Proceedings of the ASME

FLUIDS ENGINEERING DIVISION SUMMER MEETING
– 1996 –

VOLUME 3

- VORTEX FLOWS AND VORTEX METHODS
- NUMERICAL DEVELOPMENTS IN CFD
- FINITE ELEMENT APPLICATIONS IN FLUID DYNAMICS
- ADVANCES IN NUMERICAL MODELING OF FREE SURFACE & INTERFACE FLUID DYNAMICS
- COMPUTATIONAL AEROACOUSTICS
- CFD MODELING TECHNIQUES FOR LARGE STRUCTURES & FACILITIES
- FLUID MACHINERY

presented at
THE 1996 ASME FLUIDS ENGINEERING DIVISION SUMMER MEETING
JULY 7–11, 1996
SAN DIEGO, CALIFORNIA

sponsored by
THE FLUIDS ENGINEERING DIVISION, ASME

conference chair
H. W. COLEMAN

sessions organized by

P. S. BERNARD	P. E. RAAD
A. O. DEMUREN	A. S. LYRINTZIS
M. N. DHAUBHADEL	O. BAYSAL
W. G. HABASHI	G. SANCHEZ
R. K. AGARWAL	A. OGUT
M. S. ENGELMAN	U. S. ROHATGI

THE AMERICAN SOCIETY OF MECHANICAL ENGINEERS
UNITED ENGINEERING CENTER / 345 EAST 47TH STREET / NEW YORK, N.Y. 10017

ISBN No. 0-7918-1793-8

Library of Congress Number 96-85441

FOREWORD

The papers presented at the 1996 ASME Fluids Engineering Division Summer Meeting (San Diego, California, July 7–11, 1996) are published in four Proceedings volumes. I extend my greatest appreciation to the symposium and forum organizers who are listed on the following page. It was their hard work and diligence that made the meeting a success.

Hugh W. Coleman
University of Alabama, Huntsville

1996 FLUIDS ENGINEERING DIVISION SUMMER MEETING
ORGANIZING COMMITTEE

P. S. Bernard, University of Maryland, College Park, Maryland, USA
A. O. Demuren, Old Dominion University, Norfolk, Virginia, USA
M. N. Dhaubhadel, Ford Motor Company, Dearborn, Michigan, USA
P. E. Raad, Southern Methodist University, Dallas, Texas, USA
G. Tryggvason, University of Michigan, Ann Arbor, Michigan, USA
T. T. Huang, David Taylor Model Basin
B. Ramaswamy, Rice University, Houston, Texas, USA
M. Kawahara, Chuo University, Tokyo, Japan
D. Ganjoo, ANSYS, Inc.
A. S. Lyrintzis, Purdue University, West Lafayette, Indiana, USA
O. Baysal, Old Dominion University, Norfolk, Virginia, USA
G. Sanchez, Parsons Brinckerhoff, New York, New York, USA
R. Agarwal, Wichita State University, Wichita, Kansas, USA
A. Ogut, Rochester Institute of Technology, Rochester, New York, USA
U. S. Rohatgi, Brookhaven National Laboratory

CONTENTS

VORTEX FLOWS AND VORTEX METHODS

Introduction
Peter S. Bernard and Ayodeji O. Demuren 1
Fast Vortex Methods
John A. Strain 3
3D Vortex Simulation of Intake Flow in an Off-Centered Port and Cylinder
With a Moving Piston
Adrin Gharakhani and Ahmed F. Ghoniem.. 13
Vortex Particle Modelling of Stall on Rotors: An Application to Wind Turbines
Spyros G. Voutsinas and Vasislis A. Riziotis 25
Vortex Methods and Turbulent Flow Simulation
Peter S. Bernard... 33
Behavior of Quasi-Streamwise Vortices in Near-Wall Turbulence
Yutaka Miyake and Koichi Tsujimoto.. 41
Experimental Measurement and Matching Simulation of a Vortex Ring
Impinging on a Wall
Drazen Fabris, Dorian Liepmann, and Daniel Marcus..................................... 49
Vortex Ring Interaction With an Inclined Wall
Zuxing Chen, Jerry D. Swearingen, and Robert A. Handler............................. 57
Numerical Study of the Tip Vortex Flow Over a Finite-Span Hydrofoil
Chao-Tsung Hsiao and Laura L. Pauley... 65
The Three-Dimensional Vortical Structure in Time-Developing Mixing Layer
With Cross Shear
Shen Liping, Lin Jianzhong, and Fu Bin 75
Vorticity, Circulation and Vortices
John F. Foss 83
Wavelet Cross-Correlation Analysis and Its Application to Two-Dimensional
Vortex Flow
Hui Li and Tsutomu Nozaki.. 97
Confined Swirling Flow Simulation Using Spectral Galerkin and Finite Volume
Methods
Alexander Y. Gelfgat, Pinhas Z. Bar-Yoseph, and
Alexander Solan 105
Gas Core Shape and Velocity Distribution Around a Bathtub Vortex
S. Sakai, H. Madarame, and K. Okamoto.. 113
Numerical Simulation of Turbulent Jets With Rectangular Cross-Section
Robert V. Wilson and Ayodeji O. Demuren.. 121
Why Turbulence Theories Cannot Be Like the Kinetic Theory of Gases
Alexandre J. Chorin... 129
On 3D Vortex Schemes
Georges-Henri Cottet.. 135
On the Formulation of the Large-Eddy Simulation for Turbulent Vortical Flows
in Complex Domains
Stephen A. Jordan 141

NUMERICAL DEVELOPMENTS IN CFD

Introduction
Manoranjan N. Dhaubhadel... 149
Influence of Segregation on the Efficiency of Finite Volume Methods for the
Incompressible Navier-Stokes Equations
Helmar Van Santen, Danny Lathouwers, Chris R. Kleijn, and
Harry E. A. Van Den Akker 151
Application of TVD Schemes in Pressure-Based Finite-Volume Methods
R. I. Issa and M. H. Javareshkian 159

3-D Turbulent Subsonic Compressible Flow Predictions Using High-Order
Schemes and Comparison With Measurements
    Guoqing Zhang and Dennis N. Assanis 165
A Pressure-Based Preconditioner for Multi-Stage Artificial Compressibility
Algorithms
    Fotis Sotiropoulos and George Constantinescu 173
Improving Convergence Rates for Low Pressure Material Processing
Calculations
    Christopher D. Moen 181
Approximate Riemann Solvers to Compute Turbulent Compressible One and
Two-Equation Models
    Thierry Buffard and Jean-Marc Hérard 189
Spurious Unsteady Solutions Due to the Quick Scheme in Numerical Solution
of the Navier-Stokes Equations
    Jeffrey Guoping Li 197
An Algorithm for Simulation of Turbulent Free Surface Flows
    Natarajan Ramanan, Vahé Haroutunian, and
        Michael S. Engelman 205
Coupling Flow Solvers and Grids Through an Edge-Based Adaptive Grid
Method
    Marie-Gabrielle Vallet, Julien Dompierre, Yves Bourgault, Michel Fortin,
        and Wagdi G. Habashi 209
A Study of Multidomain Compact Finite Difference Schemes for Stiff Problems
    Adrian S. Sabau and Peter E. Raad 217
Implementation and Performance of a Data Parallel Algorithm for the Dynamic
Subgrid-Scale Stress Model on a Massively Parallel Computer
    Fady M. Najjar and Danesh K. Tafti 225
Application of a New Incompressible Flow Algorithm to Flows in a Variety of
Shear-Driven Cavity Configurations
    Michael C. Wendl and Ramesh K. Agarwal 233

FINITE ELEMENT APPLICATIONS IN FLUID DYNAMICS
Introduction
    Manoranjan N. Dhaubhadel 239
Theoretical Investigation on Needle Tip Deviation of a Multihole
V. C. O. Nozzle for D.I. Diesel Engine
    Luigi Fiorentino and Domenico Laforgia 241
Underhood Thermo-Fluids Simulation for a Simplified Car Model
    M. N. Dhaubhadel and T. S. Shih 249
Mathematical Modeling of Two-Phase Fluid Flow in Vacuum-Degassing of
Steel
    Bulent Kocatulum 255
Numerical Investigation of Free Convection Heat Transfer in Vertical Channels
With Backward-Facing Step
    R. K. Sahoo, A. Sarkar, and V. M. K. Sastri 263
Numerical Simulation of Newtonian Fluid Flow Through a Multiple Channel
Honeycomb Monolithic Structure
    Maher M. Shariff, Hussein J. Hussein, Kenneth A. Debelak, and
        John W. Williamson 271
Laminar Backward-Facing Step Flow Using the Finite Element Method
    Barbara T. Kornblum, Rose C. McCallen, Mark A. Christon, and
        Wolfgang Kollmann 277
Preliminary Model of an Oil-Water Settling Process Using FIDAP
    Michael A. Langerman, Matthew J. Meiners, and
        Warren Rice 285
Implementation of One-Point Quadrature in a Finite Element CFD Code
    M. Tabatabai, D. Metzger, and R. Sauvé 293

A Finite Element Method for Heat Transfer Prediction in Cooled Turbine Blades
  J.-M. Zhou, M. P. Robichaud, M. F. Peeters, and W. G. Habashi 299
Three-Dimensional Thermal Analysis Simulation of Spent Nuclear Fuel
Canister Using FIDAP
  Davoud A. Eghbali 309
A Finite Element Method for Free Surface Flows With Merging and Breakup
  J. Rosenberg and M. S. Engelman 317
Application of MEI Finite Elements to a Store Separation
  Amir A. Mobasher, Ounyoung Park, and Edward L. Bernstein............................ 323

ADVANCES IN NUMERICAL MODELING OF FREE SURFACE AND INTERFACE FLUID DYNAMICS

Introduction
  Peter E. Raad, Grétar Tryggvason, Tom T. Huang, Bala Ramaswamy,
    Mutsuto Kawahara, and Deepak Ganjoo.. 331
A Finite Amount About Finite Difference Methods for Free-Surface Flows:
Yesterday, Today and Tomorrow
  Robert L. Street 333
Free Surface Mixing With Heat Transfer
  Dani Fadda and Peter E. Raad 335
Computations of Film Boiling
  Damir Juric and Grétar Tryggvason... 341
A Fully-Implicit Multigrid Driven Algorithm for Time-Resolved Non-Linear
Free-Surface Flow on Unstructured Grids
  Biing-Horng Liou, Luigi Martinelli, and Antony Jameson.................................. 349
An Adaptive Level Set Approach for Incompressible Two-Phase Flows
  Mark Sussman, Ann S. Almgren, John B. Bell, Phillip Colella,
    Louis H. Howell, and Michael Welcome 355
Tree-Dimensional, Nonlinear, Viscous Wave Interactions in a Sloshing Tank
  Ben R. Hodges and Robert L. Street 361
Flow Over a Cylindrical Containment Dike
  Adrian S. Sabau and Peter E. Raad 369
Dynamics of Polydisperse Bubbly Flows in Periodic Domains
  Asghar Esmaeeli and Grétar Tryggvason... 375
An Advection and Interface Reconstructing Scheme for Incompressible Flow
Calculations
  José Ronaldo C. de Melo and Angela O. Nieckele.. 385
Numerical Simulation of Nonlinear Wave Over Permeable Submerged
Breakwater
  Tsutomu Sakakiyama.. 391
A Numerical Study on the Collision Behavior of Droplets
  Albert Y. Tong 397
A Numerical Scheme for Liquid-Liquid System: Deformation of a Falling
Liquid Droplet
  H. Zhang, T. Y. Hou, and V. Prasad... 403
Numerical Simulation of the Shallow Water Equations
  S. Chippada, C. N. Dawson, M. L. Martinez, and
    M. F. Wheeler.. 409
Three-Dimensional Instabilities in Heated Falling Films: A Full-Scale Direct
Numerical Simulation
  S. Krishnamoorthy, B. Ramaswamy, and S. W. Joo.. 415
Free Surface Flow Computation Using a Fully Consistent Method
  Pompiliu Donescu and Lawrence N. Virgin.. 421
A Picard Algorithm for the Solution of Unsteady Free Surface Flows
  Natarajan Ramanan and Michael S. Engelman 427
Simulation of Two-Fluid Flows by the Least-Squares Finite Element Method
Using a Continuum Surface Tension Model
  Jie Wu, Sheng-Tao Yu, and Bo-nan Jiang... 433

Numerical Computation of Surface Tension Effects
    David J. Burt, John W. J. Ferguson, and Harbi Pordal.................... 439
3-Dimensional Analysis of Incompressible Flow Around Circular Cylinder
    Shinji Ohta, Akira Maruoka, Hirokazu Hirano, and
       Mutsuto Kawahara.................... 445
Numerical Analysis of Run-Up on a Conical Island by Finite Element Method
    Hirokasu Kondo, Toshimitsu Takagi, and Mutsuto Kawahara.................... 451
Quasi 3-Dimensional Nearshore Current Simulation
    Toshimitsu Takagi and Mutsuto Kawahara.................... 457

COMPUTATIONAL AEROACOUSTICS
Introduction
    A. S. Lyrintzis and O. Baysal.................... 463
Experiences in the Practical Application of Computational Aeroacoustics
    Philip J. Morris, Lyle N. Long, Ashok Bangalore, Thomas Chyczewski,
       David P. Lockard, and Yusuf Ozyoruk.................... 465
From Jet Flow Computations to Far-Field Noise Prediction
    J. L. Estivalezes and L. Gamet.................... 473
Numerical Simulation of the Mixing Noise in Turbulent Flows
    M. E. Hayder, Y. Zhou, and R. Rubinstein.................... 479
Acoustic Radiation From Oscillating Rigid Bodies in Mean Compressible Flow
    Ramesh K. Agarwal and Kevin S. Huh.................... 485
Computation and Verification of the Effects of Finite Length Flexible Segments
on Acoustic Wave Propagation in One-Dimensional Systems
    Brian V. Chapnik and I. G. Currie.................... 497
Algorithmic Extensions of Low-Dispersion Scheme and Modeling Effects for
Acoustic Wave Simulation
    Dinesh K. Kaushik and Oktay Baysal.................... 503
Approximate Nonreflecting Boundary Conditions for Cylindrical Acoustic
Waves
    Karl D. von Ellenrieder and Brian J. Cantwell.................... 511

CFD MODELING TECHNIQUES FOR LARGE STRUCTURES AND FACILITIES
Introduction
    Greg Sanchez and Ramesh Agarwal.................... 517
Ventilation Requirements for New Phoenix Ballpark
    S. L. Gamble, R. J. Sinclair, K. M. Matsui, and
       M. R. D. Barrett.................... 519
Computational Fluid Dynamics Tracking of UF_6 Reaction Products Release
Into a Gaseous Diffusion Plant Cell Housing
    Mark W. Wendel, Norbert C. J. Chen, Seok-Ho H. Kim, Rusi P. Taleyarkhan,
       Kenneth D. Keith, and Russell W. Schmidt.................... 529
Progress in Modelling External Atmospheric Flows Around Buildings
    Jon A. Peterka, Leighton S. Cochran, Roger A. Pielke, and
       Melville E. Nicholls.................... 535
Designing a Micro-Climate for a New International Airport Using CFD
Techniques to Develop Parameters and Analyze the Effectiveness of the Design
    Peter Simmonds.................... 541
CFD Validation of Natural Smoke Movement in a Model Tunnel
    M. Tabarra, B. Kenrick, and R. D. Matthews.................... 543
CFD Modeling Considerations for Train Fires in Undeground Subway Stations
    Mark P. Deng, Paul C. Miclea, and Dan McKinney.................... 547
Numerical Simulation of Subway Station Fires and Ventilation
    Steven R. Elias, Michael J. Raw, and Peter Bostwick.................... 557
CFD-Based Design of the Ventilation System in the Major Facility Hall for
the PHENIX Detector
    L. Parietti, W. S. Gregory, and R. A. Martin.................... 559

Analysis of Airflow Around an Oil Production Platform
    Mark Seymour, Paul Rose, and Farzad Baban.. 563

FLUID MACHINERY
Introduction
    Ali Ogut and Upendra Singh Rohatgi.. 571
Fluid Dynamics and Performance of Automotive Torque Converters:
An Assessment
    T. W. von Backström and B. Lakshminarayana.. 573
Performance of Different Diffusers for Centrifugal Compressors
    Abraham Engeda 589
A Study of Fundamental Interrelation Between the Magnitude of Centrifugal
Forces and the Hydraulic Energy Losses Caused in an Axial Flow Pump
    Takaharu Tanaka.. 595
Aerothermodynamic Parameters Influence on the Noise and Vibration of a
Reciprocating Compressor
    N. H. Mostafa and Larry D. Mitchell.. 601
Theory, Design, and Test of an Efficient Subsonic Diffuser
    G. Fonda-Bonardi.. 609
Optimization of Symmetrical Profiles for the Wells Turbine Rotor Blades
    L. M. C. Gato and J. C. C. Henriques.. 623
Simulation of the Three-Dimensional Turbulent Flow Inside a Centrifugal
Fan Impeller
    R. I. Issa and G. Xi.. 631
Development of a Rapid Method of Analysing the Flow Through
Turbomachineries
    Thabet Belamri, Robert Rey, Farid Bakir, Smaine Kouidri, and
      Riccardo Noguera.. 639
Numerical Simulation of Three-Dimensional Viscous Flow in a Multiblade
Centrifugal Fan
    X. Chen, Kwang-Yong Kim, and Se-Yun Kim.. 647
An Analytical Design Method for Linearized Free-Vortex Type Flow in
Turbomachines
    Nhan T. Nguyen 653
A Design Procedure for Turbocharging Compressors
    Sarim N. Al-Zubaidy 663
Transient Response of Multiphase Pumps in Petroleum Applications
    Rune Mode Ramberg and Lars E. Bakken 669
Modeling Techniques for Predicting Compressor Performance During Surge
and Rotating Stall
    E. S. El-Mitwally, M. Abo-Rayan, N. H. Mostafa, and
    A. H. Hassanien 681
Commentary ASME Code Section III Pumps
    Douglas B. Nickerson, Paul Burchett, Robert E. Cornman, Alex Fraser,
      and Hassan Tafarrodi.. 689
Surge Prediction Modeling for Low Pressure Compression Process
    M. A. Rayan and R. N. Azoole.. 697

Author Index 705

VORTEX FLOWS AND VORTEX METHODS

Introduction

Peter S. Bernard
University of Maryland
College Park, Maryland

Ayodeji O. Demuren
Old Dominion University
Norfolk, Virginia

This symposium brings together works incorporating a wide range of numerical schemes for computing flows in which vorticity plays a dominant role, as well as several experimental works promoting the understanding of the physics of vortical flows. Deterministic and random vortex methods, vortex particle methods, boundary element, finite difference, higher order Godunov methods, pseudo-spectral, finite volume and finite element methods are represented. Applications of the schemes encompass flows in internal combustion engine cylinders, wind turbines, boundary layer turbulence, vortex ring/boundary interactions, hydrofoils, mixing layers, swirling flows, bathtub vortices, and rectangular turbulent jets. An important sub-theme of the symposium concerns the vortical nature of turbulence; vortex schemes for turbulent flow simulation, vortex dynamics in turbulence and the fundamental connection between the physics of turbulence and the thermodynamics of vortex systems. Strategies for turbulent flow analysis via large eddy simulations based on vortex methods are considered. Finally, the relationship between vorticity and vortices is explored.

The organizers wish to thank the participating authors for the high quality of their contributions to the symposium. Through their considerable efforts, the collection of papers succeeds in demonstrating the advanced understanding of turbulent flows which has been and can be achieved through analysis of the vorticity field.

FED-Vol. 238, 1996 Fluids Engineering Division Conference
Volume 3
ASME 1996

FAST VORTEX METHODS

John A. Strain

Mathematics Department and
Lawrence Berkeley National Laboratory
University of California
Berkeley, California 94720

ABSTRACT

We present three fast adaptive vortex methods for the 2D Euler equations. All obtain long-time accuracy at almost optimal cost by using four tools: adaptive quadrature, free-Lagrangian formulation, the fast multipole method and a nonstandard error analysis. Our error analysis halves the differentiability required of the flow, suggests an efficient new balance of smoothing parameters, and combines naturally with fast summation schemes. Numerical experiments with our methods confirm our theoretical predictions and display excellent long-time accuracy.

INTRODUCTION

Vortex methods solve the 2D incompressible Euler equations in the vorticity formulation by discretizing the Biot-Savart law with the aid of the flow map. They have been extensively studied, widely generalized and applied to complex high-Reynolds-number flows: See (Gustafson and Sethian, 1991) for a survey.

Vortex methods involve several components; velocity evaluation, vortex motion, diffusion, boundary conditions and regridding. In this paper, we improve the speed, accuracy and robustness of the velocity evaluation. We eliminate the flow map, improve the quadrature used for the Biot-Savart law, and analyze the error in velocity evaluation in a nonstandard way, requiring less differentiability of the flow and obtaining efficient new parameter balances. We employ standard techniques for the vortex motion and consider inviscid free-space flow to eliminate diffusion and boundary conditions. Our approach combines naturally with regridding and fast multipole methods.

Lagrangian vortex methods move the nodes of a fixed quadrature rule with the computed fluid velocity, preserving the weights of the rule by incompressibility. This procedure loses accuracy when the flow becomes disorganized, motivating many regridding techniques. Even before the flow becomes disorganized, however, obtaining high-order accuracy with fixed quadrature weights requires smoothing of the singular Biot-Savart kernel. Smoothing gives high-order accuracy for short times but slows down the fast multipole method and halves the order of accuracy relative to the differentiability of the flow.

In this paper, we discuss three fast adaptive vortex methods. We briefly review the triangulated vortex method of (Russo and Strain, 1994) and the quadrature-based method of (Strain, 1996a), then present the smoothed method of (Strain, 1996b). Triangulated vortex methods are robust, accurate and efficient but limited to second-order accuracy. Quadrature-based methods compute adaptive quadratures tailored to the Biot-Savart kernel at each time step, yielding free-Lagrangian methods which maintain long-time high-order accuracy at asymptotically optimal cost. The smoothed method couples kernel smoothing with adaptive quadrature rules *not* tailored to the Biot-Savart kernel, producing long-time high-order accuracy. The asymptotic slowdown produced by kernel smoothing is almost eliminated by a careful choice of smoothing functions and parameters, based on a new error analysis of the velocity evaluation.

The structure of these methods is standard: At each time step, the smoothed velocity is evaluated once and the vortices are moved with an explicit multistep method. The velocity evaluation is nonstandard, and different for each method. We have implemented and tested all of these new methods; the error is small on standard test problems and the theoretical predictions are fully verified. More complex flows are also computed.

EQUATIONS OF MOTION

The 2D incompressible Euler equations

$$\dot{u} + uu_x + vu_y + p_x/\rho = 0$$
$$\dot{v} + uv_x + vv_y + p_y/\rho = 0$$
$$u_x + v_y = 0,$$

involve the fluid velocity $u(z,t) = (u,v)$, where $z = (x,y)$, the pressure $p(z,t)$ and the constant density ρ. Taking the 2D curl eliminates the pressure, giving the vorticity equation

$$\dot{\omega} + u\omega_x + v\omega_y = 0$$

for the vorticity $\omega = v_x - u_y$. Let $z \mapsto \Phi(z,t)$ be the flow map, defined by

$$\dot{\Phi}(z,t) = u(\Phi(z,t),t). \tag{1}$$

Then vorticity is conserved along particle paths:

$$\omega(\Phi(z,t),t) = \omega(z,0); \tag{2}$$

When ω has compact support, the velocity is given by the Biot-Savart law

$$u(z,t) = \int K(z-z')\omega(z')dx'dy' \tag{3}$$

where K is the Biot-Savart kernel

$$K(z) = \frac{z^{\perp}}{2\pi r^2}, \quad z^{\perp} = (-y,x), \quad r^2 = x^2 + y^2. \tag{4}$$

Thus we have a closed system for Φ and ω, the "free-Lagrangian" equations of motion consisting of Eq. (2) coupled with

$$\dot{\Phi}(z,t) = \int K(\Phi(z,t) - z')\omega(z',t)dx'dy'. \tag{5}$$

The Lagrangian equation of motion is derived by changing variables $z' \leftarrow \Phi(z',t)$. The Jacobian is unity because the flow is incompressible, so this gives a closed system for Φ alone:

$$\dot{\Phi}(z,t) = \int K(\Phi(z,t) - \Phi(z',t))\omega(z',0)dx'dy'. \tag{6}$$

This requires values of ω only at time $t = 0$, and is the usual starting point for vortex methods.

VORTEX METHODS

Lagrangian vortex methods now discretize Eq. (6), tracking N points $z_j(t) \approx \Phi(z_j,t)$ moving with the fluid velocity, starting at $t = 0$ from the nodes z_j of a quadrature formula with weights w_j. Suppose we use a quadrature formula

$$\int g(z)dxdy = \sum_{j=1}^{N} w_j g(z_j) + E_N(g)$$

with a qth-order error bound

$$|E_N(g)| \leq Ch^q \|g\|_q \tag{7}$$

for $g \in C^q$. Here h is the mesh size of the rule and the C^q norm is defined by

$$\|g\|_0 = \max_z |g(z)|, \qquad \|g\|_q = \|g\|_0 + \sum_{\alpha+\beta=q} \|\partial_x^{\alpha}\partial_y^{\beta}g\|_0.$$

Applying this quadrature to the Lagrangian equation of motion (6) gives a system of N ordinary differential equations:

$$\dot{z}_i(t) = \sum_{j \neq i} w_j K(z_i(t) - z_j(t))\omega(z_j,0).$$

The quadrature error bound Eq. (7) is infinite since K is unbounded, so we replace K by the smoothed kernel

$$K_{\delta}(z) = \varphi_{\delta} * K(z) = f(r/\delta)K(z)$$

where $*$ denotes convolution,

$$\varphi_{\delta}(z) = \delta^{-2}\varphi(r/\delta)$$

φ is an appropriate radial "core function," and the "shape factor" f is given by

$$f(r) = 2\pi \int_0^r s\varphi(s)ds.$$

CONVERGENCE THEORY

Almost all modern vortex methods use smoothing, often with φ and the "core radius" δ chosen to give high-order convergence as the mesh size h vanishes (Chorin, 1989; Hald, 1991). This can be guaranteed by the following conditions on φ and ω:

$$\int \varphi = 1,$$
$$\int x^{\alpha}y^{\beta}\varphi = 0, \qquad 1 \leq \alpha + \beta \leq m-1, \tag{8}$$
$$\int |z|^m|\varphi| < \infty$$
$$\varphi \in C^L \quad \text{and} \quad \varphi(z) = 0 \quad \text{for} \quad |z| \geq 1, \tag{9}$$
$$\omega \in C^M \quad \text{has compact support.} \tag{10}$$

High-order accuracy requires smooth solutions, so condition (10) on ω is natural. Compact support in condition (9) can be weakened, but it is important for efficiency. Given these conditions, a typical convergence theorem follows.

Theorem 1 (Anderson and Greengard, 1985) *Assume conditions (8) through (10) are satisfied with $L \geq 3$, $M \geq \max(L+1, m+2)$ and $m \geq 4$. Let $\delta = ch^a$ where $0 < a < 1$. Suppose L is large enough to satisfy*

$$L > \frac{(m-1)a}{1-a}.$$

Then the computed flow map $\Phi_{h,\delta}$ satisfies

$$\|\Phi - \Phi_{h,\delta}\|_h \leq O(h^{ma})$$

as h and δ go to zero.

Here the discrete 2-norm is given by

$$\|g\|_h = \left(h^2 \sum_i |g(z_i)|^2 \right)^{1/2}$$

where z_i are the initial vortex positions, and similar bounds hold for the computed velocity and vorticity.

This theorem allows a close to 1 and δ close to $O(h)$ only for very smooth flows, where L and M are large. For general flows, Hald (1987) shows that $\delta = O(\sqrt{h})$ is a good choice. Then $2m$ derivatives of ω guarantee only $O(h^m)$ accuracy. Later, we reduce this to $m+1$ derivatives at the cost of redefining convergence.

COST AND ACCURACY

Convergence theory must be augmented by practical considerations of cost and accuracy. Since each velocity value is a sum

$$u_{h,\delta}(z_i) = \sum_{j=1}^{N} K_\delta(z_i - z_j) w_j \omega(z_j, 0),$$

direct evaluation costs $O(N^2)$ work. This is prohibitively expensive if the flow is complex, since many vortices are required. The expense has been reduced by fast summation schemes (Anderson, 1986; Carrier, Greengard and Rokhlin, 1988; Strain, 1992) which evaluate unsmoothed sums like

$$u(z_i) = \sum_{j=1}^{N} K(z_i - z_j) w_j$$

to accuracy ϵ in about $O(N \log \epsilon)$ work, by separating local from global interactions and separating the variables. These schemes are much faster than direct evaluation for large N.

However, this does not completely resolve the difficulty. Fast methods cannot evaluate the smoothed interaction $K_\delta(z_i - z_j)$ between vortices z_i and z_j closer than δ, because $K_\delta \neq K$. Asymptotically, there are $O(N\delta^2)$ vortices in a circle of radius δ, so if $\delta = O(\sqrt{h})$ there are a total of $O(N^2\delta^2) = O(N^2h) = O(N^{3/2})$ local interactions to be evaluated directly. Thus fast summation schemes slow down from $O(N)$ to $O(N^{3/2})$ when K is smoothed inside a radius $\delta = O(\sqrt{h})$.

Hence there is a conflict between smoothing and fast summation. If we try to make δ close to $O(h)$ to speed up fast summation, we need many derivatives of the flow for a modest order of convergence. Larger δ is more accurate for rougher flows, but hampers fast summation schemes. Our error analysis resolves this conflict by allowing another $O(\epsilon)$ in the error.

THE PERLMAN EFFECT

A completely different obstacle to accurate calculations with vortex methods is the "Perlman effect." The error bound for numerical quadrature in Eq. (7) depends on order-q derivatives of the integrand

$$g(z') = K_\delta(\Phi(z,t) - \Phi(z',t))\omega(z', 0),$$

so the derivatives of the flow map will affect the error bound. The flow map moves fluid particles far apart, developing large derivatives when the flow becomes disorganized. Thus vortex methods lose high-order accuracy in long-time calculations (Perlman 1985; Beale and Majda 1985). For example, Figure 1 plots the number of correct bits in the computed velocity of a standard test case for a fourth-order vortex method. Fourth-order accuracy—evidenced by the gain of one tick mark per line in the figure—is attained only during a very short initial time period.

The Perlman effect has motivated much research on regridding, the idea being to avoid large derivatives of the flow map by restarting before the flow becomes disorganized (Nordmark, 1991). Similarly, Beale (1988) has developed an iterative reweighting scheme. The Perlamn effect also motivated the free-Lagrangian

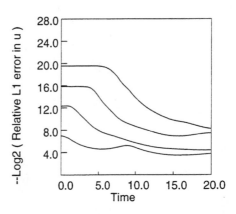

Figure 1: Correct bits in u for the Lagrangian vortex method.

vortex methods reviewed here, which eliminate the flow map from the Biot-Savart integral. Thus

$$\dot{\Phi} = \int K(\Phi - z')\omega(z', t)dx'dy',$$

replaces the Lagrangian equation of motion Eq. (6). Since ω values are known only at the moving points $z_j(t)$, each velocity evaluation requires adaptive quadratures with new weights adapted to the current vortex positions. We now present three such methods.

TRIANGULATED METHODS

Triangulated vortex methods evolve points $z_j(t)$ by

$$\dot{z}_j(t) = \int K(z_j(t) - z')\omega_h(z', t)dx'dy', \qquad (11)$$

where ω_h is a piecewise linear interpolant to the vorticity values

$$\omega_h(z_j(t), t) = \omega_h(z_j, 0) = \omega(z_j, 0)$$

and the nodes $z_j(t)$ form the vertices of a triangulation of $\mathbf{R}^2$.

Given any piecewise linear function ω_h on a triangulation of $\mathbf{R}^2$, one can evaluate the corresponding velocity u_h exactly, with results depending very strongly on the triangulation. In (Chacon Rebollo and Hou, 1990), this observation was combined with a fixed triangulation carried by the flow. While convergent, the resulting scheme costs $O(N^2)$ work per time step with a large constant, and loses accuracy very quickly because the triangulation degenerates.

We developed practical triangulated vortex methods in (Russo and Strain, 1994); a fast summation scheme brought the cost down to $O(N^{4/3})$ and a fast Delaunay triangulation scheme gave excellent long-time accuracy. An adaptive initial triangulation technique made the method robust enough to compute even discontinuous patches of vorticity. Figure 2 plots errors for the test case used in Fig. 1. The error displays no Perlman effect; second-order accuracy (one tick per line) is maintained uniformly in time. The triangulated approach is now being applied to flows in three dimensions with viscosity and boundaries (Huyer and Grant, 1994). Difficulties obtaining higher-order accuracy motivated the next approach.

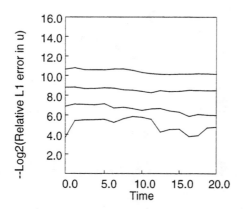

Figure 2: Correct bits in u in 1-norm, computed by the triangulated vortex method.

QUADRATURE-BASED METHODS

Higher-order free-Lagrangian methods were developed in (Strain, 1996a). They use time-dependent quadrature weights $w_{ij}(t)$ giving high-order accuracy in the Biot-Savart law:

$$u(z_i, t) = \int K(z_i - z')\omega(z', t)dx'dy'$$
$$\approx \sum_{j=1}^{N} w_{ij}(t)K(z_i - z_j)\omega(z_j, t).$$

For example, high-order product integration weights make smoothing unnecessary, but the i-dependence of $w_{ij}(t)$ precludes fast summation methods. Thus we construct weights with the "locally-corrected property" that $w_{ij} = w_j$ for almost all j, where w_j are the weights of some "smooth" quadrature rule with points z_j. Such rules can be built and the velocity evaluated in $O(N \log^2 N)$ work. The price for efficiency is a redefinition of convergence. The error bound for these quadratures is $O(\epsilon + h^q)$, where ϵ is an arbitrary user-specified error tolerance and the constant in the $O(N)$ cost depends weakly on ϵ. Thus one gets order-q convergence only down to $O(\epsilon)$. This is sufficient for three reasons: computer arithmetic has finite precision, practical computations can afford only rather low accuracy, and fast summation methods introduce an $O(\epsilon)$ error as well. High-order accuracy can be maintained for long times, though these rules are somewhat expensive to implement.

A FAST ADAPTIVE METHOD

We now describe a high-order fast adaptive vortex method which aims to avoid obstacles both to speed and to accuracy. The key ingredients are

○ A free-Lagrangian formulation to avoid the Perlman effect.

○ Adaptive quadrature rules *not* tailored to the Biot-Savart kernel.

○ New error bounds requiring fewer derivatives of the vorticity and leading to an efficient new smoothing strategy.

These ingredients combine to give a method with almost optimal efficiency and long-time high-order accuracy, without excessive differentiability requirements on the flow.

OVERVIEW

We begin with quadrature. Given N nodes $z_j \in \mathbf{R}^2$, we compute the weights of a quadrature rule with order-q accuracy on C^q functions if the nodes are well distributed. We partition the nodes into rectangular cells and build order-q rules on each cell. The union of these rules is globally accurate of order q (Strain, 1995). After quadrature, we discuss smoothing. We state a standard smoothing error bound and construct a family of arbitrary-order accurate core functions. Next we present a new error analysis which leads to an efficient new balance between quadrature and smoothing. We conclude with some numerical results.

A TREE STRUCTURE

Let $B = [a, b] \times [c, d]$ be a rectangle containing the nodes z_j. Our quadratures partition B into rectangular cells B_i, each containing enough nodes to construct an order-q quadrature. There are $q(q+1)/2$ monomials $x^\alpha y^\beta$ of degree $\alpha + \beta \leq q - 1$, so we will need at least $p \geq q(q+1)/2$ nodes per cell. Thus we build a tree structure to partition B into cells containing p or $p + 1$ nodes each.

Let $B = B_1$ be the level-0 root of the tree. Divide B_1 in half along its longest edge, with the dividing plane located so that each half of B_1 contains either $\lfloor N/2 \rfloor$ or $\lfloor N/2 \rfloor + 1$ nodes. This gives the level-1 cells B_2 and B_3. Recursively, split B_2 and B_3 along their longest edges to get B_4 through B_7, each containing $\lfloor N/4 \rfloor$ or $\lfloor N/4 \rfloor + 1$ nodes z_j. Repeat this procedure L times to get $M = 2^L$ cells B_i on the finest level L, numbered from $i = M$ to $i = 2M - 1$, each containing $p = \lfloor N/M \rfloor$ or $p + 1$ nodes z_j. The union of all the cells on any given level is B. The tree structure is stored by listing the boundaries of each cell $B_i = [a_i, b_i] \times [c_i, d_i]$ from $i = 1$ to $i = 2M - 1$, a total of $4 \cdot 2M$ numbers, and indexing the nodes into a list so that the nodes $z_j \in B_i$ are given by $j = j(s)$ for $s = b(i), \ldots, e(i)$ and three integer functions j, b and e. This can be done in $O(N \log N)$, but the simplest method requires sorting each cell before each subdivision, giving a total cost $O(N \log^2 N)$ for the tree construction with an $O(N \log N)$ sorting method such as Heapsort.

QUADRATURE RULES

We now construct qth-order quadrature rules on B with N quadrature nodes z_j given. Assume $N \geq m := q(q+1)/2$, and choose $L \geq 0$ with $p := \lfloor N/2^L \rfloor \geq m$. The tree structure divides B into $M = 2^L$ rectangular cells B_i, each containing either p or $p + 1$ nodes z_j. On each B_i, we construct local weights W_j^i for

$z_j \in B_i$ by solving the following system of m linear equations in at least p unknowns:

$$\sum_{z_j \in B_i} P_\alpha(x_j)P_\beta(y_j)W_j^i = \int_{B_i} P_\alpha(x)P_\beta(y)dxdy$$

for $0 \leq \alpha + \beta \leq q - 1$. Here $P_\alpha(x)P_\beta(y)$ are the two-variable Legendre polynomials on B_i. Since $p \geq m$, this system of m equations in at least p unknowns generically has solutions. We compute the solution W_j^i of least 2-norm, using a complete orthogonal factorization from LAPACK (Anderson et al.,1992). The weights of the rule W are then defined to be $W_j = W_j^i$ where $z_j \in B_i$. This rule integrates all polynomials of degree less than q exactly over all level-L cells B_i. This property implies order-q accuracy:

Theorem 2 (Strain, 1995) *Suppose $B = \cup_{i=1}^M B_i$ and W integrates $x^\alpha y^\beta$ exactly over each cell B_i for $0 \leq \alpha + \beta \leq q - 1$. Then for any C^q function g on B, the quadrature error*

$$E = \int_B g(z)dxdy - \sum_{j=1}^N W_j g(z_j)$$

satisfies the bound

$$|E| \leq \Omega |B| \frac{h^q}{q!} \|g\|_q$$

where h is the longest cell edge, $\Omega = 1 + \frac{1}{|B|}\sum_{j=1}^N |W_j|$ and $|B| = (b-a)(d-c)$ is the area of B.

The condition number Ω cannot be bounded a priori for arbitrary points, but we can easily compute it a posteriori, yielding an excellent diagnostic for the quality of the rule.

SMOOTHING

The following theorem is a standard error bound for smoothing with a core function satisfying moment conditions of order m:

Theorem 3 (Raviart, 1985) *Assume the compactly supported core function φ satisfies the moment conditions*

$$\int \varphi = 1, \qquad \int x^\alpha y^\beta \varphi = 0, \quad 1 \leq \alpha + \beta \leq m - 1,$$

$$M = \frac{1}{m!}\int |z|^m |\varphi| < \infty.$$

Suppose u belongs to the Sobolev space $W^{m,p}$ of functions with m derivatives in L^p, where $1 \leq p \leq \infty$. Then

$$\|\varphi_\delta * u - u\|_{L^p} \leq M\delta^m \sum_{\alpha+\beta=m} \|\partial_x^\alpha \partial_y^\beta u\|_{L^p}.$$

Suppose φ is a continuous radial function and write $\varphi(z) = \varphi(r)$ where $r^2 = |z|^2 = x^2 + y^2$. Then $\int x^\alpha y^\beta \varphi(z)dxdy = 0$ if α or β is odd, so the moment conditions simplify to

$$\int_0^1 \varphi(r)rdr = 1/2\pi, \quad \int_0^1 \varphi(r)r^{2j+1}dr = 0, \quad j = 1,\ldots,n$$

where $m = 2n + 2$ is even. A standard calculation gives

$$K_\delta(z) = \varphi_\delta * K(z) = f\left(\frac{r}{\delta}\right)K(z)$$

where the "shape factor" f is given by

$$f(r) = 2\pi \int_0^r \varphi(s)sds.$$

Since $\varphi(r) = 0$ for $r > 1$, we have $f(r) = 1$ for $r > 1$ so $K_\delta(z)$ is identical to $K(z)$ for $r > \delta$. This facilitates the application of fast summation methods.

A convenient ansatz for the shape factor is

$$f(r) = \varrho^p \left[a_d\varrho^d + \cdots + a_0\right] + 1 \tag{12}$$

where $\varrho = (1 - r^2)_+ = \max(0, 1 - r^2)$ and $\varphi(r) = \frac{1}{2\pi r}f'(r)$. The $d + 1$ coefficients a_i must be chosen so that φ satisfies $n + 1$ moment conditions, so we cannot expect a solution unless $d \geq n$. If $d > n$, the linear system of moment conditions is underdetermined, and we use a complete orthogonal factorization routine to find the solution with smallest 2-norm. Given the coefficients a_i, we have

$$K_\delta(z) = \frac{z^\perp}{2\pi r^2}\left[(1 - r^2/\delta^2)_+^p (a_d(1 - r^2/\delta^2)_+^d + \cdots + a_0) + 1\right],$$

where $z^\perp = (-y, x)$. Since $f(0) = 0$, we can reduce roundoff problems for small r by finding a polynomial g such that

$$f(r) = r^2 g(\varrho) = r^2 \left[b_{p+d-1}\varrho^{p+d-1} + \cdots + b_0\right].$$

In terms of g, we have a convenient formula

$$K_\delta(z) = \frac{z^\perp}{2\pi \max(r^2, \delta^2)}g((1 - r^2/\delta^2)_+).$$

Figure 3 shows several of the shape factors f; the increasing oscillation as n increases follows naturally from the vanishing of more moments.

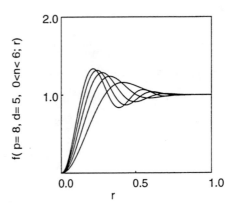

Figure 3: Piecewise polynomial shape factors f.

TIME STEPPING

Since the Euler equations are not stiff and we are constructing high-order vortex methods, we discretize time with explicit s-step Adams methods. These methods require an accurate procedure for computing the s starting values. Suppose we use an explicit s-step Adams method with a fixed time step Δ_f. We begin with a tiny time step $\Delta_i << \Delta_f$ and 1-step Adams, giving error $O(\Delta_i^2)$. Since our final method is order-s accurate, we should choose $\Delta_i = O(\Delta_f^{s/2})$. We now increase the order of the Adams method by 1 at each step until order s is reached, simultaneously increasing Δ_i by a factor $R \leq 2$ until Δ_f is reached. The final non-equidistant step is adjusted to land precisely at $t = \Delta_f$.

BALANCE OF ERROR

We now balance the errors due to smoothing and quadrature. The error in velocity evaluation splits naturally into two parts

$$
\begin{aligned}
E &= |u(z) - \sum_{j=1}^{N} w_j K_\delta(z - z_j)\omega(z_j)| \\
&\leq |K * \omega(z) - K_\delta * \omega(z)| \\
&\quad + |K_\delta * \omega(z) - \sum_{j=1}^{N} w_j K_\delta(z - z_j)\omega(z_j)| \\
&= E_\delta + E_{N,\delta}.
\end{aligned}
$$

The first term is the smoothing error, which satisfies

$$E_\delta \leq M \delta^m \|u\|_m$$

if φ satisfies moment conditions of order m and $u \in C^m$. The second term is the quadrature error, which satisfies

$$E_{N,\delta} \leq \Omega |B| \frac{h^q}{q!} \|g\|_q$$

for each fixed z. Here $g(z') = K_\delta(z - z')\omega(z')$, so by a standard inequality for the C^q norm of a product

$$\|g\|_q \leq C(\|K_\delta\|_q \|\omega\|_0 + \|K_\delta\|_0 \|\omega\|_q).$$

Scaling gives

$$K_\delta(z) = \delta^{-1} \int \varphi\left(\frac{z}{\delta} - z'\right) \frac{z'^\perp}{2\pi|z'|^2} dx' dy',$$

so there is some constant C depending only on φ, such that

$$\|\partial_x^\alpha \partial_y^\beta K_\delta\|_0 \leq C\delta^{\alpha+\beta-1}$$

if $\varphi \in C^{\alpha+\beta}$. Thus if $\varphi \in C^q$, we have

$$\|g\|_q \leq \frac{1}{\delta} C(\delta^{-q} \|\omega\|_0 + \|\omega\|_q)$$

so the error in velocity evaluation satisfies

$$E \leq C(\delta^m \|u\|_m + \delta^{-1} \left(\frac{h}{\delta}\right)^q \|\omega\|_0 + \delta^{-1} h^q \|\omega\|_q).$$

where q is the order of quadrature and $\varphi \in C^q$ satisfies moment conditions of order m.

We choose δ as a function of h to make

$$\delta^{-1}\left(\frac{h}{\delta}\right)^q \leq \epsilon,$$

where ϵ is a user-specified error tolerance, fixed as h vanishes. This implies

$$\delta = O(\epsilon^{-1/(q+1)} h^{q/(q+1)}) = O(h^a), \qquad a = 1 - \frac{1}{q+1},$$

and our error bound becomes

$$E \leq C(\epsilon \|\omega\|_0 + h^{\frac{mq}{q+1}} \|u\|_m + h^{\frac{q^2}{q+1}} \|\omega\|_q).$$

The choice $m = q$ balances the two remaining terms, so

$$E \leq C \left[\epsilon \|\omega\|_0 + h^k(\|\omega\|_q + \|u\|_q) \right] = O(\epsilon + h^k)$$

where $k = q^2/(q+1) = q - 1 + \frac{1}{q+1} > q - 1$. For quadrature of orders $q = 2, 4, 6, 8, 10$, the exponent a in $\delta = O(h^a)$ is 0.66, 0.80, 0.86, 0.89, 0.91 respectively, with order of accuracy k equal to 1.33, 3.20, 5.14, 7.11, 9.09 rapidly approaching $q - 1$ from above as q increases. Thus δ is very close to $O(h)$ for methods of high order k, with only q derivatives of ω required. This allows us to use fast summation methods with excellent efficiency: the fast multipole method with this δ costs $O(N^b)$ with $b = 1 + \frac{1}{q+1} = $ 1.33, 1.20, 1.14, 1.11, 1.09, very close to 1.

We combine this order-k velocity evaluation with an Adams method of order $s = q > k$, because the first-order Euler equations imply that the velocity should have the same order of differentiability in time as in space, with particle positions one order smoother by the flow map equation Eq. (1). An $O(\epsilon + h^k)$ error in the velocity u at each time step does not accumulate in the multistep solution of

$$\dot{\Phi}(z, t) = u(\Phi(z, t), t)$$

so we expect to obtain an error

$$O(\epsilon + \Delta_f^s + h^k)\|\omega\|_q$$

in Φ as h and Δ_f vanish. This would imply similar estimates for the velocity and vorticity by standard arguments.

RESULTS AND DISCUSSION

We implemented the algorithms described above and studied the performance of the fast adaptive method. First, we measured the accuracy and efficiency of the velocity evaluation scheme in isolation. Then we measured the error in long-time calculations with the full method. Finally, we studied the interaction of several smooth patches of vorticity.

We studied the accuracy of the velocity evaluation of orders $k = 1.33, 3.20, 5.14$ and 7.11 corresponding to $m = q = 2, 4, 6,$ and 8, using the Perlman vorticity (Perlman, 1985)

$$\omega_P(z) = \left(\max(0, 1 - r^2)\right)^P$$

where $P = 10$. The vorticity ω_P is a C^{P-1} function on $\mathbf{R}^2$, while the corresponding velocity fields are C^P:

$$u(z) = (1 - \omega_{P+1}(z)) \frac{z^\perp}{(2P + 2)r^2}.$$

This is a stationary radial solution of the Euler equations with shear and a popular test case for vortex methods.

We tested our method with a random initial grid. Given N and n with $n^2 \leq N$, the grid has n^2 vortices uniformly distributed over a rectangle, and the remaining $N - n^2$ vortices distributed in regions where the vorticity is large, providing some degree of random adaptivity.

We generated $N = 500, 1000, 2000, \ldots, 64000$ vortices in such a grid with $n^2 \approx N/10$ and evaluated the velocity at each of the vortices, using core functions and quadratures of orders $m = q = 2, 4, 6, 8$. The number of correct bits

$$B_l = \max\left(0, -\log_2\left[\frac{\|u - u_{h,\delta}\|_l}{\|u\|_l}\right]\right)$$

in the computed velocity $u_{h,\delta}$ in L^1 and L^∞ norms, the CPU times T (in seconds on a Sparc-2 workstation) and other statistics are reported in Table 1. The velocity evaluation produces error $O(\epsilon + N^{-k/2})$ with $k/2 = 0.67$, 1.60, 2.57 and 3.55 in $O(N^b \log \epsilon)$ CPU time with $b = 1.33$, 1.20, 1.14 and 1.11 and a constant of proportionality depending very weakly on the order q. Note that when N doubles, the average cell size h decreases by a factor $\sqrt{2}$, so we expect to gain $k/2$ bits per line in each table until $O(\epsilon)$ is reached.

For first-order methods, the $O(N^{-2/3})$ errors dominate so the $O(\epsilon)$ limit on accuracy never appears. For higher-order methods, we get higher-order convergence in the region where the smoothed kernel is resolved. After the $O(\epsilon)$ limit is reached, convergence continues slowly.

We also tested the long-time accuracy of the method on several Perlman-type test cases for $0 \leq t \leq 20$, a final time at which the fastest fluid particles have completed 1.6 revolutions while the slowest have completed only 0.2. This strong shear is usually considered a severe test for a vortex method. We started with an adaptive random grid with $n^2 \approx 0.8N$, and used core functions, quadratures and Adams methods of orders $m = q = s = 2$, 4 and 6, yielding adaptive vortex methods of orders $k = 1.33$, 3.20 and 5.14. We tested each method on a Perlman patch of minimal smoothness, with $P = q + 1 = 3$, 5 and 7. In particular, the errors at different orders are unrelated. The correct bits in L^1 in the velocity are plotted in Fig. 4. The plots are individually scaled and ticked in such a way that the number of correct bits should increase by half a tick mark at each line. These results clearly confirm the long-time high-order accuracy of the method; they do not show the loss of accuracy observed in Lagrangian vortex methods (for example in Fig. 1). The errors are highly oscillatory on a small scale, because a new quadrature rule is built from scratch at each step.

As a more complex example, we used the order-3.20 method to compute 20 interacting smooth patches of vorticity. Thus the initial vorticity is given by

$$\omega(z, 0) = \sum_{j=1}^{Q} \Omega_j \left(1 - |z - z_j|^2\right)^P$$

where $Q = 20$, $P = 5$ and z_j and Ω_j are random. Some sample vorticity contours are shown in Fig. 5.

$m = q = 2$, $p = 4$, $d = 1$, $k = 1.33$					
N	h	δ	B_1	B_∞	T
500	0.497	0.631	1.95	1.42	4.83
1000	0.328	0.479	2.48	2.03	13.8
2000	0.205	0.351	3.28	2.79	43.6
4000	0.142	0.275	3.91	3.41	142.7
8000	0.089	0.203	4.74	4.26	336.2
16000	0.064	0.163	5.38	4.88	1155
32000	0.039	0.118	6.29	5.79	2051
64000	0.028	0.095	6.93	6.41	6493

$m = q = 4$, $p = 6$, $d = 2$, $k = 3.20$					
N	h	δ	B_1	B_∞	T
500	1.300	1.481	1.02	0.52	6.87
1000	0.807	1.011	2.26	1.79	22.2
2000	0.443	0.625	4.49	3.71	75
4000	0.300	0.457	6.00	5.21	209
8000	0.180	0.305	8.16	7.22	632
16000	0.128	0.232	9.71	9.00	1485
32000	0.078	0.156	11.9	10.3	4498
64000	0.057	0.121	13.3	12.0	8111

$m = q = 6$, $p = 8$, $d = 3$, $k = 5.14$					
N	h	δ	B_1	B_∞	T
500	1.760	1.948	0.0	0.0	8.66
1000	1.170	1.374	0.31	0.0	26.9
2000	0.721	0.905	4.49	2.67	90.6
4000	0.386	0.529	8.21	5.51	281
8000	0.263	0.381	10.2	7.18	774
16000	0.158	0.245	12.0	6.74	1574
32000	0.114	0.185	14.0	9.30	4988
64000	0.068	0.118	15.0	10.1	7634

$m = q = 8$, $p = 10$, $d = 4$, $k = 7.11$					
N	h	δ	B_1	B_∞	T
500	1.810	2.033	1.34	0.48	9.22
1000	1.690	1.912	0.0	0.0	34.9
2000	1.100	1.304	3.34	2.23	111
4000	0.677	0.848	7.79	6.29	358
8000	0.362	0.486	10.4	6.89	960
16000	0.247	0.346	11.9	8.00	2923
32000	0.146	0.217	12.9	8.15	5828
64000	0.106	0.162	15.1	9.99	14650

Table 1: Velocity evaluation results for a Perlman-type vorticity field ω_{10} with N adaptive random points: Correct bits B_1 and B_∞ in u, CPU times T, cell size h and core radius δ. Here q is the quadrature order, m is the moment order, $p - 2$ the order of smoothness and d the degree of the core function. The final results have order k.

ACKNOWLEDGMENTS

This research was supported by a NSF Young Investigator Award, Air Force Office of Scientific Research Grant FDF49620-93-1-0053, and the Applied Mathematical Sciences Subprogram of the Office of Energy Research, U.S. Department of Energy under Contract DE-AC03-76SF00098.

REFERENCES

C. R. Anderson, 1986, "A method of local corrections for computing the velocity field due to a collection of vortex blobs," *Journal of Computational Physics*, Vol. 62, pp. 111–127.

C. Anderson and C. Greengard, 1985, "On vortex methods," *SIAM Journal of Mathematical Analysis*, Vol. 22, pp. 413–440.

E. Anderson, Z. Bai, C. Bischof, J. Demmel, J. Dongarra, J. du Croz, A. Greenbaum, S. Hammarling, A. McKenney, S. Ostrouchov, and D. Sorensen, 1992, *LAPACK Users' Guide*, SIAM, Philadelphia.

J. T. Beale, 1985, "On the accuracy of vortex methods at large times," in B. Engquist, M. Luskin and A. Majda, editors, *Computational fluid dynamics and reacting gas flow*, vol. 12 of *IMA Volumes in Mathematics and Applications*, Springer-Verlag.

J. T. Beale and A. Majda, 1985, "High order accurate vortex methods with explicit velocity kernels," *Journal of Computational Physics*, Vol. 58, pp. 188–208.

J. Carrier, L. Greengard, and V. Rokhlin, 1988, "A fast adaptive multipole method for particle simulations," *SIAM Journal of Scientific and Statistical Computing*, Vol. 9, pp. 669–686.

A. J. Chorin, 1989, *Computational Fluid Mechanics: Selected Papers*, Academic Press.

T. Chacon Rebollo and T. Y. Hou, 1990, "A Lagrangian finite element method for the 2-D Euler equations," *Communications in Pure and Applied Mathematics*, Vol. XLIII, pp.735–767.

K. E. Gustafson and J. A. Sethian, editors, 1991, *Vortex methods and vortex motion*, SIAM, Philadelphia.

O. H. Hald, 1987, "Convergence of vortex methods for Euler's equations III," *SIAM Journal of Numerical Analysis*, Vol. 24, pp. 538–582.

O. H. Hald, 1991, "Convergence of vortex methods," in Gustafson and Sethian (1991), pp. 33–58.

S. A. Huyer and J. R. Grant, 1994, "Incorporation of boundaries for 2D triangular vorticity element methods," Technical Report, NUWC.

H. O. Nordmark, 1991, "Rezoning for higher-order vortex methods," *Journal of Computational Physics*, Vol. 97, pp. 366–387.

M. Perlman, 1985, "On the accuracy of vortex methods," *Journal of Computational Physics*, Vol. 59, pp.200–223.

P. A. Raviart, 1985, "An analysis of particle methods," in F. Brezzi, editor, *Numerical methods in fluid dynamics (Lecture notes in mathematics; 1127) Fondazione C.I.M.E., Firenze*, Springer-Verlag, 1985.

G. Russo and J. A. Strain, 1994, "Fast triangulated vortex methods for the 2D Euler equations," *Journal of Computational Physics*, Vol. 111, pp. 291–323.

J. A. Strain, 1992, "Fast potential theory II: Layer potentials and discrete sums," *Journal of Computational Physics*, Vol. 99, pp. 251–270.

J. A. Strain, 1995, "Locally-corrected multidimensional quadrature rules for singular functions," *SIAM Journal of Scientific and Statistical Computing*, Vol. 16, pp. 1–26.

J. A. Strain, 1996a, "2D vortex methods and singular quadrature rules," *Journal of Computational Physics*, Vol. 124, pp. 1–23.

J. A. Strain, 1996b, "Fast Adaptive 2D Vortex Methods," *Journal of Computational Physics*, 32 pp., submitted.

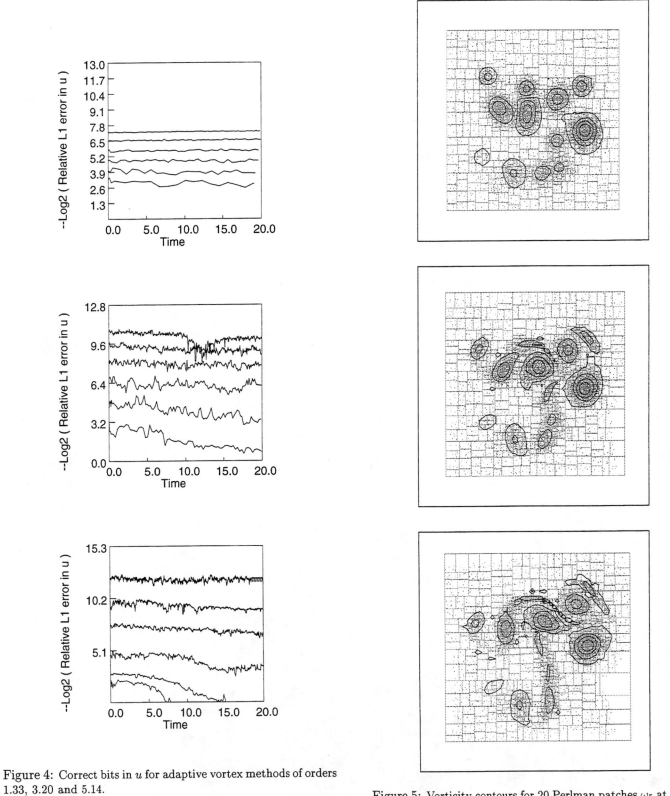

Figure 4: Correct bits in u for adaptive vortex methods of orders 1.33, 3.20 and 5.14.

Figure 5: Vorticity contours for 20 Perlman patches ω_5 at $t = 0$, 8, and 16.

FED-Vol. 238, 1996 Fluids Engineering Division Conference
Volume 3
ASME 1996

3D VORTEX SIMULATION OF INTAKE FLOW IN AN OFF-CENTERED PORT AND CYLINDER WITH A MOVING PISTON

Adrin Gharakhani and Ahmed F. Ghoniem
Department of Mechanical Engineering
Massachusetts Institute of Technology
Cambridge, MA 02139

ABSTRACT

A grid-free approach has been developed for the simulation of high Reynolds number unsteady flow inside three-dimensional domains with moving boundaries. For this purpose, the Navier-Stokes equations are expressed in terms of the vorticity transport formulation. The convection and stretch of vorticity are obtained using the Lagrangian vortex method, while diffusion is approximated by the random walk method. The boundary element method is used to solve a potential flow which is formulated to impose the assigned normal flux on the boundary of the domain. The no-slip boundary condition is satisfied by a vortex tile generation mechanism at the boundary which takes into account the time-varying boundary surfaces due to, e. g., a moving piston. The proposed approach is entirely grid-free within the fluid domain, and virtually free of numerical diffusion. The capability of the method to capture the complex vortical structures inside time-varying confined geometries is demonstrated by simulating the intake process inside an off-centered port-cylinder configuration with a harmonically driven piston.

INTRODUCTION

Since a decade ago, the literature on automotive engines has seen an explosion of research on the application of computational fluid dynamics for the prediction of turbulent flow in reciprocating engines. The range of applications has varied from the idealized 2D/axisymmetric flow in port-cylinder configurations (Butler et al., 1979; Gosman et al., 1978, 1980; Martins & Ghoniem, 1991; Morse et al., 1980,) with and without a poppet valve, to the more realistic three-dimensional flow in the intake ports and the cylinder of the engine, including moving valves (Errera, 1987; Khalighi, 1995; Naitoh et al., 1990; Taghavi & Dupont, 1988.) Most solution methods have been based on the structured control-volume derivation with a body-fitted coordinate system, although finite element methods have also appeared in publications.

The accurate, efficient and automatic meshing of the complicated unsteady three-dimensional domain of engines is a serious concern in grid-based methods. The algorithm for the mesh generation must consider the wide spectrum of geometric length scales, which range from the valve lift to the cylinder diameter and stroke length. It should also be capable of capturing the high velocity gradients within the thin concentrated jets, as well as the large scale turbulent flows, which include recirculation, swirling flows, and multiple separation zones that evolve in time. A direct consequence of the inappropriate meshing of the domain is the introduction of false diffusion - a numerically induced dissipation term - into the flow field, which is associated with weaker large eddies and faster decay of the vortical structures in the engine problem. To reduce numerical diffusion, one can either increase the mesh resolution, which can be costly, or streamline the mesh along the local flow direction, which can lead to degenerate meshes.

The application of heuristic closure models to predict the turbulent flow field in engines is another cause for concern. In most of these models, turbulence is assumed to be homogeneous, and the empirical constants in them may ignore the effect of confinement on the turbulent field and may discount the possible coexistence of multiple flow regimes within the engine, all of which limit the accuracy of the predictions. In addition, since traditional computational methods maintain a degree of false diffusion, it is often difficult to assess the accuracy of the turbulence models with certainty. Perhaps the most critical disadvantage of turbulence modeling is that information about the field is presupposed and supplied to the equations, rather than retrieved from them.

The Lagrangian vortex method is an attractive alternative to the finite volume approach for simulating high Reynolds number flows that contain large vortical structures. The method is grid free in the fluid domain. It is self adaptive and capable of dynamically concentrating computational elements in regions with significant velocity gradients, such as in shear layers, jets and recirculation zones. Furthermore, due to the Lagrangian nature of the method, numerical diffusion is minimized - making the scheme an excellent tool for analyzing flow at high Reynolds numbers.

To this end, a hybrid random vortex-boundary element method was recently developed to simulate unsteady flow in 3D geometries, with moving boundaries of the type encountered in engines. In this approach, the Navier-Stokes equations are formulated in terms of the velocity and the vorticity variables, and the latter is discretized using a collection of spherical vortex elements. The element velocity is expressed as a superposition of a vortical component evaluated by the Biot-Savart law, and a potential component obtained from the solution of a 3D Neumann problem over the domain. The convection of vorticity is evaluated by tracking the trajectory of the elements in the Lagrangian frame of reference. The diffusion is obtained by the random walk method. Additionally, the elemental vorticity vectors are properly adjusted to account for the stretch of vorticity. The boundary element method is used to solve a 3D Laplace equation, which prescribes a potential flow that imposes the normal flux boundary condition on the boundary surfaces - without having to discretize the domain interior. The no-slip boundary condition is satisfied by generating infinitesimally thin vorticity tiles at the boundaries, which subsequently convect and diffuse into the domain interior in the Lagrangian frame of reference - according to the Prandtl equations. Beyond a thin prespecified region near the boundary, the vortex tiles are treated as spherical vortex elements. At present, the boundary surface is idealized by a union of rectangular planar boundary elements and tiles, analogous to the staircase discretization in 2D. The extension to the more general quadrilateral elements is currently under development.

The vortex-boundary element method has been used successfully to simulate the unsteady wake behind a cube in an impulsively started flow (Gharakhani & Ghoniem, 1996.) A massively parallel version of the method has also been completed to take advantage of its inherent parallel properties (Gharakhani & Ghoniem, 1995.) A detailed formulation of the vortex-boundary element method and a parametric test of its accuracy can be found in (Gharakhani, 1995.) In this paper, we present a simulation of flow inside a cylinder confined by an off-centered port and a harmonically driven piston, using the 3D vortex-boundary element method - which, we believe, has not been attempted in the past. The circular cross-section of this geometry is simplified by a staircase. The Reynolds number based on the piston diameter and its maximum speed is set at 350. The objectives of this simplified intake flow problem are (1) to demonstrate the potential advantage of using an internally grid free simulation technique, (2) to verify that the extension of the 3D vortex-boundary element method to a case with moving piston produces a qualitatively reasonable flow field in the cylinder, and (3) to explore, qualitatively, the initiation and growth of large unsteady vortex structures in the field.

FORMULATION

The equations of motion of an incompressible flow within a three-dimensional domain D and with boundary surfaces ∂D are expressed in the vorticity transport form of the Navier-Stokes equations as follows:

$$\frac{\partial \omega}{\partial t} + u.\nabla \omega = \omega.\nabla u + \frac{1}{Re}\nabla^2 \omega \qquad x \in D \qquad (1a)$$

$$\nabla.u = 0 \qquad x \in D \qquad (1b)$$

$$u(x, t) = (u.\tau, u.\rho, u.n) \qquad x \in \partial D \qquad (1c)$$

$$\omega(x, t = 0) = \omega_o \quad , \quad u(x, t = 0) = u_o \qquad x \in D \qquad (1d)$$

where $x = (x, y, z)$ is the position in the Cartesian coordinates normalized by a reference length, L; $u(x, t) = (u, v, w)$ is the velocity vector normalized by a characteristic speed, U; t is the time normalized by L/U; $Re = UL/v$ is the Reynolds number and v is the kinematic viscosity. $\omega(x, t) = (\omega_x, \omega_y, \omega_z)$ is the vorticity vector and is defined as the curl of the velocity vector, $\omega(x, t) = \nabla^\wedge u$. At the boundary surfaces, velocity is expressed in terms of the local orthogonal coordinate system, τ-ρ-n, where $n = (n_x, n_y, n_z)$ is the unit outward normal, and $\tau = (\tau_x, \tau_y, \tau_z)$ and $\rho = (\rho_x, \rho_y, \rho_z)$ are the unit tangents to the boundary.

The Interior

We begin the solution of Eq. (1) by discretizing the vorticity field into a collection of N_V vortex elements, each centered at x_j with element volume ΔV_j and vorticity vector ω_j:

$$\omega(x, t) = \sum_{j=1}^{N_V} \widetilde{\Gamma}_j(t) g_\sigma(x - x_j) \qquad (2)$$

where $\widetilde{\Gamma}_j(t) = \omega_j(t)\Delta V_j$ is the volumetric vorticity, and $g_\sigma(x) = \frac{1}{\sigma^3}g(\frac{|x|}{\sigma})$ is the vortex core function with a spherical core of radius σ. We used the second order core function $g(x) = \frac{3}{4\pi}[1 - tanh^2(|x|^3)]$, selected from a list of functions given by Beale & Majda (1985.)

Given the vorticity distribution (2) and applying the viscous splitting algorithm (Beale & Majda, 1981,) the discrete Lagrangian form of Eq. (1) is integrated in time as follows:

$$\chi_i^*(x_i, t_{k+1}) = \chi_i(x_i, t_k) + \Delta t F[u_i(\chi_i, t_k)] \qquad (3a)$$

$$\widetilde{\Gamma}_i(\chi_i, t_{k+1}) = \widetilde{\Gamma}_i(\chi_i, t_k) + \Delta t F[\widetilde{\Gamma}_i(\chi_i, t_k).\nabla u_i(\chi_i, t_k)] \qquad (3b)$$

$$\chi_i(x_i, t_{k+1}) = \chi_i^*(x_i, t_{k+1}) + \eta_i \qquad (3c)$$

$$\chi_i(x_i, t_o) = \chi_{i,o} \quad , \quad \widetilde{\Gamma}_i(\chi_i, t_o) = \widetilde{\Gamma}_{i,o} \qquad k = 0, 1, ... \quad , \quad i = 1, ..., N_V$$

where χ_i describes the trajectory of the i-th vortex element initially at $\chi_{i,o}$ and with vorticity $\widetilde{\Gamma}_{i,o}$, t_o is the time it is introduced into the domain, $\Delta t = (t_{k+1} - t_k)$ is the integration timestep, and $F[.]$ represents the time integration scheme. We experimented with the modified Euler and the fourth order Runge Kutta methods and selected the former for its economy and acceptable accuracy.

Equation (3c) is the stochastic solution for the diffusion equation, and $\eta_i = (\eta_x, \eta_y, \eta_z)_i$ are independent random variables selected from a Gaussian distribution with zero mean and variance equal to $2\Delta t/Re$. The accuracy and convergence properties of the vortex element method have been demonstrated by Beale & Majda (1982a, 1982b, 1984,) Goodman (1987,) Hald (1979) and Long (1988.)

In Eqs. (3a) and (3b), the velocity and its gradients at the elements are evaluated as the sum of a vortical field in free space and a potential flow, such that continuity, Eq. (1b), and the normal flux boundary condition are satisfied. Given the vorticity distribution (2), the discrete regularized vortical velocity and its gradients (Anderson & Greengard, 1985) are evaluated as follows:

$$u_\omega(x_i, t) = \sum_{j=1}^{N_V} K_\sigma(x_i(t) - x_j(t))^\wedge \tilde{\Gamma}_j(t) \tag{4a}$$

$$i = 1, ..., N_V$$

$$\nabla u_\omega(x_i, t) = \sum_{j=1}^{N_V} \nabla K_\sigma(x_i(t) - x_j(t))^\wedge \tilde{\Gamma}_j(t) \tag{4b}$$

where $K_\sigma(x) = -\dfrac{x}{4\pi|x|^3} f(\dfrac{|x|}{\sigma})$, $K_\sigma(0) = 0$, $\nabla K_\sigma(x) = (\dfrac{\nabla x}{x} - 3\dfrac{\nabla|x|}{|x|})K_\sigma(x)$

$-x\dfrac{\nabla|x|}{|x|}g_\sigma(x)$, and $\nabla K_\sigma(0) = -\dfrac{\nabla x}{4\pi\sigma^3}$, and $f(r) = 4\pi\int_0^r g(r')r'^2 dr' = tanh(r^3)$.

The potential component of the velocity and its gradients are evaluated subsequent to the solution of the following 3D Neumann problem for the interior:

$$\nabla^2\Phi(x) = 0 \qquad\qquad x \in D \tag{5a}$$

$$q(x_o) = -u_P(x_o).n = -(u(x_o) - u_\omega(x_o)).n \qquad x_o \in \partial D \tag{5b}$$

where $\Phi(x)$ is the unknown potential distribution, the gradient of which yields the potential velocity, and $q(x_o)$ is its normal flux at the boundary. We solved Eq. (5) by the boundary element method, assuming a piecewise-linear variation of Φ and q across the boundary elements. (See Gharakhani (1995) for the details of the accurate solution of this problem.) Given Φ and q at the boundary, the potential velocity and its gradients at the vortex element locations are evaluated by the following regularized formulations (Gharakhani, 1995; Sladek & Sladek, 1992:)

$$u_{Pj}(x_i) = \sum_{k=1}^{M} \int_{\partial D_k} -G_{,p}(x_o, x_i)\{\varepsilon_{jpl}[\rho_l^k\Phi_{k,\tau}(x_o) -$$

$$\tau_l^k\Phi_{k,\rho}(x_o)] - \delta_{jp}q_k(x_o)\}dS_k(x_o) \tag{6a}$$

$$\frac{\partial u_{Pj}(x_i)}{\partial x_m} = \sum_{k=1}^{M} \int_{\partial D_k} -G_{,p}(x_o, x_i)\{\varepsilon_{jpl}[(\rho_l^k\tau_m^k\Phi_{k,\tau\tau}(x_o) -$$

$$\tau_l^k\rho_m^k\Phi_{k,\rho\rho}(x_o)) + (\rho_l^k\rho_m^k - \tau_l^k\tau_m^k)\Phi_{k,\tau\rho}(x_o) +$$

$$(\rho_l^k q_{k,\tau}(x_o) - \tau_l^k q_{k,\rho}(x_o))n_m^k] +$$

$$\delta_{jp}[q_{k,\tau}(x_o)\tau_m^k + q_{k,\rho}(x_o)\rho_m^k -$$

$$(\Phi_{k,\tau\tau}(x_o) + \Phi_{k,\rho\rho}(x_o))n_m^k q_k(x_o)]\}dS_k(x_o) \tag{6b}$$

$$(j, l, m, p) = 1, 2, 3 \quad , \quad i = 1, ..., N_V$$

where $G(x_o, x_i) = \dfrac{1}{4\pi|x_o - x_i|}$; j, l, m and p indices indicate direction with respect to the global coordinate system and follow the Einstein rule, $(.)_{,r}$ represents differentiation with respect to x_o in the r-th direction, δ_{jp} is the Kronecker delta, and ε_{jpl} is the antisymmetric permutation tensor. M is the total number of rectangular boundary elements and $S_k(x_o)$ is the surface area of the k-th element. Note that, compared to the classical derivation, the regularized formulation for the velocity and its gradient reduces the order of the integrand singularity by one and two, respectively. This leads to a more accurate evaluation of the velocity and, in particular, its gradients near the boundary. However, the reduction in the singularity order is at the expense of having to prescribe the first and second degree derivatives of the potential and its normal flux at the boundary. In this paper, the tangential derivatives of Φ and q are assumed to be piecewise-linear across the elements, and their nodal values are evaluated by the following approximation. The variation of Φ, for example, across element k is described by $\Phi^k(\xi, \zeta) = \sum_{j=1}^{4} \Theta^j(\xi, \zeta)\Phi^{k,j}$; where $\Theta^j(\xi, \zeta)$ is the standard bilinear shape function, ξ and ζ are the local orthogonal coordinates, and $\Phi^{k,j} = \Phi^k(\xi_j, \zeta_j)$ is the nodal value of Φ at the j-th node of element k. Similarly, the tangential derivative of Φ with respect to the ζ direction is constructed by $\Phi_{,\zeta}^k(\xi, \zeta) = \sum_{j=1}^{4} \Theta^j(\xi, \zeta)\Phi_{,\zeta}^{k,j}$; where $\Phi_{,\zeta}^{k,j} = \dfrac{1}{n^{k,j}}\sum_{m=1}^{M}\sum_{jj=1}^{4}\Theta_{,\zeta}^{jj}(\xi_{k,j}, \zeta_{k,j})\Phi^{m,jj}$, $(\xi_{k,j}, \zeta_{k,j})$ refers to the local coordinates of the node on element m which corresponds to the global coordinates of node j of element k, and $n^{k,j}$ denotes the number of boundary elements that share node j and can be used to compute Φ. The summation over the m boundary elements includes only those which share node j and are in the plane of element k. Therefore, $n^{k,j}$ is equal to one, two or four if node j is at a corner, an edge or elsewhere on the boundary, respectively. The piecewise-linear second derivatives are constructed using the same approach.

The Boundary Region

In this section, the process of vorticity generation on a rectangular wall segment and its evolution within a thin region near the wall are presented. (The algorithm is applied to all wall segments simultaneously.) All variables are defined with respect to the local coordinate system, z is selected normal to the wall and into the domain interior, and $z = 0$ represents the wall surface.

The application of the normal flux boundary condition to the evolution of the vorticity field in the interior, Eq. (3), induces a tangential velocity distribution on the walls, which is generally different from the prescribed no-slip boundary condition. This velocity jump is precisely the amount of surface vorticity that must be generated on the walls to satisfy the no-slip boundary condition. We discretize the latter over a set of rectangular vortex tiles; each with sides $h_{x_i}^t$ and $h_{y_i}^t$, and with surface vorticity $\overline{\gamma}(x_i, y_i, 0, t)$ at the center, $(x_i, y_i, 0)$. The tile vorticity is linked to the velocity jumps at the center of the boundary elements, and is obtained by summing the area-weighted jump contributions from all boundary elements that are shadowed by the vortex tile:

$$\bar{\gamma}_j(x_i, y_i, 0, t) = \varepsilon_{kj3} \sum_{m=1}^{M_B} \overline{\Delta u_{k_m}} \Lambda(x_i, x_m, h_{x_i}^t, h_{x_m}^b) \Lambda(y_i, y_m, h_{y_i}^t, h_{y_m}^b) \quad (7)$$

$$(j, k) = 1, 2$$

where M_B is the number of boundary elements on a wall segment. Each element is defined by its sides $h_{x_m}^b$ and $h_{y_m}^b$ and an area-averaged velocity jump Δu_{k_m} at its center, $(x_m, y_m, 0)$. $\Lambda(x_i, x_m, h_{x_i}^t, h_{x_m}^b) = (\frac{h_{x_i}^t + h_{x_m}^b}{2} - Max(\frac{|h_{x_i}^t - h_{x_m}^b|}{2}, Min(|x_i - x_m|, \frac{h_{x_i}^t + h_{x_m}^b}{2})))/h_{x_i}^t$ is used to assign the area-weighted velocity jump contributions from the boundary elements to the tile. (Indices 1 and 2 used with the surface vorticity and the velocity jump denote the x and y directions, respectively.) To maintain a finer discretization of the flow in the direction normal to the wall, each tile may be split into $N_{S,i} = (|\bar{\gamma}(x_i, y_i, 0, t)|/\gamma_{max} + 0.5)$ stacks of tiles with surface vorticity equal to $\tilde{\gamma}(x_i, y_i, 0, t) = \bar{\gamma}(x_i, y_i, 0, t)/N_{S,i}$ (Ghoniem & Ng, 1987; Ghoniem & Gagnon, 1987; Fishelov, 1990; Puckett, 1989.) γ_{max} is a user-specified maximum surface vorticity.

Once vorticity is generated on the wall, its evolution within a thin region D_b near the boundary is assumed to be locally two-dimensional and is approximated by the Prandtl equations (Chorin, 1978, 1980:)

$$\frac{\partial \omega}{\partial t} + u.\nabla \omega = \frac{1}{Re} \frac{\partial^2 \omega}{\partial z^2} \qquad x \in D_b \qquad (8a)$$

$$\nabla.u = 0 \qquad x \in D_b \qquad (8b)$$

$$\omega(x, t_o) = \omega_o \qquad x \in D_b \qquad (8c)$$

$$u(x, y, z = 0, t) = (0, 0, 0) \;,\; u(x, y, z = b, t) = (U_\infty, V_\infty, 0) \qquad (8d)$$

where $\omega(x, t) = (\omega_x, \omega_y, \omega_z) \equiv (-\partial v/\partial z, \partial u/\partial z, 0)$, and $(U_\infty, V_\infty, 0)$ is the velocity at the edge of the boundary as seen by the wall and is obtained from the Navier-Stokes solution in the interior. $b = BLTC \sqrt{2\Delta t / Re}$ is a user specified boundary thickness, where $BLTC$ is usually assigned in the range 1.0 - 3.0 so that the tiles will jump into the flow interior in a few timesteps with relatively high probability (Fishelov, 1990; Martins & Ghoniem, 1991.)

For a given tile distribution within layer b, the discretized u and v velocity components at the tile centers (x_i, y_i, z_i) are derived by directly integrating the approximate definitions for ω_y and ω_x, respectively, and applying the velocity boundary conditions (8d):

$$u_j(x_i, t) = U_{j,\infty}(x_i, y_i, b, t) + \varepsilon_{kj3} \left[\frac{1}{2} \tilde{\gamma}_k(x_i, t) + \sum_{\substack{l=1 \\ l \neq i}}^{N_T} \tilde{\gamma}_k(x_l, t) \varphi_l(x_i, y_i) s(z_l - z_i) \right] \qquad (9)$$

$$(j, k) = 1, 2 \;,\; i = 1, ..., N_T$$

where $\varphi_l(x_i, y_i) = \Lambda(x_i, x_l, h_{x_i}^t, h_{x_l}^t)\Lambda(y_i, y_l, h_{y_i}^t, h_{y_l}^t)$, N_T is the total number of vortex tiles, s is the step function, and $(U_{1,\infty}, U_{2,\infty}) \equiv (U_\infty, V_\infty)$. The w component is obtained by satisfying continuity:

$$w(x_i, t) = -\frac{(I_x^+ - I_x^-)}{h_{x_i}^t} - \frac{(I_y^+ - I_y^-)}{h_{y_i}^t} \qquad i = 1, ..., N_T \qquad (10)$$

where the divided difference rule is applied to approximate the derivatives and

$$I_x^\pm = U_\infty(x_i \pm \frac{h_{x_i}^t}{2}, y_i, b, t)z_i - \sum_{l=1}^{N_T} \tilde{\gamma}_y(x_l, t) \varphi_l(x_i \pm \frac{h_{x_i}^t}{2}, y_i) Min(z_i, z_l)$$

$$I_y^\pm = V_\infty(x_i, y_i \pm \frac{h_{y_i}^t}{2}, b, t)z_i + \sum_{l=1}^{N_T} \tilde{\gamma}_x(x_l, t) \varphi_l(x_i, y_i \pm \frac{h_{y_i}^t}{2}) Min(z_i, z_l) \qquad (11)$$

The Lagrangian tile solution of Eq. (8a), using a first order Euler time integration, is obtained as follows:

$$x_i^*(t_{k+1}) = x_i(t_k) + u_i(x_i, t_k)\Delta t \qquad (12a)$$

$$k = 0, 1, ... \;,\; i = 1, ..., N_T$$

$$z_i(t_{k+1}) = |z_i^*(t_{k+1}) + \eta_i| \qquad (12b)$$

where (x_i, y_i, z_i) describes the tile trajectory in the current context. Equation (12b) simulates diffusion normal to the wall and into the domain interior by reflecting tiles that jump below the wall back into the field (Puckett, 1989.)

The numerical algorithm is as follows: During each timestep, vortex elements convect, stretch and diffuse in the interior. If a vortex element leaves the domain or jumps into the boundary region it is eliminated. (The trajectory of the elements is such that the normal flux boundary condition is imposed on the flow.) The tiles in the boundary domain are convected concurrently with the evolution of vorticity in the interior. New tiles are then created on the solid walls to satisfy the no-slip boundary condition. Finally all tiles, old and new, are diffused normal to the wall - signifying the end of the computational timestep. If a tile jumps into the flow interior, it is converted into a vortex element with volumetric vorticity $\tilde{\Gamma}(x, t) = \tilde{\gamma}(x, t)h_x^t h_y^t$ and core radius $\sigma = Max(h_x^t, h_y^t)$. This sets the beginning of the next timestep. (See Gharakhani (1995) for the details of the vortex-boundary element method.)

RESULTS

Results from the simulation of the intake process inside an idealized engine cylinder with an off-centered port and a moving piston are presented herein. The circular cross-section of the engine is modeled by a piecewise constant (staircase) idealization, as depicted by the schematic diagram in Fig. 1.

The flow was generated by the harmonic displacement of the piston from rest at the top dead center (TDC) to rest at the bottom dead center (BDC) positions. The uniform flow through the inlet of the port was obtained by simply assigning the no-flux boundary condition to the remaining boundary surfaces and satisfying the continuity requirement. The no-slip boundary condition was applied to all solid boundaries. All dimensions were normalized by the cylinder diameter, D_c, and their values assigned as shown in Fig. 1. The velocity was normalized by the maximum piston speed at 90° crank angle, V_m. The Reynolds number based on D_c and V_m was set at 350. The induction process was discretized by 200 equal timesteps, corresponding to a 0.9° crank angle. Other parameters of importance were set as follows: $\gamma_{max} = 0.5$, $BLTC = 1.5$.

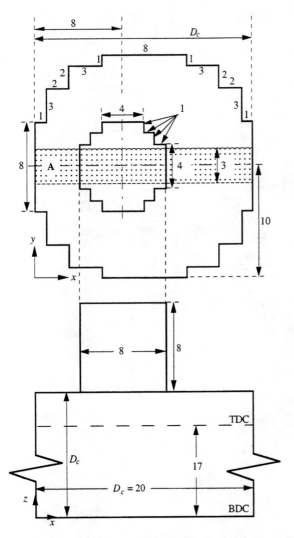

Figure 1. Schematic diagram of the port-cylinder configuration. Integers refer to units of length 0.05.

A time-varying number of boundary elements was used to discretize the cylinder walls, which undergo length change due to the piston motion. The criterion was to assign a maximum number of boundary elements, N_{max}, to discretize the maximum cylinder length, L_{max}, at BDC. The instantaneous number of elements, N, was obtained using the relation $N = Max(1, N_{max}L_c/L_{max} + 0.5)$, where L_c is the instantaneous length of the cylinder. The same procedure was repeated for the vortex tiles. In addition to saving

computational time, this approach maintains a nominal elemental mesh size in the order of L_{max}/N_{max}. In contrast, selecting a fixed value for N would yield extremely thin elements at the beginning of the computation and would generate inaccurate solutions. The boundary element and tile sizes were set at 0.05 and 0.1, respectively, for all stationary surfaces. These values were also assigned as the maximum mesh size for the cylinder walls. The number of boundary elements used to discretize the domain ranged from 1,176 at TDC to 2,536 at BDC. The tile discretization required 356 and 740 tiles, respectively. The number of vortex elements in the interior reached 9,444 at the end of the simulation.

Figure 2 depicts the side view of the trajectory and the velocity of the vortex elements within a slice of volume with 0.15 thickness, and plane of symmetry which rests on the plane of symmetry of the engine - region A in Fig. 1. The velocity vectors are represented by fixed-length sticks whose origins are positioned at the vortex element locations and depicted as solid circles. The colors indicate the magnitude of the velocity vectors, normalized by the instantaneous maximum speed in the field. The combination of the fixed-length vector and the time-varying color coding (based on the instantaneous normalization of the field) offers the following advantages for flow visualization purposes: (1) When the length of the velocity vector is scaled by the maximum or some nominal value of the velocity in the field, near stagnant or small scale recirculation regions become visually difficult to evaluate. On the other hand, while scaling the field by the smaller values of the velocity improves the clarity of the previously hard-to-detect regions of the flow, it leads to large overlapping velocity vectors elsewhere. However, the alternative of using fixed length vectors is useful in identifying even the weakest recirculation zones as clearly as the more dominant features of the flow. (2) A serious handicap with the traditional scaling approach, when visualizing 3D vectors on the paper plane, is that vectors that have a large component in the direction normal to the plane are practically indistinguishable from small in-plane vectors. However, this difficulty is partially alleviated with the present approach as vectors that have a nominal length represent flow along the paper plane, and the shorter ones indicate flow into or out of it. Additionally, solid and hollow circles may be used to identify the flow direction in or out of the paper. (3) Lastly, color coding the vectors based on the normalization by the instantaneous maximum velocity - rather than the absolute peak speed at approximately 90° crank angle - allows one to uncover the *relative* strengths of various processes in the domain within *each* time frame, irrespective of how small the instantaneous maximum velocity may be compared to the absolute peak speed.

Back to Fig. 2. Immediately after the harmonic motion of the piston proceeds from rest at TDC, a potential flow is established in the intake port and the chamber. The continuity constraint sets the area-averaged velocity in the port at 6.25 times the piston speed. This implies that by 9.3° crank angle the mean velocity in the port is already higher than the peak piston speed at 90° crank angle. Furthermore, at 9.3°, the piston has moved away from TDC by less than 0.007. Therefore, the flow dynamics inside the chamber are influenced by the intake port jet, instantly. In addition, during the entire induction step, the chamber is continuously supplied with

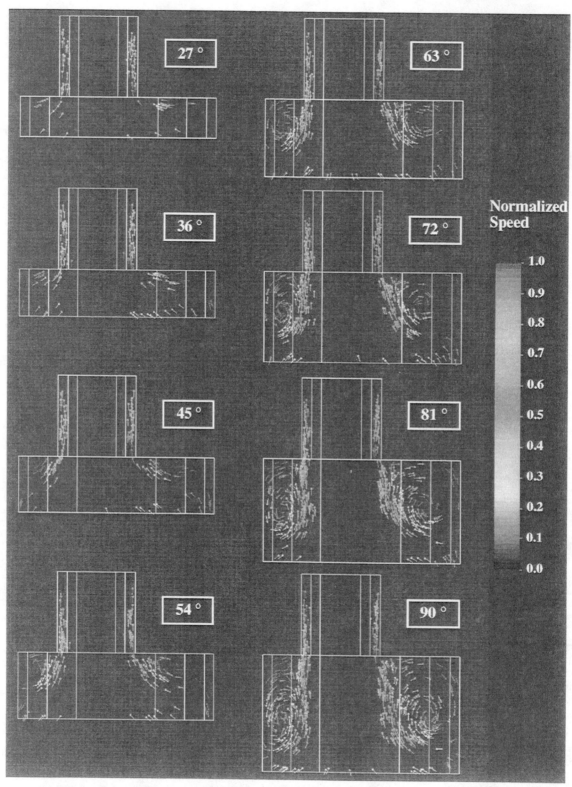

Figure 2: Vortex element trajectories within volume A of Fig. 1. Velocity vectors are fixed in length. Normalization in each time frame is based on the instantaneous maximum speed in the field.

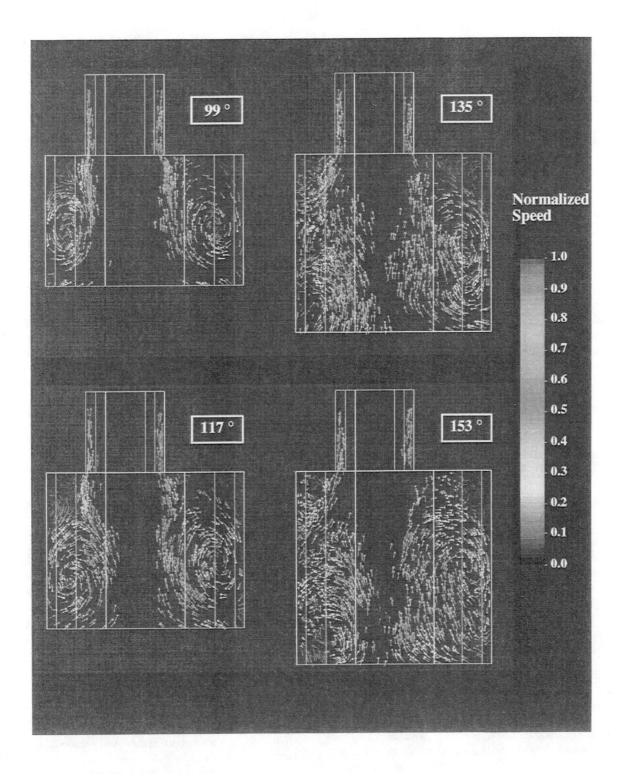

Figure 2 (Continued)

high speed vorticity, generated at the intake port walls. Thus, it is reasonable to assume that the jet issued from the intake port, rather than the moving piston, is the more significant controlling mechanism in this flow. For this reason, $Re = 875$, based on the port diameter and its peak speed, may be a more appropriate measure of the flow characteristics - especially as it relates to the formation and growth of eddies in the chamber.

The envelope of the vortex elements in the port depicts the development of the familiar boundary layer on its walls. Note that the boundary layer does not develop to its fullest at the axial centerline of the port, and a wide potential core exists in the intake port which extends into the cylinder. A longer port and/or a smaller port diameter is necessary to obtain a fully developed profile at the inlet of the cylinder. However, results from the present computation compare quite favorably with those from the 2D vortex simulation of an analog problem, using a smaller port diameter and a fully developed inlet velocity profile (Martins & Ghoniem, 1991). Therefore, the extra computational overhead associated with extending the port length is avoided here. Also notice that as the piston accelerates from TDC to its peak speed at 90° crank angle and decelerates thereafter to rest at BDC, the boundary layer thickness on the intake port walls experiences a commensurate decrease and increase, respectively. This is to be expected, because the harmonic motion of the piston changes the effective Reynolds number in the port as a function of the crank angle.

In contrast to the flow in the port, where a boundary layer is developed instantly, the flow in the chamber remains weak and essentially potential until 30° crank angle. This is evident from the absence of a sizable number of vortex elements inside the chamber; in particular, there is only negligible vorticity generation on the cylinder walls. Moreover, the trajectory of the vortices at the chamber top, which originate from the port, are closely parallel to the boundary contour - similar to streamlines in potential flow.

During the induction step, a jet is issued from the intake port into the chamber, which separates from the port due to the sudden expansion at the interface of the port and the chamber, and begins to roll up in the cylinder into a donut-shaped toroidal eddy. Note that the formation of the vortex torus near the cylinder head, and at a very early stage in the process, confirms that the jet is the primary mechanism responsible for generating the torus and that the piston acts more as a confining medium. The cross-section of the torus is depicted in the figure as two distinct eddies on the two sides of the port. The rotational directions of the eddies are consistent with the direction of jet flow. The high-speed vortex elements in the cylinder, which extend from the intake port boundary layer elements, represent the shear layer caused by the momentum difference between the high-speed jet and the relatively slow field in the chamber. At the early stages of the flow, up to around 60° crank angle, the curvature and orientation of the left and right shear layers are determined by the piston position, or the crank angle, and the relative position of the port with respect to the cylinder. This can be verified by recognizing that each shear layer is streamlined such that a curve through it extrapolates out to the intersection of the cylinder wall and the piston.

As the piston motion proceeds, the toroidal eddy convects slowly away from the chamber top, and grows by entraining most of the fluid from the jet and some of the fluid which already exists in the cylinder. Up to 63° crank angle, the left and right cross-sections of the toroidal eddy grow in size at an equal rate, and maintain similar shapes and profiles. However, this symmetry is lost beyond 63°. The left side of the eddy, which already has an effective core diameter equal to the distance between the port and the cylinder wall on the left, continues to grow *along* the cylinder - due to the availability of volume between the eddy and the piston. In the mean time, the larger area under the right expansion side allows the right side of the eddy to continue its radial growth to an effective diameter that is equal to the distance between the port and the cylinder wall on the right (at approximately 81°.) Beyond this point, both sides of the eddy continue to grow along the axial direction, while occupying most of the volume under their respective expansion sides. The coherence of the toroidal vortical structure is preserved until 90° after TDC (ATC.) Notice the development of a weak counter-rotating vortex ring at approximately 72°, at the corner of the cylinder head and the side walls. This ring stays at the corner and remains insignificantly weak. In addition to the primary vortex torus, a small secondary torus starts to develop at 99° crank angle. In contrast to the primary torus, the core of this torus is azimuthally non-uniform from inception, and its left side appears to be larger than the one on the right. The average core size is equivalent to the initial clearance height - the distance between the piston at TDC and the cylinder top.

In spite of the observed symmetry between the left and right sides of the eddy during the initial stages of the flow development (up to 63°,) the line passing through the eddy centers is slightly slanted with respect to the horizontal, due to the off-center location of the port. An azimuthally uniform torus is initially created around the jet, near the cylinder head, due to the jet separation into the cylinder. As the flow progresses, the torus rolls forward in the jet direction and expands out radially, while it enlarges its core size as a result of further entrainment of the jet and the chamber fluid. Prior to its first contact with the cylinder side walls at approximately 63°, during which the wall effects are negligible, the torus behaves strikingly similar to a ring vortex in an unbounded domain. Beyond 90° ATC, and as will be confirmed by the plots showing the iso-surfaces of the dotproduct of the vorticity vector with itself, this vortex loses its coherence and starts to break up into a number of large structures. The break up appears to occur first around the azimuth of the torus, leading to the formation of a number of vortices whose primary direction is along the cylinder axis. In the following, we attempt to explain this observation qualitatively using the dynamics of vortex rings.

As we mentioned earlier, the vortical structure forming at the cylinder head (up to 90°) strongly resembles a vortex ring moving in free space (see also Fig. 4.) The dynamics of the latter have been analyzed extensively (Saffman, 1978; Widnall et al., 1974,) as well as investigated experimentally (Maxworthy, 1977; Sullivan et al., 1973) and computationally (Knio & Ghoniem, 1988) in free space and in wall confined flows. In fact, Ekchian (1978) was able to predict vortex breakdown in axisymmetric engines with poppet valves, using linear theories of the inviscid instability of ring vortices. In a parametric study by Knio and Ghoniem (1988,) vortex rings were excited by a sinusoidal perturbation in the radial direction, using an integer number of waves around the azimuth of the rings. The computations predicted the development and growth of streamwise vortices around the ring azimuth, and the mode of stability was shown to depend on the nature of the perturbation as well as the ring. More specifically, the most unstable wavenumbers were found to be proportional to the ratio of the ring radius to the core size. Additionally, outside a narrow band around the most unstable wavenumbers, the rings were shown to oscillate stably. In long time computations, these perturbations grow - leading to the break up of the ring. In the present computation, the circular cross section of the port is discretized by 20 unequal staircase segments, as depicted in Fig. 1. As a result, the contour of the discretized circle imparts small radial perturbations around the azimuth of the primary torus; albeit, with multiplicity of wavenumbers. The growth of these perturbations, via the mechanism mentioned before, leads to the development of streamwise vortices around the azimuth of the torus, accompanied by mild oscillations. Eventually, as the waves grow further, the break up is observed (see Fig. 4, at 153°.) While the origin of the initial perturbation is numerical (the discretization of the circle into a staircase-shaped polygon,) in practice one expects to encounter other perturbations due to turbulence that would lead to a similar break up of the vortex.

Figure 3 depicts the perspective view of the trajectory of the vortex elements generated by the piston face, due to the interaction of the latter with the intake jet. The fixed length vectors represent the vorticity, and the colors represent the magnitude normalized by the instantaneous maximum vorticity in the field. The jet at the exit of the intake port is 6.25 times faster than the moving piston. Consequently, it impinges upon the piston face and disperses out radially, generating circular vortex rings parallel to the piston face. The direction of these rings is opposite the direction of the toroidal vortex in the cylinder. The inner most circular area directly below the port is the stagnation region and is, therefore, devoid of vortex elements.

The accelerated motion of the piston towards 90° crank angle is accompanied by a corresponding increase in the jet speed as it impinges on the piston, which leads to an increase in the radial velocity of the rings generated on the piston. This, combined with the fact that the outermost rings - being closer to the chamber walls - are relatively slower than the inner rings, leads to the formation of a well defined closely packed vortex torus. The torus is nearly symmetric with respect to the plane of symmetry of the engine. As the wavefront of the expanding vortex torus contacts the cylinder walls, it encounters the corners of the staircase that is used to discretize the cylinder walls. As a result, strong waviness appears around the periphery of the vortex ring, near the walls, which again leads to the strong growth of lobes around its periphery. These lobes correspond to vortex structures whose axes are aligned in the direction of the cylinder axis. However, the relative magnitudes of these vortices are small compared to the ones generated in the chamber due to the jet separation.

Figure 4 depicts the evolution of $|\omega|^2 = 0.2$ surfaces, where ω is the local vorticity, normalized by the instantaneous maximum vorticity in the field. The local value of the vorticity was evaluated on a uniform grid, divergence free, using its definition as the curl of the velocity. $|\omega|^2$ corresponds to the enstrophy, which can also be regarded as a measure of the energy dissipation rate per unit volume, and can be used to detect regions of high energy dissipation, shear and mixing within a configuration. During the early stages of the induction process, before 45° crank angle, the boundary layer in the intake port contributes substantially to the vorticity, hence the energy dissipation, within the cylinder. The figure confirms the earlier suggestion that the flow in the cylinder is essentially potential during this stage, and that the jet from the port is the only significant source of vorticity or shear. The development and roll up of the donut shaped vortex torus due to the sudden expansion of the jet in the cylinder is prominently displayed in the figure. The iso-surface evolves from a cylindrical shape inside the port into a donut shape in the cylinder. The latter is clearly the structure which stores most of the incoming shear/vorticity/rotational energy. A mild waviness can be seen on the iso-surface, for up to 72° crank angle. The perturbations associated with these waves grow and lead to the break up of the torus in the later stages. Also note that beyond 81° crank angle, the eventual formation of the secondary vortex near the cylinder head, and around the port, begins to contribute to the total dissipation.

CONCLUSIONS

A recently developed three-dimensional random vortex-boundary element method was extended to simulate the intake flow inside a chamber, fitted with an off-centered port at one end and a harmonically moving piston at the other. The Reynolds number based on the piston diameter and its maximum speed was set at 350. A time-varying number of surface meshes was used to discretize the cylinder walls. Initially, 356 vortex tiles and 1,176 boundary elements were used, which grew to 740 and 2,536, respectively.

Results show that the flow inside the cylinder is primarily dominated by the jet issued from the intake port, which separates at the top of the cylinder and forms a primary vortex torus. The latter continues to entrain the jet and grows to fill a significant portion of the cylinder at BDC. In addition, the jet separation is seen to give rise to a secondary vortex torus, which maintains a nominal core size in the order of the initial clearance height in the cylinder. A weak counter-rotating torus (generated by the cylinder) is also evident at the top corner of the chamber, which remains weak but stable. The boundary layer in the port is the major source of vorticity in the cylinder; at least, during the early stages of the intake process. Later, the primary toroidal eddy contains the highest level of vorticity. The structure of the primary torus is coherent until 90° crank angle. Beyond this stage, the introduction of perturbations around the azimuth of the eddy leads to the growth of strong vorticity along its axis of rotation and the eventual break up of the eddy. Zones of high vorticity are also regions of strong energy dissipation. The oscillations which are observed around the azimuth of the primary toroidal eddy and the piston-generated eddy result from perturbations introduced by the staircase discretization

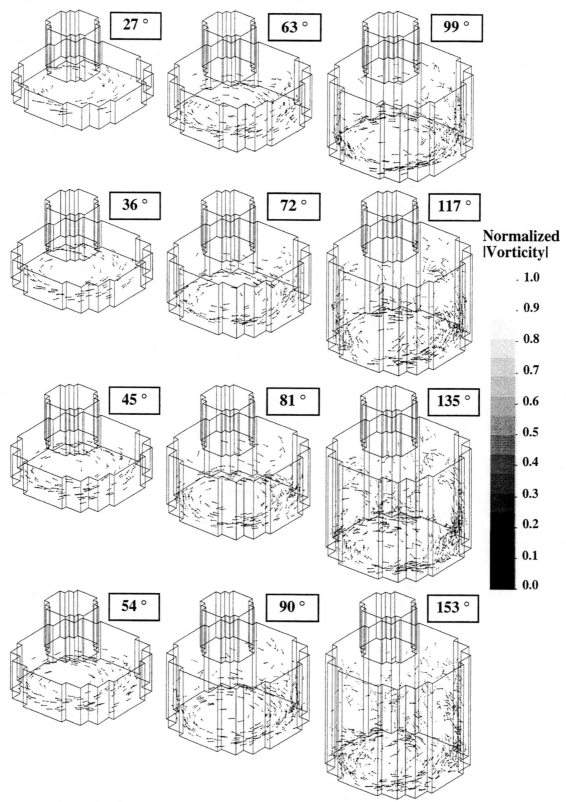

Figure 3: Perspective view of vortex elements generated on the piston.
Vorticity vectors normalized by the instantaneous maximum vorticity in the field.

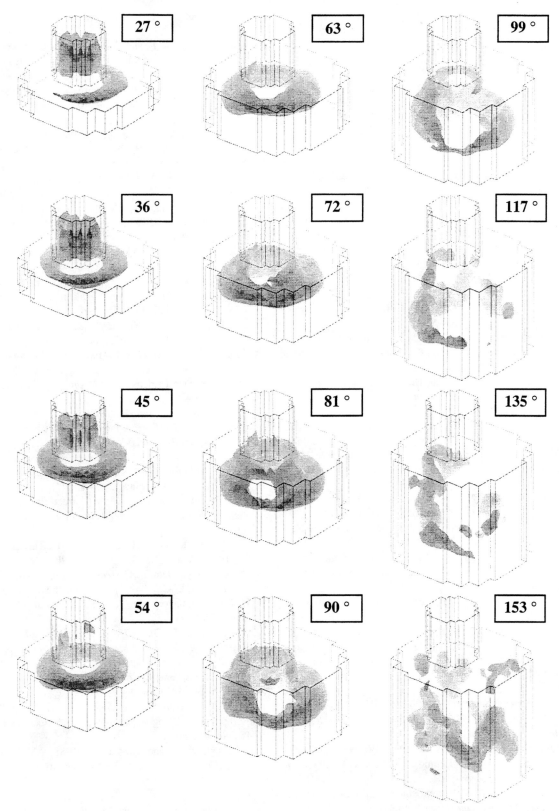

Figure 4: Iso-surfaces of $\omega.\omega = 0.2$. ω is vorticity normalized by the instantaneous maximum field vorticity.

of the engine surface. In practice, the structure of these perturbations could be the turbulence present in the incoming flow.

ACKNOWLEDGMENTS

This project was funded by FORD Motor Company and Gas Research Institute. The numerical experiments were performed on the Cray C90 at the Pittsburgh Supercomputing Center.

REFERENCES

Anderson, C. and Greengard, C., 1985, "On Vortex Methods," *SIAM J. Numer. Anal.*, Vol. 22, No. 3, pp. 413-440.

Beale, J. T. and Majda, A., 1981, "Rates of Convergence for Viscous Splitting of the Navier-Stokes Equations," *Math. Comput.*, Vol. 37, No. 156, pp. 243-259.

Beale, J. T. and Majda, A., 1982a, "Vortex Methods. I: Convergence in Three Dimensions," *Math. Comput.*, Vol. 39, No. 159, pp. 1-27.

Beale, J. T. and Majda, A., 1982b, "Vortex Methods. II: Higher Order Accuracy in Two and Three Dimensions," *Math. Comput.*, Vol. 39, No. 159, pp. 29-52.

Beale, J. T. and Majda, A., 1984, "Vortex Methods for Fluid Flow in Two or Three Dimensions," in *Contemporary Mathematics*, Amer. Math. Soc., Vol. 28, pp. 221-229.

Beale, J. T. and Majda, A., 1985, "High Order Vortex Methods with Explicit Velocity Kernels," *J. Comput. Phys.*, Vol. 58, pp. 188-208.

Butler, T. D., Cloutman, L. D., Dukowicz, J. K. and Ramshaw, J. D., 1979, "CONCHAS: An Arbitrary Lagrangian-Eulerian Computer Code for Multi-Component Chemically Reactive Fluid Flow at All Speeds," Los Alamos Scientific Laboratory Report No. LA-8129-MS.

Chorin, A. J., 1978, "Vortex Sheet Approximation of Boundary Layers," *J. Comput. Phys.*, Vol. 27, pp. 428-442.

Chorin, A. J., 1980, "Vortex Models and Boundary Layer Instability," *SIAM J. Sci. Stat. Comput.*, Vol. 1, No. 1, pp. 1-21.

Ekchian, A., 1978, "Flow Visualization Study of the Intake Process of An Internal Combustion Engine," Ph.D. Thesis, M.I.T., Cambridge, MA.

Errera, M. P., 1987, "Numerical Prediction of Fluid Motion in the Induction System and the Cylinder in Reciprocating Engines," *SAE Technical Paper No. 870594*, pp. 1-11.

Fishelov, D., 1990, "Vortex Methods for Slightly Viscous Three-Dimensional Flow," *SIAM J. Sci. Stat. Comput.*, Vol. 11, No. 3, pp. 399-424.

Gharakhani, A. and Ghoniem, A. F., 1995, "Massively Parallel Implementation of A 3D Vortex-Boundary-Element Method," *2nd International Workshop on Vortex Flows and Related Numerical Methods*, (Montreal, Canada.)

Gharakhani, A. and Ghoniem, A. F., 1996, "Vortex Simulation of the Three-Dimensional Wake Behind A Cube," *AIAA-96-0170 34th Aerospace Sciences Meeting*, (Reno, Nevada, Jan.) pp. 1-22.

Gharakhani, A., 1995, "3-D Vortex-Boundary Element Method For The Simulation Of Unsteady, High Reynolds Number Flows," Sc.D. Thesis, M.I.T., Cambridge, MA.

Ghoniem, A. F. and Ng, K., 1987, "Numerical Study of the Dynamics of a Forced Shear Layer," *Phys. Fluids*, Vol. 30, No. 3, pp. 706-721.

Ghoniem, A. F. and Gagnon, Y., 1987, "Vortex Simulation of Laminar Recirculating Flow," *J. Comput. Phys.*, Vol. 68, No. 2, pp. 346-377.

Goodman, J., 1987, "Convergence of the Random Vortex Method," *Commun. Pure Appl. Math.*, Vol. 40, No. 2, pp. 189-220.

Gosman, A. D., Meling, A., Watkins, A. P. and Whitelaw, J. H., 1978, "Axisymmetric Flow in a Motored Reciprocating Engine," *Proc. Instn. Mech. Engrs.*, Vol. 192, pp. 213-223.

Gosman, A. D., Johns, R. J. R. and Watkins, A. P., 1980, "Development of Prediction Methods for In-Cylinder Process in Reciprocating Engines," Mattavi, J. N. and Amann, C. A., eds, *Combustion Modeling in Reciprocating Engines*, Plenum, New York, pp. 69-129.

Hald, O., 1979, "Convergence of Vortex Methods for Euler's Equations," *SIAM J. Numer. Anal.*, Vol. 16, No. 5, pp. 726-755.

Khalighi, B., 1995, "Multidimensional In-Cylinder Flow Calculations and Flow Visualization in a Motored Engine," *J. Fluids Engrg.*, Vol. 117, No. 2, pp. 282-288.

Knio, O. M. and Ghoniem, A. F., 1988, "On the Formation of Streamwise Vorticity In Turbulent Shear Flows," *AIAA-88-0728 26th Aerospace Sciences Meeting*, (Reno, Nevada) pp. 1-17.

Long, D.-G., 1988, "Convergence of the Random Vortex Method in Two Dimensions," *J. Amer. Math. Soc.*, Vol. 1, No. 4, pp. 779-804.

Martins, L.-F. and Ghoniem, A. F., 1991, "Vortex Simulation of the Intake Flow in A Planar Piston-Chamber Device," *Int. J. Numer. Methods Fluids*, Vol. 12, pp. 237-260.

Maxworthy, T., 1977, "Some Experimental Studies of Vortex Rings," *J. Fluid Mech.*, Vol. 81, No. 3, pp. 465-495.

Morse, A., Whitelaw, J. H. and Yianneskis, M., 1980, "The Influence of Swirl on the Flow Characteristics of A Reciprocating Piston-Cylinder Assembly," *J. Fluids Engrg.*, Vol. 102, No. 4, pp. 478-480.

Naitoh, K., Fujii, H., Urushihara, T., Takagi, Y. and Kuwahara, K., 1990, "Numerical Simulation of the Detailed Flow in Engine Ports and Cylinders," *SAE Technical Paper No. 900256*, pp. 1-18.

Puckett, E. G., 1989, "A Study of the Vortex Sheet Method and Its Rate of Convergence," *SIAM J. Sci. Stat. Comput.*, Vol. 10, No. 2, pp. 298-327.

Saffman, P. G., 1978, "The Number of Waves On Unstable Vortex Rings," *J. Fluid Mech.*, Vol. 84, No. 4, pp. 625-639.

Sladek, V. and Sladek, J., 1992, "Non-Singular Boundary Integral Representation of Stresses," *Int. J. Numer. Methods Eng.*, Vol. 33, pp. 1481-1499.

J. P. Sullivan, S. E. Widnall and S. Ezekiel, 1973, "A Study of Vortex Rings Using A Laser-Doppler Velocimeter," *AIAA Jl*, Vol. 11, No. 10, pp. 1384-1389.

Taghavi, R. and Dupont, A., 1988, "Multidimensional Flow Simulation in An Inlet Port/Combustion Chamber Assembly Featuring A Moving Valve," *ASME Internal Combustion Div.*, ICE v6, pp. 9-15.

Widnall, S. E., Bliss, D. B. and Tsai, C-Y, 1974, "The Instability of Short Waves on A Vortex Ring," *J. Fluid Mech.*, Vol. 66, pp. 35-47.

FED-Vol. 238, 1996 Fluids Engineering Division Conference
Volume 3
ASME 1996

VORTEX PARTICLE MODELLING OF STALL ON ROTORS.
APPLICATION TO WIND TURBINES.

Spyros G. Voutsinas and Vasilis A. Riziotis

National Technical University of Athens,
Department of Mechanical Engineering,
P.O Box 64070, 15710 Zografou, Hellas
Tel: (+)301-7721096, Fax: (+)301-7721057,
e_mail: spyros@fluid.mech.ntua.gr
e_mail: vasilis@fluid.mech.ntua.gr

ABSTRACT

Dynamic stall is of particular interest to rotor aerodynamics because of its connection to structural vibrations and control malfunctions. Due to inherent difficulties in most cases stall on rotors is approximated by simple models as those used within the context of blade element theory. However, their predictions are not always satisfactory and thus improvement is necessary. Since complete Navier-Stokes solvers are too expensive to afford, improvement is sought in between at an intermediate level. In the present work, a vortex model is proposed, based on the double wake concept corresponding to two vortex sheets originating from the trailing edge and the separation point respectively. Results on 2D steady stall, on dynamic stall of a pitching airfoil and finally of stall on a wind turbine rotor operating in yaw showed that the model reproduces the physics in a satisfactory way as compared with measurements.

ROTOR AERODYNAMICS & STALL MODELLING

Unsteady aerodynamics and dynamic stall in particular, play an important role in the design of rotors since they determine the excitation of structural dynamics which can lead to malfunctions or even failure. Dynamic inflow and yaw induced stall are two examples of unsteady flow situations appearing quite often on both helicopter rotors and wind turbines. For wind turbines with which we will be dealing specifically herein, the turbulent character of the flow environment within which they operate, renders these excitation mechanisms highly oscillating over the whole range of frequencies. Therefore models capable of providing satisfactory predictions are necessary in order to well design rotors.

From the prediction point of view, we still do not dispose reliable methods for stall. In many aspects we lack of fundamental knowledge on flows at high Reynolds numbers which are of direct relevance with the occurrence and evolution of stall. For example, it is still unclear even in the case of a pitching airfoil how the reduced frequency and the Reynolds number affect the unsteady loading of the airfoil (Ekaterinaris et al 1995). As for 3D viscous calculations which could give a better insight to the problem, they are beyond our current computational capabilities. First attempts to perform such calculations in steady state conditions have been reported only recently (AGARD 1995, IEA 1994).

In spite of all difficulties, the importance of stall induced effects in engineering design, made necessary the development of approximate models capable of providing reliable quantitative information. In this connection several so called *engineering* models have been developed within the context of the classical blade-element theory (Johnson 1980, Hansen and Butterfield 1993, Snel and Scheppers 1994). In these models, stall is accounted for by appropriately modifying the sectional lift and drag characteristics either through a time-delay scheme on the angle of attack as in the Boeing-Vertol model or by solving a set of equations as in the Leishman-Beddoes and ONERA models (Leishman and Beddoes 1986, Leishman and Crouse 1989, Petot 1989, Truong 1993). In the case of wind turbines, experimental evidence as well as numerical results suggest that engineering models can be incorrect especially at the inboard part of the blade.

Part of the discrepancies between predictions and measurements are due to inherent weaknesses engineering models have. The assumptions from strip theory used in order to formulate the flow equations, suppress 3D effects. In addition, wake effects are taken into account only indirectly through induction factors assuming equilibrium. In this way several dynamic inflow effects are incorrectly reproduced by the models. Consequently, amelioration of the predictions can be at first sought by using more elaborate aerodynamic models such as the lifting-surface or the full three-dimensional free-wake models (Voutsinas et al 1995, Voutsinas 1995). This improves the quality of the flow information provided to the stall model. Moreover, the feedback of the stall consequences to the overall flow is made possible. It is noted that in most engineering models the stall model will only modify the loads and not the velocity field. In the models proposed herein this feedback link is realized through the free vorticity.

VORTEX-TYPE STALL MODELS

Stall is a typical case of vortex flow. Near the solid boundary and downstream of separation, vorticity is massively released and then convected in the outer flow. Thus a pronounced shear layer is formed whose evolution controls stall (McCroskey 1976, Favier et al 1988). In view of developing a numerical model with reasonable computational requirements it was clear that viscous effects should be included indirectly by their consequences on the overall flow. In this respect vortex methods are particularly well suited not only because they are formulated with respect to vorticity but also because they are grid-free since they are based on the Lagrangian (material) description of the flow (Leonard 1985, Smith 1986). Previous experience has showed that vortex methods need not model viscous effects in detail in order to give good predictions. This fits well with our intention to keep only the essentials of the whole stall problem in the model. More specifically, the flow is represented by surface (bound) vorticity whereas all free shear layers are assumed thin vortex sheets. In order to introduce separation, points (2D case) or lines (3D case) are specified on the solid boundaries where from vorticity is shed. In fact it is at these locations that the bound vorticity is transformed into free vorticity. For each airfoil section either isolated or as part of a rotor blade, there can be at most two shedding locations for the vorticity: the trailing edge, and the separation point that is somewhere between the leading edge and the trailing edge. The two shear layers that are gradually generated, constitute the double-wake concept. They correspond to the classical trailing wake and the boundary of the separation bubble. Both shear layers are simulated by vortex particles. The basic advantage of the particle approach is its flexibility and its computational economy. This is especially true in the case of three-dimensional calculations.

Because stall is definitely of viscous origin, a standalone inviscid model as the one described above, is unable to handle it. Therefore we have to complete the model with viscous-type enhancements such as the specification of the location of separation or of the rate with which vorticity is released (Katz 1981, Vezza and Galbraith 1985).

In the present paper new vortex-type stall models are proposed for both the two-dimensional as well as the three-dimensional case. The 2D model concerns a moving airfoil for which we specify the history of the separation point by means of an empirical model. Steady as well as dynamic stall are discussed and results are shown for all the aerodynamic characteristics (lift, drag and moment). The 3D model concerns the modelling of wind turbine rotors operating in yaw. Adopting the thin-wing approximation for the blades stall is modelled as leading edge separation. In this case the free parameter is the rate with which vorticity is shed from the leading edge. Numerically it is specified by means of the ONERA stall model applied in a section-by-section procedure over the whole blade. In the sequel the two models are presented separately together with some typical results. Comparisons with measurements show that the predictions can reproduce the real flow quite well.

THE 2D STALL MODEL

Theory

According to the double wake concept two vortex sheets are formed originating from the trailing edge and the point of separation $P_s(t)$ respectively (Fig. 1). It is assumed that the location of P_s is known a priori as a function of time. Using Green's theorem the velocity field $\vec{u}(\cdot;t)$ is represented by means of singularity distributions. More specifically on the airfoil we distribute sources $\sigma(.;t)$ and surface vorticity $\gamma(.;t)$. As for the double wake it is formed by its near part consisted of two vorticity segments carrying surface vorticities $\gamma_w(t)$ and $\gamma_s(t)$, and the far part consisted of a collection of vortex particles which represent the vorticity released at previous times. Details on the discrete model can be found in Morfiadakis et al (1991) where the case of the attached flow is treated.

For attached flows $\gamma(.;t)$ is considered constant over the entire airfoil and this because Kelvin's theorem being a scalar relation, permits the introduction of only one degree of freedom (d.o.f.). When this formulation was applied to the stalled case a sharp pressure jump appeared just at the separation point, showing the necessity of introducing locally a significant velocity jump at separation. Noting that the angle formed by the vortex sheet at separation and the surface of the airfoil is theoretically zero we decided to impose a stagnation point just after separation which led to the desired velocity jump. In order to satisfy such a condition we had to increase the number of d.o.f. by one. Because surface vorticity is closely related to tangential velocity we decided to add this new d.o.f to $\gamma(.;t)$. As shown in Fig. 1, $\gamma(.;t)$ is a two-valued function with $\gamma_1(t)$ and $\gamma_2(t)$ being the constant values on either side of the separation point.

The piecewise constant source distribution is determined by the implementation of the non entry boundary condition whereas $\gamma_1(t)$ and $\gamma_2(t)$ are determined by the stagnation condition satisfied at the first control point just downstream $P_s(t)$ and Kelvin's theorem. This means that the details of the velocity distribution over the airfoil are basically determined by the source distribution whereas $\gamma_1(t)$ and $\gamma_2(t)$ fix the circulation of the airfoil. As for the remaining unknowns:

(a) The intensities $\gamma_w(t)$ and $\gamma_s(t)$ of the two near wake elements, are determined at the trailing edge and separation point by taking them equal to the local discontinuity of the velocity as indicated in Fig. 2 & 3 (Δt denotes the time step of the numerical scheme).

(b) The lengths Δl_w and Δl_s of the two near wake segments, are determined by the local mean velocity multiplied by Δt (See Fig. 2&3).

(c) At the trailing edge because of the wedge-like configuration, θ_w is chosen so as the segment is parallel either to the upper or to the lower surface of the airfoil according to the sign of the circulation around the airfoil (Fig. 2). On the contrary at separation, θ_s is found by averaging locally the convection directions (Fig. 3).

Because Δl_w, Δl_s, θ_w and θ_s are implicitly related to the rest of the d.o.f., an iterative scheme is followed at every time step. Experience showed that up to 5 iterations were enough. Finally, it is noted that $P_s(t)$ was always set at a node. This means that in the dynamic case as it moves on the surface of the airfoil, a remeshing is necessary. This is done over the whole mesh so as the spacing remains reasonable. Of course interpolation is needed in order to calculate derivatives in time. Otherwise we did not remark any numerical instabilities.

Results and Discussion

We first tested the model in the case of steady stall. In Fig. 4 the pressure coefficient distribution over a $GA(W)-1$ airfoil at $20.05°$ of incidence is shown. In Fig. 5 for the same airfoil the predicted $C_L - \alpha$ curve is compared to measured data. In both cases the position of separation was taken from measurements (McGhee and Beasley 1973). The comparison with the experiments is absolutely satisfactory.

Next the case of a pitching $NACA$ 0012 was considered. In this case the position of separation must be input as a function of time. Because relevant measured information is not available, an empirical model had to be used. In the present work the example of a simplified form of the hysteresis has been adopted. As shown in Fig. 6(d) the location of separation x_s, is defined by the incidence at four points, A, B, C, D (Point B' in this case corresponds to the steady location of separation for the maximum incidence). An idea about the position of A, B, C, D, can be obtained from models as Leishman-Beddoes or the Boeing Vertol models. Extensive tests were performed to check the sensitivity of the predictions to variations of the shape of the hysteresis loop of x_s. It was found that most sensitive is the moment and less sensitive is the normal force. Although a definite rule has not been devised we concluded that appropriate loops of x_s can give quickly reliable predictions as shown in Fig. 6. From a certain point of view the positions of A, B, C and D can be considered as parameters of an empirical model to be defined by means of regression analysis over a collection of cases for which experimental data exist (Voutsinas, Riziotis 1996).

The quality of the predictions presented indicates that the location of separation is the essential information that an otherwise inviscid model needs in order to approximate stall. In terms of computational cost, a full run lasts about 30 min on processors running at 200 Specfp92. This time corresponds to 300 time-steps per period and three cycles which are required to reach periodicity.

THE 3D STALL MODEL FOR ROTORS

Theory

Three dimensional calculations are much more complicated and computationaly expensive as compared to their two dimensional counterparts. Besides that when dealing with rotors, in true configurations, instead of a single body as before, multibody configurations are usually encountered. In our case we consider the case of an N-bladed wind turbine rotor. Aiming at retaining the computational cost to reasonable levels, we applied the double wake concept to the thin-wing formulation of the problem. This approximation leads to a somewhat different treatment of stall. First the location of separation is fixed at the leading edge. Second the evolution of stall is now controlled by specifying the rate with

which vorticity is released. This is done by means of an empirical model. After testing several alternatives we finally selected the ONERA model which we found most appropriate. As for the rest of the discrete model, a combination of the panel and the vortex particle methods is used. Panels carrying constant dipole distribution (as in the vortex-lattice method) are used on the blades as well as over the near parts of the wakes (Fig.7). In the far part of the wake instead of vortex segments as in the vortex-lattice method, we use vortex particles.

At the end of each time step the near-wakes are convected with the local velocity. This process is combined with the transformation of the near-wakes into a number of vortex particles. Fig. 8 shows this sequence of transformations for the trailing as well as the separated vortex sheets. In principle we merge the vortex segments we have on the boundaries of the panel as a result of the piecewise constant dipole distribution we use. Depending on the integration scheme, the vortex particle can be either positioned at the centre of the near wake panel or at its contour. We tried both schemes. It was found that the computations became more stable when the second scheme was used at the leading edge. According to our experience, the reason for such a behaviour is that the vortices after their release, will follow paths which do not pass over control points. So during their convection over the blade they will always give significant contribution to the normal velocity at the near-by control points. In this way the consequences of stall are fedback to the flow equations and more specifically to the non entry boundary condition which seems to have a stabilising effect. Details of the numerical method can be found in Voutsinas et al (1995), Voutsinas and Riziotis (1995). In brief,

(a) The non entry boundary condition on the blades is used to determine the bound vorticity,

(b) The Kutta condition along the trailing edge and the tip which sets the vorticity along the edge equal to zero is used to specify the amount of vorticity to be shed.

(c) For every section the ONERA model is used to determine the amount of vorticity to be shed from the leading edge. Due to its two-dimensional origin, the stall model needs some modifications before applied to 3D calculations. The equations used by the ONERA model depend also on the angle of attack corresponding to the attached flow case. Thus first the fully attached flow calculations are performed wherefrom at each section, the angle of attack is determined as the direction normal to the total force.

Results and Discussion

The evaluation of the 3D model was carried out with reference to the Cranfield experiment (Bellia and Hales 1990). It concerned a series of outdoors measurements on a small 3m diameter, three-bladed wind turbine rotating at approximately 340 RPM. The turbine was mounted on a trailer and trucked at constant speed in an airfield. This was done in order to have the best possible conditions at a full scale.

The 3D model was run for several cases. In all runs the period of rotation was divided in 80 time steps. Regarding convergence it was found that three rotations after stall is included, are adequate to reach periodicity. For the preliminary attached flow calculation a wake development up to 2.5 diameters downstream of the rotor plane is needed. A total of 30 CPU hours is required for a full run. Results from a representative case are given in Fig. 9 and 10 corresponding to the 35% and 75% spanwise sections of the blade respectively (Further results can be found in Voutsinas and Riziotis 1995). In every set, predictions are given of the normal and tangential to the blade forces as functions of the azimuth angle (Fig. 9,10(a,b)), and as functions of the angle of attack as calculated from the attached run (Fig. 9,10(c,d)). The dot in these last figures denotes the starting point of the loop which is the point of zero azimuth angle i.e. when the blade is upgoing and horizontal. The loops were left open to indicate their direction. In Fig. 9-10(e) the loops of the normal force coefficient C_N are shown as function of the angle of attack together with the steady 2D experimental curves as well as the corrected ones which account for 3D effects according to Snel's correction (Snel et al 1993). Finally in Fig.9,10(f) the angle of attack obtained from the attached calculation is given as function of the azimuth angle. In the figures, GENUVP and GENUVP+Stall correspond to results from the attached and stalled runs respectively.

As expected the variation of the normal force is well predicted even by the "attached" model (Fig.9-10(a)). The stall model in this case makes some shape modifications which are in the direction of improving the quality of the predictions. On the contrary, the "attached" predictions of the tangential force are wrong even in shape (Fig.9-10(b)). In this case the stall model changes completely the shape. At the 75% section the predictions are good whereas at the 35% section there are significant differences around the 180⁰ azimuth angle. Part of these discrepancies are due to the presence of the nacelle which shades this range of azimuth positions (Due to lack of data we did not included the nacelle in the computations). A very interesting remark can be made on the sense of the normal and tangential force loops (Fig.9-10(c,d)). At the 35% section the stall is deep as shown in Fig.9-10(e) whereas at the 75% section we have light stall. This is clearly revealed by the loops. For light stall the introduction of the stall model will modify only the position of the loops whereas in the case of deep stall the model will also change the sense of the loops from anti-clockwise to clockwise. This is an essential stall driven characteristic and the fact that the model reproduces it is very important.

REMARKS ON THE IMPLEMENTATION OF THE MODELS
(a) The discrete problems were solved by a 2nd order Adams Bashford time marching scheme.
(b) Although in the text each condition is corresponded to a certain d.o.f., all discrete equations involve the complete set of d.o.f.
(c) The vortex particles were regularised by exponential cut-off functions: $1-\exp(r/\varepsilon)^n$ where ε denotes the cut-off length and n the dimension of the problem (=2 or 3). In the 2D model ε was chosen proportional to $\sqrt{\Delta t}$ with coefficient smaller than 2. In the 3D model it was chosen so as the cores of the particles overlap (Beale, Majda 1985).

CONCLUSIONS
In the present paper the double wake concept has been successfully used to devise vortex type stall models. In the 2D case it was proven that it is enough to prescribe the location of separation in order to get good predictions. In the 3D case the combination of a detailed free-wake model and the ONERA stall model is proposed. The application to the case of a wind turbine rotor in yaw gave satisfactory results in the sense that the main physical mechanisms are reproduced, the predictions are close to measurements with differences acceptable at least for design purposes. The relatively low computational cost of the models make them quite attractive for engineering applications.

ACKNOWLEDGEMENTS
The present work was partially financed by the DG-XII of the CEU (Commission of the European Union) under the JOU2-CT93-0345 project.

REFERENCES
AGARD-CP-552, 1995, "Aerodynamics and Aeroacoustics of Rotorcraft," Berlin 1995

Beale,J.T. and Majda,A., 1985, "Higher order accurate vortex methods with explicit velocity Kernels," *J. Computational Physics*, Vol. 58, pp. 188-208

Belia,J.M. and Hales,R.L., 1990, "An Experimental Investigation of HAWT Aerodynamics in Natural Conditions," Cranfield Institute of Technology, Final Report of the EN3W/0033/GB CEC project.

Ekaterinaris,J.A., Srinivasan,G.R. and McCroskey,W.J., 1995, "Present capabilities of predicting 2D-Dynamic Stall," *AGARD-CP-552 Proc. Aerodynamics and Aeroacoustics of Rotorcraft*, Berlin, paper 2

Favier,D., Agnes,A., Barbi,C. and Maresca,C., 1988, "Combined Translation/Pitch motion: a new airfoil dynamic stall simulation," *J. of Aircraft*, Vol. 25, No. 9, pp. 805-814

Hansen,A.C. and Butterfield,C.P., 1993, "Aerodynamics of Horizontal-Axis Wind Turbines," *Ann. Rev. Fluid Mechanics*, Vol. 25, pp. 115-149

IEA, 1994, "Aerodynamics of wind turbines," *8th IEA Symposium*, Pedersen,B.M.(ed), Lyngby 1994

Johnson,W., 1980, "Helicopter Theory," Princeton Univercity Press

Katz,J., 1981, "A discrete vortex method for the non-steady separated flow over an airfoil," *J. of Fluid Mech.*, Vol. 102, pp. 315-328

Leishman,J.G. and Beddoes,T.S., 1986, "A Generalised model for Airfoil Unsteady Aerodynamics Behaviour and Dynamic Stall using the Indicial Method," *Proc. 42th Annual Forum of the American Helicopter Society*, Washington D.C., pp. 243-265

Leishman,J.G and Crouse,G.L., 1989, " State-Space Model For Unsteady Airfoil Behaviour and Dynamic Stall," Presented as paper 89-1319 at the AIAA/ASME/ASCE/AHS/ASC 30th Structures, *Structural Dynamics and Materials Conference*, Mobile, Alabama, pp. 1372-1383

Leonard,A., 1985, "Computing three-dimensional incompressible flows with vortex filaments," *Ann. Rev. Fluid Mech.*, Vol. 17, pp. 523-559

McCroskey,W.J., 1976, "Dynamic Stall experiments on Oscillating airfoils," *AIAA*, Vol. 14, No. 1, pp. 57-63

McGhee,R.J. and Beasley,W.D., 1973, "Low speed aerodynamic characteristics of a 17-percent-thick airfoil section designed for general aviation applications," NASA TN D-7428

Morfiadakis,E., Voutsinas,S.G., Papantonis,D., 1991, "Unsteady Flow Calculation in a Radial Centrifugal Pump with Spiral Casing," *Int. Journal of numerical methods in fluids*, Vol. 12, pp 895-908

Petot,D. 1989, "Differential equation modelling of dynamic stall," *Rech. Aerosp.*, paper no.5

Smith,J.H.B., 1986, "Vortex flows in aerodynamics," *Ann. Rev. Fluid Mech.*, Vol. 18, pp. 221-242.

Snel,H. and Schepers,J.G., 1994, "Joint Investigation of Dynamic Inflow Effects and Implementation of an Engineering Method," ECN report ECN-C--94-107, Netherlands

H.Snel, R.Houwink, J.Bosschers, W.J.Piers, G.J.W van Bussel, A.Bruining, 1993, "Section al Prediction of 3D effects for Stalled flow on Rotating Blades and Comparison with Measurements", *Proceedings of ECWEC'93*, Travemunde.

Truong,V.K., 1993, "A 2-D Dynamic Stall Model Based on a Hopf Bifurcation," *Nineteenth European Rotorcraft Forum*, paper no. 23

Vezza,M. and McD Galbraith,R.A., 1985, "An inviscid model of unsteady aerofoil flow with fixed upper surface separation", *J. for Numerical Methods in Fluids*, Vol. 5, pp. 577-592

Voutsinas,S.G, Belessis,M.A. and Rados,K.G., 1995, "Investigation of Yawed Operation of Wind Turbines by means of a Vortex Particle Method", *AGARD-CP-552 Proc. Aerodynamics and Aeroacoustics of Rotorcraft*, Berlin, paper 11

Voutsinas,S.G., 1995, "Development of a New Generation of Design Tools for HAWT", Final Report of the JOU2-CT92-0113 CEU project

Voutsinas,S.G. and Riziotis,V.A., 1995, "Vortex Particle Modelling of Stall," Final Report of the JOU2-CT93-0345 CEU project

Voutsinas,S.G. and Riziotis,V.A., 1996, "Validation of a Vortex-Type Stall Model," NTUA Report

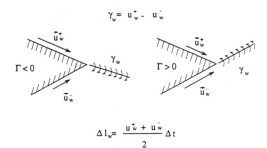

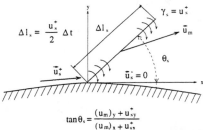

Figure 2: Vorticity emission at the trailing edge

Figure 3: Vorticity emission at separation

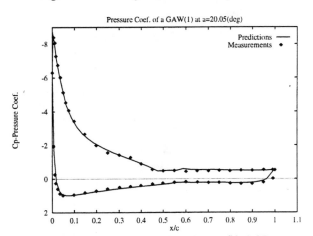

Figure 4: Num. of panels=65, Δt.c/U=0.05

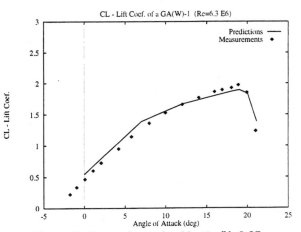

Figure 5: Num. of panels=66, Δt.c/U=0.05

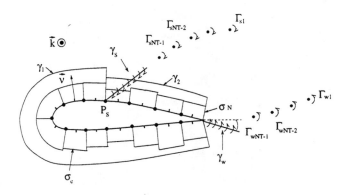

Figure 1: The discrete analogue

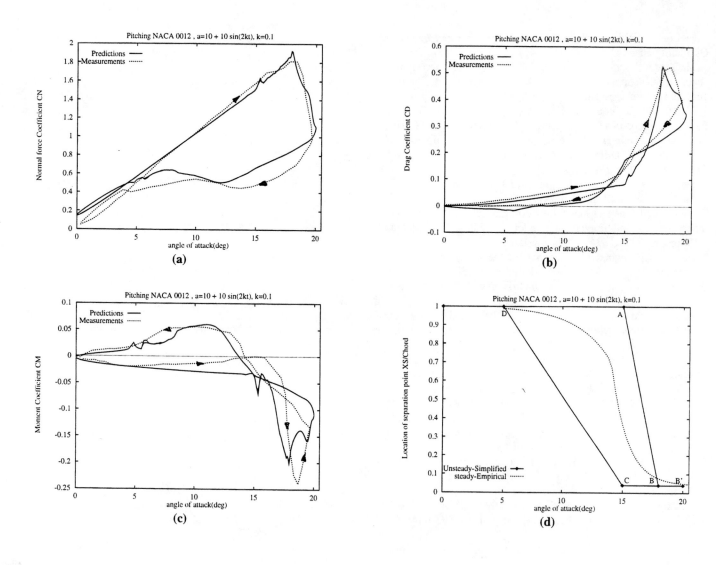

Figure 6: Results for a pitching airfoil, Num of panels=60, Δt.c/U=0.1

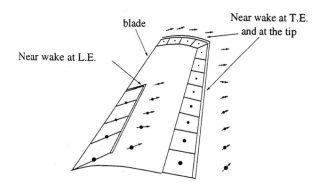

Figure 7: The separation model for a rotor blade

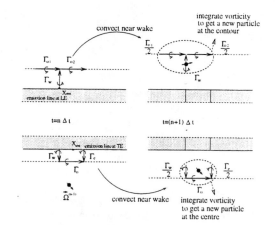

Figure 8: The formation of vortex particles

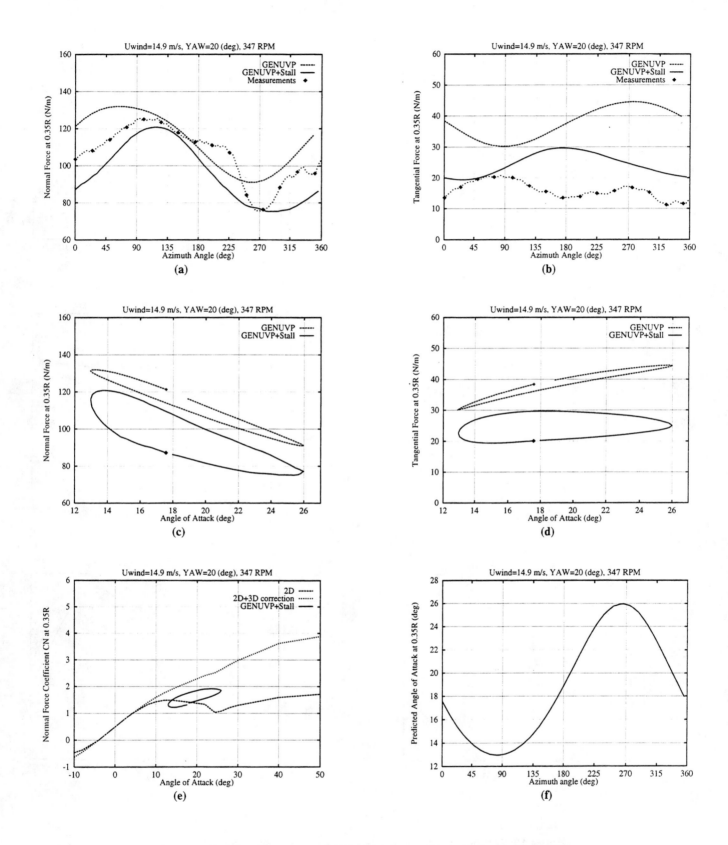

Figure 9: Sectional results at 0.35R, grid size on blade 8×9, Δt = Period/80

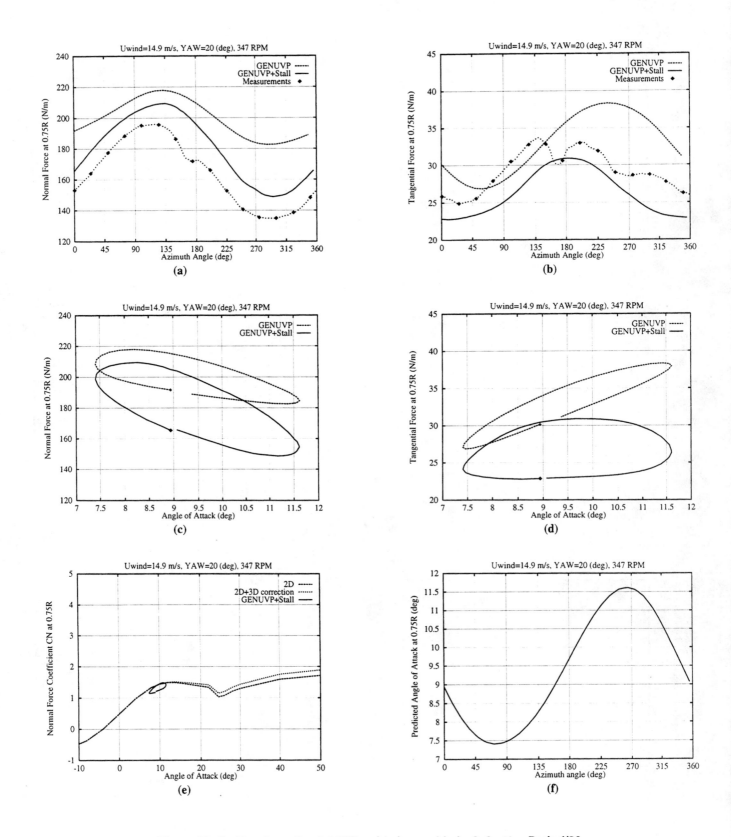

Figure 10: Sectional results at 0.75R, grid size on blade 8×9, Δt = Period/80

FED-Vol. 238, 1996 Fluids Engineering Division Conference
Volume 3
ASME 1996

VORTEX METHODS AND TURBULENT FLOW SIMULATION

Peter S. Bernard
Department of Mechanical Engineering
University of Maryland
College Park, Maryland

ABSTRACT

A three-dimensional vortex method suitable for simulating turbulent flows at high Reynolds numbers in complex geometries is developed. Dynamically evolving vortical structures in the turbulent flow are represented as vortex tubes and filaments, while smoothed vortex sheets are used in the immediate vicinity of solid boundaries to efficiently accommodate the primarily wall-normal viscous vorticity diffusion occurring in this region. New structures are introduced into the computation in mimicry of the process by which pre-existing quasi-streamwise vortices self-replicate. Numerical efficiency is enhanced through use of Chorin's hairpin removal algorithm to limit the range of resolvable scales. The computational scheme is designed for execution on highly parallel computers. Progress in capturing the self-replication process for quasi-streamwise vortices is described, as well as preliminary results of a turbulent channel flow simulation using the vortex method. In view of its grid-free character, the approach may be readily generalized to flows in complex geometries.

INTRODUCTION

A primary motivation for developing vortex methods has been the belief that they should provide an efficient means for predicting the high Reynolds number turbulent flows encountered in complex engineering applications. In particular, they are largely free of two of the principle limitations of more traditional numerical schemes, namely, the need for a computational grid and the Reynolds number restriction imposed by numerical diffusion. Previous applications of vortex methods to high Reynolds number flows have often been in two-dimensions (e.g. Gagnon, et al. 1993). Their stochastic character is brought about through use of a random walk model of diffusion, rather than instabilities associated with vortex stretching. Three-dimensional calculations (e.g. Fishelov, 1994) have not systematically documented the nature of the random field they produce to verify that turbulence is being simulated correctly. In particular, such benchmark turbulent flows as that in a channel, which have been successfully simulated using spectral or finite difference algorithms (Kim et al., 1987) have yet to be considered. The object of the present work is to bring closer to fruition the promise that vortex methods hold for simulating turbulence. As a step in this direction, a vortex method is described which is specifically aimed at reproducing the principal physical characteristics of canonical turbulent flows containing boundaries.

The present approach departs from previous efforts by using some of the chief distinguishing physical attributes of turbulence to achieve significant gains in numerical efficiency. Among these are the expectation that viscous vorticity diffusion can be confined primarily to wall normal viscous diffusion occurring in a thin layer on solid boundaries. Secondly, the vortex element representation is limited to only the most dynamically significant structures, in the belief that a full accounting of the Reynolds stress does not require inclusion of smaller scales (Bernard et al., 1993). Resolution of the vortical structures is controlled via the implementation of a self-replication model for generating new structures in the wall region, as well as a hairpin removal algorithm (Chorin, 1993), to effect a physical space renormalization of the flow. Thus, to the extent that it models 'subgrid' motions, the current scheme has the characteristics of a large eddy simulation (LES). If successful, the approach eliminates the prohibitive expense of tracking fine scale folding and stretching vortex tubes which has been a significant hindrance to the implementation of previous vortex methods.

The numerical scheme incorporating these ideas builds on the three-dimensional filament scheme described by Chorin (1993). To accommodate boundaries, smoothed vortex sheet elements are used as an economical representation of the high gradient vorticity field near walls, where primarily one-dimensional viscous vorticity diffusion takes place. At the same time, vortex filaments provide an efficient representation of the essentially inviscid interactions of vortex tubes − both coherent or otherwise − populating the region further from the wall, i.e. beyond the direct influence of viscous wall effects (see Fig. 1). A small overlap between the region of sheets and tubes serves to accommodate the creation of new vortical structures. For convenience, all vortex elements sufficiently close to the boundary are assumed to have interchangeable tube-like and sheet-like properties. Which of them is in force depends on the circumstances. For example, diffusion is carried out under the sheet-like manifestation, while the stretching and convection process assumes a tube-like state. The velocity field due to a tube in close wall proximity is that due to the equivalent sheet, while sheets appear tube-like in their far fields.

Numerical results described here include an investigation of the feasibility of capturing the self-replication process with a vortex method. In this, the evolution of tilted vortices in a channel flow is computed, revealing an induced flow in the wall vortex sheets which may be

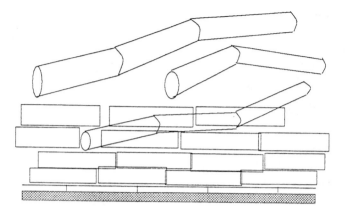

Fig. 1. Layout of vortex elements. Sheets and filaments coexist in an intermediate region where new structures are created.

taken as new vortical structures. Using a preliminary self-replication criterion, simulations of channel flow are carried out. These show the development of new structures contributing to maintenance of the turbulent field.

SHEETS AND FILAMENTS

The evolution of the vorticity field, $\mathbf{\Omega}(\mathbf{x}, t)$, in three-dimensional flow is governed by the transport equation

$$\frac{\partial \mathbf{\Omega}}{\partial t} + (\nabla \mathbf{\Omega})\mathbf{u} = (\nabla \mathbf{u})\mathbf{\Omega} + \frac{1}{R}\nabla^2 \mathbf{\Omega} \qquad (1)$$

where R is the Reynolds number, $\mathbf{u} = (u_1, u_2, u_3)$ is the velocity field and $\nabla\mathbf{u}$ is the velocity gradient tensor with components $(\nabla\mathbf{u})_{ij} = \partial u_i/\partial x_j$. Approximate solutions to (1) are sought in which $\mathbf{\Omega}$ is represented as a collection of vortex sheets or "tiles" in the near wall region and vortex filaments in the outer flow. For the present discussion, $y = 0$ is the boundary, in which case sheets are located in $0 \leq y \leq y_s$ and filaments in say $y > y_f$. Generally, y_f is chosen to be slightly smaller than y_s so as to create an overlap region where sheets and filaments can coexist.

Vortex sheets at locations $\mathbf{x}_i$, $i = 1, ..., N_s$ with dimensions $2l \times 2h \times 2d$ in the streamwise, wall-normal and spanwise flow directions, respectively, initially fill up a grid covering the region between the wall and y_s. Since the geometry of the bounding surface must be specified in any application of the method, creating such a mesh poses little significant handicap to applying the approach to complex geometries. The sheets have large aspect ratio, i.e. $h << l, d$, and are assumed to have uniform vorticity $\mathbf{\Omega}_i$. A layer of sheets of half thickness, arranged along the wall, are kept stationary during the calculation consistent with the view that they are full sized sheets whose centers are on the wall surface and hence non-moving. The vorticity of these elements is assigned at each time step in such a way as to satisfy the no-slip boundary condition. When conditions at inflow boundaries or near a solid wall warrant it, the sheets are allowed to change size in order to enhance the efficiency with which full coverage of the near-wall region can be maintained — a requirement of deterministic diffusion schemes.

Vortex tube segments are prescribed by their circulation Γ_i, length Δs_i and orientation $\mathbf{s}_i = \mathbf{x}_i^2 - \mathbf{x}_i^1$ where $\mathbf{x}_i^1$ and $\mathbf{x}_i^2$, are the vector distances to the beginning and end points of the ith filament, respectively. Segments are joined together to form filaments. If desired, groups of filaments can be used to represent tubes.

VELOCITY FIELD

In vortex methods the velocity field is computed as a sum of the contributions from individual elements as derived from the Biot-Savart law (Puckett, 1993). For the ith tube segment, the smoothed velocity field induced at a point $\mathbf{x}$ is given by

$$-\frac{\Gamma_i}{4\pi}\frac{\mathbf{r}_i \times \mathbf{s}_i}{|\mathbf{r}_i|^3}\phi(r/\sigma) \qquad (2)$$

where $\mathbf{r}_i = \mathbf{x}_i - \mathbf{x}$, $r = |\mathbf{r}|$, $\phi(r) = \left(1 - \left(1 - \frac{3}{2}r^3\right)\right)e^{-r^3}$ is a higher order smoothing function and σ is a scaling parameter. The physical radius of a vortex tube is $\sigma/2.5$.

The velocity field due to the ith sheet is determined from the smoothed Biot-Savart integral

$$\int_{V_i} K_\eta(\mathbf{x} - \mathbf{x}')\mathbf{\Omega}(\mathbf{x}', t)d\mathbf{x}', \qquad (3)$$

where V_i is the volume of the sheet,

$$K_\eta = \begin{cases} K & |\mathbf{x}| \geq \eta \\ K\left(\frac{5}{2} - \frac{3}{2}\left(\frac{\mathbf{x}}{\eta}\right)^2\right)\frac{|\mathbf{x}|^3}{\eta^3} & |\mathbf{x}| < \eta \end{cases}$$

$$K(x,y,z) = -\frac{1}{4\pi|\mathbf{x}|^3}\begin{pmatrix} 0 & -z & y \\ z & 0 & -x \\ -y & x & 0 \end{pmatrix},$$

and η is a cutoff parameter. Assuming that $\mathbf{\Omega}$ is constant for each sheet, (3) becomes

$$\left[\int_{V_j} K_\eta(\mathbf{x} - \mathbf{x}')d\mathbf{x}'\right]\mathbf{\Omega}_i. \qquad (4)$$

In view of the high aspect ratio of the vortex sheets, the y integration in (4) can be approximated by a midpoint rule. Furthermore, the x and z integrals can be done analytically for all values of $\mathbf{x}$ and $\mathbf{x}'$ yielding

$$\int_{V_i} K_\eta(\mathbf{x}-\mathbf{x}')d\mathbf{x}'\,\mathbf{\Omega}_i = \begin{pmatrix} 0 & W_i & -V_i \\ -W_i & 0 & U_i \\ V_i & -U_i & 0 \end{pmatrix}\mathbf{\Omega}_i, \qquad (5)$$

where the form taken by the coefficients U_i, V_i and W_i depends on whether or not any part of the ith sheet intersects a sphere of radius η around the point $\mathbf{x}_i$. If not, $K_\eta = K$ in (4) and integration yields the far field formulas:

$$U_i = -\frac{h_j}{8\pi}\ln\left(\frac{r_{11} - Z_1}{r_{11} + Z_1}\frac{r_{21} + Z_1}{r_{21} - Z_1}\frac{r_{22} - Z_2}{r_{22} + Z_2}\frac{r_{12} + Z_2}{r_{12} - Z_2}\right) \qquad (6)$$

$$V_i = -\frac{h_j}{4\pi}\left(\tan^{-1}\frac{X_2 Z_2}{Y r_{22}} - \tan^{-1}\frac{X_2 Z_1}{Y r_{21}}\right.$$
$$\left. - \tan^{-1}\frac{X_1 Z_2}{Y r_{12}} + \tan^{-1}\frac{X_1 Z_1}{Y r_{11}}\right) \qquad (7)$$

$$W_i = -\frac{h_j}{8\pi} \ln\left(\frac{r_{11}-X_1}{r_{11}+X_1}\frac{r_{21}+X_1}{r_{21}-X_1}\frac{r_{22}-X_2}{r_{22}+X_2}\frac{r_{12}+X_2}{r_{12}-X_2}\right)$$

$$(8)$$

where $r_{mn}^2 = X_m^2 + Y^2 + Z_n^2$, $m,n = 1,2$, $X_1 = (x-x_i-l_i)/\eta$, $X_2 = (x-x_i+l_i)/\eta$, $Z_1 = (z-z_i-d_i)/\eta$, $Z_2 = (z-z_i+d_i)/\eta$ and $Y = (y-y_i)/\eta$. A geometrical interpretation of r_{mn} is given in Fig. 2. The evaluation of U_i, V_i and W_i in the local case involves carrying out the integration of K_η over a region formed by the intersection of a sheet with a sphere of radius η around the point $\mathbf{x}_i$. The high aspect ratio of the sheets causes the condition $\eta < l, d$ to be satisfied so that no sheet can fit entirely within a ball of radius η around $\mathbf{x}_i$. The local formulas are too lengthy to write down here, though a FORTRAN subroutine based on these results is available from the author upon request.

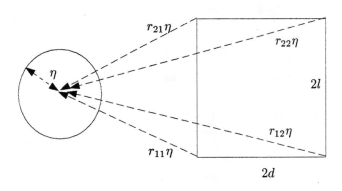

Fig. 2. Geometry of sheet interactions.

The far field velocities associated with a sheet and tube at the same location are indistinguishable from each other if the condition

$$\mathbf{\Omega}_i\, V_i = \Gamma_i\, \mathbf{s}_i \qquad (9)$$

is met. Here

$$\mathbf{s}_i = \frac{\mathbf{\Omega}_i}{|\,\mathbf{\Omega}_i\,|}\Delta s_i, \qquad (10)$$

Δs_i is the length of the tube segment and $V_i = 2l\cdot 2h\cdot 2d$. From (9) and (10) it follows that

$$|\,\mathbf{\Omega}_i\,|\, V_i = |\,\Gamma_i\,|\,\Delta s_i. \qquad (11)$$

Equation (2) is considerably cheaper to evaluate numerically than (5), so a substantial gain in computational speed may be had by converting sheets to tubes for the far field velocity summation. In converting a sheet to a tube, Δs_i can be chosen arbitrarily – with Γ_i then determined from (11) – since (2) depends only on the product $\Gamma_i \Delta s_i$. Conversely, when transforming a tube segment into a sheet, the dimensions of the sheet are kept the same as the others, implying that the vorticity of the sheet is determined uniquely from (9).

From the previous results it follows that the velocity field due to a collection of N_s sheets and N_f filaments is given by

$$\mathbf{u}(\mathbf{x},t) = \sum_{i=1}^{N_s}\begin{pmatrix} 0 & W_i & -V_i \\ -W_i & 0 & U_i \\ V_i & -U_i & 0 \end{pmatrix}\mathbf{\Omega}_i$$
$$-\frac{1}{4\pi}\sum_{i=1}^{N_f}\frac{\mathbf{r}_i \times \mathbf{s}_i}{|\,\mathbf{r}_i\,|^3}\Gamma_i\phi(r/\sigma). \qquad (12)$$

For a flat plate boundary layer or channel flow, the sums in (12) include a set of image sheets and filaments which enforce the non-penetration boundary condition. For more general geometries, the latter condition can be satisfied by appending to (12) a grid-free potential flow solution (Hess and Smith, 1967) belonging to a surface source distribution.

The intersection of boundaries with the support of the smoothing functions in (12) must be specifically compensated for to prevent a loss of information in determining the velocity field. Since filaments are prohibited from close contact with the boundaries, it is only necessary to specially modify the sheet calculation near walls. An effective technique in this regard, which is compatible with the implementation of the boundary conditions, is to force sheets within η of the wall to contribute to the velocity at points between themselves and the wall surface according to the far field formulas (6) - (8) only. This can be done by reducing η for these sheets. By this approach, the wall sheet lying immediately over a point on the wall contributes the amount $-h_i(\Omega_3)_i$ to the u velocity at this location, i.e., exactly what is expected from a physical analysis of the local vortex sheet. This result is a consequence of the difference in arctangent terms in (7) which will be approximately π in this case. A similar result holds for the spanwise velocity where the sheet above a point contributes $h_i(\Omega_1)_i$.

The boundary values of the components of vorticity tangential to the wall may be determined by setting (12) to zero at the location of each wall sheet. For planar walls containing M fixed sheets on the wall, this yields two sets of M coupled equations which are readily solved by iteration.

VORTEX TUBE ALGORITHM

The filament part of the calculation is adapted directly from the computer code developed by Chorin (1993). The end points of each segment are moved in time according to a fourth order Runge-Kutta discretization of the kinematic identity

$$\frac{d\mathbf{x}_i}{dt} = \mathbf{u}(\mathbf{x}_i(t),t). \qquad (13)$$

The stretching and reorientation terms in (1) are accommodated automatically by this procedure. Folded vortex segments forming hairpins are removed when the interior angle is less than a critical angle. Here we take this to be 45°. Long segments are divided in two whenever they stretch too far, while short segments are joined to larger ones.

Coherent vortex filaments and tubes in a turbulent flow presumably have a finite life span. The demise of such structures as coherent entities may be a natural outcome of their interactions with other vortices. The end result is a release of their vorticity into the background, non-coherent vorticity, with some role played in this by viscous diffusion. In the case of a periodic flow, such as in a channel, it is particularly important to accommodate the life cycle of coherent vortex tubes since otherwise the numerical scheme will see a monotonic growth in the number of structures as new ones are created. In external flows the problem is much less severe since the destruction of vortices presumably takes place downstream after they have exited the flow domain.

Core spreading was previously introduced (Leonard, 1975, 1980) as a means of modeling viscous spreading of vortex tubes. While the numerical inconsistencies (Greengard, 1985) of this approach may be correctable (Rossi, 1995), it is not well suited to the present purposes since it yields a field of ever thickening structures. A more useful approach is to allow vortices which are not being sufficiently stretched to lose an appropriate amount of their circulation at each time step, specifically, that amount which would be contained in the outward diffusing vorticity. Vortices whose circulations drop below a threshold, can then be eliminated.

A model for this phenomenon can be fashioned from the Gaussian core solution (Leonard, 1980). In this, a tube whose length increases from Δs to $\Delta s'$ in time Δt must have a radius equal to

$$r_e \equiv 2 \sqrt{\frac{\Delta t}{R_e(\Delta s'/\Delta s - 1)}} \qquad (14)$$

if the stretching rate is to be in equilibrium with viscous spreading. Generally, it can be expected that the tube radii will be inconsistent with the rate of stretching. A tube segment for which $\Delta s' > \Delta s$, will thicken if its radius $r < r_e$, and a calculation yields that the necessary adjustment of circulation is:

$$\Gamma^{n+1} = \Gamma^n \left(1 - \frac{4\Delta t}{R_e} \left(\frac{1}{r^2} - \frac{1}{r_e^2}\right)\right). \qquad (15)$$

If $r \geq r_e$, the circulation may be left untouched, i.e.

$$\Gamma^{n+1} = \Gamma^n. \qquad (16)$$

If contraction takes place, i.e. $\Delta s' < \Delta s$, then the maximum circulation can be assumed to be lost so that

$$\Gamma^{n+1} = \Gamma^n \left(1 - \frac{4\Delta t}{R_e} \frac{1}{r^2}\right). \qquad (17)$$

For tubes composed of multiple segments, (15) - (17) may be applied using the average rate of stretching along the tubes.

VORTEX SHEET ALGORITHM

The possibility of interchanging vortex elements with tube-like or sheet-like properties enables a significant simplification of the numerical solution to (1) for vortex sheets. In particular, the convection and stretching terms can be modeled by replacing the sheets by equivalent tubes using (9), convecting their end points to find the new sheet location, and then using (9) in reverse to update the sheet vorticity.

A rationale for using sheets near the wall is that they are well suited to capturing wall normal viscous diffusion from the boundary. A number of deterministic schemes can be adapted to a field of sheets. Here, the Fishelov (1990) method is considered as well as a simple mesh based scheme. The former is a particle exchange method based on differentiating smoothed representations of the vorticity field. For a field of sheets, one-dimensional diffusion can be captured in the relation

$$\frac{1}{R}(\nabla^2 \mathbf{\Omega})_i \approx \frac{1}{R} \sum_j \frac{\gamma_{ij} \mathbf{\Omega}_j^n h_j}{\sqrt{\pi}\delta^3} \left[e^{-\tilde{y}^2} 16 \left(\tilde{y}^2 - \frac{1}{2}\right) \right.$$
$$\left. + \sqrt{2} e^{-\tilde{y}^2} \left(1 - \tilde{y}^2\right) \right] \qquad (18)$$

where $\tilde{y} \equiv (y_i^n - y_j^n)/\delta$ and γ_{ij} represents the fractional overlap of the ith and jth sheets. More precisely $\gamma_{ij} \equiv m((x_i - l_i, x_i + l_i) \cap (x_j - l_j, x_j + l_j))/(2l_i) \cdot m((z_i - d_i, z_i + d_i) \cap (z_j - d_j, z_j + d_j))/(2d_i)$ where $m(S)$ is the rectilinear measure of the set S. Thus $\gamma_{ij} = 1$ when $x_i = x_j, z_i = z_j, l_i = l_j$, and $d_i = d_j$, while $\gamma_{ij} = 0$ if $(x_i - l_i, x_i + l_i) \cap (x_j - l_j, x_j + l_j) = \emptyset$ or $(z_i - d_i, z_i + d_i) \cap (z_j - d_j, z_j + d_j) = \emptyset$. Since only a relatively small subset of the complete collection of vortical elements intersect $(x_i - l_i, x_i + l_i) \times (z_i - d_i, z_i + d_i)$, the numerical expense of computing (18) is not prohibitive.

As in the velocity field calculation, the use of (18) near a boundary requires compensation for the intersection of the wall with the support of the smoothing function used in its derivation. Failure to do so results in an underprediction of the diffusion rate. It was shown previously (Bernard, 1995), that boundaries may be accommodated by appending to (4) a collection of sheets reflected through the boundary with quadratically extrapolated vorticity.

The success of deterministic vorticity redistribution schemes depends on maintaining full coverage of the flow domain with vortex elements. In the present case, gaps between sheets will inevitably form as they are convected in the irregular shear flow. To circumvent this, the domain must be periodically resheeted by imposing the original surface layer grid structure and interpolating the vorticity values back into the grid. The interpolation scheme

$$\mathbf{\Omega}(\mathbf{x}_i) = \frac{\sum_j \gamma_{ij} \theta_{ij} \mathbf{\Omega}_j}{\sum_j \gamma_{ij} \theta_{ij}} \qquad (19)$$

is used here where $\mathbf{x}_i$ is now meant to denote an arbitrary point in the flow, and $\theta_{ij} \equiv m((y_i - h_i, y_i + h_i) \cap (y_j - h_j, y_j + h_j))/(2h_i)$. The denominator of (19) is necessary to compensate for overlap of the vortex elements if this should occur. The sum in (19) is just over those vortices in the immediate neighborhood of a point, so it is of minimal computational cost.

The need for special image vortices in implementing (18) near walls creates significant hardship in treating irregular boundaries. At the same time, the need to remesh has the potential to add a degree of unwanted numerical diffusion to the deterministic scheme, though this is mitigated somewhat by the relatively small region within which viscous diffusion is computed. In view of these considerations, it is not self-evident that equal success in capturing viscous diffusion cannot be had using a standard one-dimensional finite difference formula on a fixed mesh. Such an approach avoids resheeting and is easily implemented on arbitrary three-dimensional boundaries. Both diffusion schemes are employed in the calculations given below.

36

PHYSICAL CONSIDERATIONS

The hairpin removal and quasi-streamwise vortex replication models act to maintain the numerical system at a resolvable scale appropriate to a large eddy simulation. With use of a finer resolution of vortices the approach may approximate a direct numerical simulation in some sense. An important question, which will be taken up in later aspects of the study, is to consider what the appropriate or necessary filament resolution should be at a given Reynolds number.

The success of our numerical scheme depends on developing a convincing methodology for capturing the process by which pre-existing vortical structures induce new ones in the flow. This involves interactions between parent vortices and the abundant vorticity produced at the solid boundary. A number of studies (Brooke and Hanratty, 1993, Bernard, et al., 1993, Miyake et al., 1995) have considered the physical nature of vortex self-replication. While there is not yet complete consensus on how this occurs, or complete knowledge of what is occurring, nonetheless, the general outlines of the process appears to be partly understood. In this, tilted parent structures of sufficient circulation and proximity to the boundary, cause the creation of new vortices. Without ruling out the possibility that other mechanisms might exist and be important, there is some evidence to suggest two particular scenarios. In the first, counter-rotating streamwise vorticity generated at the surface in response to a parent vortex accumulates on the upwash side forming a new counter-rotating structure relatively close to the wall. Secondly, and perhaps more commonly, the downwash flow of a parent vortex forces the reorientation of initially spanwise vorticity into the wall-normal direction. This subsequently is sheared into the streamwise direction in counter-rotation to the parent vortex, at a similar altitude from the wall.

Much latitude exists in how the vortex creation processes can be reproduced numerically. These have to contend with the intrinsic difficulty of locating structure in three-dimensional numerical flow fields — there being few guideposts yet as to the appropriate conditions, e.g. time and location, when the identification should be made. Since the primary object of interest is new quasi-streamwise vortices, algorithms built directly around this condition are used here. As of this writing, this consists of the following: At each time step, and on each individual $x-y$ planar set of sheets, the point where the maximum of the product $\Omega_1\Omega_2$ is located, say (x_m, y_m), is determined. If this is far enough from the wall, say $y_m > y_{crit}$ and if $(\Omega_1\Omega_2)_{max} > (\Omega_1\Omega_2)_{crit}$ where y_{crit} and $(\Omega_1\Omega_2)_{crit}$ are values to be determined, then the contour line of magnitude $\beta(\Omega_1\Omega_2)_{crit}$, $0 \leq \beta < 1$ is found. Below we take $\beta = .5$. If this proves to be a closed region, then within it $(\Omega_1\Omega_2)_{max} \geq \beta(\Omega_1\Omega_2)_{crit}$. Having found an acceptable contour, the average direction of the vector $(\Omega_1\Omega_2)$ over the nodes interior to it are found, say θ_m. At the same time, the largest distance from (x_m, y_m) to the contour is computed as well as its direction, say θ_d. If θ_d is close to θ_m (or $\theta_m + \pi$) then it is assumed that the region within the contour forms a new structure. In particular, it is a reasonably coherent, elongated volume of fluid of elevated vorticity magnitude, whose vorticity projection in the $x-y$ plane is approximately along its own axis. A new vortex is

then created with circulation

$$\sum_i \sqrt{\Omega_1^2 + \Omega_2^2}\, 2l \cdot 2d \cdot 2h/\Delta s$$

where the sum is over the interior nodes of the contour. The length, Δs, is as long as the physical contour region. Finally, the Ω_1 and Ω_2 components of the underlying vorticity in the mesh are set to zero. Thus, the new vortex is considered to be a replacement for vorticity contained in the vortex sheets.

NUMERICAL RESULTS

Calculations performed to date have focused on the nature of the self-replication process and how it can be captured in the numerical scheme, as well as simulations of turbulent channel flow using a preliminary form of the vortex identification procedure. In the former case, single or pairs of tilted vortices are inserted into a mean channel flow, after which their time development is tracked. Their effect on the vorticity field is examined with a view to establishing when a new structure has emerged and how this can be represented numerically.

The channel flow is defined by holding the average flow velocity at the centerline fixed at $U_{cl} = 1.165$, corresponding to the value computed in a spectral DNS of channel flow at $R_\tau = U_\tau h/\nu = 290$, where U_τ is the friction velocity and h is the channel width. Here U_{cl} and other velocities are scaled by the average mass flow velocity. The computational domain is $2.155 \times 1 \times 2.155$ units in the streamwise, wall-normal and spanwise directions, respectively, where $y = .5$ is the centerline of the channel. In wall units this is $625 \times 290 \times 625$ The initial grid of sheets on each wall is $16 \times 10 \times 16$ for a total of 2560. For these, $l = d = .135$ while $h = .016$, so that the sheets cover only the regions $0 \leq y \leq .144$ and $.856 \leq y \leq 1$. In terms of wall variables, the sheets are $39.2 \times 4.64 \times 39.2$.

The initial vorticity distribution in the sheets is taken to be that corresponding to the mean vorticity profile in the channel flow simulation. Thus, the initial field is one dimensional consisting of just the spanwise vorticity. A number of calculations were performed following the development of tilted vortex tubes. The initial and final configurations for a typical calculation with a single vortex, as viewed from the side, i.e. $x-y$ plane, are shown in figures 3a and 3b. Contours of the spanwise vorticity (taken from the sheets) on a plane slightly to the upwash side of the vortex ($z = 1.01$) show the relationship between the vortex and the wall sheets. In these calculations, a single filament is used to represent the vortex. Similar results have been obtained using multiple filaments. Initially the vortex tube has length .54 and is inclined at an angle of 22.5°. After an elapsed time of 1.31 (260 time steps) the vortex has convected across the periodic domain and its length is seen to have increased significantly through vortex stretching. The Ω_3 contours are seen to be compressed by the flow underneath the vortex tube.

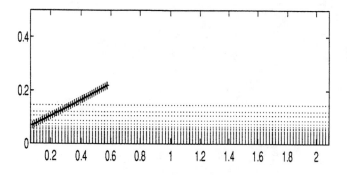

Fig. 3a. Initial position of tilted vortex. Dotted lines are Ω_3 contours in plane $z = 1.01$.

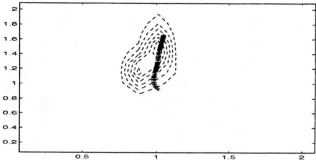

Fig. 4a. Ω_1 contours on plane $y = .147$ and projection of tilted vortex. Flow is from bottom to top.

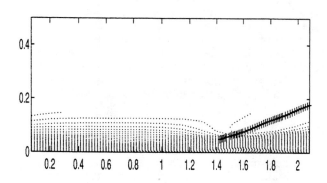

Fig. 3b. Final position of tilted vortex. Dotted lines are Ω_3 contours in plane $z = 1.01$.

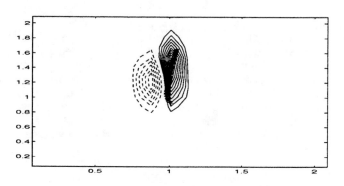

Fig. 4b. Ω_2 contours on plane $y = .147$ and projection of tilted vortex. Dashed lines are negative, solid are positive. Flow is from bottom to top.

The interest of these calculations is in examining the extent to which the interaction of the tilted vortices with the wall region vorticity generates a vorticity field which may be identified as a next generation of coherent streamwise vortices. A single tilted vortex was found to generate a relatively distinct vorticity pattern as shown in figures 4a and 4b. The view is at an intermediate time $t = .86$. Since the initial time, the vortex has caused an upwelling of high spanwise vorticity on the upwash side. At this instant there is an interesting plus and minus arrangement of Ω_2 vorticity at the upper levels of the sheet region as shown in figure 4b. This vorticity has formed by shearing of the uplifted spanwise vorticity. A conceptualization of the process is shown in figure 5.

The corresponding streamwise vorticity field — which is counterrotating to the parent vortex — is shown in figure 4a. Examination of Ω_1 contour plots in the $x - y$ plane show that the origin of this vorticity may be traced to forward shearing of the wall normal vorticity. In particular, it is not evidently a result of the very significant streamwise vorticity generated at the surface which collects on the upwash side of the vortex as indicated in figure 5. It is likely that the latter process may also lead to new structures, as was observed in Bernard et al.

(1993). However, in view of the close wall proximity of this vorticity, it is not evident that it is advantageous to include the associated mechanism in the numerical scheme.

The coherent vorticity region which has developed in figure 4 is the kind of event to which the numerical search algorithm has been tuned. Figure 6 shows that the continued development of the flow results in the creation of two new counter-rotating filaments to the parent vortex. Though it is too early to reach a definitive conclusion about the degree to which this model captures the true physics of self-replication, it is interesting to note the similarity of the pattern in figure 6 with previous studies (Bernard et al., 1993, Miyake et al., 1995). In particular the oblique angle formed by the new vortices in relation to the parent.

To simulate channel flow, a collection of vortices found in a spectral DNS is added to the mean field to create a quasi-turbulent inital state. The vorticity field continues to develop as the calculations proceeds in time with the addition and removal of vortices as circumstances warrant. A successful turbulent flow simulation requires the attainment of an equilibrium flow state with correct velocity statistics and a relatively stable population of vortical elements. At a minimum, the calculation should proceed until the initial vortical population has been fully replaced by new structures.

Calculations of long duration have yet to be completed, though figure 7 shows the vorticity field in a turbulent channel flow simulation after 450 time steps covering an elapsed time of 2.43. One of the original structures has been deleted and several new ones have been created. The latter appear in spatially intermittent, relatively active, zones, as indicated by the accompanying spanwise vorticity contours at the outer edge of the sheet layer. The new filaments appearing toward the right side of the figure fit the pattern observed in the test calculation with a single tilted vortex. In particular, they have formed on the outer side of the region of intense spanwise vorticity caused by the upwelling fluid of the parent vortex.

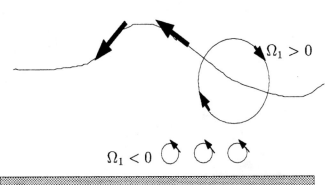

Fig. 5. Conceptualization of self-replication process. Ω_2 vorticity is formed into a + and - pattern from uplifted spanwise vorticity.

6. CONCLUSIONS

A three-dimensional vortex sheet method has been constructed for simulation of turbulent flow. Numerical studies of the self-replication process have been made which suggest a criteria to incorporate in a general setting. In particular, the appearance of localized regions of sizable streamwise and wall-normal vorticity — at some distance from the wall surface — may be taken as a workable criteria for inserting new filaments.

Long time calculations of channel flow must be completed to assess the degree to which the method is able to accurately model real turbulent flows. In view of the ease with which the code can be modified to accommodate complex geometries, preparations are also being made for simulating the flow in practical configurations. In particular, implementation of the scheme for the case of flow past a 6:1 prolate spheroid is planned for the near future. The intent is to get an early indication of the effectiveness of the methodology in design work.

ACKNOWLEDGEMENT

This research was supported by ONR Grant N00014-93-10184, Dr. L. P. Purtell, project monitor.

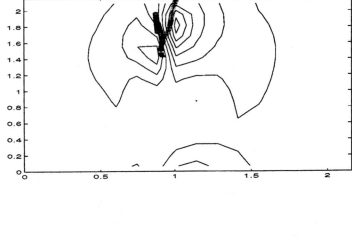

Fig. 6. New vortices generated by tilted vortex. Ω_3 contours on $y = .147$, + original vortices, o new vortices.

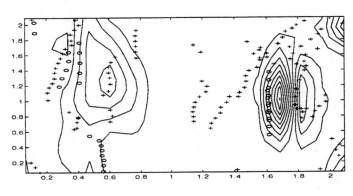

Fig. 7. Channel flow simulation. Ω_3 contours on $y = .097$, + original vortices, o new vortices.

REFERENCES

Bernard, P. S. 1995, "A deterministic vortex sheet method for boundary layer flow," *J. Comput. Phys.*, Vol. 117, pp. 132 - 145.

Bernard, P. S. Thomas, J. M., and Handler, R. A., 1993, "Vortex dynamics and the production of Reynolds stress," *J. Fluid Mech.*, Vol. 253, pp. 385 - 419.

Brooke, J. W., and Hanratty, T. J., 1993, "Origin of turbulence-producing eddies in a channel flow," *Phys. Fluids A*, Vol. 5, pp. 1011 - 1022.

Chorin, A. J., 1993, "Hairpin removal in vortex interactions II," *J. Comput. Phys.* Vol. 107, 1 - 9.

Chorin, A. J., 1994, *Vorticity and Turbulence*, Springer-Verlag, New York.

Fishelov, D., 1990, "A new vortex scheme for viscous flows," *J. Comput. Phys.*, Vol. 86, pp. 211 - 224.

Fishelov, D., 1994, "Simulation of three-dimensional turbulent flow in non-cartesian geometry," *J. Comput. Phys.* Vol. 115, pp. 249 - 266.

Gagnon, Y. Giovannini, A. and Hebrard, P., 1993, "Numerical simulation and physical analysis of high Reynolds number recirculating flows behind sudden expansions, *Phys. Fluids A*, Vol. 5, pp. 2377 - 2389.

Greengard, C., 1985, "The core spreading vortex method approximates the wrong equation," *J. Comp. Phys.*, Vol. 61, pp. 345 - 348.

Hess, J. L. and Smith, A. M. O., 1967, "Calculation of potential flow about arbitrary bodies," *Prog. Aero. Sci.*, Vol. 8, pp. 1 - 138.

Kim, J., Moin, P. and Moser, R. D., 1987, "Turbulence statistics in fully-developed channel flow at low Reynolds number," *J. Fluid Mech.*, Vol. 177, pp. 133 - 166.

Leonard, A., 1975, "Numerical simulation of interacting, three-dimensional vortex filaments," *Lec. Notes in Phys.*, Vol. 35, pp. 245 - 250.

Leonard, A., 1980, "Vortex methods for flow simulation," *J. Comp. Phys.*, Vol. 37, 289 - 335.

Miyake, Y., Ushiro, R., Morikawa, T., 1995, "On the regeneration of quasi-streamwise eddies," Proc. Tenth Symp. on Turbulent Shear Flows, Penn State University, 15-7 — 15-12.

Puckett, E. G., 1993, "Vortex methods: an introduction and survey of selected research topics," in *Incompressible computational fluid dynamics: trends and advances*, edited by M. D. Gunzburger and R. A. Nicolaides, Cambridge University Press, Cambridge, pp. 335 - 407.

Rossi, L. F., 1995, "Resurrecting core spreading vortex methods: a new scheme that is both deterministic and convergent," *SIAM J. Sci. Comp.*, Vol. 17, pp. 370 - 388.

FED-Vol. 238, 1996 Fluids Engineering Division Conference
Volume 3
ASME 1996

BEHAVIOR OF QUASI-STREAMWISE VORTICES IN NEAR-WALL TURBULENCE

Yutaka Miyake
Department of Mechanical Engineering
Osaka University
2-1, Yamada-oka, Suita 565 Japan

Koichi Tsujimoto
Department of Mechanical Engineering
Osaka University
2-1, Yamada-oka, Suita 565 Japan

ABSTRACT

Authors new findings concerning the behavior of a quasi-streamwise vortex is described in this paper. Specifically, the mechanism of self-sustenance of a vortex and a novel process of its regeneration as well as its mechanism is mentioned. The discussion is based on the large-scale spatial field data of consecutive discrete time instants obtained by a large scale full three-dimensional simulation of a channel flow. Also a quasi-three-dimensional simulation is conducted to consolidate the discussion. It is demonstrated that a single streamwise vortex is capable of sustaining by itself similarly to a pair of counter-rotating streamwise vortices of legs of a hair-pin type vortex. Stretching is proved to be the major mechanism of the sustenance. A novel type of regeneration of a quasi-streamwise vortex to upstream is also presented. Tilting generates new vortex above and upstream-end of a parent vortex but shortly after of its birth, the new vortex acquires self-sustenance ability by stretching. Brief comment to give a reasoning for the suppression of turbulence by spanwise oscillation of a wall, extending the discussion made for self-sustenance.

INTRODUCTION

Large scale numerical simulations of wall turbulence have promoted enormously the understanding of the physics of turbulence in the near-wall region (Robinson, 1993, Kasagi & Shikazono, 1995). The role of quasi-streamwise vortices whose axis are nearly in the direction of mean flow has been found to be crucially important in the process of all the events taking place in the layer close to the wall. Since the local Reynolds number is small there, small scale vortices are hard to survive and longitudinally elongated vortices becomes dominant and hence coherent structure is observed.

Recent investigations revealed that manipulation at wall such as micro-jet and/or spanwise slip (Choi et al. 1993) and that of wall itself such as spanwise oscillation (Jung et al. 1992, Laadhari,F. et al. 1994) allow us to manage wall turbulence. Since turbulent energy is mostly supplied from the near-wall region, it is quite reasonable that whole wall turbulence is modified by controlling the turbulence in the near-wall region. So, it is of vital importance to understand the behavior of quasi-streamwise vortices, specifically the mechanisms of their generation and sustenance.

As for the generation of quasi-streamwise vortices, many works have been presented. Brooke et al. (1993) found that they are regenerated beneath downstream-end of a grown-up streamwise vortex and Bernard et al. (1993) demonstrated that the regeneration is also possible beneath upstream-end of a parent vortex. So, it is inferred that some different kinds of regeneration exist.

In this article, it is intended to summarize the authors' findings about the self-sustenance mechanism of a single vortex, not of a counter-rotating pair of vortices and a novel evolution process of quasi-streamwise vortices including its mechanism (Miyake et al. 1995, 1996).

A set of huge field data of three-dimensional velocity and pressure of a turbulent channel flow of every $\Delta t^+ = 3.6$ where time t is non-dimensionalized to t^+ by ν, the kinematic viscosity and mean friction velocity on the wall u_τ obtained numerically is stored and used as the data-base for this analysis. In case that cross-flow oscillation is applied on one wall, the mean friction velocity is that on the oscillating wall. The Reynolds number $Re_\tau = Hu_\tau/\nu$ where H is the distance between two walls of channel is around 300. Also a quasi-three-dimensional simulation of a flow of a single quasi-streamwise vortex located close to a wall in an otherwise uniform laminar flow having velocity distribution of turbulent flow is conducted.

SAMPLING OF VORTICES

A picture of the vortex field obtained by specifying some threshold value on the magnitude of streamwise vorticity ω_x, say 0.2, gives a random distribution of vortices, both in local density and in individual scale. Therefore, some kind of conditional sampling is needed to pick up and classify typical streamwise vortices. A group of vortices thus collected has its own property which is different each other depending on the conditions of sampling.

The quasi-streamwise vortices discussed in this paper are those collected under the following sampling conditions.

Strong downwash $v^3/v_{rms}^3 \leq -15$ where v is wall-normal velocity, on the plane parallel to the wall whose distance from the wall is $y^+ = 15$ is used as the signal to detect a quasi-streamwise vortex. This detection method gives the points of upstream-end portion of a

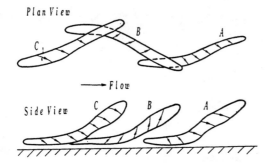

Fig.1 A typical coherent structure of quasi-streamwise vortices in near-wall region. A,C, : $\omega_x > 0$, B : $\omega_x < 0$.

quasi-streamwise vortex where strong wall-normal velocity v is induced by its strong circulation velocity. In addition to this condition, another one that the streamwise length l^+ of the sampled vortices should be within $48 \leq l^+ \leq 80$ when measured on the plane $y^+ = 15$ is added. Vortices thus sampled are similar in scale and are located close to the wall. Among various streamwise vortices, these are active and constitute the major element of coherent structure of near-wall layer, surviving long time. Interesting is that the vortices are not usually found as a single filament but as a group of two or more filaments arranged in the streamwise direction, as shown conceptually in Fig.1. Namely, the upstream portion of a vortex is located close to and nearly parallel to a wall and its tail portion lifts up itself and the top view of a vortex axis is slightly slanted to mean flow, either to the left or to the right depending on its direction of rotation. Upstream end of a vortex is below the tail of another vortex situated upstream to itself.

A typical top view of two quasi-streamwise vortices arranged in the manner mentioned above is shown in Fig.2. The flow is from bottom to top and the vortex A_2 is of negative vorticity, or with counter-clockwise rotation seen from upstream and A_1 is a positive vortex. In this arrangement, sign of vortex is alternating from one to the next. The numbers in Fig.2 means distance from a wall in wall variable and the lines are the contours of $|\omega_x^+| = 0.2$ on each plane.

SELF-SUSTENANCE OF A QUASI-STREAM - WISE VORTEX

In order to get an idea how a quasi-streamwise vortex sustain for long time, budget of production rate of streamwise vorticity ω_x is useful.

$$\frac{D\omega_x}{Dt} = \omega_x \frac{\partial u}{\partial x} + \omega_y \frac{\partial u}{\partial y} + \omega_z \frac{\partial u}{\partial z} + \frac{1}{Re_\tau}\nabla^2 \omega_x$$
$$= \omega_x \frac{\partial u}{\partial x} - \frac{\partial w}{\partial x}\frac{\partial u}{\partial y} + \frac{\partial v}{\partial x}\frac{\partial u}{\partial z} + \frac{1}{Re_\tau}\nabla^2 \omega_x \quad (1)$$

The second line of above equation is to reduce numerical error and each member of the right-hand side of the second line is termed here as stretching term, tilting term, twisting term and viscous diffusion term in the order from the first to the fourth. The time evolution of the streamwise distribution of integrated production

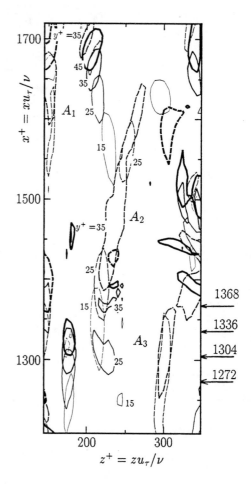

Fig.2 Top view of a chain of quasi-streamwise vortices. Contour lines of $|\omega_x| = 0.2$ in planes $y^+ = 15$(fine), 25, 35, 45(thick). Solid lines : $\omega_x > 0$, broken lines : $\omega_x < 0$.

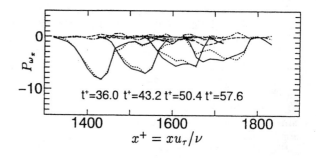

Fig.3 Time evolution of streamwise distribution of integrated production rate P_{ω_x} of a grown-up vortex A_2. Dotted lines : stretching $\omega_x\,(\partial u/\partial x)$, broken lines : tilting $-(\partial w/\partial x)(\partial u/\partial y)$, chained lines : twisting $(\partial v/\partial y)\,(\partial u/\partial z)$, solid lines : sum of these three.

rate P_{ω_x} which is cross sectional integration of production rate in the area where the magnitude of vorticity

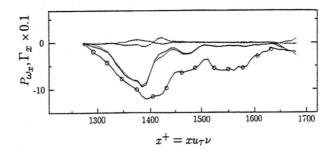

Fig.5 Time evolution of streamwise distribution of integrated production rate P_{ω_x} and circulation Γ_x of a grown-up vortex A_2, at $t^+ = 32.4$. Thin solid line with circles : circulation Γ_x, others, see caption Fig.3.

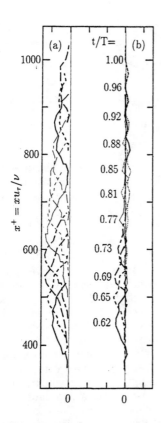

Fig.4 Evolution of streamwise distribution of (a) circulation Γ_x^+ and (b) total production rate of vorticity $P_{\omega_x}^+$.

$|\omega_x|$ exceeds 0.2 for the vortex A_2 of Fig.2 is given in Fig.3. Total production rate which is the sum of first three terms of righthand side of eq.(1) and shown by solid lines gradually attenuates as time marches suggesting that the vortex is already in a grown-up stage, though it is still growing, since the diffusion due to viscosity is less than the total production rate. Figure 4 shows another example of evolution of (a) cross-sectional circulation and (b) the total production rate of every $t^+ = 3$. It strongly suggests that a vortex can survive long even after the vorticity production has ceased.

Figure 5 is a detailed version of Fig.3 in whole length of the vortex A_2 at the particular time instant of $t^+ = 32.4$. In the figure, streamwise variation of circulation is also included. Interesting properties of a grown-up vortex are observed in the figure. Firstly, total production rate is nearly completely occupied by the integrated production rate due to stretching, which is true for other time instant. Secondly, only the upstream-end portion of about 1/3 of whole length of a vortex actively produces vorticity and the rest does not but just receives vorticity by convection. The tail part lifts up and goes farther away from the wall. In this sense, the large part of a vortex is inactive. So, to manage a quasi-streamwise vortex, it is needed to focus on the active upstream-end portion.

In order to investigate the mechanism of the production due to stretching, two-dimensional vortex lines which are obtained by integrating $dy/\omega_y = dz/\omega_z$ in a cross-stream plane are calculated. The vortex lines for

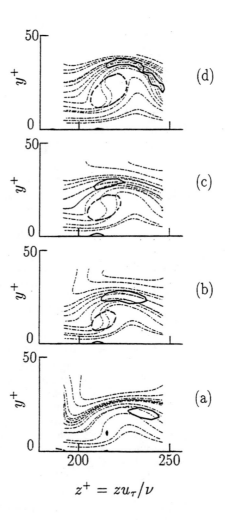

Fig.6 Two-dimensional vortex lines in cross-stream sections. (a) $x^+ = 1272$, (b) $x^+ = 1304$, (c) $x^+ = 1336$, (d) $x^+ = 1368$. Broken lines : A_2, solid lines : A_3

A_2 in $x^+ = 1272, 1304, 1336$ and 1368 at $t^+ = 32.4$ are shown in Fig.6 (a) through (d). Although physical mean

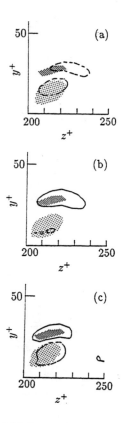

Fig.7 Area of high production rate of ω_x in a cross-section $x^+ = 1336$ at $t^+ = 32.4$. (a) : production rate due to stretching, (b) : due to tilting, (c) : total production rate. Broken line : $P_{\omega_x} < 0$, solid line : $P_{\omega_x} > 0$, hatched area : A_3, dotted area : A_2.

ing of these lines is ambiguous, it has been confirmed that they are quite similar to the full three-dimensional vortex lines projected to a cross-stream plane. The figure indicates that the portion of vortex lines passing through the vortex A_2 are nearly vertical. Since the upstream-end portion of vortex A_2 currently in concern is located close to the wall where high gradient of streamwise velocity $\partial u / \partial y$ exist, stretching of vortex lines passing through the vortex by $\partial u / \partial y$ becomes efficient.

The corresponding production rate distribution in a cross-flow plane $x^+ = 1336$ is given in Fig.7 in which (a) is the production rate due to stretching, (b), due to tilting and (c) sum of these two. The dotted area is the cross section of the vortex A_2 where $\omega_x \leq -0.2$ and the hatched area is that of A_3 where $\omega_x \geq 0.2$. Broken lines show the area in which $P_{\omega_x}^+ \leq -0.015$ and solid lines, $P_{\omega_x}^+ \geq 0.015$. It is reconfirmed from the figure that for a grown-up vortex A_2, stretching is almost unique source to supply streamwise vorticity, producing large amount in the strong vorticity area.

Tilting contributes favorably in this section, though very small, but the contribution is not consistently favorable in the whole length as seen in Fig.5. Summing up two effects, the area of high total production rate becomes nearly coincident with that of high vorticity. So it is concluded that the core of a vortex of strong vorticity is the area where production of vorticity is actively

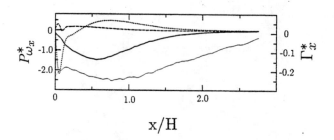

x/H

Fig.8 A quasi-streamwise vortex obtained by a quasi-3D simulation. Thin solid line : circulation, solid line : production rate by stretching, dotted line : tilting, broken line : twisting.

taking place.

The vortex lines shown in Fig.6 give approximate configuration of folded vortex sheet of strong spanwise vorticity representing high wall-normal gradient of streamwise velocity. Heave of this sheet by self-induced velocity of a streamwise vortex is a key process which allows application of stretching to spanwise vortex by streamwise flow. The similar mechanism of conversion of spanwise vorticity to that of streamwise component is found at the leg of a hair-pin vortex in which a pair of counter rotating streamwise vortices generates upward flow in between and heave of vortex sheet is caused. But it is to be noted that even in a single streamwise vortex, the self-sustenance by supplying streamwise vorticity by itself is possible and important is that this process takes place only in the upstream-end portion of a long streamwise vortex. The rest part lifts up itself and the core of vortex cross section there is located farther away from the wall where gradient of streamwise velocity is small and stretching becomes inefficient.

A quasi-three-dimensional simulation has been also conducted to confirm above mentioned mechanism and to verify that the self-sustenance of a streamwise vortex is possible independently on surrounding vortices. In the simulation, spatial marching to downstream direction from a initial cross-stream plane $x = 0$ is carried out, solving two-dimensional flow in a cross-stream plane in each step. In the initial plane, a round vortex of uniform streamwise vorticity is assumed to be located close to the wall. An example of an obtained streamwise vortex is shown in Fig.8 in which streamwise distribution of circulation is denoted by thin solid line and those of integrated production rate due to stretching, by solid line, due to tilting, by dotted line, due to twisting, by broken line.

The quantities in the figure are non-dimensionalized using wall separation H and mean friction velocity u_τ and denoted with superscript (*). The left-end part of the curves of the figure $x/H = 0 \sim 0.2$ includes errors due to physically unreasonable assumption in the initial plane and hence must be put aside in discussion. The simulation confirms the results of full three-dimensional simulation. That is, stretching is dominant and tilting shows similar variation as in Fig.5. Circulation as well varies along with total production rate as in full three-dimensional simulation.

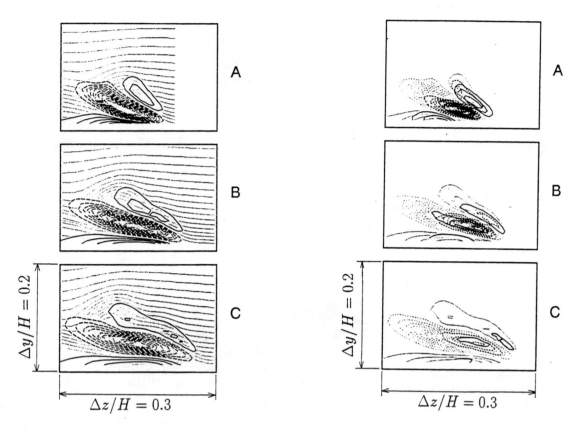

Fig.9 Iso-vorticity contours (solid lines : $\omega_x^* > 0$, broken lines $\omega_x^* < 0$, increment $\Delta\omega_x^* = 10$) and 2-D vortex lines (light lines). A,B,C : $x/H = 0.45, 1.12, 1.57$, respectively.

Fig.10 Iso-production rate contours of ω_x (solid lines : positive tilting, broken lines : negative stretching, increment $\Delta P_{\omega_x}^* = 100$) and iso-vorticity contours (light lines)

However, fundamental difference also appears in this simulation compared with full 3-D one. That is, the vortex axis is not slanted to the wall but is nearly parallel in whole length. Furthermore, the cross section of the vortex is not round but flattened as depicted in Fig.9. In the figure, broken lines are iso-contours of negative vorticity of every $\Delta\omega^* = 10$, and the solid ones are those of positive vorticity and the sections A,B,C are at $x/H = 0.45, 1.12, 1.57$, respectively. The two-dimensional vortex lines in each cross-section obtained in a same manner as in Fig.6 are shown by light lines. Cross sectional view of vortices are fundamentally identical with that of full 3-D simulation. Namely, weak vortex having opposite rotation is found above the major one as well as the sheet of streamwise vorticity below.

Some vortex lines pass through the core of major vortex but they are strongly inclined to horizontal direction as well as the longitudinal axis of vortex sections. It means that vortex sheet is strongly folded and hence, the production due to stretching becomes inefficient, the difference of streamwise velocity between the top and the bottom of a vortex line being small. The reason for this strong folding is not understood well but this is enhanced more in the downstream section and accordingly, the vorticity production decreases.

Figure 10 shows the cross sectional distribution of area of high production rate in three sections A,B,C that are same as in Fig.9. Dotted lines are contours of every $\Delta P_{\omega_x}^* = 100$, of negative production rate due to stretching and solid lines, positive production rate due to tilting. The light lines are vorticity contours brought from Fig.9. In these three sections, stretching produces only negative vorticity and tilting, only positive. These two effects conflict each other in the main vortex core but as in full 3-D simulation, the larger the vorticity, the higher the production rate. The figure supports the discussion mentioned above. That is, in this simulation, the weakening of production is not because of lift-up of body of vortex but because of unsuitable configuration of folded vortex sheet. Therefore, it is suggested that only quasi-streamwise vortices located at appropriate distance from the wall and make a suitable folding of vortex sheet of strong spanwise vorticity can sustain by themselves.

REGENERATION OF QUASI-STREAMWISE VORTICES

According to investigations of the present authors, streamwise vortices are not homogeneously distributed even within a plane parallel to a wall, but concentrated in some area and sparse in the rest. That is, clusters of

$$x^+ = x u_\tau / \nu$$

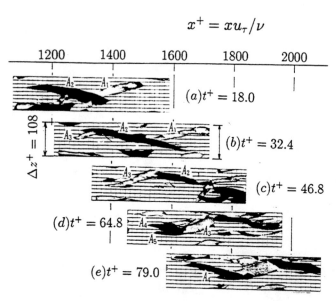

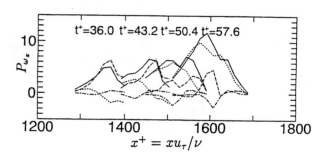

$$x^+ = x u_\tau / \nu$$

Fig.12 Time evolution of streamwise distribution of integrated production rate P_{ω_x} of a regenerating vortex A_3. See caption Fig.3.

Fig.11 Regeneration of quasi-streamwise vortices to upstream. Top view of a parent vortex A_2 and regenerating vortices A_3 and A_4. Black : $\omega_x < 0$, light : $\omega_x > 0$

vortices appear. The life-time of a cluster is usually longer than that of individual vortices inside a cluster. So, it is expected that active regeneration of vortices is taking place commonly in the near-wall layer.

In fact, a couple of types of regeneration have been reported in the literature, as mentioned earlier. Here, it is intended to describe one novel regeneration process. A representative example of the process of establishing a chain of streamwise vortices conceptually depicted in Fig.1 is demonstrated in Fig.11. Shots of top view of every $\Delta t^+ = 14.4$ in the figure illustrate an evolution of quasi-streamwise vortices. Figure 2 is an alternative drawing of the shot at $t^+ = 32.4$ of Fig.11. Black bodies (A_2) are negative vortices and light ones (A_1, A_3) are positive. The flow is from left to right and the vortices are convected to downstream whose speed is estimated by their streamwise location referring to the scale at the top of the figure.

Initial combinations of A_1 and A_2 at $t^+ = 18.0$ is modified to a zig-zag form adding a new vortex A_3 at $t^+ = 32.4$. Although the configuration of A_3 given by top view in Fig.2 is ambiguous because segments of iso-contours in consecutive planes appear discontinuously, the vortex A_3 is a similar continuous filament as others. The newly born vortex A_3 grows up gradually as time marches ($t^+ = 46.8$) and again it regenerates new vortex A_4 ($t^+ = 64.8$).

That is, a grown-up vortex generates new one of opposite rotation to itself at its upstream-end and above itself. Interesting is that this process takes place repeatedly.

The mechanism of this regeneration is discussed in the

following.

The time evolution of streamwise distribution of integrated production rate P_{ω_x} of A_3 is shown in Fig.12. Broken line means P_{ω_x} due to tilting, dotted line, due to stretching, chained line, due to twisting and solid line, the sum of these three. At the early stage of its growth, tilting is dominant in the total production rate but as time marches, stretching becomes more than tilting and twisting contributes little. So, it can be concluded that the early stage growth is mainly by tilting and when a vortex has grown up, stretching sustain its strength. A more detailed picture of above one demonstrates that in the 2/3 upstream-end portion of A_3, tilting is overwhelming but in the rest downstream-end portion, two effects conflict with each other.

The corresponding cross sectional distribution of high production rate area is found in Fig.7 in which hatched area is the cross section of A_3. In this section, stretching suppresses its growth and tilting drives it. Figure 7 demonstrates that the total production rate becomes positive and the area of strong total production rate coincides exactly with that of strong vorticity. The same maps in other upstream sections, though not shown here, are in accordance with the implementation of the curves in Fig.12.

As shown in Fig.6(a), vortex lines passing through the cross section of A_3 are smooth and no complicated folding of vortex sheet occurs. However, a high-shear layer of strong spanwise vorticity is found between A_2 and A_3 in a longitudinal section including these two vortices, an example of which is shown in Fig.13. It gives a flow in a longitudinal section of $z^+ = 222$ at $t^+ = 32.4$ in which solid closed curve is the contour of $\omega_x = 0.2$ of A_3 and that of broken line, $\omega_x = -0.2$ of A_2 and arrows mean the fluctuating velocity vectors projected to the plane.

Thin solid lines show wall-normal distributions of streamwise velocity u. Since this section is located in a up-wash region of induced flow of A_2, low-speed streak appears. It should be noted that the low speed streak extends long to upstream of the vortex itself, as a trace of its passing.

The above-mentioned high shear layer is caused by bringing low speed fluid from the layer closer to the wall

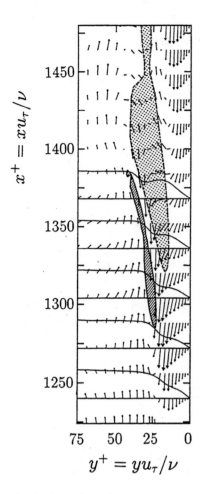

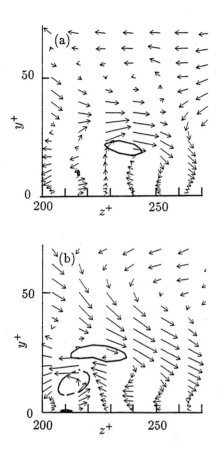

Fig.14 Velocity vector maps in cross-stream sections (a) $x^+ = 1272$ and (b) $x^+ = 1304$. Closed lines are cross sections of vortices, top : A_3, bottom : A_2.

Fig.13 High-shear layer between a parent vortex and a regenerating vortex. Solid lines : streamwise velocity distribution, broken line : $\omega_x^* \geq 20$, dotted line : $\omega_x^* \leq -60$

by circulating flow of A_2. This spanwise vorticity can be converted to streamwise component by streamwise velocity gradient $\partial u/\partial z$, which is again due to the self-induced velocity of A_2, i.e., on one side upwash of low speed fluid and on the other side, downwash of high-speed fluid. This production is mostly that of stretching mentioned above and not of twisting.

The reasoning for tilting is rather complicated. Figure 13 as well as those of other spanwise place indicates that body of A_2 grows and lifts up to downstream in the upstream-end portion where new vortex A_3 is generated. This is because that high production of vorticity there magnifies circulation to downstream as demonstrated in Fig.5. Then, spanwise velocity w induced by circulatory motion of A_2 increases to downstream, that is, in this case, $\partial w/\partial x < 0$, since the circulating flow is counter-clockwise of negative w. Accordingly, positive wall-normal vorticity ω_y is generated.

This ω_y is tilted quickly by above-mentioned high-shear layer $\partial u/\partial y > 0$ producing positive streamwise vorticity. If the circulation of the parent vortex is opposite, the wall-normal vorticity is downward or negative and hence, produced streamwise vorticity is reversed. This mechanism is not peculiar for this particular vortex but can take place commonly in other vortices.

The mechanism of tilting in the upstream of the upstream-end of A_2 is similar fundamentally, but the reasoning of generation of $\partial w/\partial x$ is slightly different. As exhibited in Fig.14 which shows velocity vector maps in cross-flow sections and vortex sections of A_2 and A_3 at (a) $x^+ = 1272$ and (b) $x^+ = 1304$, the circulating flow attenuates to upstream. Because at the section $x^+ = 1304$, the strong circulating

flow is generated by cooperation of A_2 and A_3, but in the more upstream section of $x^+ = 1272$, it is due to A_3 itself. Shortly after this instant, the new vortex A_3 gains self-sustenance ability by stretching.

A streamwise vortex above upstream portion of a grown-up streamwise vortex is reproduced also by a quasi-three dimensional simulation. The formation of the vortex corresponding to A_3 is exhibited in Fig.9 shown earlier. The conflict of tilting and stretching in the vortex currently in concern and superior effect of the former is also shown in Fig.10. These results support the conclusions of full 3-D simulation. In addition, high shear layer between two vortices of opposite rotation is also reproduced in this quasi-3D simulation.

DRAG REDUCTION BY SPANWISE OSCILLATION OF A WALL

Much effort has been devoted to reduce drag of near-wall turbulence and many ideas have been presented.

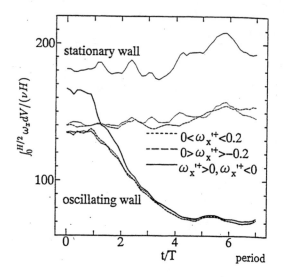

Fig.15 Attenuation of streamwise vorticity ω_x by spanwise simulation of a wall (thick lines). Total vorticity inside half computational volume of oscillating wall side. Solid line : $\omega'_x > 0$ and < 0, broken line : $0 > \omega'_x > 0.2$, dotted line : $\omega'_x < 0$.

Among them, method of cross-streamwise oscillation of a wall (Jung et al. 1992, Laadhari et al. 1994) attract attention as to be realizable in practical situation.

A simulation in a channel whose upper wall is oscillating with period $T^+ = 100$ reproduced reduction of friction drag presented by Jung et al.(1992). The drag reduction proceeds gradually and at the end of 5th period of oscillation, it attains saturated reduction rate. Along with this evolution, the streamwise vortices parallely attenuates. Figure 15 shows an example of evolution of total streamwise vorticity which is the integration of ω_x in half horizontal volume of flow passage. Thick lines are for oscillating wall side and the thin lines, for stationary side. Solid lines mean the evolution of total vorticity and dotted and broken lines mean those of negative and positive weak vortex of $|\omega_x| \leq 0.2$, respectively. One finds that attenuation of vortex takes place from stronger one, suggesting that for the management of near-wall turbulence, priority should be on the strongest vortices.

It is found from the simulation that in one period of oscillation, streamwise vortices are activated temporarily, but the root portion or the upstream-end portion of a vortex which is of major importance in its sustenance stays almost consistently under low production. This suppression of production is caused by unfavorable folding of spanwise vortex sheet, namely, too heavy in some fraction of one period and too weak in some other.

CONCLUDING REMARKS
In this article, birth, growth and sustenance of a quasi-streamwise vortex are discussed using a three-dimensional field data fabricated by a large scale numerical simulation.

Strong quasi-streamwise vortices inducing strong downwash at a plane close to the wall constitute a major element of coherent structure in the near-wall turbulence. These vortices are commonly observed in a combination of single vortices arranged in streamwise direction and are capable of sustaining by themselves converting spanwise vorticity which is the unique source of vorticity supplied to the flow field, to streamwise component. The mechanism of its conversion is mostly due to stretching effect taking advantage of sharp wall-normal gradient of streamwise velocity. But in order that this effect arises effectively, winding or folding of vortex sheet by self-induced velocity of a streamwise vortex is crucial. Drag reduction by spanwise oscillation of a wall is reasonably explained by the extension of the sustaining mechanism.

The zig-zag combination of vortices is not peculiar in the vortices exhibited herein but common in near-wall layer. This pattern is built by regeneration to upstream of a parent vortex. The early stage of regeneration is due to tilting, but shortly after of its birth, the regenerated vortex gain the self-sustenance ability due to stretching.

It is hoped that the discussions summarized in this article are extended to realize management of near-wall turbulence.

REFERENCES
Bernard, P.S., Thomas, J.M., Handler, R.A. 1993, "Vortex dynamics and the production of Reynolds stress", J. Fluid Mech., Vol.253, pp.385-419.

Brooke, J.W., Hanratty, T.J., 1993, "Origin of turbulence-producing eddies in a channel flow", Phys. Fluids, A Vol.5, pp.1011-1022.

Choi, H., Moin, P., Kim, J., 1994, "Active turbulence control for drag reduction in wall-bounded flows", J. Fluid Mech., Vol.262, pp.75-110.

Jung, W. J., Mangiavacchi, N., Akhavan, R., 1992, "Suppression of turbulence in wall-bounded flows by high-frequency spanwise oscillations", Phys. Fluids, A Vol.4, pp.1605-1607.

Kasagi, N., Shikazono, N., 1995, "Contribution of direct numerical simulation to understanding and modeling turbulent transport," Proc. R. Soc. Lond. A, Vol. 451, pp. 257-292.

Laadhari, F., Skandaji, L., Morel, R., 1994, "Turbulence reduction in a boundary layer by a local spanwise oscillating surface", Phys. Fluids, Vol.6, pp.3218-3220.

Miyake, Y., Ushiro, R., Morikawa, T., 1995, "On the regeneration of quasi-streamwise eddies", Proc. 10th Symp. Turb. shear Flows, Aug.14-16, 1995, Penn. State Univ., 15-7-15-12.

Miyake, Y., Tsujimoto, K., Morikawa, T., 1996, "Mechanism of self-sustenance and regeneration of quasi-streamwise vortices of near-wall turbulence", (to appear in Intern. J. JSME)

Robinson,S.K., 1991, "Coherent motions in the turbulent boundary layer", Annu. Rev. Fluid Mech., Vol.23, pp.601-639

FED-Vol. 238, 1996 Fluids Engineering Division Conference
Volume 3
ASME 1996

EXPERIMENTAL MEASUREMENT AND MATCHING SIMULATION OF A VORTEX RING IMPINGING ON A WALL

Drazen Fabris and Dorian Liepmann
Department of Mechanical Engineering
University of California, Berkeley, California 94720

Daniel Marcus
Lawrence Livermore National Laboratory
Livermore, California 94550

ABSTRACT

A joint experimental and computational methodology is developed and applied to investigate a vortex ring (Reynolds number 1000) impinging normally on a wall. The method uses Digital Particle Image Velocity measurements to provide the initialization and validations for a second-order finite difference projection method. The experiment and the computations both show shedding of the boundary layer and formation of a secondary ring of opposite signed vorticity. The simulation indicates a second rebound in the position of the peak of vorticity. Two comparison cases are simulated with Gaussian vorticity profiles to consider the effect of assumptions in the initialization. The comparison shows that the initialization derived from measurements produces the most accurate simulation.

INTRODUCTION

Recent improvements in experimental and numerical methods open up the possibility of combined investigations which will substantially increase our understanding of complex fluid flows. Specifically, the development of Digital Particle Image Velocimetry (DPIV) (Willert and Gharib, 1991) enables accurate experimental measurements of two-dimensional instantaneous velocity fields, whereas previous efforts were limited to flow visualization or ensembles of single point measurements (LDV). These measurements can be integrated with simulations to provide both a validation of the evolution of the simulation and more signifi-

cantly, a physically realistic initialization. The validated numerical simulation can then be confidently used to probe the fluid dynamics on a finer spatial and temporal scale than possible experimentally. In the following paper, we develop a methodology for combining experimental and numerical methods to quantitatively investigate the normal impingement of a vortex ring with a wall. To demonstrate the importance of the initial conditions the experimental results are compared to simulations based on measured and idealized vorticity initializations. The interest lies in understanding the accuracy of the measured DPIV characterization, as well as, comparing the overall accuracy of the numerical method, and the effect of the choice of initialization.

A vortex ring interaction with a wall encorporates fundamental inviscid and viscous boundary layer dynamics. The interaction exhibits four primary stages of development: 1) vortex stretching as the ring approaches the wall, 2) viscous boundary layer growth, 3) boundary layer development and separation, and 4) coalescence of the separated boundary layer into a ring of opposite signed vorticity (secondary ring). Further dynamics of the flow include an inviscid and viscous interaction between the opposite signed vortices, a repeat of the boundary layer shedding forming a tertiary ring, and instability of the secondary vortex. Extended descriptions of the phenomena were originally proposed by Walker et al. (1987) and Orlandi and Verzicco (1993), and a stability analysis and computation was done by Swearingen et al. (1995).

The process of vortex ring formation and translation is well described (Didden, 1979; Saffman, 1992; Weigand, 1993) but an accurate 2-D characterization of the core vortex distribution is uncertain. Theoretically, many different distributions are proposed with interest in determining advection velocity or stability (Norbury, 1973; Widnall and Sullivan, 1973; Ye and Chu, 1995) A fundamental assumption in most theoretical models is a ring with a small core diameter relative to the ring diameter, and a circular and symmetric distribution of vorticity in the core. Numerically, a variety of distributions are modeled (Chu et al., 1995; Liepmann et al, 1991; Orlandi and Verzicco, 1993; Stanaway et al., 1988) from a Kelvin-Hicks ring (core in solid body rotation) to a Hill's vortex (thick diffuse ring). In addition, vortex generation methods in experiments vary without consistent comparisons of velocity or vorticity fields (Maxworthy, 1977; Pullin, 1979; Shariff and Leonard, 1992). Therefore, in order to accurately describe and simulate a vortex ring the distribution of the core vorticity needs to be known. The effect of core distribution should be especially important in the interaction with a wall. Cores with the same circulation (Reynolds number = Γ/ν) but different strength of peak vorticity and distributions will lead to different strengths in the boundary layer flow and hence to secondary rings with different circulations and strengths.

METHODOLOGY

The general approach is to apply DPIV to measure the two-dimensional velocity field in a plane through the center of a laminar vortex ring. From the velocity field we compute vorticity which is used to initialize the simulation. The flow is simulated with a finite-difference projection method which resolves the boundary layer and the secondary vortex roll up with greater detail than experimentally possible. The experiment and simulation are then compared at later times for mutual verification.

Figure 1 shows a schematic of the experiment. The diameter of the generating tube is 2.54 cm. The ring is generated 4 diameters from the wall to allow formation transients to die out (Didden, 1979). Two dimensional velocities are measured in a planar (r-x) cut with a DPIV method developed by Willert and Gharib (1991). The Reynolds number is chosen to be 1000 to ensure a two dimensional vortex ring which is verified through flow visualization. The seed particles are fluorescein embedded polystyrene spheres of 80 micron diameter and are illuminated with an argon ion LASER light sheet. For improved spatial resolution, the field of view focuses on only half of the ring. Thirty velocity fields are generated per second of flow time with

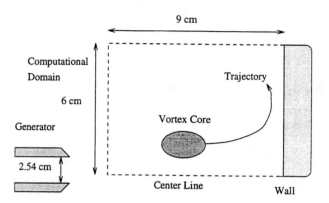

Figure 1: Experimental configuration.

799 realizations overall. For the case presented, the DPIV measurements result in no spurious vectors and are unfiltered in order not to degrade the maxima and minima of velocity and vorticity in the field.

The computations implement a second-order projection method for the incompressible, axisymmetric Navier-Stokes equations developed by Bell, Colella, and Glaz (1989) (Bell and Marcus, 1992; Chorin, 1969). The method incorporates a variant of the unsplit second-order Godunov methodology developed by Colella (1990) for inviscid, compressible flows for the evaluation of the nonlinear advection terms in the momentum equations. This provides a temporal discretization that is second-order for smooth flows and stable in regions with steep gradients, even for singular initial data and in the limit of vanishing viscosity. These properties make the method extremely well suited for flows which are characterized by fine structure and a wide range of length scales.

Two versions of the second order finite difference method are used. In the interest of extending the cases considered, the simulations are repeated and extended with the second and newer method. The first uses a pressure grid staggered from the velocity, a continuity projection based on an orthonormal decomposition, and a conjugate gradient solver (Bell and Marcus, 1992; Marcus and Bell, 1994). The second method uses for advection a marker-and-cell stencil which locates the pressure at the cell centers, an approximate projection, and a multigrid solver (Almgren et al., 1996; Lai et al., 1993). Both methods extrapolate advective terms with a Godunov method. The bulk of the results use the first simulation while the trajectories in figure 9 are computed with the second method. Little variation between the methods is expected.

The primary interest is to be able to accurately characterize an experiment and simulate directly that specific run. To provide an initialization we average a limited number of DPIV measurements (seven) to characterize the vortex ring. Only half of the symmetric vor-

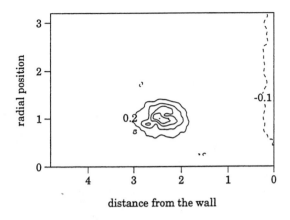

Figure 2: Initial vorticity field. Positive contours every 0.2 and negative at -0.1. (Lengths are non-dimensionalized with initial ring radius and vorticity with initial peak vorticity.)

	Experiment	Gaussian I	Gaussian II
Γ cm^2/sec	10.89	10.89	10.89
Vorticity (Max.) sec^{-1}	7.26	4.77	7.26
Width Squared cm^2	N/A	0.7278	0.4778
Kinetic Energy $milli - Joules$	946.8	946.8	1125
Impulse $Newtons/sec$	2.556	2.758	2.833
Enstrophy cm^3/sec^2	32.53	26.01	39.57
Position (R) cm	1.802	1.802	1.802

Table 1: Possible cases for Gaussian matching. The Gaussian is matched to two global quantities. The Reynolds number (Γ/ν) is always matched. Width is defined by the 1/e height of the Gaussian.

tex is considered and the centerline is determined by the position of a square contour integral which maximizes circulation. In averaging, the DPIV velocity fields are translated by the advection distance of the ring over the time difference of the measurements (30 hertz) to avoid spreading the distribution. With this averaging experimental noise should be reduced. Finally the simulation is initialized with vorticity which is projected by the simulation onto a divergence free basis. The second method is initialized with a velocity field numerically solved from the vorticity with a stream function.

The vorticity field used to initialize the simulation is shown in figure 2. The vortex ring is started at 2.5 ring radii from the wall. A boundary layer exists in the initialization which is partially attributed to natural convection. For the simulation, the boundary layer is left in the initialization. The computational method is not considered to be sensitive to the smoothness and continuity of the initialization field. High frequency noise in the field will damp on its own and the projection in the code would immediately enforce continuity. In short, prefiltering of the initial data is unwarranted.

In addition to validation of the simulation, we are interested in the differences induced by assumed initial conditions. As a simplest characterization the core is taken to be Gaussian in vorticity distribution. With this distribution we can match two physical quantities in addition to the ring radius. The Reynolds number is always matched (Γ/ν) and other quantities considered are peak vorticity, kinetic energy, and fluid impulse. Values are tabulated based on vorticity included in the ring core with kinetic energy and impulse calculated with a stream function solver. Table 1 presents the measured quantities and mismatches for the different Gaussian distributions. Matching impulse was found not to be possible.

The first simulations are evolved on a 200 by 300 grid (6cm by 9cm) for 8 seconds of flow time and then the domain is redrawn to a 300 by 150 grid to prevent artificial boundary influences. The simulation employed free slip boundary conditions at the centerline and viscous no-slip conditions at the other boundaries. A small jump in some quantities, such as centroids, occurs when the flow is projected onto the new domain. The second set of simulations are evolved on a 256 by 256 grid (9cm by 9cm) over the entire run. Lower and higher resolution cases are run for a short time to determine if the simulation is fully resolved. In addition, a simulated case is run with the initial data passed through a smoothing filter. The smoothed run shows no significant departure in the trajectory of the ring during the approach but a slightly lower value of the peak vorticity and is not continued for this reason.

For quantitative comparisons integral information from the experiment, kinetic energy and enstrophy, is interpolated and tabulated on spatial grids with the same resolution as the computation. All quantities are non-dimensionalized using R_o^2/Γ_o for time and R_o(initial radius) for length, and vorticity, circulation and kinetic energy are normalized with their initial values.

RESULTS

Through DPIV measurements we are able to identify and characterize the vorticity distribution of the ring and follow the interaction with the wall closely. The initial vorticity field shows that the ring is very thick with a large core radius relative to the ring radius, and that the core shape is clearly not circular but oblong and slightly weighted towards its centerline (fig. 2). The front stagnation point and the rear stagnation point are different in shape which shows the lack of reflective symmetry in the core. The distributions show Gaussian characteristics with different broadening widths of 0.254 in the radial direction and 0.426 in the x direction. This comparison points out that spatial cross-sections can lead to misinterpreting the core as Gaussian and illustrates the value in making a planar measurements.

For a general comparison we look at vorticity contours in between the secondary and tertiary vortex shedding (fig. 3). In general, the simulation agrees extremely well with the experiment showing identical features and comparing quantitatively. This close matching gives us confidence that we are simulating the flow accurately. Variations are attributed to experimental noise and effects due to the natural convection boundary layer in the experiment. The separation point of the boundary layer remains relatively fixed on the wall at r = 2.5, and the primary ring sweeps negative vorticity from the wall past the separation point. In both cases the circulation of the secondary ring is substantially weaker than that of the primary, but is strong enough to cause the primary ring to rebound through an inviscid interaction but not to cause the primary ring to contract radially.

To compare the simulation to the experiment quantitatively we look for a reduced characterization of the vortex dynamics in the trajectories of the primary and secondary vortices. These are shown for the experiment and the computations in figs. 4a and b. The positions of the primary and secondary ring are determined by the positions of the local extrema of the vorticity. Due to high noise in the peak value and position, the experimental trajectory of the peak of vorticity is curve fit with a seventh order polynomial. Both the primary and secondary vorticity peaks in the experiment and simulation follow nearly the same path. The simulation undergoes a transitory phase initially while the high frequency variations in vorticity dissipate and forms a distribution which is stable during advection. Figure 4c shows the centroid of positive vorticity. The centroid provides an integral measurement of the position of ring and shows global dynamics of the flow. The experimental trajectory biased away from the wall due to noise in the far field.

Close inspection of the trajectory of peak vorticity, fig. 4a, shows that the actual positions of the exper-

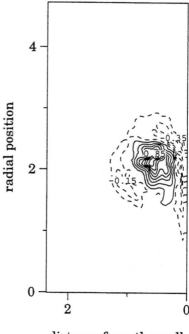

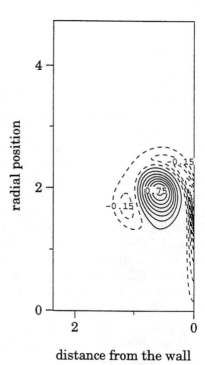

Figure 3: Vorticity contours in the experiment and the simulation at t = 26.0 (after the roll up of the boundary layer into the secondary vortex and before the generation of the third).

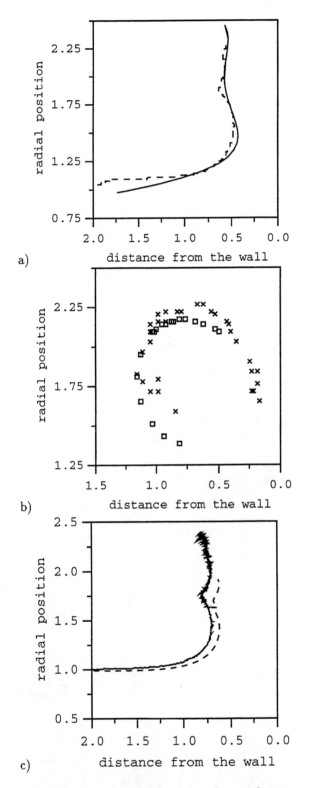

a)

b)

c)

Figure 4: Trajectories of primary and secondary vortices: a) trajectory of peak of positive vorticity, b) positions of the peak of the secondary vortex, and c) trajectory of the centroid of positive vorticity. The experiment is shown in solid lines and x's. The simulation is shown in dashed lines and boxes.

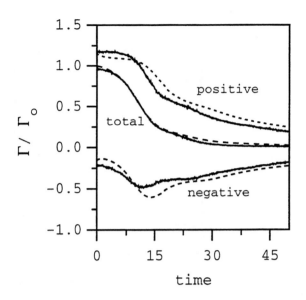

Figure 5: Positive, negative and total circulation.

imental and numerical rings agree very well. We are able to identify the vortex peak and follow the structure for longer times than in dye visualization studies. The straight approach towards the wall shown in fig. 4c compares well with Walker et al. (1987). The rebounds of the primary ring from the wall in the experiment and the computation agree qualitatively. The first bounce is suggested in the experimental trajectory (fig. 4a) and distinctly indicated in the centroid trajectory (fig. 4c). The simulation clearly shows the bounce at non-dimensional time t = 22.0, r = 1.91 (peak of rebound) and also shows a second bounce at t = 42 and r = 2.2 (fig. 4a) which is seen experimentally but comparable to the noise. The first rebound is an inviscid interaction with the secondary vortex and the second rebound is an interaction with the tertiary. The ring continues to expand at this Reynolds number, which agrees with earlier studies (Lim et al., 1991; Walker et al., 1987). In addition, the secondary vortex ring in both cases follows the same path. In the simulation the genesis of the secondary vortex is identified where the separating boundary layer develops a local minimum. Experimentally the secondary vortex appears earlier, but, considering noise and resolution, the exact point of formation is difficult to judge.

A comparison of global quantities, such as circulation history, provides a good consistency check for the simulation. Figure 5 shows the positive (in the ring), negative (in the boundary layer) and total circulation. Circulation is calculated by summing the vorticity of the appropriate sign over the entire field. Again, the simulation can be seen to undergo a transient stage (time = 0 to 4) where the high frequency variations in vorticity cancel. These variations occur both in the vortex ring and in the far field. The overall circulation

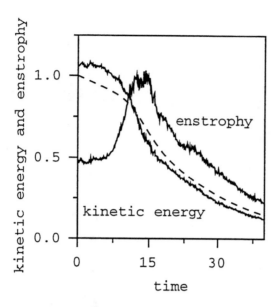

Figure 6: Kinetic energy and enstrophy. Only the experimental enstrophy is shown.

is very well represented which indicates that we have a good characterization of the flow. At later times we expect the experimental measurements to undervalue the circulation due to difficulties in resolving the fine structure of the boundary layer. Looking at the negative circulation one can see strong boundary layer growth from time 6 to 12 with shedding of vorticity from the boundary layer indicated here at the minimum of the negative circulation. The highest rate of decay of total circulation occurs early, time = 6 to 14, while there is strong development of the boundary layer. After this point the strong vortex layer rolls up into the secondary ring and diffuses with the primary ring. A repeat of this process with the formation of the tertiary ring can be seen from time 24 to 36.

Figure 6 shows the history of kinetic energy and enstrophy. The kinetic energy decay prior to the interaction with the wall (time = 0 to 8) shows a large viscous effect which supports the thick ring characterization with diffusion during the advection process. The dissipation greatly increases as the ring interacts with the wall. The growth in the enstrophy corresponds primarily with boundary layer growth. The decay occurs during the rebound and is due to vorticity diffusion and cancellation. Evidence of the repeat of the boundary layer growth and shedding is inferred from the leveling of enstrophy from time 21 to 24.

A comparison of the simulation with real initial conditions with the Gaussian case illustrates the importance of using appropriate starting conditions. Figure 7 shows the interaction of the Gaussian core with the wall. The more diffuse core creates a stronger sec-

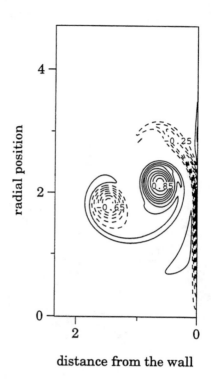

distance from the wall

Figure 7: Vorticity contours of the simulation with Gaussian initial conditions at the same point in time as figure 3.

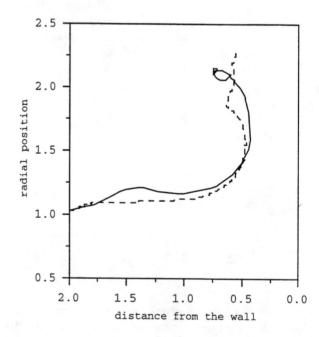

Figure 8: Trajectories of the peak of positive vorticity for the two simulated cases. The Gaussian case is solid and the case with real initial conditions is shown dotted.

ondary vortex due to a longer time of interaction before the secondary vortex was shed. The comparison of the position of peak vorticity for the two simulations is shown in fig. 8. The Gaussian initial condition is unstable due to its large and diffuse distribution and goes through a process of development as it approached the wall. The same effect is reported in other numerical work (Orlandi and Verzicco, 1993; Shariff et al., 1994; Stanaway et al., 1988). The simulation with real initial conditions shows two rebounds with continued expansion while the Gaussian case expands further and then undergoes a loop. This contraction isn't seen at this Reynolds number in our experiment, but is reported for higher Reynolds numbers (Orlandi and Verzicco, 1993), but not seen with great confidence in the dye visualization studies (Walker et al., 1987). The significant over-estimation of the secondary vortex circulation drives the primary ring contraction. This case illustrates a simple point that accurate experimental characterizations and initializations are vital to simulating a physically consistent condition.

Figure 9 shows the trajectories of the centroids of positive vorticity for the newer simulations compared with the experiment. In addition to the two simulations previously shown, the Gaussian case II (matching peak vorticity in table 1) is considered. The primary and secondary rebounds of the vorticity centroid give an indication of the negative vorticity flux coming from the boundary layer. The case with the experimental data as initial conditions again comes the closest to the experiment. The Gaussian condition with matched kinetic energy performs better than the case with matched peak vorticity. The radial positions of the rebounds and the maximum radial extent of the ring is the strongest indication of how well the code follows the physics. A reduced radial expansion of the ring indicates over-estimation of negative vorticity flux from the boundary layer which will further affect the dynamics of the stability of the secondary vortex. As mentioned before, the experimental trajectory is biased slightly away from the wall.

CONCLUSIONS

An overall methodology for combining modern experimental and numerical techniques is applied to a laminar vortex ring interacting normally with a wall. The vorticity distribution in the core of the ring is measured with DPIV and found to be nonsymmetric. The flow is simulated with a second order finite difference method. The simulated cases include initializations with the measured data and two Gaussian vorticity distributions matching Reynolds number and either peak vorticity or kinetic energy.

The experimental results agree qualitatively with

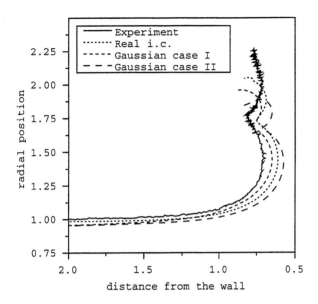

Figure 9: Trajectory of the centroid of positive vorticity for the three different simulations and experiment.

previous work (Walker et al., 1987) and in this study global and local quatities are measured such as circulation, kinetic energy and trajectories. The boundary layer is seen to roll up into an opposite signed vortex whose magnitude is sufficient to induce a rebound of the primary ring but substantially smaller than the primary. The primary vortex continues to expand and the boundary layer shedding process repeats with the formation of the tertiary ring. The stages of development can been seen in the circulation, kinetic enegy, and enstrophy histories.

A matching numerical simulation is evolved using experimental data as an initialization. The profiles of kinetic energy and circulation compare well. The trajectories of the rings along with positions, and strengths of the shed vortices are consistent. From the greater detail available in the simulation the position of the peak of vorticity in the primary ring is identified to rebound a second time from the wall.

To demonstrate the importance of a physically accurate initialization for computations, an initialization of a circular, Gaussian ring is simulated. Historically, vortex ring simulations assume initial conditions, typically Gaussian, and use estimates of circulation from dye studies. Without an accurate measurement of physical quantities, such as kinetic energy and impulse, there exists uncertainty in choosing the Gaussian's size and strength. In all cases the Gaussian distributions mismatch some measured quantities by 10% to 20%. These mismatches are a result of the non-circular shape of the ring core. The Gaussian cases show qualitatively and quantitatively different results. The peak vorticity in the secondary vortex is too high and the trajectory of the primary ring undergoes a contraction which is physically unrealistic for this flow. Of the two cases the matching of kinetic energy comes closer to the real flow than matching the peak vorticity.

Acknowledgements

The authors would like to thank for their contributions and advice: Alexander Weigand, Ömer Savaş, and Phillip Colella. Research at UC Berkeley was supported in part by the US Department of Energy HPCCP grant DE-FG03-92ER25140 . The work of Dan Marcus was performed under the auspices of the U.S. Department of Energy by the Lawrence Livermore National Laboratory under contract No. W-7405-Eng-48. Support under contract No. W-7405-Eng-48 was provided by the DOE Office of Scientific Computing Applied Mathematical Sciences Program DOE HPCC Program.

References Adrian, R.J., 1991, "Particle-imaging techniques for experimental fluid mechanics," *Annu. Rev. Fluid Mech.* **23**, pp. 261-304.

Almgren, A.S., Bell, J.B., and Szymczak, W.G., 1996, "A Numerical Method for the Incompressible Navier-StokesEquations Based on an Approximate Projection", SIAM. J. Sci. Comput. **17** no. 2.

Bell, J.B., Colella, P., and Glaz, H.M., 1989, "A second-order projection method for the incompressible Navier-Stokes equations," *J. Comp. Physics* **85**, pp. 257-283.

Bell, J.B., and Marcus, D.L., 1992, "A second-order projection method for variable-density flows," *J. Comp. Physics* **101**, pp. 334-348.

Chorin, A.J., 1969, "On the convergence of discrete approximations to the Navier-Stokes equations," *Math. Comp.* **23**, p. 341.

Chu, C.-C., Wang, C.-T., and Chang, C.-C., 1995, "A vortex impinging on a solid plane surface-Vortex structure and surface force", *Phys. Fluids* **7**, pp. 1391-1401.

Colella, P., 1990, "Multidimensional upwind methods for hyperbolic conservation laws," *J. Comp. Physics* **87**, p. 171.

Didden, N., 1979, "On the formation of vortex rings: rolling-up and production of circulation," *J. App. Math. and Physics (ZAMP)* **30**, pp. 101-116.

Lai, M., Bell, J.B., and Colella, P., 1993, "A Projection Method for Combustion in the Zero Mach Number Limit", Proceedings, 11th AIAA Computational Fluid Dynamics Conference, Orlando, FL July 6 - 9, p. 69.

Liepmann, D., Dommermuth, D. and Weigand, A., 1991, "Quantitative Experimental and Numerical Investigation of a Vortex Ring Impinging on a Wall," *Bull. Amer. Phy. Soc.*, **36** (10), p. 2320.

Lim, T.T., Nichols, T.B., and Chong, M.S., 1991, "A note on the cause of rebound in the head-on collision of a vortex ring with a wall," *Exp. in Fluids 12*, pp. 41-48.

Marcus, D. L. and Bell, J.B., 1994, "Numerical simulation of a viscous vortex ring interaction with a density interface," *Phys. Fluids* **6**, pp. 1505-1514.

Maxworthy, T., 1977, "Some experimental studies of vortex rings," *J. Fluid Mech.* **81**, pp. 465-495.

Norbury, J., 1973, "A family of steady vortex rings," *J. Fluid Mech.* **57**, pp. 417-431.

Orlandi, P. and Verzicco R., 1993, "Vortex rings impinging on walls: axisymmetric and three-dimensional simulations," *J. Fluid Mech.* **256**, pp. 615-646.

Pullin, D.I., 1979, "Vortex ring formation at tube and orifice openings," *Phys. Fluids* **22**, pp. 401-403.

Saffman, P.G., 1992, *Vortex Dynamics*, Cambridge Univer. Press, Cambridge.

Shariff, K. and Leonard, A., 1992, "Vortex Rings," *Annu. Rev. Fluid Mech.* **24**, pp. 235-279.

Shariff, K., Verzicco, R., and Orlandi, P., 1994, "A numerical study of three-dimensional vortex ring instabilities: viscous corrections and early nonlinear stage," *J. Fluid Mech.* **279**, pp. 351-375.

Stanaway, S., Shariff, K., and Hussain, F., 1988, "Head-on collision of viscous vortex rings," *Proc. Summer Program*, Center for Turb. Research, Stanford, pp. 287-309.

Swearingen, J.D., Crouch, J.D., and Handler, R.A., 1995, "Dynamics and stability of a vortex ring impacting a solid boundary," *J. Fluid Mech.* **297**, pp. 1-28.

Walker, J.D.A., Smith, C.R., Cerra, A.W., Dogilaski, T.L., 1987, "The impact of a vortex ring on a wall," *J. Fluid Mech.* **181**, pp. 99-140.

Weigand, A., 1993, *The response of a vortex ring to a transient, spatial cut*, Ph.D. thesis, Univer. Calif., San Diego.

Widnall, S.E., and Sullivan, J.P., 1973, "On the stability of vortex rings," *Proc. R. Soc. Lond. A.* **332**, pp. 335-353.

Willert, C.E. and Gharib, M., 1991, "Digital particle image velocimtry," *Exp. Fluids* **10**, p.181.

Ye, Q.-Y. and Chu, C.K., 1995, "Unsteady evolution of vortex rings," *Phys. Fluids* **7**, pp. 795-801.

FED-Vol. 238, 1996 Fluids Engineering Division Conference
Volume 3
ASME 1996

VORTEX RING INTERACTION WITH AN INCLINED WALL

Zuxing Chen

Jerry D. Swearingen

University of Kansas, Department of Mechanical Engineering, Lawrence, Kansas 66045

Robert A. Handler

Naval Research Laboratory, Remote Sensing Division, Washington, D.C. 20375-5351

ABSTRACT

Direct numerical simulations were used to study the dynamics of a vortex ring impacting a wall inclined to the propagation axis of the ring. Separation of the boundary layer formed as the primary vortex ring approaches the wall occurs in a complex fashion leading to the creation of a secondary vortex loop. During this process, vortex stretching and cancellation lead to the annihilation of the primary vortex ring. These results are in good agreement with the experimental observations of Lim (1989). Simulations at two different Reynolds numbers are also compared.

1. INTRODUCTION

Vortex motions at various scales are known to be of great importance to the turbulence generation/maintenance processes in both transitional and turbulent wall-bounded shear flows (Robinson 1991, Smith et al. 1991, Doligalski et al. 1994). As such, there long has been a strong interest in developing a basic understanding of the dynamics of vortex formation, evolution, and interaction. In this regard, the fundamental dynamics governing the motion of vortex tubes or rings, and their interactions, have been studied extensively as models for more complex behavior observed in turbulent flows, such as unsteady separation, vortex stretching/intensification, and vortex instability. A recent review of these phenomena and how they may be important in applications has been given by Doligalski et al. (1994). In particular, vortex ring interaction with a solid boundary has often been studied (Walker et al. 1987, Chu and Falco 1988, Swearingen et al. 1995), however there are many unanswered questions about the nature and physics of the interaction. In this study, as a means of examining the complex vortex dynamics associated with the wall-bounded turbulence production processes, the interaction between a laminar vortex ring propagating through a quiescent fluid and a solid wall is also investigated. Impingement at non-normal incidence has been directly simulated using psuedospectral 3D computations at initial vortex-ring Reynolds numbers ($Re_0 = V_0D_0/n$, based on the

initial propagation velocity V_0 the initial ring diameter D_0 and the kinematic viscosity ν) in the range $Re_0 \approx 600 - 1000$ and at inclinations of the wall (θ) with respect to the ring propagation direction in the range 0 - 90°. Since the sequence of events observed is similar over this range of Reynolds number and for comparison with the experimental results of Lim (1989), a representative case at $Re_0 \approx 635$ and $\theta = 51.5°$ is the primary basis for discussion. Core trajectories, 3D visualizations, vorticity maps, and core statistics (radius and circulation) are used to explain the evolution.

2. NUMERICAL SIMULATIONS

2.1 Computational Technique

The vortex ring evolution was simulated by solving the Navier-Stokes equations in rotational form subject to the incompressibility condition and no-slip boundary conditions. A single vortex ring was generated dynamically by introducing an appropriately prescribed impulsive body force directly into the equations of motion as described briefly below. Cartesian coordinates (x, y, z) were used, where x and y are the planar or horizontal coordinates and z is perpendicular to the wall, corresponding to the velocity field (u, v, w), where w denotes the component of velocity in the direction normal to the wall. Here, all variables are non-dimensionalized by a length scale corresponding to the half-height between upper and lower boundaries, and by a unit velocity scale. The governing equations, formulated in the manner suggested by Orszag and Patera (1981) and as implemented by Kim et al. (1987), consist of a fourth-order equation for the vertical velocity, w:

$$\left(\frac{\partial \nabla^2}{\partial t} - \nu \nabla^4\right)w = \left(\frac{\partial^2}{\partial x^2} + \frac{\partial^2}{\partial y^2}\right)H_z - \frac{\partial}{\partial z}\left(\frac{\partial}{\partial x}H_x + \frac{\partial}{\partial y}H_y\right) \quad (1)$$

and a second-order equation for the vertical vorticity, Ω_z :

$$\left(\frac{\partial}{\partial t} - \nu\nabla^2\right)\Omega_z = \frac{\partial}{\partial y}H_x - \frac{\partial}{\partial x}H_y \qquad (2)$$

where $H_x = (V\times\Omega)_x + f_x$, $H_y = (V\times\Omega)_y + f_y$, $H_z = (V\times\Omega)_z + f_z$. Here, the instantaneous velocity vector is given by V, the instantaneous vorticity vector is defined by $\Omega = \nabla\times V$, f is a body force described below, and ν is the kinematic viscosity.

Equations (1) and (2) are solved using a psuedospectral discretization of the velocity field in which Chebyshev modes are used in the wall normal (z) direction and Fourier modes are employed in the horizontal (x-y) plane. The calculations were performed on a $96\times96\times65$ computational grid in the x-, y-, and z-directions respectively corresponding to a domain size of $L_x = L_y = 5$ in the horizontal plane and height $L_z = 2$ in the normal coordinate direction. Nominally, a laminar vortex ring with an initial ring diameter of 1 was generated at a distance of 0.5 from the upper boundary of the domain located at $z = +1$ and then allowed to propagate unimpeded through quiescent fluid before interacting with the solid boundary at $z = -1$. A schematic showing the computational domain and the parameters defining the vortex-ring characteristics is given in Fig. 1. For clarity only one-half of the vortex ring is sketched and only a portion of the domain is shown; however, the simulations utilized a fully three-dimensional vortex ring. Typically, the ring diameter was chosen to be $D_0 = 1$ and initial (primary) vortex rings with $Re_0 \approx 600-1000$ were studied. Additionally, the primary-ring core was relatively thin with an intial-core radius to ring-radius ratio of $a_0/R_0 \approx 0.2$.

2.2 Vortex Ring Generation

Analogous to the experimental methodology conventionally used to generate a vortex ring (momentary ejection of fluid through a circular sharp-edged orifice), this study used an impulsive body force applied to a cylindrical region of fluid to generate a vortex ring with the desired properties. The impulsive body force introduced directly into the equations of motion was of the form

$$f(x,y,z,t) = \mathcal{A}\cdot\mathcal{T}(t)\cdot\mathcal{F}(x,y,z) \qquad (3)$$

Here, $\mathcal{A}$ is an amplitude constant which was adjusted to obtain a ring of the desired circulation strength and function $\mathcal{T}(t)$ was used to ensure that the force was only applied momentarily during the ring generation process. Function $\mathcal{F}(x,y,z)$ was used to confine the impulsive force to a cylindrical region corresponding analogously to the cylindrical fluid slug which emerges from the orifice to form the ring experimentally. Generally functions $\mathcal{T}(t)$ and $\mathcal{F}(x,y,z)$ are both based on a tanh distribution so that they are applied smoothly. The exact forms of these distributions and further details of this ring generation methodology are given in Swearingen et al. (1995). For this study, both the wall-normal component of the force, f_z, and the streamwise component, f_x, were precisely specified along with $f_y = 0$ to produce rings inclined with any desired incidence angle θ to the solid boundary. The vortex rings generated in this way were prescribed to approximately match those observed in the experimental work of Lim (1989).

3. RESULTS

Two simulations are discussed and compared: case 1 with $Re_0 \approx 635$, $\theta = 51.5°$ (approximately the conditions in the experiments of Lim 1989); and case 2 with $Re_0 \approx 935$, $\theta = 51.5°$. Here the increase in Reynolds number for case 2 was accomplished by decreasing the kinematic viscosity in the calculation. Note also that a third simulation with $Re_0 \approx 635$, $\theta = 35-40°$ was attempted but problems in the ring generation process precluded inclusion of the results at this time. A time sequence of three-dimensional visualizations of the primary-ring interaction with the boundary for case 1 is given in Fig. 2. The perspective views of the vortex ring development are shown by plotting a surface of constant vorticity magnitude in three dimensions. As the primary vortex ring (PVR) approaches the wall, a boundary layer (i.e. secondary vorticity) is formed because of the no-slip condition there and the radial flow induced by the ring. The visualizations of the interaction process show that separation of the secondary vorticity generated at the boundary is initiated as the segment of the PVR closest to the wall approaches as in Fig. 2a. This separation of secondary vorticity continues as the remainder of the PVR moves toward the wall and the secondary vorticity sheet is then continually wound around the PVR in a complex fashion leading to the creation of a secondary vortex loop over the portion of the PVR which was initially furthest from the wall. In this process, the PVR core is subjected to differing rates of vortex stretching along its circumference, which in turn leads to a variation in its core size as seen particularly in Fig. 2d. Due to the stretching, vorticity cancellation is enhanced and ultimately the PVR is almost completely annihilated as the entire structure moves axially along the wall. These results are in good agreement with the experiments of both Lim (1989) and Batill and Doligalski (1987).

The temporal evolution of the PVR and the secondary vorticity field it generates as it approaches the wall is shown in Fig. 3 for case 1 in the form of contours of constant vorticity (Ω_y here) plotted on the (x,z)-plane of symmetry for six discrete time steps. As with the PVR approaching a wall at normal incidence (see Swearingen et al. 1995), the separation of the boundary layer at the wall produces an elongated region of concentrated secondary vorticity which eventually pinches off to form a secondary vortex structure. However, in this case, this does not occur symmetrically about the original direction of propagation of the PVR. The trailing portion of the PVR core which reaches the wall first initiates this process and subsequently the entire PVR core produces separated secondary vorticity which evolves into a coherent secondary vortex structure as shown for $t = 5$. As this complex interaction takes place, the vortex structures propagate slowly in the x-direction to the right and the secondary vortex loop structure is created. The secondary vortex apparently gains strength throughout this process at the expense of the PVR until it is almost completely dissipated. Note also that the vortex stretching effect can be seen clearly in the area-of-interest (AOI) contours plotted on a larger scale for the trailing portion of the cores. The size of the PVR core decreases significantly while its peak vorticity increases comensurately.

A comparison between the experimental results of Lim (1989) and the case 1 simulation results of the present study is given in Fig. 4. The trajectories of the PVR cores in the (x,z)-plane of symmetry are shown. The location of a vortex core at any instant in time is given by the center of vorticity (i.e. the first moment of the vorticity distribution); details of the trajectory determination methodology are given in Swearingen et al. (1995). The agreement between the two results is very good, including the rebound of the leading portion of the PVR core. Discrepancies in the location of the trailing portion of the PVR core are attributed to inaccuracies inherent in the experimental determination through visual means.

Figure 5 shows the temporal evolution of the PVR and the secondary vorticity field it generates for case 2. Contours of constant Ω_y vorticity are again plotted on the (x,z)-plane of symmetry as in Fig. 3 previously. It is observed that the initial free propagation of the case 2 PVR (see frame for $t = 1$) is essentially identical to that of case 1 since the effect of viscosity has not yet come into play. In case 2 as the PVR comes in proximity to the wall, the boundary layer formed is somewhat thinner and contains larger velocity gradients (seen for $2 \leq t \leq 4$). The evolution of the secondary vorticity happens in much the same way as for case 1, but the smaller viscosity used in the higher Reynolds number case 2 produces much less dissipation which leads to a more intense secondary vortex core structure as seen for $4 \leq t \leq 6$.

The vortex core trajectories for cases 1 and 2 are given respectively in Fig. 6a and 6b to facilitate comparison; the trajectories for both the PVR cores and the readily identifiable secondary vortex (SV) cores are shown. The cores in cases 1 and 2 basically follow the same trajectories even though their Reynolds numbers differ by approximately 50%. The coincidence is particularly true for the trajectories of the trailing cores. In both cases it is observed that the generation and evolution of the secondary vorticity near the trailing PVR core portion occurs while the PVR core position remains relatively fixed (hence the clustering of the PVR trajectory points). A similar observation was made by Swearingen et al. (1995) for the evolution of the secondary-ring core in the ring/wall interaction problem with $\theta = 90°$.

In Fig. 6 it can also be observed that the leading cores in both cases 1 and 2 show significant rebound away from the wall. Note that in Fig. 6a for case 1 with $Re_0 \approx 635$, the leading PVR core cannot be tracked reliably for later times using the current core-locating algorithm (Swearingen et al. 1995) and thus it was not plotted. However, this was not the circumstance for case 2 with $Re_0 \approx 935$ and consequently it only appears to have a significantly larger rebound away from the wall. The difficulty in tracking the leading PVR core for case 1 probably stems from its more complex topology due to the higher level of viscous dissipation at its lower Reynolds number. In both cases, it is obvious that the vortex loop structure structure created by the leading PVR core portion is moving away from the wall at a significant rate as time proceeds.

A comparison of cases 1 and 2 can also be made in terms of the vortex core characteristics, the circulation Γ and the vortex-core radius a, as shown in Fig. 7. The methodology used for determining these characteristics is given in Swearingen et al. (1995). Figures 7a and 7b respectively show the vortex-core circulation (scaled with R_0^2) and the non-dimensional core radius a/R_0 as a function of time. These characteristics are given for both cases 1 and 2 segregated into values for the PVR trailing and leading portions. Figure 7a shows that the circulation measured initially in each of the four circumstances is

the same, as expected. At $t \approx 2.3$, the trailing core circulation decreases significantly as it begins its viscous interaction at the solid boundary. Similarly, but starting later in time at $t \approx 4.2$, the circulation of the leading core decreases significantly (a factor of approximately 6) as it reaches the wall and interacts viscously. It is interesting to note that the circulation of the leading core for case 2 (i.e. higher Reynolds number, lower viscosity) decreases at a faster rate and to a somewhat lower value. The apparent explanation of this is that the lower viscous dissipation leads to a circumstance where energy is transferred more readily to the secondary vortex structure (i.e. the loop vortex structure that results for later times). This effect can be seen by comparing the contours in Fig. 3 (case 1) and Fig. 5 (case 2) at $t = 6$; the leading secondary core appears more intense and smaller in size. Similar observations can be made from Fig. 7b; initially the cores in all four circumstances presented have the same size. The vortex stretching effect can be seen for the trailing core as its radius decreases during its viscous interaction at the wall. For the trailing core, the change in size with time occurs in the same manner as observed in Swearingen et al. (1995) for the ring/wall interaction problem with $\theta = 90°$. Interestingly, the radius of the leading vortex core increases during the initial period of its viscous interaction at the wall ($4 \leq t \leq 5.5$). This is then followed by a significant decrease for later times ($t \geq 5.5$). The explanation of this behavior is unclear at this time.

4. SUMMARY & CONCLUSIONS

The flow associated with a vortex ring interacting with a wall inclined to its axis of propagation was investigated by direct numerical simulations. The results at similar Reynolds number compare very well with the experimental results of Lim (1989), but also allow access to the quantitative details of the flow. The viscous interaction of the PVR with the wall produces a separated sheet of secondary vorticity which is continually wound around the PVR in a complex way. This ultimately leads to the creation of a secondary vortex loop. In this process, the PVR core is subjected to differing rates of vortex stretching which enhances vorticity cancellation. The secondary vortex gains strength at the expense of the PVR until it is almost annihilated. The simulation for the higher Reynolds number shows much the same behavior, except that the lower viscous dissipation produces a more intense secondary vortex core structure. In these simulations for the ring impacting at angle of attack, the evolution appears not to be instability dominated as in the case of the ring/wall interaction at normal incidence (Walker et al. 1987, Swearingen et al. 1995).

ACKNOWLEDGEMENTS

This work was supported with project start-up funding from the University of Kansas, School of Engineering. The authors also gratefully acknowledge the continued use of the direct numerical simulation code originally created at the Naval Research Laboratory, Washington, DC in collaboration with Dr. R. I. Leighton and Dr. T. F. Swean, Jr.

REFERENCES

Batill, S. M., and Doligalski, T. L., 1987, "Three-dimensional vortex structures in wall bounded flows," In Flow Visualization IV (ed. C. Véret), Hemisphere Publishing Corp., pp. 437-441.

Chu, C. C., and Falco, R. E., 1988, "Vortex ring/viscous wall layer interaction model of the turbulence production process near walls," Experiments in Fluids, Vol. 6, pp. 305-315.

Doligalski, T. L., Smith, C. R., and Walker, J. D. A., 1994, "Vortex interaction with walls," Annual Review of Fluid Mechanics, Vol. 26, pp. 573-616.

Kim, J., Moin, P. and Moser, R., 1987, "Turbulence statistics in fully developed channel flow at low Reynolds number," Journal Fluid Mechanics, Vol. 177, pp. 133-166.

Lim, T. T., 1989, "An experimental study of a vortex ring interacting with an inclined wall". Experiments in Fluids, Vol. 7, 453-463.

Orszag, S. A., and Patera, A. T., 1981, "Subcritical transition to turbulence in planar shear flows," In Transition and Turbulence (ed. R.E. Meyer), Academic Press, Inc., pp. 127-146.

Robinson, S.K., 1991, "Coherent motions in the turbulent boundary layer," Annual Review of Fluid Mechanics, Vol. 23, pp. 601-639.

Smith, C.R., Walker, J. D. A., Haidari, A. H., and Sobrun, U., 1991, "On the dynamics of near-wall turbulence," Philosophical Transactions of the Royal Society of London - A, Vol. 336, pp. 134-175.

Swearingen, J. D., Crouch, J. D., and Handler, R. A., 1995, "Dynamics and stability of a vortex ring impacting a solid boundary," Journal of Fluid Mechanics, Vol. 297, pp. 1-28.

Walker, J. D. A., Smith, C. R., Cerra, A. W., and Doligalski, T. L., 1987, "The impact of a vortex ring on a wall," Journal of Fluid Mechanics, Vol. 181, pp. 99-140.

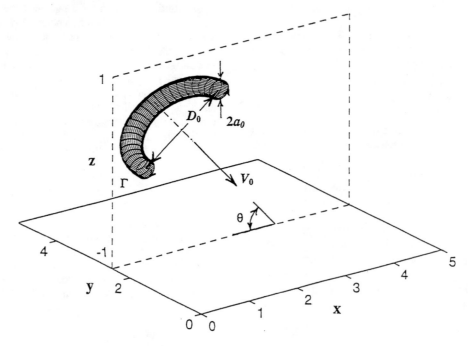

Figure 1. Schematic of the vortex ring located in the computational domain.

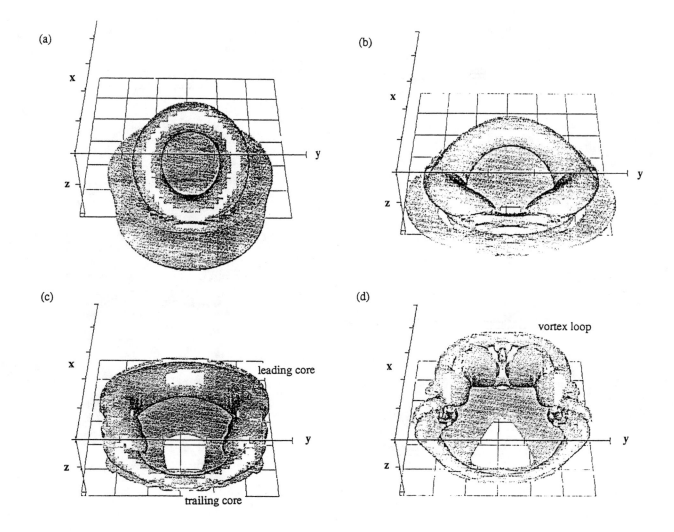

Figure 2. Perspective views of a vortex ring impinging on a wall with $Re_o \approx 635$, $\theta = 51.5°$. (a) t = 2.5, (b) t = 3.5, (c) t = 4.5, (d) t = 5.5.

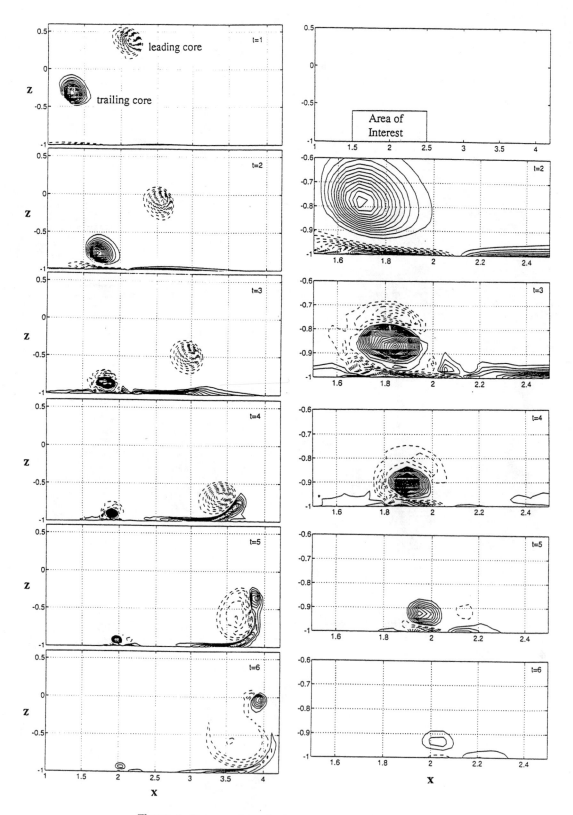

Figure 3. Temporal evolution of the primary and secondary vorticity for $Re_o \approx 635$, $\theta = 51.5°$ (case 1). Contours are of constant vorticity (Ω_y) and the wall is at $z = -1$. Negative vorticity contours are shown as dashed lines.

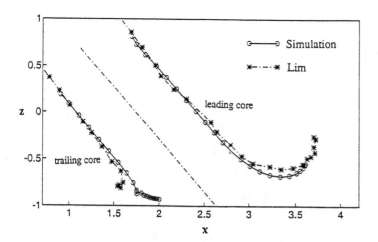

Figure 4. Trajectories of the PVR cores. Simulation for $Re_o \approx 635$, $\theta = 51.5°$; experiments (Lim 1989) for $Re_o \approx 600$, $\theta = 51.5°$.

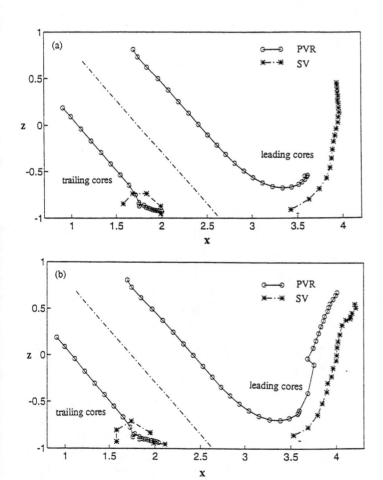

Figure 5. Temporal evolution of the primary and secondary vorticity for $Re_o \approx 935$, $\theta = 51.5°$ (case 2). Contours are of constant vorticity (Ω_y) and the wall is at $z = -1$. Negative vorticity contours are shown as dashed lines.

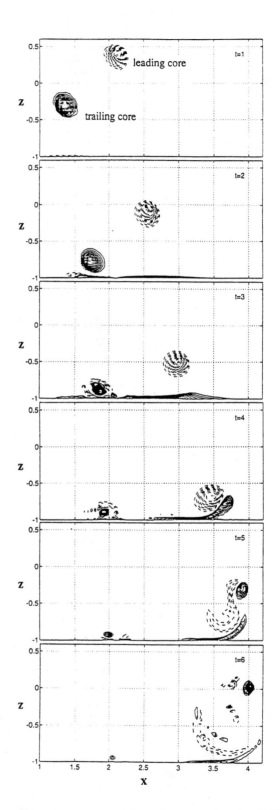

Figure 6. Trajectories of the primary vortex ring (PVR) and the secondary vortex (SV): (a) case 1 with $Re_o \approx 635$, $\theta = 51.5°$; (b) case 2 with $Re_o \approx 935$, $\theta = 51.5°$.

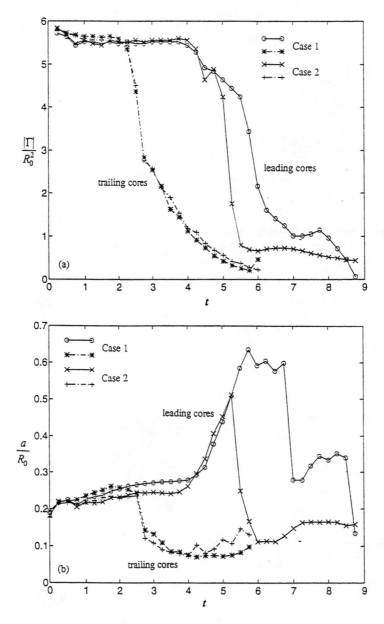

Figure 7. Properties of the PVR for cases 1 and 2: (a) circulation magnitude; (b) core radius.

FED-Vol. 238, 1996 Fluids Engineering Division Conference
Volume 3
ASME 1996

NUMERICAL STUDY OF THE TIP VORTEX FLOW
OVER A FINITE-SPAN HYDROFOIL

Chao-Tsung Hsiao and Laura L. Pauley

Mechanical Engineering Department
The Pennsylvania State University
University Park, Pennsylvania

ABSTRACT

The flow over a finite-span hydrofoil creating a tip vortex was numerically studied by computing the full Navier-Stokes Equations. Favorable comparison was achieved between the numerical solution and available experimental data. The steady-state roll-up process of the tip vortex was described in detail from the numerical results. The effect of the angle of attack, the Reynolds number, and the hydrofoil planform on the tip vortex was investigated. The axial and tangential velocities within the tip-vortex core in the near-field wake region was greatly influenced by the angle of attack. An increase in the axial velocity within the tip-vortex core was found at high angle of attack while a decrease in the axial velocity was found at low angle of attack. Increasing the Reynolds number was found to increase the axial velocity but only had a slight impact on the tangential velocity. Finally, a swept hydrofoil planform was found to attenuate the strength of the tip vortex due to the low-momentum boundary layer traveling into the tip vortex on the suction side.

1. INTRODUCTION

It is well known from classical wing theory that a tip vortex is generated for all finite-span lifting surfaces. The tip-vortex flow is a very complicated three-dimensional viscous flow phenomenon. The details of the flow in the tip region can have a major effect in determining the performance of lifting surfaces in both aerodynamic and hydrodynamic applications.

Since the tip vortex is often considered detrimental, extensive studies have been conducted to understand the formation process of the tip vortex in order to alleviate, if not eliminate, the effects of the tip vortex. In early years, most studies which have focused on the tip vortex problem have been either experimental or analytical efforts. Analytical studies are confined primarily to inviscid tip-vortex roll-up or viscous decay of an isolated vortex. Although the experimental studies have extensively explored many aspects of the tip-vortex flow, some physical measurements such as the pressure field in the tip-vortex core are incomplete. Therefore, a numerical study can serve as a good supplement to experiments in complex flows. Numerical solution of the Navier-Stokes equations was not extensively utilized in early years, especially for hydrodynamic applications, due to the limitations of computational resources. In recent years, however, numerical simulation has been more frequently applied.

Early numerical simulations usually made assumptions to simplify the Navier-Stokes equations to the Parabolized Navier-Stokes equations (PNS) (Shamroth & Briley, 1979 and Tsai et al. 1988) or the Thin-Layer Navier-Stokes equations (TLNS) (Mansour 1984, Srinivasan et al. 1988). However, for separated flows with large secondary velocities such as lift-off of the tip vortex, the streamwise diffusion effect neglected by both PNS and TLNS is significant. Previous studies using PNS or TLNS were unable to determine the tip-vortex formation adequately. Recently, Dacles-Mariani et al. (1993) carried out a full Navier-Stokes simulation with the one-equation Baldwin-Barth turbulence model (1990) and applied the inflow and outflow boundary conditions from the experimental data. The particular tip-vortex studies were conducted on a rectangular planform with a NACA0012 cross section at a chord Reynolds number of 4.6 million. Although they showed an improvement over numerical results obtained by previous researchers, the tip vortex formation was still underpredicted. The less than perfect agreement between computations and experiments was attributed to the insufficient grid density near the tip vortex and the transition/turbulence modeling.

The goal of the present study is to advance the understanding of tip-vortex formation, especially in the near-field wake region. To achieve this goal a three-dimensional incompressible Navier-Stokes flow solver, INS3D-UP, developed by Rogers *et al.* (1991) is applied in the current study. In order to obtain an appropriate grid distribution and sufficient grid density for the near-field wake region and the tip-vortex core, a combination of algebraic and elliptic grid generation techniques is implemented.

2. GEOMETRY AND GRID GENERATION

The current study considers a uniform flow past a rectangular hydrofoil having a NACA0015 airfoil cross section with a round tip and an aspect ratio Ar equal to 3 (based on semi-span) without twist or taper. The edge shape of the round tip is formed by rotation of the hydrofoil section about its camber line based on the local thickness.

From previous numerical studies, it is known that a sufficiently dense grid must exist near the tip-vortex core and the hydrofoil surface in order to adequately resolve the tip vortex and predict boundary-layer effects. Although a conventional elliptic grid generation technique (Sorenson 1989) can be used to create a smooth grid, it is rather difficult to specify the clustering of the grid inside the computational domain. Conversely, algebraic grid generation techniques can easily create the desired grid distribution, but this grid is usually not smooth. A combination of algebraic and elliptic grid generation techniques is therefore implemented. This grid generation scheme is accomplished by generating the initial grid distribution with an algebraic method and applying the elliptic routine to smooth out the grid.

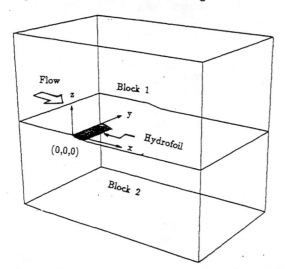

Fig. 1   The two-block structure grid for the finite-span hydrofoil.

In order to easily control the computational domain and grid distribution on both pressure and suction sides independently, an H-H grid topology with two blocks (one for the pressure side and one for the suction side) is applied in the three-dimensional computational domain (see Figure 1). Since the tip vortex always sheds

from the suction side of a finite-span hydrofoil and approaches asymptotically to the angle of attack, additional grid clustering can be added on the suction side to capture the tip vortex without adding the same number of grid points on the pressure side. Therefore, in addition to generating the grid clustering near the tip in the spanwise direction, the grid clustering is also arranged to capture the tip vortex trajectory as shown in Figure 2. Another benefit of using the block structure is that one can reduce the amount of computer memory required by the flow solver as the data from only one block needs to be present in memory at once; the other block can be buffered out of memory.

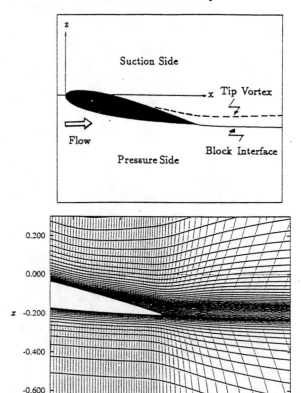

Fig. 2   The grid clustering used to capture the tip vortex trajectory.

3. NUMERICAL METHOD

The three-dimensional incompressible Navier-Stokes flow solver, INS3D-UP, developed by Rogers *et al.* (1991) is based on the artificial-compressibility method. In the artificial-compressibility method, a time derivative of pressure is added to the continuity equation to couple it with the momentum equations. As a consequence, a hyperbolic system of equations is formed and can be solved using a time-marching scheme. This method can be marched in pseudo-time to reach a steady-state solution. To obtain a time-dependent solution, a sub-iterative procedure for pseudo-time needs to be performed in each physical time step such that the continuity equation is satisfied. The spatial differencing of the convective terms uses a fifth-order accurate flux-difference splitting based on Roe's method (1981). A second-order central differencing is used for the viscous terms. The resulting system of algebraic equations are solved by a Gauss-Seidel line-relaxation method in which several line-relaxation sweeps through the computational domain are performed before the solution is updated at the new pseudo-time step.

The INS3D-UP code is also accompanied by the Baldwin-Barth one-equation turbulence model (Baldwin & Barth 1990) which is derived from a simplified form of the standard $k - \epsilon$ equation. This model is not only simpler than the two-equation model, but also eliminates the need to define the turbulent mixing length which is required in Baldwin-Lomax algebraic model.

4. BOUNDARY CONDITIONS

Since the multiblock scheme is used in the present study, there are two types of boundaries where conditions have to be specified: 1) the physical boundaries, such as inflow, outflow, far field, and solid surfaces; and 2) the block-interface boundaries across which all flow quantities must be continuous. In order to allow the use of large pseudo-time steps, implicit boundary conditions need to be applied at all of the boundaries.

On the solid hydrofoil surface, no-slip flow and zero normal pressure gradient conditions are used. Freestream velocity and pressure are specified at the far-field boundary and the inflow boundary while the first-order extrapolation for all variables is used at the outflow boundary. For a finite-span hydrofoil, a complicated three-dimensional separated flow usually occurs on the joined solid surface at the root section. To resolve this flow field requires large computational resources (Burke 1989). Since the present study is only concerned with the tip flow field, a slip boundary condition is applied at the root boundary instead of a no-slip boundary condition.

The convergence rate and stability of the implicit scheme can be severely limited by an explicit boundary condition at the interface between blocks in a multiblock scheme. An explicit boundary condition is applied if the block-interface boundaries are updated after all blocks are calculated by an implicit solver. For the current Gauss-Seidel line-relaxation method, several sweeps need to be performed for each block before the solution is updated. Therefore, a semi-implicit method of passing the boundary conditions between blocks can be easily accomplished by updating the velocities and pressure at the block-interface after each sweep of a block. The next sweep through the other block would utilize the updated values at the common block interface.

5. RESULTS AND DISCUSSION

As a base case, a computation is conducted at Reynolds number $Re = 1.5 \times 10^6$ (based on the chord length and the freestream velocity) and angle of attack $\alpha = 12°$ for a rectangular hydrofoil with a NACA 0015 cross section and a round tip. Before comparing the results with the available experimental data to validate the current numerical scheme, several numerical experiments have been performed to assess the influence of the computational domain and the grid density. After validation, the steady-state roll-up process of the tip vortex is described in detail. Finally, the effect of the Reynolds number, the angle of attack, and the hydrofoil planform on the tip vortex are addressed.

5.1 Assessment of Critical Numerical Aspects

Since the flow field around the hydrofoil is considered as an external flow in the present study, the outer boundaries can not be placed too close to the solid surface. Otherwise, the freestream boundary approximation will break down and result in an overconstraint of the flow. Two different computational domains, with two different far-field boundaries locations (at 6 and 10 chord lengths), were tested. The grid density for these two computational domains was the same near the hydrofoil and grid points were added in the extended portion of the larger computational domain. No significant difference was found from comparison of the two flow fields. Therefore, all results shown in the present study are obtained from the smaller computational domain.

The primary grid used in the present study contains $135 \times 91 \times 61$ for suction side and $135 \times 91 \times 41$ for pressure side in the streamwise, spanwise and normal direction respectively. In the primary grid, 81 of the 135 streamwise grid points and 61 of the 91 spanwise grid points are used on the hydrofoil. The first grid spacing on the hydrofoil surface is specified as 1×10^{-5}. The tip-vortex core includes at least 17 grid points in the crosswise direction and 28 grid points in the spanwise direction. It is computationally prohibitive to perform a grid independence study by doubling the grid points in each direction for a complex three-dimensional flow. However, a grid with higher local density near the hydrofoil tip and tip-vortex core was tested and compared with the primary grid. This grid is generated by adding 20 more grid points on the hydrofoil surface in the streamwise direction, 10 more grid points on the hydrofoil surface in the spanwise direction, and 20 more grid points in the normal direction for both sides of the hydrofoil. Only a slight discrepancy between the results from these two grids was observed.

5.2 Validation of the Numerical Results

The steady-state numerical solution is first compared to the experimental data of Spivey & Morehouse (1970) and McAlister & Takahashi (1991). Figure 3 shows the surface pressure distribution at two spanwise stations away from the tip region from computation and experiments. It is important to note that Spivey and Morehouse's experimental results were all performed on a lifting wing with a square tip. However, previous studies (Srinivansan *et al.* 1988, McAlister and Takahashi 1991) confirm that the differences in the flow fields produced by different tip caps (square and round tip caps) are confined to the outermost 3%-10% of the span depending on the Reynolds number and angle of attack. Although the drastic alteration of the flow field is confined to the tip region, the induced downwash of the tip vortex and wake vortex sheet will influence the flow along the span and cause the leading edge suction peak and local lift coefficient to decrease from root to tip.

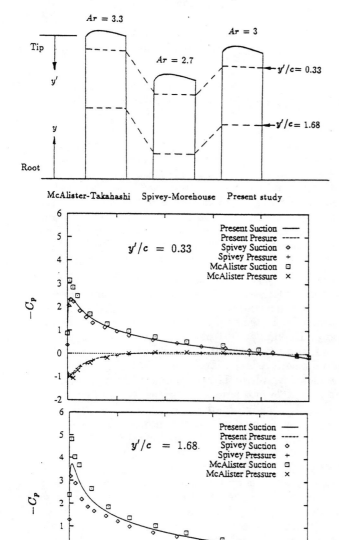

Fig. 3 The chordwise pressure distribution on the hydrofoil surface at two different spanwise stations ($y'/c = 0.33, 1.68$) away from the tip region for $\alpha = 12°$ and $Re = 1.5 \times 10^6$.

Comparison with the experimental data shows that the current suction side numerical solution is slightly higher than Spivey and Morehouse's experimental data

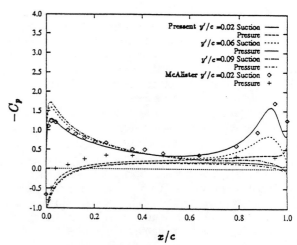

Fig. 4 The chordwise pressure distribution on the hydrofoil surface near the tip region.

while slightly lower than McAlister and Takahashi's experimental data. McAlister and Takahashi also compared their results with Spivey and Morehouse and attributed the differences to two factors. First, wall corrections to the experimental data were not made in McAlister and Takahashi's study. This may lead to a larger negative pressure coefficient, $-C_p$. Second, tuft studies during the Spivey and Morehouse test revealed that an increased updraft (along the span) due to an opening around the base of the floor-mounted model may have produced sizeable wing-wall effects when those data were acquired.

The influence of the tip vortex on the chordwise pressure distribution near the tip region is shown in Figure 4 and compared with the previous experimental data of McAlister and Takahashi (1991) with a round tip. In addition to the leading-edge suction peak, a second suction peak that appears in the tip region can be observed. This additional suction peak is associated with the tip vortex that forms on the suction side of the tip region. From the comparison, the present result shows a good agreement with the experimental data on the suction side but only a qualitative agreement on the pressure side. The region influenced by the tip vortex can be seen from the details of the surface "oil flow" pattern in the tip region shown in Figure 5. Comparison between the experimental surface oil flow (Srinivasan et al. 1988) and the computed result shows a good agreement on the suction side near the tip. The major and secondary separation lines (convergent lines) and reattachment line (divergent line) observed in the experiment are well predicted.

Further quantitative comparison with McAlister and Takahashi's experimental data is made for the velocity field around the tip-vortex core. A new coordinate ($\bar{y}, \bar{z}$) with its origin located on the tip-vortex core is defined for plotting the velocity field around the tip-vortex core. The axes $\bar{y}$ and $\bar{z}$ are aligned in the directions of y and z but the origin of the coordinate system is translated. From Figure 6 it is observed that the vertical w (z component) and axial u (x component) velocities

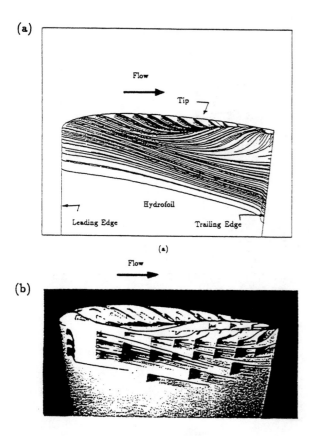

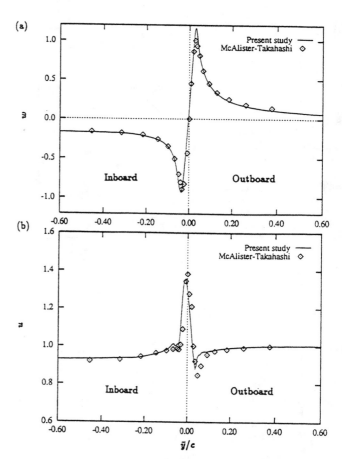

Fig. 5   The surface "oil flow" pattern near the tip region (a) the computed result (b) the experimental results (Srinivasan *et al.* 1988) for $\alpha = 12°$ and $Re = 1.5 \times 10^6$.

Fig. 6   Comparison of the vertical and axial velocity components across the tip-vortex core in inboard-outboard direction at $x/c = 1.1$ for $\alpha = 12°$ and $Re = 1.5 \times 10^6$.

of the tip-vortex core in the inboard-outboard direction are well predicted in the present study within the near-field wake region. In Figure 7, however, the flow field far downstream shows an over-diffusive error within the tip-vortex core. The vertical velocity is much smaller and the tip-vortex core is much larger than the experimental data. In addition, the axial velocity within the tip-vortex core displays a deficit instead of the excess obtained experimentally. Further mesh refinement on the tip-vortex core was tested, but no significant improvement was found.

It is known that the flow is dominated by the pressure gradient between the pressure and the suction sides near the hydrofoil tip. From the momentum equations, one can see that the viscous terms will have only a secondary effect on the tip-vortex flow. However, as the tip vortex continues downstream and away from the hydrofoil, the pressure gradient is not dominant and the viscous terms will play an important role. Since all the eddy viscosity models use the Boussinesq approximation for the Reynolds stress and incorporate it into the viscous terms, an inappropriate turbulence model will cause an error in the viscous dissipation. This also explains why a good agreement with the experimental data can be obtained in the very near-field wake region although the present turbulence model can not adequately model

the tip-vortex turbulence. Therefore, we attribute the over-diffusive error and excessive dissipation to the turbulence model used in the current study. Higher order turbulence modeling such as the $k - \epsilon$ two-equation model is not expected to significantly improve the results since the turbulence around a tip vortex is thought to be highly non-isotropic.

5.3 The Origin of the Tip Vortex

In the present numerical study the tip vortex can be visualized by creating particle traces near the tip region. The formation and lift-off of the tip vortex are shown in Figure 8 as the traces of unrestricted fluid particles released at several locations. It is seen that the roll-up process of the tip vortex consists of the braiding of fluid particle traces released from both suction and pressure sides of the hydrofoil surface. The fluid particles released on the pressure side smoothly cross over the hydrofoil tip and braid with the particles released on the suction side. This tightly braided ribbon of fluid particles defines a tip vortex that is distinct from the rest of the wake vortex sheet. While the braiding process is still in progress, the vortex lifts off the surface and, as it rolls up, it also starts rolling inboard of the hydrofoil tip. Further downstream

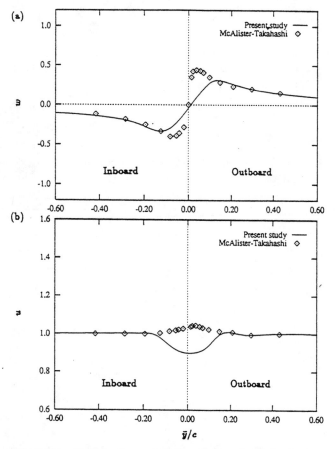

Fig. 7 Comparison of the vertical and axial velocity components across the tip-vortex core in the inboard-outboard direction at $x/c = 5$ for $\alpha = 12°$ and $Re = 1.5 \times 10^6$.

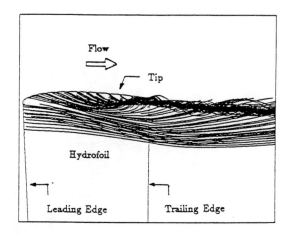

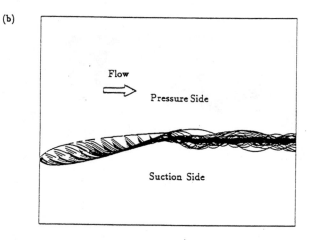

Fig. 8 Particle traces of the tip vortex (a) on $x - y$ plane (b) on $x - z$ plane for $\alpha = 12°$ and $Re = 1.5 \times 10^6$.

of the hydrofoil, it continues to roll inboard and stays distinctly above the shed wake vortex sheet.

The detailed initial roll-up process can be well described from the topology of three-dimensional separated flows. According to the definition of Wang (1976), this initial roll-up phenomenon of the tip vortex can be classified as an "open" (vs "closed") separation, *i.e.* flow upstream can access the separation region. From the surface "oil flow" pattern in the hydrofoil tip region, the tip vortex roll-up also satisfies the definition of "local" (vs "global") separation described by Tobak and Peake (1982), *i.e.* the line of separation starts from a non-critical point. While there are still disputes about the definition of "open" or "local" separation (Wang 1983), the streamsurface bifurcation was introduced by Hornung and Perry (1984) to define the different types of separated flows. According to their definition the tip vortex roll-up is a type of slightly asymmetric open negative streamsurface bifurcation. In the asymmetric open negative streamsurface bifurcation, a free vortex sheet begins to roll-up from its free edge in a direction given by the component of vorticity in the streamline direction on the sheet. The streamwise vorticity gathers into a vortex, which induces a velocity away from the wall on one of its flanks and a velocity towards the wall on

the other. The latter effect necessitates the presence of a positive streamsurface bifurcation beside a negative one. Hornung and Perry illustrated this type of vortex roll-up in a perspective view looking upstream, shown in Figure 9. The free sheet S_1 of the open negative bifurcation issues from the open negative bifurcation line PQ and induces the positive streamsurface bifurcation S_2 along the open positive bifurcation line $P'Q'$. The negative bifurcation and the positive bifurcation lines are related to the convergent and divergent lines respectively in the surface "oil flow".

5.4 Angle of Attack Effect

Three different angles of attack, $\alpha = 4°, 8°$ and $12°$ are studied to investigate the effect on the tip-vortex flow at a fixed Reynolds number $Re = 1.5 \times 10^6$. Figure 10 shows the surface "oil flow" for these three angles of attack investigated. It is found that as the angle of attack is increased, the roll-up location of the tip vortex moves further upstream. The previous discussion suggests that if the vortex continues to roll up and lift off the surface, the flow induced towards the wall by the vortex will also gradually form a second open negative streamsurface bifurcation and become a secondary vor-

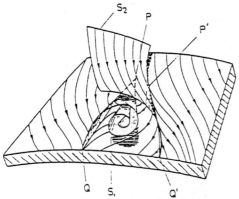

Fig. 9 Sketch of vortex rollup showing an open negative and an open positive streamsurface bifurcation. (Hornung and Perry, 1984).

tex. This secondary vortex will roll up in the opposite direction. For higher angles of attack at $\alpha = 8°$ and $12°$, the surface "oil flow" shows a second convergent line near the trailing edge. This second convergent line is referred to as the second open negative bifurcation line. Although the second convergent line is not found at $\alpha = 4°$, a negative streamwise vorticity is still generated due to the induced flow beneath the major vortex.

Figure 11 shows the vertical velocity of the tip-vortex core in the inboard-outboard direction at three downstream locations. The negative streamwise vorticity carried outboard by the induced flow beneath the tip vortex interacts with the major vortex and causes a "kink" in the outboard vertical velocity. Downstream this "kink" smooths as the secondary vortex merges with the primary vortex. At $\alpha = 4°$, the inboard vertical tip-vortex velocity also contains a "kink" due to the hydrofoil wake. This interaction also occurs in the axial velocity of the tip vortex at the lowest angle of attack (Figure 12). At higher angles of attack, the tip vortex lifts off the hydrofoil surface and above the hydrofoil wake. The inboard vertical velocity distribution, therefore, is not modified when the angle of attack is high.

The effect of the angle of attack on the axial velocity of the tip-vortex core is shown in Figure 12 in the inboard-outboard direction at one downstream location. The axial-flow pattern is found to be highly influenced by the angle of attack. An increase in the axial flow is found within the tip-vortex core at higher angle of attack while a decrease in the axial flow occurs at lower angle of attack. Since the vortex forms further upstream at higher angle of attack, a larger pressure gradient will convey more fluid from the pressure side to the suction side which will significantly increase the velocity, both tangential and axial components, within the tip-vortex core.

5.5 Reynolds Number Effect

To study the effect of the Reynolds number on the tip vortex, computations at $Re = 1.5 \times 10^6$ and 3.5×10^6 are conducted for $\alpha = 12°$. From previous two-dimensional airfoil studies, it is known that increasing the Reynolds

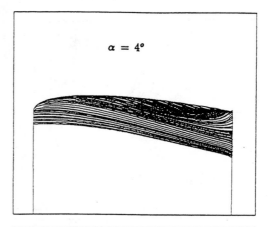

$\alpha = 4°$

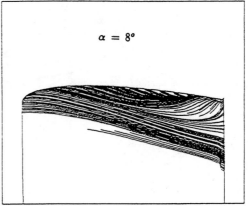

$\alpha = 8°$

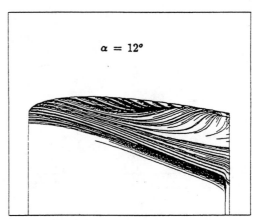

$\alpha = 12°$

Fig. 10 Comparison of the surface "oil flow" for $\alpha = 4°, 8°$ and $12°$.

number will not alter the lift coefficient of the airfoil when the boundary layer remains attached although it will decrease the boundary-layer thickness. The present results show that as the Reynolds number is increased, the pressure distribution is only influenced in the tip region where the second suction peak appears. Figure 13 shows that a higher Reynolds number leads to a higher second suction peak corresponding to an increased strength of the tip vortex. The effect of increasing the Reynolds number on the tip-vortex core can also be found from the velocity field. Figure 14 shows that increasing the Reynolds number increases the maximun axial velocity by 4.8% but has a minor impact on the

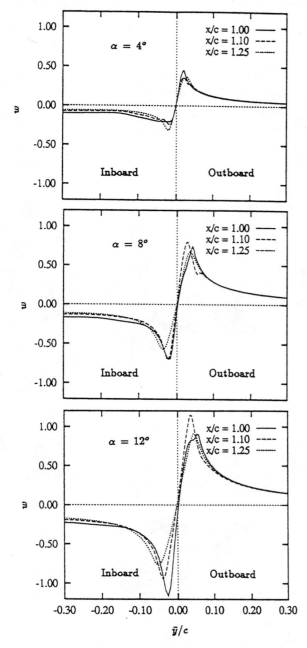

Fig. 11   Comparison of vertical velocity across the tip-vortex core in inboard-outboard direction at $x/c = 1.0, 1.1, 1.25$ for $\alpha = 4^\circ, 8^\circ$ and 12° and $Re = 1.5 \times 10^6$.

vertical velocity.

5.6 Hydrofoil Planform Effect

To study the influence of planform geometry, a hydrofoil with a 30° swept angle is considered and results compared to those from the rectangular hydrofoil. Computations are conducted at $Re = 1.5 \times 10^6$ and $\alpha = 12^\circ$ for both geometries. Both rectangular and swept hydrofoil studies presented here have an aspect ratio $Ar = 1.5$. This is different than the aspect ratio used for the computations reported in the previous sections ($Ar = 3$).

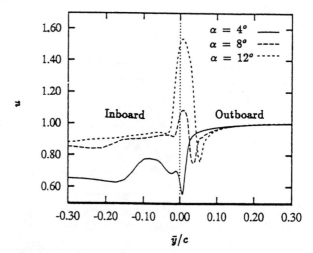

Fig. 12   Comparison of axial velocity across the tip-vortex core in inboard-outboard direction at $x/c = 1.0$ for $\alpha = 4^\circ, 8^\circ$, and 12° and $Re = 1.5 \times 10^6$.

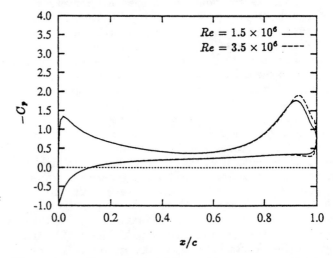

Fig. 13   Comparison of the surface pressure distribution at $y'/c = 0.02$ for $Re = 1.5 \times 10^6$ and 3.5×10^6 at $\alpha = 12^\circ$.

It is expected that the swept hydrofoil will induce a spanwise secondary flow toward the tip on both pressure and suction sides due to the spanwise pressure gradient. Figure 15 shows the comparison of the surface "oil flow" between the swept and the rectangular hydrofoils. It is seen that the tip vortex forms further upstream and induces a secondary vortex earlier in the swept hydrofoil. In contrast to the rectangular hydrofoil, the boundary-layer flow on the suction side for the swept hydrofoil also travels toward the tip region near the trailing edge. By comparing the pressure coefficient along the tip-vortex core shown in Figure 16, it is found that the strength of the tip vortex of the swept hydrofoil is weaker than that of the rectangular hydrofoil. It should be noted that the tip trailing edge is at $x/c = 0.978$ for the rectangular hydrofoil and $x/c = 1.844$ for the swept hydrofoil.

From the pressure distribution near the tip region on both pressure and suction sides shown in Figure 17, one can find that the swept hydrofoil has a higher pressure

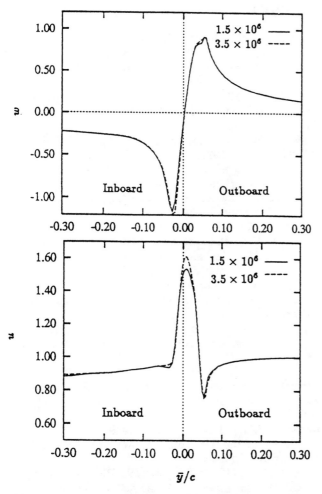

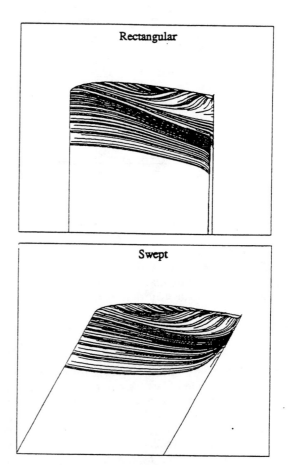

Fig. 14 Comparison of the vertical and axial velocities across the tip-vortex core in inboard-outboard direction at $x/c = 1.0$ for $Re = 1.5 \times 10^6$ and 3.5×10^6 at $\alpha = 12°$.

gradient between the pressure side and the suction side near the leading edge. This larger pressure gradient, therefore, drives a stronger flow across the tip from the pressure side to the suction side and leads to an earlier vortex roll-up. As the flow travels further downstream, however, the low-momentum boundary-layer flow on the suction side will enter the tip vortex and attenuate the strength of the tip vortex.

7. CONCLUSIONS

The present study applied full Navier-Stokes computations with the Baldwin-Barth one-equation turbulence model and an H-H type grid to study the finite-span hydrofoil flow. Comparison with the available experimental data showed that the present results favorably predicted the tip-vortex flow on the hydrofoil and near-field wake region. However, over-diffusive error and excessive dissipation were found downstream in the tip vortex. Due to highly non-isotropic turbulence around the tip vortex, current eddy viscosity models were not able to accurately model this free shear layer turbulence. Non-

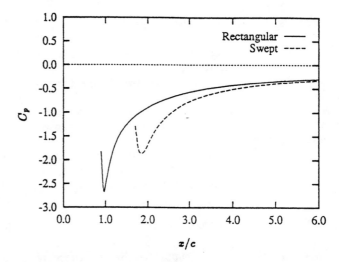

Fig. 15 Comparison of the surface "oil flow" for the rectangular and swept hydrofoil at $Re = 1.5 \times 10^6$ and $\alpha = 12°$.

Fig. 16 Comparison of the pressure coefficient along the tip-vortex core for the rectangular and swept hydrofoil at $Re = 1.5 \times 10^6$ and $\alpha = 12°$.

isotropic turbulence models such as a Reynolds-stress model or Large Eddy Simulation may be required to resolve accurately the tip vortex downstream.

The roll-up process of the tip vortex was studied from the numerical results. The initial roll-up process of the

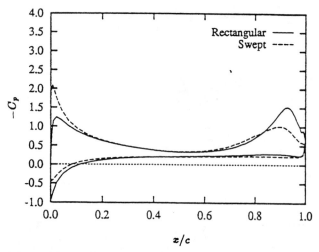

Fig. 17 Comparison of the surface pressure distribution for the rectangular and swept hydrofoil at $y/c = 0.02$ for $Re = 1.5 \times 10^6$ and $\alpha = 12°$.

tip vortex was well described from the topology of three-dimensional separated flow introduced by Hornung and Perry (1984).

In the present study, multiple vortex roll-up was observed at higher angle of attack. A secondary vortex was induced by the major vortex when the major vortex rolled up and lifted off the hydrofoil surface. From comparison of three different angles of attack, it was found that the profile of the axial velocity in the tip-vortex core was greatly influenced by the angle of attack. In the near-field wake region, an increase in the axial velocity within the tip-vortex core was found at high angle of attack while a decrease in the axial velocity was found at low angle of attack.

From the comparison at two different Reynolds numbers, it was found that increasing Reynolds number increased the axial velocity but only slightly altered the vertical velocity of the tip vortex in the near-field wake region. The strength of the tip vortex was also enhanced by increasing Reynolds number.

A swept hydrofoil planform was considered to study its effect on the tip vortex. The swept hydrofoil induced a spanwise flow toward the tip on both pressure and suction sides. As the low-momentum boundary layer on the suction side was carried into the tip vortex, the strength of the tip vortex was attenuated.

ACKNOWLEDGEMENTS

This research has been supported by the Office of Naval Research under contract N00014-90-J-1169 monitored by Dr. Edwin P. Rood. Computational facilities were provided by the NAVOCEANO Supercomputer Center and the CEWES High Performance Computing Center. These contributions are gratefully acknowledged.

REFERENCES

Baldwin, B. S., Barth, T. J., (1990), "A One-Equation Turbulence Transport Model for High Reynolds Number Wall-Bounded Flows," NASA TM 102847.

Burke, R. W., (1989), "Computation of Turbulent Incompressible Wing-Body Junction Flow," AIAA Paper 89-0279.

Dacles-Mariani, J., Rogers, S. E., Kwak, D., Zilliac, G., Chow, J., (1993), "A Computational Study of Wingtip Vortex Flowfield," AIAA paper 93-3010.

Mansour, N. N., (1984), "Numerical Simulation of the Tip Vortex off a Low-Aspect Ratio Wing at Transonic Speeds," AIAA Paper 84-522.

McAlister, K. W., Takahashi, R. K., (1991), "NACA0015 Wing Pressure and Trailing Vortex Measurements," NASA Technical Paper 3151.

Perry, A. E., Hornung, H. G., (1984), "Some Aspects of Three-Dimensional Separation, Part I: Streamsurface Bifurcations," *Zeitschrift für Flugwissenschaften und Weltraumforschung*, 8, PP. 77-87.

Roe, P. L., (1981), "Approximate Riemann Solvers, Parameter Vectors, and Difference Schemes," *Journal of Computational Physics*, Vol. 43, pp. 357-372.

Rogers, S. E., Kwak, D., Kiris, C., (1991), "Steady and Unsteady Solutions of the Incompressible Navier-Stokes Equations," *AIAA Journal*, Vol. 29, No. 4, pp. 603-610.

Shamroth, S. J., Briley, W. R., (1979), "A Viscous Flow Analysis of the Tip Vortex Generation Process," AIAA paper 79-1546.

Sorenson, R. L., (1989), "The 3DGRAPE Book: Theory, Users' Manual Examples," NASA TM 102224.

Spivey, W. A., Morehouse, G. G., (1970), "New Insights into the Design of Swept-Tip Rotor Blades," 26th Annual National Forum Proceedings of the American Helicopter Society, Washington, D. C.

Srinivasan, G. R., McCroskey, M. J., Baeder, J. D., Edwards, T. A., (1988), "Numerical Simulation of Tip Vortices of Wings in Subsonic and Transonic Flows," *AIAA Journal*, Vol. 26, No. 10, pp. 1153-1162.

Tobak, M., Peake, D. J., (1982), "Topology of Three-Dimensional Flow Separations," *Annual Review of Fluid of Fluid Mechanics*, Vol. 14, pp. 61-85.

Tsai, T. M., de Jong, F. J., Levy, R., (1988), "Computation of the Tip Vortex Flowfield for Advanced Aircraft Propellers," NASA CR-182179.

Wang, K. C., (1983), "On the Disputes About Open Separation," AIAA Paper 83-0296.

Wang, K. C., (1976), "Boundary-Layer Separation in Three Dimensions," Review in Viscous Flow, Proceedings of the Lockheed-Georgia Company Viscous Flow Symposium, Marietta, GA. pp. 341-414.

FED-Vol. 238, 1996 Fluids Engineering Division Conference
Volume 3
ASME 1996

THE THREE-DIMENSIONAL VORTICAL STRUCTURE
IN TIME-DEVELOPING MIXING LAYER WITH CROSS SHEAR

Shen Liping   **Lin Jianzhong**
Fu Bin

Department of Mechanics
State Key Laboratory of Fluid Power Transmission and control
Zhejiang University,Hangzhou,310027,China

ABSTRACT

A new method used to describe three-dimensional mixing layers with discrete vortex filaments is studied. Based on this method, the three-dimensional mixing layers are computed numerically. The vortical structure, distribution of mean velocity and momentum loss thickness in different time are given. The effects of shear rate and intensity of disturbance on flows are analysed. Some computed results are compared with experimental ones, they show a good agreement. The results given in the paper are helpful to understand such flows.

INTRODUCTION

The vortical structures in two-dimensional mixing layer have been studied widely and many valuable results , such as vortex rolling-up, pairing and amalgamating have been achieved. However, some problems have evoked much controversy, for example coherent structures are whether two-dimensional or three-dimensional(LeBoeuf and Metha, 1993; Lasheras et.al,1986). The dimension of vortex is relative to shear and disturbance along the span, so making research directly on the mixing layer with shear along stream and span, i.e. three-dimensional mixing layer(shown in Fig.1), is helpful to gain a clear idea of dimension of coherent structure. Furthermore, the research of three-dimensional mixing layer has practical interest, such as the flow in a combustion chamber and flow behind an airfoil. In these flow field, there are many problems which have not been solved

yet,such as what kind vortex is there in the field, how do shear rate and disturbance effect vortical structure, what is the difference of the average velocity profile and momentum thickness between two-dimensional and three-dimensional mixing layers, and what is the characteristic of this flow field ? Knowledge about all these questions will be helpful to save energy and reduce the production cost in the practical usage. So this flow field has been studied experimentally(Lin and Wei,1993; Shen and Lin,1995).In this paper, it is numerically simulated with discrete vortex filament method.

The discrete vortex dynamics method is a new but very important means of research on vortical structure. The method used popularly is point vortex method, but it can't describe the three-dimension flow. In order to simulate the evolution of there-dimensional vortical structure, the discrete vortex filament method must be used. To the flow field studied in this paper, it is the first time to be simulated with discrete vortex filament method because in this flowfield it is not very obvious that the flow is described equivalently with a series of vortex elements. In this paper by means of reasonable arrangement of vortex filaments and corresponding bound-ary condition, the evolution of three-dimensional mixing layer is numerically simulated. By comparing with the experimental results, the answer of above questions are given.

ANALYSIS OF FLOW MODEL

In the mixing layer shown in figure 1, two streams are

separated by a very thin splitter plate, velocities of over and below plate are U_1 and U_2 respectively, the angle between two streams is $2\theta(\theta \neq 0)$,and the downstream flow of plate is named three-dimensional mixing layer. In this paper the time-developing model is studied. i.e. the flow formed in the surface of two streams after a sudden disappearance of splitter plate, though such flow is not fully equivalent to space-development model, they are very similar in mechanism.

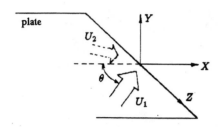

Fig.1. Three-dimensional mixing layer flow

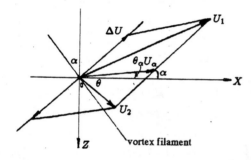

Fig.2. Velocity decomposition

There is a velocity jump after a sudden disappearance of splitter plate, and the velocity jump can be replaced with a infinite plane vortex layer. According to figure 2, velocities of two streams can be analysed as follows:

$$U_1 = U_a + \frac{1}{2}\Delta U$$
$$U_2 = U_a - \frac{1}{2}\Delta U$$

(1)

where $\Delta U(= (U_1 - U_2))$ is the velocity difference between the two streams, on which the shear rate and shear direction depends, which also determines the strength and

direction of vortex element. $U_a = \frac{1}{2}(U_1 + U_2)$, is called convection velocity. According to Eq(1), the initial flow can be decomposed into two parts, one is a two-dimensional mixing layer with a velocity difference of Δ **U** and the other is a convection flow with a velocity of U_a,and there is an angle between them. The part of two-dimensional mixing layer can be replaced with equivalent vortex layer,which can be discreted into a series of vortex filaments. From the figure 2, we can get:

$$tg\theta_a = \frac{U_1 - U_2}{U_1 + U_2} tg\theta$$

(2)

$$tg\alpha = \frac{U_1 + U_2}{U_1 - U_2} tg\theta$$

(3)

So the angle between vortex filaments and x axis is $\frac{\pi}{2} - \alpha$, and angle between average velocity and vortex filaments is $\frac{\pi}{2} - (\alpha - \theta_a)$ .Here **Q**=15°(the same degree with experiment).

COMPUTATIONAL METHOD
1 Induced Velocity.

Flow can be discreted into a series of vortex filaments with a convection velocity U_a between which and x axis there is an angle of $\pi/2 - \alpha$, every filament is represented by a number of nodes. The velocities of node are evaluated according to a modified Biot-Savart law and the temporal evolution of the flow can then be obtained by advancing the nodes over a small time step with their respective velocities. The expression of modified Biot-Savart law is given as follows based on the assumption of an invariant vorticity distribution along the filaments.

$$\gamma_i(x - r_i) = \frac{3\beta\sigma_i^2}{4\pi(|x - r_i|^2 + \beta\sigma_i^2)^{3/2}}$$

(4)

The advantage of this assumption is that no singular appear when velocity are integrated along filaments. According to above equation, the vorticity distribution caused by a filament with circulation Γ_i follows as:

$$\omega(x,t) = \Gamma_i \int_{C_i} \gamma_i [(x - r_i(s))] \frac{\partial r_i(s)}{\partial s} ds$$

(5)

where $r_i(s)$ is location of the filament centreline described with arclengths. $\beta\sigma_i^2$ is a measurement of the vorticity distribution for ith filament, σ_i is the core radius of the ith filament, different vorticity distribution can be obtained by changing the value of **B** in the condition of the same vortex core, here **B**=0.413.

Putting this vorticity distribution into the Biot-Savart formula and integrating over the arclength of all N filaments, we have the velocity **u** at position **x**

$$u(x,t) = -\frac{1}{4\pi} \sum_{i=1}^{N} \Gamma_i \int_{C_i} \frac{[x - r_i(s,t)] \times \hat{e}(s)}{([x - r_i(s,t)]^2 + \beta \sigma_i^2)^{3/2}} ds$$

(6)

where $\hat{e}(s)$ is the tangent vector of filament. In this modified Biot-Savart formula velocity remains finite even for $x \to r_i$. Taking the diameter of vortex core as the reference length. i.e. $\sigma = 0.5$, and taking the circulation of unity length as reference velocity, we can get the dimensionless form of all values.

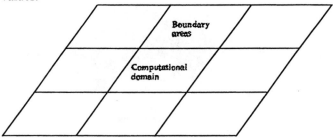

Fig.3 computational domain and boundary areas

2 Accuracy of computation.

In order to make the Biot-Savart integer have two-order accuracy in space, we represent the filament centerline by a cubic spline function with distance between the node points as the spline parameter. This allow us to determine the tangent vector at each node in order to maintain a satisfactory resolution. The spatial resolution depends on the arclength between two successive nodes and the local curvature. In the whole computational process, the number of node increase continuously, so is the computational cost of every step. In order to obtain two-order accuracy in temporal integration as the accuracy in space, the nodes are advanced in time according to a predictor-corrector scheme.

$$x' = x(t) + u(t)\Delta t$$
$$x(t + \Delta t) = x(t) + \frac{1}{2}(u(t) + u')\Delta t$$

(7)

The time step is continuously adjusted to satisfy the requirement of accuracy for predictor-corrector scheme. Thus the time step is reduced continuously, and the above integral corresponds to four order Runge-Kutta integral for time (Ashurst and Meiburg,1988).

3 Boundary Condition.

We confine our calculation to a finite computational domain(shown in figure 3). In order to describe infinite in space,the periodic condition in two directions(streamwise and span direction) is taken into consider. All boundary areas (shown in figure 3) are assumed to have the same vortical structure with computational domain. So the velocity of a node in computational domain depends on the all areas shown in figure 3. Each node in the domain evolves with time under the induced velocities. then the evolution of vortical structure can be obtained. In this paper, seven periodic images are used in streamwise and five ones used in spanwise.

4 Effect of Viscosity.

In the calculation process, based on the conservation of vorticity of whole flow field, the method of vortex core expansion is used to simulate the diffusion of vorticity. Because of viscosity, the distribution of vorticity in the flow field will turn uniformity, and the vortex core will expand

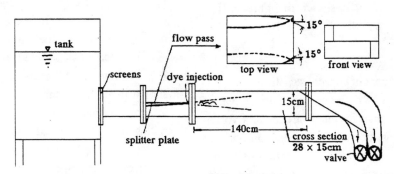

Fig.4. Experimental facility

according to the expression of vorticity distribution (Chorin, 1973). Thus we can simulate the diffusion of vorticity by means of the growth of vortex core.

5 Disturbance.

In order to simulate the time-development of disturbance in the flow, the three-dimensional periodic disturbance is introduced into initial distribution of vortex filaments.Along the spanwise a small amplitude(0.01) sinusoidal disturbance is added to every filament, and along the stream the initial disturbance is represented by a small displacement of the filament out of the plane of vortex layer. The expressions of disturbance are given in Eq(8,9). The evolution of disturb-ance in the free mixing layer can be obtained by computation. There include twice wavelength of disturbance along spanwise and once along streamwise in the computational domain.

$$x = A\{1 + \cos[2\pi(z - z_0)/\lambda_1]\}/2$$
$$z = A\{1 + \cos[2\pi(z - z_0)/\lambda_1]\}/2 \tag{8}$$
$$y = B\cos[2\pi(x/\lambda_2)] \tag{9}$$

RESULTS AND DISCUSSION

The numbers of node increase continuously in the computation, which leads to the increase of calculation cost. On the other hand, because of the requirement of accuracy in time, the interval of time step must be reduced continuously. Thus the calculations become slower and slower. For the limitation of computer, the calculation time is limited in a week on PC LEO486/33 computer. The flowfield is discreted initially into fifty filaments and each filament is represented with seventeen nodes.

The corresponding experiment is also made,the comparison of computational and experimental results is given. The experimental facility is shown in figure 4. The velocity of water stream is controlled by two valves.

1 Vortical structure.
(1) Formation and development of vortical structure.

The vortical structures of different stages are shown in figure 5. Every curvature stands for the centreline of a vortex filament. The centralization of vortex filaments means the centralization of vorticity, which forms the regions of vortex core. Furthermore, the centralization of vortex filaments which arrange equably in plane means the vortex rolling-up.

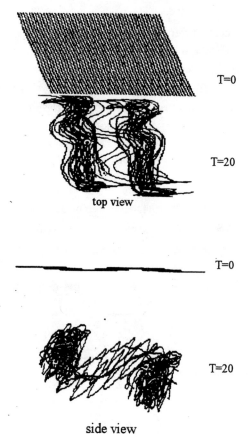

Fig.5. Development of vortical structure
(R=0.5,A=0.01,B=0.005)

The initial disturbance is amplified gradually. For the Kelvin-Helmholz instability, the streamwise disturbances develop very quickly, which leads to the vortex rolling-up. Because the angle between two streams is small in this paper, the pattern of vortical structure are similar to two-dimensional ones, there exist vortex core regions and braid regions also. The vortex filaments in the vortex braid enwind at the vortex core regions. The curvature of vortex core means that the vortical structure is three-dimensional. There are also some similarities between three-dimensional and two-dimensional mixing layer flow in the primary instability.

(2) The effect of shear intensity on the vortical structure.

Rolling-up of vortex with different shear intensity is shown in figure 6, the above has a greater shear intensity. We can see that the greater shear intensity will accelerate the rolling-up of vortex and vortical structures develop faster in the case of the greater shear intensity. So increasing shear intensity is an important means to enhance the mixing of flow.

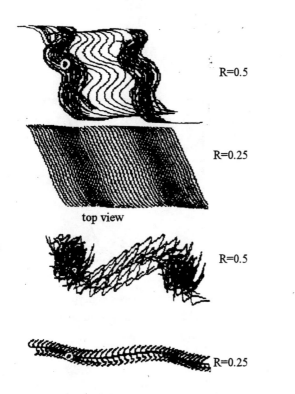

R=0.5

R=0.25

top view

R=0.5

R=0.25

side view

Fig.6. The effect of shear intensity on the vortex structure
(T=15.A=0.01.B=0.005)

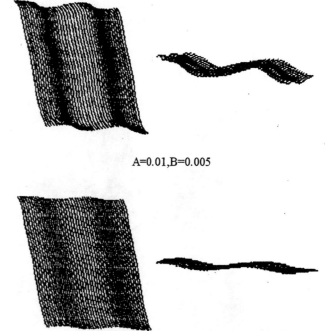

A=0.01,B=0.005

A=0.005,B=0.002

Fig.7. The effect of disturbance on the vortex structure
(T=10,R=0.3)

(3) The effect of disturbance on the vortical structure.

Free mixing layer flow is unstable to any kind of disturbance, so it's possible to control the development of mixing layer with different external excitement. The different disturbance can change the pattern of flow field, such as the secondary instability and the interaction of neighboring vortices. In this paper only the effect of disturbance strength is considered, the results with disturbance of different strength are shown in Fig.7. and the above is the case of stronger

disturbance. In the figure, we can see that disturbance is amplified gradually and the initial phase of disturbance is kept. Additionally, the stronger disturbance accelerates the formation of vortical structure, so the secondary instability occurs earlier, thus the mixture of flow will be more fully. The disturbance make vortex filaments become three-dimensional curves, and cause vorticity distribution in three direction, so it's also an important factor to make filament become three-dimensional curves.

(4) Comparison with experimental results

The top view of the span vortical structure of computational and experimental results are shown in Fig.8, which shows that they are very similar. In the Fig.9, the above is computational result, which is the track of a series of passive particles. It's similar to the picture(below) in flow visualization experiment. In both figures the helical vortex is obvious. The reason of formation of this helical vortex is the existence of convection velocity and shear in two direction.

2 The computation of flow parameters

(1) The average velocity profile.

The average velocity profiles in different time are shown in figure 10, it shows that velocity gradient reduces gradually because of the mixture of fluid between two streams. Scaled with the momentum loss thickness, we can find out that the velocity profile in different time are self-similarity as shown in figure 11.

(2) The momentum loss thickness.

We can calculate the momentum loss thickness from the average velocity (Aref and Siggia,1980),

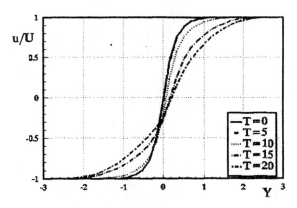

1:T=0;2:T=5;3:T=10;4:T=15;5:T=20
Fig.10.　The average velocity profiles in streamwise

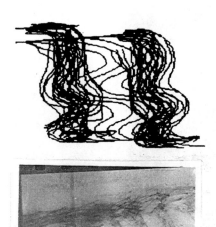

Fig.8. The comparison of span vortical structure

(T=20,A=0.01,B=0.005,R=0.5)

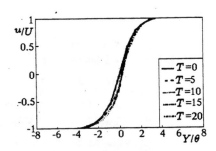

1:T=0;2:T=5;3:T=10;4:T=15;5:T=20
line:two-dimensional,　dash:three-dimensional
Fig.11.　Self-similarity of velocity profiles

Fig.9.　Comparison of helical vortical structure

(R=0.5,A=0.01,B=0.005)

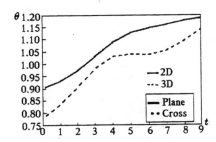

Fig.12. Increase of the momentum loss thickness

$$\theta(t) = \int [0.25 - (\bar{u}/U)^2] dy \qquad (10)$$

The variation of the momentum loss thickness for three-dimensional and two-dimensional mixing layer are shown in figure 12, We can find out that the increase of the momentum thickness in two-dimensional case is faster than in three-dimensional flow. The momentum loss thickness is an important parameter in mixing layer flow, so we can control the flow by changing the angle between two streams in mixing layer.

CONCLUSION

The disturbance in the three-dimensional mixing layer flow is amplified gradually, meanwhile the helical vortical structure is formed. The larger shear ratio and stronger disturbance is, the faster the vortical structures develop. With the increase in time, the velocity gradients in two direction reduce and velocity profiles keep self-similarity. In the same condition, the momentum loss thickness in the three-dimensional mixing layer flow develop slower than in two-dimensional case, so we can control the increase of momentum loss thickness by changing the angle between two streams.

There are still many things to do in three-dimensional mixing layer flow, such as the vortical structures in different shear angle and different disturbance patterns(which include the different disturbance wave number and phase). The interaction between vortical structures after the secondary instability need to be studied further.

ACKNOWLEDGMENT

This research is supported by National Nature Science Foundation and ZheJiang University Science Foundation

REFERENCES

Aref,H,and Siggia E.D.,1980, Vortex dynamics of the two-dimensional turbulent shear layer,*J.Fluid Mech.*, Vol. 100, pp. 705-737.

Ashurst, W.T and Eckart Meiburg,1988,Three-dimensional shear layers via vortex dynamics, *J.Fluid Mech.*, Vol. 189, pp. 87-116.

Chorin, A.J, 1973, Numerical study of slightly viscous flow, *J. Fluid Mech.*, Vol. 57, pp. 359-381.

Lasheras, J.C., Cho, J.S. and Maxworthy, T., 1986, On the Origin and evolution of streamwise vortical structures in a plane free shear layer, *J.Fluid Mech.*, Vol. 173, pp. 231-258.

LeBoeuf, R.L. and Metha, R.D., 1993, Streamwise vortex meander in a plane mixing layer, *Phys. Fluids*, Vol.5, pp.1983-1991.

Lin Jianzhong and Wei Zhonglei,1993, The experimental research on the flow characteristic in the cross free mixing layer, *Experimental Mechanics*, Vol.8,No.1,pp.63-69.

Shen Liping and Lin Jianzhong,1994, The research on the coherent structure and turbulent characteristic in cross free shear layer, *Journal of Hydrodynamics*,Vol.10,pp.77-82.

FED-Vol. 238, 1996 Fluids Engineering Division Conference
Volume 3
ASME 1996

VORTICITY, CIRCULATION AND VORTICES

John F. Foss
Department of Mechanical Engineering
Michigan State University
East Lansing, MI 48824

ABSTRACT

"Vorticity" and "circulation" are advanced as useful descriptors of physical flow fields. In contrast, it is argued that "vortices" should not be used in other than "casual conversation". Experimental observations, supported by theoretical considerations, are used to clarify and support the above assertions.

INTRODUCTION

The present contribution to this Symposium is to record experimental observations, in the context of appropriate theoretical considerations, that most effectively speak to the Symposium's theme: "Vortex Flows and Vortex Methods." Specifically, it is argued that the words "vortex" and "vortices" are not subject to definitions that provide "precision of communication" regarding experimental observations and for most computational (e.g., DNS, LES, RANS, etc) results. Hence, "vortex" and "vortices" should be reserved for communications where general and qualitative attributes of the flow are to be represented. It is also argued that "vorticity" and "circulation" provide both mathematical precision and a quite useful conceptual framework for describing flow fields. This exposition is presented following a review into the matters of vorticity, circulation, and vortices. The third section will provide specific examples of experimental observations that build upon the considerations of Section 2. The examples used in Section 2 primarily derive from the author's (and his students') experience. Complementary, if not superior, examples may exist. Correspondents, who add to the author's knowledge base by explicitly noting these additional examples, will receive statements of gratitude.

VORTICITY, CIRCULATION AND VORTICES

A principal objective of this section is to explicitly demonstrate the precision of the first two words of its title and to recommend that usage of the third (vortices) be limited to "casual conversation" where similarly non-precise or ill-defined words such as "sky" might be utilized. (Specifically, whereas the expression: "the sky is quite blue today" might have qualitative substance, the speaker would be hard-pressed to answer the question: "how high up does the sky start?" Definitions of a vortex core will be given below; however, it will also be apparent that these offer little utility in the service of flow field analysis.)

Primitive Definitions

Vorticity. Shapiro (1969), in an excellent motion picture discussion of vorticity, notes that "A fluid dynamic particle can rotate, deform and translate. If, at time t, the particle were frozen, then it could translate and rotate. The rotation vector $\bar{\Omega}$ after freezing would be one-half the vorticity before freezing." The 3-D vector representing vorticity is expressed as

$$\vec{\omega} = \nabla \times \vec{V} \qquad (1)$$

with, e.g., an x-y plane projection as

$$\omega_z = \frac{\partial v}{\partial x} - \frac{\partial u}{\partial y}. \qquad (2)$$

As clarified in numerous texts (e.g., Panton (1984) and Potter and Foss (1975)) and as demonstrated in the Shapiro movie, this expression can be interpreted as the rotation of a fluid cross centered upon the particle of interest.

Vorticity filaments and the solenoidal condition

In direct analogy to the streamline field that is everywhere tangent to $\vec{V}$, the field of vorticity filaments is tangent to $\vec{\omega}$. (The concepts expressed in this section complement those addressed by Foss and Wallace (1989)). This analogy is especially useful in its clarification that the magnitude of $\vec{\omega}$, along the filament, need not be a constant in the same manner that $\vec{V}$ need not be constant along a streamline. Such filaments can end on a surface (analogous to a stagnation point) or they can form closed loops. (The latter is the general rule). This can be expressed by the condition that a ring, encircling such a filament, can never be slid off the end of the filament.

An instructive example of the application of this concept in a two-stream shear layer is presented schematically in Figure 1 for the time averaged flow. As shown, the $\bar{\omega}$ filaments of the approach boundary layers (Fig. 1b) form closed loops in their respective channels and similar loops (c) in the free shear layer region -- on the high speed side. The $\bar{\omega}_z > 0$ vorticity of the low speed approach flow is "lost through diffusion" between the upstream and downstream locations.

Fig. 2 presents a measured time series of ω_z at the centerline of a two-stream mixing layer. A dramatically different image of the vorticity field (cf the $\bar{\omega}$ representation) is suggested by these data. Specifically, the rapid and strong $\pm$ swings of ω_z imply that the filaments which intercept the probe are segments of loops that do not extend to the upper and lower tunnel walls but are segments of smaller, compact loops with $|\omega_z|$ values that are dramatically larger than the mean value. (Note that the peak $|\omega_z|$ value is nominally 600 times larger than the mean value.) The basis for the large amplitudes is clarified below. Compact, in this sense, can be interprted as "of the order of the Taylor microscale."

Vorticity filaments and streamlines of the velocity field are defined <u>at an instant of time</u>. The motion picture: "Flow Visualization" by S.J. Kline (1969), provides an excellent sequence which demonstrates the dramatic changes with respect to time that can be exhibited by the streamline pattern in a flow field. (Refer to the discussion of streamlines, streaklines and pathlines past an oscillating flat plate.) Similarly dramatic changes in the vorticity filaments can be experienced as described below.

Circulation

The circulation, about an arbitrary contour "c" is

$$\Gamma_c = \oint_c \vec{V} \cdot d\vec{S}. \tag{3}$$

By the Stokes theorem, this can also be written as the flux of vorticity through an area bounded by c:

$$\Gamma_c = \int_A \vec{\omega} \cdot \hat{n} dA. \tag{4}$$

As an example of (3) and (4) consider the circuit c_1, of Fig. 1a. The distribution of velocity near the channel center clearly shows that $\Gamma_1 < 0$ per (3). Also, the $\omega_z(<0)$ on the left side of the splitter plate results in $\Gamma_1 < 0$.

Stream tubes, vortex tubes

A cluster (i.e., a finite area) of streamlines or filaments constitutes a tube. The mass flow $(\dot{m})$ and Γ are the conserved quantities that characterize the integral properties of such

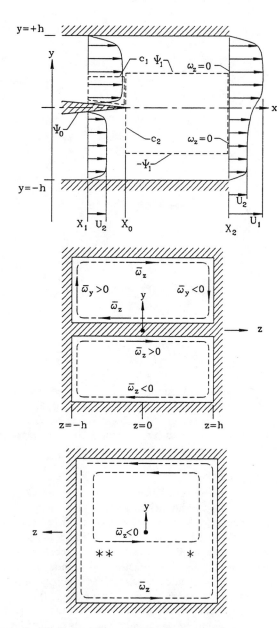

Figure 1: The time averaged (mean) vorticity filaments in a two-stream mixing layer.

a) Plan view of the mean velocity field. Note the irrotational core flows. b) Elevation view of the channel looking downstream. (Planar filaments are not implied). c) Elevation view of the channel looking upstream. Note, * shows region where the lower time mean boundary layer vorticity region merges with the shear layer vorticity. ** shows a similar region of separation at the upper boundary layer.

tubes for streamlines and vorticity filaments respectively. In this section, the time mean vorticity field for a turbulent flow (or the instantaneous vorticity for a laminar flow) will be used to define the subject filaments. A collection of the filaments for $y > 0$, x_1 in Fig.

1b provides an obvious example of such a vortex tube. The splitting (at **) and rejoining (at *) of the filament clusters in Fig. 1c would provide a means of identifying two vortex tubes that connect the left side $(y \lesssim +h)$ of the tunnel to the central $(y \approx 0)$ and also to the right hand side $(y \gtrsim -h)$ regions of the flow field at x_2.

Governing Equations

The transport equation for $\vec{\omega}$ follows directly from the Navier-Stokes equation (for a linearly viscous and an incompressible fluid in a non-accelerating reference frame) as

$$\nabla \times \left[\frac{D\vec{V}}{Dt} = -\frac{\nabla p}{\rho} + \nu \nabla^2 \vec{V} \right] \tag{5a}$$

or

$$\frac{D\vec{\omega}}{Dt} = \vec{\omega} \cdot \nabla \vec{V} + \nu \nabla^2 \vec{\omega}. \tag{5b}$$
$$\text{(I)} \qquad \text{(II)} \qquad \text{(III)}$$

The Lagrangian derivative of $\vec{\omega}$ (i.e., the time rate of change of $\vec{\omega}$ as stated by I (of (5b)) for a given fluid dynamic particle can be non-zero as a result of II (of (5b)) which represents stretching ($\pm$) and by the viscous diffusion described by III (of 5b). (If the components of $\vec{\omega}$ are considered, then (II) may contribute to a given component by reorienting existing $\vec{\omega}$ into that component direction.) Note that $\vec{\omega}$ <u>cannot</u> dissipate; that is, unlike kinetic energy, it cannot irreversibly change to something else (internal energy in the latter case). The enstrophy, $(\vec{\omega}, \vec{\omega}/2)$ is the "equivalent" of the kinetic energy $(\vec{V} \cdot \vec{V}/2)$ This quantity is subject to dissipation, diffusion, and convective transport and its describing equation has provided the basis for numerical modeling schemes and as the focus of experimental measurements. For the latter, see e.g. Foss and Wallace (1989).

The large and rapid fluctuations in $\omega_z(t)$ as shown in Fig. 2 are interpreted to be a result of term II of (5b). Given that a momentary observation of ω_z at the measurement location implies that this segment of a vorticity line is connected to itself through a loop (as noted above) and given the straining effect of the turbulence field which, on average, will lengthen line segments in a turbulent flow, the large ω_z fluctuations ($\pm$ amplifications about a small mean value) are rational.

The effect of III in (5b) is also apparent in the schematic result of Fig. 1c. Note that the sign of $\bar{\omega}_z$ on the $y < 0$ side of the splitter plate (Fig. 1b) is clearly > 0 whereas the central region $\bar{\omega}_z(x_2)$ is uniformly negative. Since term II <u>only</u> amplifies or diminishes the magnitude of ω_z, it is apparent that those fluid dynamic elements arriving at (x_2) from $(y < 0, x_1)$, have been acted upon by term III. The effect of term III of (5b) is also evident by the bounded character of the $\omega_z(t)$ fluctuations in Fig. 2 since sufficiently steep gradients result in a limitation (by diffusion) of the amplification effects of term II.

The parallel equation for Γ is also derived from the Navier-Stokes equation given the operation

$$\int_c \left[\frac{D\vec{V}}{Dt} = -\frac{\nabla p}{\rho} + \nu \nabla^2 \vec{V} - \vec{a}_I \right] \cdot d\vec{S} \tag{6}$$

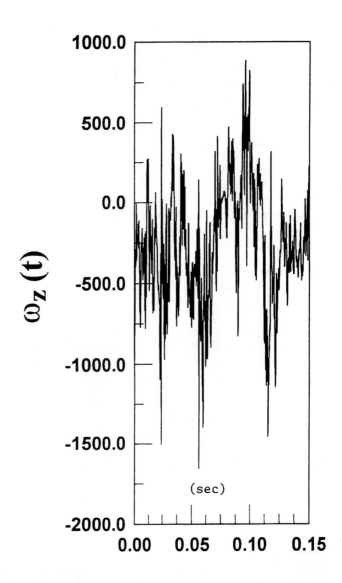

Figure 2: Time resolved $\omega_z(t)$ measurements at $x_2 = 6.94$ m, $y = z = 0$ in the University of Houston, Two-Stream Shear layer Tunnel using the MSU vorticity probe and algorithms described in Wallace and Foss (1995). Note, the mean value of ω_z is -25 sec^{-1} for this measurement location; the large fluctuations with respect to the mean are apparent.

where the pseudo body force terms of a non-inertial reference frame are now included for generality. To clarify the role of $\vec{a}_I$ in (6), recall that the inertial acceleration $(\vec{A})$ can be described in a non-inertial reference frame, $(\ )_{NI}$, as

$$\vec{A}_I = A_{NI} + \frac{d^2\vec{S}}{dt^2} + \vec{\Omega} \times \vec{\Omega} \times \vec{R} + 2\vec{\Omega} \times \vec{V} + \frac{d\vec{\Omega}}{dt} \times \vec{R} \tag{7a}$$

or

$$= \vec{A}_{NI} + \vec{a}_I \tag{7b}$$

where the terms are given standard interpretations (see, e.g., Panton (1984) or Potter and Foss (1975)) inclusive of $A_{NI} = dV/dt$ as seen by the non-inertial observer. The a_I terms are included in (6) since they serve as important source terms in such problems as pitching airfoils and impulsively started bodies.

Equation (6) can be rewritten as

$$\frac{D\Gamma}{Dt} = -\int_c \frac{\nabla p}{\rho} \cdot d\vec{S} + \int_c \nu \nabla^2 \vec{V} \cdot d\vec{S} - \int_c \vec{a}_I \cdot d\vec{S}. \qquad (8)$$
$$\quad\quad\quad IV \qquad\qquad V \qquad\qquad VI$$

Term IV represents a non-barotropic effect that was not explicitly included in the incompressible equation (5b) for $D\vec{\omega}/Dt$. Term V represents the immensely important "source term" wherein "vorticity enters the flow by rolling down the pressure hill." Specifically, for

$$\frac{D\vec{V}}{Dt} = 0 \quad \text{at a solid surface}, \qquad (9a)$$

the pressure gradient - viscous balance (for $a_I = 0$)

$$\frac{\nabla p}{\rho} = \nu \nabla^2 \vec{V} \qquad (9b)$$

is achieved and term V of (8) becomes a descriptor for the "source of circulation" or the "diffusive flux of vorticity into the flow" given a pressure gradient at a no-slip boundary. Note that (9b) has returned to the inertial form of the governing equations. If non-inertial effects are present, (9b) would apply to that portion of the surface pressure gradient that is not associated with the $a_I \neq 0$ effects.

Equation (8) has been presented and interpreted by numerous authors see, e.g., Lighthill (1963) and Panton (1984). Its Lagrangian nature, however, makes its evaluation and intuitive interpretation somewhat awkward. Potter and Foss (1975) developed an Eulerian form for this equation; viz.,

$$\frac{d\Gamma_c}{dt} = -\int_A \nabla \times (\vec{\omega} \times \vec{V}) \cdot \hat{n} dA - \oint_c \vec{a}_I \cdot d\vec{s} - \int_c \frac{\nabla p}{\rho} \cdot d\vec{s} + \oint_c \nu \nabla^2 \vec{V} \cdot d\vec{s} \qquad (10)$$
$$\quad\quad\quad\quad VII \qquad\qquad VIII \qquad\quad IX \qquad\quad X$$

from which they clarified the relationship of X from equation (10) on a no-slip boundary to the net "flux" of vorticity (VII of (10)) with respect to the fixed (Eulerian) circulation domain (C). A specific example of this net flux condition is shown in Fig. 3. Potter and Foss (1975), show how term VII of (10) can be expressed as a "flux-like" effect where the "flux" is past a line and not through an area. Specifically, for the example shown,

$$\int_A \nabla \times (\vec{\omega} \times \vec{v}) \cdot \hat{n} dA = \int_{x_2} u \omega_z dy - \int_{x_1} u \omega_z dy. \qquad (11)$$
$$\quad\quad\quad\quad\quad\quad XI \qquad\qquad XII$$

Figure 3 has been prepared for the conditions of a steady flow laminar boundary layer on the indicated obstruction. The symbol S_{final} shows the streamwise position at which the surface pressure is zero (gage) and all of the boundary layer vorticity ($\omega_z < 0$) has been introduced into the flow. A similar location could be defined for the time averaged flow in a turbulent boundary layer. However, the $\pm$ $\partial p/\partial x$ and $\partial p/\partial z$ gradients of the latter are important instantaneous source terms for ω_z and ω_x respectively. In the example of Fig. 3 term XII of (11) is zero whereas term XI shows the presence of ω_z in the boundary layer. The lhs of (10) is clearly zero in this steady state flow field.

It was noted above that diffusive effects are responsible for the absence of $\bar{\omega}_z > 0$ at x_2 in the shear layer of Fig. 1. The contour c_2 of Fig. 1a can likewise be addressed using (10). Note that $\psi = 0$ is the streamline of the splitter plate and $\pm \psi_1$ show streamlines in the irrotational core flow. The $x =$ constant lines connect to $\pm \psi_1$ to form c_2. Terms VIII, IX, and X are clearly zero as is the $d\Gamma_c/dt$ of equation (10). Term VII is, therefore, also zero with the consequence that

$$\lim_{T \to \infty} \int_0^T \left\{ \iint_A \nabla \times (\vec{\omega} \times \vec{V}) \cdot \hat{n} dA \right\} dt = \int_{-\psi_1}^{\psi_1} \overline{u \omega_z} dy]_{at\, x_2} - \int_{-\psi_1}^0 \overline{u \omega_z} dy]_{at\, x_0}$$
$$\quad\quad\quad\quad\quad\quad\quad\quad\quad\quad\quad\quad XIII \qquad\qquad\qquad XIV$$

$$- \int_0^{\psi_1} \overline{u \omega_z} dy]_{at\, x}$$
$$\quad\quad\quad XV$$

In this physical situation, the efflux of negative sign vorticity, (XIII), is balanced by the combination of the larger magnitude, flux of negative $\bar{\omega}_z$, (XIV), and the smaller magnitude of the flux of positive ω_z, (XV). It is interesting to note that the right-hand side integrals, without $\bar{\omega}_z$ in the integrands, also sum to zero.

A Vortex

In contrast to the above quantities, but in concert with the words: laminar and turbulent, a vortex cannot be given a "satisfying" definition. However, in a manner similar to "laminar" and "turbulent", "vortex" is an oft-used word.

Cantwell (1978), as well as Dallman (1983), Vollmers (1983) and Perry and Chong (1994), offer the (paraphrased) definition for the core of a vortex:

"In a flow field, if a selected point represents an isolated singular point, and if the velocity field (around that singular point) exhibits a spiral node (or a focus) for a plane that passes through the point, then at that point and in that plane, there exits a "vortex core."

The present author, having been vexed by arbitrary if not argumentative definitions of a "vortex", is pleased to reiterate the definition of these authors and to note that their definition provides a clearly stated method to evaluate a vortex core. It also confirms the inconsequential nature of so doing. That is, the identification process is precise but, having done so (at a point), no further information can (apparently) be inferred about the flow field. (This inference was confirmed by Prof. Perry in a private discussion (Nov. 1995)). It is noteworthy that the above definition is, however, fully compatible with the in-plane measurement techniques that are discussed in Section 3. These data bases can easily be interrogated to evaluate such rotational patterns.

Jeong and Hussain (1995), provide an extensive discussion under the title: "On the identification of a vortex". They also provide a further guide to the definitions of a vortex given by previous authors. A striking feature of their exposition is the authors' consideration of other definitions using arguments that are seemingly based upon an a'priori understanding of what constitutes a vortex in an incompressible flow. The other definitions are concluded by them to

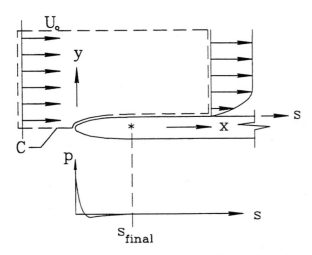

Figure 3: The addition of negative ω_z into a boundary layer flow via the action of the pressure gradient $(\partial p/\partial x < 0)$. Note, see equations (9b) and (10) for the corresponding discussion.

be inadequate and the definition: $\lambda_2 < 0$, given the eigenvalues $(\lambda_1, \lambda_2, \lambda_3)$ of the quantity:

$$[S^2 + \Omega^2],$$

where S and Ω are the symmetric and anti-symmetric components of the velocity (u_i) gradient $(\partial(\ )/\partial x_j)$ tensor: $\partial u_i/\partial x_j$, is advanced as the definition of a vortex core. The "extent" of the vortex, perhaps like the "height at which the sky starts", is not addressed. (It can be parenthetically observed that a rather complete knowledge of the flow field, e.g., from a DNS solution, would be required to evaluate $\lambda_2 < 0$ for the Jeong and Hussain vortex). As is well recognized, DNS solutions will be limited to Reynolds number values dramatically below those of typical engineering interest for the foreseeable future and the experimental 3-D velocity vector field data bases sought using holographic PIV (for example, by Meng and Hussain (1995)) seems to also be a somewhat distant prospect. These constraints mean that the effective utilization of this definition is rather limited. The technique of Scalar Imaging Velocimetry (SIV) by Dahm and co-workers, see, e.g., Dahm, et al. (1992), could be used for this purpose but, to-date, it has not been so used. It is also true that SIV is limited to very low velocities (of order several mm/sec) to accommodate the scanning rate between planes.

The numerous definitions of a vortex (two of which are explicitly noted here) prompt the following summary comments for this section. It is noted that the word "vortex" is in the eye of the beholder and, if the beholder finds solace in a formal definition, then it is the wise person who holds contrary opinions as a private matter. One is reminded of the interaction between Alice and Humpty Dumpty as communicated by Lewis Carroll in Through the Looking Glass. "When I use the word", Humpty Dumpty said in a rather scornful tone, "it means just what I choose it to mean -- neither more nor less." (Appreciation is expressed to Prof. J. Dressel (Central Michigan University) for locating the precise quote.) The reaction, on the part of the present author to all such definitions, would change

if, like $\bar{\omega}$ and Γ, the identified "vortex" could be used to gain further knowledge or understanding about a flow field. The favored definition (that of Cantwell (1978) and others) is obviously one which carries "no deeper meaning."

A similarity between the words "sky" and "vortex" was proposed above. It is useful to further note that the addition of modifying adjectives appears to make both words more "acceptable". "Cloudy" and "deep blue" shift the focus from "sky" to the descriptors. The same is true of "wing tip" and "bound" (the latter as applied to a jet in cross flow). However, the modifiers do not contribute to the problem of providing a general meaning for the noun "vortex".

NOTEWORTHY PROPERTIES OF A FIELD OF VORTICITY

Addition of Vorticity into a Flow Field

Equation (9) and Fig. 3 are associated with a discussion of the role of surface pressure gradients regarding the introduction of vorticity into a flow field. Once entered by this mechanism, the vorticity will convect and diffuse per the local prescriptions of equation (5b). A particular example is provided by the work of Bohl and Foss (1995); see Figure 4 for a schematic representation of a tabbed jet geometry and the measured upstream pressure field on the inner wall of the approach nozzle. The tabbed jet, and its near field of concentrated streamwise vorticity regions, is a manifestation of the importance of these source terms. Figure 5 presents the distribution of the mean streamwise vorticity as derived from

$$\bar{\omega}_x = \frac{\partial \bar{w}}{\partial y} - \frac{\partial \bar{v}}{\partial z} \qquad (12)$$

and the measured $\bar{w}(y,z)$ and $\bar{v}(y,z)$ distributions at $x/b = 1.2$. The presence of counter rotating vortex motions is apparent. (The present use of the word "vortex" in this discussion is advanced as an example of the casual use which is found to be appropriate. Specifically no precision is asked of its use to characterize the two regions which exhibit concentrations of streamwise vorticity). As noted in Figure 5, these regions can be related to the following physical effects: i) the reorientation of the boundary layer vorticity into the $\pm\omega_x$ concentrations that exist on the outer $\mp y$ locations (i.e., the "necklace vortex") and ii) the "pressure hill induced vortex" motions that are of opposite sign, interior to and stronger than (i.e., larger Γ) the vortex of (i). It is evident that the coherent motions at $x/b = 1.2$ can be traced upstream to the jet exit plane. At this plane they form relatively compact regions of vorticity filaments (see Bohl and Foss (1995)) which must be connected to the similar filaments on the $y > 0$ side of the tab. This connection is made by loops that form upstream of the tab. The filaments of the pressure hill vortex will be connected in the separated flow region upstream of the tab. (The farthest upstream location of this region is at the saddle point of separation between the approach flow and the reversing flow forward of the tab).

The identification of a necklace vortex, that "wraps around" the obstruction that produced it, can be made in any flow with an obstruction that interrupts the approach boundary layer. A tutorial discussion of such a flow might include reference to the approach vorticity as if it were a "flexible string that bends around the

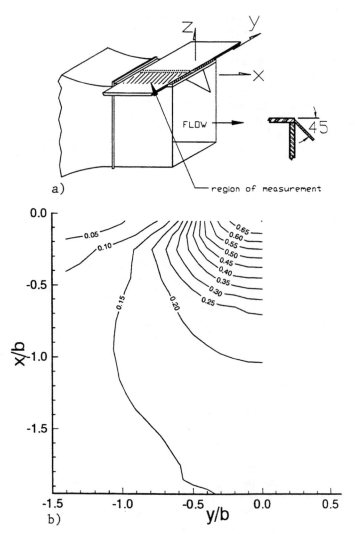

a)

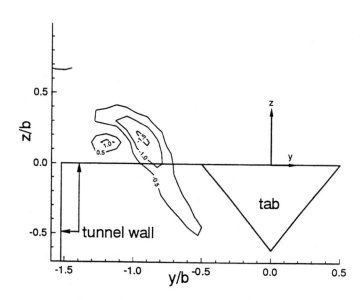

Figure 5: Time mean streamwise vorticity values $(\bar{\omega}_z b/U_o)$ at $x/b = 1.2$. Notes, 1) the positive values (max value shown = 1.0) derive from the reoriented boundary layer vorticity of the approach flow; 2) the negative values (max = -1.5) derive from the "pressure hill" forward of the tab. See equation (10) and Fig. 5; 3) full lines show traces of tab and walls at $x = 0$.

Figure 4: Definition of tabbed jet flow field and surface pressure distribution

a) Square jet exit (61×61 cm³) with equilateral-triangular tab (base = b = 20 cm) b) Pressure $[p^* = (p(x,z) - p_{atm})]/0.5 \rho U_o^2]$ distribution forward of the tab

obstruction". This can be very misleading for the tutoree!

Figure 6 has been prepared to emphasize the difference between such a "string" -- i.e., that which can be thought of as a material line in the flow -- and a vorticity filament. (In the rare event of an inviscid, vortical flow, these two attributes of a flow field would be the same.)

The approaching filament (shown at time $t = 1$) and the material line are characterized by the marked fluid particles: $A(1)$ and $B(1)$. The same particles are shown at time $t = 2$ as $A(2)$ and $B(2)$. By definition they remain on the same material line. The important point is that the vorticity filament which passes through $A(2)$ does not pass through $B(2)$. These separate filaments are shown schematically at the downstream (or "2") positions. Viscous diffusion of vorticity, term III of (5b), will have acted to modify the $\bar{\omega}$ field such that

the material line (i.e., the flexible extensible string) which connects A to B is different from either of the two filaments that pass through those material elements. Specifically, a flux of countersign vorticity into the flow will be associated with the decelerating fluid (A) and this will diminish the magnitude of its $\bar{\omega}$ for A. Conversely, the accelerative effect along the trajectory of B will add common sign vorticity to this particle. At each "time step" of the process, the vorticity filaments passing through A and B must (and will) be "reformulated" to represent the state of the flow field.

Vorticity as a Diffusive Variable

The influence of the surface flux of vorticity on the connectivity of the vorticity filaments was considered in the prior section. It also plays a significant role in the oblique impingement of an axisymmetric jet as investigated by Foss and Kleis (1976); see Fig. 7. It is useful in this discussion to consider a series of time steps that begin ($t = 0$) with the jet fluid approaching the plate. Fluid dynamic particles, in a plane perpendicular to the jet axis will be marked for discussion. Consider the jet, in this plane, to be axisymmetric. The marked particles -- $A(0)$:*, $B(0)$: ◯, $C(0)$: ☐, $D(0)$: ★ -- are designated at time (0) and they will be the subject of the following interpretive discussion for subsequent times ($0 < t < t_j$). Note that the upper and lower symmetric fluid elements are joined by the same -- time mean -- vorticity filaments at $t = 0$. Specifically, $A(0)$-$D(0)$ and $B(0)$-$C(0)$ are so joined.

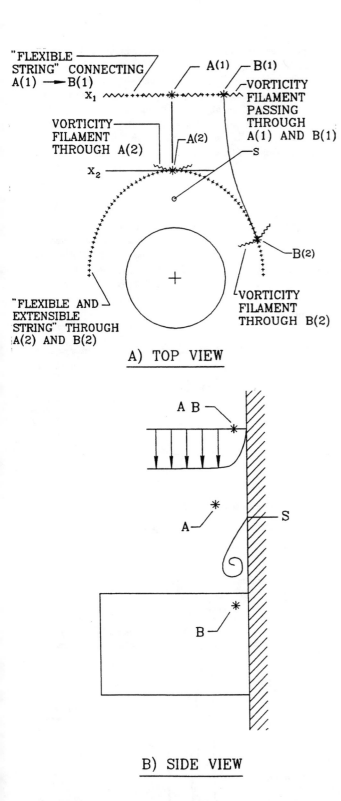

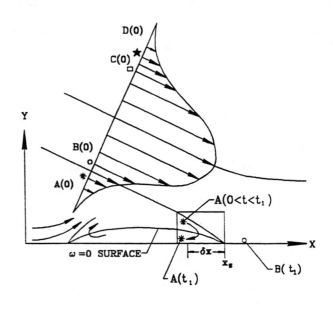

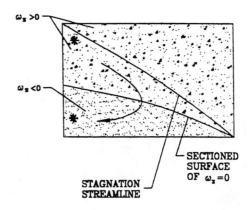

It was shown (Foss and Kleis (1976)) that the stagnation streamline, for the shallow incidence angles of that study, was taken from the low speed, vortical region of the jet's outer perimeter. That is, $A(0)$ and $B(0)$ bracket the stagnation streamline of the approach flow. As a consequence, the mean vorticity of the fluid on the approach streamline that was positioned below the stagnation streamline (i.e., $A(0)$) changed sign as it (i.e., $A(t_1)$) flowed upstream from the stagnation point. As stated above, for $t \approx 0$, $A(0)$ would have been joined to a fluid element $D(0)$ on the top of the jet. For a time (t_1) at which A was moving upstream (away from the stagnation point), it would have been joined to $B(t_1)$ (by definition). It is evident that this involved a dramatic change in the connectivity of the time mean vorticity filaments between time $(t=0)$ and (t_1). Similarly, $C(t_1)$ and $D(t_1)$ (not shown on the figure) are connected to downstream flowing filaments that were originally above $B(0)$. Again, a dramatic change in connectivity is implied.

"FLEXIBLE STRING" CONNECTING $A(1) \longrightarrow B(1)$

x_1

$A(1)$ — $B(1)$

VORTICITY FILAMENT PASSING THROUGH $A(1)$ AND $B(1)$

VORTICITY FILAMENT THROUGH $A(2)$

$A(2)$

x_2

s

$B(2)$

"FLEXIBLE AND EXTENSIBLE STRING" THROUGH $A(2)$ AND $B(2)$

VORTICITY FILAMENT THROUGH $B(2)$

A) TOP VIEW

A B

s

A

B

B) SIDE VIEW

Figure 6: Schematic representation of the "necklace vortex" as an example of the effects of diffusion on the vorticity field. Note, "s" shows the separation point for the approach boundary layer <u>and</u> the farthest upstream location of the "necklace vortex"

$D(0)$

$C(0)$

Y

$B(0)$

$A(0)$

$A(0<t<t_1)$

$\omega = 0$ SURFACE

$A(t_1)$

δx

x_s

X

$B(t_1)$

$\omega_z > 0$

$\omega_z < 0$

SECTIONED SURFACE OF $\omega_z = 0$

STAGNATION STREAMLINE

Figure 7: Physical characteristics of the shallow angle, oblique jet impingement. Note, x_s = stagnation point.

89

A second dramatic example of the role of diffusive effects on the vorticity field was provided by Oshima and Asaka (1977a,b) in their original studies and by Schatzle (1987) in his PhD dissertation that qualitatively and quantitatively extended the former investigations. The interested reader is referred to the Schatzle thesis for quantitative details regarding this experiment as well as photographic records of the sequence of events which follow from a shallow impingement angle between two simultaneously "fired" vortex rings.

A schematic representation of the "fusion-fission" process is shown in Fig. 8. This representation is based upon the Oshima and Asaka observations in which two dyed vortex rings (red and gold) are directed toward the "impact region" (i.e., showing the fusion process) followed by the departure of two rings "half-red/half-gold" from the impact region. This latter phase represents the "fission" process. The centers of the departing rings define a plane that is 90 degrees to the approach plane. This dramatic experiment shows that the dye — as a non-diffusive marker — was equally shared by the departing vortex rings. Hence, the departing rings, are a product of a very rapid diffusion of vorticity that permits the filaments to be locally realigned in the interaction region. The diffusive vorticity defines the rings. The non-diffusive dye allows the rings to be visualized but the dyes do not define the rings.

Hussain and co-workers have characterized such interactions as "cut-and-connect", see, e.g. Melander and Hussain (1988). This is arguably misleading (again, for a tutoree) since it implies that a physical object — such as a flexible string — characterizes a vorticity filament and is therefore subject to being "cut". The preferred conception is that, at an instant, a filament field exists and the variable effects of diffusion along its length will result in a new (possibly dramatically different) configuration of filaments at a future time. The two preceding examples in this section are offered as excellent reasons why this latter conceptualization is appropriate.

Vorticity and Coherent Vortex Motions

An experiment, involving quantitative measurements in an air flow and visualization observations in water, was executed and reported by Walter, et al. (1992) and Foss, et al. (1993). The purpose of their work was to create an unambiguous, large scale coherent vortex motion and to determine if it could be identified by its time resolved vorticity signature. The apparatus is shown schematically in Fig. 9.

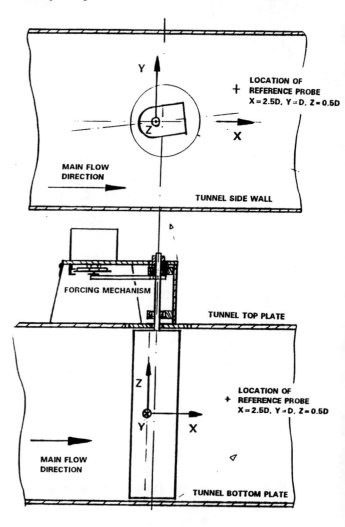

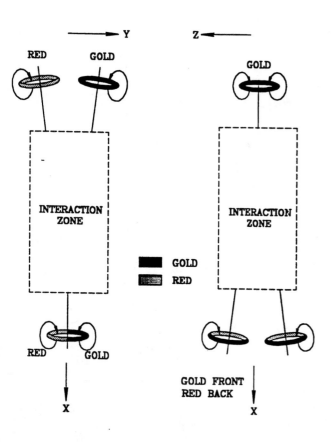

Figure 8: A schematic representation of the Oshima and Asaka (1977) obliquely colliding vortex rings experiment.

Figure 9: Oscillating (± 1 degree) inverted D shaped obstruction.

The drive mechanism created ± 1 degree oscillations about the indicated axis; the excitation frequency was set to the "natural" shedding frequency

$$(S_T = fD/U = 0.242).$$

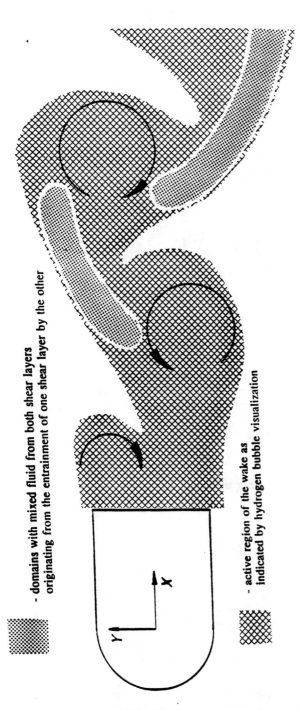

Figure 10: A tracing of the dye visualizations: hydrogen bubbles and two dye colors released from the aft edges -- $x \leq D$, $y = \pm D/2$.

Cross correlation observations from two probes: $x/D=2.5$, $y/D=1$, $z/D=+1$ and $z/D=-1$ showed a non-decaying peak-to-peak amplitude of $\pm 0.8 \sqrt{u_1'^2}\sqrt{u_2'^2}$. Hence, judging by these pressure-field-driven oscillations of the velocity in the external potential flow, an exceptionally well defined and regularly spaced set of coherent vortex motions was established. This inference was confirmed in the dye and hydrogen bubble visualizations which were in excellent agreement with the quantitative phase averaged hot-wire data.

Specifically, Figure 10 presents tracings of the visualized flow field at the phase angle $\phi = 135$ degrees. The visualized markers were differently colored dye streams from taps near the juncture of the circular and the straight walls of the obstruction. The dye streak markers were complemented by phase locked hydrogen bubbles released from a wire located at 0.05 D downstream from the trailing edge and perpendicular to the axis of the cylinder. The pulsed segments of bubbles clealry showed the in-sweep (toward the centerline) in a pattern that confirmed the large scale motions suggested by the dye markers. The indications from these qualitative markers are supported by the quantitative (u,v) measurements. Namely, these velocity values were obtained as time series values at the discrete locations and processed as phase averaged quantities. The phase averaged streamwise and lateral velocities, $<u(\phi)>$, $<v(\phi)>$, are shown in Fig. 11. (Phase sampling: data samples are sorted by reference to the pitch-up, zero-angle angle of attack position of the D-shaped obstruction). Note that the convection velocity has been subtracted from the measured $<u(\phi)>$ values for this representation. The convection velocity was determined by identifying the elapsed time (τ_{max}) to the peak of the autocorrelation function:

$$R_{12}(x_1,y_1,\pm z_1,\delta x,\tau) = \overline{u_1'(x_1,y_1,+z_1,t)u_2'(x_1+\delta x,y_1,-z_1,t+\tau)}, \quad (13)$$

and then defining u_c as

$$u_c = \frac{\delta x}{\tau_{max}}. \quad (14)$$

These figures provide independent confirmations of the well defined coherent vortex motions created by the oscillating D-shaped obstruction.

Figure 12 shows the time resolved $\omega_z(t)$ measurements using the MSU technique as discussed in Foss and Wallace (1989) and Wallace and Foss (1995). These four samples are representative of all such records. Namely, their "local average" (for the range of D-shaped pitch angles: $135 \leq \phi \leq 180$) agrees well with the long term phase average from the complete time record. However, in comparison to the instantaneous values, these "local averages" are quite small with respect to the irregular excursions of the $\omega_z(x=4.2D, y=0.3D, t)$ signatures. Statistical expressions of the latter are shown in Fig. 13 where the lack of any signature pattern is again expressed.

In conclusion, one can note that even for this relatively low Reynolds number flow field: $UD/\nu = 23,000$, an instantaneous trace of $\omega_z(t)$ cannot be used to infer the presence of a large scale coherent vortex motion. (Note that "relatively low Reynolds number", as used above, is in reference to flows of typical interest in Fluids Engineering. Conversely, this Reynolds number is quite large with respect to those of academic interest. The IUTAM

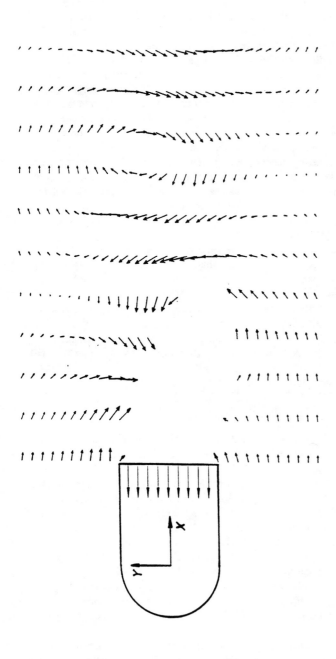

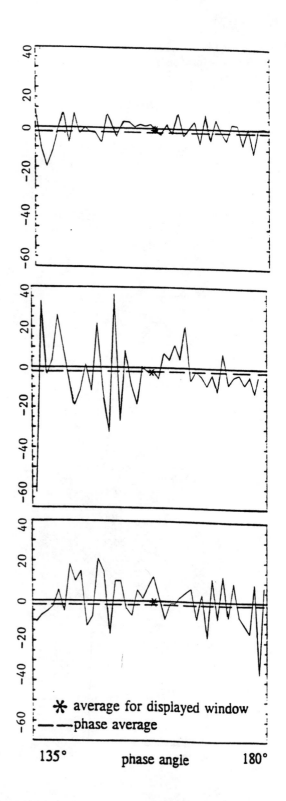

Figure 11: Phase sampled, $(\bar{u}-U_c)$ and $\bar{v}$ time mean velocity profiles for 135 degrees. Note, U_c is the convection speed; see equation 13.

Figure 12: Three representative samples of $\omega_z(t)$ at $x = 4.2D$, $y = 0.3D$ spanning phase angles $135 \rightarrow 180$ degrees. Note, this time series will cut through the center of the "vortex" that is revealed by the visualized and phase averaged observations.

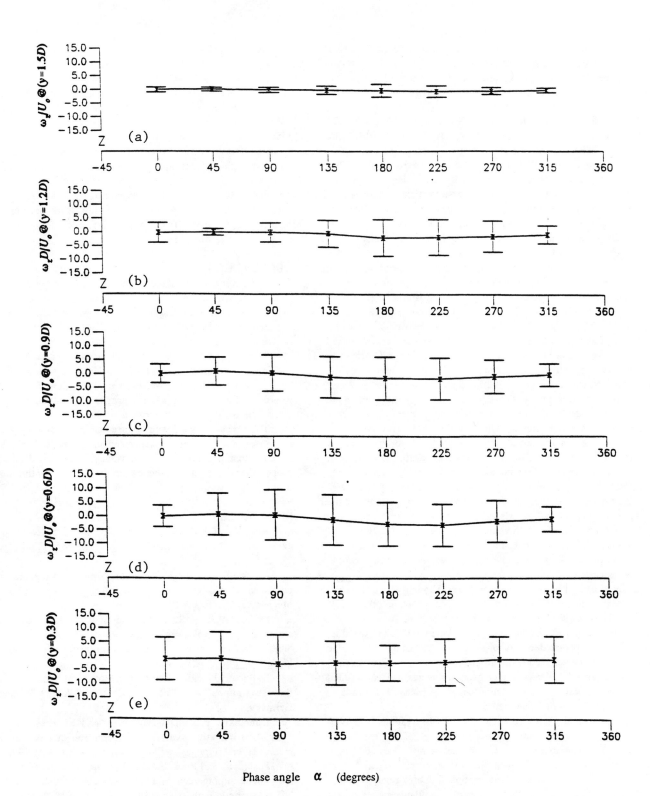

Figure 13: Phase sampled mean and rms values of $\omega_z(t)$
Notes, a: $y=1.2D$, b: $y=0.9D$, c: $y=0.6D$,
d: $y=0.3D$, e: $y=0$, * shows mean value; I shows rms
Ordinate represents $(\omega D/U_o)$, abscissa
shows phase angle.

Symposium: Bluff Body Wakes, Dynamics and Instabilities (1992), provides numerous examples of the latter interests). The contribution of these results is to help one understand the limits of the phrase: "coherent vortex motions."

EXPERIMENTAL METHODS FOR "VORTEX" IDENTIFICATIONS: VORTICITY AND CIRCULATION MEASUREMENTS

The experience of Walter, et al. (1992) and Foss, et al. (1993), for technologically small, albeit academically large, Reynolds numbers was that time resolved transverse vorticity measurements were not useful in the identification of vortex motions. Given the understanding that the vorticity must fulfill two roles:

i) $\omega_z(t)$ must provide, as a spatial integral, the correct value of Γ (per equation (4)), and

ii) $\omega_z(t)$ must be compatible with the small scales of the motion that provide the turbulence kinetic energy dissipation.,

and since the former constraint can be satisfied with a large number of $\omega_z(t)$ distributions, it is apparent (as shown in Fig. 12) that the second "role" (i.e., (ii)) is the physically determining one for turbulent flows. Hence, it is inferred that experimentally based "vortex" identifications should rely on the integral property: circulation. (A statistical exception to this "rule" is provided by the work of Nguyen, et al. (1992). Specifically, their vorticity measurements, utilizing a 12-sensor (hot-wire) probe were quite successful in extracting the dominant shedding frequency of spanwise vortex motions from a circular cylinder at $R_d = 2050$. However, these authors do not describe an attempt to identify "a vortex" from its $\omega_z(t)$ signature. Their results do, however, confirm the ability of the 12-sensor probe to discriminate between vorticity components).

Particle image velocimetry (PIV) observations by Rockwell (1992), which were processed to yield vorticity magnitudes of the component parallel to the axis of the generating cylinder, proved quite useful in identifying the coherent motions aft of a cylinder at $R_D = 5000$. Measurements for a non-uniform diameter cylinder were also presented at much lower R_D values (≈ 150).

It can be expected that, at higher R_D values, the ω_{axial} contours will show behaviors as characterized by hot-wire probes and as presented above. However, a major contribution of the PIV method is to "switch" to circulation measurements which, if the spatial domain is sufficiently small, will mimic the ("point" variable) vorticity. The planar domains for the circuit "C" of the Γ value would need to be selected with "insight"; however, the PIV scheme, like all planar — full field — imaging measurements, is ideally suited for such identifications of circulation values. Adrian (1991) provides an excellent review of these methods.

Oakley, et al., have reported on PIV observations in a two-stream shear layer as characterized by Fig. 1. Their use of the individual realizations to compute $\bar{\omega}_z$, but not the rms value of the ω_z population, is in keeping with the above observations. Their observations do provide useful information about the relatively large scale attributes of this flow field. In particular, they emphasize that the conceptual image of well ordered "eddies and braids," that derive from lower Reynolds number investigations as characterized by Dimotakis, et al. (1981) -- $R_\delta \approx 2.5 \times 10^3$ -- are not evident in their images — $R_\delta \approx 2.6 \times 10^4$. The time series $\omega_z(t)$ values of Fig. 2 are nomially an order of mangitude larger than those of Oakley, et al., viz. $R_\delta \approx 2 \times 10^5$. These quantitative values reinforce the Oakley, et al. observations that the well ordered "eddies and braids" are not observed at higher Reynolds numbers.

Particle image velocimetry is a popular (i.e., a widely used) and an effective measurement tool. Modifiers: "digital" and "photographic" have been added to the PIV description to represent video (fast, easy, limited resolution) and photographic (still) film methods (slow, difficult, maximum resolution and information content). Other planar imaging techniques can be employed as well. As one example, there exists a class of methods termed "Molecular Tagging Velocimetry (MTV)" as coined by M.M. Koochesfahani. The most recent representation of his work is contained in Koochesfahani, et al. (1996). Other references to such studies are provided in that document.

CONCLUSIONS

Vorticity and circulation are "praised" as robust flow field descriptors whose fundamental nature and analytical descriptions provide instructive representations of flow fields. Examples and narrative expositions are provided (Section 2) to clarify the contributions of "vorticity" and "circulation."

"Vortex" and "vortices" are advanced as words that should be restricted to "casual" conversation. "Untested and unchallenged," they provide appropriate words to describe flow fields. Specific references for, and examples of, usages of vortex and vortices that are useful are given in the above text.

Time resolved vorticity measurement methods are <u>not</u> endorsed as "vortex identification" measurement methods. Rather, "full" field methods that provide circulation values for specified domains are proposed as the most effective experimental tools for the focus areas of this Symposium.

REFERENCES

Adrian, R.J., 1991, "Particle imaging techniques for experimental fluid mechanics", <u>Annual Review of Fluid Mechanics</u>, <u>23</u>, 261-304.

Cantwell, B.J., 1978, "Coherent turbulent structures as critical points in unsteady flow", <u>Arch. Mech. Strosow.</u> (Archives of Mechanics) <u>31</u>, 707-721.

Dahm, W.J.A., Su, L.K. and Southerland, K.B., 1992, "A scalar imaging velocimetry technique for fully resolved four-dimensional vector velocity field measurements in turbulent flows", <u>Physics of Fluids A</u>, <u>4</u>, p. 2191.

Dallman, U., 1983, "Topological structures of three-dimensional flow separations", DFVLR Rep. IB 221-82-A07, Göttingen, West Germany.

Dimotakis, P.E., Debussy, F.D. and Koochesfahani, M.M., 1981, "Particle streak velocity measurements in a two-dimensional mixing layer," <u>Physics of Fluids</u>, <u>24</u>, No. 6, pp. 995-999.

Foss, J.F. and Kleis, S.J., 1976, "Mean flow characteristics for the oblique impingement of an axisymmetric jet", AIAA Jour. <u>14</u>:6, 705-6 (Synoptic with extended M.S. on file at NTIS N76-21425).

Foss, J.F. and Wallace, J.M., 1989. "The measurement of vorticity in transitional and fully developed turbulent flows", <u>Advances in Fluid Mechanics Measurements</u>, M. Gad-el-Hak, Ed., Springer-Verlag, Berlin, 263-321.

Foss, J.F., Walter, B., and Koochesfahani, M.M., 1993, "Velocity and vorticity measurements in the near wake of a D-shaped cylinder", Ninth Turbulent Shear Flows Conference, Kyoto, Japan.

Jeong, J. and Hussain, F., 1995, "On the identification of a vortex", Jour. Fluid Mech., 285, pp. 69-94.

Kline, S.J., 1969, Flow Visualization, a motion picture (21607) distributed by the Encyclopedia Britanica Ed. Corp., 425 N. Michigan Ave, Chicago, IL 60611.

Koochesfahani, M.M., Cohn, R.K., Gendrich, C.P. and Nocera, D.G., 1996, "Molecular Tagging Diagnostics for the Study of Kinematics and Mixing in Liquid Phase Flows," Proceedings, Eighth International Symposium on Applications of Laser Techniques to Fluids Mechanics, Lisbon, Portugal.

Lighthill, M.S., 1963, "Introduction to Boundary Layer Theory," Laminar Boundary Layers, Clarendon Press (ed. Rosenhead, L), Chap. 2.

Melander, M. and Hussain, F., 1988, "Cut-and-connect of two antiparallel vortex tubes", Center for Turbulence Research Report, CTR S 88, pp. 257-286.

Meng, H. and Hussain, A.K.M.F., 1995, "Instantaneous flow field in an unstable vortex ring measured by holographic particle velocimetry", Phys. of Fluids, 7, pp. 9-11.

Nguyen, P.H., Marasli, B. and Wallace, J.M., 1992, "The vortical structure of the near wake of a circular cylinder", IUTAM Symposium, Bluff Body Wakes, Dynamics and Instabilities, ed., H. Echelmann, J.M.R. Graham, P. Huerre, and P. Monkewitz, Springer Verlag, pp. 81-84.

Oakley, T.R., Loth, E. and Adrian, R.J., 1996, "Cinematic particle image velocimetry of high-Reynolds-number turbulent free shear layer," AIAA Journal, 34, No. 2, pp. 299-308.

Oshima, Y. and Asaka S., 1977a, "Interaction of two vortex rings along parallel axes in air", J. Phys. Soc. Japan, 42, 708-713.

Oshima, Y. and Asaka, S., 1977b, "Interaction of two vortex rings," Proceedings of the International Symposium on Flow Visualization, Tokyo, Hemisphere Publishing Corp., 81-86.

Panton, R.L., 1984, Incompressible Flow, John Wiley and Sons, Inc.

Perry, A.E. and Chong, M.S., 1994, "Topology of flow patterns in vortex motions and turbulence", Applied Scientific Research, 53, 357-374.

Potter, M.C. and Foss, J.F., 1975, Fluid Mechanics, The Ronald Press Co. (Now published by Great Lakes Press Co, Okemos, MI 48864).

Rockwell, D., 1992, "Quantitative visualization of bluff body wakes via particle imaging velocimetry", IUTAM Symposium, Bluff Body Wakes, Dynamics and Instabilities, pp. 263-270.

Schatzle, P.R., 1987, "An experimental study of fusion of vortex rings", PhD Thesis, Calif. Inst. of Tech.

Shapiro, A.H., 1969, Vorticity (parts 1 and 2), motion picture (21605, 21606) distributed by the Encyclopedia Britanica Ed. Corp. 425 N. Michigan Ave, Chicago, IL 60611.

Vollmers, H., 1983, "Separation and vortical-type flow around a prolate spheroid. Evaluation of relevant parameters", AGARD Symposium on Aerodyn. of Vortical Type Flow in Three-Dimensions, Rotterdam, AGARD-CP 342, pp. 14.1-14.14.

Wallace, J.M. and Foss, J.F., 1995, "The measurement of vorticity in turbulent flows", Ann Reviews of Fluid Mechanics.

Walter, B., Koochesfahani, M.M. and Foss, J.F., 1992, "Transverse vorticity measurements in the wake of an inverted D-shaped cylinder", proc. of IUTAM Conference on Bluff Body Wakes, Springer Verlag.

FED-Vol. 238, 1996 Fluids Engineering Division Conference
Volume 3
ASME 1996

WAVELET CROSS-CORRELATION ANALYSIS AND ITS APPLICATION TO TWO-DIMENSIONAL VORTEX FLOW

Hui Li
Department of Mechanical Engineering
Kagoshima University
1-21-40, Koorimoto
Kagoshima city, Japan
E-mail li@mech.eng.kagoshima-u.ac.jp

Tsutomu Nozaki
Department of Mechanical Engineering
Kagoshima University
1-21-40, Koorimoto
Kagoshima city, Japan
E-mail nozaki@mech.eng.kagoshima-u.ac.jp

ABSTRACT

A new combination of familiar techniques of signal processing, which is called a wavelet cross-correlation analysis, is proposed and its main properties are also presented. The wavelet cross-correlation analysis can express the cross-correlation characteristics of two arbitrary signals as a function of time delay. As the practical application to vortex flow, the cross-correlation characteristics of the two velocity signals in a plane turbulent jet at various positions are analyzed for revealing the similar structure of the eddy and apparent flapping motions in terms of time delay and period.

INTRODUCTION

Since a wavelet analysis was first proposed in 1981 by the geophysicist Morlet (1981), it has been applied mostly to various fields, for example, harmonic analysis and partial differential equations in pure mathematics, signal and image processing in computer science, fluid engineering and electrical engineering because of its ability to describe a signal simultaneously in time and in scale.

Recently, the wavelet analysis has also been applied mostly in fluid mechanics. In the limited open literature available from 1993 at the time of submission (some literature until 1993 were summarized by Li and Nozaki (1995a)), Dallard and Browand (1993) have reported extensive results of wavelet analysis from phase-averaged 2-D velocity fields in an acoustically forced mixing layer. The extension of the usual definitions of wavelet functions in one dimension to the 2-D case and their applications to the experimental data in fluid mechanics have been considered by Dallard and Spedding (1993). Spedding et al. (1993) applied the wavelet transform analytical tools to obtain a space-scale decomposition of a 2-D surface wave field. Lewalle (1994a) explored the application of wavelet transforms to some equations of fluid mechanics. The wavelet-based algorithm was formulated by Lewalle (1994b) as sequences of modular algorithms that characterized and/or enhance specific features of dynamical interest. The velocity signals in the inner mixing layer of a coaxial jet were analyzed by the wavelet transform in order to analyze the dominance of non-periodic vortices at a given time scale (Lewalle et al., 1994). Higuchi et al. (1994) applied wavelet analysis to map the intermittent near-periodic structures in the wake of two flat plates. Wang and Brasseur (1993) developed the three dimensional wavelet transform as a Fourier-spectral space filter to analyze the anisotropic turbulence structure from the results of the direct numerical simulation, and Brasseur (1994) has also discussed the relationships between multi-dimensional continuous physical Fourier and wavelet spaces. A wavelet decomposition of fluctuating velocities in a planar jet was used to the Reynolds stress in scale space by Gordeyev and Thomas (1995). Iima and Toh (1995) applied wavelet analysis to analyzing the energy transfer processes within and across scales due to spatial structures. Zimin and Hussain (1995) developed a simple model for the locally isotropic turbulence using a vector wavelet decomposition of the velocity field and applied it to representing the small-scale turbulence in LES schemes. Li and Nozaki (1995a) displayed very different scale eddies, the breakdown of a large eddy and the successive branching of a large eddy structure in the plane turbulent jet by analyzing the velocity signals at various positions with the wavelet analysis. In order to reveal self-similarity structure of the eddies in the plane turbulent jet, Li and Nozaki (1995b, 1996) proposed a wavelet auto-correlation analysis. The wavelet auto-correlation analysis is a new useful combination of familiar techniques of signal processing which can decompose auto-correlation of arbitrary signals in both scale and time delay, thus overcoming classical limitations of auto-correlation which only describes auto-correlation by time delay.

The major objective of the present investigation is first to propose a new cross-correlation, which is called a wavelet cross-correlation and characterizes the statistical cross-correlation of two arbitrary signals in terms of scale and time delay. The wavelet cross-correlation will overcome limitations of the classical cross-correlation which only describes the cross-correlation of two signals by time delay. Until now, the classical correlation analysis has played an important role, but the information of coherence in frequency space can not been obtained yet. This information is very important for analyzing similarity structure of two signals whether in fluid engineering or other fields.

Finally, the velocity signals at various positions in a plane turbulent jet are analyzed by the wavelet cross-correlation analysis and reveal the coherent structure of the eddies.

BASICS OF WAVELET TRANSFORM

It is now well-known that for any function $f(t) \in L^2(\Re)$ ($L^2(\Re)$ denotes the Hilbert space of measurable and square-integrable one-dimensional function) the wavelet transform (Holschneider, 1995) can be defined as

$$Wf(b,a) = \frac{1}{a} \int_{-\infty}^{\infty} f(t)\overline{\psi}\left(\frac{t-b}{a}\right)dt, \qquad (1)$$

where $Wf(b,a)$ is called the wavelet coefficient, a and b are the wavelet scale (inverse wavenumber) and analyzing position respectively. $\psi(t)$ is a function of $L^2(\Re)$ called an analyzing wavelet or mother wavelet (here ‾ stands for complex conjugate), satisfying the following admissibility condition

$$C_\psi = \int_{-\infty}^{\infty} \frac{|\hat{\psi}(\omega)|^2}{|\omega|}d\omega < \infty. \qquad (2)$$

It is well known that some kind of functions, such as

Morlet, Mexican hat, Gabor and so on, are often used as an analyzing wavelet. The Mexican hat function is well-localized in time, although it has a poor frequency localization. But Morlet function has the very-high localization in frequency and is poor localized in time. The Gabor function has higher localization than Morlet function in the time space and is better localization than Mexican hat function in the frequency space. In this paper the following Gabor function (see Fig.1(a)) is used as an analyzing wavelet and called a Gabor wavelet:

$$\psi(t) = \left(\frac{\omega_0}{\gamma}\right)^{\frac{1}{2}} \pi^{-\frac{1}{4}} e^{\left(\frac{(\omega_0 t/\gamma)^2}{2} + i\omega_0 t\right)}, \qquad (3)$$

where $\gamma = \pi\sqrt{2/\ln 2}$. Its Fourier transform (see Fig.1(b)) is written as

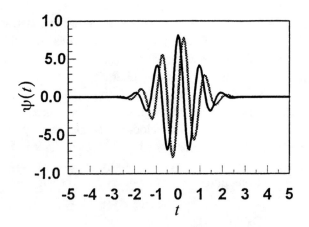

Fig.1 (a) The Gabor wavelet in the time representation (—— real part, ‥‥‥ imaginary part)

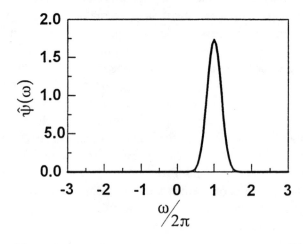

Fig.1 (b) The Gabor wavelet in the frequency representation

$$\hat{\psi}(\omega) = \frac{\gamma^{\frac{1}{2}}}{\pi^{\frac{1}{4}}}\left(\frac{2\pi}{\omega_0}\right)^{\frac{1}{2}} e^{\left[-\frac{\gamma^2}{2}\left(\frac{\omega}{\omega_0}-1\right)^2\right]}. \tag{4}$$

From Fig.1 it is obvious that $\psi(t)$ is localized around $t = 0$, and $\hat{\psi}(\omega)$ is localized around the central frequency $\omega = \omega_0$. In applications of signal processing it has been found that a particularly useful value for the central frequency ω_0 is the one for which the wavelet scale a presents the period or frequency. Therefore the central frequency is defined as $\omega_0 = 2\pi$ in this paper. Then $\frac{1}{a}\overline{\psi}\left(\frac{t-b}{a}\right)$ is localized around the position b and around the central frequency ω_0/a. Therefore, from Eq.(1) the wavelet coefficient can describe a signal as localized strength of the signal over a time-period plane.

The wavelet transform can also be expressed in Fourier space via

$$Wf(b,a) = \frac{1}{2\pi}\int_{-\infty}^{\infty}\hat{f}(\omega)\overline{\hat{\psi}}(a\omega)e^{ib\omega}d\omega, \tag{5}$$

where $\hat{f}$ and $\hat{\psi}$ are the Fourier transform of f and ψ respectively.

WAVELET CROSS-CORRELATION FUNCTION

It is a well-known fact that classical cross-correlation method determines the coherent structure of the two signals only by means of a time delay, and aims at examining their similarity behaviors relative to the different time delay. But this method can not determine the cross-correlation distributions at various periods.

The wavelet coefficients can describe a signal as strength of the signal at various periods and any time, which is a zero-mean random process. In order to obtain the coherent structure of the two signals $f_x(t)$ and $f_y(t)$ for various periods at any time delay, we use their wavelet coefficients $Wf_x(b,a)$ and $Wf_y(b,a)$ to define a new cross-correlation function, which is called a wavelet cross-correlation function $WC_{xy}(a,\tau)$, by the formula

$$WC_{xy}(a,\tau) = \lim_{T\to\infty}\frac{1}{T}\int_{-\frac{1}{2}T}^{\frac{1}{2}T}\overline{Wf_x}(b,a)Wf_y(b+\tau,a)db, \tag{6}$$

where τ is a time delay of the wavelet coefficients in the wavelet space, or the time delay of the two signals. Equation (6) can exhibit an important similarity feature, which is second-order statistical property, not only relative to a time delay τ, but also relative to a period a.

The wavelet cross-correlation function $WC_{xy}(a,\tau)$ can

also be written as

$$WC_{xy}(a,\tau) = \frac{1}{2\pi}\int_{-\infty}^{\infty}S_{xy}(\omega)\left|\hat{\psi}(a\omega)\right|^2 e^{i\tau\omega}d\omega, \tag{7}$$

where $S_{xy}(\omega)$ is the classical cross-spectrum. Here we define an local wavelet cross-spectrum function $WL_{xy}(a,\omega)$ as follows

$$WL_{xy}(a,\omega) = S_{xy}(\omega)\left|\hat{\psi}(a\omega)\right|^2. \tag{8}$$

Substituting Eq.(8) into Eq.(7), we obtain

$$WC_{xy}(a,\tau) = \frac{1}{2\pi}\int_{-\infty}^{\infty}WL_{xy}(a,\omega)e^{i\tau\omega}d\omega. \tag{9}$$

With the inverse Fourier transform the above equation becomes

$$WL_{xy}(a,\omega) = \int_{-\infty}^{\infty}WC_{xy}(a,\tau)e^{i\tau\omega}d\tau. \tag{10}$$

From Eqs. (9) and (10) it is obvious that $WL_{xy}(a,\omega)$ may be defined as the Fourier transform of $WC_{xy}(a,\tau)$, and $WC_{xy}(a,\tau)$ may be obtained from the inverse Fourier transform of $WL_{xy}(a,\omega)$. This relationship is very similar to that of the classical cross-correlation.

From the definition of the wavelet cross-correlation function in Eq. (6) or (7), it is evident that $WC_{xy}(a,\tau)$ is complex-valued and consists of a real part $RWC_{xy}(a,\tau)$ and a imaginary part $IWC_{xy}(a,\tau)$. $RWC_{xy}(a,\tau)$ can express the strength of correlation and the phase of correlation $\theta WC_{xy}(a,\tau)$ can be given by $IWC_{xy}(a,\tau)/RWC_{xy}(a,\tau)$.

In order to analyze the structural similarity of two arbitrary signals, it is convenient to introduce a wavelet cross-correlation coefficient $WR_{xy}(a,\tau)$ from the real part of the wavelet cross-correlation function $RWC_{xy}(a,\tau)$ by

$$WR_{xy}(a,\tau) = \frac{RWC_{xy}(a,\tau)}{\sqrt{RWC_x(a,0)RWC_y(a,0)}}. \tag{11}$$

Here, we will now describe some of main properties of the wavelet cross-correlation function. They are

(1) $WC_{xy}(a,\tau) = WC_{yx}(a,-\tau)$ or $WR_{xy}(a,\tau) = WR_{yx}(a,-\tau)$,

(2) $-1 \leq WR_{xy}(a,\tau) \leq 1$,

(3) $\frac{\partial}{\partial\tau}WC_{xy}(a,\tau) = \lim_{T\to\infty}\frac{1}{T}\int_{-\infty}^{\infty}\frac{\partial}{\partial b}\overline{Wf}_x(b,a)Wf_y(b+\tau,a)db$,

(4)

$$\frac{\partial^2}{\partial\tau^2}WC_{xy}(a,\tau) = -\lim_{T\to\infty}\frac{1}{T}\int_{-\infty}^{\infty}\frac{\partial}{\partial b}\overline{Wf}_x(b,a)\frac{\partial}{\partial b}Wf_y(b+\tau,a)db.$$

In this paper the classical cross-correlation function $C_{xy}(\tau)$ and its coefficient $R_{xy}(\tau)$ (such as Hino, 1977) for two signals $f_x(t)$ and $f_y(t)$ are also used and defined as

$$C_{xy}(\tau) = \lim_{T \to \infty} \frac{1}{T} \int_{-\frac{2}{T}}^{\frac{2}{T}} \overline{f_x(t)} f_y(t+\tau) dt,$$

$$R_{xy}(\tau) = \frac{C_{xy}(\tau)}{\sqrt{C_x(0)C_y(0)}}.$$

APPLICATION TO A PLANE TURBULENT JET
Experimental Conditions

The physics of a plane turbulent jet has been widely investigated for many years (Gutmak, 1976; Moum et al., 1979; Gervantes et al., 1981; Krothapalli et al., 1981; Antonia et al., 1983; Oler et al., 1984; Hsiao et al., 1994). Although the space-time correlation, along with the power spectra, is well established classical techniques for gaining information into the nature of large-scale eddy motion in a plane turbulent jet which exhibits an symmetric, periodic and apparent flapping motion in the similarity region, local period with respect to space-time are changing for the eddy motion and its structural similarity of various periods have not been clear yet. In the present study, we use the wavelet cross-correlation method to analyze the coherent structure of large scale eddy motions over a two-dimensional time-period plane in more detail.

A definition sketch of a plane jet is shown in Fig.2, where x is the streamwise coordinate, y is the lateral coordinate. The jet is generated by a blower-type wind tunnel having flow-straightening elements, screens, settling length and a 24:1 contraction leading to a 350x25 mm nozzle. For all measurements, the jet is operated at a constant Reynolds number Re=3330 (exit velocity is 2m/s) based upon nozzle width. The velocity of the x-component of the plane jet is measured simultaneously using two standard hot wire probes located in the (x,y)-plane. The recording frequency is 2 kHz and the record length is 1.5 seconds. Two types of measurements presented in this investigation are in Fig.2, while the different probe locations used in the two types are listed in Table 1. They are described in the following subsections.

Wavelet Cross-Correlation on the Center Line (Type I)

The wavelet cross-correlation coefficients $WR_{xy}(a,\tau)$ of the x-component of the velocities are determined for varying Δx separation distance along the jet center line at

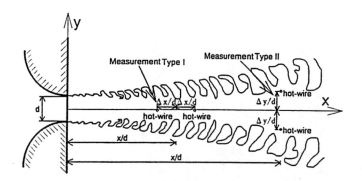

Fig.2 Sketch of the experimental configuration

Table 1 Probe Configurations

(a) Measurements type I

x/d	5	6	7	8	9	10	11	12	13	14	15
$\Delta x/d$	0.5,1	0.5,1	0.5,1	0.5,1	0.5,1	0.5,1	0.5,1	0.5,1	0.5,1	0.5,1	0.5,1
	1.5	1.5,2	1.5,2	1.5,2	1.5,2	1.5,2	1.5,2	1.5,2	1.5,2	1.5,2	1.5,2
			2.5	2.5	2.5	2.5					

(b) Measurements type II

x/d	5	6	7	8	9	10
$\Delta y/d$	0.25, 0.5	0.25, 0.5	0.25, 0.5	0.25, 0.5	0.25, 0.5	0.25, 0.5
	0.75, 1	0.75, 1	0.75,1	0.75,1	0.75,1	0.75,1
	1.25		1.25 ,1.5	1.25 ,1.5	1.25 ,1.5	1.25 ,1.5
				1.75	1.75	1.75, 2

x/d stations of 5, and are shown on the (a,τ) B&W plane representation in Fig.3. respectively. Under these B&W plates, the results of the classical cross-correlation coefficients $R_{xy}(\tau)$ are also illustrated.

At first, let us analyze the wavelet cross-correlation of the two velocity fluctuations for $\frac{2\Delta x}{d} = 2$ apart at $x/d = 5$ on the jet center line. Making a comparison between $WR_{xy}(a,\tau)$ and $R_{xy}(\tau)$ in Fig.3 (a), we find that the positive and negative peaks of $WR_{xy}(a,\tau)$ in the large-period region correspond to large peaks of $R_{xy}(\tau)$, and the peaks of $WR_{xy}(a,\tau)$ in small period region equivalent to small peaks of $R_{xy}(\tau)$. From the distributions of $WR_{xy}(a,\tau)$ the branching structures, in which the correlation of a large period consists of that of small periods, is observed clearly. In other words, the large-scale periodic coherent structure (or large eddy motion) contains that of smaller scale (or small eddy motions). From Fig.3 (a) as the time delay τ increases, the

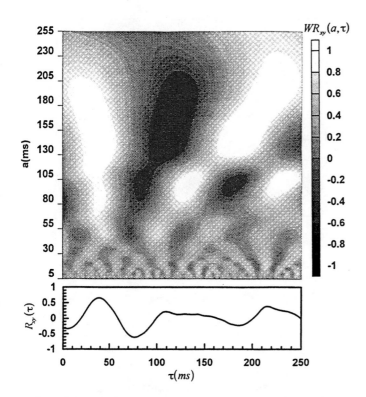

Fig.3 (a) Wavelet cross-correlation analysis of the two velocity fluctuations at $x/d = 5$, $2\Delta x/d = 2$

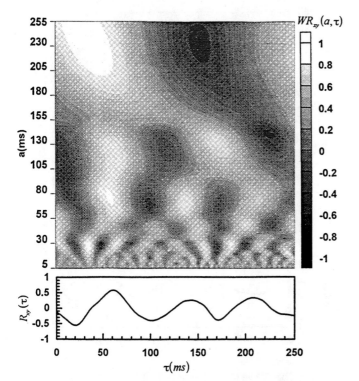

Fig.3 (b) Wavelet cross-correlation analysis of the two velocity fluctuations at $x/d = 5$, $2\Delta x/d = 3$

succession of positive and negative peaks for various periods are observed. The dominant feature of this figure is the periodic oscillation at $a=100ms$ and $150ms$ after delay time 85 ms and 100ms respectively. For $\tau > 40ms$ 4 cycles of oscillations at $a=50ms$ can be observed. That indicates that the periodic motions of $a=50$, 100 and 150ms pass through the mixing region. For small-scale motion there is a weaker pattern in the 20-30ms range and only weaker periodic motions appear. The first positive peak of $R_{xy}(\tau)$ corresponds to the positive peaks of $WR_{xy}(a,\tau)$ at $a = 50 \sim 180ms$ which gives the periods of motion. Because $WR_{xy}(a,\tau)$ has a strongly negative peak at period $a = 80ms$ at zero time delay, $R_{xy}(\tau)$ exhibits a negative value. But this does not mean the negative correlation at all period range.

Then, Fig.3 (b) illustrates the wavelet cross-correlation coefficients $WR_{xy}(a,\tau)$ for the two velocity fluctuations of $2\Delta x/d = 3$ apart at $x/d = 5$ on the jet center line. The main features are the periodic oscillation at $a = 230ms$, $a = 70ms$ (for $\tau > 63ms$), $a = 50ms$ (for $\tau > 85ms$) and $a = 30ms$. Nearly-periodic correlation peaks at $a = 125 - 140ms$ for $\tau > 63ms$ seem to increase significantly. It is well-known that the classical cross-correlation of velocity fluctuations have been used extensively to determine the convection velocities by which the vortices are convected in different turbulent flows. Although Goldschmide et al. (1981) considered both broadband and wave-number-dependent convection velocities, from the distribution of peaks for $WR_{xy}(a,\tau)$ we can easily determine the convection velocities for various periods by the following way. The convection velocity for some period is defined as the ratio of the longitudinal separation distance Δx between two probes and the time delay τ_{max} between local maximum or minimum of $WR_{xy}(a,\tau)$ at the period, or the ratio of the longitudinal separation distance Δx and the period a_{max} at which $WR_{xy}(a,\tau)$ has local maximum or minimum value. From the distribution of peaks of $WR_{xy}(a,\tau)$ for various periods, it is found the convection velocities is period dependent. The time delay between local maximum or local minimum of $WR_{xy}(a,\tau)$ indicates that the large-scale motion moves slower than the small scales.

Wavelet Cross-Correlation in the Mixing Layer (Type II)

Type II measurements were performed for the probes at equal distance from the jet center line and at various locations. The B&W plate of the wavelet cross-correlation coefficients $WR_{xy}(a,\tau)$ of the two velocities for $2\frac{\Delta y}{d} = 0.5$ and $2\frac{\Delta y}{d} = 2$ separations at $x/d = 5$ in the mixing layer is shown in Fig.4. They all exhibit a positive value of the wavelet cross-correlation coefficients $WR_{xy}(a,\tau)$ at zero time delay and periodic oscillation for some periods as the time delay increases. This indicates that the symmetric and coherent structural motions for some scales exist in the mixing layer.

For $2\frac{\Delta y}{d} = 0.5$ separation in Fig.4(a), the dominant distributions of the periodic oscillations at $a = 180ms$, $a = 80ms$ and $a = 45ms$ are evident, and weaker periodic peaks exist in the range of $a < 30ms$. This implies that the two-dimensionality of the vortex street contains three periodic vortices and some irregular small vortices on opposite sides of the centerline.

With $2\frac{\Delta y}{d} = 2$ apart in Fig.4(b), the obvious periodic oscillations happen at $a = 160ms$ and $a = 65ms$. This two periods are the average period of occurrence of the vortical structures on opposite sides of the centerline. Comparing to Fig.4(a), the dominant scales of periodic motion decrease clearly with increasing separation distance $2\frac{\Delta y}{d}$ from the jet centerline..

At the downstream distance $x/d = 10$, the variation of $WR_{xy}(a,\tau)$ with $2\frac{\Delta y}{d} = 0.5$ separations are illustrated in Fig.5. In this figure, it is apparent that the strong periodic coherence occur at $a = 230ms$, $a = 105ms$, $a = 70ms$ (fading after $\tau = 110ms$) and $a = 50ms$, there are weaker periodic peaks at $a = 25ms$ and $a = 10ms$. It is well-known that the turbulent plane jet exhibits an apparent sideways and flapping type motion. The apparent flapping motion is generally detected by the negative correlation of the velocity on opposite sides of the jet centerline. In this study we can determine the flapping motion in period space. From the positive peaks of $WR_{xy}(a,\tau)$ at zero time delay, the symmetric periodic motions are still remained at $a = 230ms$, $a = 70ms$ and $a = 50ms$. However, because $WR_{xy}(a,\tau)$ at $a = 105ms$ and small period range exhibit a negative peak at zero time delay, they appear the apparent flapping behaviors which are hidden in the large-scale symmetric periodic motion.

From these results, it is clearly that the apparent

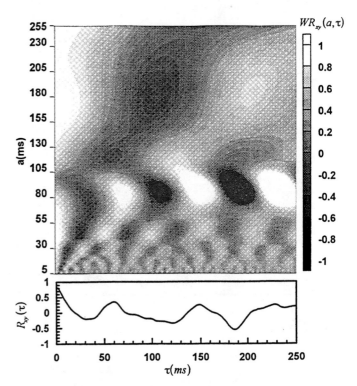

Fig.4 (a) Wavelet cross-correlation analysis of the two velocity fluctuations at $x/d = 5$, $2\Delta y/d = 0.5$

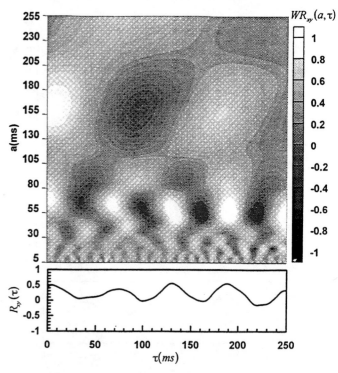

Fig.4 (b) Wavelet cross-correlation analysis of the two velocity fluctuations at $x/d = 5$, $2\Delta y/d = 2$

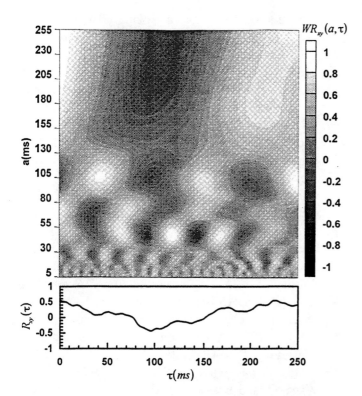

Fig.5 Wavelet cross-correlation analysis of the two velocity fluctuations at $x/d=10$, $2\Delta y/d=0.5$

flapping behavior appears firstly in the medium periodic motions. From the distributions of the classical cross-correlation, it is difficult to obtain the information about the growth of the apparent flapping motions for various scales.

CONCLUSIONS

The main conclusions are now summarized. A new combination of familiar techniques of signal processing, which is called a wavelet cross-correlation analysis, is proposed and its main properties are also described. As the practical application to fluid engineering, the cross-correlation of the two velocity signals in a plane turbulent jet at various positions are analyzed for revealing the similar structure of the various scale motions in terms of time delay and period. The following results can be drawn.
(1)The peaks of $WR_{xy}(a,\tau)$ in large period region correspond to large peaks of $R_{xy}(\tau)$, and the peaks of $WR_{xy}(a,\tau)$ in small period region are equivalent to small peaks of $R_{xy}(\tau)$.
(2)From the distribution of $WR_{xy}(a,\tau)$, the structural

similarity of various scale motions can be easily determined in terms of period and time delay.
(3) The branching structures of $WR_{xy}(a,\tau)$, in which the cross-correlation of a large period consists of that of small periods, in other words, a large-scale motion contains the motions of smaller scale, is observed clearly.
(4) By the time between local maximum or minimum of $WR_{xy}(a,\tau)$ or the period of peaks, the convective velocities of various scales can be easily computed, and it is found that the large-scale motion moves slower than that of the small-scale.
(5)The symmetric periodic eddy motions at various periods appear in the mixing layer at $x/d=5$.
(6)The large eddies still remain symmetric and periodic motion in the mixing layer at $x/d=10$. But the apparent flapping behavior appears in the region of medium periodic motions.

It is believed that the wavelet cross-correlation analysis can be widely applied to various fields for revealing structural similarity, involving signal processing and pattern recognition.

ACKNOWLEDGMENT

This work was performed as part of the research which was supported by a scientific research fund granted by Japanese Ministry of Education, Science and Culture (No.07750202).

REFERENCES

Antonia, R. A., Browne, L. W., Rajagopalan, S. and Chambers, A. J., 1983, "On the Organized Motion of a Turbulent Plane Jet", *J. Fluid Mech.*, Vol.134, pp.49-66.

Brasseur, J. G., 1994, "The Wavelet Decomposition: Locality in Fourier Space, Locality in Physical Space, and the Relationship between the Two", *AIAA Paper 94-2280*.

Dallard, T. and Browand, F.K., 1993a, "Scale Transitions at Defect Sites in the Mixing Layer: Application of the 2-D Arc Wavelet Transform", *J. Fluid Mech.*, Vol.247, pp.339-368.

Dallard, T. and Spedding, G.R., 1993b, "2-D Wavelet Transform: Generalisation of the Hardy Space and Application to Experimental Studies", *Eur. J. Mech. B/Fluids*, Vol.12, pp.107-134.

Gervantes, de Gortari, J. G., and Goldschmidt, V. W., 1981, "The Apparent Flapping Motion of a Turbulent Plane Jet - Further Experimental Results", *ASME Journal of Fluids Engineering*, Vol.103, No.1, pp.119-126.

Gordeyev, S. V. and Thomas F. O., 1995, "Measurement of Reynolds Stress Reversal in a Planar Jet by Means of a Wavelet Decomposition", *Turbulent Flows ASME*, FED-Vol.208, pp.49-54.

Goldshmidt, V. W., Young, M. F. and Ott, E. S., 1981, "Turbulent Convective Velocities (Broadband and Wavenumber Dependent) in a Plane Jet", *J. Fluid Mech.*, Vol.105, pp.327-345.

Gutmark, E., 1976, "The Planar Turbulent Jet, *J. Fluid Mech.*, Vol.73, Part 3, pp.465-495.

Higuchi, H., Lewalle J. and Crane P., 1994, "On the Structure of a Two-Dimension Wake behind a pair of Flat Plates", *Physics Fluids*, Vol.6, No.1, pp.297-305.

Hino, M., 1977, "Spectral Analysis" (in Japanese), Asakura Press.

Holschneider, M., 1995, "Wavelets An Analysis Tool", Oxford Science Publications.

Hsiao, F. B. and Huang, J. M., 1994, "On the Dynamics of Flow Structure Development in an Excited Plane Jet", *ASME Journal of Fluids Engineering*, Vol.116, No.4, pp.714-720.

Iima, M. and Toh, S., 1995, "Wavelet Analysis of the Energy Transfer Caused by Convective Terms: Application to the Burgers Shock", *Physical Review E*, Vol.52, No.6, pp.6189-6201.

Krothapalli, A., Baganoff, D., and Karamcheti, K., 1981, "On the Mixing of a Rectangular Jet", *J. Fluid Mech.*, Vol.107, pp.201-220.

Lewalle, J., 1994a, "Wavelet Transforms of Some Equations of Fluid Mechanics", *Acta Mechanica*, Vol.104, pp.1-25.

Lewalle, J., 1994b, "Wavelet Analysis of Experimental Data: Some Methods and the Underlying Physics", *AIAA Paper* 94-2281.

Lewalle, J., Petagna P. and Buresti G., 1994, "Wavelet Statistics of the Near-Field Structure of a Coaxial Jet", *AIAA Paper* 94-2323.

Li, H., and Nozaki, T. 1995a, "Wavelet Analysis for the Plane Turbulent Jet (Analysis of Large Eddy Structure)", *Transactions of JSME International Journal, Fluids and Thermal Engineering*, Vol.38, No.4, pp.525-531.

Li, H., and Nozaki, T., 1995b, "Wavelet Auto-correlation Analysis of a Plane Turbulent Jet", *Proceedings of the Seventh International Symposium of Flow Visualization*, Seattle USA, pp.365-370.

Li, H., and Nozaki, T., 1996, "Wavelet Auto-correlation Analysis (Application to the Plane Turbulent Jet)", Submitted to *Transactions of ASME, Journal of Fluids Engineering*.

Morlet, J., 1981, "Sampling Theory and Wave Propagation", *Proc. 51st Annu. Meet. Soc. Explor. Geophys.*, Los Angeles.

Moum, J. N., Kawall, J. G., and Keffer, J. F., 1979, "Structure Features of the Plane Turbulent Jet", *Physics Fluids*, Vol.22, No.7, pp.1240-1249.

Oler, J. W., and Goldschmidt, V. W., 1984, "Coherent Structures in the Similarity Region of Two-Dimensional Turbulent Jets", *ASME Journal of Fluids Engineering*, Vol.106, No.2, pp.187-192.

Spedding, G.R., Browand , F.K., Huang N.E. and Long S.R., 1993, "A 2-D Complex Wavelet Analysis of an Unsteady Wind-Generated Surface Wave Field", *Dynamics of Atmospheres and Oceans*, Vol.20, pp.55-77.

Wang, Q. and Brasseur, J. G., 1993, "Application of Nonsymmetrical 3D Wavelet Filters to the Analysis of Anisotropic Data", Forum on Turbulent Flows ASME 1993, FED-Vol.155, pp.137-142.

Zimin, V. and Hussain, F., 1995, "Wavelet Based Model for Small-Scale Turbulence", *Physics Fluids*, Vol.7, No.12, pp.2925-2927.

FED-Vol. 238, 1996 Fluids Engineering Division Conference
Volume 3
ASME 1996

CONFINED SWIRLING FLOW SIMULATION
USING SPECTRAL GALERKIN AND FINITE VOLUME METHODS

Alexander Yu. Gelfgat,   Pinhas Z. Bar-Yoseph[*],   and   Alexander Solan

Computational Mechanics Laboratory, Faculty of Mechanical Engineering,
Technion - Israel Institute of Technology, Haifa 32000, Israel

ABSTRACT

A numerical investigation of steady states, their stability, onset of oscillatory instability, and slightly supercritical unsteady regimes of an axisymmetric swirling flow of a Newtonian incompressible fluid in a closed circular cylinder with independently rotating top and bottom is presented. Influence of co– and counter–rotation of the bottom on steady flows, the vortex breakdown and the onset of the oscillatory instability is studied. Two different numerical approaches are applied. The global spectral Galerkin method is used for calculation of steady flows, analysis of their stability and weakly nonlinear analysis of bifurcations. The finite volume method is used for calculation of steady and supercritical unsteady flows. The values of the critical Reynolds number Re_{cr} and the frequency ω_{cr} of oscillations are calculated for different values of the aspect ratio γ and the rotation ratio ξ. A weakly nonlinear asymptotic analysis of slightly supercritical flows is carried out. Various patterns of steady flows, the dominant perturbations of steady flows, and patterns of unsteady flows are discussed. In particular, the new results for $Re_{cr}(\gamma)$ and $\omega_{cr}(\gamma)$ at $\xi = 1$ show that the oscillatory instability sets in as a result of a Hopf bifurcation.

INTRODUCTION

A confined axisymmetric swirling flow in a cylinder with independently rotating top and bottom and stationary sidewall is investigated numerically using two different numerical approaches – a global Galerkin method and a second order finite volume method based on the SIMPLE algorithm and three–level scheme in time. A particular case – flow in a cylinder with a rotating lid has been intensively studied experimentally (Escudier, 1984; Roesner, 1989) and numerically (Lopez and Perry, 1992; Sørensen and

Christensen, 1995; Gelfgat et al. 1995,1996a,b,c). It is known that at a certain value of the Reynolds number Re a vortex breakdown appears in this flow, and that at another value of Re the transition from steady to oscillatory state takes place. Steady and oscillatory flows observed in experiments are well reproduced numerically. However, a more thorough study is needed to complete the investigation of instability phenomena and transitions between different states of the flow. In the present work the steady flows, their stability, oscillatory instability onset and weakly nonlinear supercritical states of the flow are investigated numerically. The global Galerkin spectral method is used for the calculation of steady states, analysis of their stability and weakly nonlinear analysis of supercritical flows. The finite volume method is used for the calculation of steady states and for the calculation of slightly supercritical oscillatory flows by the solution of the full unsteady Navier-Stokes equation.

As was previously shown (Gelfgat et al., 1996a,b,c) that the vortex breakdown takes place not as a result of instability but as a continuous change of the steady states with the variation of the Reynolds number. It was shown also that a weak *counter–rotation* of the bottom suppresses the vortex breakdown. Conversely, a weak *co–rotation* promotes the appearance of the vortex breakdown in the flow. Stronger *co–rotation* may lead to the detachment of the recirculation zone from the axis and to the formation of a separation vortex ring.

Transition from steady to oscillatory state for different values of the aspect ratio and the rotation ratio was analyzed in Gelfgat et al. (1995, 1996a,b,c). The dependence of the critical Reynolds number on the aspect ratio for the case of rotating top and stationary bottom was studied in Gelfgat et

[*] Corresponding author, Fax: 972-4-832-4533, e-mail: merbygr@cmlp.technion.ac.il

al. (1996a). The dependence of the critical Reynolds number on the rotation ratio for fixed aspect ratio was studied in Gelfgat et al. (1996b,c). In the present work the attention is focused on the dependence of the critical Reynolds number on the aspect ratio in the case when the top and the bottom rotate with the same angular velocity ($\xi=1$). It is shown that the transition from steady to oscillatory flow takes place due to a Hopf bifurcation. Patterns of the most unstable perturbations and snapshots of the supercritical oscillatory flows are reported and discussed.

FORMULATION OF THE PROBLEM

The axisymmetric flow of an incompressible Newtonian fluid is described by the axisymmetric momentum and continuity equations with the corresponding boundary conditions. The problem in the dimensionless form is formulated in the domain $0 \leq r \leq 1$, $0 \leq z \leq \gamma$ for the velocity vector $\mathbf{v} = (v_r, v_\varphi, v_z)^T$ and the pressure p as

$$\frac{\partial \mathbf{v}}{\partial t} + (\mathbf{v} \cdot \nabla)\mathbf{v} = -\nabla p + \frac{1}{Re}\Delta \mathbf{v}, \quad \nabla \cdot \mathbf{v} = 0 . \quad (1,2)$$

$$v_r = v_\varphi = \frac{\partial v_z}{\partial r} = 0 \qquad \text{at } 0 \leq z \leq \gamma, r = 0; \quad (3)$$

$$\mathbf{v} = 0 \qquad \text{at } 0 \leq z < \gamma, r = 1; \quad (4)$$

$$\mathbf{v} = \xi r \, \mathbf{e}_\varphi \qquad \text{at } 0 \leq r < 1, z = 0; \quad (5)$$

$$\mathbf{v} = r \, \mathbf{e}_\varphi \qquad \text{at } 0 \leq r < 1, z = \gamma. \quad (6)$$

Here $Re = \Omega^*_{top} R^{*2}/\nu^*$ is the Reynolds number, $\xi = \Omega^*_{bottom}/\Omega^*_{top}$ the rotation ratio, and $\gamma = H^*/R^*$ the aspect ratio of the cylinder; Ω^*_{top} and Ω^*_{bottom} are the angular velocities of the top and the bottom respectively; $\mathbf{e}_\varphi$ is the unit vector in the azimuthal direction.

NUMERICAL TECHNIQUE

The main results of this investigation are obtained using global Galerkin spectral method. The approach is as in Gelfgat et al. (1996a). The meridional velocity vector $\mathbf{u}=(v_r,v_z)^T$ and the azimuthal velocity component v_φ are approximated by the truncated series

$$\mathbf{u} \approx \sum_{i=0}^{N_r} \sum_{j=0}^{N_z} c_{ij}(t) \, \mathbf{u}_{ij}(r,z), \quad (7)$$

$$v_\varphi \approx \Phi(r,z) + \sum_{i=0}^{M_r} \sum_{j=0}^{M_z} d_{ij}(t) \, w_{ij}(r,z) . \quad (8)$$

Here $c_{ij}(t)$ and $d_{ij}(t)$ are time-dependent coefficients to be found; N_r, N_z, M_r, M_z are numbers of basis functions used for the approximation of the velocity in radial and axial directions; $\mathbf{u}_{ij}$ and w_{ij} are vector and scalar basis functions defined as in Gelfgat et al. (1996a):

$$\mathbf{u}_{ij}(r,z) = \left\{ \begin{array}{l} \frac{1}{2}r \sum_{m=0}^{4} a_{im}T_{i+m}(r) \sum_{m=0}^{4} b_{jm}U_{j+m-1}\left(\frac{z}{\gamma}\right) \\ -\sum_{m=0}^{4} a_{im}\bar{U}_{i+m-1}(r) \sum_{m=0}^{4} \frac{b_{jm}}{2(j+m)}T_{j+m}\left(\frac{z}{\gamma}\right) \end{array} \right\} \quad (9)$$

$$w_{ij}(r,z) = r\left(T_i(r) + p_iT_{i+1}(r)\right)\left(T_j\left(\frac{z}{\gamma}\right) + q_{1j}T_{j+1}\left(\frac{z}{\gamma}\right) + q_{2j}T_{j+2}\left(\frac{z}{\gamma}\right)\right) \quad (10)$$

where T_n and U_n are the Chebyshev polynomials of the 1st and 2nd type respectively and $\bar{U}_n = T_{n+1} + (n+1)rU_n$. Using the relation $\frac{d}{dx}T_{n+1}(x) = 2(n+1)U_n(x)$ it is easy to see that the basis functions (9) are divergence-free.

The function $\Phi(r,z)$ is defined as the solution of the Stokes problem $\Delta v_\varphi = 0$ with the corresponding boundary conditions (3-6) for v_φ. Since the function $\Phi(r,z)$ satisfies the inhomogeneous boundary conditions (5,6), all the boundary conditions for the basis functions w_{ij} are homogeneous.

Substitution of (7-10) into the boundary conditions (3-6) defines a system of linear algebraic equations for the coefficients a_{im}, b_{jm}, p_i, q_{1j} and q_{2j}. Once these coefficients are determined (with the help of symbolic computations), the approximations (8) satisfy all boundary conditions and the continuity equation analytically.

Since the basis functions $\mathbf{u}_{ij}$ are divergence-free and satisfy no-penetration boundary conditions the pressure gradient is orthogonal to each of the functions $\mathbf{u}_{ij}$. No approximation for the pressure is necessary because the projection of the meridional part of the equations (1) on the basis $\mathbf{u}_{ij}$ eliminates the pressure from the numerical model. Once the Galerkin method with the basis functions (9,10) is applied, the problem (1-7) is reduced to a system of ordinary differential equations (ODEs) for the time-dependent coefficients $c_{ij}(t)$ and $d_{ij}(t)$ that can be written in the following form (the summation convention on repeated indices is assumed):

$$\frac{dX_i}{dt} = F_i(\mathbf{X}; Re) = L_{ij}X_j + N_{ijk}X_jX_k + Q_i . \quad (11)$$

Here X_i stands for one of the coefficients $c_{ij}(t)$ or $d_{ij}(t)$.

The completely explicit form of the system (11) allows us to use standard numerical methods developed for an ODE system both for obtaining steady and unsteady solutions and for the investigation of the stability of solutions. Thus, a stationary solution $\mathbf{X}^0$ of the system (11) is unstable if the Jacobian matrix calculated at $\mathbf{X}=\mathbf{X}^0$ has at least one eigenvalue $\lambda=\lambda^r+i\lambda^i$ with positive real part $\lambda^r > 0$. Thus, the investigation of stability for a given aspect ratio requires the calculation of a value of Re such that the real part of the dominant eigenvalue (eigenvalue with the maximal real part) $\Lambda=\Lambda^r+i\Lambda^i$ is zero: $\Lambda^r = 0$. The eigenvector $\mathbf{V}$ corresponding to the dominant eigenvalue Λ with $\Lambda^r = 0$ ($J_{mk}V_k = \Lambda V_m = i\Lambda^i \mathbf{V}_m$) defines the most unstable perturbation of the system (11). The corresponding perturbation of the flow may be calculated using series (8) with coefficients c_{ij} and d_{ij} defined as components of the eigenvector $\mathbf{V}$.

If for some value of Re the dominant eigenvalue has zero real part $\Lambda^r = 0$ and $\frac{\partial \Lambda^r}{\partial Re} \neq 0$, then $\Lambda^i \neq 0$ means a bifurcation to a periodic solution, called a Hopf bifurcation (Hopf, 1942). In the case of the Hopf bifurcation the imaginary part Λ^i of the dominant eigenvalue gives an estimate of the circular frequency of the oscillatory solution branching from the steady state after the onset of the oscillatory instability. The branching periodic solution may be approximated as (Hassard et al., 1981):

$$Re = Re_{cr} + \mu \varepsilon^2 + O(\varepsilon^4), \quad T(Re) = \frac{2\pi}{\omega_0}\left[1 + \tau \varepsilon^2 + O(\varepsilon^4)\right],$$

$$X(t;Re) = X^0(Re_{cr}) + \varepsilon \, \text{Real}\left[\mathbf{V} \exp\left(\frac{2\pi i}{T}t\right)\right] + O(\varepsilon^2). \tag{12}$$

Here $(Re - Re_{cr})$ is the supercriticality, T is the period of oscillations, and X is the asymptotic solution of the ODE system (11) for the Reynolds number defined in (12a). ε is a formal small parameter, μ and τ are coefficients to be calculated. The parameter μ defines the direction of bifurcation: the bifurcation is supercritical if $\mu > 0$, and subcritical if $\mu < 0$. A numerical algorithm for the calculation of the parameters μ and τ is described in Hassard et al. (1981). Some details of application of this algorithm to the dynamic system (11) and the corresponding results for the considered problem may be found in Gelfgat et al. 1996a.

The finite volume method based on the three time levels pressure-correction SIMPLE algorithm was used to verify the accuracy of the spectral method. The comparison was made both for steady and for oscillatory states of the flow.

TEST CALCULATIONS

A comparison of results obtained by the Galerkin method and the finite volume method for a steady state at $Re = 2000$, $\gamma = 2.5$, $\xi = 0$ is shown in Table 1. The comparison of local maxima and minima of the stream function ψ and the azimuthal vorticity η is presented. The two most accurate results for 38×38 basis functions and for the 300×300 stretched grid are shown in bold. As it is seen, 30×30 basis functions of the Galerkin method provide the accuracy comparable with that obtained using the 300×300 stretched finite volume grid, while the numerical solution obtained on the uniform grid, even with 300×300 nodes, is not very accurate. The obvious reason for this is the existence of thin boundary layers near the rotating top and the sidewall of the cylinder.

The values of the critical Reynolds number and the critical frequency of oscillations obtained by the Galerkin method are compared with the results of time marching calculations in Table 2. The use of 26×26 basis functions provides rather good approximation of the critical parameters, which are in agreement with the results of time marching numerical integration. Note that in the present time marching solution

by the finite volume method the critical Re was not calculated. The frequencies shown in Table 2 are calculated by FFT from time series corresponding to slightly supercritical flows. Further increase of the number of the basis functions up to 38×38 showed, that in the considered cases 26×26 basis functions provide at least 3 correct digits of Re_{cr} and 4 correct digits of ω_{cr}.

Slightly supercritical flows asymptotically approximated using (12) and calculated by the finite volume method were compared in Gelfgat et al. (1996a).

RESULTS

One of the objectives of the present work is to investigate the influence of *co-* and *counter-rotation* of the bottom on the vortex breakdown which takes place in a cylinder with rotating top. It was found that a weak *counter-rotation* suppresses vortex breakdown while a weak *co-rotation* may induce vortex breakdown in the flow. This is in agreement with the experiments (Roesner, 1989) and with the experimental and numerical investigation of the vortex breakdown in the polar region between two rotating spheres (Bar-Yoseph et al., 1992).

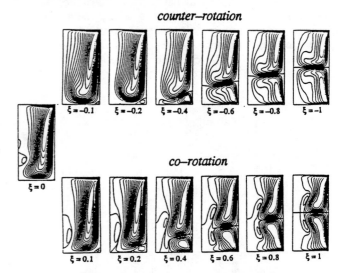

Fig.1 Streamlines of steady flows for different values of ξ. ($Re = 2000$, $\gamma = 2$)

An example of flows with *co-* and *counter-rotating* bottom is shown in Fig.1 for $\gamma = 2$. With decrease of the rotation ratio from $\xi = 0$ to $\xi = -1$ the separation vortex bubble disappears (already at $\xi < -0.1$) and another counter-clockwise meridional vortex grows. At $\xi = -1$ the meridional flow consists of two antisymmetric vortices. The influence of *co-rotation* is different. Weak *co-rotation* leads to growth of the separation vortex bubble. Stronger *co-rotation* leads to the detachment of the recirculation zone from the axis ($\xi = 0.6$) and to the formation of two additional meridional vortex rings. At $\xi = 1$ the whole meridional flow (that consists of two main vortices and two separation vortex rings) becomes antisymmetric with respect to the midplane of the cylinder.

The appearance and evolution of the vortex breakdown with the increase of the Reynolds number in the antisymmetric case $\xi = 1$ is shown in Fig.2 for $\gamma = 2$. Here, two antisymmetric separation vortex bubbles appear when the Reynolds number reaches a value $Re = 500$. With the increase of the Reynolds number the size of the separation bubbles grows. With further increase of Re the upper and the lower stagnation points on the axis of the cylinder move towards the middle stagnation point at $r = 0$, $z = \gamma/2$ ($Re = 1000$). When the Reynolds number increases further, the three stagnation points coincide and the recirculation zones detach from the axis ($Re = 1500$). More details about the influence of *co-* and *counter-rotation* on the vortex breakdown in cylinders with different aspect ratios are reported in Gelfgat et al. (1996b,c).

According to the results of the stability analysis the appearance and disappearance of the vortex breakdown (Figs.1 and 2) are not due to instability. This means that all the eigenvalues of the spectrum of the problem linearized in the vicinity of the steady state (spectrum of the Jacobian matrix, see above) have negative real parts. The appearance and disappearance of the vortex breakdown take place along a single branch of a steady axisymmetric solution. Steady states remain stable until the oscillatory instability sets in. For more details about the cylinder with rotating top and stationary bottom see Gelfgat et al. (1996a).

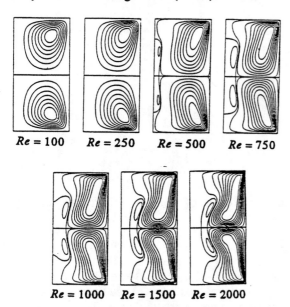

Fig.2. Streamlines of steady flows for different values of Re ($\xi = 1$, $\gamma = 2$). Effect of *co-rotation*.

Analysis of oscillatory instability onset was carried out for $\xi = 0$, $1 \leq \gamma \leq 3.5$ in Gelfgat et al. (1996a) and for $\gamma = 1.5$, $-1 \leq \xi \leq 1$ in Gelfgat et al. (1996b,c). Here new results for $\xi = 1$, $1 \leq \gamma \leq 3$ are described. For $\xi = 1$ the

numerical studies of the full unsteady problem were carried out by Lopez (1995) for $\gamma = 3$ and by Gelfgat et al. (1996c) for $\gamma = 1.5$. These studies showed that slightly supercritical oscillatory flows remain symmetric with respect to the plane $z = \gamma/2$. This allows us to consider the stability problem in one half of the whole flow region by imposing the boundary conditions of symmetry at $z=0$. Namely, boundary conditions (5) and (6) are replaced by

$$v_z = \frac{\partial v_r}{\partial z} = 0 \qquad \text{at } 0 \leq r < 1, z = 0; \qquad (13)$$

$$v = r\, e_\varphi \qquad \text{at } 0 \leq r < 1, z = \frac{\gamma}{2}. \qquad (14)$$

The dependencies $Re_{cr}(\gamma)$ and $\omega_{cr}(\gamma)$ for $\xi = 1$, are shown in Fig.3. Along the whole neutral curve $Re_{cr}(\gamma)$ the oscillatory instability sets in as a result of the Hopf bifurcation, which is indicated by the change of the sign of the real part of two complex conjugate eigenvalues. Other conditions of the Hopf theorem (Hopf, 1948) also hold. This is in contradiction with the conclusion of Lopez (1995) whose straight-forward numerical solution of the full problem for $\gamma = 3$ showed that stable steady and oscillatory states may exist at the same value of the Reynolds number. Note, that the critical parameters obtained by Lopez (1995) and in the present study are very close (see Table 2). A possible explanation of the disagreement in the conclusion about the type of the bifurcation here and in Lopez (1995) is the following. The increments of the Reynolds number used in Lopez (1995) for increasing Re were about 1–2% or less. Using such small increments the computational process converged to a steady solution for $Re \leq 3200$. The present investigation showed that when the Reynolds number exceeds its critical value the dimensionless growth rate (e.g., positive real part of the dominant eigenvalue) remains of order 10^{-2}. This means that the dimensionless time necessary to increase the amplitude of the perturbation by a factor of e is about 10^2. The time step used in Lopez (1995) for numerical integration was 0.005, which means that several tens of thousands of time steps were needed to allow a small perturbation to grow to a significant value. Possibly, the numerical solutions in Lopez (1995) converged to steady states before the perturbation grew larger than the tolerance of the numerical method.

The curves $Re_{cr}(\gamma)$ and $\omega_{cr}(\gamma)$ (Fig.3) consist of four continuous branches which indicates that there are four different modes of the dominant perturbation. The eigenvector V of the Jacobian matrix J corresponding to the dominant eigenvalue Λ ($J_{mk}V_k = \Lambda V_m$, $\Lambda^r = 0$) defines the dominant perturbation of the stationary solution of the dynamical system (11). The oscillatory instability sets in as an appearance of oscillations with exponentially growing amplitude when the Reynolds number exceeds the value Re_{cr}. The distribution of this amplitude in the flow region coincides, within multiplication by a constant, with the distribution of the modulus of the most unstable perturbation (recall that the perturbation is a complex function). This means that the patterns of the absolute value of the perturbation describe the amplitude of the oscillatory state near the threshold of instability, and may give additional insight into the physics of the instability. The absolute values of the perturbations (amplitude of the most unstable mode) is chosen for plotting because this property does not depend on time and phase. It may be easily used for comparison of results obtained with different spatial discretizations as well as with different numerical approaches.

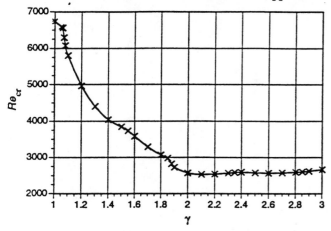

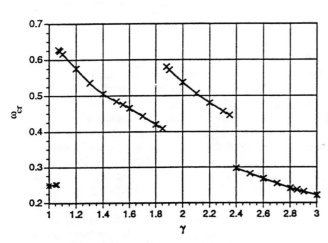

Fig.3. Stability diagram for $\xi = 1$, $1 \le \gamma \le 3$.
Re_{cr} and ω_{cr} versus γ.

Streamlines of steady flows at the critical values of parameters are shown in Fig.4, and the corresponding dominant perturbations of ψ and $\mathcal{M}_\varphi = rv_\varphi$ are shown in Fig.5. All flows are symmetric with respect to the horizontal midplane – the plots show the upper half of the flow domain. The four examples shown in Figs.4 and 5 correspond to the four continuous branches of the neutral curve $Re_{cr}(\gamma)$ (Fig.3). Figure 4 shows that the critical steady states are characterized by the existence of the detached vortex breakdown. Patterns of the perturbation of the stream function are different at the different branches of the neutral curve (Fig.5), while patterns of the perturbation of $\mathcal{M}_\varphi$ have a common feature – the global maximum of this perturbation is located on the plane

of symmetry $z = \gamma/2$ in the area of the vortex breakdown (the vertical line in the middle of plots in Fig.5 corresponds to the axis of the cylinder). This allows us to suppose that the oscillatory instability is connected with the disturbances of the azimuthal velocity which begin to grow inside the separation vortex bubble.

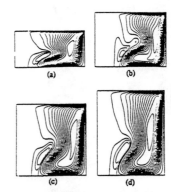

Fig.4. Steady states streamlines of the flow at Re_{cr}. $\xi = 1$.
   (a) $\gamma = 1$, $Re_{cr}=6745$, (b) $\gamma = 1.5$, $Re_{cr}=3845$,
   (c) $\gamma = 2$, $Re_{cr}=2567$, (d) $\gamma = 2.5$, $Re_{cr}=2577$.

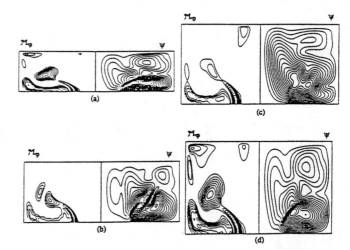

Fig.5. Dominant perturbations of ψ and $\mathcal{M}_\varphi$. $\xi = 1$.
   (a) $\gamma = 1$, $Re_{cr}=6745$, (b) $\gamma = 1.5$, $Re_{cr}=3845$,
   (c) $\gamma = 2$, $Re_{cr}=2567$, (d) $\gamma = 2.5$, $Re_{cr}=2577$,

The slightly supercritical oscillatory flows obtained by asymptotic approximation (12) are shown in Figs. 6 and 7. The temporal changes of the streamlines are similar to those obtained by a solution of the full unsteady problem (Lopez, 1995; Gelfgat et al. 1996c). It is seen that oscillations of the meridional flow (Figs. 6 and 7) contain simultaneously two types of the pulsating separation vortex bubbles – those attached to the axis and those detached from it. The simultaneous existence of the attached and detached oscillatory vortex breakdown is a common property of the supercritical oscillatory flows for strong corotation, namely for the interval $0.8 \le \xi \le 1$. Note that only detached vortex breakdown exists in the subcritical steady states (Fig.4), and only oscillating detached vortex breakdown is observed in the supercritical states for smaller ξ (Fig.8). The additional oscillating separation vortex bubble, attached to the axis, appears as a result of the oscillatory instability. This is analogous to the appearance of the oscillating vortex breakdown in the case of $\xi = 0$ and $\gamma \le 1.7$ described in Gelfgat et al. (1996a).

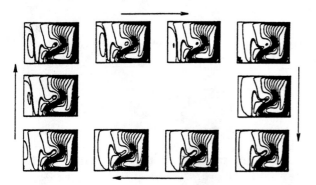

Fig.6. Instantaneous streamlines of the meridional flow plotted for equal time intervals (period/10) covering the complete period. $\xi = 1$ (symmetric case), $\gamma = 1.5$, $Re = 3845$.

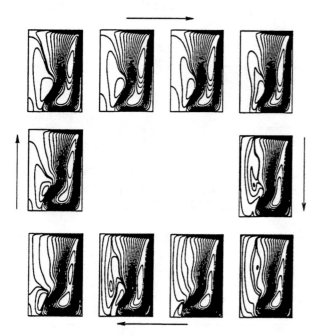

Fig.7. Instantaneous streamlines of the meridional flow (as in Fig.6). $\xi = 1$ (symmetric case), $\gamma = 3$, $Re = 2800$.

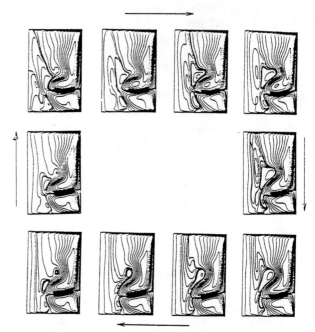

Fig.8. Instantaneous streamlines of the meridional flow (as in Fig.6). $\xi = 0.6$, $\gamma = 1.5$, $Re = 4500$. Calculation by the finite volume method using 150×150 stretched grid.

CONCLUDING REMARKS

Steady states, linear stability of steady states and weakly supercritical states of a confined swirling flow were investigated numerically by two different numerical approaches. As a rule, numerical investigation of stability for realistic confined flows is very difficult. The main numerical difficulties arise from the eigenvalue problem of a very high order which is equal to the number of degrees of freedom used by a numerical method. To decrease the number of degrees of freedom the spectral Galerkin method with globally defined basis functions was used. The appropriate choice of the basis functions, which satisfy all the boundary conditions and the continuity equation, allowed to exclude the pressure from the numerical model and to decrease the number of degrees of freedom to a relatively small value. The total number of Galerkin modes used in the present calculations did not exceed 3500. This allows to perform not only the analysis of linear stability of a calculated steady state, but also to carry out weakly non-linear analysis of a calculated bifurcation. For comparison, the use of the finite volume method with a grid of 150×150 nodes for the calculation of slightly supercritical states (Gelfgat et al., 1996a,b,c) gives 90,000 degrees of freedom.

The main disadvantage of the global spectral approach is connected with the huge amount of computer memory needed to store the coefficients of the dynamic system (11). The matrix N_{ijk} contains $2n^6$ non-zero elements, where n is the number of basis functions used in one spatial direction. The storage can be significantly reduced by recalculating the elements of N_{ijk} whenever the right hand side vector (11) is evaluated. A characteristic run contains calculation of steady states, stability analysis and weakly nonlinear analysis and requires several tens of calculations of the right hand side vector. The CPU time for a representative run with 30×30 basis functions is about 3-4 hours on DIGITAL 7000/660. Calculations with 40×40 basis functions require about 40 hours. The CPU time for calculating a single steady state flow for 30×30 and 40×40 basis functions respectively is about 40 minutes and 5 hours. For comparison, the calculation of a steady state by the finite volume method with the 150×150 grid consumes from 3 to 6 hours depending on the Reynolds number and initial values. Calculation of a slightly supercritical oscillatory flow using the same grid requires several tens of hours.

The appearance and disappearance of the vortex breakdown in steady states of the confined swirling flow considered here are not connected with the stability of the flow. The vortex breakdown appears and develops as a continuous change of the meridional flow with the variation of the Reynolds number.

The weak *counter–rotation* of the bottom may suppress the vortex breakdown which exists in a cylinder with rotating top and stationary bottom. Weak *co-rotation* of the bottom of the cylinder leads to the appearance of the vortex breakdown at lower values of the Reynolds number than in the case of the stationary bottom. Stronger *co-rotation* may lead to detachment of the separation vortex bubble from the axis of the cylinder and formation of two separation vortex rings. It was shown that the single separation bubble, characteristic for the case of stationary bottom, and the antisymmetric vortex rings, characteristic for *co-rotation* of the top and the bottom with the same angular velocity, continuously transform one into another with the continuous change of the rotation ratio.

The oscillatory instability was studied for the case of *co-rotation* of the top and the bottom ($\xi = 1$) and for the aspect ratio of the cylinder varying in the interval $1 \leq \gamma \leq 3$. It was found that the oscillatory instability sets in due to Hopf bifurcation in all the cases considered. The corresponding stability diagram in the plane of the control parameters (Re, γ) was obtained. Along with the stability diagram the dependencies of the critical frequency on the aspect ratio was calculated. It was shown that the neutral curve $Re_{cr}(\gamma)$, and the curve $\omega_{cr}(\gamma)$ consist of four continuous branches corresponding to several distinct eigenmodes of the linearized problem.

It was shown that in the case of strong *co-rotation* ($\xi \geq 0.8$) vortex breakdown bubbles attached to the axis and detached from it may exist simultaneously in slightly supercritical steady states.

ACKNOWLEDGEMENT

This research was supported by the Center for Absorption in Science, Ministry of Immigrant Absorption, State to Israel (to A.Gelfgat), by the Y.Winograd Chair of Fluid Mechanics and Heat Transfer at the Technion, and by the Fund for the Promotion of Research at the Technion.

REFERENCES

Bar-Yoseph, P.Z., Roesner, K.G. and Solan, A., 1992, "Vortex Breakdown in the Polar Region Between Rotating Spheres," Phys. Fluids A, Vol. 4, pp. 1677-1686.

Gelfgat, A.Yu., and Tanasawa, I., 1993, "Systems of Basis Functions for Calculation of Three-Dimensional Fluid Flows in Cylindrical Containers with the Galerkin Spectral Method," Proc. of Institute of Industrial Science, Univ. of Tokyo, Vol. 45, No. 8, pp. 60-63.

Gelfgat, A.Yu., and Tanasawa, I., 1994, "Numerical Analysis of Oscillatory Instability of Buoyancy Convection with the Galerkin Spectral Method," Numerical Heat Transfer, Part A: Applications, Vol. 25, pp. 627-648.

Gelfgat, A.Yu., Bar-Yoseph, P.Z., and Solan, A., 1995, "Numerical Investigation of a Confined Swirling Flow in a Cylinder with Rotating Top and Bottom by the Galerkin Spectral Method," 6th International Symposium on Computational Fluid Dynamics (ed. M.Hafez), Lake Tahoe, Nevada, September 4-8, pp. 355-360.

Gelfgat A.Yu., Bar-Yoseph P.Z., and Solan A., 1996a, "Stability of Confined Swirling Flow with and without Vortex Breakdown," Journal of Fluid Mechanics, Vol. 311, pp. 1-36.

Gelfgat A.Yu., Bar-Yoseph P.Z., and Solan A., 1996b, "On Steady and Unsteady Patterns in Confined Swirling Flow," Proc. 36th Israel Aerospace Conference, Tel-Aviv/Haifa, February 22-23, Omanuth Press, pp. 12-23

Gelfgat A.Yu., Bar-Yoseph P.Z., and A.Solan, 1996c, "Steady States and Oscillatory Instability of Swirling Flows in a Cylinder with Rotating Top and Bottom" (submitted for publication).

Escudier, M.P., 1984, "Observation of the Flow Produced in a Cylindrical Container by a Rotating Endwall," Exp. Fluids, Vol. 2, pp. 189-196.

Hassard, B.D., Kazarinoff, N.D., and Wan, Y.-H., 1981, "Theory and Applications of Hopf Bifurcation," London Math. Soc. Lecture Note Series Vol. 41.

Hopf, E., 1942, "Abzweigung Einer Periodischen Losung von Einer Stationaren Losung Eines Differentialsystems" Ber. Verh. Sachs. Acad. Wiss. Leipzig Math.-Nat., Vol. 94, pp. 3-22.

Lopez, J.M., and Perry, A.D., 1992, "Axisymmetric Vortex Breakdown. Part 3: Onset of Periodic Flow and Chaotic Advection," J. Fluid Mech., Vol. 234, pp. 449-471.

Lopez, J.M., 1995, "Unsteady Swirling Flow in an Enclosed Cylinder with Reflectional Symmetry," Phys. Fluids, Vol. 7, pp. 2700-2714.

Roesner, K.G., 1989, "Recirculation Zones in a Cylinder With Rotating Lid," Proc. IUTAM Symp. on Topological Fluid Mechanics. (eds. A.Tsinober & H.K.Moffat) Univ. of Cambridge, pp. 699-708.

Sørensen J.N., and Christensen E.A., 1995, "Direct Numerical Simulation of Rotating Fluid Flow in a Closed Cylinder," Phys. Fluids, Vol. 7, pp. 764-778.

Valentine D.T., and Jahnke C.C., 1994, "Flows Induced in a Cylinder with Both Endwalls Rotating," Phys. Fluids, Vol. 6, pp. 2702-2711.

Table 1. Comparison of results obtained by the global Galerkin method and the finite volume method with uniform and stretched grids. Steady state $Re = 2000$, $\gamma = 2.5$, $\xi = 0$.

Method	Discretization	$\psi_{max} \times 10^2$	$\psi^1_{min} \times 10^5$	$\psi^2_{min} \times 10^6$	η_{max}	η_{min}
Galerkin method	22×22 basis functions	0.7723	-0.6252	-0.5240	0.4847	-0.3812
	30×30 basis functions	0.7646	-0.7424	-0.5434	0.4663	-0.4033
	38×38 basis functions	**0.7648**	**-0.7489**	**-0.5526**	**0.4637**	**-0.4016**
Finite volume method	100×100 stretched grid	0.7667	-0.5304	-0.6034	0.4721	-0.3907
	200×200 stretched grid	0.7653	-0.6989	-0.5770	0.4664	-0.3959
	300×300 stretched grid	**0.7649**	**-0.7291**	**-0.5642**	**0.4653**	**-0.3993**
	100×100 uniform grid	0.7881	-1.442	-3.054	0.4974	-0.4305
	200×200 uniform grid	0.7771	-1.313	-1.774	0.4801	-0.4281
	300×300 uniform grid	0.7709	-1.015	-1.098	0.4717	-0.4143

Table 2. Comparison of critical values obtained by the linear stability analysis (global Galerkin method) with the results of numerical solution of full Navier-Stokes equation.
[1] - Lopez and Perry, 1992; [2] - Sorensen and Cristensen, 1995; [3] - Lopez, 1995.

		Galerkin method (present)		Finite volume (present)	Finite difference method		
					[1]	[2]	[3]
		26×26 basis functions	30×30 basis functions	150×150 stretched grid	61×151 stretched grid	100×200 uniform grid	101×151 stretched grid
$\gamma = 1$ $\xi = 0$	Re_{cr}	3152	3152	< 3600			
	ω_{cr}	0.39090	0.39090	0.392			
$\gamma = 1.25$ $\xi = 0$	Re_{cr}	2871	2871	< 3050			
	ω_{cr}	0.29958	0.29958	0.302			
$\gamma = 1.5$ $\xi = 0$	Re_{cr}	2724	2724	< 2800			
	ω_{cr}	0.23675	0.23675	0.239			
$\gamma = 2$ $\xi = 0$	Re_{cr}	2584	2581			< 2600	
	ω_{cr}	0.23486	0.23485			0.24	
$\gamma = 2.5$ $\xi = 0$	Re_{cr}	2706	2705	< 2765	2650 + 2675		
	ω_{cr}	0.17241	0.17243	0.176	0.1746		
$\gamma = 1.5$ $\xi = 1$	Re_{cr}	3850	3846	< 3845			
	ω_{cr}	0.4849	0.4849	0.485			
$\gamma = 3$ $\xi = 1$	Re_{cr}	2662	2663				2640
	ω_{cr}	0.2212	0.2212				0.223

FED-Vol. 238, 1996 Fluids Engineering Division Conference
Volume 3
ASME 1996

Gas Core Shape and Velocity Distribution around a Bathtub Vortex

S.SAKAI, H.MADARAME and K.OKAMOTO
Nuclear Engineering Research Laboratory
University of Tokyo
Tokai-mura, Ibaraki, 319-11, JAPAN
Ph: +81-29-287-8413/ Fx: +81-29-287-8488/ Email: seigo@utnl.gen.u-tokyo.ac.jp

ABSTRACT

Flow field around a bathtub vortex was investigated. Velocity distribution around a gas core at the vortex center was measured using a cylindrical vessel. The test vessel had a tangential inlet open channel at the top, and a vertical outlet pipe at the bottom center. Gas core shape, a radius of stagnant region, and a radius of fast downward flow region were measured simultaneously.

Circulation was uniform in a major part of the vessel, which decreased near the center. The downward velocity in the central region was proportional to a distance from the original surface without the gas core except in the neighborhood of the outlet.

A new flow field model was proposed which based on the expanding vortex flow. The gas core shape calculated with the new model showed good agreement with the experimental result.

1. INTRODUCTION

Reducing the size of liquid metal fast breeder reactor (LMFBR) components is regarded as of major importance in view of decreasing the construction cost. It affects the coolant flow in the components, then the velocity of coolant should be set high in order to secure sufficient heat removal. One of the problems arising from the compact design is cover gas entrainment at the free surface of the sodium coolant. If a significant concentration of gas is entrained by the sodium flow, bursts of gas bubbles may pass through the reactor core, causing a change in reactivity. The bubbles may inhibit the removal of heat from the fuel rods. Gas entrainment must be carefully prevented in FBR design.

There are three types of entrainment; (1)vortex formation, (2)breaking of surface waves, and (3)waterfall formation (Laithwaite and Taylor, 1970). Among them, the entrainment at vortices in a liquid surface is the most difficult to find a proper countermeasure. A number of researchers (Baum, 1974, Baum and Cook, 1975, Takahashi et al., 1988a and 1988b) have proposed empirical correlations of the gas entrainment inception using parameters such as the total flow rate and the vessel diameter. The results entirely depended on the configuration of equipments, thus the applicability of the correlations are limited.

The flow field near the center of vortex is quite peculiar; the concentration of angular momentum not only causes very steep gradient of the tangential velocity in the radial direction but also induces considerably high axial flow near the center. It is the neighboring velocity distribution that affects the bubble formation at the tip of the vortex gas core. Thus it is important to examine the flow distribution around the vortex center.

Though the vortex flow has been studied by many researchers both analytically (Rott, 1958, Long, 1961, Lewellen, 1962 and Belcher et al., 1966) and experimentally (Granger, 1966, Toyokura and Akaike, 1969 and Sadahiro and Hanaoka, 1985), most of them dealt with only an idealized flow condition; the outlet is far from the surface so that the effect of outlet shape can be neglected, and the gas core does not affect the surrounding liquid velocity. In that condition, there is an exact solution of the Navier-Stokes equations, which is called the expanding vortex flow. The gas core shape, i.e., the radius and the depth, is formulated for the expanding vortex flow. However, the solution does not agree in the neighborhood of the outlet even if the gas core is shallow. The vortex flow in a vessel of finite size is different from the expanding vortex flow.

In order to clarify the flow field around the vortex, it is important to examine circulation and downward flow at

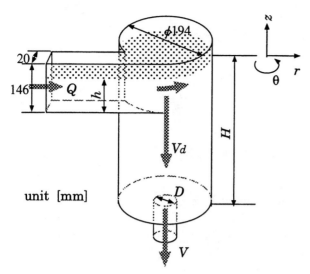

Fig.1 Test section

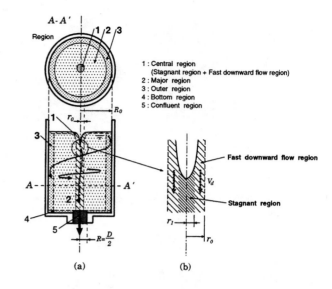

Fig.2 Flow pattern in the vessel

Table 1 Experimental parameters

Outlet pipe diameter	D [mm]	10.5,15.1,17.8, 19.8,22.1,24.0, 25.8,28.1,30.0, 32.0,34.1,36.1, 39.1,40.9,50.3
Height of inlet jet	h [mm]	50 (const)
Flow rate	Q [ℓ/min]	5,7,10,12, 15,20,25
Depth of vessel	H [mm]	400 (const)

the vortex center. Shiraishi et al. (1995) proposed a new flow field model revising the expanding vortex flow. They dealt with a symmetrical two-dimensional flow field considering radial inward velocity, axial downward velocity and viscosity. However the model did not exactly simulate the practical flow field.

In this paper, the velocity distribution around the gas core at the vortex center was measured and discussed. A new symmetrical two-dimensional flow field model was proposed, revising the expanding vortex flow. The calculated gas core shape was compared with experimental result.

2. EXPERIMENTAL APPARATUS AND METHOD

The test section is shown in Fig.1. The vessel was made of acrylic resin so that the velocity distribution could be measured by flow visualization using ink or particles as tracers. Water entered tangentially into the cylindrical vessel through a rectangular open channel with total flow rate, Q. The inlet flow gave circulation to the internal flow, and a vortex was made almost on the axis of the cylindrical vessel. Water flowed downward with velocity, V_d, near the vortex center and flowed out from an outlet pipe at the

bottom center with velocity, V. The outlet pipe at the bottom center could be easily replaced with pipes of various sizes. The cylindrical vessel was enveloped in an acrylic rectangular vessel filled with water in order to minimize the refractive image distortion.

Experimental parameters are shown in Table 1. The height of the inlet jet, h, and the depth of the vessel, H, were fixed in this study. The gas core shape and the velocity distribution were measured with varying the outlet pipe diameter, D, and the total flow rate, Q.

3. RESULT AND DISCUSSION

3.1 Flow pattern

In the experiment, the gas core was formed at the center of the vessel. Figure 2 shows the schematic of the flow pattern in the vessel. The flow in the vessel was classified into five flow regions as follows.

1. **Central region**
   A fast downward flow existed in this region. The downward velocity, V_d, was considerably high, which increased with approaching the outlet. Figure 2-(b) shows the detail of the central region. In the larger Q condition, the stagnant region appeared near the axis of the vortex surrounded by the fast downward flow region. The central region was divided into two regions. One was the stagnant region with radius, r_1, and another was the fast downward flow region with radius, r_0, as shown in Fig.2-(b). The radius of the central region was also expressed by r_0.

2. **Major region**
   The major region occupied the most of the vessel. In this region, circulation was constant. Since the radial inward velocity and the downward velocity were so small compared with the tangential velocity, there seemed to be only rotational motion.

3. **Outer region**

The region was very thin layer within 20mm from the outer wall of the vessel. The axial velocity in the outer region was a little higher than that in the major region.

4. **Bottom region**

The very thin layer on the vessel bottom was the Eckman layer (Sadahiro and Hanaoka, 1985). Water from the outer region flowed to the center in this region. The tangential velocity, v_θ, was smaller than that in the major region because of the bottom wall friction, resulting in the lower centrifugal force. Then the flow had negative radial velocity, i.e., the Eckman layer.

5. **Confluent region**

Flow from the central region and that from the bottom region joined in this region, resulting in so much complication of the flow field. The downward velocity should be increasing to the outlet velocity, V, because of the continuity.

3.2 Distribution of circulation

The radial distribution of circulation ($\gamma = rv_\theta$) in the vessel was measured by the tracer particles, as shown in Fig.3. It did not coincide with the incoming circulation because of dissipation near the inlet. However, it was almost constant in the major region. The distribution of the circulation was also uniform in the vertical direction, thus the following equation was satisfied in this region.

$$\frac{\partial \gamma}{\partial z} = 0 \qquad (1)$$

This equation is also one of the most important basic assumption of the expanding vortex flow. The assumption was confirmed to hold in the real flow field except in the bottom region.

The circulation in the major region, γ_0, was proportional to 1.25th power of the total flow rate as shown in Fig.4, though the incoming circulation was proportional to Q. It hardly depended on the outlet pipe diameter.

3.3 Downward velocity near the vortex center

Downward velocity near the vortex center $V_d(= -v_z(r,z)|_{r\approx0})$ was measured by tracking the edge of the ink tracer. Figure 5 shows the measured V_d in the case of $D = 24.0$[mm]. The downward velocity was proportional to the distance from the surface position without the gas core. Thus the following relationship existed near the vortex center except in the neighborhood of the outlet.

$$V_d = \alpha z \qquad (2)$$

where the downward velocity gradient, α, was constant. The expanding vortex flow is a strict solution of the Navier-Stokes equations on the assumption that the radial velocity component, v_r, and the tangential velocity component, v_θ, are uniform in the axial direction and the axial velocity component, v_z, is proportional to the distance from the

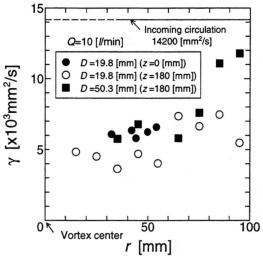

Fig.3 Radial distribution of circulation

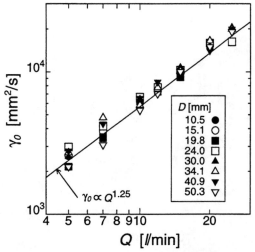

Fig.4 Relation between Q and γ_0

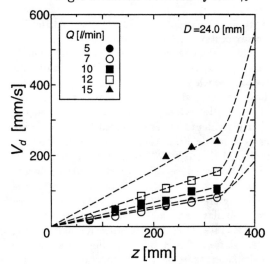

Fig.5 Downward velocity

115

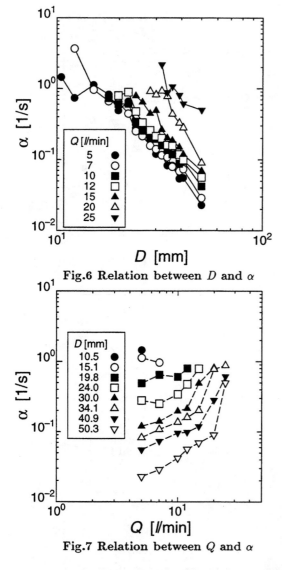

Fig.6 Relation between D and α

Fig.7 Relation between Q and α

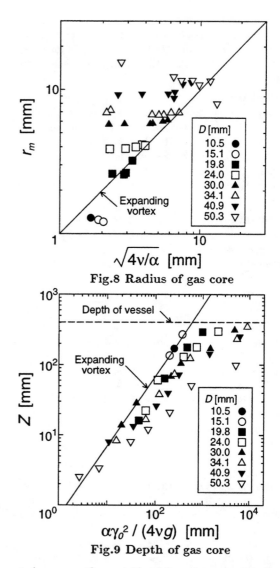

Fig.8 Radius of gas core

Fig.9 Depth of gas core

surface (Rott, 1958). The downward velocity distribution near the vortex center agreed well with the expanding vortex flow except in the confluent region. The axial velocity component of the expanding vortex flow is uniform in the radial direction, which was not correct in this experiment using a finite size of vessel. The downward velocity rose suddenly to the outlet velocity in the confluent region.

The velocity gradient, α, was measured for various tank geometries as shown in Figs.6 and 7. Experimental results in Fig.6 indicated that $\alpha \propto D^{-3} \sim D^{-4}$, therefore the velocity gradient was not proportional to the outlet velocity, V, which was inversely proportional to the square of the outlet pipe diameter($V \propto D^{-2}$). If the flow pattern in the vessel remains similar, the gradient should be proportional to the total flow rate, $Q(\alpha \propto Q)$. Figure 7 illustrates the experimental relation of $\alpha \propto Q^0 \sim Q^3$ depending on the outlet pipe diameter, therefore the proportion of flow quantity in the central region to the total flow was not constant. The flow pattern depended on the flow rate. When the flow

rate increases, the centrifugal force increases together with the circulation in the vessel. Decrease of pressure near the vortex center is proportional to the square of the circulation, thus a larger portion of fluid gathers in the central region, making the velocity gradient steeper.

3.4 Shape of gas core

The gas core shape, i.e., the radius and the depth, were measured from photographs. In the case of the expanding vortex flow, the gas core radius at its half depth, r_m, is given by

$$r_m = \sqrt{\frac{4\nu}{\alpha}} \tag{3}$$

where ν is the kinematic viscosity. The experimental results scattered widely as shown in Fig.8. The radius could not be estimated by Eq.(3).

The gas core depth Z (the distance from the surface position without the gas core to tip of the core) was measured as shown in Fig.9. In the case of the expanding vortex flow, the depth is expressed by the following equation.

$$Z = 0.69 \frac{\alpha \gamma_0^2}{4\nu g} \tag{4}$$

where g is acceleration of gravity. While the measured core radius could not be estimated by the expanding vortex flow, the measured core depth was well approximated by the expanding vortex flow except in the case the tip approached the outlet. The expanding vortex flow explains the real flow only partially. There was a stagnant region in the central region under some condition. So that it is necessary to propose a new flow field model revising the expanding vortex flow model and discuss in the next section.

4. THEORETICAL CONSIDERATIONS

4.1 Numerical calculations

Though the expanding vortex flow is an exact solution of the Navier-Stokes equations, it cannot explain the real flow. Shiraishi et al. (1995) assumed the downward velocity in the central region as follows.

$$v_z(r, z) = \alpha z F(r),$$

$$F(r) = \begin{cases} 1 & (0 \leq r \leq R) \\ 0 & (R < r) \end{cases} \tag{5}$$

where R is radius of the outlet pipe. They solved the velocity distribution using the continuity equation and the Navier-Stokes equations. However, their model did not agree with the experimental results.

As mentioned in section 3.1, the downward velocity in the central region, V_d, was higher than that of the surroundings. The downward velocity in the central region was not uniform in the radial direction. The central region was divided into the stagnant region and the fast downward flow region. So the downward velocity distribution should be assumed as follows.

$$v_z(r, z) = \alpha z F(r),$$

$$F(r) = \begin{cases} 0 & (0 \leq r \leq r_1) \\ 1 & (r_1 < r \leq r_0) \\ 0 & (r_0 < r) \end{cases} \tag{6}$$

where r_1 is the radius of the stagnant region and r_0 is the radius of the center region, i.e., the fast downward flow region. The circulation, γ, and $\partial \gamma / \partial r$ is continuous at r_1 and r_0 as boundary conditions. The radial and tangential velocity components (v_r, v_θ) are given from the continuity equation and the Navier-Stokes equations in axisymmetric cylindrical co-ordinates (r, θ, z).

$0 \leq r \leq r_1$;

$$v_r(r) = 0 \tag{7}$$

$$\gamma(r) = \gamma_1 \frac{r^2}{r_1^2} \tag{8}$$

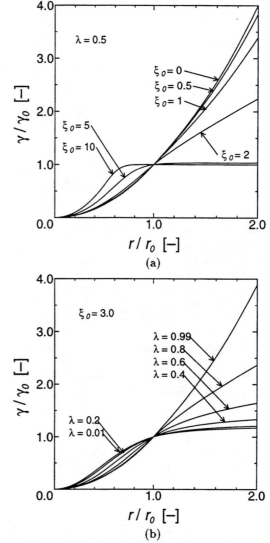

Fig.10 Calculated distribution of circulation

$r_1 \leq r \leq r_0$;

$$v_r(r) = -\frac{\alpha}{2} \frac{1}{r}(r^2 - r_1^2) \tag{9}$$

$$\gamma(r) = \gamma_1 F_{\gamma 1}\left(\sqrt{\frac{\alpha}{\nu}} r\right) \tag{10}$$

$r_0 \leq r$;

$$v_r(r) = -\frac{\alpha}{2} \frac{1}{r}(r_0^2 - r_1^2) \tag{11}$$

$$\gamma(r) = \gamma_1 F_{\gamma 2}\left(\sqrt{\frac{\alpha}{\nu}} r\right) \tag{12}$$

where γ_1 is circulation at $r = r_1$. The tangential velocity component is calculated as $v_\theta = \gamma/r$ from the definition. Defining non-dimensional numbers as $\xi = r\sqrt{\alpha/\nu}$, $\xi_1 = r_1\sqrt{\alpha/\nu}$ and $\xi_0 = r_0\sqrt{\alpha/\nu}$, $F_{\gamma 1}(\xi)$ and $F_{\gamma 2}(\xi)$ are expressed as

$$F_{\gamma 1}(\xi) = 1 + \frac{2\exp\left(\frac{\xi_1^2}{4}\right)}{\xi_1^{2+\frac{\xi_1^2}{2}}} \int_{\xi_1}^{\xi} \xi^{1+\frac{\xi_1^2}{2}} \exp\left(-\frac{\xi^2}{4}\right) d\xi$$

$$F_{\gamma 2}(\xi) = F_{\gamma 1}(\xi_0) + A\left\{\left(\frac{\xi}{\xi_0}\right)^{2-\frac{\xi_0^2-\xi_1^2}{2}} - 1\right\}$$

respectively, where

$$A = \frac{2}{2 - \frac{\xi_0^2 - \xi_1^2}{2}}\left(\frac{\xi_0}{\xi_1}\right)^{2+\frac{\xi_1^2}{2}} \exp\left(\frac{\xi_1^2 - \xi_0^2}{4}\right)$$

γ_1 and γ_0 are the values of the circulation at $r = r_1$ and $r = r_0$ respectively, so $\gamma_0 = \gamma_1 F_{\gamma 1}(\xi_0)$.

Figure 10-(a) shows the radial distribution of the circulation calculated with varying ξ_0 under the condition of $\lambda = r_1/r_0 = 0.5$. The circulation γ converged on $\gamma_0(r/r_0)^2$ when $r \to 0$. In the case of $\xi_0 \leq 2$, the circulation diverged when $r \to \infty$. However, in the case of $\xi_0 > 2$, the circulation for $r_0 < r$ tended to be almost constant. The circulation in the experiment was also constant in the major region. It suggests that ξ_0 might be greater than 2.

The radial distribution of the circulation for several λ with $\xi_0 = 3$ are shown in Fig.10-(b). The circulation was constant at smaller r with decreasing λ. The circulation had a finite value unless λ was nearly equal to 1.

On the any horizontal plane, the velocity distributions are assumed to satisfy Eqs.(6) $\sim$ (12). Pressure, p, is assumed to be continuous on the plane. Under the boundary condition of $p = 0$ at $r = 0$, the following equations represents the radial distribution of the pressure.

$$p(r) = \frac{\rho\gamma_1^2\alpha}{2\nu}\frac{1}{\frac{\alpha}{\nu}r_1^2}\left(\frac{\xi}{\xi_1}\right)^2 \qquad (0 \leq r \leq r_1) \qquad (13)$$

$$p(r) = \frac{\rho\gamma_1^2\alpha}{\nu}F_{p1}(\xi) \qquad (r_1 \leq r \leq r_0) \qquad (14)$$

$$p(r) = \frac{\rho\gamma_1^2\alpha}{\nu}F_{p2}(\xi) \qquad (r_0 \leq r) \qquad (15)$$

where ρ is the density of fluid. $F_{p1}(\xi)$ and $F_{p2}(\xi)$ are expressed as

$$\begin{aligned}F_{p1}(\xi) &= \frac{1}{2\xi_1^2} + \int_{\xi_1}^{\xi}\frac{1}{\xi^3}\{F_{\gamma 1}(\xi)\}^2 d\xi \\ &\quad - \frac{\varepsilon}{8}\{F_{\gamma 1}(\xi_0)\}^2\frac{(\xi^2-\xi_1^2)^2}{\xi^2}\end{aligned}$$

$$\begin{aligned}F_{p2}(\xi) &= F_{p1}(\xi_0) + \int_{\xi_0}^{\xi}\frac{1}{\xi^3}\{F_{\gamma 2}(\xi)\}^2 d\xi \\ &\quad - \frac{\varepsilon}{8}\{F_{\gamma 1}(\xi_0)\}^2(\xi_0^2-\xi_1^2)^2\left(\frac{1}{\xi_0^2}-\frac{1}{\xi^2}\right)\end{aligned}$$

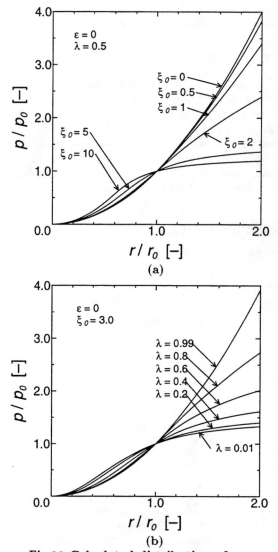

Fig.11 Calculated distribution of pressure

respectively, where $\varepsilon = (\nu/\gamma_0)^2$. In the experiment, ε was smaller than 10^{-6} and had little influence on the distribution of the pressure. So that the calculation had done under the assumption of $\varepsilon = 0$. The pressure at $r = r_0$ was expressed as $p_0 = \rho\gamma_1^2\alpha/(2\nu\xi_1^2)F_{p1}(\xi_0)$.

Figure 11-(a) shows the radial distribution of the pressure calculated with varying ξ_0 under the condition of $\lambda = 0.5$. Similar to the distribution of the circulation, the pressure converged on $p_0(r/r_0)^2$ when $r \to 0$. In the case of $\xi_0 \leq 2$, the pressure diverged when $r \to \infty$. However, for the larger ξ_0, the pressure for $r_0 < r$ was almost constant.

Figure 11-(b) shows the radial distribution of the pressure for several λ with $\xi_0 = 3$. Similar to the distribution of the circulation, the pressure was almost constant at smaller r with decreasing λ. The pressure did not diverge when $\lambda = 1$.

In the case of $\xi_0^2 - \xi_1^2 > 2$, $p(\infty) = p_\infty$ has a finite value shown as

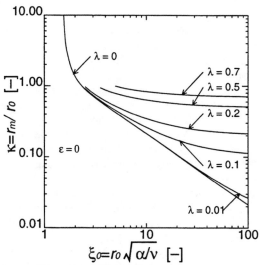

Fig.12 Relation between ξ_0 and κ

$$\frac{p_\infty}{\frac{\rho r_1^2 \alpha}{\nu}} = F_{p1}(\xi_0) + \frac{1}{2\xi_0^2}\left[\{A - F_{\gamma1}(\xi_0)\}^2\right.$$

$$-\frac{8}{\xi_0^2 - \xi_1^2}A\{A - F_{\gamma1}(\xi_0)\}$$

$$\left.+ \frac{2}{\xi_0^2 - \xi_1^2 - 1}A^2\right] \tag{16}$$

The core radius, r_m, is defined where $p(r)/p_\infty = 0.5$. The non-dimensional core radius, $\kappa(= r_m/r_0)$, is a function of ξ_0 and λ, as shown in Fig.12. For small ξ_0, κ had no solution, since the pressure distribution diverged to infinity. When λ is not zero, κ is smaller than 1, that is, r_m is smaller than r_0. At the constant $\xi_0(= r_0\sqrt{\alpha/\nu})$, κ increased together with λ.

When $\lambda = 0$ (no stagnant region, $r_1 = 0$) and $\xi_0 < \sqrt{2}$, the pressure diverged infinity, resulting in κ to be infinity. For $\xi_0 \gg \sqrt{2}$ and $\lambda = 0$, κ tended to an asymptote of $2.121/\xi_0$, that is, the following equation.

$$r_m = 2.121\sqrt{\frac{\nu}{\alpha}} \tag{17}$$

The gas core radius, r_m, is independent of r_0 when $\xi_0 \gg \sqrt{2}$ and $\lambda = 0$. In the expanding vortex flow, $r_m = 2\sqrt{\nu/\alpha}$ as shown in Eq.(3). The relationship of Eq.(17) is almost similar to the expanding vortex flow. Equation (17) did not explain the whole experimental results well as shown in Fig.8. In the model of Shiraishi et al. (1995), λ was assumed to be zero as shown in Eq.(5), therefore their model did not represent the core radius well.

4.2 Comparison with experimental results

The radius of stagnant region, r_1, and the radius of fast downward flow region, r_0, were visualized by ink dye and measured. Figures 13 and 14 show measured r_1 and r_0 respectively. In the case of $Q = 5[\ell/min]$, no stagnant region was observed for all outlet pipe diameter, D. Both r_1 and

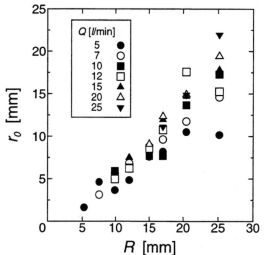

Fig.13 Measured radius of
fast downward flow region

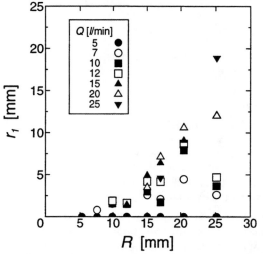

Fig.14 Measured radius of stagnant region

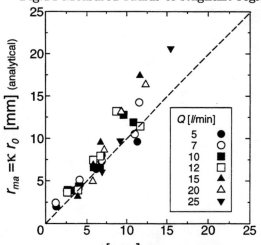

Fig.15 Experimental and analytical
gas core radii

r_0 increased with the outlet pipe radius, R. The radius of the fast downward flow region, r_0, depended on the outlet pipe diameter, $2R$, while the radius of the stagnant region, r_1, depended on the total flow rate.

Using the measured data of r_1, r_0 and α, $\lambda(= r_1/r_0)$ and $\xi_0(= r_0\sqrt{\alpha/\nu})$ were calculated, resulting in $\kappa(= r_m/r_0)$ to be obtained from Fig.12. The analytical gas core radius, $r_{ma}(= \kappa r_0)$, was compared with the measured gas core radius, r_m, as shown in Fig.15. Both radii showed good agreement. The proposed downward velocity distribution shown in Eq.(6) explains the actual flow field well. That is, the velocity distribution in the center region was expressed by Eq.(6) with 3 empirical parameters, r_1, r_0 and α. r_0 was assumed to be determined by the outlet pipe diameter, D. r_1 and α were thought to be determined by the flow rate in the center region.

5. CONCLUSION

The velocity distribution around the gas core was measured and the following conclusions were obtained.

- The downward velocity in the central region was proportional to the distance from the surface position without the gas core, which was similar to the expanding vortex flow.

- The measured gas core depth agreed with the expanding vortex flow.

- A new flow field model was proposed in which the central region was divided into the stagnant region and the fast downward flow region. With this assumption, the radial distribution of the circulation and the pressure could be analytically calculated, resulting in the analytical gas core radius, r_{ma}, to be calculated.

- The radius of the stagnant region, r_1, and the radius of the fast downward flow region, r_0 were measured. The analytical gas core radius showed good agreement with the experimental gas core radius, r_m. Therefore, the new flow field model explained the actual flow field well.

REFERENCES

Laithwaite J.M., and Taylor A.F., 1970, "Hydraulic Problems in the PFR Coolant Circuit", Proceedings, IAEA Symposium on Sodium Cooled Fast Reactor Engineering, Monaco, pp.75-85.

Baum M.R., 1974, "Gas Entrainment at the Free Surface of a Liquid: Entrainment Inception at a Laminar Vortex", BNES Journal, Vol.13, No.2, pp203-209.

Baum M.R., and Cook M.E., 1975, "Gas Entrainment at the Free Surface of a Liquid: Entrainment Inception at a Vortex with an Unstable Gas Core", Nuclear Engineering and Design, Vol.32, pp239-245.

Takahashi M., Inoue A., Aritomi M., Takenaka Y., and Suzuki K., 1988a, "Gas Entrainment at Free Surface of Liquid, (I) Gas Entrainment Mechanism and Rate", Journal of Nuclear Science and Technology, Vol.25, No.2, pp131-142.

Takahashi M., Inoue A., Aritomi M., Takenaka Y., and Suzuki K., 1988b, "Gas Entrainment at Free Surface of Liquid, (II) Onset Conditions of Vortex-Induced Entrainment", Journal of Nuclear Science and Technology, Vol.25, No.3, pp245-253.

Rott N., 1958, "On the Viscous Core of a Line Vortex", ZAMP, Vol.IXb, pp543-553.

Long R.R., 1961, "A Vortex in an Finite Viscous Fluid", Journal of Fluid Mechanics, Vol.11, Part 4, pp.611-624.

Lewellen W.S., 1962, "A Solution for Three-Dimensional Vortex Flows with Strong Circulation", Journal of Fluid Mechanics, Vol.14, Part 3, pp.420-432.

Belcher R.J., Burggraf O.R., and Stewartson K., 1972, "On Generalized-Vortex Boundary Layers", Journal of Fluid Mechanics, Vol.52, Part 4, pp.753-780.

Granger R., 1966, "Steady Three-Dimensional Vortex Flow", Journal of Fluid Mechanics, Vol.25, Part 3, pp.557-576.

Toyokura T., and Akaike S., 1969, "Study on a Bathtub Vortex", JSME Transaction 2., Vol.35, No.275, pp.1466-1473 (in Japanese).

Sadahiro M., and Hanaoka Y., 1985, "Experimental Study of a Bathtub Vortex with Free Surface", JSME Transaction B., Vol.51, No.463, pp.789-797 (in Japanese).

Shiraishi T., Watakabe H, and Nemoto K., 1995, "Fundamental Study on Gas Entrainment due to a Vortex", Proceedings The 3rd JSME/ASME Joint International Conference On Nuclear Engineering, Japan, pp.577-582.

FED-Vol. 238, 1996 Fluids Engineering Division Conference
Volume 3
ASME 1996

NUMERICAL SIMULATION OF TURBULENT JETS WITH

RECTANGULAR CROSS-SECTION

Robert V. Wilson and Ayodeji O. Demuren

Old Dominion University
Department of Mechanical Engineering
Norfolk, Virginia 23529, USA
Tel: (804)-683-6363; Fax: (804)-683-5344; Email: demuren@mem.odu.edu

ABSTRACT

Three-dimensional turbulent jets with rectangular cross-section are simulated with a finite-difference numerical method. The full Navier-Stokes equations are solved at low Reynolds numbers, whereas at the high Reynolds numbers filtered forms of the equations are solved along with a sub-grid scale model to approximate the unresolved scales. A 2-N storage, third-order Runge-Kutta scheme is used for temporal discretization and a fourth-order compact scheme is used for spatial discretization. Computations are performed for different inlet conditions which represent different types of jet forcing. The phenomenon of axis- switching is observed, and it is confirmed that this is based on self-induction of the vorticity field

INTRODUCTION

Turbulent jets are present in many physical processes and technological applications. Turbulent jets can be found in combustors where the fuel and oxidizer are introduced as co-flowing jets. The efficiency of such a process is largely determined by the mixing of the jets. Recently, jet aircraft noise has received much attention due to plans for a high-speed civil transport. A critical issue for the project's success is reducing jet noise to acceptable levels near populated areas. The belief is that acoustic patterns can be altered by manipulating the large scale structures in turbulent jet flows through external forcing. Non-circular jets can also be used to enhance the mixing of hot jet gases with the surroundings and thus avoid aircraft detection. In industrial applications, efficient mixing is required to dilute pollutants issuing from smokestacks with the ambient air to minimize its harmful effects.

Experiments (Quinn 1989) have shown that three-dimensional (3-D) jets can be used to enhance mixing and entrainment rates in comparison to nominally two-dimensional (2-D) jets. A fundamental understanding of the dynamics of complex, turbulent jets is required for their prediction and control. The present study is concerned with the understanding of the role of vorticity in the spatial evolution of incompressible 3-D jets in the near to medium field and the effects of external forcing thereupon.

MATHEMATICAL FORMULATION

The partial differential equations governing the incompressible jet fluid flow are the Navier-Stokes equations which can be written in Cartesian tensor form, for dimensionless variables as:

$$\frac{\partial u_i}{\partial t} + u_j \frac{\partial u_i}{\partial x_j} = -\frac{\partial p}{\partial x_i} + \frac{1}{Re_{D_e}} \frac{\partial^2 u_i}{\partial x_j \partial x_j} \qquad (1)$$

where, u_i are the Cartesian velocity components in the Cartesian coordinate directions x_i, p is the pressure and Re_{D*} is the Reynolds number based on the equivalent diameter. These equations must be solved in conjuction with the continuity equation:

$$\frac{\partial u_i}{\partial x_i} = 0 \qquad (2)$$

which expresses the divergence-free velocity condition.

The Navier-Stokes equations (1) are discretized temporally with explicit Runge-Kutta (RK) schemes and spatially with implicit compact finite difference schemes. The discretized equation has the form:

$$u_i^{n+1} = u_i^n + b^M \Delta t [H_i^M - \delta_{x_i} P^M] \qquad (3)$$

with

$$H_i^M = -u_j \delta_{x_j} u_i^M + \frac{1}{Re_{D_e}} \delta_{xx_j} u_i^M$$

i.e., the sum of convection and diffusion (CD) terms.

In Eq.(3), n represents the time step and M stands for the Mth stage of the RK scheme, with the corresponding coefficient b^M. δ_{x_j} and δ_{xx} are compact first and second derivative operators, respectively. In the present study low-storage RK schemes are utilized. The low-storage requirement is accomplished by continuously overwriting the storage location for the time derivatives and unknown variables at each sub-stage:

$$\hat{H}_i^M \leftarrow a^M \hat{H}_i^{M-1} \qquad (4)$$

$$u_i^{M+1} \leftarrow u_i^M + b^M \Delta t \hat{H}_i^M \qquad (5)$$

where $\hat{H}_i^M = H_i^M - [\partial p^M / \partial x_i]$ and the notation $\leftarrow$ is used to indicate that the storage locations, $\hat{H}_i^{M-1}$, u_i^M are overwritten by, $\hat{H}_i^M$, u_i^{M+1}, respectively. The constants a^M and b^M for the low-storage, third--order scheme (Williamson, 1980; Lowery and Reynolds 1986) are,

Table 1: Coefficients of the third-order RK scheme

M	a^M	b^M
1	0	0.500
2	-0.68301270	0.91068360
3	-1.33333333	0.36602540

Compact finite-difference schemes (Lele 1992) to approximate derivatives which appear in Eqs. (1) and (2) involve implicit treatment of discrete derivatives and explicit treatment of discrete functions. Only tri-diagonal schemes are utilized in this study. For example:

$$\alpha \phi'_{i-1} + \phi'_i + \alpha \phi'_{i+1} = \frac{a}{2\Delta x_i}(\phi_{i+1} - \phi_{i-1}) \qquad (6)$$

where ϕ'_i represents the first derivative of the generic variable ϕ with respect to x_i, and α, a are the coefficients of the compact scheme which determine the accuracy. For the fourth-order scheme: $\alpha = 1/4$; $a = 3/2$. The LHS of Eq. (6) contains the unknown derivatives at grid points i and $i \pm 1$ while the RHS contains the known functional values ϕ_i at the grid points $i \pm 1$. Similarly, the second derivative terms present in the viscous terms of the momentum equation and the Laplacian operator of the Poisson equation for pressure are approximated using fourth-order compact finite differences:

$$\alpha \phi''_{i-1} + \phi''_i + \alpha \phi''_{i+1} = \frac{a}{(\Delta x_i)^2}(\phi_{i+1} + 2\phi_i + \phi_{i-1}) \qquad (7)$$

where ϕ''_i represents the second derivative of the generic variable ϕ_i with respect to x_i, and α, a, b are the coefficients of the compact scheme. For the fourth-order scheme: $\alpha = 1/10$; $a = 6/5$. The tri-diagonal system of algebraic equations are solved using the Thomas algorithm. At the boundary third-order, one-sided differences are used

to close the system of equations arising from the first or second derivative schemes.

A major requirement in the computation of incompressible flow is the satisfaction of the divergence-free velocity condition. This is made particularly difficult by the absence of an evolution equation for pressure. This condition must be satisfied indirectly through the solution of a Poisson equation derived by taking the divergence of the momentum equations:

$$\nabla^2 P^M = \delta_{x_j}\left[H_i^M + \frac{u_i^M}{b^M \Delta t}\right] \qquad (8)$$

The discretization of the Laplacian operator ∇^2 results in:

$$\delta_{xx_i}P^M = \delta_{x_i}\left[H_i^M + \frac{u_i^M}{b^M \Delta t}\right] \qquad (9)$$

It is necessary to solve this equation completely at every substage of the RK scheme. Although the computational matrix is sparse, direct methods of solutions are not feasible. An iterative multi-grid method was found to be most efficient, with reasonably good convergence rates. Nevertheless, the solution of the Poisson equation accounts for about 50% of the total computational effort.

In order to solve a well posed problem, the boundary and initial conditions for the jet simulations are defined. The ellipticity in the spatial terms of the governing equations requires that boundary conditions be defined on all boundaries. In the laboratory, jet flows are commonly generated by the use of a fan which forces fluid along an enclosed duct of nozzle. The jet leaves the exit plane of the nozzle where it interacts with the ambient fluid. Prior to exit, the jet can be considered as a relatively uniform freestream and a curved boundary layer at the walls of the nozzle. A short distance downstream of the nozzle exit, the boundary layer is smoothened so that the streamwise velocity can be modeled using the hyperbolic tangent (tanh) function. The tanh function enables the streamwise velocity to transition in the radial direction from the uniform velocity at the core of the jet to that of the ambient fluid in the freestream. The inflow boundary of the computational domain is placed at a short distance downstream of the nozzle exit which is not actually included in the jet simulations.

The mean or time-averaged streamwise velocity component at the inflow boundary is given by:

$$\overline{u}_1(0, x_2, x_3) = U_c + \frac{(U_H - U_L)}{2}\tanh\left(\frac{r}{2\theta_o}\right) \qquad (10)$$

where $U_C = (U_H + U_L)/2$ is the convective velocity and UH, UL, represent the velocities of the jet core, and ambient fluid, respectively. The variable r, represents the minimum directed distance from the point, (0, x2, x3) to the line of constant convective velocity of the boundary layer. The momentum thickness of the boundary layer at the inflow plane, θ_o is used to normalize the directed distance, r. If the point (0, x2, x3) is "outside" the boundary layer, r is defined to be negative, otherwise r is defined to be positive in the point lies on the inside of the boundary layer. Equation (8) produces a constant thickness boundary layer if the momentum thickness, θ_o, is constant at all azimuthal positions along the boundary layer. Non constant thickness boundary layers are generated by specifying the desired variation of θ_o along the perimeter of the boundary layer. The mean major and minor direction velocity components at the inflow plane, u2(0, x2, x3) and u3(0, x2, x3) are specified from experiment.

Due to limitations in computational resources a time dependent forcing function of low intensity is added to the mean velocity components at the inflow boundary to promote unsteady motion. At higher Reynolds numbers or large computational lengths small round-off errors would grow to produce unsteady motion of the unstable shear layers thus obviating the need for forcing functions. Two classes of perturbations are used in the current study; (i) sinusoidal perturbations with frequency and amplitudes related to the most unstable modes found from viscous stability analysis (Wilson and Demuren 1996); (ii) perturbations having an experimentally measured velocity spectrum and transverse root mean square (rms) value.

Perturbations having a broad spectrum resembling that of fully-developed, mostly random, 3-D turbulence were generated (Wilson 1993). The perturbations are typical of those found in the experimental jets originating from contoured nozzles. The power spectrum and rms values are taken from experiment. Because phase information is not included in the power spectrum, a random phase relationship for the modes comprising the spectrum was assumed. The random inlet boundary conditions are the spatial analog to the random perturbations generated for initial conditions in the temporal simulation.

MODEL PROBLEMS

Spatial simulations of rectangular jet flows are performed in this study in which a fixed region of the flow is computed and disturbances grow in the streamwise direction. This can be contrasted with a temporal simulation in which a small region of the flow is followed in time and the domain moves in the streamwise direction. Spatial simulations are closer to reality, but are computationally more demanding. As a result of the spatial reference frame, initial conditions are of minor importance because they are quickly convected out of the domain and the dynamics of the jet flow are determined by the forcing functions applied at the inflow plane, until the inherent instabilities of the flow take over or the onset of transition to turbulent flow. Simulations are started on coarser grids with the velocities specified at the inflow plane used to initialize the velocity field in the interior at t = 0. After several flow through times (the time required for a fluid particle to convect from the inflow to the outflow plane at the jet core velocity, Ue) the initial conditions are "washed" from the domain. Simulations on finer grids are commenced with initial fields obtained by prolongating the coarser grid results using a standard, 2nd-order accurate interpolation formula.

The rectangular jet of the present study has a nominal aspect ratio of 2:1. This corresponds to the configuration of some jet issuing from contoured nozzle studied by Quinn (private communication). Only the lower Reynolds number computations are presented here, in which case the flow is fully resolved, no sub-grid scale model is utilized. The Reynolds number based on the core velocity and the equivalent diameter is 750. Three cases are simulated, each corresponding to different types of inlet forcing functions, as explained previously, namely; (i) sinusoidal perturbations with the fundamental mode at an rms of 3%; (ii) sinusoidal perturbation with the fundamental and first subharmonic modes, each at an rms of 1.5%; (iii) random broad-mode perturbations with an rms of 5%. Case (i) was simulated in a domain with size (10 x 5 x5) on a uniform computational grid of (80 x 65 x 65), whereas both cases (ii) and (iii) were simulated on a (10 x 10 x 10) domain with computational grids of (100 x 129 x 129)

RESULTS AND DISCUSSION

Figures 1-3 show the computed vorticity fields for cases (i) - (iii), respectively. In case (i), the flow remains symmetrical about the major and minor axes, just like the inlet mean flow and perturbation velocities, hence the flow has remained laminar and transition to turbulence did not occur in the 10 diameters computed. The phenomenon of axis switching can be observed to be taking place by the end of the domain. The source of this is seen to be clearly in the complex vorticity field. It is most likely due to self-induction, since there is no streamwise vorticity at the inlet plane. In case (ii), the vorticity field is even more complex, indicating the effects of the sub-harmonic component in inducing multiple vortex pairings. Near the end of the computed domain, some asymmetry can be discerned, indicating the beginning of the transition process. Figure 3 shows that in case (iii) with random perturbations, signatures of turbulence can be seen, from about 6 diameters, i.e., beyond the potential core. The structures are completely asymmetric. The phenomenon of axis-switching can be seen at x/D=10, where the extent of the jet has become larger along the minor axis. The present results are promising and more detailed study is planned, especially in longer domains and for higher Reynolds numbers.

CONCLUDING REMARKS

Direct numerical simulation of jets with rectangular cross-section have been performed using third-order Runge-Kutta temporal discretization and fourth-order compact schemes. The phenomenon of axis-switching is observed, and it is confirmed that this is based on self-induction of the vorticity field.

REFERENCES

Lele, S. K. (1992) Compact Finite Difference Schemes with Spectral-Like Resolution. J. Comp. Phys. 103, pp. 16.

Lowery, S. L. and Reynolds, W. C. (1986) Numerical Simulation of a Spatially-Developing Mixing Layer. Report TF-26, Mech. Engr. Dept., Stanford Univ.

Quinn, W. R. (1989) On Mixing in an Elliptic Turbulent Free Jet. Phys. Fluid. A, Vol. 1, No. 10, pp. 1716-1722.

Williamson, J. (1980) Low Storage Runge-Kutta Schemes. J. Comp. Phys., 35, pp. 48-56.

Wilson, R. V. (1993) Numerical Simulation of Two-Dimensional, Spatially Developing Mixing Layers. Masters Thesis, Old Dominion University.

Wilson, R. V. and Demuren, A. O. (1996) Two-Dimensional Spatially-Developing Mixing Layers, Numerical Heat Transfer, Part A.

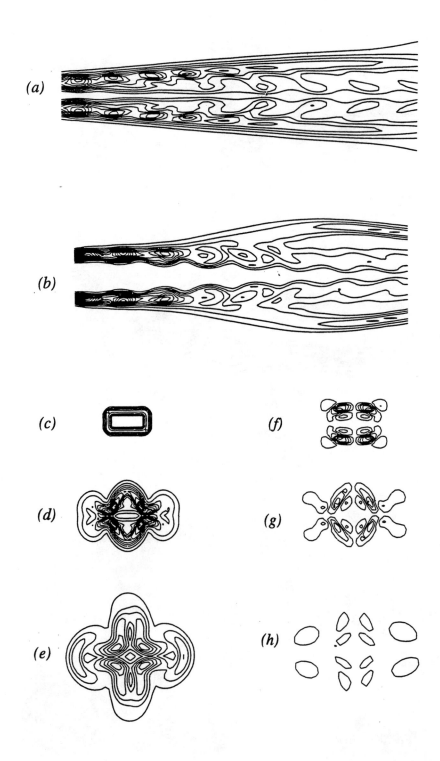

Figure 1. Vorticity magnitude *(a) - (e)* and streamwise vorticity *(f) - (h)* contours at $t = 2$ flow through times for fundamental forcing function. *(a)* minor axis plane, $z/d = 0$, *(b)* major axis plane, $y/d = 0$, *(c)* cross flow plane, $x/d = 0$, *(d)* $x/d = 5$, *(e)* $x/d = 10$, *(f)* $x/d = 2.5$, *(g)* $x/d = 5$, and *(h)* $x/d = 10$.

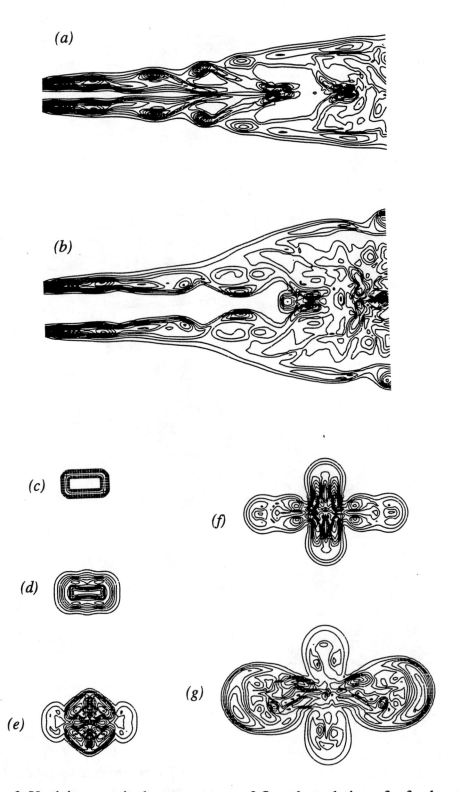

Figure 2. Vorticity magnitude contours at $t = 2$ flow through times for fundamental and first sub-harmonic forcing function. *(a)* minor axis plane, $z/d = 0$, *(b)* major axis plane, $y/d = 0$, *(c)* cross flow plane, $x/d = 0$, *(d)* $x/d = 2.5$, *(e)* $x/d = 5$, *(f)* $x/d = 7.5$, and *(g)* $x/d = 10$.

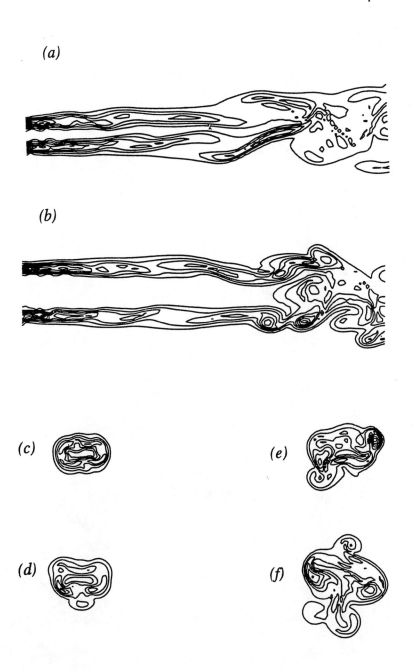

(a)

(b)

(c)   *(e)*

(d)   *(f)*

Figure 3. Vorticity magnitude contours at $t = 2$ flow through times for broad mode forcing function. *(a)* minor axis plane, $z/d = 0$, *(b)* major axis plane, $y/d = 0$, *(c)* cross flow plane, $x/d = 2.5$, *(d)* $x/d = 5$, *(e)* $x/d = 7.5$, and *(f)* $x/d = 10$.

FED-Vol. 238, 1996 Fluids Engineering Division Conference
Volume 3
ASME 1996

WHY TURBULENCE THEORIES CANNOT BE LIKE

THE KINETIC THEORY OF GASES

Alexandre J. Chorin

Department of Mathematics
University of California
Berkeley, CA 94720

ABSTRACT

Recent work on random solutions of the Euler and Navier-Stokes equations is summarized, with emphasis on field-theoretical ideas and linear response theory. Implications for practical turbulence modelling are sketched. The main theoretical conclusion is that turbulent states correspond to critical points in a certain phase diagram; this criticality, defined in the text, arises because one must assign probabilities to sets of flows, i.e., to continua, and it is absent in other well-known statistical theories in mechanics; it is the main reason for the qualitative difference between turbulence theory and other statistical theories in mechanics.

INTRODUCTION

You all know the story: Einstein dies and asks the angel Gabriel to explain the structure of the universe. Gabriel swiftly complies with a few equations. then Einstein asks about the structure of turbulence, and Gabriel answers "No one here knows."

A joke often reflects reality, but this one does not. A lot of deep insight about turbulence has accumulated in recent years; I would like to summarize some of this new knowledge from my own idiosyncratic point of view. By "turbulence" I mean "random behavior in fluids and plasmas" (and in this talk I will omit the plasmas). I shall also concentrate on fully-developed turbulence.

The goal of turbulence theory is two-fold: To gain a mathematical understanding of the nature of random solutions of the Navier-Stokes and related equations, and to use this understanding in practical modelling. Good practical modelling is unlikely to come without solid understanding. The reason random solutions are appropriate is the chaotic nature of hydrodynamics; arbitrarily small variation in the data are amplified, no experimental apparatus is identical to any other, and the flow one sees depends on the specific experiment — the very definition of a random solution.

Fully developed turbulence has many degrees of freedom; the natural machinery for dealing with many degrees of freedom is field theory — the realm of functional integrals, gauge invariance, Feynman diagrams and renormalization. Most of us engineers dislike this realm, because it is unfamiliar, and because early messengers from the realm did not bring important news. I believe that the second reason is now obsolete, and therefore the first must be overcome. Field theory offers the right tools for dealing with random functions.

It is natural to focus first on stationary random solutions of the Euler or Navier-Stokes equations, just as it is natural in the kinetic theory of gases to focus first on stationary distributions of the momenta and positions of particles. A stationary random solution in turbulence is the obvious generalization of a statistically steady state in a system of N particles; it is a collection ("space") of functions, in which one has identified subsets, each with an attached probability that a function in the space belong to the subset (see e.g. Gelfand & Vilenkin (1964)). As the functions in the space evolve according to the equations of motion, they move in and out of the various subsets, in such a way that the probability that a function belong to a given subset does not change; those that leave the subset are replaced by others. One difficulty present in turbulence that is absent in the case of N particles is the need for a correct characterization of the space of solutions; if one assigns positive probabilities to functions that cannot appear in natural flows (for example, to collections of wild distributions), the effort is wasted.

Stationary solutions are important because they may attract others — i.e., one may be able to replace long-time averages by averages over a stationary statistical solution (i.e., over the appropriate space of solutions with its time-independent probabilities), and also because non-stationary solutions depend on initial and boundary conditions and few general conclusions can be reached about them. It is understood that stationary solutions may provide only a partial description of real solutions; in turbulence, this partial description usually applies to the small scales.

Stationary flows come in two flavors: equilibrium and non-equilibrium. An equilibrium is what happens after a long-time in an isolated system or a portion of an isolated system. In an isolated system with only energy as an invariant, equilibrium can be characterized by a "micro-canonical" distribution, i.e., equipartition over the set of appropriate equal-energy systems; it can also be characterized by the Gibbs probability distribution, in which the probability of a collection of states is the integral of $Z^{-1}e^{-\beta H}$, with β the "inverse temperature", H the Hamiltonian (or a suitable generalization), and Z, the "partition function", is a normalizing factor, see for example Huang (1963). One often thinks of the Gibbs distribution as describing a system in contact with a "heat bath", but it is also possible to identify the heat bath with the remainder of the system when one considers only a portion of it.

Non-equilibrium steady states are the analogs of what one obtains in kinetic theory when one considers, for example, the distribution after a long time of velocities and momenta of gas particles between two walls at different temperatures. That distribution of momenta and locations is stationary but not Gibbsian. Unlike a Gibbsian equilibrium, it allows for the irreversible transport of mass, momentum and energy across the system.

The great discovery of Onsager, Callen, and Welton (see e.g. Evans & Morriss (1989)) is that in a system not too far from a Gibbsian equilibrium, non-equilibrium properties (e.g., transport coefficients) can be evaluated on the basis of equilibrium properties. An example is heat capacity, which is perfectly well defined at equilibrium, but measures the response of the system to outside (i.e., non-equilibrium) perturbations. (For an introduction to such "fluctuation-dissipation" theorems, see e.g. Chandler (1987), Forster (1975)). Most of the theory of non-equilibrium processes deals with systems not far from equilibrium. Clearly, stationary turbulence is not in Gibbsian equilibrium, in particular because it features an irreversible energy transfer from large to small scales. The interesting question is: Can turbulence be viewed as a small perturbation of a suitable Gibbsian equilibrium? The key word here is "suitable". The usual answer is "no", but the answer here will be "yes".

Note that the temperature, energy, entropy, etc., to be discussed, refer to the properties of the macroscopic solutions of the Navier-Stokes or Euler equation and are not necessarily related to the temperature, etc., of the molecular motion of the particles that make up the fluid. It is easiest to visualize the difference for incompressible flow, where the macroscopic and molecular degrees of freedom are uncoupled (see e.g. Chorin (1994)).

THE HOPF EQUILIBRIUM, THE KOLMOGOROV SPECTRUM, DIAGRAMMATIC EXPANSIONS

There are two reasons why one usually thinks of turbulence as being far from equilibrium: the identification of equilibrium with the Hopf equilibrium and the historical interpretation of the Kolmogorov spectrum.

In 1952 Hopf and others (Hopf (1952), Lee (1952)) constructed an "equilibrium" for incompressible fluid flow based on properties of Fourier expansions. To save writing, I will present a one-dimensional version of their development. Consider the model equation $\partial_t u + \partial_x(u^2) = 0$, $\left(\partial_t = \frac{\partial}{\partial t}, \text{ etc.}\right)$, where u is periodic with period 1. Expand u in Fourier series: $u = \sum \hat{u}_k e^{ikx}$; $\hat{u}_k = \hat{u}_k(t)$ satisfies

$$\frac{d}{dt}\hat{u}_k + ik \sum_{k'} \hat{u}_{k'} \hat{u}_{k-k'} = 0. \tag{1}$$

Assume $\hat{u}_0 = \int_0^1 u\,dx = 0$, and $\hat{u}_k = 0$ for $|k| \geq K$, where K is a cut-off. One can readily check that $E = \frac{1}{2}\sum|\hat{u}_k|^2$ is invariant under (1). One can further check that the uniform distribution of the set of $\hat{u}_k$'s on the sphere $E = $ constant is also invariant under (1). This distribution can be viewed as a microcanonical distribution. The formal limit $K \to \infty$ produces a probability measure on a function space. Completely analogous constructions can be carried out for the two- and three-dimensional incompressible Euler and even Navier-Stokes equations.

The result is a legitimate probability distribution on a space of functions, which is formally invariant under

Euler flow ("formally" means that all questions of existence and convergence are disregarded). A typical "flow" in this collection of flows is a wild distribution, nowhere differentiable. The average energy at a point is infinite. Even more disturbing from the point of view of statistical mechanics, the truncated systems do not have the same constants of motion as the original differential equations. The natural reaction is: If this is equilibrium, real flow must be far from it.

Another source of the belief that turbulence is far from equilibrium is the usual interpretation of Kolmogorov's law; that law states that in the inertial range of scales, across which energy "cascades" from the stirring scales to the dissipation scales, the energy spectrum $E(k)$, i.e., the energy E per wave number k, has the form $E(k) = C\epsilon^{2/3}k^{-5/3}$, where C is an absolute constant and ϵ is the rate of energy dissipation. Neither the idea of a cascade nor the dimensional analysis that leads to this law prejudges the issue of distance from equilibrium. However, the presence of ϵ in the spectral law creates the impression that it is the dissipation that creates the law. An alternate interpretation can be produced, according to which the amount of energy dissipated depends on the amount of energy present, i.e., $\epsilon = (E(k))^{3/2} k^{5/2}$, when $E(k)$ may be determined by equilibrium considerations. Examples from polymer theory with power laws similar to Kolmogorov's and where the rate of energy dissipation enters the spectrum in a way similar to what has just been suggested are offered in Chorin (1996b).

Be that as it may, the idea that irreversibility dominates the small scales of turbulence leads naturally to a particular formalism (see e.g. McComb (1989), Lesieur (1990)). The dominant effect is assumed to be the provision of energy at large scales and its removal by viscosity at small scales. Both can be represented by a linear Stokes equation with forcing, which can readily be solved. The nonlinear terms in the Navier-Stokes equations can then be represented as a perturbation expansion ordered by the Reynolds number R. The various terms in this expansion can be represented by Feynman diagrams, and the panoply of perturbative field theory can be used in the attempt to extract useful information. This is an awesome and uncompleted task, as the jump from $R = 0$ to $R = \infty$ is large, and it would be desirable to avoid it by constructing perturbation expansions on other premises.

ALTERNATE EQUILIBRIA IN HYDRODYNAMICS

We now set out to look for more reasonable equilibria for the Euler equations, in the hope that turbulence can be found in their vicinity. Here too we start with a discretization of the equations of motion and plan to take an appropriate limit at the end.

A general procedure for doing so would be as follows: Assume the turbulence lives in a finite volume V; divide V into small pieces of side h and volume h^3; construct a finite number of variables by integrating appropriate continuum variables, for example, the components of the vorticity vector ξ, over the small volumes. (The condition div $\xi = 0$ must be enforced, and there is a machinery for doing that.) The energy E discretizes into a sum E_h over the boxes, and for each h, one can construct an equilibrium Gibbs distribution $Z_h^{-1}\exp(-\beta E_h)$, where β is an "inverse temperature". The question is: what happens to these equilibria as $h \to 0$?

First note that the question can be asked and answered for the discretized spectral equilibria of the previous section. Given a cut-off K, standard methods show that the temperature $T = \beta^{-1}$ is proportional, for constant energy E, to $E/(K^d)$, where d is the dimension of the space. Thus $T \to 0$ as one approaches the continuum limit.

For the systems discretized by chopping up the vorticity in physical space several things can happen. In two dimensions generally T increases as h decreases, and then T goes beyond into the "negative" (trans-infinite region). (see Chorin (1994, 1996c)). In three space dimensions a richer variety of behaviors may appear.

A reminder of some properties of phase transitions is needed here. The same collection of particles may exist in several phases, for example, $H_2 0$ can make up ice, water, or vapor. At $0°$C water becomes ice, a "phase transition" of "first order", i.e., one in which the usual thermodynamic functions exhibit a discontinuity. "Higher order" or "critical" phase transitions are less dramatic; an example is the transition of ^{4}He from the normal to the superfluid phase. At a phase transition the correlation length of a physical system is infinite (or else the thermodynamic properties of the system are analytic in parameters such as T). Furthermore, at a critical phase transition a system is "scale invariant", which roughly means the following: If the system is discretized, or is already discrete to start with and its variables are collected into groups in a way that preserves energy, then the properties of the system are invariant under changes in the scale of the discretization or of the grouping. The relation between scale invariance and phase transition comes about because scale invariance can occur only when the correlation length is infinite. If the correlation length is finite, a change of discretization changes the correlation length (for example, if a length that characterizes the discretization is doubled, the correlation length is halved) and thus the system changes.

The question whether alternate equilibria in turbulence can be found now becomes: Does the family of equilibria with parameters β and h have multiple phases with a curve separating them in the (β, h) plane? If yes, the intersection β^* of this phase transition line with the $h = 0$ axis is our candidate for a "reasonable" value of β, and the corresponding equilibrium is our thermal equilibrium.

Note that this is where the fact that we are looking for probability distributions over continuous flows impinges on the analysis. For a discrete collection of particles, invariance under a change of discretization is usually not a relevant consideration; here, however, we have to make sure that our systems have a meaningful continuum limit, and this forces us to consider systems invariant under a refinement of the discretization, and thus forces us towards phase transitions. Phase transitions and critical phenomena have a number of unusual properties that make the use of some standard approximations difficult.

A similar problem has been investigated for superfluid and superconductor vortex systems, where a phase transition is well-known and reasonably well-understood. A heuristic analysis that maps superfluid results onto classical fluid results has been carried out, and will be discussed below by a method that can be generalized to non-equilibrium conditions as long as one does not de-

part too much from equilibrium. The superfluid vortex system and the Euler/Navier-Stokes fluid systems are not identical (see e.g. Zhou (1996)) and the applicability of the analysis to fluid mechanics is not yet an established fact. However, if the analysis is applicable, certain well-known properties of turbulence are immediately explained, for example, the failure of moment closures — moment expansions always fail near critical points; the feasibility of large-eddy simulation — in other fields, procedures similar to large-eddy simulation require in general a change in the equations for large-scale quantities, except near critical points.

A SIMPLIFIED EQUILIBRIUM MODEL

To give some feeling for the alternate equilibria whose existence has just been postulated, we simplify the description of three-dimensional flow and assume that it consists of a sparse collection of circular vortex loops. This is a far-reaching simplification, but it it leads to relatively simple models. We shall assign probabilities to various arrangements of vortex loops, and the consider what happens when the number of loops increases. The significant parameters of the problem are $\beta = 1/T$ and μ, the "chemical potential" that measures the energy per unit length of a vortex. The chemical potential increases as a vortex is stretched and becomes thinner. Note that this description makes short-shrift of the detailed structure of vortex filaments, though recent work has shown that this structure plays a key role in hydrodynamics. The analysis proceeds via a "dielectric" formalism (Williams (1987)) patterned after work on two-dimensional conductor/insulator transitions (see e.g. Itzykson & Drouffe (1989)). This formalism is not unique (Chorin & Hald, (1996)), and we pick its easiest version (Chorin & Hald, (1995)). The overall strategy described in the previous section will be maintained.

Here I will launch into a technical discussion, so that the paper is not merely a collection of generalities. The gist of this discussion is that fairly standard manipulations that make use of the well-known magnetostatics/hydrodynamics analogy (Chorin (1994)), make possible the construction of appropriate probabilities. They are built up, in a certain approximation, by considering a vortex loop in gas of vortex loops, and making the interaction of the loop and its background self-consistent.

Suppose for a moment that the temperature T of the system of vortex loops is small; there will be very few loops in the system and the impulse they carry will be small. The impulse of a vortex loop is the integral $\frac{1}{2}\kappa \int_{\text{loop}} \mathbf{x} \times d\mathbf{s}$, where κ is the circulation in the loop and $d\mathbf{s}$ is an element of arc length; if the loop is planar, the impulse reduces to κA, where A is the area spanned by the loop (See e.g Chorin (1994)). As the temperature increases, more and larger loops appear in the system. The growth in the number of loops and in the size of the loops are related: If one takes a large loop and places inside it a smaller loop with opposite orientation, the energy of the combined configuration is reduced and its appearance is more likely (this is "polarization"); thus a cloud of small loops allows large loops to form. Eventually, it becomes possible for an infinite loop to form. The result is a phase transition in the vortex system. In the theory of superfluids, this phase transition corresponds to the transition from a superfluid to a normal fluid; we shall argue below that this is also the attracting equilibrium for a classical fluid (i.e., for the set of "excitations", or modes of motion, that make up turbulence in the usual type of fluid). Roughly speaking, classical turbulent systems and superfluid systems are on opposite sides of the transition.

To characterize the phase transition quantitatively, consider a single vortex loop; assume that all the other loops create a polarizable background that modifies the energy of the loop, and look for the range of the parameters β, μ for which this picture is self-consistent. The boundary of that region will be the phase transition line.

Suppose a velocity $\mathbf{u}$ is imposed on the cloud of vortex loops. The loops will orient themselves so as to oppose that velocity. The reduction in energy due to the presence of an impulse $\mathbf{m}$ is $\frac{1}{2}\mathbf{m} \cdot \mathbf{u}$. The average polarizability of the loop, i.e., the average value of $\mathbf{m} \cdot \mathbf{u}$ divided by $u = |\mathbf{u}|$ is $\frac{1}{12}\beta m^2$, where $m = |\mathbf{m}|$. This calculation can be found e.g in Chorin & Hald (1995): One averages over all solid angles, weighing each by the appropriate Gibbs factor which favors lower energies. We already know that $m = \kappa \pi r^2$, where r is the radius of the loop; thus polarizability is a function of r. Next one has to find the density of loops of radius r. We view the number of loops as variable, and it is the grand-canonical ensemble that is relevant (see Huang (1963)).

The grand-canonical partition function is an expansion in powers of the fugacity $y = \exp(-\beta\mu_{\text{loop}})$, where μ_{loop} is the energy needed to create a single loop of radius r. For an isolated circular loop this energy equals $\mu r \log r$, where μ is the energy per unit length of the vortex loop. The coefficient of y is the partition function for a one-loop system, the sum of possible states of that system per unit volume times their Gibbsian weights (Huang (1963)). If the fugacity is small enough one can be content with this single term, which is then the density of the the loops of radius r. (Note that the zero-order term in y does not contribute to the polarization).

To enumerate all states one needs an estimate of the smallest length scale in the problem. For a collection of thin circular filaments it is natural to take the small diameter δ of the filaments as this smallest length scale. In a unit cube there are δ^{-3} possible loop centers. All orientations of the loops are possible, albeit with different probabilities; there are $4\pi r^2 dr \delta^{-3}$ distinct orientations of a loop with radius between r and $r + dr$. Each of these has to be multiplied by the corresponding Gibbs factor $\exp(-\beta E/e)$, where E is the energy of interaction between the loop under discussion and all the others, and $e = e(r)$ is the dielectric "constant", which, in the absence of a scale separation between large and small loops, may well be a function of r. In fact, one must figure out how a loop of radius r is formed and write a history-dependent expression for the potential in the Gibbs factor, but we shall not need this degree of refinement: In a low-fugacity system, E is negligible. The dielectric constant is the sum of all these contributions as r ranges from δ to infinity. It is customary to introduce the function $K = K(r)$ by $e(r) = \beta/K(r)$. Note that the unknown e or K appears in the exponential. We shall assume for simplicity that K is in fact a constant; the equation for K is nonlinear:

$$K^{-1} = \beta^{-1} + c_1 \int_\delta^\infty r^6 \exp(-K c_2 r \log r)) dr, \quad (2)$$

where the constant c_1 can be evaluated from the preceding discussion, and is proportional to δ^{-6}. (More precisely, $c_1 = (4/3)\pi^4 \kappa^2 \delta^{-6}$; The powers of π come about as follows: Two from the formula for polarizability, one from the enumeration of states due the rotations of the loops, and one from the 4π in the relation between loops and the induced velocity.). The expression $c_2 r \log r$ is what we have called μ_{loop}, where c_2 is an appropriate constant. The estimation of c_2 involves some elaborate manipulations. The easiest way to find it is as follows: Assume the energy of a loop can be found as the product of an energy μ per unit length of the filament times the length; this requires dropping $\log r$ from the definition of the energy of a loop — a small error (In Chorin & Hald (1995) it is shown that this simplification is entirely legitimate for fractal loops, but we are not invoking a fractal loop model.). Once this simplification has been carried out, μ can be found from standard arguments about the energy associated with vortex.

Equation (2) can now be rewritten in the form

$$T = \beta^{-1} = K^{-1} - c_1 \int_\delta^\infty r^6 \exp(-K\mu r) dr. \quad (3)$$

The right-hand side of (3) is a convex function of K with a single maximum T_0 at some K_0. For $T > T_0$ equation (3) cannot be satisfied with K real, and we are outside the region of validity of the "dielectric" approximation, i.e., we have crossed the phase transition line. As μ varies one obtains different values of $\beta_0 = 1/T_0$ which trace out the phase transition line, sketched for a particular choice of parameters in Figure 1. If one now allows vortex stretching to lengthen the vortex lines, or if one tries to approach classical hydrodynamics by lengthening and thickening the vortex lines, one approaches the phase transition lines from any reasonable starting point (motion marked on Figure 1). Both phenomena are special cases of the general fact, already noted above, that only "critical" states survive a continuum limit at a finite energy. The expectation is that the points on the phase transition line approximate possible turbulence states. We are of course dealing with an approximation since the equations of motion have not yet been taken into account.

LINEAR RESPONSE THEORY

So far, the equations of motion have not been taken into account, and it is too much to expect that they will produce the equilibria we have constructed without some discrepancy. We wish to use linear response theory to evaluate the modifications needed to get a possible asymptotic state of the Euler or Navier-Stokes equations; this should yield at the same time a model of the effect of small scales on the large scales in a numerical "large-eddy" calculation because this effect is presumably contained in the equations of motion; in performing this modification we are correcting for a mismatch (hopefully small) between the equilibrium we have found and the set of solutions of the Navier-Stokes or Euler equations. That such a mismatch exists is of course obvious because turbulence is dissipative. Our analysis is closely related to earlier work on superfluids (see for example Ambageokar et al. (1978)). We sketch its simplest forms.

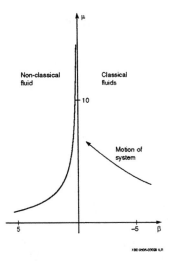

Figure 1: Phase diagram according to the approximate theory.

The zero-th order form of this correction is simple indeed: Assume the vortex system is very sparse, for example because a long time has passed since it was stirred and all small-scale structures have been lost. Then the parameter μ is large, and an easy calculation shows that the phase transition occurs at an infinite temperature T. At this temperature $\beta = 0$, there is no polarization, and small loops can be simply removed without harming the large scales. The removal modifies the equilibrium and creates an energy cascade from large to small scales, because the small scales are continuously replenished and must be continuously removed.

It would be desirable to do better. The difficulty lies in the fact that the equilibrium we are starting from is critical, and involves long range interactions and large fluctuations. Many of the standard perturbation schemes do not apply. One way of proceeding that may work in this situation is the following: Consider the distribution of vortex loops created by our equilibrium ensemble. Suppose we resolve all scales $\geq h$ in a flow, say by a finite-difference scheme. Consider the effect of the scales left unresolved on the scales that have been kept. these unresolved scales create a dielectric constant $e = e(h) = 1 + c_1 \int_\delta^h r^6 \exp(-K\mu r) dr$ (see equation (2)). If the computed velocity $\mathbf{u}$ in a cell of volume h^3 changes, equilibrium is not reached immediately; the time constant τ that characterizes the decay to equilibrium at scale r is $\tau = D/r^2$ (on dimensional grounds), where D is a diffusion coefficient that can be calculated from models of vortex interactions (Donnelly & Roberts (1971)). Thus the dielectric constant becomes time-dependent: $e = e(h,t) = 1 + C_1 \int_\delta^h r^6 \exp(-K\mu r)(1 - \exp(-t/\tau(r)) dr$. The simplest approximation is $D = $ constant. The complex part of the Fourier transform $\hat{e}(h,t)$ represents energy dissipation by the small scale equilibrium. As a result, the vorticity has two parts, one visible on the grid and one on subgrid scales; both affect the velocity and the second has a built-in delay that causes energy loss. An expansion of the delay function in a Taylor series produces an eddy viscosity model; the retention of the full delay function produces a rather simple integro-differential equation for the mean velocity. The whole machinery belongs to the class of approximation that go under the name of

"linear response theory", and that are applicable in the immediate neighborhood of thermal equilibria. The obvious advantage of the approach is that it is based on an expansion in a parameter, the fugacity, which is typically quite small, rather than on an expansion in a Reynolds number R which is very large in all problems of interest. These ideas are now being tried on the computer (for example, in Kast & Chorin (1996)).

CONCLUSION

I have sketched a theory of turbulence, i.e., a set of a priori assumptions about the statistical solutions of the Navier-Stokes equations, of which the main one is that in three space dimensions one can find a Gibbsian ensemble of incompressible flows, with turbulence living in its vicinity. I think that this is a well-motivated theory, and likely to be true (in fact, a partial experimental verification has turned out to be possible, see Barenblatt & Chorin (1996)).

To make this theory into a practical computing tool one has to construct a practically implementable perturbation expansion around the equilibrium. While this is in principle a more tractable task than the more commonly attempted expansions that start from the Stokes equations, one must face the difficulties that arise from the critical nature of the proposed initial state, with its long range correlations. The tools proposed for performing this expansion come from condensed-matter physics, and there is good hope is that they will succeed. The obvious caveat is that many seemingly fool-proof theories of turbulence have failed in the past.

It is the criticality of the basic equilibrium that constitutes the major qualitative difference between turbulence theory as it has just been described and other statistical theories in fluid dynamics and kinetic theory. This criticality is closely connected to the fact that one must deal with collections of functions rather with ensembles of discrete particles.

ACKNOWLEDGMENTS

This work was supported in part by the Applied Mathematical Sciences subprogram of the Office of Energy Research, U.S. Department of Energy, under Contract Number DE-AC03-76SF00098, and in part by the National Science Foundation under grant number DMS89-19074

REFERENCES

Ambegaokar, V., Halperin, B.I., Nelson, D. and Siggia, E., 1978, Dissipation in two-dimensional superfluids, Physical Review Letters, 40, 783–786.

Barenblatt, G.I. and Chorin, A.J., 1996, Small viscosity asymptotics for the inertial range of local turbulence and for the wall region of wall-bounded turbulent shear flow, Proceedings of the US National Academy of Sciences, in press.

Chandler, D., 1987, Introduction to Modern Statistical Mechanics, Oxford.

Chorin, A.J., 1993, Hairpin removal in vortex interactions, Journal of Computational Physics, **107**, 1–9.

Chorin, A.J., 1994, Vorticity and Turbulence, Springer, NY.

Chorin, A.J., 1996a, Turbulence as a near-equilibrium process, Lectures in Applied Mathematics, 31, 235–248.

Chorin, A.J., 1996b, Turbulence cascades through equilibrium spectra, Manuscript, University of California, Berkeley, Mathematics Department.

Chorin, A.J., 1996c, Partition functions and invariant states in two-dimensional and nearly two-dimensional turbulence, manuscript, University of California, Berkeley, Mathematics Department.

Chorin, A.J. and Hald, O., 1995, Vortex renormalization in three space dimensions, Physical Review B, 51, 11969–11972.

Chorin, A.J. and Hald, O., 1996, Analysis of Kosterlitz-Thouless transition models, Manuscript, Mathematics Department, University of California, Berkeley.

Donnelly, R.J. and Roberts, P.H., 1971, Stochastic theory of the nucleation of quantized vortices in superfluid helium, Philosophical Transactions of the Royal Society of London, A 271, 6–100.

Evans, D. and Morriss, G., 1990, Statistical Mechanics of Non-Equilibrium Liquids, Academic, NY.

Forster, D., 1975, Hydrodynamics Fluctuations, Broken Symmetry and Correlation Functions, Benjamin, Reading.

Gelfand, I.M. and Vilenkin, N. Ya., 1964, Generalized Functions, Vol 4: Applications of Harmonic Analysis, Academic, NY.

Hopf, E., 1952, Statistical hydromechanics and functional calculus, Journal of Rational Mechanics and Analysis, 1, pp. 87–141.

Huang, K., 1963, Statistical Mechanics, Wiley, NY.

Itzykson, C. and Drouffe, J. M., 1989, Statistical Field Theory, Cambridge University Press.

Kast, A. and Chorin, A.J., 1996, linear response theory for random flow, Manuscript, Lawrence Berkeley National Laboratory.

Lee, T.D., 1952, On some statistical properties of hydrodynamical and magnetohydrodynamical fields, Quarterly of Applied Mathematics, 10, pp. 69–72.

Lesieur, M., 1990, Turbulence in Fluids, Kluwer, Dordrecht.

McComb, W.D., 1989, Physical Theories of Turbulence, Cambridge University Press.

Williams, G., 1987, Vortex ring model of the superfluid lambda transition, Physical Review Letters, 59, pp. 1926–1929.

Zhou, H., 1996, On the motion of slender vortex lines, Ph.D. thesis, Mathematics Department, University of California, Berkeley.

FED-Vol. 238, 1996 Fluids Engineering Division Conference
Volume 3
ASME 1996

ON 3D VORTEX SCHEMES

Georges-Henri Cottet
LMC-IMAG
Université Joseph Fourier
Grenoble, France

ABSTRACT

We investigate various 3D vortex schemes, with a particular emphasis on the fulfillment of the divergence free constraint for the vorticity.

INTRODUCTION

Vortex methods (Chorin 1973, Leonard 1980) although based on the same principle for 3d and 2d flows, namely the concept of weak measure solutions to advection equations, have specific difficulties in 3d related to the divergence free constraint on the vorticity. Vortex filament methods are very particular from this point of view, as they use particles which are adapted to the geometry of the flow and thus implicitly enforce this condition. Apart from this particular case, which does not allow to easily handle diffusion in the method, it seems difficult to design a vortex method which would keep the basic features of vortex methods and guarantee a physically acceptable vorticity field. Let us recall that this issue is to some extent related to the conservativity of the method. Indeed, for the continuous Euler equations the preservation of the total vorticity directly follows from the fact that it is divergence free. Moreover the divergence free condition on the vorticity is crucial to ensure that the velocity is given in terms of the vorticity by the Biot-Savart law. Finally the fact that the vorticity remains divergence-free for all times in turn results from the fact that the divergence of the vorticity is advected by the flow. This is actually how one can check that the vorticity-velocity formulation is equivalent to the original velocity-pressure formulation. This is to say that the question of the divergence of the vorticity is central in the 3D fluid equations in vorticity form, not only from the physical and numerical point of view but also from the mathematical point of view. The goal of this paper is to review old or more recent recipes in vortex methods to address this issue. Numerical experiments illustrating the efficiency of these recipes will be presented elsewhere.

The paper is structured as follows: we first outline the definitions and main properties of the basic available vortex schemes. We then show several ways to improve these schemes in order to better fulfill the divergence free constraint, either by modifying the stretching term in the vorticity equation, or by projecting the vorticity at each time step on divergence free vector fields. We finally discuss several LES models in the light of the tools described in the course of the paper.

BASIC 3D VORTEX SCHEMES

In this section we recall the basic vortex schemes available for the 3D Euler equations written in velocity-vorticity:

$$\frac{\partial \omega}{\partial t} + \text{div}(u : \omega) - (\omega \cdot \nabla)u = 0 \quad (1)$$

$$\omega(\cdot, 0) = \omega_0 \quad (2)$$

$$u = K \star \omega. \quad (3)$$

The kernel K is a matrix valued function defined by

$$K \star \omega(x) = \frac{1}{4\pi} \int \frac{x - y}{|x - y|^3} \times \omega(y)\, dy = \text{curl}\, (G \star \omega)$$

where $G(x) = (4\pi|x|)^{-1}$ and $\times$ denotes the vector product.

We will be concerned with approximations of the vorticity of the type

$$\omega \simeq \sum_p v_p \omega_p \delta(x - x_p) \quad (4)$$

where v_p and ω_p are respectively the volume and the local vorticity at the particle p. These methods are sometimes called vortex *particle* methods as opposed to vortex filament methods where vorticity is concentrated on lines rather than points. Note also that these schemes are grid-free as they solely rely on particles, even for the evaluation of the velocity in (3). We will mention alternative schemes, called Vortex-In-Cell methods, where the velocity is first computed on a grid, through a classical Poisson solver, then interpolated to particles.

The original grid-free scheme is based on the weak exact measure solution of (1),(2) with initial vorticity given by (4). This solution reads

$$\omega^h(x, t) = \sum_p v_p \omega_p^h(t)\delta(x - x_p^h(t))$$

where the volumes v_p remain constant, as imposed by the incompressibility of the flow, and

$$\frac{d\omega_p^h}{dt} = \left[\nabla u^h(x_p^h, t)\right]\left[\omega_p^h\right] ; \quad \frac{dx_p^h}{dt} = u^h(x_p^h, t) \quad (5)$$

$[\nabla u^h]$ denotes the matrix with coefficients the 3 partial derivatives of the 3 components of u^h. The initial values necessary to solve this system of ODE are given by the initial vorticity and positions of the particles. If particles initially lie on a regular lattice of meshsize h, $v_p = h^3$.

The velocity u^h and its derivatives are computed from the Biot-Savart law (3), where however the kernel K is regularized to avoid infinite values resulting from short range interactions of particles. The construction of the regularized kernel K_ε is generally done through the convolution by a *cut-off* function ζ_ε. Using spherically symmetric cut-off leads to explicit simple expressions of K_ε (Beale and Majda 1985).

Although this scheme is a straightforward extension of 2d schemes, with a natural way to handle the stretching, its major difficulty is that is does not conserve the basic invariants of the flow, starting with the total vorticity.

To overcome this difficulty, a variant of this scheme has been proposed (Choquin and Cottet 1988, Winckelmans and Leonard 1988). It is based on the remark that, if $\omega = \operatorname{curl} u$, something which is true for the continuous equation but not at the discrete level, $[\nabla u]\omega = [\nabla u]^t \omega$. The so-called transpose scheme is based on the second form of the stretching term. It thus reads

$$\frac{d\omega_p^h}{dt} = \left[\nabla u^h(x_p^h, t)\right]^t \left[\omega_p^h\right]$$

The conservativity of this method follows from straigthforward algebra, as soon as the regularization preserves the symmetry properties of the kernel K; if we focus on the component k of the vorticity:

$$\left(\sum_p \frac{d\omega_p}{dt}\right)_k = \sum_{p,i} \frac{\partial u_i}{\partial x_k}(\omega_p)_i$$
$$= \sum_{p,p',i} \left(\frac{\partial K_\varepsilon}{\partial x_k}(x_p - x_{p'}) \times \omega_{p'}\right)_i (\omega_p)_i$$
$$= \sum_{p,p'} \left(\frac{\partial K_\varepsilon}{\partial x_k}(x_p - x_{p'}) \times \omega_{p'}\right) \cdot (\omega_p)$$
$$= \sum_{p,p'} \left(\frac{\partial K_\varepsilon}{\partial x_k}(x_p - x_{p'}), \omega_{p'}, \omega_p\right)$$

Exchanging indices p, p' in the above determinant turns the sum into its opposite, which therefore must vanish.

Leonard and Winckelmans (1993) report results which confirm the improvement of this scheme in terms of conservation of the invariants of the flow (including angular impulse and energy). However, other results, concerning shear layer calculations (Knio and Ghoniem 1990) or comparison with tabulated ring

clusions. As a matter of fact, the transpose scheme has the drawback to destroy one nice property of the original scheme, namely the fact that it allows particles lying along vortex lines to remain so. The reason is that integrating (5) yields

$$\omega_p^h(t) = \left[\exp\left(\int_0^t [\nabla u^h(X_p^h(s), s)]\, ds\right)\right][\omega_p^h(0)]$$
$$= \left[D_x X^h(x_p; t, 0)\right][\omega_p^h(0)]$$

In the above expression $D_x X$ stands for the derivatives of the flow map. As a result, if the vorticity at a given particle points towards a neighbor, then, to the leading order, this property will be preserved for all time, and vortex filaments are conserved by the numerical methods. An alternative way to explain why the original scheme can be superior to the transpose scheme is to differentiate its master equation (1). One easily obtains

$$\frac{\partial(\operatorname{div}\omega^h)}{\partial t} + \operatorname{div}(u^h(\operatorname{div}\omega^h)) = 0 \quad (6)$$

This means that if one starts from a divergence free initial distribution of particles (ideally a continuous distribution along filaments of vorticity), vortex lines will not be broken by the method. This property is not satisfied by the transpose scheme.

In any case, both schemes fail to give a correct topology of the filaments as soon as particles are strained apart from one another, something which in general happens very soon if the flow becomes fully three-dimensional. The rest of the paper is devoted to recipes which aim at improving this aspect of 3D vortex methods.

Let us conclude this section by some comments on the convergence properties of these methods. As usual for numerical methods, convergence is a consequence of consistency and stability. Consistency analysis looks at the truncation errors produced by the method. They come from 2 sources: the regularization error resulting from the use of K_ε instead of K in the Biot-Savart law, and the initialization error resulting from replacing a continuous initial vorticity field by a discrete set of particles. To further analyze the first error, it is convenient to compare the exact solution to the solution u_ε of the continuous regularized Euler equation, that is (1)-(3) with K_ε instead of K. It is not difficult to show that $u - u_\varepsilon$ is of the order of ε^{r+1}, where r is the number of vanishing moments of the cut-off used for the regularization. To control the stability and the effect of the initialization error, one can observe that both ω^h and ω_ε are solutions to advection equations, so one can easily form an equation satisfied by $\omega^h - \omega_\varepsilon$. It is then possible to design distribution spaces where

- bounds of the initial error exactly translate classical estimates for quadrature rules

- optimal stability estimates hold.

translate error bounds for the vorticity in these weak norms into more conventional norms for the velocity (say energy norms). Typically one obtains $u^h - u_\varepsilon$ of the order of $h^m \varepsilon^{1-m}$ for smooth solutions, where m is the order of the quadrature rule on which is based the initialization of particles. It is worthwhile to emphasize that essentially the same arguments apply to the original or transpose scheme, to VIC or grid-free methods, and to vortex filament methods.

DISSIPATION OF DIVERGENCE PROCEDURE

This procedure has been used in the context of Maxwell equations, where it is crucial to preserve the divergence free nature of the magnetic field in order to conserve the electric charge. The idea is to add to the vorticity equation (1) an artificial viscosity term whose effect is to dissipate the divergence eventually produced by the numerical method. The master equation is now

$$\frac{\partial \omega}{\partial t} + \mathrm{div}(u\omega) - (\omega \cdot \nabla)u = \sigma \mathrm{grad}(\mathrm{div}\,\omega) \qquad (7)$$

Taking the divergence of this equation indeed yields

$$\frac{\partial(\mathrm{div}\,\omega)}{\partial t} + (u \cdot \nabla)(\mathrm{div}\,\omega) = \sigma\Delta(\mathrm{div}\,\omega)$$

Particle Strength Exchange schemes have enough flexibility to handle any kind of second order differential operator (Degond and Mas-Gallic 1989), and in particular the one in the right hand side of (7). We recall that the general recipe form constructing such schemes is to start from an integral approximation of this operator, then to discretize the integrals on the vortices. The first step gives

$$\frac{\partial^2 \omega}{\partial x_i \partial x_j} \simeq$$
$$-\frac{\lambda_{ij}}{\varepsilon^4}\int[\omega(x) - \omega(y)](x_i - y_i)(x_j - y_j)\theta_\varepsilon(x - y)\,dy$$

where the coefficients λ_{ij} must be such that

$$\lambda_{ij}\int x_i^2 x_j^2 \theta(x-y)\,dy = \begin{cases} 2 & \text{if } i = j \\ 1 & \text{if not} \end{cases}$$

θ is a cut-off with spherical symmetry and ε is a small parameter. Up to a normalization of θ, typical values in 3D are $\lambda_{ii} = 2$, and, for $i \neq j$, $\lambda_{ij} = 3$. Stability analysis can be made on both the equation (7) and on its integral approximation. Choosing σ of the order of ε^2 leads to a time step constraint $\Delta t \leq 1$. The resulting vortex scheme, based on the original form of the stretching term is (from now on, for simplicity, we will drop the superscript h and use instead the index k to refer to the component numbers of the velocity and vorticity fields)

$$\frac{d\omega_p^k}{dt} = \sum_j \frac{\partial u^k}{\partial x_j}(x_p, t)\omega_p^j - \sigma\varepsilon^{-4}$$
$$\sum_{j,q} \lambda_{kj}v_q(\omega_p^j - \omega_q^j)(x_p^k - x_q^k)(x_p^j - x_q^j)\theta_\varepsilon(x_p - x_q)$$

Note that this diffusion procedure can be combined with the transpose scheme, in which case it gives a conservative scheme. The numerical experiments we have performed seem to indicate that this method is very efficient in damping the divergence of the vorticity but that it may produce undesired dissipation on the vorticity itself.

MODIFYING THE STRETCHING TERM

The schemes we are going to described are based on the conservative form $\mathrm{div}(\omega : u)$ of the stretching term. The reason for using this form is that, if we take the divergence of the resulting vorticity equation and use the fact that u is divergence free, we obtain

$$\frac{\partial}{\partial t}(\mathrm{div}\,\omega) = 0$$

which is better than (6). In particular, unlike (6), it does not allow exponential increase of the divergence of the vorticity. The question is how to discretize this term on particles. Note that with that expression of the stretching term, we have lost the nice form of an advection equation, so the usual rule to derive particle schemes do not apply any more. Let us develop the stretching term in the conservative form. If u is divergence free, we get

$$\mathrm{div}(\omega : u) = (\omega \cdot \nabla)u + u(\mathrm{div}\,\omega)$$

To derive a vortex scheme, we thus need to discretize $\mathrm{div}\,\omega$, given a particle description of ω. To do so the general recipe is to regularize ω, then to differentiate the resulting smooth field and finally to evaluate it on the particles. If in addition, we seek a conservative scheme, which is natural in view of the fact that the master equation is now written in conservative form, we need to somewhat alter the way derivatives of velocity are usually derived to compute the term $(\omega \cdot \nabla)u$. Instead of differentiating the Biot-Savart law, it seems more clever to use formulas of finite-difference type:

$$\partial_i u(x) = \sum_p v_p u_p \partial_i \zeta_\varepsilon(x - x_p)$$

where x_p, v_p are the locations and volumes of particles, and u_p are their velocities obtained through the regularized Biot-Savart law. We then obtain the following vortex scheme

$$\frac{d\omega_p}{dt} = h^3 \sum_{j,q}(u_q\omega_p^j + u_p\omega_q^j)\frac{(x_p^j - x_q^j)}{|x_p - x_q|}\zeta'_\varepsilon(|x_p - x_q|)$$

(for simplicity we have assumed here that all volumes are equal to h^3 and that the cut-off ζ has spherical symmetry). This scheme is clearly conservative.

137

natural in the context of Vortex-In-Cell methods (however we do not think it has ever been used). A VIC scheme based on the conservative form of the stretching term would consist in

- assign vorticity to grid points

- call a Poisson solver to compute the stream function on the grid

- differentiate on the grid to obtain velocity values; multiply them with grid vorticity values already available

- differentiate quantities of the type $u^i \omega^j$ on the grid and interpolate them back to particles

at each time step.

CORRECTION OF DIVERGENCE BASED ON HELMHOLTZ DECOMPOSITION

The idea is to decompose, at each time step the vorticity into a gradient and a rotational part:

$$\omega = \operatorname{grad} \pi + \operatorname{curl} \phi \qquad (8)$$

and to recover a divergence free field by substracting the gradient part of ω. This is actually equivalent to using a lagrange multiplier in the vorticity equation to enforce the divergence free constraint on the vorticity (similar to the pressure in the velocity-pressure formulation), and to use a transport-projection algorithm. The issue is to compute π in a vortex code. We will distinguish between Vortex In Cell and grid free approaches.

VIC implementation

Taking the divergence of (8) yields

$$\Delta \pi = \operatorname{div} \omega$$

which has to be supplemented with boundary conditions which depend on the problem under consideration. This system can be easily solved on a grid, once vorticity values have been determined. So a typical sequence is, starting from particle weights ω_p, to

- assign vorticity to the grid

- compute $\operatorname{div} \omega$ on the grid

- call a Poisson solver, compute π then $\operatorname{grad} \pi$ on the grid

- interpolate $\operatorname{grad} \pi$ back to the particles and write

$$\omega'_p = \omega_p - (\operatorname{grad} \pi)_p$$

This procedure actually allows to get rid of the divergence of ω on the grid if one can check that assigning the particle values $(\operatorname{grad} \pi)_p$ on the grid will lead back to its grid values as computed in the second step above, or, in other words, if interpolation

It is well-known that this is not true in general if one uses a naive interpolation procedure. This is a classical problem in particle methods which can be stated as follows: given a grid quantity α_j, we wish to find corresponding particle values α_p such that assigning these values on the grid will lead to α_j. Since there are in general more particles than grid points, this is not a well posed linear system. However one can try to solve the linear system

$$IA(\alpha_p) = I(\alpha_j)$$

where I and A denote respectively the interpolation and assignment operators. The above linear system can be solved by an iterative process which essentially consists in alternating interpolation and assignment steps.

Grid-free implementation and Novikov calculation

In a grid-free code (that is when velocities are computed by the Biot-Savart law) π must be given an integral representation. Assuming that ω vanishes at infinity, it is natural to write

$$\pi = G_\varepsilon \star \operatorname{div} \omega$$

where G_ε is a regularized version of G. The new particle vorticity which results from this is therefore

$$\omega' = \omega - \nabla G_\varepsilon \star \operatorname{div} \omega \qquad (9)$$

Let us compare this vorticity field to the one suggested by Novikov. Novikov's vorticity is the curl of the velocity (this is an obvious way to enforce a divergence free vorticity):

$$\omega'_N = \operatorname{curl} u_\varepsilon \text{ where } u_\varepsilon = \operatorname{curl} G_\varepsilon \star \omega$$

This continuous field must then be sampled on the existing particles. Straightforward calculation yields

$$\omega'_N = \omega_\varepsilon - \nabla G_\varepsilon \star \operatorname{div} \omega \qquad (10)$$

where ω_ε is the original regularized vorticity field. Let us compare formulas (9) and (10); the later clearly induces some extra dissipation: if the original particle vorticity is already divergence free, (9) does not change it, whereas there is still a regularization step in (10) which will thus spread the vorticity carried by one particle among the neighbors. The trouble with (9) is however that the vorticity field it gives, unlike ω'_N, is not exactly divergence free, because of the cut-off required in the evaluation of π. This difficulty is very much related to the assignment-interpolation issue raised above by the VIC approach. The cure for this problem is very similar: one just needs to process the weights of the particles before applying formula (9). More precisely one has to find weights β such that, if we denote by $\star_d$ discrete convolution,

$$\beta \star_d \zeta_\varepsilon = \nabla G_\varepsilon \star_d \operatorname{div} \omega \qquad (11)$$

on all particles This is a linear system which can be solved by iterative techniques, just as in the case of VIC methods. The grid free code is now, at each time step

Novikov calculation

- solve the linear system (11)
- substract the weights β from the vorticity weights ω.

Note that this scheme is very close to the W-scheme of Leonard and Winckelmans (1993), with however the difference that in this reference the processing step is done on the whole vorticity field and not on its gradient part.

To conclude this section, let us insist on the fact that all the tools presented here should in practice be combined with remeshing procedures to ensure a correct accuracy in all parts of the flow, as soon as the strain starts creating a large amount of distortion in the particle mesh.

LES MODELS

Although the motivation in LES models has little to do with enforcing a divergence free vorticity, we wish to consider them here from this point of view. If one has in mind direct extension to vortex methods of existing, well documented LES models, it seems that a good candidate for the vorticity equation is, written component by component (Mansour and al. 1978)

$$\frac{\partial \omega_i}{\partial t} + \operatorname{div}(u\omega_i) - \sum_j \omega_j \frac{\partial u_i}{\partial x_j} =$$
$$\sum_j \frac{\partial}{\partial x_j}\left(\nu_t(\frac{\partial \omega_i}{\partial x_j} - \frac{\partial \omega_j}{\partial x_i})\right) \qquad (12)$$

where the turbulent viscosity ν_t is of the order of $\varepsilon^2|\omega|$. Taking the divergence of this equation gives

$$\frac{\partial(\operatorname{div}\omega)}{\partial t} + (u \cdot \nabla)(\operatorname{div}\omega) =$$
$$\sum_{ij} \frac{\partial^2}{\partial x_i \partial x_j}\left(\nu_t(\frac{\partial \omega_i}{\partial x_j} - \frac{\partial \omega_j}{\partial x_i})\right) = 0 \quad (13)$$

(as it is seen by exchanging indices i and j in the right hand side). This form of the diffusion term is thus well designed for not contributing to divergence production.

It is worth noticing that the right hand side of (12) can be split in 2 terms, one being a classical Smagorinsky term

$$\frac{\partial}{\partial x_j}\left(\nu_t \frac{\partial \omega_i}{\partial x_j}\right)$$

the other being a correction precisely of the type used in (7) to dissipate the divergence of ω. On the basis of what we have said in this section, we believe that this correction may not be the best gradient term to control the divergence of the vorticity, and that a projection algorithm could be more efficient to take

both the vorticity transport scheme and the diffusion scheme. Let us point out that, even if these approaches are equivalent at the continuous level, they are not at the discrete level (in particular notice that, in the particle diffusion scheme, derivatives are not dealt with the same way as they would be to evaluate the divergence of the vorticity, so, for the numerical method, cancellations do not apply any more to give (13) from (12)).

Let us now shortly comment on other diffusion models which have been designed more specifically for vortex methods (Cottet 1995). In these models, one carefully looks at truncation errors produced by vortex methods and selectively corrects part of this error which can be responsible for spurious small scales. In vortex methods, truncation errors come from the regularization used in the calculation of the velocity. To account for this error, it is possible to form an equivalent equation satisfied by the regularized vorticity $\omega_\varepsilon = \sum_p v_p \omega_p \zeta_\varepsilon(x - x_p)$ (or the collection of vortex blobs, as opposed to vortex particles). One finds an advection equation plus a term which, for positive cut-off, can be seen as a second order operator:

$$\frac{\partial \omega_\varepsilon}{\partial t} + \operatorname{div}(\tilde{u}\omega_\varepsilon) = \qquad (14)$$
$$c\varepsilon^2 \operatorname{div}\left([\nabla u_\varepsilon]\nabla \omega\right) + O(\varepsilon^4)$$

where $\tilde{u}$ is a divergence free $O(\varepsilon^2)$ perturbation of u_ε and c is the second order monemtum of the cut-off function. The diffusion model proposed by Cottet (1995) consists in cancelling the part of the right hand side above which could increase the enstrophy. It is shown that this can be done by the following Particle Strength Exchange scheme

$$\frac{d\omega_p}{dt} = \qquad (15)$$
$$\sum_q ((\omega_p - \omega_q)v_q \left\{[u(x_p) - u(x_q)] \cdot \nabla\zeta_\varepsilon(x_p - x_q)\right\}_-$$

where the index - means that the exchange of vorticity takes place only when the quantity between brackets is negative; if the cut-off is a decreasing function of the distance, this occurs when particles diverge from one another.

A similar approach can be used in 3D. To form an equivalent equation one needs to determine the effect of the cut-off on the 2 non linear terms in the left hand side of (1). The first one will give a similar expression as in 2D; the stretching will clearly give another term and the issue is to find out what is the appropriate correction for this term. The strategy followed to deal with the right hand side of (14) does not work any more for the error term coming form the stretching: there is no reason to require that this term should not produce enstrophy (it results form the stretching term which itself is supposed to produce enstrophy). Instead, it seems natural to use precisely the correction which will cancel the divergence of the vorticity resulting from (15). The 3D a projection step on divergence free vorticity fields, using the tools described in the previous section.

CONCLUSION

We have explored several ways to improve the efficiency of vortex particle methods for 3D incompressible flows. It seems that dealing with the stretching term in conservative form can be a way to combine the advantages of the original scheme (conservation of filaments) and the transpose scheme (conservation of total vorticity). On the other hand, projection methods based on Helmholtz decomposition of vector fields can be easily incorporated in vortex schemes. They however require some care and a processing stage to make sure that they significantly reduce the divergence of the vorticity.

These methods, combined with Particle Strength Exchange schemes, also allow to handle various turbulent viscosity schemes.

REFERENCES

Beale, J.T., Eydeland, A., and Turkington, B., 1991, "Numerical tests of 3-D vortex methods using a vortex ring with swirl," *Lectures in Applied Mathematics*, Vol. 28, pp. 1 - 10.

Beale, J.T., and Majda, A., 1985, "High order accurate vortex methods with explicit velocity kernels," *J. Comp. Phys.*, Vol 58, pp. 188 - 208.

Choquin, J.-P., and Cottet, G.-H., 1988, "Sur l'analyse d'une classe de méthodes de vortex tridimensionnelles,", *C. R. Acad. Sci.*, Vol. 306, pp. 739 - 742.

Chorin, A.J., 1973, "Numerical study of slightly viscous flow,", *J. Fluid. Mech.*, Vol. 57, pp. 785 - 796.

Cottet, G.-H., 1995, "Artificial viscosity models for vortex and particle methods," submitted to *J. Comp. Phys.*

Degond, P., and Mas-Gallic, S., 1989, "The weighted particle method for convection-diffusion equations," *Math. of Comp.*, Vol. 53, pp. 485 - 526.

Knio, O.M., and Ghoniem, A.F., 1990, "Numerical study of three dimensional vortex methods,", *J. Comp. Phys.*, Vol. 86, pp. 75 - 106.

Leonard, A., 1980," Vortex methods for flow simulation," *J. Comp. Phys.*, Vol. 37., pp. 289 - 335.

Winckelmans, G.S., and Leonard, A., 1988, "Weak solutions of the three-dimensional vorticity equation with vortex singularities," *Phys. Fluids*, Vol. 31, pp. 1838 - 1839.

Winckelmans, G.S., and Leonard, A., 1993, "Contributions to vortex particle methods for the computation of three-dimensional incompressible unsteady flows," *J. Comp. Phys*, Vol. 109, pp. 247 - 273.

Mansour, N.N., Ferziger, J.H., and Reynolds, W.C., 1978, "Large-eddy simulation of a turbulent mixing layer,", Reprt TF-11, Thermosciences Div., Dept. Mech. Eng., Stanford University.

FED-Vol. 238, 1996 Fluids Engineering Division Conference
Volume 3
ASME 1996

ON THE FORMULATION OF THE LARGE-EDDY SIMULATION
FOR TURBULENT VORTICAL FLOWS IN COMPLEX DOMAINS

Stephen A. Jordan
Naval Undersea Warfare Center
Newport, RI 02841

ABSTRACT

When deriving a governing set of generalized large-eddy simulation (LES) equations for resolving turbulent flows in complex domains, two mathematical operations are formally necessary. These operations comprise execution of the spatial filter and transformations to the generalized curvilinear coordinate system. In the derivation, the order of these operations can produce two separate LES systems that differ only by their representation of the metric coefficients. This paper presents both LES systems and reasons for choosing one formulation instead of the other. Two explicit box filters are designed, one for the physical domain and the other for the curvilinear space. The energy damping effects in wavenumber space and the computational cost of each filter are compared using results from a direct numerical simulation of the turbulent near wake of a circular cylinder at a Reynolds number of 3400.

INTRODUCTION

The large-eddy simulation (LES) is gaining popularity as a viable numerical alternative to the traditional Reynolds-Averaged Navier Stokes (RANS) approach for engineering solutions of complex turbulent flows. Its success rests primarily on the rapid advancements in supercomputer technology as well as the recent developments in the LES methodology itself. Unlike the full-scale modeling inherent in a RANS technique, the LES method requires resolution of the dominate energy-bearing scales of the turbulent field while modeling only the remaining finer eddies which tend toward homogeneous and isotropic characteristics. Demarcation between the resolved and modeled scales is formally instituted by spatially filtering the basic governing equations of the fluid motion. In most computations however, this filter is actually treated implicitly through the spatial resolution of the implemented grid. Those physics lying beneath the grid resolution embody the subgrid scales (SGS) of the turbulent field

and usually encompass most of the equilibrium range of the kinetic energy. Under this premise of an energy balance, today's SGS models are much simpler in form and better delineate the turbulent physics of their assigned scales as opposed to the typical full-turbulence models used in the RANS computations.

Over the past twenty five years, LES results have uncovered the complex turbulent physics in numerous engineering applications with variations of the channel flow being the most popular problem. It is common knowledge now that Deardorff (1970) performed one of the earliest investigations of this canonical flow which clearly demonstrated the feasibility of the LES approach for resolving turbulence. In a more recent work, Yang and Ferziger (1993) investigated the Reynolds stress statistics of the channel where rectangular ribs were mounted periodically on the floor. Other notable examples of this flow include Shimomura (1991) who studied the anisotropic laminarization of a magnetohydrodynamic turbulent channel when subjected to a uniform magnetic field and Akelvoll and Moin (1993) who precisely predicted the channel reattachment length of the separated turbulent region behind a backward facing step. Finally, Zang and Piomelli (1990) investigated the transition process to turbulence in a plane channel using the dynamic SGS eddy viscosity model designed by Germano et al. (1991). Besides the channel flow, a few other LES applications include the shear driven cavity (Jordan and Ragab, 1994 and Zang et al., 1993), a jet in a crossflow (Jones and Wille, 1995) and the near wake behind either a square (Murakami et al., 1993) or circular (Balachandar and Mittal, 1995) cylinder.

The LES applications sited above (as well as most others) are geometrically simple in a sense that the grid boundaries were regular and the governing fundamental equations were written in cartesian coordinates. Few exceptions include Schumann and Krettenauer (1990) who simulated the turbulent convection over a sinusoidal undulated terrain at an infinite Rayleigh number and Lund and Moin (1995) who resolved the turbulence statistics in the spatially-evolving boundary layers along the upper and lower concave-walls of a turbulent channel. Although these exceptions required coordinate transformation of the cartesian form of the governing equations to accommodate a boundary fitted grid to the wall curvature, no formal treatment of the accompanying metrics was addressed. As in a RANS approach, their coordinate transformations were performed after obtaining the proper cartesian form of the LES equations which can be viewed principly as a mathematical convenience to align the flow solutions with the respective grid lines.

The present work aims to formally derive a curvilinear coordinate form of the LES equations with special emphasis directed toward treatment of the transformation metrics. Because this derivation requires two operations (the grid filter and the coordinate transformation), the curvilinear form can not be acquired in a unique manner. The question to be answered is whether one should filter the governing equations before or after the coordinate transformation. This order is especially important when employing mixed modeling concepts where the Leonard term is evaluated explicitly. By contrast, an order of operations does not arise when transforming a RANS set of equations because only that single operation in needed to arrive at the final generalized system. In the following sections, the filter operation is restricted to only that which is synonymous with the spatial resolution of the generated grid. Subsequent filtering such as the test filter operation which defines use of a dynamic SGS model Germano et al. (1991) will not be addressed specifically herein.

As just mentioned, two approaches are possible when formulating a set of LES equations in a curvilinear coordinate framework. The difference rests solely on the representation, interpretation and evaluation of the transformation metrics. As an alternate to the traditional approach, if the transformations are performed prior to the filter operation (rather than after), then the accompanying metrics should be considered as filtered quantities. In the present paper, important issues of both formulations are discussed that deal with satisfaction of the commutative property between the filter and the differentiation, the resultant truncation error and the filtering of the metric coefficients. Two box filters are designed for application in either the physical domain or the transformed space. Finally, these filters are tested and evaluated using the DNS results of a classic vortical flow involving flow past a circular cylinder

FORMULATION

To derive a generalized curvilinear coordinate formulation of the LES equations for incompressible turbulent flows, we begin with the well-known cartesian system comprising the continuity and the Navier-Stokes equations. In primitive variables, the non-dimensional system appears as

$$\frac{\partial u_i}{\partial x_i} = 0 \tag{1}$$

$$\frac{\partial u_i}{\partial t} + \frac{\partial u_j u_i}{\partial x_j} = \frac{\partial p}{\partial x_j} + \frac{1}{Re}\frac{\partial^2 u_i}{\partial x_j \partial x_j} \tag{2}$$

where Re symbolizes the Reynolds number and the variables u_i and p represent the velocity and pressure quantities, respectively.

Solving these equations without modification necessitates resolution of all the spatial scales of the turbulent field which is classified as a direct numerical simulation (DNS). One can now choose to either filter this DNS system, followed by a transformation operation, or vice versa to acquire the LES formulation in generalized curvilinear coordinates (ξ^k). The resultant equations differ only by their mathematical depiction of the metric quantities.

The first order of operations proposed here involves filtering the DNS system prior to any transformations. This particular order produces the governing equations

$$\frac{\partial \sqrt{g}\,\xi_i^k\,\overline{u}_i}{\partial \xi^k} = 0 \tag{3}$$

$$\frac{\partial \sqrt{g}\,\overline{u}_i}{\partial t} + \frac{\partial \sqrt{g}\,\xi_{x_j}^k\,\overline{u}_j\overline{u}_i}{\partial \xi^k} = \frac{\partial \sqrt{g}\,\xi_{x_j}^k\,\overline{p}}{\partial \xi^k}$$
$$+ \frac{\partial \tau_i^k}{\partial \xi^k} + \frac{1}{Re}\frac{\partial}{\partial \xi^k}\left[\sqrt{g}\,g^{k\ell}\frac{\partial \overline{u}_i}{\partial \xi^\ell}\right] \tag{4}$$

where each term is shown in its non-dimensional strong conservation-law form (Vinokur, 1974). The coefficients $\xi_{x_j}^k$ (as well as $g^{k\ell}$) and $\sqrt{g}$ denote the contravariant metrics and the Jacobian of the transformation, respectively. In these equations, only the flow quantities are filtered as designated by an overbar.

This order is equivalent to the traditional procedure where the basic cartesian form of the respective equations is derived prior to any coordinate transformations. In a RANS formulation for example, the overbar would denote the mean motion instead of the resolved turbulent quantity as shown. Inasmuch as the filtering operation appears before the transformation, the types of filter functions are identical to those in the literature for cartesian coordinate systems (Leonard, 1974). Under this approach, the SGS stress tensor (τ_i^k) is defined as

$$\tau_i^k = \sqrt{g}\,\xi_j^k\,(\overline{u}_j\overline{u}_i - \overline{u_j u_i}) \tag{5}$$

which is simply a transformation of its cartesian counterpart (τ_{ij}) to curvilinear coordinates .

There are many difficulties when numerically implementing the above derivation over a boundary fitted grid as well as assessing the finite differencing effects in the wavenumber space. Because the filter function is formally represented in cartesian coordinates, evaluation of the Leonard term ($L_{ij} = \overline{\overline{u}_i\,\overline{u}_j} - \overline{u}_i\,\overline{u}_j$) would be cumbersome to resolve consistently along the curvilinear lines in the physical domain. Moreover, the spectral physics of the Leonard term in wavenumber space would be difficult to isolate from the attenuation effects due to the spatial approximations used for each derivative. In the above formulation, the metric coefficients are represented as continuous functions which are evaluated exactly. Although their analytical determination is certainly possible for a particular grid, the order of the leading term in the truncation error of both the first and second-order derivatives is actually reduced compared to that obtained through their difference approximation. To this end, the first approach can only be viewed as a valid LES methodology if one ignores these salient drawbacks associated with its implementation.

An alternate approach to the above derivation is to filter the DNS system after performing the transformations. This order gives the LES equations

$$\frac{\partial \overline{\sqrt{g}\,\xi_i^k\,u_i}}{\partial \xi^k} = 0 \tag{6}$$

$$\frac{\partial \overline{\sqrt{g}\,u_i}}{\partial t} + \frac{\partial \overline{\sqrt{g}\,\xi_{x_j}^k\,u_j\,\overline{u}_i}}{\partial \xi^k} = \frac{\partial \overline{\sqrt{g}\,\xi_{x_i}^k\,p}}{\partial \xi^k}$$
$$+ \frac{\partial \tau_i^k}{\partial \xi^k} + \frac{1}{Re}\frac{\partial}{\partial \xi^k}\left[\sqrt{g}\,g^{k\ell}\frac{\partial u_i}{\partial \xi^\ell}\right] \tag{7}$$

Because the transformations are performed first, the filter operation is now sensibly directed along the grid lines where the independent spatial variables are the curvilinear coordinates. Explicit filtering in this approach can occur in either the physical domain or the computational space with both applications having characteristic filter widths defined by the local metric coefficient (see Fig. 1). With the filter defined in curvilinear coordinates, one can easily show that the partial differentiation and the filtering commute for each transformed term. Furthermore, decomposition of the filtered non-linear term into its resolved and model elements will yield Leonard, cross and Reynolds stresses similar in form to their cartesian counterparts. However, the SGS stress field shown in equations (6) and (7) assumes that this initial filter operation is applied implicitly through the spatial resolution of the implemented grid. The Leonard term is assumed negligible and the cross and Reynolds stress terms are combined to define the SGS field field as

$$\tau_i^k = \overline{\sqrt{g}\,\xi_j^k\,u_j}\,\overline{u}_i - \overline{\sqrt{g}\,\xi_j^k\,u_j\,u_i} \tag{8}$$

At this point, the contravariant velocity components can be introduced into the LES equations. Each metric coefficient can be declared resolved and independent from its respective resolved turbulent quantity because the metrics should be conceived as smooth functions which are numerically evaluated and devoid of any fluctuations. It is important to note that the difference approximation used for each metric coefficient at the field points can be viewed as a separate mechanism of spatial filtering. By substituting the resolved contravariant velocity components ($\overline{U}^k$) into equations (6) and (7), we obtain

$$\frac{\partial \overline{U}^k}{\partial \xi^k} = 0 \tag{9}$$

$$\frac{\partial \overline{\sqrt{g}\,u_i}}{\partial t} + \frac{\partial \overline{U}^k\,\overline{u}_i}{\partial \xi^k} = \frac{\partial \overline{\sqrt{g}\,\xi_{x_i}^k\,p}}{\partial \xi^k}$$
$$+ \frac{\partial \sigma_i^k}{\partial \xi^k} + \frac{1}{Re}\frac{\partial}{\partial \xi^k}\left[\overline{\sqrt{g}\,g^{k\ell}}\frac{\partial \overline{u}_i}{\partial \xi^\ell}\right] \tag{10}$$

where the SGS stress tensor (σ_i^k) is expressed as

$$\sigma_i^k = \overline{U^k}\,\overline{u}_i - \overline{U^k\,u_i} \tag{11}$$

and the Leonard term becomes

$$L_i^k = \overline{\overline{U^k}\,\overline{u}_i} - \overline{U^k\,u_i} \tag{12}$$

which could be evaluated explicitly along the curvilinear lines in either the physical domain or contravariant space using an appropriately designed filter.

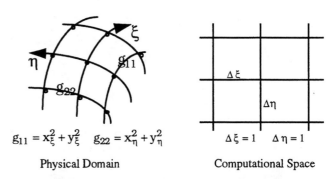

$$g_{11} = x_\xi^2 + y_\xi^2 \qquad g_{22} = x_\eta^2 + y_\eta^2$$

Physical Domain   Computational Space

Figure 1. Filtering Along the Curvilinear Lines

FILTERING

The most common filtering functions used in LES are those of the sharp cut-off, Gaussian and box filters. To assume that all contributions from the Leonard term vanish (as is assumed in the above formulations as well as many others), the grid-filter function is essentially an implicit sharp cut-off filter which prohibits any energy transfer beyond the cut-off wavenumber. This viewpoint excludes any implicit damping of energy due to the finite difference approximations used for the fluid motion derivatives. For example, if the non-linear term is approximated by low-order finite differences, the Leonard term will be completely masked by the truncation error. Conversely, when high-order finite-differences are used and the Leonard term is evaluated explicitly, such as in a dynamic or mixed model computation, the box filter is often chosen because its explicit application resides in the physical domain.

When the transformation operation is performed prior to filtering, one should consider each metric coefficient as a filtered quantity. This viewpoint is justified due to the implicit filtering inherent in the finite differencing schemes used to evaluate the metric coefficients. For example, numerical approximation of the metric coefficient x_ξ by second-order central differences carries a built-in box-type filter of finite width $\delta\xi$. We can show the exact relation between this differencing scheme and the box filter as

$$x_\xi \approx \frac{\delta x}{\delta \xi} = \frac{x(\xi+1) - x(\xi-1)}{2} = \frac{\delta}{\delta \xi}\left\{\frac{1}{2}\int_{\xi-1}^{\xi+1} x(\xi)\delta\xi\right\} \tag{13}$$

where the integral in the parentheses is a definition for the box filter. Thus, approximation of the metric coefficients by second-order finite differences (as well as higher order schemes) implicitly attenuates all the spectral components of the dependent grid variables in wavenumber space (k) except at k = 0.

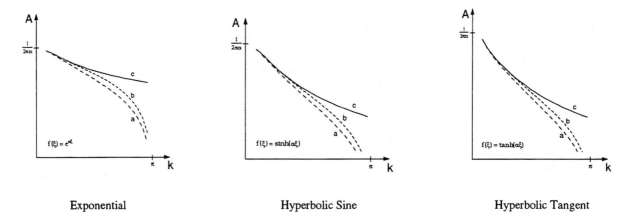

| Exponential | Hyperbolic Sine | Hyperbolic Tangent |

**Figure 2 Attenuation of the Fourier Amplitudes of Three Stretching Functions
Caused by Finite Difference Approximations of the Metric Coefficients**

In grid generation, the most common analytical expressions used to stretch the spatial distribution of the finite points are the exponential, hyperbolic sine and hyperbolic tangent functions (Thompson et al., 1985). Attenuation of their Fourier amplitudes in wavenumber space by the implicit box filter in equation (13) is shown in Fig. 2 as curve (a) where the maximum resolved scaled wavenumber ($w = 2\pi k / N$) of each function is π; N+1 is the number of grid points and $1 \leq k \leq N / 2$. In this figure, the exact Fourier amplitudes (no filtering) of each function are designated by curve (c). One can see that significant attenuation of the spectral components begins at very low wavenumbers. At $w = \pi / 2$ for example, each Fourier amplitude is damped by about 34 percent. Curve (b) in Fig. 2 illustrates the damping effect using a fourth-order-accurate central scheme. At the cost of additional CPU time, one can delay significant damping of the metric coefficients until much higher wavenumbers. At $w = \pi / 2$, attenuation of the improved fourth-order approximation is less than 1/2 (13 percent) of that caused by the second-order scheme.

For the curvilinear coordinate formulation proposed here, an explicit filter can be designed (for example to resolve the Leonard stress) that is executed in either the physical domain or the computational space. In the physical domain however, this filter is usually CPU intensive due to the local spatial irregularity of the boundary fitted grid. By contrast, the filters administered in the computational space can be identical in form to those in the literature for simple cartesian coordinate systems because the respective grid framework of the transformed domain is conveniently regular and completely uniform. The difference between the two filter operations in the cartesian and curvilinear coordinate systems is not the filter itself, but in the variable being filtered. For explicit filtering to occur in the computational space, the resolved turbulent quantity must be transformed to its contravariant form, filtered and finally transformed again back to the physical domain. Obviously, concerns about this manner of filtering include the additional CPU cost of the transformations,

but more importantly, comparisons to the former approach must show no discernible energy loss of the filtered turbulence. In the following section, two three-dimensional kernels are designed (one for each domain) having forms similar to the standard box-type filter. These filters essentially implement either volume-weighting in the physical domain or volume-averaging (Schumann, 1974) in transformed space of the particular resolved turbulent quantity.

The basic one-dimensional discretized form of the box filter has the functional form in the physical domain as

$$\overline{\phi}_i = \phi_i + S/(1+a)(\phi_{i+1} + a\phi_{i-1} - (1+a)\phi_i) \qquad (14)$$

where S is the filter coefficient and the parameter (a) is a local weighting function which accounts for the non-uniform grid spacing. To insure that this kernel attenuates the Fourier elements without a phase change, the filter coefficient is simply set to the constant S = 0.5. The magnitude of the corresponding response function |R(k)| with uniform curvilinear spacing is

$$|R(k)| = \frac{1}{2(1+a)}\left\{[(1+a)(1+\cos k)]^2 + [(1-a)\sin k]^2\right\}^{1/2} \qquad (15)$$

which dampens all Fourier components except at wavenumber k = 0. As illustrated in Fig. 3, the effect of the weighting function is additional damping of the spectral components. Expanding the box filter in equation (14) to three-dimensions (3D) produces a 27-point operator of the form

$$\overline{\Phi}_{i,j,k} = \Phi_{i,j,k} + D_1\left[(1+a)(\Phi_{i,j+1,k} + b\Phi_{i,j-1,k}) + (1+b)(\Phi_{i+1,j,k} + a\Phi_{i-1,j,k})\right]$$
$$+ D_2\left[(1+a)(\Phi_{i,j+1,k\pm1} + b\Phi_{i,j-1,k\pm1}) + (1+b)(\Phi_{i+1,j,k\pm1} + a\Phi_{i-1,j,k\pm1})\right]$$
$$+ D_3\left[\Phi_{i+1,j+1,k} + a\Phi_{i-1,j+1,k} + b\Phi_{i+1,j-1,k} + ab\Phi_{i-1,j-1,k}\right]$$
$$+ D_4\left[\Phi_{i+1,j+1,k\pm1} + a\Phi_{i-1,j+1,k\pm1} + b\Phi_{i+1,j-1,k\pm1} + ab\Phi_{i-1,j-1,k\pm1}\right] \qquad (16)$$
$$+ D_1\left[\frac{1}{2}(1+a)(1+b)\Phi_{i,j,k\pm1}\right] - 4\left[(D_1+D_2) + \frac{1}{2}(D_3+D_4)\right]\Phi_{i,j,k}$$

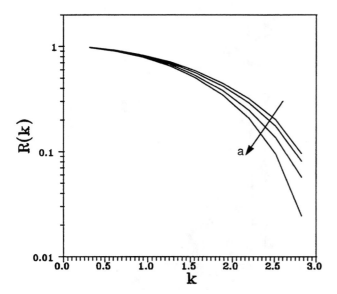

Figure 3. Additional Damping of a Filtered Quantity Caused by Local Weighting

where

$$D_1 = S(1-S)^2 \big/ (1+a)(1+b),$$

$$D_2 = \tfrac{1}{2}S^2(1-S)\big/(1+a)(1+b),$$

$$D_3 = S^2(1-S)\big/(1+a)(1+b) \text{ and}$$

$$D_4 = \tfrac{1}{2}S^3 \big/ (1+a)(1+b)$$

In the physical domain, the non-uniformity of the grid spacing is accounted for through the local weights $a = \sqrt{g_{11}^+/g_{11}^-}$ and $b = \sqrt{g_{22}^+/g_{22}^-}$ in the ξ and η directions, respectively. In this 3D operator the spanwise spacing is considered uniform, therefore no weight respectively appears for that particular direction. The box filter derived in equation (16) can be applied in either the physical domain or the computational space. As noted above, the latter choice requires transformations of the turbulent quantity to and from the computational space in addition to the filtering. However, both weights a and b of the 3D operator have unit values in the computational space due to the spatial regularity of the grid points.

RESULTS AND DISCUSSION

The net result of explicit (or implicit) filtering on the metric coefficients depends strongly on the distribution function used to manipulate the grid spacing. To illustrate this point, consider the discretized box filter function in equation (14) rewritten with a = 1 as

$$\overline{\phi}_i = \phi_i + \frac{S}{2}\frac{d^2\phi}{d\xi^2} \qquad (17)$$

In general, most distribution functions follow the relation

$$x_i(\xi^k) = q\big(\alpha\xi^k\big/N^k\big) \qquad (18)$$

where N^k denotes the total number of points along the curvilinear line ξ^k. By substituting this relationship into equation (17) and choosing the example i = k = 1, the filtered metric coefficient $\overline{x}_\xi$ relative to its unfiltered component becomes

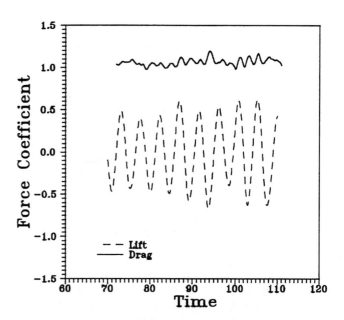

Figure 4. Profiles of the Drag and Lift Coefficients of Cross-Flow Over a Circular Cylinder (Re=3400).

$$\overline{x}_\xi = x_\xi(1+\beta) \qquad (19a)$$

where the smoothing parameter β is defined as

$$\beta = S/2\,(\alpha N)^2 (x_\xi)_{\xi\xi}\big/(x_\xi) \qquad (19b)$$

The degree of metric smoothing as given by the order of the parameter β for the exponential, hyperbolic sine and hyperbolic tangent functions is listed in Table 1 for two extreme cases of grid stretching. The first case restricts the point stretching to insure the correct accuracy of simple second-order central differences for terms like $\xi_x \partial u/\partial \xi$. The smoothing is minimal only for the exponential distribution function suggesting that the net effect of filtering can be negligible. However, this stretching restriction is unrealistic and rarely satisfied in most boundary-fitted grids. The other extreme case illustrates the effect of smoothing when the subsequent grid point spacing is doubled. Although this stretching exceeds that allowable by the truncation error of most finite difference schemes, the hyperbolic functions seem least effected by the box filter. In general, Table 1 shows the hyperbolic functions as most favorable stretching to use when attempting to minimize the net effects of filtering. These particular distributions have also been identified as the best overall choice for resolving viscous layers (Thompson et al., 1985)

Table 1. Smoothing Effects of Box Filtering

Function $q(\xi/N)$	Weighting Function (a)			
	$(x_\xi)_1/(x_\xi)_0 = 1 + (x_\xi)_0$		$(x_\xi)_1/(x_\xi)_0 = 2$	
	α	β	α	β
$\dfrac{\exp(\alpha\xi/N)-1}{\exp\alpha -1}$	0.42	$O(10^{-2})$	1.39	$O(1)$
$\dfrac{\sinh(\alpha\xi/N)}{\sinh\alpha}$	1.24	$O(10^{-1})$	1.92	$O(10^{-1})$
$1-\dfrac{\tanh[\alpha(1-\xi/N)]}{\tanh\alpha}$	0.92	$O(10^{-1})$	1.26	$O(10^{-1})$

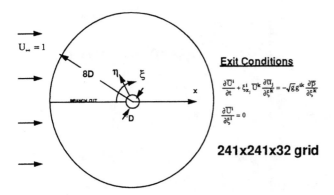

Exit Conditions

$$\frac{\partial \overline{U}^l}{\partial t} + \xi^l_{x_j} \overline{U}^k \frac{\partial \overline{u}_j}{\partial \xi^k} = -\sqrt{g}\,g^{lk}\frac{\partial \overline{p}}{\partial \xi^k}$$

$$\frac{\partial \overline{U}^l}{\partial \xi^{l'}} = 0$$

241x241x32 grid

Figure 5. Grid Point Distribution, External Boundaries, and Flow Conditions Used for Direct Numerical Simulation of Cylinder Flow at Re = 3400.

To investigate the energy damping effects in wavenumber space and the computational efficiency of the explicit box filters in equation (16), the results were used from a DNS computation of the vortical wake motion of a circular cylinder at Re = 3400 where the Reynolds number is based on the cylinder diameter (D). To acquire these results, the DNS formulation of Rai and Moin (1989) in cartesian coordinates was recast into generalized curvilinear coordinates. The Reynolds number of 3400 was chosen in view of the experimental results of Wei and Smith (1986) where the fine-scale spanwise cellular deformation of the shed Strouhal vortices showed little development. The lack of this spanwise characteristic helped relax the resolution requirement on the corresponding grid point spacing. Several grids were generated and tested with varying degrees of refinement to insure that sufficient spatial resolution was achieved of the dissipation scale within the wake formation region.

Profiles of the computed drag and lift force coefficients over eight vortex shedding cycles are plotted in Fig. 4. The mean drag is 1.08 ± 0.038 and the lift coefficient is ± 0.525. Fourier transforms of these profiles (sampling at 20 Hz) gave highest peaks at non-dimensional frequencies $f_D = 0.43$ and $f_L = 0.23$ which identify the shedding frequencies of the Strouhal vortices in the drag and lift coefficient profiles, respectively. These statistics reasonably agree with the experimental evidence available in the literature.

The final grid along with the boundary conditions are given in Fig. 5. An exponential interpolation function (see Table 1) was used to uniformily cluster the circumferential ξ lines toward the cylinder surface so that the restriction $<y^+> \le 2$ was maintained during the computation of the first ξ line within the wake formation region. The η lines shown in the figure eminated normally from the cylinder periphery (s) and where uniformly distributed circumferentially ($\Delta s \approx 0.008\pi$) which produced a single-valued metric coefficient g_{11} along each constant ξ line. This particular distribution therefore permits analysis of the explicit box filters along the curvilinear ξ lines in either the physical domain or computational space because only the radial distribution of the grid point spacing varied locally.

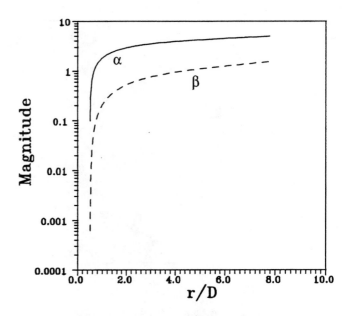

Figure 6. Local Parameters α and β of an Exponential Radial Grid Point Distribution Used for the DNS Computation.

The importance of explicitly filtering the metric coefficients in the application of the curvilinear form of the box filter is illustrated in Fig. 6 where the parameters α and β of the exponential distribution function listed in Table 1 are plotted from the cylinder surface ($r/D = 0.5$) radially to the truncated external boundary ($r/D = 8$). The relative local contributions of filtering the metric coefficients as given by the β parameter is only unimportant within one radii from the cylinder periphery. Beyond four diameters, this parameter is on the same order of magnitude as the unfiltered metric coefficient itself for this particular grid. Figure 6 also justifies representation of the metric coefficients as filtered quantites in the LES formulation using this particular grid point distribution.

Attenuation of the spectral energy in wavenumber space of the vertical fluctuations caused by explicit application of the two box filters in shown in Fig. 7. This figure also gives a sense of energy damping when the first-order non-linear terms of the LES formulation is approximated by a finite difference scheme. Each profile in the figure represents ensemble averages of DNS datasets saved at four separate Strouhal shedding cycles as well as spatial averages in the spanwise direction. Both the physical domain and curvilinear space forms of the box filter were applied along a constant ξ line which corresponds to approximately $r/D = 0.69$. This particular line lies within the primary vortical formation region of the turbulent wake. Kolmogorov's -5/3 scale law is included in Fig. 7a which indicates an inertial sub-range of $10 < w < 50$. The box filter begins to show substantial damping of the spectral energy within this sub-range. Notice that no discernible differences are shown between either filter application. The expanded profiles in Fig. 7b strongly illustrate this point. Conversely, the computational efficiency of the physical domain application is nearly twice that in the

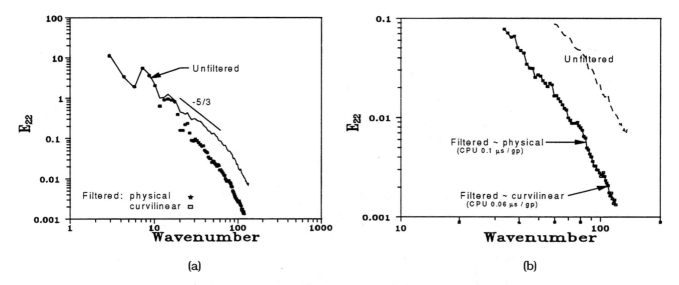

(a)   (b)

Figure 7. Comparisons of the Damping Effects on the Spectral Energy Caused by the Explicit Box Filters Designed for Application in the Physical Domain and Computational Space.

computational space even including the transformations. The additional cost of the physical domain filter is due to its direct dependence on the local weighting functions.

CONCLUDING REMARKS

Two formulations are possible when formally deriving a set of large-eddy simulation (LES) equations in generalized curvilinear coordinates for application in complex domains. These possibilities arise because the derivation itself requires a filter operation as well as coordinate transformations. The final LES equations of each approach differ only by their representation of the metric coefficients. When the filter operation is performed after the coordinate transformations, the accompanying metric coefficients formally appear as filtered quantities. It was shown in this paper that this consideration seems appropriate since these coefficients are commonly evaluated numerically, which inherently results in an implicit dampening of the Fourier amplitudes of the dependent non-uniform cartesian coordinates.

Two explicit forms of the box filter were designed for application in either the physical domain or the computational space. Their damping effects were compared in wavenumber space using direct numerical simulation results of flow past a circular cylinder at a Reynolds number of 3400. No differences were detected between each filter except that the box filter administered in the physical domain cost twice as much as the computational space filter. The additional CPU time results directly from the filter's dependence on the local grid non-uniformity in terms of weighting functions. Finally, the box filter designed for the computational space has a form identical to the volume-averaging filters commonly used for uniform cartesian coordinate systems. But in the present application, the turbulent quantity must be transformed to the computational space, filtered and then again transformed back to the physical domain. The

filtering in the computational space is actually performed on the contravariant components.

ACKNOWLEDGMENTS

The author gratefully acknowledges the support of the Office of Naval Research (Contract No. N00014-95-WX-20147, Dr. L.P. Purtell, Scientific Officer) and the Independent Research Program (Dr. S. Dickinson, Coordinator) at the Naval Undersea Warfare Center.

REFERENCES

Akselvoll, K. and Moin, P., (1993), 'Application of the Dynamic Localization Model to Large-Eddy Simulation of Turbulent Flow Over a Bachward Facing Step,' FED-Vol. 162, *Engineering Applications of Large-Eddy Simulations ASME*, pp. 1-6.

Balachandar, S. and Mittal, R., (1995), 'Momentum and Vorticity Transport by 3-D Vortical Structures in Bluff Body Wakes,' *10th Symposium on Turbulent Shear Flows*, (Pennsylvania State University, University Park, PA, August 14-16, 1995.

Deardoff, J.W., (1970), 'A Numerical Study of Three-Dimensional Turbulent Channel Flow at Large Reynolds Numbers', *Journal of Fluid Mechanics*, Vol. 41, pp. 453-480.

Germano, M., Piomelli, U., Moin, P. and Cabot, W.H., (1991), 'A Dynamic Subgrid-Scale Eddy Viscosity Model,' *Physics of Fluids A*, Vol 3, pp. 1760-1765.

Jordan, S.A. and Ragab, S.A., (1994), 'On the Unsteady and Turbulent Characteristics of the Three-Dimensional Shear Driven-Cavity Flow,' *Journal of Fluids Engineering*, Vol. 116, pp. 439-449.

Jones, W.P. and Wille, M., (1995), ' Large-Eddy Simulation of a Jet in a Cross Flow,' *10th Symposium on Turbulent Shear Flows*, (Pennsylvania State University, University Park, PA, August 14-16, 1995).

Leonard, A., (1974), 'Energy Cascade in Large-Eddy Simulations of Turbulent Fluid Flows', *Advanced Geophysics*, Vol. 18a, pp. 237-248.

Lund, T.S. and Moin, P., (1995), 'Large-Eddy Simulation of a Boundary Layer on a Concave Surface,' *10th Symposium on Turbulent Shear Flows*, (Pennsylvania State University, University Park, PA, August 14-16, 1995).

Murakami, S., Rodi, W., Mochida, A. and Sakamoto, S., (1993), 'Large-Eddy Simulation of Turbulent Vortex Shedding Flow Past Two-Dimensional Square Cylinders, FED-Vol. 162, *Engineering Applications of Large-Eddy Simulations ASME*, pp. 113-120.

Rai, M.M. and Moin, P., (1989), "Direct Simulations of Turbulent Flow Using Finite-Difference Schemes," *AIAA* 89-0369.

Schumann, U., (1975), "Subgrid Scale Model for Finite Difference Simulation of Turbulent Flows in Plane Channel and Annuli," *Journal of Computational Physics*, No. 18, pp. 376-404.

Schumann,U. and Krettenauer, K., (1990), 'Numerical Simulation of Turbulent Convection Over Wavy Terrain,' *Journal of Fluid Mechanics*, Vol. 63. pp. 21-32.

Shimomura, Y., (1991), 'Large-Eddy Simulation of Magnetohydrodynamic Turbulent Channel Flows Under a Uniform Magnetic Field,' *Physics of Fluids A*, Vol. 3, pp. 3098-3106.

Tompson, J.F., Warsi, Z.U.A. and Mastin, C.W., (1985), 'Numerical Grid Generation - Foundations and Applications,' Elsevier Science Publishing Co., NY, NY.

Vinokur, M., (1974), 'Conservative Form of Gas Dynamic Equations,' *La Recherche Aerospatiale,* No. 1974-1, pp. 65-68.

Wei, T. and Smith, C.R., (1986), "Secondary Vortices in the Wake of Circular Cylinders," *Journal of Fluid Mechanics*, Vol. 169, pp. 513-533.

Yang, K.S. and Ferziger, J.H., (1993), 'Large-Eddy Simulation of Turbulent Obstacle Flow Using a Dynamic Subgrid-Scale Model,' *AIAA Journal*, Vol 31, No. 8, pp. 1406-1413.

Zang, T.A. and Piomelli, U., (1990), 'Large-Eddy Simulation of Transition Flow,' *Instability and Transition*, Springer-Verlag, Vol 2, pp. 1-17.

Zang, Y., Street, R.L. and Koseff, J.R., (1993), 'A Dynamic Mixed Subgrid-Scale Model and Its Application to Turbulent Recirculating Flows,' *Physics of Fluids A*, Vol. 5, pp. 3186-3196.

NUMERICAL DEVELOPMENTS IN CFD

Introduction

Manoranjan N. Dhaubhadel
Ford Motor Company
Dearborn, Michigan

The 1996 ASME Symposium on Numerical Developments in CFD is the second in the series sponsored by the ASME Fluids Engineering Division. The symposium is intended to provide a forum for presentation of significant numerical developments in solving fluid flow equations. This volume contains papers in varied topics such as, influence of segregation on finite volume methods, TVD schemes in pressure-based finite volume methods, turbulent compressible flow predictions using high order schemes, pressure-based preconditioner for multi-stage artificial compressibility algorithms, improving convergence rates for low pressure material processing calculations, approximate Riemann solvers for compressible one and two equation models, spurious unsteady solutions due to the QUICK scheme in the numerical solution of the Navier-Stokes equations, algorithm for simulation of turbulent free surface flows, coupling of flow solvers and grid through an edge-based adaptive grid method, multi-domain compact finite difference scheme for stiff problems, implementation and performance of a data parallel algorithm and application of new incompressible flow algorithm to shear-driven cavity flows.

I gratefully acknowledge the efforts of Professors Wagdi G. Habashi and Ramesh K. Agarwal as co-organizers of the symposium.

We express our appreciation to the authors for their contributions. We hope that the symposium will be seen as a window on the current developments in numerical aspects of CFD.

FED-Vol. 238, 1996 Fluids Engineering Division Conference
Volume 3
ASME 1996

INFLUENCE OF SEGREGATION ON THE EFFICIENCY OF FINITE VOLUME METHODS FOR THE INCOMPRESSIBLE NAVIER-STOKES EQUATIONS

Helmar Van Santen, Danny Lathouwers, Chris R. Kleijn and **Harry E. A. Van Den Akker**
Kramers Laboratorium voor Fysische Technologie, J. M. Burgers Centre for Fluid Mechanics,
Delft University of Technology, Prins Bernhardlaan 6, 2628 BW Delft, The Netherlands
Tel +31 15 2782839, Fax +31 15 2782838, E.mail helmar@klft.tn.tudelft.nl.

ABSTRACT

The finite volume discretisation is commonly applied for the numerical solution of the Navier-Stokes equations. The efficiency, accuracy and robustness of algorithms for solving the resulting system of algebraic equations greatly depend on the segregation of the equations. This paper discusses the effect of decoupling the continuity and the momentum equations (resulting in pressure correction algorithms) and the effect of decoupling the momentum equations per direction (Picard versus Newton linearisation) for both steady and transient problems.

The coupled solution of momentum and continuity equations for steady problems is very robust and can significantly reduce the necessary number of iterations. The memory and time costs per iteration however are still high, therefore this method is not efficient for transient problems. Picard linearisation is more robust than Newton linearisation, allowing larger time steps, corresponding to less iterations for steady problems. For transient problems, Newton linearisation is more efficient and allows for a straightforward implementation of second-order time accuracy.

1 INTRODUCTION

The finite volume discretisation is widely applied for the numerical solution of the Navier-Stokes equations [5]. Initially, because of the small amount of internal computer memory available, line solvers were used to solve the resulting system of non-linear algebraic equations in a highly segregated form [8]. Presently however, owing to the tremendous increase in memory capacity and with the developments in non-stationary iterative solvers and precon-

ditioners for non-symmetric matrices, the efficiency and robustness of finite volume methods can be significantly increased by reducing the segregation of the equations. Therefore it seems opportune to re-evaluate the various solution strategies.

In most algorithms the continuity equation is decoupled from the momentum equations, resulting in pressure correction type methods. These methods enforce the use of time or time-like steps, even when a time independent solution is sought. In the present paper pressure correction schemes are compared with algorithms where continuity and momentum equations are solved in a coupled way, theoretically eliminating the need for time-stepping in steady problems [10].

Two linearisation methods are commonly applied for the non-linear terms in the momentum equations: Picard linearisation, resulting in a decoupling of the momentum equations per direction (an indirect coupling remains when momentum and continuity equations are solved simultaneously) and Newton linearisation, resulting in a strong coupling between all momentum equations. This paper shows the properties of these linearisations both for pressure correction schemes and for schemes where momentum and continuity equations are solved in a coupled way.

The effect of the linearisation method and the decoupling of continuity and momentum equations are studied for two steady examples: the driven cavity at a Reynolds number Re = 1,000 and the backward facing step with Re = 500, and two time-dependent examples: the driven cavity with Re = 13,000 and the initial transient of a rotating cavity with Re = 20,000.

2 METHOD

Discretisation

For the spatial discretisation of the 2D Navier-Stokes equations for incompressible viscous flow a staggered grid is used [3]. Central differences are used for the convective fluxes and the discrete continuity equations are used to eliminate part of the centre coefficient in the momentum equations. The reason for the latter is that the matrix properties improve reducing the time for their solution. The resulting set of constrained ordinary differential equations can be written as:

$$\frac{dU}{dt} = F(U) + G(p) \tag{1}$$

$$DU = h(t) \tag{2}$$

where U is the vector containing the velocities in both directions in all grid points; t is time; $F(U)$ contains the convective and diffusive fluxes and the body forces; p is pressure; $G(p)$ represents the discrete pressure gradient; D is the discrete divergence operator and $h(t)$ absorbs boundary conditions. After time discretisation this can for Euler backward and Backward-2 be rewritten to:

$$\frac{1}{\Delta t}\left\{(1+\xi)U^{n+1} - (1+2\xi)U^n + \xi U^{n-1}\right\} =$$
$$F(U^{n+1}) + G(p^{n+1}) \tag{3}$$

$$DU^{n+1} = h^{n+1} \tag{4}$$

where $n + 1$ is the new time level and where ξ takes the value 0 for the first-order Euler backward scheme, whereas it is $\frac{1}{2}$ for the second-order Backward-2 scheme. Backward-2 is slightly less accurate than the Cranck-Nicholson scheme, the latter however is suffering from the disadvantage of asymptotic oscillatory decay.

Equation (3) and (4) represents a set of coupled non-linear algebraic equations that has to be solved in each time step. In the next section various algorithms for the solution of this system are presented.

Solution algorithms

Direct. The system of equations (3) and (4) can be solved directly although still some linearisation for the non-linear terms is required. Then, for steady problems, the time term can be omitted, leaving the solution of a single set of non-linear equations. A restriction however is that without the time term the initial estimate should be in the region of convergence for the linearisation method used.

Newton and Picard linearisation can be used for the non-linear terms. For steady problems, close to the solution Newton linearisation results in quadratic convergence while Picard only allows linear convergence. For transient problems Newton linearisation retains the second-order time accuracy of the Backward-2 scheme while Picard linearisation only allows first-order time accuracy. Picard linearisation however has the property of anti-symmetric

Figure 1: Sparsity patterns of the various algorithms.

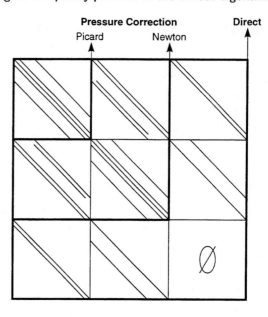

convection terms and a non-zero, positive centre coefficient in the momentum equations which is advantageous for the iterative matrix solvers.

After linearisation a system of linear equations $\hat{A}\mathbf{x} = \mathbf{b}$ results where $\hat{A}$ has a sparsity pattern as is shown in Fig. 1, denoted with 'Direct'. The upper-middle and middle-left block are zero for Picard linearisation (in a rotating frame of reference these are not zero, then however the fill-in is converted to a source term and put in $\mathbf{b}$). The algorithms where the whole system of Fig. 1 is solved will be denoted with 'Direct'.

The direct approach is especially valuable for steady problems where multiple stable flows obey the boundary conditions. Because of the absence of the time term the direct solution then allows to calculate all solutions, also the the implied linearly unstable flows. The reason is that the direct method corresponds to solving a set of non-linear equations, irrespective of the time-stability. When more solutions exist, the solution that will be obtained is determined by the initial estimate. Special techniques however are available that allow to determine all solutions including the linearly unstable solutions [6].

Pressure correction There are several problems involved in solving the equations directly, mainly connected to the large zero block on the bottom-right in Fig 1. Therefore the continuity equations are usually decoupled from the momentum equations resulting in the pressure correction method. This method consists of two steps: the prediction step and the correction step. In the prediction step an intermediate velocity $\tilde{U}^{n+1}$ is computed using the pressure at the old time level p^n:

$$\frac{1}{\Delta t}\left\{(1+\xi)\tilde{U}^{n+1} - (1+2\xi)U^n + \xi U^{n-1}\right\} =$$
$$F(\tilde{U}^{n+1}) + G(p^n) \qquad (5)$$

The velocity after prediction in general does not satisfy the continuity constraint (4). In the correction step the new pressure p^{n+1} corresponding to a new velocity U^{n+1} is calculated to the effect that the continuity constraint is satisfied. This results in the discrete Poisson equation for the pressure:

$$\mathrm{DG}\left(p^{n+1} - p^n\right) = \frac{(1+\xi)}{\Delta t}h^{n+1} - \mathrm{D}\tilde{U}^{n+1} \qquad (6)$$

The new velocity then follows from:

$$\frac{(1+\xi)}{\Delta t}\left\{U^{n+1} - \tilde{U}^{n+1}\right\} = \mathrm{G}\left(p^{n+1} - p^n\right) \qquad (7)$$

Solving equation (5) still requires some linearisation for the non-linear terms. Again Newton linearisation and Picard linearisation can be used, and the corresponding sparsity patterns are the upper left 2×2 block and the upper left block in Fig. 1 respectively. Newton linearisation retains the second-order accuracy of the Backward-2 scheme as has been proven by Van Kan (1986). Picard linearisation has the advantage that smaller systems have to be solved, second-order time accuracy can only be attained when iterations are made within the prediction step as will be illustrated below.

Matrix solvers and Preconditioners

The solution algorithms for the discretised equations result in large sparse systems of linear equations. In the last decade several efficient non-stationary iterative solvers for symmetric and non-symmetric matrices have been developed. In the field of preconditioners for these solvers, still much work is being done [2].

Discrete Poisson equation. For incompressible flows with a constant density on orthogonal grids, the discrete Poisson equation (6) results in a symmetric matrix that is equal in each time step. The Conjugate Gradient (CG) solver [4] is used in combination with two preconditioners. (i) A linear combination of the Incomplete Choleski decomposition (IC) where only the Diagonal is determined (ICD) and a Modified IC decomposition (MICD) where the sum of the fill-in is subtracted of the diagonal. This is usually referred to as Relaxed ICD (RICD) [1]:

$$D_i^{RICD} = \alpha D_i^{MICD} + (1-\alpha)D_i^{ICD} \qquad (8)$$

where α is chosen close to 1 [11]. (ii) IC(ϵ), allowing fill-in where the elements, scaled with the row sum are larger than ϵ. When ϵ was chosen equal to 0.001, the fill-in on larger grids was of the order of 24 elements per row (so

approximately 12 extra vectors had to be stored). As the preconditioner has to be calculated only once, the time involved in generating this preconditioner is of little influence on the total computing time.

RICD and IC(ϵ) require approximately an equal amount of computer time. Only when the termination criterion is stringent, the IC(ϵ) preconditioner is faster owing to the super linear convergence behaviour of CG when the preconditioned matrix is well conditioned. RICD is selected because of the low storage requirements. The value of α is chosen 0.99 when the pressure matrix is non-singular (*e.g.* when pressure outflow boundary conditions are used) and 0.975 when the matrix is singular [14]. When the same termination criterion is used for the pressure and the momentum equation, the time consumption of the correction step is of the same order of magnitude as the prediction step (approximately a factor 5 slower for the small time steps in the time-dependent problems and a factor five faster for the larger time steps in time independent problems).

Momentum system. For the momentum equations GMRES(m) [9] and BiCGSTAB [12] have been tested. The preconditioner was the Relaxed Incomplete LU preconditioner allowing fill-in in the corresponding elements of the matrix have a fill in (RILU(0)) (for Picard linearisation RILU(0) corresponds to RILUD). The value of α is selected 0.95. The storage required for GMRES(m) is 5+m vectors and for BiCGSTAB 10 vectors. For the smaller time steps used for the transient problems GMRES(5) is approximately 40% more time efficient than BiCGSTAB while their storage requirements are the same. For the larger time steps used in the steady problems, BiCGSTAB is approximately 25% more time efficient than GMRES(m) and much more memory efficient as a restart of approximately 20 is required.

Complete coupled system. The linear system in the direct methods is solved with GMRES(m) because of the robustness of this method. The preconditioner required for this system is more complex than the preconditioners mentioned above as these are only efficient if the matrix is well conditioned, usually corresponding to a large diagonal. This is certainly not the case for the system that has to be solved in the direct methods because of the large zero block to the bottom-right (see Fig. 1).

The following solution is selected to partly overcome this problem. For steady problems and not too high velocity gradients and cell Peclet numbers, the upper-left 2×2 block is well conditioned especially when Picard linearisation is used. For non-steady problems this block is well conditioned because of the time term on the diagonal. The equations for the pressure however are very ill-conditioned. Therefore, from the upper 2×2 block an ILU(ϵ) decomposition is made, allowing fill-in in just part of the block to limit the computing time. With this decomposition P1,

P2 and P3 are determined to obey:

$$\begin{bmatrix} I & 0 & 0 \\ 0 & I & 0 \\ P1 & P2 & P3 \end{bmatrix} \cdot \begin{bmatrix} UU & UV & PU \\ VU & VV & PV \\ 0 & 0 & I \end{bmatrix}$$
$$\approx \begin{bmatrix} UU & UV & PU \\ VU & VV & PV \\ DU & DV & 0 \end{bmatrix} \quad (9)$$

where again just the larger elements of P1...P3 are retained. From P3 an ILU(ϵ) decomposition is made.

For steady problems this preconditioner results in a fill-in of approximately 30 elements per row and requires 5 to 10 minutes on and HP 735 for a 100×100 grid. This preconditioner however only has to be calculated two or three times because after a few iterations little changes. The restart value m is selected 40 which is relatively high and then still several restarts have to be made.

Termination criteria. A few important remarks apply to the termination criteria for the iterative solvers. The residual is required to decrease with a certain factor. The computing time is highly dependent on the magnitude of this factor. For steady problems, the accuracy of the intermediate solutions is of little importance. Then for some cases a termination criterion of a decrease factor 10 leads to the same answer and the same number of iterations as a factor 10^6 but to a reduction in computing time of a factor 20! For the cases discussed below factors of 10 to 10^6 are used, depending on the problem.

3   RESULTS

Steady problems

Preliminary test. The test case of a square driven cavity with Re = 200 and a 50×50 grid is used to show various aspects of the effect of the decoupling of the continuity equations. The distribution of the grid points is given by:

$$\frac{x_i}{W} = \frac{i - \frac{1}{2}}{i_{max}} - \frac{\alpha}{2\pi} \sin\left(2\pi \frac{i - \frac{1}{2}}{i_{max}}\right) \quad i = 1, 2, ... i_{max} \quad (10)$$

where α is the stretching parameter, which is set to $\frac{1}{2}$. The reason for the low Reynolds number is that then for the direct methods the zero initial solution is in the region of convergence for both the Newton and the Picard linearisation.

Figure 2 shows the influence of the selected time step on the number of time steps required to reach a maximal time derivative of 10^{-6} (for the direct methods if the time step is larger than 1, the maximal change in the velocities is required to be less than 10^{-6}). The direct solution follows the physical time scale for much larger time steps to eventually arrive at the asymptotic value of the respective linearisation: 6 for Newton and 15 for Picard. These are considerably lower than the number of iterations required for pressure correction methods.

Figure 2: Number of iterations required for the various algorithms.

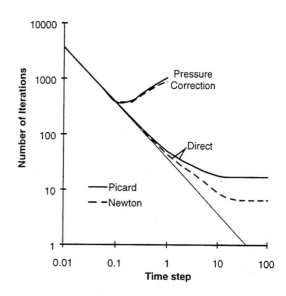

Table 1: Calculation statistics for the various solution methods

	Direct		Pressure Correction	
	N	P	N	P
Memory [Mb]	39	39	7	3.5
CPU-time (relative)	2.1[†]	2.5[†]	1.4	1[‡]
Number of Iterations	6	22	643	617

[†] To go from Re = 500 to Re = 1,000

[‡] Corresponding to 20 minutes on an HP 735

For this low Reynolds number there is little difference between Picard and Newton linearisation. The differences become apparent when the Reynolds number is increased: for the direct solution method the zero initial solution is within the region of convergence for Picard linearisation for Re up to 1,300, while Newton only converges for Re smaller than 300. A similar phenomenon occurs with pressure correction methods. This is further discussed below within the context of the example of the backward facing step.

Driven cavity at Re = 1,000. The time and memory requirements of the different methods are illustrated using the example of the driven cavity at Re = 1,000 on a 128×128 grid, partitioned as given by equation (10). The dimensionless time step used for the Pressure Correction schemes is 0.25. To start in the region of convergence of both linearisation methods, the initial solution for the direct methods was the solution at Re = 500. Some calcu-

Figure 3: Convergence behaviour of the direct solution algorithms.

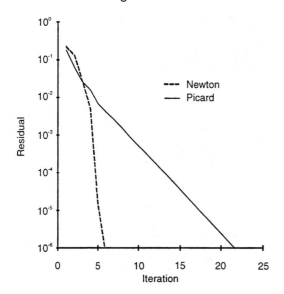

Figure 3: Convergence behaviour of the direct solution algorithms.

Table 2: Time accuracy of the various solution methods.

	Time step		
	1/64	1/128	1/256
Picard PC	20	2.7	2.2
Picard2 PC	25	4.2	4.1
Newton PC	26	4.1	4.2
Picard Direct	2.6	2.1	2.0
Newton Direct	4.2	4.1	4.0

lation statistics are given in Table 1. Figure 3 shows the convergence behaviour of the two direct methods.

The pressure correction methods are most time and especially memory efficient. For these methods Picard and Newton require approximately the same amount of iterations when the same time step is used. Then, as one Newton step is more time consuming than one Picard-step (the Newton system larger system and worse conditioned), Picard is with the same time step more time-efficient than Newton. This is further discussed within the context of the next example).

Nevertheless, the direct methods have their own value. Figure (3) shows that close to the solution the convergence of these methods is very fast, in contrast to pressure correction methods which tend to slow down for lower residuals. When a very accurate solution is required direct methods become increasingly efficient. An optimum might be a combination of the two methods. A second application of direct methods occurs when a solution is to be calculated as a function of a tuning parameter, $e.g.$ the Reynolds number. Then usually a good starting estimate for the direct methods is available and one or two iterations may suffice.

Backward facing step at Re = 500. The example of the backward facing step at Re = 500 (based on step height and the maximum of the inlet velocity) is used to illustrate the effect of the linearisation method. The step height is one third of the channel height [7]. A 30×120 non-uniform grid is used and at the outflow zero pressure is imposed.

For the pressure correction schemes convergence was attained for dimensionless time steps up to 1 and 0.1 for Picard and Newton respectively, for the direct methods these numbers are 4 and 0.1. Similar behaviour is seen in

different problems with relatively high cell Peclet numbers. This shows that Picard linearisation is more robust than Newton linearisation.

An interesting other conclusion that follows from these numbers is that for larger cell Peclet numbers in pressure correction schemes Picard linearisation breaks down because the mass conservation equations are not imposed. Newton linearisation however does not break down because the mass conservation equation are not imposed. On the other hand if the time step is selected too large, Newton linearisation results in too large adjustments ($e.g.$ in the presence of some velocity gradient very easily a recirculation is formed) causing break down.

For steady problems Picard linearisation is most efficient as each step is cheaper in time and in memory and larger time steps can be taken corresponding to less iterations.

Transient problems

Time accuracy. The accuracy in time of the various schemes was verified on a square cavity with Re = 20 and a 20×20 grid, partitioned as given by equation (10). The equations were integrated with time steps Δt 1/64, 1/128, 1/256, 1/512 and 1/1024 from $t = 0$ to $t = 1$. The quantity

$$\frac{\|u(\Delta t) - u(\frac{1}{2}\Delta t)\|}{\|u(\frac{1}{2}\Delta t) - u(\frac{1}{4}\Delta t)\|} \qquad (11)$$

is a measure for the time accuracy and should be equal to 4 for second-order accuracy and 2 for first-order accuracy.

Table 2 shows the results for the different methods. In Picard2, the momentum systems are solved twice in the prediction step updating the velocities in the convection terms. The values agree well with the expected values. The direct methods keep the time accuracy for much larger time steps than the pressure correction methods. In most time dependent problems however the required time accuracy results in time steps that are sufficiently small. Then pressure correction schemes are more efficient due to their low time and memory costs. If storage is a premium, Picard2 is the most efficient solver, the higher costs for the prediction step usually being small compared to the costs of a whole cycle as the correction step is the most time consuming.

Figure 4: Power Density Spectrum for the lid driven square cavity.

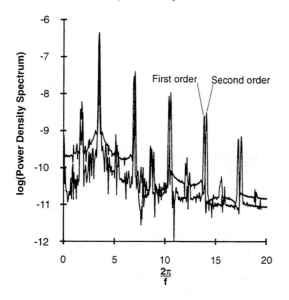

Figure 5: Streamlines of the rotating square cavity at t = 4 and Re = 20,000.

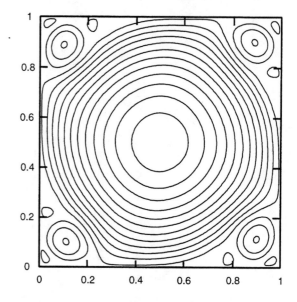

Driven cavity at Re = 13,000. In two dimensions, the flow of the two-dimensional driven cavity converges to a steady state for Reynolds numbers up to 10,000. For larger Reynolds numbers the flow undergoes a transition to unsteadiness. For Re between 11,000 and 15,000, the flow converges to a purely periodic solution with a period of 1.8 [13]. The 2D driven cavity at Re = 13,000 is used to study the influence of the linearisation method. The 128×128 grid mentioned above is used and the dimensionless time step is 0.01. Although locally cell Peclet numbers in excess of 200 occur, central differences for the convection term did not cause any problems.

Figure (4) shows the power density spectra for both Picard and Newton linearisation of v_x in the point (x,y) = (0.1,0.9) (the top is moving in the x-direction at y = 1). A time series of 12,000 time steps is used, starting from a statistically stable solution. The solution for both Picard and Newton linearisation is periodic and the energy is approximately equally distributed over the first and higher order harmonics. The main difference between the two linearisations shows off as a difference in period which is 0.02, of order the order of the time step ($\Delta t = 0.01$).

Rotating cavity at Re = 20,000. To illustrate the influence of an additional body force, the time behaviour of a square cavity that at $t = 0$ is given an angular velocity of Ω around its centre is studied. In a rotating frame of reference the transition will occur to the solution with velocities zero and an equilibrium between pressure and centrifugal forces. If the axes of reference are rotating steadily with $-\Omega$ the fictitious Coriolis force $2\Omega \times \mathbf{u}$ has to be modelled while the centrifugal force is incorporated in the pressure. The Coriolis force is for this case a lin-

ear term. When Picard linearisation is used, however this term is treated as a source. Similar experiments as mentioned above show that this treatment does not affect the second-order accuracy of Picard2.

The rotating cavity is calculated for a Reynolds number Re = 20,000 (based on angular velocity and side). The 128×128 grid mentioned above is used. Figure (5) shows the streamlines when the equations are integrated from $t = 0$ to $t = 4$ with Picard2 and a time step of 0.02.

4 CONCLUSIONS

The finite volume discretisation of the 2D incompressible Navier-Stokes equations leads to three coupled sets of coupled non-linear algebraic equations: the momentum equations in each direction and the continuity equations. The effect of decoupling these three sets of equations has been studied.

The set of continuity equations can be decoupled leading to pressure correction schemes. For transient problems this is most efficient. For steady problems however this forces to take time steps and then an interesting alternative is the fully coupled direct solution. This results in a large decrease in the number of iterations and offers several opportunities that are not available in pressure correction schemes. To become really competitive, the preconditioners for the resulting linear system of equations need to be improved.

The sets of momentum equations can be decoupled by using Picard linearisation for the non-linear terms. Picard linearisation is more robust than Newton linearisation. This means for steady problems that larger time steps can be taken resulting in a significant decrease in computer time. For transient problems however Newton linearisation allows straight forward and efficient implementation of second-order time accuracy.

REFERENCES

[1] O. Axelsson and G. Lindskog. On the eigenvalue distribution of a class of preconditioning methods. *Numer. Math.*, 48:479–498, 1986.

[2] R. Barrett, M. Berry, T. Chan, J. Demmel, J. Donato, J. Dongarra, V. Eijkhout, R. Pozo, C. Romine, and H. Van Der Vorst. *Templates for the solution of linear systems: building Blocks for iterative methods.* SIAM, Philadelphia, 1992. Can be obtained through anonymous ftp at netlib2.cs.utk.edu in the directory /templates).

[3] F. J. Harlow and J. E. Welch. Numerical calculatioin of time dependent viscous incompressible flow of fluids with free surface. *Phys. Fluids*, 8:2182–2189, 1965.

[4] M. R. Hestenes and E. Stiefel. Methods of conjugate gradients for solving linear systems. *J. Res. Natl. Bur. Stand.*, 49:409–436, 1954.

[5] C. Hirsch. *Numerical computation of internal and external flows Vol 1: Fundamentals of numerical discretization.* Wiley, Chichester, 1988.

[6] H. B. Keller. Numerical solution of bifurcation and nonlinear eigenvalue problems. In P. H. Rabinowitz, editor, *Applications of bifurcation theory*, pages 45–52, New York, 1977. Dekker.

[7] K. Morgan, J. Periaux, and F. Thomasset. Analysis of laminar flow over a backward facing step. In *Notes on numerical fluid mechanics Volume 9*, Vieweg and Sohn Braunschweig/Wiesbaden, 1984. Proceedings of a GAMM-workshop, 1984.

[8] S. V. Patankar. *Numerical heat transfer and fluid flow.* McGraw-Hill, New York, 1980.

[9] Y. Saad and M. H. Schultz. GMRES: A generalized minimum residual algorithm for solving nonsymmetric linear systems. *SIAM J. Sci. Stat. Comput.*, 7:931–869, 1986.

[10] A. Van Der Ploeg. *Preconditioning for sparse matrices with applications.* PhD thesis, Rijksuniversiteit Groningen, 1994.

[11] H. A. Van Der Vorst. High performance preconditioning. *SIAM J. Sci. Stat. Comput.*, 10(2):1174–1185, 1989.

[12] H. A. Van Der Vorst. Bi-CGSTAB: A fast and smoothly converging variant of Bi-CG for the solution of nonsymmetric linear systems. *SIAM J. Sci. Stat. Comput.*, 13(2):631–644, 1992.

[13] R. Verstappen, J. G. Wissink, and A. E. P. Veldman. Direct numerical simulation of driven cavity flows. *Appl. Sci. Res.*, 51:377–381.

[14] C. Vuik. Fast iterative solvers for the discretized incompressible Navier-Stokes equations. 1993. Technical Report 93-98, Delft University of Technology, Faculty of Technical Mathematics and Informatics, Delft, The Netherlands. Can be obtained through anonymous ftp at ftp://ftp.twi.tudelft.nl in directory /pub/publications/tech-reports/1993).

FED-Vol. 238, 1996 Fluids Engineering Division Conference
Volume 3
ASME 1996

Application of TVD Schemes in Pressure-Based Finite-Volume Methods

R. I. Issa and M.H. Javareshkian
Imperial College of Science, Technology and Medicine
Dept of Mechanical Engineering, London, SW7 2BX
United Kingdom

ABSTRACT

The paper presents a general implementation of TVD schemes into an implicit finite volumes procedure which uses pressure as a working variable. The boundedness criteria determined from TVD schemes are applied to the fluxes of the convected quantities directly, including mass flow. The finite-volume procedure into which these schemes are implemented uses a co-located variable arrangement and utilises the pressure correction technique to obtain the solution to the discretised equations.

The method is applied to the computation of steady subsonic and transonic flows over a bump-in-channel geometry as well as to the transient shock-tube problem. The results are compared with other computations published in the literature.

INTRODUCTION

The capturing of sharp gradients associated with shock waves and contact discontinuities has been the subject of much research and development. The work has resulted in the devising of various high resolution bounded schemes notably the total variation diminishing(TVD) technique (Harten 1983, Yee et al. 1985). Most of these schemes, and especially the latter have been implemented in density-based numerical algorithms which are specific to highly compressible flows. This imposes a restriction on the applicability of the methodology and precludes from its use in multi-propose CFD procedures that can be applied equally to incompressible as well as compressible flows. Alternatively, pressure-based methods offer the capability of handling both of these classes of flow in a unified manner. The objective of the present work is to developed a general method for implementing TVD schemes in pressure-based procedures and demonstrate the validity of such an implementation.

Although this is not the first attempt at the introduction of TVD schemes into pressure-based methods, it is more general in that the implementation is effected to the hyperbolic system of equations directly rather than to individual conservation equation for different variables. Lien and Leschziner (1994) introduced a MUSCL (Van Leer, 1974) type of TVD scheme into their pressure-based procedure; the slope-limiter in their work relies on the gradients of the dependent variables solved for. A density-retardation technique tantamount to upwinding on pressure-gradient is introduced to account for the hyperbolic nature of the conservation equations. There is also the work of Shyy and Thakur (1994) who developed what they call the controlled variation scheme(CVS) which is based on the formalism of the TVD concept, introduced in the context of incompressible flow. Those authors expressed the view that existing TVD schemes do not generalise to pressure-based methods for two reasons. The first is related to contemporary sequential-iteration methods of solution which treat the pressure-gradients as source terms in the momentum equations; this is unlike simultaneous algorithms which treat gradients as part of the flux vectors. The second reason is the lack of definition of local characteristics on which the flux limiters of the TVD schemes are based.

In both of the above cited works, the gradients of either the conserved or primitive variables are used in formulating the flux-limiting function. This is different from constructing the flux limiter on characteristic variables which are considered to be more appropriate for compressible flow problems. Indeed, Mulder and Van Leer (1985) who carried out extensive numerical experiments found that at least for one-dimensional flow, the best accuracy was obtained using the Riemann variables. This can perhaps be explained by the fact that only one of the these variables will undergo a small change through a wave or a contact front, whereas large changes take place in conserved or primitive variables.

The present work bases the flux-limiting function on the Riemann variables and this is accomplished within the context of a method that employs pressure as a dependent variable. The implementation takes into account the fact that pressure-gradient terms are part of the flux vectors, but formulate them in such a way that they appear explicitly in the momentum equations.

FINITE VOLUME DISCRETIZATION

The basic equations which describe conservation of mass, momentum and scalar quantities can be expressed in the following vector form, which is independent of coordinate system used:

$$\frac{\partial \rho}{\partial t} + div(\rho \vec{v}) = S_m \qquad (1)$$

$$\frac{\partial (\rho \vec{v})}{\partial t} + div(\rho \vec{v} \otimes \vec{v} - \vec{T}) = \vec{S}_v \qquad (2)$$

$$\frac{\partial (\rho \phi)}{\partial t} + div(\rho \vec{v} \phi - \vec{q}) = \vec{S}_\phi \qquad (3)$$

where the density ρ, velocity vector $\vec{v}$ and scalar quantity ϕ appear as the basic dependent variable, $\vec{T}$ is the stress tensor and $\vec{q}$ is the scalar flux vector. The latter two are usually expressed in terms of basic dependent variables. The stress tensor for a Newtonian fluid is:

$$\vec{T} = -(P + \frac{2}{3}\mu \, div \, \vec{v})\vec{I} + 2\mu \vec{D} \qquad (4)$$

and the scalar flux vector is usually given by the Fourier-type law:

$$\vec{q} = \Gamma_\phi \, grad \, \phi \qquad (5)$$

For the purpose of illustration Eq.(3) may be expressed in 2D Cartesian coordinates as:

$$\overbrace{\frac{\partial (\rho \phi)}{\partial t}}^{transient\,term} + \overbrace{\frac{\partial (\rho u \phi)}{\partial x} + \frac{\partial (\rho v \phi)}{\partial y}}^{convection} -$$

$$\underbrace{\frac{\partial}{\partial x}(\Gamma_\phi \frac{\partial \phi}{\partial x}) - \frac{\partial}{\partial y}(\Gamma_\phi \frac{\partial \phi}{\partial y}))}_{diffusion} = \overbrace{S_\phi}^{source} \qquad (6)$$

Integration of Eq.(6) over a finite volume (see e.g. Fig.1) and application of the Gauss Divergence Theorem yield a balance involving the rate of change in ϕ, face fluxes and volume-integrated net source. The transient term is approximated by the Euler implicit scheme for the purposes of this work, although other temporal schemes are also possible.

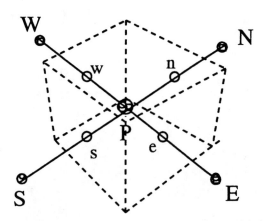

Fig. 1 Finite volume and storage arrangement

The diffusion flux is approximated by central differences and can be written for cell-face e of the control volume in Fig.(1) as an example as:

$$I_e^D = D_e(\phi_P - \phi_E) - S_e^u \qquad (7)$$

The discretization of the convective flux, however, requires special attention and is the subject of the various schemes developed. A representation of the convective flux is :

$$I_f^c = (\rho.v.A)_f \phi_f = F_f \phi_f \qquad (8)$$

The value of the dependent variable ϕ_f is not known and should be estimated using an interpolation procedure, from the values at neighbouring grid points. The details of how the interpolation is made is dealt with later; it suffices to say that the discretised equations resulting from each approximations take the form:

$$A_p.\phi_p = \sum_{m=E,W,N,S} A_m.\phi_m + S_\phi' \qquad (9)$$

where the A's are coefficients the expressions for which are given later.

CONVECTIVE FLUXES

The expression for the mass, momentum and energy fluxes in Eq.(8) are determined by the TVD scheme used for interpolation from nodes at the neighbouring points, say nodes i and $i+1$. The expression can be written in general (see Roe, 1981) as:

$$F_{i+1/2} = \frac{1}{2}[F_i + F_{i+1} + R_e\Phi_e] \qquad (10)$$

where $R_e\Phi_e$ is a dissipation term, based on the characteristic field decomposition of the flux difference. The quantity R_e stands for the right eigenvector matrix, while Φ_e is a vector containing the components of the anti-diffusive flux terms.

According to Yee et al.(1985), a spatially second-order upwind formula for the components of Φ_e is given by:

$$\phi_e^l = \frac{1}{2}\psi(a_e^l)(g_i^l + g_{i+1}^l) - \psi(a_e^l + \gamma_e^l)\alpha_e^l \qquad (11)$$

The eigenvalues of the Jacobian matrix are denoted by a. The spatial increments of the characteristic variables α are obtained by:

$$\alpha_{i+1/2}^l = R_{i+1/2}^{-1}(u_{i+1}^l - u_i^l) \qquad (12)$$

For γ one can take (Yee et al., 1985):

$$\gamma_{i+1/2}^l = \frac{1}{2}\psi(a_{i+1/2}^l)\begin{cases} \frac{g_{i+1}^l - g_i^l}{\alpha_{i+1/2}^l} & \alpha_{i+1/2}^l \neq 0 \\ 0 & \alpha_{i+1/2}^l = 0 \end{cases}$$

The function ψ is required to prevent non-physical solutions such as expansion shocks and introduces a small amount of viscosity. Following Harten's suggestion, it is taken as:

$$\begin{aligned} \psi(z) &= \frac{z^2}{4\epsilon} + \epsilon \; for & |z| < 2\epsilon \\ &= |z| & for & |z| \geq 2\epsilon \end{aligned} \qquad (13)$$

where ϵ is a arbitraryly small number. The most important factor in Eq.(11) is the flux-limiter, g, which determines the accuracy and TVD-property of the scheme. Among the proposals, which have been discussed by, for example, Chakravarthy and Osher (1986) and Yee et al. (1990) are the following limiters which have been applied in our investigation:

$$\begin{aligned} g_{i,j}^l &= SMax(0, min[2.|\alpha_{i+1/2,j}^l|, S\alpha_{i-1/2,j}^l], \\ & \quad min[|\alpha_{i+1/2,j}^l|, 2S\alpha_{i-1/2,j}^l]), \qquad (14) \\ with & \qquad S = sign(\alpha_{i+1/2,j}^l), \end{aligned}$$

which corresponds to the superbee limiter of Roe (1985) and,

$$g_{i,j}^l = minmod(\alpha_{i+1/2,j}^l, \alpha_{i-1/2,j}^l) \qquad (15)$$

$$minmod(x,y) = sign(x).Max(0, min[|x|, y\,sign(x)]) \qquad (16)$$

which corresponds to the Minmod limiter of Harten (1983). In the present work, it was found that the Superbee limiter

gives a somewhat sharper resolution of the waves and contact fronts; this is in agreement with the findings by Roe (1985). However, it was also found that convergence of the solution process with the Superbee scheme was somewhat troublesome; hence in the present work, a "blend" of the two limiters for steady state flows was used.

With the above assumption the convective momentum fluxes(for a typical cell-face) for two dimensional flow in non-orthogonal coordinates can be derived as:

$$I_e^{cx} = \frac{1}{2}[I_E^{cx} + I_P^{cx} + R_e\phi_e^{2x}]$$

$$I_e^{cy} = \frac{1}{2}[I_E^{cy} + I_P^{cy} + R_e\phi_e^{2y}]$$

Where

$$\begin{aligned} I_E^{cx} &= (\rho u^2)_E + P_E & I_P^{cx} &= (\rho u^2)_P + P_P \\ I_E^{cy} &= (\rho uv)_E & I_P^{cy} &= (\rho uv)_P \\ I_E^c &= F_E U_E + P_E & I_P^c &= F_P U_P + P_P \end{aligned}$$

Hence:

$$I_e^c = \frac{1}{2}[F_E^c U_E + F_P^c U_P] + \frac{1}{2}[P_E + P_P] + \frac{1}{2}[R_e\phi_e^{2x} + R_e\phi_e^{2y}] \qquad (17)$$

Similarly, the mass flux is given by:

$$F_e^{cx} = \frac{1}{2}[F_E^{cx} + F_P^{cx} + R_e\phi_e^{1x}]$$

$$F_e^{cy} = \frac{1}{2}[F_E^{cy} + F_P^{cy} + R_e\phi_e^{1y}]$$

Where

$$\begin{aligned} F_E^{cx} &= (\rho u)_E & F_P^{cx} &= (\rho u)_P \\ F_E^{cy} &= (\rho v)_E & F_P^{cy} &= (\rho v)_P \\ F_E^c &= F_E^{cx} + F_E^{cy} & F_P^c &= F_P^{cx} + F_P^{cy} \end{aligned}$$

Hence:

$$F_e^c = \frac{1}{2}[F_E^c + F_P^c + R_e\phi_e^{1x} + R_e\phi_e^{1y}] \qquad (18)$$

When all other fluxes at the various cell faces are assembled and introduced into the discretised equations, the coefficients in Eq.(9) become:

$$\begin{aligned} AE &= D_e - \frac{F_E}{2} & AN &= D_n - \frac{F_N}{2} \\ AW &= D_w + \frac{F_W}{2} & AS &= D_s + \frac{F_S}{2} \end{aligned}$$

$$with \quad AP = AE + AW + AN + AS + \frac{\rho\delta v}{\delta t} \qquad (19)$$

The dissipation contribution to the convective fluxes is put into the source terms of the discretised equations; thus, in the continuity it takes the form:

$$S_1 = \frac{1}{2}(R_e\Phi_e^{1x} + R_e\Phi_e^{1y} - R_w\Phi_w^{1x} - R_w\Phi_w^{1y}$$
$$+ R_n\Phi_n^{1x} + R_n\Phi_n^{1y} - R_s\Phi_s^{1x} - R_s\Phi_s^{1y})U_p \quad (20)$$

while for momentum it is:

$$S_2 = -\frac{1}{2}(R_e\Phi_e^{2x} + R_e\Phi_e^{2y} - R_w\Phi_w^{2x} - R_w\Phi_w^{2y}$$
$$+ R_n\Phi_n^{2x} + R_n\Phi_n^{2y} - R_s\Phi_s^{2x} - R_s\Phi_s^{2y}) \quad (21)$$

Preferably they are calculated explicitly when their signs are positive and when the signs are negative they are evaluated implicitly. The source term in the momentum equation will in addition contain the pressure gradient term which appears as follows:

$$S_p^u = \frac{1}{2}(P_E.A_E - P_W.A_W + P_N.A_N - P_S.A_S) \quad (22)$$

SOLUTION ALGORITHM

Most contemporary pressure-based methods employ a sequential iteration technique in which the different conservation equations are solved one after another. The common approach taken in enforcing continuity is by combining the equation for continuity with those of momentum to derive an equation for pressure or pressure-correction.

The present work employs the PISO technique (Issa, 1986) in which the implicitly discretised equations are solved at each time step by a sequence of predictor and corrector steps. This scheme is especially efficient for unsteady flows as it does not involve expensive iteration. For steady flows, time-marching is effected until the steady-state is reached.

RESULTS

Both two-dimensional steady and one-dimensional transient flows are computed and the results are compared either with existing numerical solutions obtained by others or with the analytic solution when available. The test cases chosen are the normal benchmarks to which methods such as the one presented here are applied. The first case is that of the classical shock tube problem and the second is the bump-in-channel case.

Fig. 2 shows the spatial distribution of pressure, Mach number, density and velocity along the shock tube at a given instant in time in a shock-tube for an initial pressure of 10. The results of computation on a mesh of 100 nodes using two flux limiters: Minmod and Superbee,

are compared with the analytic solution. The quality of the resolution of both TVD schemes as implemented in the pressure-based implicit procedure is similar to those obtained from the same schemes when applied in density-based solution methods.

In Fig. 3(a) the geometry of a 10% thick bump on a channel wall is shown together with the mesh used(98×25) to compute this steady two-dimensional inviscid flow case. Two cases were considered, one with an inlet mach number of 0.5 resulting in a subsonic flow throughout, the other with inlet Mach number of 0.675 leading to transonic flow over the bump.

In Figs 3(b) and 3(c) the surface Mach number distributions on the upper and lower walls are depicted for the subsonic and transonic cases respectively. The corresponding pressure distribution for the transonic case is shown in Fig. 3(d). The present computations for the transonic case are compared with those of Widermann and Iwamoto (1994) which were carried out with an explicit density-based method. The agreement between the two solutions is remarkable, thus once again verifying the validity of the present TVD generalization.

CONCLUSION

The TVD technique has been implemented in a general manner into a pressure-based, finite-volume procedure which uses an implicit solution algorithm. The implementation is based on limiting the fluxes directly by reference to an approximate Riemann solution: this is unlike previous implementations which apply slope limiters to the dependent variables themselves, and not to the conserved fluxes.

The method is applied to both transient and steady state flows and the results, compare very well with corresponding ones using the same or similar TVD schemes in conjunction with density-based methods. It can therefore be concluded that TVD schemes are equally applicable to both pressure and density based techniques contrary to previous conjecture in the literature which suggested otherwise

Fig. 2 Shock-tube results for an initial pressure ratio $\frac{P_H}{P_L}=10$ at time $t_o=6.0$ ms

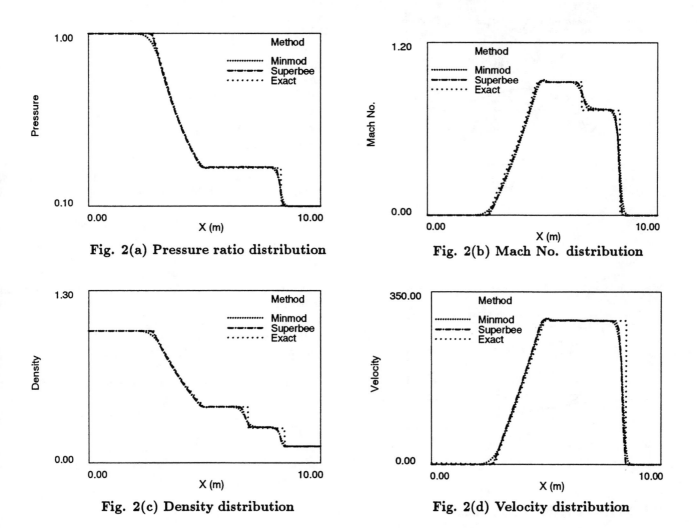

Fig. 2(a) Pressure ratio distribution

Fig. 2(b) Mach No. distribution

Fig. 2(c) Density distribution

Fig. 2(d) Velocity distribution

Fig. 3 Inviscid subsonic and transonic flows

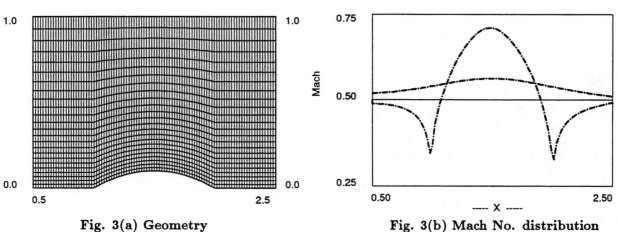

Fig. 3(a) Geometry

Fig. 3(b) Mach No. distribution

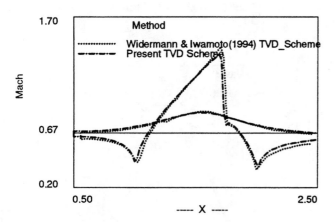

Fig. 3(c) Mach No. distribution

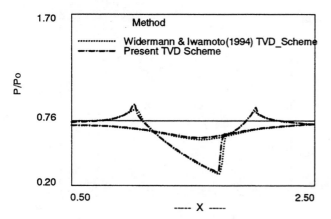

Fig. 3(d) Pressure ratio distribution

REFERENCES

Chakravarthy S.R. and Osher S.,1986, "Computing with high-resolution upwind schemes for hyperbolic equations", Lect. Appl. Math. 22(1), 57

Harten, A.,1983, "High Resolution Scheme for Hyperbolic Conservation Laws", J. of Computational Physics, Vol.49, pp.357-93

Issa R.I., 1986, "Solution of implicit discretised fluid flow equations by operator splitting", J. Comput. Phys. Vol.62, pp.40

Lien, F.S. and Leschziner M.A., 1994, "A general non-orthogonal collocated finite volume algorithm for turbulent flow at all speeds incorporating second-moment turbulence-transport closure", Comput. Methods Appl. Mech. Engg Vol.114, pp.123-148

Mulder W.A. and Van Leer B.,1985, "Experiments with implicit upwind methods for the Euler Equations", J. of Computational Physics, Vol.59 pp.232-246

Roe P.L, 1981, "Approximate Riemann Solvers, Parameter Vectors and Difference Schemes", Journal Computational Physics, Vol.43, pp.357-72

Roe, P.L.,1985, "Some contributions to the modelling of discontinuous flows, Proc(1983) AMS-SIAM summer seminar on large scale computing in Fluid Mechanics, Lectures in Applied Mathematics", Vol. 22,pp.163-93 SIAN, Philadelphia

Shyy W. and Thakur S., 1994, "Controlled Variation Scheme in a Sequential Solver for Recirculating Flows", Heat Transfer, part B, 25, pp.245-272

Van Leer B.,1974, "Towards the Ultimate Conservation Difference Scheme. II. Monotonicity and conservation combined in second order scheme", J. of Computational Physics, Vol.14, pp.361-370

Widermann A. and Iwamoto J.,1994, "A Multigrid TVD-Type scheme for computing inviscid and viscous flows", Computers Fluids Vol.23, No.5, pp.711-735

Yee, H. C., Warming R. F. and Harten A.,1985, "Implicit Total Variation Diminishing(TVD) Schemes for Steady State Calculations", J. of Computational Physics, Vol.57, pp.327-360

Yee, H.C. Klopfer G.H. and Montagne J.L.,1990, "High-resolution shock capturing schemes for inviscid and viscous hyperbolic flow", J. comput. Phs. 88, 32

FED-Vol. 238, 1996 Fluids Engineering Division Conference
Volume 3
ASME 1996

3-D TURBULENT SUBSONIC COMPRESSIBLE FLOW PREDICTIONS USING HIGH-ORDER SCHEMES AND COMPARISON WITH MEASUREMENTS

Guoqing Zhang and Dennis N. Assanis
W. E. Lay Automotive Laboratory
Department of Mechanical Engineering and Applied Mechanics
University of Michigan
Ann Arbor, MI 48109-2121, U. S. A.

A calculation procedure for three-dimensional, steady, compressible, turbulent flows in complex geometries is presented using the k-ε turbulence model. The numerical solver is an extension of a segregated, iterative solver developed by Zhang, Assanis and Tamamidis (1996) for laminar compressible subsonic flows. The method uses a collocated finite volume scheme in body fitted coordinates. With the segregated approach for solving the continuity, momentum, turbulence, and state equations, high order schemes can be readily implemented. The third-order QUICK scheme is used for discretizing convective terms, while a third order TVD scheme has been implemented for the k-ε model equations. A non-linear cell-face interpolation scheme is adopted to eliminate checker-board oscillations that can arise with collocated schemes in conjunction with the segregated approach. The purpose of this paper is to evaluate the performance and accuracy of the code in the light of experimental results. Benchmark tests are performed for turbulent flows in a 90° curved duct and an S-duct of circular cross sections. The results show that accurate solutions can be obtained by the present method.

NOMENCLATURE

g^{ij}	Contravariant metric factor
U^i	Contravariant velocity component
C_v, C_p	Specific heat
e_t	Total internal energy
F, G, H	Convective terms
Q	Variable vector
F_v, G_v, H_v	Viscous terms
C_p	Pressure coefficient
Δt	Time step
J_a	Jacobian of the transformation
k	Turbulent kinetic energy
p	Pressure
R	Right hand side
R_e	Reynolds number
T	Temperature
t	Time
U,V,W	Contravariant velocity component
u,v,w	Cartesian velocity component
x,y,z	Cartesian coordinate

Greek

$\Gamma_{ij}{}^k$	Christoff symbol of the second kind
ξ, η, ζ	Coordinate in the transformed space
ρ	Density
Γ_ϕ	Diffusion coefficient
μ	Dynamic viscosity
$\sigma_K, \sigma_\varepsilon$	Parameters in k-ε model
ε	Turbulent dissipation rate

Subscript

cf	Cell face
cvt	Convective terms
E,W,N,S	East, west, north, south
p	Pressure
u	Velocity
vis	Viscous terms
w	Solid wall
ξ, η, ζ	Derivative in computational space
x,y,z	Derivative in physical space

INTRODUCTION

In recent years, much progress has been made in the development of faster and more accurate methods for solving the compressible Navier-Stokes equations, as reviewed by Lakshminarayana (1991), MacCormack (1985), and Shang (1985). The Finite Volume Method (FVM) has been one of the commonly used approaches to solve the Navier-Stokes equations using collocated grids and a coupled formulation for continuity, momentum, energy, and turbulence. However, many of those methods are not appropriate in the low Mach number limit (Van Doormal, et. al., 1987). In addition, programming difficulties are often encountered in the implementation of accurate, high order schemes using the coupled approach, since the variable storage requirements and computational time are considerably increased (Lien and Leschziner, 1993).

As an alternative to coupled solution approaches for compressible flows, segregated methods have been introduced as extensions of incompressible flow, SIMPLE-based algorithms (Patankar, 1971; Issa and Lockwood, 1977; Hah, 1984; Van Doormal et. al., 1987; Karki and Patankar, 1989; Kobayashi and Perira, 1992, Shyy et al, 1992). Instead of using SIMPLE-based pressure updating algorithms for the uncoupled solution of compressible flows, a more direct but yet segregated approach has been introduced for the solution of laminar flows (Zhang, et. al., 1996). The method solves iteratively the continuity, momentum, and state equations for the density, velocity, and pressure fields. In order to be able to use collocated grids in conjunction with the proposed segregated approach for subsonic compressible flows, a non-linear cell-face interpolation scheme has been introduced to relate control volume surface values to nodal point values, thus avoiding checker-board pressure problems (Zhang, et al., 1996).

This paper extends the segregated, laminar compressible flow solver so as to compute turbulent compressible flows in complex geometries. Turbulence is modeled by using the standard two-equation k-ε model of Launder and Spalding (1973). The high order QUICK scheme of Leonard (1979) is implemented for the spatial discretization of the convective terms in the continuity and momentum equations. A third order TVD scheme developed by Chakravarthy and Osher (1985) has been implemented to solve the k-ε turbulence model equations. The purpose of this paper is to evaluate the performance and accuracy of the compressible, turbulent flow code in the light of experimental results. Benchmark tests are performed for turbulent flows in 90° curved and S-duct of circular cross sections. The results show that accurate solutions can be obtained by the present method.

THEORETICAL FORMULATION

With Favre's density-weighted averaging procedure, and the FVM formulation, the transformed governing equations (with k-ε model) for unsteady, compressible flows in generalized curvilinear coordinates (ξ, η, ζ) can be written in the following format:

$$\frac{\partial \hat{Q}}{\partial t} + \frac{\partial (\hat{F} - \hat{F}_v)}{\partial \xi} + \frac{\partial (\hat{G} - \hat{G}_v)}{\partial \eta} + \frac{\partial (\hat{H} - \hat{H}_v)}{\partial \zeta} = R \tag{1}$$

Where
$$\hat{Q} = J_a \rho (1, u, v, w, k, \varepsilon)^T \tag{1a}$$

$$\hat{F} = J_a \rho U (1, u, v, w, k, \varepsilon)^T \tag{1b}$$

$$\hat{F}_v = J_a \mu_{eff} g^{11} \left(0, \frac{\partial u}{\partial \xi}, \frac{\partial v}{\partial \xi}, \frac{\partial w}{\partial \xi}, \frac{1}{\sigma_k}\frac{\partial k}{\partial \xi}, \frac{1}{\sigma_\varepsilon}\frac{\partial \varepsilon}{\partial \xi} \right)^T$$

$$\hat{G} = J_a \rho V (1, u, v, w, k, \varepsilon)^T$$

$$\hat{G}_v = J_a \mu_{eff} g^{22} \left(0, \frac{\partial u}{\partial \eta}, \frac{\partial v}{\partial \eta}, \frac{\partial w}{\partial \eta}, \frac{1}{\sigma_k}\frac{\partial k}{\partial \eta}, \frac{1}{\sigma_\varepsilon}\frac{\partial \varepsilon}{\partial \eta} \right)^T \tag{1c}$$

$$\hat{H} = J_a \rho W (1, u, v, w, k, \varepsilon)^T$$

$$\hat{H}_v = J_a \mu_{eff} g^{33} \left(0, \frac{\partial u}{\partial \zeta}, \frac{\partial v}{\partial \zeta}, \frac{\partial w}{\partial \zeta}, \frac{1}{\sigma_k}\frac{\partial k}{\partial \zeta}, \frac{1}{\sigma_\varepsilon}\frac{\partial \varepsilon}{\partial \zeta} \right)^T \tag{1d}$$

$$R = J_a \left(0, -\frac{\partial p}{\partial \xi_i}\frac{\partial \xi_i}{\partial x}, -\frac{\partial p}{\partial \xi_i}\frac{\partial \xi_i}{\partial y}, -\frac{\partial p}{\partial \xi_i}\frac{\partial \xi_i}{\partial z}, s_k, s_\varepsilon \right) \tag{1e}$$

$$U^i = J_a \left[u\frac{\partial \xi_i}{\partial x} + v\frac{\partial \xi_i}{\partial y} + w\frac{\partial \xi_i}{\partial z} \right] \tag{1f}$$

$$s_k = J_a (G - \rho\varepsilon), s_\varepsilon = J_a \frac{\varepsilon}{k} (C_1 G - C_2 \rho\varepsilon) \tag{1g}$$

Note that the viscous terms have been simplified by ignoring the cross terms, which are only important in very low Re number flows and highly non-orthogonal grids. For our work, total enthalpy is assumed to be constant. This assumption is warranted for viscous compressible flows with unity Prandtl number and adiabatic conditions on the solid wall.

The equation of state and Sutherland's equation of viscosity will be used as the supplementary equations.

Boundary conditions :

The boundary conditions for subsonic flows are given by Ruddy and Strikwerda (1981) and Poinsot and Lele (1992) as follows:

(i) On solid wall: $U=U_W$, $V=V_W$, $W=W_W$, $\frac{\partial p}{\partial n}=0$,

$\frac{\partial T}{\partial n}=0$

For turbulent flow the wall function method was implemented to determine the velocity on the second grid line from the wall. The turbulent kinetic energy k, and its dissipation rate ε on the second grid line from the wall are determined using the local equilibrium assumptions.

(ii) Outflow conditions:

For subsonic flows, pressure is specified at the outlet boundary, while other parameters are extrapolated from the interior points.

(iii) Inflow conditions:

There are totally seven independent variables : ρ, u, v, w, T, k, ε. Since one variable is specified at the outlet boundary, the remaining six variables should be determined at the inlet boundary. In this paper, u, v, w, H, k, ε are specified, while ρ is extrapolated from the interior flow field.

Method of solution:

The FVM is used to solve Eq. (1) using collocated grids in conjunction with the segregated approach. In this method, all variables are stored at the centroid of the brick-type elements, following the approach of Rhie (1988), thus achieving simplicity and low cost of computations. The first step to solve Eq. (1) is to integrate it over a control volume in the computational space shown in Fig. 1:

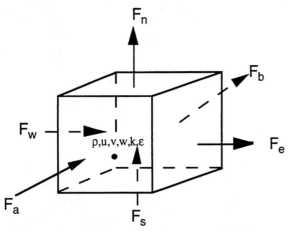

Fig. 1 Arbitrary Cube-Type Finite Volume in the Computational Space

$$\frac{\hat{Q}^{n+1} - \hat{Q}^{n}}{\Delta t} \Delta\xi\Delta\eta\Delta\zeta + (\bar{F}_E - \bar{F}_W)\Delta\eta\Delta\varsigma +$$

$$(\bar{F}_N - \bar{F}_S)\Delta\xi\Delta\varsigma + (\bar{F}_A - \bar{F}_B)\Delta\xi\Delta\eta = R\Delta\xi\Delta\eta\Delta\zeta \qquad (2)$$

where the tildes denote convective and diffusive terms. The convection-diffusion terms are defined as following:

$$\left(\bar{F}_i\right)_{cf} = \left(F_i\right)_{cf} + \left(F_{i,v}\right)_{cf} \qquad (3)$$

where $(F_1, F_2, F_3) = (F, G, H)$, $(\xi_1, \xi_2, \xi_3) = (\xi, \eta, \zeta)$, and cf stands for cell face. For convenience, $\Delta\xi, \Delta\eta, \Delta\zeta$ are set to be unity. The convective terms are computed according to the different schemes used. The third order upwind-biased QUICK scheme of Leonard (1979) is implemented in this paper. The

third order TVD scheme of Chakravarthy and Osher (1985) is implemented for the k-ε model equations.

Grouping the various terms together we obtain a system of equations of the following format:

$$\frac{\hat{Q}^{n+1} - \hat{Q}^{n}}{\Delta t} = RHS \qquad (4)$$

As described by Patankar (1980), a "checker-board pressure problem" and a "wavy velocity field" would arise when collocated grids are used in conjunction with a decoupled pressure-velocity approach for incompressible flows. A similar problem would occur in predicting compressible viscous flows when using a segregated approach and collocated grids (Lien and Leschziner, 1993). To avoid the checker-board pressure field, a "non-linear interpolation" scheme has been used to calculate the cell-face contravariant velocity components (Zhang, Assanis and Tamamidis 1996). The cell-face contravariant velocities are related to the velocities and pressures at the adjacent cell centers through the following equation, illustrated in one dimension for clarity

$$U_{i+1/2}^{n+1} = \left(-g^{11}(p_{i+1} - p_i) + \frac{\rho}{\Delta t}U_{i+1/2}^n + 2\rho(U^+U_i - U^-U_{i+1})\right.$$

$$+ 2(J_a g^{11}\mu)_{i+3/4}U_{i+1} + 2(J_a g^{11}\mu)_{i+1/4}U_i + \rho(\Gamma_{11}^1 UU)_{i+1/2}\bigg) \div \qquad (5)$$

$$\left(\frac{\rho}{\Delta t} + 2\rho(U^+ - U^-) + 2(J_a g^{11}\mu)_{i+3/4} + 2(J_a g^{11}\mu)_{i+1/4}\right) \qquad (5)$$

where $U^+ = \frac{\left(U_{i+1/2} + |U_{i+1/2}|\right)}{2}, U^- = \frac{\left(U_{i+1/2} - |U_{i+1/2}|\right)}{2}, \Delta\xi = 1$

and Γ_{ij}^m is the Christoff symbol of the second kind. Clearly, $U_{i+1/2}$ is not only related to U_i and U_{i+1}, but also to p_i, p_{i+1}.

A four-stage scheme is employed to advance the solution of Eq. (4) in time (Jameson, 1983; Swanson and Turkel, 1985; Cabuk et al. 1992). This multi-stage scheme is fourth-order accuracy in time for linear equations, while it is second-order accuracy for non-linear equations.

The solution is declared convergent when the root-mean-square of the velocity and density residuals decreases by at least two orders of magnitude from their starting values. Here, the residual of a variable is defined as:

$$R = \frac{\sqrt{\frac{\sum_{i=1}^{N} Er_i^2}{N}}}{reference} \qquad (6)$$

where N is the number of nodes, Er_i is the change of a variable at a node:

$$Er_i = \left(q_i^{n+1} - q_i^n\right) \qquad (6a)$$

COMPARISON OF PREDICTIONS WITH MEASUREMENTS

Turbulent Flow in a 90 Degree Circular Duct

The first test case deals with the prediction of the turbulent flow in a 90 degree curved duct of circular cross-section. This test problem has been selected to explore the convergence and accuracy of the compressible code near the low Mach number limit. Our numerical results are compared with the Laser Doppler velocimetry study of Enayet et al. (1982) for incompressible turbulent flow of water. The prediction uses a moderately-dense grid 61 x 17 x 17. The Reynolds number for this problem is 43000.

Figure 2 shows the flow development in the vertical mid-plane. The "core" fluid, defined as fluid of velocity greater than about 0.9 of the maximum at each streamwise station, is found closer to the suction surface of the duct, upstream of the bend. The fluid near the suction surface continues to accelerate at $\theta=30^{\circ}$. After that section, the position of maximum velocity gradually shifts toward the pressure surface of the duct, with a correspondingly low velocity region adjacent to the inner-radius wall. This redistribution of streamwise velocity is caused by the secondary flow in the duct. The presence of a large central region of uniform velocity flow influences significantly the development of the secondary flow downstream. This secondary motion is directed towards the side walls along the outer-radius wall and towards the symmetry plane along the inner-radius wall. It is gradually weakened in the straight part after the bend at the further downstream stations. The predicted flow development is very similar to that illustrated by the incompressible flow computations of Tamamidis and Assanis (1993).

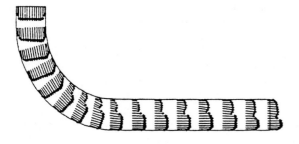

Fig. 2 Velocity Vectors In the Vertical Mid-plane

To explore the accuracy of the predictions near the low Mach number limit, the magnitudes of the predicted velocities have been compared with the measurements of Enayet et al. (1982) at several mid-span locations along the duct. In Fig. 3, the velocities have been normalized with respect to the "bulk velocity" as in Enayet et al. (1982). Further, the radial distance r has been normalized according to the relation

$$r^* = \frac{r - r_o}{r_m - r_o}.$$ where, r_o and r_m are the outer and mean radii, respectively. The predictions generated using the third order QUICK scheme are in very good agreement with the measurements at the 30°, 60° and 75° stations, but some discrepancies exist at the station one hydraulic diameter downstream of the bend Overall, the QUICK scheme yields satisfactory numerical prediction in this test case. The discrepancies between the numerical computation and the experimental data at the downstream section, also observed by Tamamidis and Assanis (1993), are partly attributed to the limitation of the wall function approximations, and the limitations of the k-ε model in flows with streamline and surface curvature, and anisotropic turbulence.

The computation requires 1260 iterations to converge, i.e. for residuals to drop by three orders of magnitude, with a CPU time of 8 minutes on the Cray Y/MP. It should be noted that initial calculations with the standard k-ε model could not converge using the QUICK scheme. This unstable convergence was originated from the solution of the k- and ε-equations using the high order non-monotonic scheme. In order to obtain convergent and accurate results, a third order TVD scheme developed by Chakravarthy and Osher (1985) was used. Fig. 4 compares predicted and measured turbulent intensity distributions at the 30°, 60°, 75°, and 1d downstream stations. Reasonable quantitative agreement was reached at the 30° section, while only qualitative agreement was seen at the other three sections. Again, these discrepancies are attributed to the limitations of the k-ε turbulence model, and the wall function approximation.

Turbulent Flow in an S-Shaped Duct of Circular Cross-Section

The second test case deals with the prediction of subsonic turbulent flow at a higher Mach number in an S-shaped duct of circular cross-section. Our numerical results are compared with the Laser Doppler Velocimetry study of Vakili et al. (1983). Again, the prediction uses a moderately-dense grid 60x21x21, but denser than for the previous test case since the flow has a higher Reynolds number. The grid is generated numerically, following the elliptic grid generation procedure of Thompson et al (1985) and is clustered near the walls to capture the expected high velocity gradients in that area. The inlet velocity profile is prescribed by fitting the experimental data at a distance of 1.5 hydraulic diameters upstream of the bend. The downstream duct length in the computation is taken to be 2.0 hydraulic diameters. The Reynolds number is taken to be 1.76×10^{6}, using the duct diameter as a reference length (Vakili et al., 1983). The diameter of the duct at each cross-section is 16.51 cm, and the radius of curvature of the center line is 83.82 cm at each bend. The angles of the first (clock-wise) and the second (counter-clock wise) bend are both 30° (Vakili et al., 1983). The average Mach number of the velocity field at the inlet cross-section is 0.6.

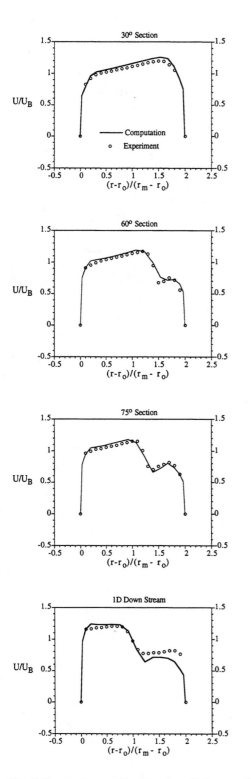

Fig. 3 Comparison of Predicted and Measured Velocity
Profiles for the 90° Curved Duct

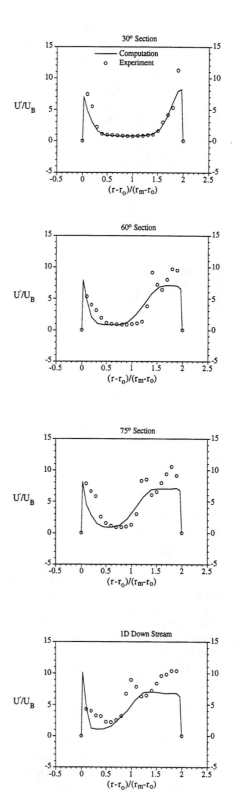

Fig. 4 Comparison of Predicted and Measured Turbulence
Intensity Profiles for the 90° Curved Duct

Figure 5 shows the flow development in the vertical mid-plane. The presence of a large central region of uniform velocity flow influences significantly the development of the secondary flow downstream. At the 15° section (first bend), the maximum velocity has been displaced toward the lower wall of the bend. At the 32°, 45°, and 60° sections, the maximum velocity has been shifted to the upper wall. In the exit section, the maximum velocity begins to shift back towards the lower wall, but at the same time, strong secondary flows exist in both the upper and lower wall regions.

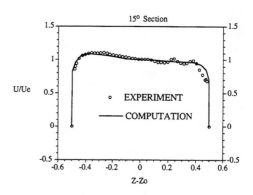

Fig. 5 Velocity Vectors in the Vertical Mid-plane

To further assess the accuracy of the method, flow velocities are compared in Fig. 6 with the measurements of Vakili et al. (1983) at several mid-span locations along the duct. The velocities have been normalized with respect to the duct central velocity at each section. Further, the distance in the Z-direction has been non-dimensionalized by setting the circular center as $Z-Z_0=0$, the lower wall as $Z-Z_0=-0.5$, and the upper wall as $Z-Z_0=0.5$. The predictions are in very good agreement with the experimental data at the 15° and 32° stations, where the velocity profiles are fairly smooth. Only slight discrepancies exist at the 45° and 60° stations.

Unfortunately, experimental data for turbulent intensity were not available for comparison with our predictions for this test. However, a qualitative impression for the development of the turbulent flow field can be extracted from study of their reported pressure contours. Figure 7 shows a good qualitative agreement between measured and computed total pressure contours at the 45° and 60° sections.

CONCLUSIONS

In this paper, the segregated calculation procedure of Zhang, Assanis and Tamamidis (1996) for laminar compressible flows has been extended for turbulent subsonic flows. The method uses a collocated finite volume scheme in body fitted coordinates, and a non-linear interpolation scheme to avoid checker board oscillations. With the segregated

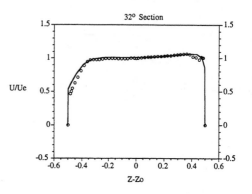

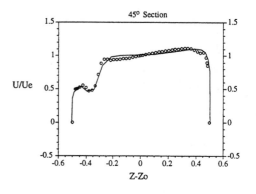

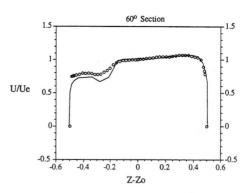

Fig. 6 Comparison of Predicted and Measured Velocity Profiles for the S-duct Problem

approach for solving the continuity, momentum, turbulence, and state equations, high order schemes have been readily implemented for discretizing the convective terms and the k-ε model equations.

To assess the accuracy and convergence of the method, benchmark computations have been performed for turbulent flows in a 90° curved duct and an S-shaped duct with circular cross-sections. Overall, given the limitations of the k-ε model and those of the wall function approach, the numerical method yields satisfactory quantitative predictions of velocities, and a good qualitative description of the pressure field. Furthermore, the method's convergence behavior, accuracy, and computational requirements are very satisfactory near the low Mach number limit. It is concluded that the method can be used to solve compressible, subsonic, turbulent problems of practical interest.

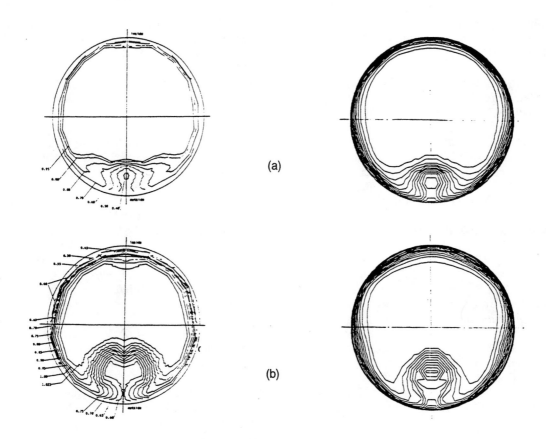

(a)

(b)

Fig. 7 Total Pressure Contours
Left: Experiment: Right: Computation
(a) 45° Section; (b) 60° Section

ACKNOWLEDGMENTS

The contributions of Dr. Panos Tamamidis in the initial development of the laminar version of the compressible CNS-3D code are gratefully acknowledged. The National Center for Super-Computer Applications at the University of Illinois at Urbana-Champaign provided the CPU time on the CRAY Y-MP system for this study.

REFERENCES

Agarwal, R. K. and Deese, J. E. (1984), "Computation of Transonic Viscous Airfoil, Inlet, and Wing Flow Fields," AIAA Paper 84-1551.

Arakawa, A. (1966), "Computational Design for Long-Term Numerical Integration of the Equations of Fluid Motion : 2D Incompressible flow, Part I," *J. of Comp. Phy.*, V1, pp. 119-143.

Cabuk, H., Sung, C.-H. and Modi, V. (1992), "Explicit Runge-Kutta Method for Three-Dimensional Internal Incompressible Flows," *AIAA Journal,* **30** (8).

Chakravarthy, S. R., and Osher, S. (1985), "A New Class of High Accuracy TVD Scheme for Hyperbolic Conservation Laws," AIAA-85-0363.

Doormaal, J. P., Raithby, G.D. and McDonald, B.H. (1987), "The Segregated Approach to predicting Viscous Compressible Fluid Flows," Trans. of ASME, J. of Turbomachinery, Vol. 109, pp. 268-277.

Enayet, M. M., Gibbson, M. M., Taylor, A. M. K., and Yianneskis, M. (1992), "Laser Doppler Measurements of Laminar and Turbulent Flow in a Pipe Bend," NASA Contractor Report 3551.

Jameson, A. (1983), "Transonic Flow Calculations for Aircraft," *Lecture Notes in Mathematics*, pp. 156-242, Edited by Dold, A. and Eckman, B., Springer-Verlag.

Ku, H. C., Hirsch, R. S., and Taylor, T. D. (1987), "A Pseudo-Spectral Method for Solution of 3D Incompressible Navier-Stokes Equations," *J. of Comp. Phy.*, V70, pp. 439-462.

Lakshminarayana, B. (1991), "An Assessment of Computational Fluid Dynamic Techniques in the Analysis and Design of Turbomachinery -- The 1990 Freeman Scalar Lecture," *J. of Fluid Eng.*, Vol. 113, pp. 315-352.

Launder, B. E. and Spalding, D. B. (1974), "The Numerical Computation of Turbulent Flows," Comp. Meth. in *Appl. Mech. and Eng.*, Vol. 3, pp. 269-275.

Leonard, B. P. (1979), "A Stable and Accurate Convective Modeling Procedure Based on Quadratic Upstream Interpolation," *Comp. Meth. in App. Mech. and Eng.*, V19, pp. 59-98.

Lien, F-S., Leschziner, M. A. (1993), "A Pressure-Velocity Solution Strategy for Compressible Flow and Its Application to Shock/Boundary-layer Interaction Using Second-Moment Turbulence Closure," J. *of Fluids Engineering*, Vol. 115, pp. 717-725.

MacCormack, R. W. (1985), "Current Status of Numerical Solutions of Navier-Stokes Equations," AIAA Paper 85-0032. Patankar, S. V. (1980), *Numerical Heat Transfer and Fluid Flow*, Hemisphere, Washington, D.C.

Poinsot, T. J. and Lele, S. K. (1992), "Boundary Conditions for Direct Simulations of Compressible Viscous Flows," *J. of Comp. Phy.*, Vol. 101, pp. 104-129.

Raw, M. R., Galpin, P. F. and Hutchinson, B. R. (1989), "A Collocated Finite Volume Method for Solving the Navier-Stokes Equations for Incompressible and Compressible Flows in Turbomachinery: Results and Applications," Canadian Aeronautics and Space Journal, **35**(4).

Rhie, C. M. and Chow, W. L. (1983), "Numerical Study of the Turbulent Flow Past an Airfoil with Trailing Edge Separation," *AIAA J.*, **21**(11).

Rhie, C. M. (1985), "A Three-Dimensional Passage Flow Analysis Method Aimed at Centrifugal Impellers," *Coput. Fluids*, Vol. 13, pp. 443-460.

Rudy, H. D. and Strikwerda, J. D. (1981), "Boundary Conditions for Subsonic Navier-Stokes Calculations," *Coput. Fluids*, Vol. 9, pp. 327-338.

Shang, J. S. (1985), " An Assessment of Numerical Solutions of the Compressible Navier-Stokes Equations," J. of Aircraft, **22**(5).

Swanson, R. C., Turkel, E. (1985), "A Multistage Time-Stepping Scheme for the Navier Stokes Equations," AIAA Paper 85-35.

Tamamidis, P., and Assanis, D. (1993), "Numerical Simulation of Turbulent Flows in Complex Geometries Using Curvature Modified k-ε Models," ASME-FED, Vol. 155, Turbulent Flows.

Thompson, J. F., Warsi, Z. V. A., and Mastin. C. W. (1985), "Numerical Grid Generation, Foundations and Applications," North-Holland, New York, N.Y.

Vakili, A., Wu, J. M., Liver, P, and Bhat, M. K., (1983), "An Experimental Investigation of Secondary flows in an S-Shaped Circular Duct," Final Report for NASA Lewis Research Center.

Yang, H. Q., and Przekwas, A. J. (1992), "A Comparative Study of Advanced Shock-Capturing Schemes Applied to Burgers' Equation," *J. Comp. Physics*, Vol. 102, pp. 139-159.

Zhang, G., Assanis D. N. and Tamamidis, P. (1996), "Segregated Prediction of 3-D Compressible Subsonic Fluid Flows Using Collocated Grids," *Numerical Heat Transfer, Part A*, **29**(8).

FED-Vol. 238, 1996 Fluids Engineering Division Conference
Volume 3
ASME 1996

A PRESSURE-BASED PRECONDITIONER FOR MULTI-STAGE ARTIFICIAL COMPRESSIBILITY ALGORITHMS

Fotis Sotiropoulos
School of Civil and Environmental Engineering
Georgia Institute of Technology
Atlanta, Georgia 30332-0355, USA

George Constantinescu
Iowa Institute of Hydraulic Research and
Department of Civil Engineering
The University of Iowa, Iowa City, Iowa 52242-1585, USA

ABSTRACT

A differential preconditioner is developed for accelerating the convergence of explicit, multi-stage, artificial compressibility algorithms using ideas from pressure-based methods. The velocity derivatives in the continuity equation and the pressure gradient terms in the momentum equations are discretized in time implicitly. The discrete system of equations is linearized in time producing a block implicit operator which is approximately factorized and diagonalized via a similarity transformation. The so derived diagonal operator depends only on the metrics of the geometric transformation and can, thus, be implemented in an efficient and straightforward manner. It is combined with the standard implicit residual smoothing operator and incorporated in a four-stage Runge-Kutta algorithm also enhanced with local time stepping and multigrid acceleration. Linear stability analysis, for the coupled Navier-Stokes equations, and calculations of three-dimensional laminar flows through strongly curved square ducts and pipes demonstrate the damping properties and efficiency of the proposed approach.

INTRODUCTION

Explicit, multistage, time-stepping schemes are widely used for simulating incompressible flows in conjunction with the artificial compressibility (AC) approach of Chorin (1967)--Choi and Merkle (1985), Farmer et al. (1994), Lin and Sotiropoulos (1996), etc. Their success and popularity is largely due to the constant-coefficient, implicit residual smoothing (IRS) procedure which is incorporated in the basic, explicit, time-stepping scheme (Jameson et al., 1981). IRS is a differential preconditioner (Turkel, 1992) which allows the use of larger Courant numbers, enhances robustness, and improves the overall damping properties of the time-stepping procedure. It is, therefore, of crucial importance for designing efficient multigrid algorithms whose performance relies heavily on the damping properties of the basic iterative scheme (multistage, Runge-Kutta in this case). These benefits are achieved at a relatively low computational overhead (typically less than ten percent of the total CPU time per iteration) since only inversions of scalar tridiagonal matrices are required. On large-aspect-ratio meshes, however, the effectiveness of the constant-coefficient IRS operator diminishes and variable-coefficient operators appear to be somewhat more effective (Martinelli, 1987).

The objective of this paper is to exploit certain properties of the incompressible flow equations to develop a differential preconditioning operator for explicit, multistage AC algorithms. Such preconditioner must: i) exhibit the simplicity and computational efficiency of the standard IRS operator; and ii) further enhance the damping of high-frequency errors so that it can be used as an effective multigrid smoother. We propose to explore the possibility of constructing such an operator by combining ideas from pressure-based, or pressure-Poisson (PP), methods with pseudo-compressible formulations. Consider a PP method in which the momentum equations are advanced in time explicitly (see for example Sotiropoulos and Abdallah (1992)). In such an algorithm the velocity derivatives in the continuity equation and the pressure gradient terms in momentum equations are discretized implicitly. The continuity and momentum equations are subsequently combined to derive a Poisson equation for the pressure field at the new time level. Solution of this equation requires the inversion of a linear Laplacian operator, which involves only transformation metrics and the time increment. Once the pressure equation is solved, the new pressure field is used to advance the momentum equations in time. An explicit AC method (Choi and Merkle (1985), Farmer et al. (1994), Lin and Sotiropoulos (1996)), on the other hand, advances the continuity and momentum equations in time simultaneously in a coupled fashion. The main advantage of coupling the governing equations is that spatial discretization techniques (scalar and matrix-valued dissipation models, flux-difference splitting upwinding, non-linear limited schemes, etc.) originally developed for the compressible flow equations can be readily extended to incompressible flows (Merkle and Athavale (1987), Lin and Sotiropoulos (1996)). Coupling also facilitates the implementation of boundary conditions using the method of characteristics (Choi and Merkle, 1985).

We propose herein to incorporate ideas from pressure-based methods in explicit AC formulations to derive an algorithm which: i) maintains the coupled formulation of the governing equations; and ii) allows the implicit treatment of the pressure in a way that only linear matrices need to be inverted. To do so, we employ the same temporal discretization for the AC system as the one used in PP formulations--that is, the velocity derivatives, in the pseudo-compressible continuity equation, and the pressure gradient terms, in the momentum equations are discretized implicitly. Rather than solving the discrete equations in a segregated fashion, the resulting system is linearized in time and formulated in delta form. This procedure produces a linear block implicit operator which is factorized, using the standard Beam and Warming (1976) approach, and subsequently diagonalized via a similarity transformation (Pulliam and Chaussee, 1981). As is the case with the pressure equation in PP methods, the resulting diagonal operator depends only on the metrics of the geometric transformation. It is combined with the constant-coefficient IRS operator and incorporated in a four-stage Runge-Kutta algorithm enhanced with local time-stepping and multigrid acceleration. Depending on the spatial discretization of the convective terms, both central and upwind preconditioners can be designed using the proposed approach.

In what follows, we first present the governing equations in Cartesian coordinates and outline an approach for incorporating ideas from pressure-based methods in AC algorithms. Based on this approach, we propose a new differential preconditioner for explicit, Runge-Kutta, time-stepping schemes and employ vector stability analysis to investigate its damping properties. The efficiency of the proposed approach is evaluated by applying it to calculate three-dimensional laminar flows through curved ducts and pipes. The governing equations and the proposed method are formulated in three-dimensional, generalized curvilinear coordinates in an Appendix at the end of this paper.

NUMERICAL METHOD

Governing Equations

For the sake of convenience, but without loss of generality, we employ the two-dimensional, incompressible Navier-Stokes equations in Cartesian coordinates to demonstrate the proposed preconditioning method. It should be emphasized, however, that the results presented in subsequent sections of this paper have been obtained using the three-dimensional Navier-Stokes equations in generalized, non-orthogonal curvilinear coordinates (see Appendix for the three-dimensional, curvilinear coordinate version of the proposed method).

The two-dimensional governing equations read in Cartesian coordinates as follows:

$$\Gamma \frac{\partial Q}{\partial t} + \frac{\partial E}{\partial x} + \frac{\partial F}{\partial y} = \frac{1}{\text{Re}} \left(\frac{\partial^2 Q}{\partial x^2} + \frac{\partial^2 Q}{\partial y^2} \right) \tag{1}$$

where:

$$\Gamma = diag(\beta, 1, 1)$$
$$Q = (p, u, v)^T$$
$$E = \left(u, u^2 + p, uv \right)^T$$
$$F = \left(v, uv, v^2 + p \right)^T \tag{2}$$

In the above equations, β is a positive constant, p, u, and v denote the pressure, and velocity components, respectively, and Re is the Reynolds number. Note that setting $\beta = 0$ in eqn. (1) produces the incompressible Navier-Stokes equations, in the form used to derive pressure-based algorithms, while $\beta \neq 0$ corresponds to the pseudo-compressible system of equations which is solved in artificial-compressibility formulations.

A Pressure-Based AC Algorithm

In this section we outline a general procedure for combining ideas from pressure-based methods with explicit AC algorithms to derive a "pressure-based" AC method. To facilitate our discussion let us split the flux vectors in eqn. (1) into a linear and a non-linear part,

$$E = E_L + E_N \quad \text{and} \quad F = F_L + F_N \tag{3}$$

where:

$$E_L = (u, p, 0)^T ; E_N = \left(0, u^2, uv \right)^T$$
$$F_L = (v, 0, p)^T ; F_N = \left(0, uv, v^2 \right)^T \tag{4}$$

That is, the E_L and F_L vectors contain the velocity terms in the continuity equation and the pressure gradient terms in the momentum equations, while the E_N and F_N vectors contain the remaining non-linear convective terms. As discussed below, this splitting facilitates the unified formulation of pressure-based and artificial compressibility algorithms. It was first introduced by Merkle et al. (1992) who compared a PISO-type pressure-based method with density-based algorithms.

By employing a simple, one-stage, Euler-type, temporal integration scheme, and incorporating eqns. (3), eqn. (1) can be discretized in time as follows:

$$\Gamma \frac{\Delta Q}{\Delta t} + \frac{\partial}{\partial x} \left(E_L^k + E_N^n \right) + \frac{\partial}{\partial y} \left(F_L^k + F_N^n \right) = \frac{1}{\text{Re}} \left(\frac{\partial^2 Q^n}{\partial x^2} + \frac{\partial^2 Q^n}{\partial y^2} \right) \tag{5}$$

where,

$$\Delta Q = Q^{n+1} - Q^n,$$

n denotes the time level, and $k=n$ or $n+1$ depending on the approach employed to integrate eqn. (5) in time.

Eqn. (5) may represent either pressure-based or artificial compressibility methods. Choosing $\beta=1$ (or in general $\beta > 0$) and $k=n$, for example, produces the standard explicit AC method in which the continuity and momentum equations are coupled and advanced in time simultaneously. On the other hand, selecting $\beta = 0$ and $k=n+1$ produces a pressure-based formulation. In this case, the governing equations need to be solved in a segregated fashion. The momentum equations are substituted in the continuity equation to derive a Poisson eqn. which is solved to obtain the pressure at the $n+1$ time level. The resulting pressure is subsequently employed to update the velocities using the momentum equations.

Here we propose to combine the two approaches so that the implicit treatment of the pressure and velocity-divergence terms, in pressure-based methods, and the coupled solution of the governing equations, in AC methods, are preserved. This can be accomplished by choosing $\beta = 1$ (i.e. $\Gamma = I$, where I is the identity matrix) and setting $k=n+1$. Upon linearization, eqn. (5) reads as follows:

$$\left[I + \Delta t \left(\frac{\partial}{\partial x} A + \frac{\partial}{\partial y} B \right) \right] \Delta Q = -\Delta t R\left(Q^n \right) \qquad (6)$$

where R is the residual vector,

$$R\left(Q^n \right) = \frac{\partial E^n}{\partial x} + \frac{\partial F^n}{\partial y} - \frac{1}{\text{Re}} \left(\frac{\partial^2 Q^n}{\partial x^2} + \frac{\partial^2 Q^n}{\partial y^2} \right) \qquad (7)$$

and A and B are the Jacobian matrices:

$$A = \frac{\partial E_L}{\partial Q} = \begin{pmatrix} 0 & 1 & 0 \\ 1 & 0 & 0 \\ 0 & 0 & 0 \end{pmatrix}$$

$$B = \frac{\partial F_L}{\partial Q} = \begin{pmatrix} 0 & 0 & 1 \\ 0 & 0 & 0 \\ 1 & 0 & 0 \end{pmatrix} \qquad (8)$$

Eqn. (6) can be factorized using the standard Beam and Warming (1976) method as follows:

$$\left[I + \Delta t \frac{\partial}{\partial x} A \right] \left[I + \Delta t \frac{\partial}{\partial y} B \right] \Delta Q = -\Delta t R\left(Q^n \right) \qquad (9)$$

Eqn. (9) appears similar to standard implicit, approximate-factorization, AC methods (see, for example, Kwak et al., 1986). The main difference between the present formulation and such methods is obviously the fact that the operator in the left hand side of eqn. (9) is linear, since we have treated implicitly only the divergence and pressure gradient terms.

The two factors in the left hand side of eqn. (9) are block matrices and their inversion would require significant computational resources. To remedy the situation, we note that the A and B Jacobians have real, distinct eigenvalues ($\lambda_1=0$, $\lambda_2=1$, $\lambda_3=-1$) and can, thus, be diagonalized via a similarity transformation (Pulliam and Chaussee (1981)). It is also rather interesting to note that the two non-zero eigenvalues are of opposite sign and equal absolute value. This indicates that every point in the solution domain is equally influenced by upstream and downstream traveling waves. This is consistent with the elliptic character of the pressure gradient terms and continuity equation which were discretized implicitly. This observation further underscores the relation between the proposed formulation and pressure-based methods whose elliptic character is associated with the implicit solution of the Poisson equation for the pressure field. By implementing the similarity transformation of A and B in eqn. (9), $A = M^{-1} \Lambda_A M$ and $B = N^{-1} \Lambda_B N$, the following diagonal algorithm is obtained:

$$M \left[I + \Delta t \frac{\partial}{\partial x} \Lambda_A \right] M^{-1} N \left[I + \Delta t \frac{\partial}{\partial y} \Lambda_B \right] N^{-1} \Delta Q = -\Delta t R\left(Q^n \right)$$

$$(10)$$

where $\Lambda_A = \Lambda_B = \text{diag}(0, 1, -1)$, and M and N are the modal matrices of the A and B Jacobian matrices, respectively, given by:

$$M = \begin{pmatrix} 0 & 1/\sqrt{2} & 1/\sqrt{2} \\ 0 & 1/\sqrt{2} & -1/\sqrt{2} \\ -1 & 0 & 0 \end{pmatrix}$$

$$N = \begin{pmatrix} 0 & 1/\sqrt{2} & 1/\sqrt{2} \\ 1 & 0 & 0 \\ 0 & 1/\sqrt{2} & -1/\sqrt{2} \end{pmatrix} \qquad (11)$$

All terms in the left hand side of eqn. (10) are constant--in generalized curvilinear coordinates these terms involve the metrics of the geometric transformation (see Appendix)--and can, thus, be computed once and stored. Furthermore, solution of eqn. (10) requires inversions of scalar, tri-diagonal matrices.

Extension to Multistage AC Algorithms

The "pressure-based" AC algorithm outlined above, eqn. (10), can be employed to derive a differential preconditioner for explicit, multistage AC methods. Let us consider the standard explicit, four-stage, Runge-Kutta procedure, enhanced with IRS, as applied to eqn. (1) (for m=1 to 4):

$$Q^{(m+1)} = Q^n - \Delta t \alpha_m \overline{\Im}^{-1} R\left(Q^{(m)} \right) \qquad (12)$$

175

where a_m are the Runge-Kutta coefficients and $\overline{\mathfrak{I}}$ is the standard IRS operator defined as follows:

$$\overline{\mathfrak{I}}(\ ) = \left(1 - \varepsilon_x \frac{\partial^2}{\partial x^2}\right)\left(1 - \varepsilon_y \frac{\partial^2}{\partial y^2}\right)(\ ) \tag{13}$$

where ε_x and ε_y are positive constants of order one.

We propose to replace eqn. (12) with the following multistage procedure (for m=1 to 4):

$$\mathfrak{I}\Delta Q^{(m)} = -\Delta t \alpha_m R\left(Q^{(m)}\right) - \left(Q^{(m)} - Q^n\right)$$
$$Q^{(m+1)} = Q^{(m)} + \Delta Q^{(m)} \tag{14}$$

where

$$\mathfrak{I}(\ ) = M\mathfrak{I}_x M^{-1} N \mathfrak{I}_y N^{-1}(\ ) \tag{15}$$

$$\mathfrak{I}_x = I + \alpha_m \Delta t \left(\frac{\partial}{\partial x}\Lambda_A - \varepsilon_x \rho(A) I \frac{\partial^2}{\partial x^2}\right)$$
$$\mathfrak{I}_y = I + \alpha_m \Delta t \left(\frac{\partial}{\partial y}\Lambda_B - \varepsilon_y \rho(B) I \frac{\partial^2}{\partial y^2}\right) \tag{16}$$

and $\rho(A)$ and $\rho(B)$ are the spectral radii of matrices A and B, respectively. The operator given by eqns. (15) and (16) combines the implicit, "pressure-based" operator, eqn. (10), with a generalized implicit residual smoothing operator, similar to eqn. (13). Attempts to employ only the "pressure-based" operator ($\varepsilon_x = \varepsilon_y = 0$ in eqn. (14)) were not successful as no converged solutions could be obtained. Both the A and B matrices have a zero eigenvalue (see also eqns. (8)) which implies that, for $\varepsilon_x = \varepsilon_y = 0$ in eqn. (16), one of the three governing equations is not being smoothed. Thus, non-zero values for ε_x and ε_y were always necessary. The spectral radii of the Jacobian matrices A and B were included in eqn. (16) to scale the second-order dissipative derivatives proportionally to the convective-like terms. Although in Cartesian coordinates they are both unity, in generalized curvilinear coordinates $\rho(A)$ and $\rho(B)$ depend on the contravariant metric tensor (see Appendix) and, thus, need to be included for proper scaling. This eigenvalue scaling is similar to that used for constructing explicit, second and/or fourth-difference artificial dissipation terms for stabilizing central-differencing schemes (Martinelli, 1987).

Implementing operator $\mathfrak{I}$ in place of $\mathfrak{I}$ increases the required CPU time per time step by approximately twenty percent because of the additional matrix-vector multiplications required for inverting eqn. (15). The subsequently presented results, however, indicate that the proposed preconditioner accelerates significantly the convergence to steady state in terms of total CPU time. Furthermore, it can be implemented in existing Runge-Kutta AC flow solvers with relatively minimal additional programming work.

Spatial Discretization

The spatial derivatives in eqns. (7) and (16) are discretized by employing three-point central, finite differencing for the second order derivatives while central or upwind differencing may be employed for the convective terms.

When central-differencing is employed--both for the convective terms in eqn. (7) and the "convective-like" terms in eqns. (16)--fourth-difference, scalar artificial dissipation terms, with eigenvalue scaling (Martinelli, (1987), Lin and Sotiropoulos (1996)), are explicitly added in the right-hand side of eqn. (7) for stability. In this case, the second-order derivatives in eqn. (16) can be interpreted as implicit artificial dissipation.

Upwind approximations of the convective terms are constructed using flux-difference splitting (Merkle and Athavale (1987), Rogers et al. (1991), Lin and Sotiropoulos (1996)). The convective-like terms in eqn. (16), on the other hand, can be upwinded in a straightforward fashion by splitting the eigenvalue matrices, Λ_A and Λ_B, into positive and negative parts--for example, $\Lambda_A = \Lambda_A^+ + \Lambda_A^-$, where $\Lambda_A^+ = diag(0,1,0)$ and $\Lambda_A^- = diag(0,0,-1)$. In the present study a second order accurate upwind scheme is used to discretize the convective fluxes in eqn. (7) while first-order accurate upwinding is employed for discretizing the convective-like derivatives in the preconditioning operator, eqn. (16). Obviously, this inconsistency, between left and right hand sides, does not affect the accuracy of the steady state solution but preserves the tri-diagonal character of each of the two factors in eqn. (15).

Multigrid Acceleration

The proposed preconditioner is implemented in a four-stage, Runge-Kutta algorithm--with coefficients α_m=1/4, 1/3, 1/2, 1, for m=1,2,3,4 respectively--in conjunction with multigrid acceleration (Jameson, 1983) and local time stepping. The multigrid method employs a standard V-cycle algorithm with three grid levels and has both full- and semi-coarsening capabilities (Lin and Sotiropoulos (1996)). One iteration is performed on the finest mesh, and two and three iterations are performed on the two coarser meshes, respectively. It should be noted that during prolongation, the coarse grid residuals are smoothed using the standard constant-coefficient IRS operator (eqn. (13)).

LINEAR STABILITY ANALYSIS

To investigate the effect of the proposed preconditioner in the damping properties of the multistage iterative algorithm, we employ Von-Neumann vector stability analysis for the coupled Navier-Stokes equations. Both the two- and three-dimensional equations are investigated. Due to space considerations, however, we only present a small but representative sample of the two-dimensional stability analysis results (a detailed discussion will be included in a future journal publication).

Fig. 1 shows the maximum eigenvalue of the amplification matrix for the proposed (eqn. (14)) and standard (eqn. (12))

176

to discretize the spatial derivatives in both algorithms. For each case, however, the stability results were obtained for the corresponding optimum Courant number and smoothing coefficients. These parameters were selected to optimize, in the linear stability sense, the damping properties of each algorithm over the entire frequency domain. As seen in Fig. 1, the proposed preconditioner yields very low amplification factors in the high-frequency region. The standard algorithm, on the other hand, does not appear to damp these frequencies at all since the amplification factor approaches unity as the phase angles approach π. These results suggest that the present method should converge much faster than the standard residual smoothing approach. It should also be very effective in conjunction with multigrid acceleration. The calculations discussed below verify these conclusions.

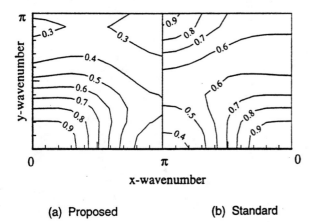

(a) Proposed   (b) Standard

Fig. 1 Amplification factors for standard and proposed AC algorithms

RESULTS AND DISCUSSION

To investigate the relative efficiency of the proposed and standard IRS preconditioners we apply them to calculate laminar flow through strongly curved, 90° square ducts and pipes. As mentioned above these calculations are carried out using the three-dimensional Navier-Stokes equations in generalized, curvilinear coordinates (see Appendix). For the square duct case, the Reynolds number, based on hydraulic diameter and bulk velocity, is Re=496 and fully-developed flow is specified at the entrance of the bend. For the pipe bend, on the other hand, plug flow is specified at the entrance of the bend and Re=1,096.

Fig. 2 shows typical plane-of-symmetry and cross-sectional views of the computational grid for the duct and pipe geometries. Two meshes are employed to discretize the duct geometry: a uniform mesh with 61x21x13 nodes (case 1a), and a highly stretched mesh (minimum near-wall spacing 8x10^{-4}) with 61x41x21 nodes (case 1b) in the streamwise, radial, and normal directions, respectively. The pipe bend is discretized using 69x41x21 grid nodes (case 2) with minimum near-wall spacing 1×10^{-3}. It should be noted that the cross-sectional mesh topology for the pipe bend (see Fig. 2) produces highly-skewed grid lines near the corners of the cross-section. This topology was specifically selected to provide a particularly acid

test for the efficiency and robustness of the proposed algorithm.

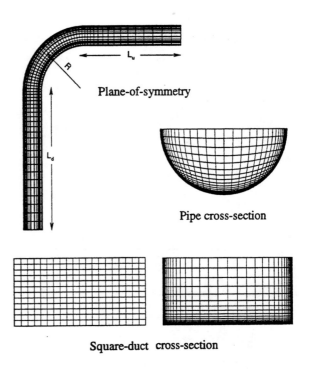

Fig. 2 Plane-of-symmetry and cross-sectional views of the computational mesh

For cases 1b and 2, calculations are carried out with the multigrid version of the standard and proposed preconditioners both with central-differencing, with explicitly added artificial dissipation, and second-order accurate flux-difference splitting upwind differencing. Case 1a, on the other hand, is calculated with the single-grid version of the two algorithms. For all cases the Courant number and smoothing coefficients were optimized via numerical experimentation with guidance from linear stability analysis. Also all calculations were carried out on a HP-750 workstation using single-precision arithmetic. To facilitate our subsequent discussion, the relative efficiency of the various algorithms is assessed based on the work they require to reduce the residuals by four orders of magnitude (corresponding residual level of the order 10^{-3}).

The convergence histories for cases 1a, 1b, and 2 are shown in figures 3, 4, and 5, respectively. Regardless the use of single or multi-grid algorithms, or whether central or upwind differencing is employed, it is seen that the proposed differential preconditioner yields substantial savings in the work required for convergence. On the uniform mesh (Fig. 3), for instance, it converges approximately two times faster than the standard residual smoothing approach. Even more encouraging is its performance on the highly stretched mesh--which is sufficiently fine for high-Reynolds number turbulent flow

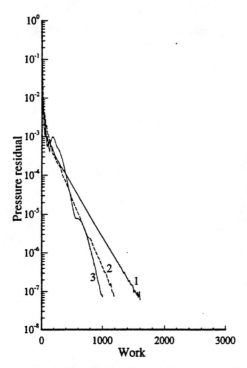

Fig. 3 Convergence histories for Case 1a (square bend; uniform mesh, single-grid): 1) Standard, central diff.; 2) Proposed, central diff.; 3) Proposed, upwind.

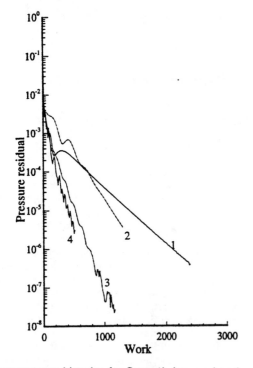

Fig. 4 Convergence histories for Case 1b (square bend; stretched mesh, multi-grid): 1) Standard, central diff.; 2) Standard, upwind 3) Proposed, central diff.; 4) Proposed, upwind.

calculations--employed in case 1b where the proposed method converges approximately three times faster. Even on the highly skewed and stretched mesh of case 2, where the performance of all algorithms consistently deteriorates, the proposed differential preconditioner requires approximately forty percent less work for achieving convergence as compared to the standard approach. Insofar as the effect of artificial dissipation is concerned (central vs. upwind differencing), it is seen that the second-order upwind consistently converges somewhat faster than central differencing--similar trends were reported by Lin and Sotiropoulos (1996) who investigated the effect of artificial dissipation on accuracy and convergence of the standard artificial compressibility approach.

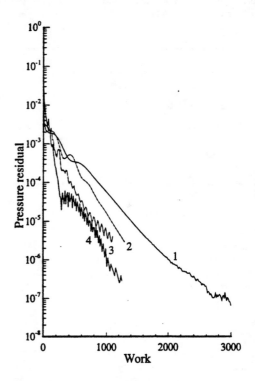

Fig. 5 Convergence histories for Case 2 (pipe bend; stretched mesh, multi-grid): 1) Standard, central diff.; 2) Standard, upwind 3) Proposed, central diff.; 4) Proposed, upwind.

CONCLUSIONS

A new differential preconditioner for explicit, multistage artificial compressibility methods is derived by incorporating ideas from pressure-based methods. The proposed preconditioner is simple to implement in existing multistage codes which utilize the standard, constant-coefficient implicit residual smoothing operator. Both central and upwind differencing formulations were developed and investigated. Vector stability analysis for the coupled Navier-Stokes equations indicates that the proposed preconditioner substantially enhances the damping of high-frequency errors and can, thus, be very effective in conjunction with multigrid acceleration. This is confirmed by a number of numerical experiments for laminar flow through strongly curved ducts and pipes using both uniform and highly stretched as well as orthogonal and highly skewed meshes. Depending on mesh quality, the proposed approach requires between 40 to 70 percent less work for achieving convergence as compared to the standard residual smoothing preconditioner. It is, therefore, a powerful tool for accelerating convergence in calculations of complex, three-dimensional shear flows. The proposed approach can be extended to unsteady flows by combining it with dual time-stepping procedures.

ACKNOWLEDGMENTS

This work was supported by a grant from the Electric Power Research Institute (EPRI), monitored by Mr. J. L. Tsou. Some calculations during the development stage of this work were carried out on the Cray-C90 at the San-Diego Supercomputing Center (SDSC).

REFERENCES

Beam, R. M., and Warming, R. F. (1976), "An Implicit Finite Difference Algorithm for Hyperbolic Systems in Conservation-Law Form," *Journal of Computational Physics*,, Vol. 22, pp. 87-110.

Choi, D. and Merkle, C. L. (1985), "Application of Time Iterative Schemes to Incompressible Flow," *AIAA Journal,* Vol. 23, No. 10, pp. 1518-1524.

Chorin, A. J. (1967), "A numerical method for solving incompressible viscous flow problems," *Journal of Computational Physics*, Vol. 2, No. 1, pp.12-26.

Farmer, J., Martinelli, L. & Jameson, A.(1994), "A Fast multigrid Method for Solving the Non-linear Ship Wave Problem with a Free Surface," Proceedings of *Sixth International Conference on Numerical Ship Hydrodynamics,* pp. 155-172, National Academy Press, Washington, D.C.

Jameson, A., Schmidt, W., and Turkel, E. (1981), "Numerical Solutions of the Euler Equations by Finite Volume Methods Using Runge-Kutta Time-Stepping Schemes," *AIAA Paper 81-1259.*

Jameson, A. (1983), "Solution of the Euler Equations by a Multigrid Method," *Appl. Math. Comput.*, 13, 327-356 (1983).

Kwak, D., Chang, J. L. C., Shanks, S. P., and Chakravarthy, S. (1986), "A Three-Dimensional Incompressible Navier-Stokes Flow Solver Using Primitive Variables," *AIAA Journal*, Vol. 24, No. 3, pp. 390-396.

Lin, F. B., and Sotiropoulos, F. (1996), "Assessment of Artificial Dissipation Models for Three-Dimensional Incompressible Flow Solutions," to appear in the *ASME Journal of Fluids Engineering.*

Martinelli, L. (1987), "Calculations of Viscous Flows with a Multigrid Method," Ph.D. Thesis, MAE Department, Princeton Uni., NJ.

Merkle C. L., Venkateswaran, S., and Buelow, P. E. O. (1992)," The Relationship Between Pressure-Based and Density-Based Algorithms," AIAA paper 92-0425.

Merkle C. L., and Athavale, M. (1987), "Time-Accurate Unsteady Incompressible Flow Algorithms Based on Artificial Compressibility," *AIAA paper* 87-1137.

Pulliam, T. H., and Chaussee, D. S. (1981), "A Diagonal Form of An Implicit Approximate-Factorization Algorithm," *Journal Computational Physics*, Vol. 39, pp. 347-363.

Rogers, S. E., Kwak, D., and Kiris, C. (1991), "Steady and Unsteady Solutions of the Incompressible Navier-Stokes Equations," *AIAA Journal*, Vol. 29, No. 4, pp. 603-610.

Sotiropoulos, F., and Adballah, S. (1992), "A Primitive Variable Method for the Solution of Three-Dimensional Incompressible Viscous Flows," *Journal of Computational Physics*, Vol. 103, No. 2, pp. 336-349.

Turkel, E. (1992), "Review of Preconditioning Methods for Fluid Dynamics," NASA Contractor Report 189712.

APPENDIX

In this appendix we present the governing equations and the proposed preconditioner in three-dimensional curvilinear coordinates.

__Governing Equations__ (repeated indices imply summation):

$$\Gamma \frac{\partial Q}{\partial t} + J \frac{\partial}{\partial \xi^j}\left(F^j - F_V^j\right) = 0$$

where

$$Q = \left[p, u_1, u_2, u_3\right]^T$$

$$F^j = \frac{1}{J}\left[U^j, u_1 U^j + p\xi_{x_1}^j, u_2 U^j + p\xi_{x_2}^j, u_3 U^j + p\xi_{x_3}^j\right]^T$$

$$F_V^j = \frac{1}{J}\frac{1}{\mathrm{Re}}\left[0, g^{mj}\frac{\partial u_1}{\partial \xi^m}, g^{mj}\frac{\partial u_2}{\partial \xi^m}, g^{mj}\frac{\partial u_3}{\partial \xi^m}\right]^T$$

In the above equations, p is the static pressure, u_i are the Cartesian velocity components, x_i are the Cartesian coordinates, J is the Jacobian of the geometric transformation, $\xi_{x_i}^i$ are the metrics of the geometric transformation, U^j are the contravariant velocity components ($U^j = u_i \xi_{x_i}^i$), and g^{ij} are the components of the contravariant metric tensor ($g^{ij} = \xi_{x_k}^i \xi_{x_k}^j$).

__The proposed Algorithm__ (no summation over repeated indices)

$$M_1 \mathfrak{S}_{\xi^1} \mathfrak{S}_{\xi^2} T \mathfrak{S}_{\xi^3} M_3^{-1}(\Delta Q) = -\Delta t \alpha_m R^{(m)} - (Q^{(m)} - Q^n)$$

where

$$\mathfrak{S}_{\xi^j} = \left[I + \alpha_m \Delta t\left(\Lambda^j \frac{\partial}{\partial \xi^j} - \varepsilon_{\xi^j}\sqrt{g^{jj}}I\frac{\partial^2}{\partial(\xi^j)^2}\right)\right]$$

$$\Lambda^j = diag\left(0, 0, \sqrt{g^{jj}}, -\sqrt{g^{jj}}\right)$$

$$S = M_1^{-1} M_2, \quad T = M_2^{-1} M_3$$

$$M_j = \begin{pmatrix} 0 & 0 & \dfrac{1}{\sqrt{2}} & \dfrac{1}{\sqrt{2}} \\[2ex] \dfrac{-(\xi_{x_2}^j + \xi_{x_3}^j)}{s^j} & \dfrac{\xi_{x_1}^j (\xi_{x_3}^j - \xi_{x_2}^j)}{s^j \sqrt{g^{jj}}} & \dfrac{\xi_{x_1}^j}{\sqrt{2}} & \dfrac{-\xi_{x_1}^j}{\sqrt{2}} \\[2ex] \dfrac{\xi_{x_1}^j}{s^j} & \dfrac{g^{jj} + \xi_{x_2}^j (\xi_{x_3}^j - \xi_{x_2}^j)}{s^j \sqrt{g^{jj}}} & \dfrac{\xi_{x_2}^j}{\sqrt{2}} & \dfrac{-\xi_{x_2}^j}{\sqrt{2}} \\[2ex] \dfrac{\xi_{x_1}^j}{s^j} & \dfrac{-(g^{jj} - \xi_{x_2}^j (\xi_{x_3}^j - \xi_{x_2}^j))}{s^j \sqrt{g^{jj}}} & \dfrac{\xi_{x_3}^j}{\sqrt{2}} & \dfrac{-\xi_{x_3}^j}{\sqrt{2}} \end{pmatrix}$$

$$s^j = \sqrt{2 g^{jj} - (\xi_{x_2}^j - \xi_{x_3}^j)^2}$$

FED-Vol. 238, 1996 Fluids Engineering Division Conference
Volume 3
ASME 1996

IMPROVING CONVERGENCE RATES FOR LOW PRESSURE MATERIAL PROCESSING CALCULATIONS

Christopher D. Moen *
Sandia National Laboratories
Livermore, CA 94551-0969

ABSTRACT

An enhanced solution strategy for the SIMPLER algorithm is presented for low pressure heat and mass transport calculations with applications in material processing. The accurate solution of highly diffusive flows requires an inflow boundary condition that preserves chemical species mass fluxes. The flux-preserving inflow boundary condition contains a scaling problem that causes the species equations to converge very slowly when using the standard SIMPLER algorithm. A gradient algorithm, coupled to a line-relaxation method, accelerates the convergence of the linear problem. Reformulation of the pressure-correction boundary conditions ensures that continuity is preserved in each finite volume at each iteration. The boundary condition scaling problem is demonstrated with a simple linear model problem. The enhanced solution strategy is implemented in a baseline computer code that is used to solve the multicomponent Navier-Stokes equations on a generalized, multiple-block grid system. Convergence rate acceleration factors of up to 100 are demonstrated for several material processing example problems.

NOMENCLATURE

A = boundary area
D = average Fickian mass diffusivity
j = mass diffusion flux
$\dot{m}$ = mass flow rate
$\mathbf{n}$ = unit normal vector to boundary
Pe = Peclet number
u = velocity
x = Cartesian coordinate
Y = mass fraction
$\overline{Y}$ = reference mass fraction
Δ = finite-difference increment
∇ = gradient operator
ϕ = potential function
ρ = density

Subscripts

g = chemical species
1 = ghost-cell point
2 = first interior point

---

*Senior Technical Staff, Thermal and Plasma Processes Department, (510) 294-3709

INTRODUCTION

Numerical simulation is a useful tool for studying heat and mass transfer in gas-phase manufacturing of materials. Numerical models predict the uniformity and deposition rate of material coatings and help design reactors and processes. Many applications occur at low pressures, such as etching and chemical vapor deposition, (Jensen, et al., 1991) and (Kleijn, 1991a). Segregated solutions algorithms are commonly used for chemical vapor deposition (CVD) modeling, (Evans and Greif, 1994), (Kleijn, et al.,1889), and (Kleijn and Hoogendoorn, 1991b). Though they can be slow, they are desirable for their simplicity and economic use of computer resources. Increased coupling between equations improves convergence for some flow regimes, discussed in the review by Patankar (1988). Fully coupled methods, (Jensen, 1991) and (Knoll, et al., 1995), are used for reacting flow, but at the cost of storing large matrices. For many applications, the coupled species transport equations are split from the heat and momentum equations (Moffat and Jensen, 1986,1988).

For highly diffusive problems, equation coupling is not as important as spatial coupling. Convergence is degraded at low pressures by poor numerical propagation of information between physical boundaries. Mass diffusivities increase with decreasing pressure and gradients in species composition can span an entire reactor. Difficulty arises at the inflow boundary where convection must balance diffusion to preserve specified species mass fluxes. Information propagates very slowly from such a boundary for a particular class of segregated solution algorithms with explicit updating of boundary conditions. Boundary condition equations should be coupled to interior equations with complete solution of the resulting lineared system.

The focus of this paper is to explain the physical processes that adversely affect the convergence rate at low pressures and modify the solution algorithm accordingly. The algorithm enhancements discussed in this article may not be beneficial to fully coupled schemes. Solution algorithm enhancements are demonstrated with a baseline computational fluid dynamics (CFD) code based on the SIMPLER algorithm (Patankar, 1980). The baseline code, CURRENT, is an extensive reformulation of the TEACH (Gosman and Pun, 1973) code by Evans (1994). He recast the governing equations in terms of a generalized body-fitted coordinate system with multiple-block grids and implemented multicomponent transport with gas-phase and surface-phase chemical reactions. Strengthening the implicit coupling between physical boundaries and across internal grid-block boundaries in the baseline code greatly enhances convergence. Furthermore, convergence rates are improved with only modifications to the species and continuity algorithms.

The solution algorithm enhancements affect both the nonlinear and linear parts of the SIMPLER algorithm. The nonlinear part is modified by including the boundary condition equations in the linearization of the transport equations. Coupling the boundary conditions allows the boundaries to directly communicate at each iteration, but it is during the solution of the linear problem in which information is numerically propagated. The convergence of the linear problem is accelerated by adding the generalized minimal residual (GMRES) gradient scheme of Saad and Schultz (1986) to the line-relaxation scheme. The gradient algorithm is matrix-free, described by Wigton *et al.* (1985) and is implemented with only minor modifications to the existing code. The solution of the continuity equation must also be modified to keep up with the improved species algorithm.

The following sections discuss the baseline code and the developments which lead to the enhanced solution strategy. First, the solution of the governing equations with the baseline solution algorithm is discussed. Then, the low pressure convergence problems are investigated for a simple model problem. Lessons from the model problem lead to modifications to the baseline solution algorithm and boundary condition treatment. Improved performance is demonstrated for two example chemical reactor problems.

TRANSPORT EQUATIONS

The governing equations used in this work, (Evans and Greif, 1994) and (Kleijn, 1989), describe the conservation of mass and the transport of momentum, energy, and chemical species, and are suitable for chemically reacting flows with multicomponent transport. The low Mach number approximation is used where the pressure is split into dynamic and thermodynamic parts and the viscous dissipation term is dropped from the thermal energy equation.

There are two types of boundary conditions: conditions at physical boundaries and conditions at grid-block interfaces. The interface conditions are the result of the block-by-block solution algorithm for the linearized equations. Ghost-cells are used around the grid-blocks to calculate fluxes and averages at boundaries and interfaces. Most boundary conditions are updated explicitly in the baseline CFD code. The ghost-cells, used to couple grid blocks along block interfaces, are locally explicit, but are updated during line-relaxation sweeps so that information propagates across the blocks.

Dirichlet conditions are traditionally applied at an inflow boundary, but they may not preserve the correct species mass flow rates when the flow is highly diffusive. If there is a gradient in chemical composition near the inflow boundary, then the more stringent condition for preserving species mass fluxes is applied:

$$\frac{\dot{m}_g}{A} = \rho u Y_g + \mathrm{j}_g. \tag{1}$$

which states that the species mass flux is balanced by the convective flux and the diffusive flux. The correct composition of chemical species entering the reactor is artificially imposed instead of moving the grid boundaries far away from the source of the composition gradient.

At an outflow boundary, variables are extrapolated from the interior to the ghost-cells. The boundary velocity is also extrapolated from the interior. Since the extrapolation for the boundary velocity does not necessarily satisfy continuity, the outflow velocities are scaled to satisfy global mass conservation.

LOW PRESSURE CONVERGENCE PROBLEM

The root of the low-pressure convergence problem is the unfavorable scaling within the chemical species mass flux-preserving inflow boundary condition, applied in highly diffusive regions. A simple linear model problem is used to demonstrate how convergence degrades with the species cell-Peclet number.

Chemical reaction rates, which usually cause convergence problems in reacting flow computations, play a lesser role in the convergence rate degradation. The reactions are relatively slow at low pressure and not very energetic so there is not a strong effect on the temperature. Surface chemistry is more problematic than gas-phase chemistry since it provides highly nonlinear sources and sinks for gas-phase species at physical boundaries.

Peclet Number Scaling

A scaling problem between convection and diffusion is artificially introduced by using a flux-inflow-boundary condition near a strong species composition gradient. For low Peclet numbers, diffusive transport dominates convective transport. Yet, for the limiting case of uniform inflow composition and no chemical reactions, the convective transport term determines the species distribution within the flow domain. The Peclet number scaling makes it difficult to enforce the convective part of the boundary condition. The scaling is demonstrated using the inflow boundary condition, Eq. (1), simplified by the assumption of Fickian diffusion:

$$\frac{\dot{m}_g}{A} = \rho u Y_g - \rho D \frac{\partial Y_g}{\partial x}. \tag{2}$$

Dividing by the total mass flux gives:

$$\overline{Y}_g = Y_g - \frac{D}{u} \frac{\partial Y_g}{\partial x}, \tag{3}$$

where $\overline{Y}_g = \dot{m}_g / \dot{m}$ represents the reference inflow mass fraction for species g. The cell-Peclet number, $Pe_{\Delta x}$, is defined by the length scale of the finite volume, Δx, the convective velocity, and a mass diffusivity, D: $Pe_{\Delta x} = u\Delta x/D$. The boundary condition is discretized about the inflow cell face using centered differences and the explicit formula for updating the boundary point is:

$$Y_{g,1} = \frac{1 - \frac{1}{2}\text{Pe}_{\Delta x}}{1 + \frac{1}{2}\text{Pe}_{\Delta x}} Y_{g,2} + \frac{\text{Pe}_{\Delta x}}{1 + \frac{1}{2}\text{Pe}_{\Delta x}} \overline{Y}_g. \qquad (4)$$

For small limiting values of the cell-Peclet number, the ghost-cell mass fraction is more dependent on the interior point, $Y_{g,2}$ than the reference value, $\overline{Y}_g$, during the explicit update. Yet, the mass fractions must approach the reference value when there are no chemical reactions or sources.

$$\lim_{\text{Pe}_{\Delta x} \ll 1} Y_{g,1} = Y_{g,2} + \text{Pe}_{\Delta x}\overline{Y}_g \qquad (5)$$

Bad initial guesses for the mass fractions result in very slow convergence to the actual solution. The interior points are strongly dependent on the boundary points because of the elliptic nature of the partial differential equations. The scaling argument indicates that any implicit scheme used to update interior points without coupling the boundary points is ineffective.

Linear Model Problem

The severity of the Peclet number scaling problem is demonstrated using a simple linear model problem. The model approximates the multicomponent transport processes with simple diffusion, described by the Laplace equation:

$$\nabla^2\phi = 0. \qquad (6)$$

The "mass flux preserving" inflow boundary condition is set over part of the boundary and the rest of the boundary has a zero-gradient condition:

$$\phi - \frac{1}{\epsilon}\nabla\phi \cdot \mathbf{n} = 1, \qquad (7)$$

$$\nabla\phi \cdot \mathbf{n} = 0, \qquad (8)$$

where $\mathbf{n}$ is the unit normal vector to the boundary. The Peclet number scaling is introduced as the parameter, ϵ, even though there is no convection in the model. The solution to these equations is $\phi = 1$ and the initial condition is $\phi = 0$. For the purposes of discussion, the scaling parameter ϵ will be referred to as the Peclet number, Pe.

Equations (6) through (8) are discretized using centered differences on a uniform multiple-block grid. The scalar variable, ϕ, is located at the center of volumes formed by grid points. The mesh consists of three grid blocks, each of size 31×11 points. The blocks stack on top of each other to form a square grid, shown in Fig. 1, with cells of unit length. The "inflow boundary" is the west face of the bottom Block 1. The discrete linear equations are solved using a line-relaxation scheme, each iteration consisting of four sweeps in alternating directions.

A large number of line-relaxation iterations are required to solve the equations when the scaling is poor (small Peclet number) and the boundary conditions are evaluated explicitly. The convergence is plotted as a function of the

L_2-norm of the linear system residual in Fig. 2. The number of iterations required to converge the problem scales with $(\frac{1}{2} + \frac{1}{\text{Pe}})$. As the Peclet number increases, the number of iterations required to converge the problem with the flux inflow boundary condition approaches that for a fixed Dirichlet boundary condition, $\phi = 1$.

Implicit coupling of the physical boundary conditions in the line-relaxation scheme improves convergence by 25%, but the work required is still excessive. The boundary information is propagated implicitly in the direction of the line-solve, but more "explicit-like" in the sweep direction. The full set of boundaries, which drive the interior equations, are not directly coupled. Each boundary point should simultaneously see every other boundary point.

Matrix-free, preconditioned gradient algorithms provide an efficient solution to the boundary communication problem. The method is similar to direct inversion, but there is no need to store inverse-matrix fill-in. The GMRES gradient algorithm is used to invert the linear system with the block-by-block line-relaxation implicit scheme acting as a preconditioner. The GMRES scheme enhances the implicitness of the line-relaxation scheme. The gradient algorithm is not restarted for the model problem and the number of search directions is limited to 20 so that outer iterations on the problem are required. The convergence history for the enhanced implicit scheme is shown in Fig. 3. The residual norm is plotted as a function of the number of preconditioning calls. Each preconditioning call is comparable in computational work to one iteration of the line-relaxation scheme alone. The overhead work of the gradient algorithm effectively increases the amount of CPU time required for each preconditioner call by 30%. The addition of the GMRES scheme accelerates the convergence of the line-relaxation scheme by anywhere from a factor of 4 to 1000, depending on the cell-Peclet number.

The GMRES acceleration scheme provides no additional benefits as the mesh density is refined. The amount of work required to converge on a finer mesh follows theoretical scaling laws for relaxation-type schemes. When the number of mesh points is increased by a factor of 16 to three 121×41 grids, the number of iterations required to reach the convergence tolerance increases by roughly an order of magnitude. The convergence rate for the GMRES accelerated scheme on the denser grid behaves similarly to the line-relaxation itself, shown in Fig. 4.

ENHANCED NAVIER-STOKES ALGORITHM

The solution algorithm enhancements to the Navier-Stokes code involve the species equations and the pressure-correction equation. The modifications to the species equations follow those described for the model problem where the boundary condition equations are treated implicitly and the linear problem is solved to completion with the GMRES algorithm. When the linearized species equations are fully converged, the solution can change too fast for the nonlinear problem and the overall solution strategy becomes unstable. Stability is increased by satisfying the continuity equation more rigorously.

Errors in continuity cause artificial sources and sinks in the species equations. In the baseline algorithm, neither continuity nor the linearized species equations are satisfied exactly at each iteration. The errors tend to offset each other and no stability problems result. Conversely, the enhanced solution algorithm does such a good job of satisfying the transport equations that they become very sensitive to mass errors.

The solution to the continuity problem is twofold. First, it is recognized that continuity errors during iteration are due to the use of zero-gradient boundary conditions for the pressure-correction on all boundaries and incomplete convergence of the linear pressure-correction equation. The zero-gradient boundary condition on the pressure-correction term does not allow outflow boundary velocities to change. The outflow boundary condition is reformulated so that the outflow velocity can be corrected in a manner consistent with continuity. Secondly, the matrix-free GMRES gradient algorithm is added to the solution algorithm for the pressure-correction equation to accelerate convergence.

The pressure-correction procedure is reformulated in a manner consistent with other projection methods for low Mach number flows, (Chorin, 1967) and (Dwyer, 1994). The pressure is still updated according to the SIMPLER algorithm. The pressure-correction is treated as a velocity potential and is set to zero at the outflow boundary ghost points. Matrix coefficients are extrapolated from the interior. A velocity correction can then be formulated at the outflow boundary and the velocity updated in a way that is consistent with continuity. The velocity potential approaches the fixed boundary value of zero everywhere upon overall convergence.

EXAMPLE PROBLEMS

Two manufacturing process examples are presented to demonstrate the convergence performance of the enhanced solution strategy. All example problems are run on a Hewlett Packard 735/125 workstation. The baseline code is compiled for 32-bit precision floating-point arithmetic and the modified code is compiled for 64-bit precision. The modified code must be compiled at 64-bit precision in order to avoid numerical precision problems with the gradient algorithm. The discrete governing equations in the code are solved using dimensional quantities in terms of the metric cgs system.

SiO_2 Deposition

Silicon dioxide dielectric growth in a rotating disk chemical vapor deposition (CVD) reactor is modeled. This problem involves gas-phase and surface-phase chemistry in a diffusive environment. The baseline CFD code does not exhibit extremely poor convergence rates for this problem, but the enhanced code improves the average convergence time by a factor of two.

In the CVD reactor, a tetraethoxysilane (TEOS) precursor gas is injected through a shower head arrangement onto a heated substrate, supplying the silicon and oxygen for the deposition. The heat applied to the substrate conducts into the flow field and dissociates the TEOS into other chemical precursors. The chemical precursors react at the substrate with intermediate surface species to form silicon dioxide.

The reactor geometry is discretized with finite volumes in a body-fitted coordinate system. The reactor grid, shown in Fig. 5, is constructed from three blocks with the following block sizes: 21×41, 21×16, and 21×16 grid points. Radial position is measured relative to the vertical centerline and axial position is measured relative to the base of the outflow face. Only half the grid is used for the computation since the reactor is axisymmetric about the vertical centerline. The thermodynamic pressure in the reactor is 1 torr. The growth substrate is maintained at 1000 K and rotates at 30 rpm. The process gas, a mixture of nitrogen and TEOS shown in Table 1, flows into the reactor at 300 K. The axial temperature distribution along the outer vertical wall is represented by a piecewise linear curve, given in Table 2.

Table 1: TEOS Inflow Conditions as a Function of Radial Position

	Inner 5.08 cm	Outer 5.08 cm
X_{TEOS}	0.5	0.75
X_{N_2}	0.5	0.25
V_{in}	20 cm/s	30 cm/s

Table 2: Wall Temperature Profile as a Function of Axial Position

Axial Position (cm)	Temperature (K)
0.0	300.0
2.54	320.0
5.08	400.0
7.62	380.0
10.16	340.0

The gas-phase species considered in the model are: N_2, $Si(OC_2H_5)_4$, $Si(OH)(OC_2H_5)_3$, C_2H_5OH, C_2H_4, and H_2O. A single gas-phase reaction describes the thermal decomposition of TEOS into triethoxysilanol and ethene:

$$Si(OC_2H_5)_4 \rightleftharpoons Si(OH)(OC_2H_5)_3 + C_2H_4.$$

The water and ethanol species are byproducts of the surface-phase reaction mechanism, given in Table 3. A short-hand notation is used involving the symbol G for describing the intermediary glass-like surface species required to form bulk dielectric, $SiO_2(D)$. The notation (D) indicates the solid material in this mechanism. The computational solution indicates that the chemical precursors are fairly well distributed across the substrate surface. One of the primary chemical radical precursors to the silicon dioxide deposition is $Si(OH)(OC_2H_5)_3$, shown in Fig. 6.

Table 3: TEOS Surface-Phase Reaction Mechanism

	Reaction
1.	$Si(OC_2H_5)_4 + SiG3(OH) \rightleftharpoons SiO_2(D) + SiGE3 + C_2H_5OH$
2.	$SiG3E \rightleftharpoons SiG3(OH) + C_2H_4$
3.	$SiG(OH)E2 \rightleftharpoons SiG(OH)2E + C_2H_4$
4.	$SiGE3 \rightleftharpoons SiG(OH)E2 + C_2H_4$
5.	$SiG(OH)2E \rightleftharpoons SiG3(OH) + C_2H_5OH$
6.	$SiG(OH)E2 \rightleftharpoons SiG3E + C_2H_5OH$
7.	$SiG(OH)2E \rightleftharpoons SiG3E + H_2O$
8.	$Si(OH)(OC_2H_5)_3 + SiG3(OH) \rightleftharpoons SiO_2(D) + SiGE3 + H_2O$

The cell-Peclet numbers at the inflow boundary are close to values that begin to cause convergence problems for the model problem. The species Peclet numbers are based on the inflow conditions and are given for a unit reference length of one centimeter: $Pe_{N_2} = 0.27$ to 0.57 and $Pe_{TEOS} = 2.0$ to 4.2. These numbers are multiplied by the wall-normal grid spacing of 0.35 cm to form the cell-Peclet numbers.

Solutions generated with the baseline code and the modified code use mostly the same input parameters. The baseline code uses an under-relaxation value of 0.5 for the temperature equation and 0.9 for the species equations. With the modified solver, the species equations are damped at a value of 0.5 and the temperature equation is damped at a value of 0.9.

The convergence rate for this problem, shown in Fig. 7, is measured in terms of the L_1-norm of the species equation. The L_1-norm is constructed from flux balances over each control volume for each species equation, scaled by the maximum species convective flux. Only the residual norm for the species equations is plotted since it is most indicative of convergence problems. The baseline code converges to the level of 10^{-6} after 4000 iterations at which point it reaches the limits of numerical precision. The baseline code runs at a rate of 0.8 seconds per iteration (averaged over 7500 iterations). The modified code with the gradient algorithm runs at a rate of 2.5 seconds per iteration (averaged over 1000 iterations). One iteration of the modified code requires many calls to the line-relaxation preconditioner. The iteration rate for the modified code varies slightly due to the variable search direction strategy in the gradient scheme.

There are actually two measures of convergence. The mathematical residual norm describes how well the discrete governing equations have been satisfied. If this measure is used, the modified code converges to the L_1-norm of 10^{-6} twenty times faster than the baseline code. At this same convergence level, the baseline code is converged as far as numerical precision will allow. The residual norm can be misleading since physical quantities of interest often converge to within engineering accuracy long before the residual norm reaches the limits of computer precision. The second measure of convergence is based on the physical quantities that are to be extracted from the simulation. The number of iterations required to converge to engineering accuracy is found by studying surface heat and mass flux profiles at the substrate.

Even though the modified code runs about three times slower per iteration than the baseline code, the modified code converges to an engineering solution twice as fast as the baseline code.

Methyltrichlorosilane Injection

The injection and mixing of cold methyltrichlorosilane (MTS) gas, CH_3SiCl_3, into hot helium gas is modeled for a silicon carbide CVD flow-tube experiment. A mixing chamber is designed such that the gases mix completely and flow uniformly out the exhaust.

The geometry consists of a cylindrical center plug with normal injectors inside a cylindrical mixing chamber, shown in Fig. 8. The center plug, with a spherical cap, is 2.5 cm in diameter and the mixing chamber is 5.0 cm in diameter. The injectors are 1.0 mm in diameter and are modeled as a continuous ring. The grid system consists of five blocks of size: 26×26, 7×26, 11×26, 36×21, and 36×26 grid points. Only half the grid is used for the computations since it is symmetric about the axial centerline.

The flow-tube model is not a low pressure problem, but it is very diffusive. The thermodynamic pressure is 100 torr. The MTS flows in at a rate of 500 sccm and a temperature of 300 K. The helium flows in at a rate of 4500 sccm and a temperature of 1400 K. The mole fraction of MTS for complete mixing is 0.1.

The cell-Peclet number at the helium inflow is low enough that convergence problems are expected. The species Peclet numbers are based on the inflow conditions and are given for a unit reference length: $Pe_{He} = 0.037$ and $Pe_{MTS} = 300.0$. These numbers should be multiplied by the wall-normal grid spacing of 0.367 cm for helium and 0.0346 cm for MTS to find the cell-Peclet numbers.

In addition to boundary condition scaling problems in the linear problem, there are transport property problems which affect the stability of the nonlinear iteration process. The mixing configuration is hard to solve because the injected gas has a molecular weight of 149.5 and the carrier gas has a molecular weight of 4. The MTS mass fraction in the completely mixed gas is about 0.8 even though the volume fraction is low. The disparities in molecular weight and transport properties cause numerical problems during the iterative phase of the nonlinear solution procedure. When the solution procedure is started, the MTS injection is impulsive. If the linearized species equations are solved exactly at each nonlinear iteration, large nonphysical errors are introduced. Solution damping is ineffective for this problem. The error is controlled by limiting the degree to which the linear problem is converged. The number of search directions for the gradient solver is selected such that the boundary conditions boundary conditions remain coupled, but not so many that physical errors from the incorrect transport properties dominate. Even with strict limits on search directions, the strong coupling between boundaries is maintained.

The convergence history for the species equations, in terms of the scaled L_1-norm of the conservation laws, is plotted in Fig. 9. The converged mixing levels are approached after about 200 iterations. The modified code runs at about six seconds per iteration for this problem. The convergence history for the baseline code is not shown because it is prohibitively slow for this case. Well over 100000 iterations are required with the baseline code. The modified code provides an acceleration of at least a factor of 100 over the baseline code.

SUMMARY

An enhanced solution strategy for the SIMPLER algorithm is presented for low pressure heat and mass transport calculations with applications in material processing. The solution strategy is implemented in an existing baseline computer code that is used to solve the multicomponent Navier-Stokes equations on a generalized, multiple-block grid system.

The adverse interaction between the inflow boundary condition scaling and the implicit line-relaxation scheme is demonstrated using a simple linear model problem. The convergence rate degrades with the species cell-Peclet number. The physical boundaries do not communicate directly during relaxation sweeps. Enhancing the solution algorithm for the linear problem with a gradient algorithm increases the convergence rate by at least two orders of magnitude. The preconditioned gradient algorithm accelerates the convergence, but the convergence rate is still proportional to the grid size. Future considerations should include the use of multigrid methods for mesh independent convergence rates.

The solution strategy modifications are consistent with the segregated solution approach of the SIMPLER algorithm. Segregation is much more attractive than using a fully coupled Newton method because it is easier to increase the chemical complexity without running out of computing resources. The code modifications are relatively nonintrusive, requiring few changes to validated sections of code. The boundary condition equations are coupled to the interior equations for the linearization. The linear problem is solved completely at each nonlinear iteration using a gradient method to accelerate the existing line-relaxation method. The modifications are only applied to the species equations and the pressure-correction equation. Boundary conditions for the pressure-correction equation are reformulated to ensure continuity is preserved in each finite volume at each iteration.

REFERENCES

Chorin, A. J., 1968, "Numerical Solution of the Navier-Stokes Equations". *Mathematics of Computation*, **22**(1):745–762.

Dwyer, H., 1991, "Calculation of Low Mach Number Reacting Flows". *AIAA Journal*, **28**(1):98–105.

Evans, G. and R. Greif, 1994, "A Two-Dimensional Model of the Chemical Vapor Deposition of Silicon Nitride in a Low-Pressure Hot-Wall Reactor Including Multicomponent Diffusion". *International Journal of Heat and Mass Transfer*, **37**(10):1535–1543.

Gosman, A. D. and W. M. Pun, 1973, "Calculation of Recirculating Flow". Unpublished lecture notes, Imperial College of Science and Technology.

Jensen, K. F., D. I. Fotiadis, and T. J. Mountziaris, 1991, "Detailed Model of the MOVPE Process". *Journal of Crystal Growth*, **107**:1–11.

Kleijn, C. R., Th. H. van der Meer, and C. J. Hoogendoorn, 1989, "A Mathematical Model for LPCVD in a Single Wafer Reactor". *Journal of the Electrochemical Society*, **136**(11):3423–4333.

Kleijn, C. R., 1991a, "On the Modelling of Transport Phenomena in Chemical Vapour Deposition and Its Use in Reactor Design and Process Optimization". *Thin Solid Films*, **206**:47–53, December 1991.

Kleijn, C. R. and C. J. Hoogendoorn, 1991b, "A Study of 2- and 3-D Transport Phenomena in Horizontal Chemical Vapour Deposition Reactors". *Chemical Engineering Science*, **46**(1):321–334.

Knoll, D. A., P. McHugh, and D. Keyes, 1995, "Newton-Krylov Methods for Low Mach Number Combustion". In 12th *Computational Fluid Dynamics Conference*, AIAA Paper 95–1672.

Moffat, H. and K. F. Jensen, 1986, "Complex Flow Phenomena in MOCVD Reactors: I. Horizontal Reactors". *Journal of Crystal Growth*, **77**:108–119.

Moffat, H. and K. F. Jensen, 1988, "Three-Dimensional Flow Effects in Silicon CVD in Horizontal Reactors". *Journal of the Electrochemical Society*, **135**(2):459–471.

Patankar, S. V., 1980, *Numerical Heat Transfer and Fluid Flow*. Hemisphere Publishing Company.

Patankar, S. V., 1988, "Recent Developments in Computational Heat Transfer". *Journal of Heat Transfer*, **110**:1037–1045.

Saad, Y. and M. H. Schultz, 1986, "GMRES: A Generalized Minimal Residual Algorithm for Solving Non-symmetrical Linear Systems". *SIAM Journal of Scientific and Statistical Computing*, **7**(3):856–869.

Wigton, L. B., N. J. Yu, and D. P. Young, 1985, "GMRES Acceleration of Computational Fluid Dynamics Codes". AIAA Paper 85–1494, 7th Computational Fluid Dynamics Conference.

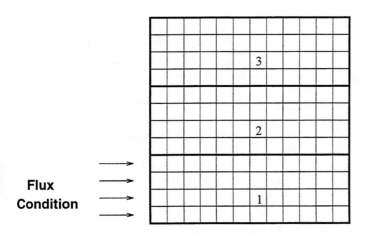

Figure 1: Three-Block Grid for Model Problem

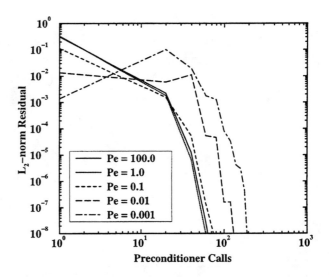

Figure 3: Line-Relaxation Convergence is Accelerated by GMRES

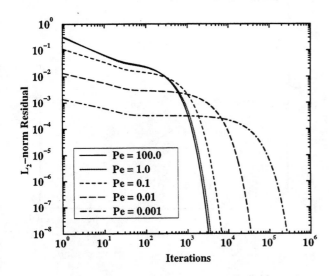

Figure 2: Line-Relaxation Convergence Scales Inversely with Peclet Number

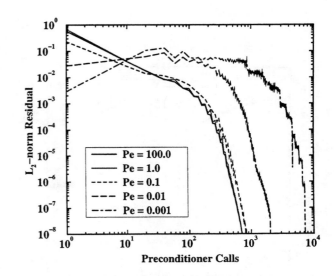

Figure 4: Line-Relaxation Convergence Accelerated by GMRES on Denser Grid

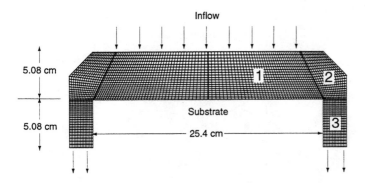

Figure 5: Three-Block Grid for TEOS Reactor

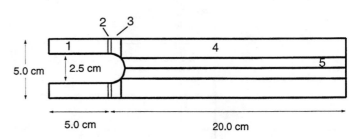

Figure 8: Five-Block MTS Grid System

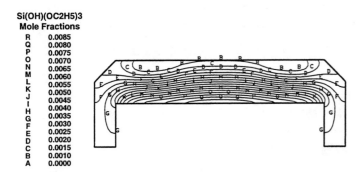

Figure 6: Triethoxysilanol Mole Fraction Contours in TEOS Reactor

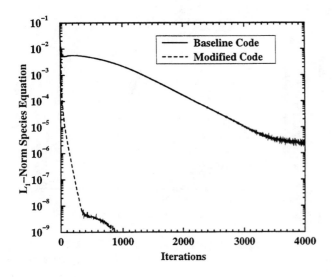

Figure 7: Convergence History for TEOS Problem

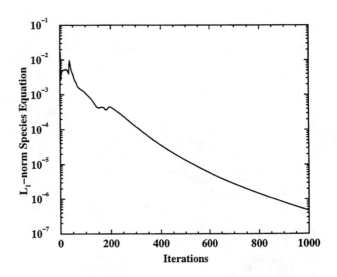

Figure 9: MTS Convergence Performance for Enhanced Solution Strategy

FED-Vol. 238, 1996 Fluids Engineering Division Conference
Volume 3
ASME 1996

APPROXIMATE RIEMANN SOLVERS TO COMPUTE TURBULENT COMPRESSIBLE ONE AND TWO-EQUATION MODELS

Thierry Buffard [1], Jean-Marc Hérard [2]

[1]. Université Blaise Pascal. Laboratoire de Mathématiques Appliquées. 63177. Aubière. FRANCE
[2]. EDF. Laboratoire National d'Hydraulique. 6, Quai Watier. 78400. Chatou. FRANCE

ABSTRACT

Two different approximate Riemann solvers are presented herein, which enable to compute the non conservative convection system arising from one-equation and two-equation turbulent compressible models. Both algorithms, which are based on the general formulation proposed in (Hérard, 1995), which extends the notion introduced by Roe in 1981, are detailed in the present contribution. Some simple but instructive computational results of shock tube test cases are briefly described and discussed.

INTRODUCTION

We focus in this paper on the numerical simulation of turbulent compressible one or two-equation models. Little attention has been paid up to now to the numerical treatment of turbulent compressible models, except in the work reported by Jansen (1994) and Jansen et al (1993), where the authors apply for the finite element strategy. The algorithms presented herein are fully different. The main objective of the contribution is to exhibit cheap, sufficiently accurate and well-suited Finite-Volume algorithms to compute non stationary compressible turbulent flows with shocks on unstructured meshes. A way to achieve this is to derive new approximate Riemann solvers, as has been done till now within the Euler frame work. However, due to the presence of a second pressure (which is usually called the turbulent kinetic energy K) which strongly couples the variation of the mean variables (namely the mean density, the mean momentum and total energy) together with the variation of K, one needs to develop new approximate (or exact) Riemann solvers to deal with the whole.

The suitability of two different approximate Riemann solvers is discussed herein. The first one is a Roe-type solver which has been designed to account for the non conservative terms which are present in the governing equations of the turbulent kinetic energy and dissipation. The second one is a straight extension of the so-called WPS algorithm, which separates convection and propagation effects ; actually, the propagation system inherits the non conservative terms issuing from the whole hyperbolic system. Hence, we may no longer apply for the classical Lax theory on conservative hyperbolic systems and we must use new results detailed in (Colombeau, 1992 ; Le Floch, 1988 ; Le Floch and Liu, 1992 ; Sainsaulieu, 1991, 1995ab ; Toumi, 1992) to deal with the latter. The contribution is organised as follows. At first, the whole set of equations is recalled, together with some recent theoretical results, the proofs of which are available in (Louis, 1995 ; Hérard et al, 1995). Afterwards, the extension of the WPS strategy is presented, and the exact solution of the one dimensional Riemann problem associated with the non conservative hyperbolic system is given. The jump conditions are exactly the same as when dealing with the whole set of equations. Then, the new Roe-type Finite Volume formulation which was proposed in (Hérard, 1995) is presented, which enables to account for the *non conservative terms* present in the system ; this applies for both the "standard" scheme and for the flux-splitting scheme. Full details of the numerical procedures are given. Computational results are eventually displayed, which confirm the suitability of the method.

1 TURBULENT MODEL

The set of equations which governs the variations of the mean density ρ, the mean momentum ρU, the mean total energy E, together with the turbulent kinetic energy K of the fluctuating field is:

$$(\rho)_{,t} + (\rho U_i)_{,i} = 0 \qquad (1)$$

$$(\rho U_i)_{,t} + (\rho U_i U_j)_{,j} + P_{,i} + \frac{2}{3} K_{,i} + (\Sigma_{ij})_{,j} = 0 \qquad (2)$$

$$(E)_{,t} + (U_j (E + P + \frac{2}{3} K) + U_i \Sigma_{ij})_{,j} + (\psi_j)_{,j} = 0 \qquad (3)$$

$$(K)_{,t} + (U_j K + \theta_j)_{,j} + \frac{2}{3} K (U_j)_{,j} = S_K - \rho \varepsilon \qquad (4)$$

$$\mu_t = \rho \, C_\mu \, R = \rho \, C_\mu \frac{(K/\rho)^2}{\varepsilon} \qquad (5)$$

$$\Sigma_{ij} = -(\mu + \mu_t) (U_{i,j} + U_{j,i} - \frac{2}{3} U_{l,l} \, \delta_{ij}) \qquad (6)$$

$$S_K = \mu_t \ (U_{i,j}+U_{j,i}-\frac{2}{3}U_{l,l} \ \delta_{ij}) \ (U_{j,i} + U_{i,j}) \ /2 \qquad (7)$$

$$\theta_j = -(\mu+\frac{\mu_t}{\sigma_K})(\frac{K}{\rho})_{,j} \quad ; \quad \psi_j = -(\mu+\frac{\mu_t}{\sigma_K}) \ (\frac{K}{\rho})_{,j} - \lambda_E \ (\frac{p}{\rho})_{,j}$$
$$(8)$$

It is also assumed that the following (averaged) perfect gas state law holds :

$$P = (\gamma -1) \ (E - \frac{1}{2} \rho \ U_j U_j - K) \qquad (9)$$

and we set : $C_\mu = 0.09$; $\sigma_K = 1$. Besides, an equation is written to provide either the rate of turbulent dissipation ε, or the turbulent eddy viscosity R (see Goldberg, 1994). Anyway, it has already been shown (Forestier et al, 1995) that the latter has no influence on the convective part of the susbset (1, 2, 3, 4) ; moreover, for both formulations, the convective part is of the form :

$$(\phi)_{,t} + (\ U_j \phi)_{,j} \ + a \ \phi \ (U_j)_{,j} = 0 \qquad (10)$$

where the constant a is equal to $(2 \ C_{\varepsilon_1} / 3)$ ($\phi = \varepsilon$, K-ε model) or to $(2 \ (2-C_{\varepsilon_1}))/ 3$ ($\phi = R$, K-R model). Thus, once an approximate Riemann solver has been derived to compute the two-equation K-ε model, a simple change of constant in the computer code enables to get the straight counterpart of the algorithm for the K-R model.

2 SOME BASIC RESULTS

We recall first that, provided that the divergence of the mean velocity and the inverse of the turbulent time scale ($\rho\varepsilon$/K or K/ρR) remain bounded, system ((1) to (10)) provides regular (C^1) solutions with positive values of the mean density, mean pressure and the turbulent kinetic energy (Hérard et al, 1995). The latter requirements also arise within the frame of incompressible flows (see Hérard, 1994ab). Actually, the realisability conditions are also valid through shocks, at least in a one dimensional framework (see propositions 2 and 3.2). Moreover, an entropy inequality may be derived, which is helpful to exhibit physically admissible discontinuous solutions of the convective part of the whole system. The entropy inequality is also useful to compute in a suitable way the production term S_K (Hérard, 1995, appendix 6).

We focus now on the behaviour of the non conservative first order differential system issuing from (1 to 4), which is :

$$(\rho)_{,t} + (\rho \ U_i)_{,i} = 0 \qquad (11)$$

$$(\rho \ U_i)_{,t} + (\rho \ U_i \ U_j)_{,j} \ + P_{,i} +\frac{2}{3} \ K_{,i} = 0 \qquad (12)$$

$$(E)_{,t} + (\ U_j \ (E +P +\frac{2}{3} \ K))_{,j} \ = 0 \qquad (13)$$

$$(K)_{,t} + (\ U_j K)_{,j} \ +\frac{2}{3} \ K \ (U_j)_{,j} = 0 \qquad (14)$$

We first recall that (Louis, 1995 ; Hérard et al, 1995) :

Proposition 2 :

(i)   The non conservative convective subset (11, 12, 13, 14) is a non strictly hyperbolic system. Its eigenvalues are in the three dimensional case :

$$\lambda_1 = U.\, n \ -c \ ; \ \lambda_k = U.\, n \ (k=2 \ to \ 5) \ ; \ \lambda_6 = U.\, n \ +c$$

with :

$$\rho \ c^2 = \gamma P +\frac{10}{9} K$$

(ii)   The one dimensional Riemann problem associated with (11, 12, 13, 14) and with the following initial conditions :

$$(\rho_L, \rho_L U_L, E_L , K_L) \ if : x < 0$$
$$(\rho_R, \rho_R U_R, E_R , K_R) \ if : x > 0$$

has a unique solution if and only if the following holds :

$$U_R \ -U_L <\ X_R \ +X_L$$

with :

$$X_i = \int_0^{\rho_i} (\frac{c \ (x=\rho \ ; \ y=p(\rho) \ ; \ z=K(\rho) \ )}{\rho}) \, d\rho$$

$$\left(\frac{\rho}{\rho_i}\right)^{5/3} = \left(\frac{K(\rho)}{K_i}\right) \quad ; \quad \left(\frac{\rho}{\rho_i}\right)^{\gamma} = \left(\frac{p(\rho)}{p_i}\right)$$

*Moreover, the **mean variables** ρ, **p** and **K** remain positive through rarefaction waves, shocks and contact discontinuities .*

States have been connected by a linear path through any discontinuity. Hence, the jump condition associated with (14) reads :

$$-\sigma [K] +[UK] \ +\frac{2}{3} \ \overline{K} \ [U]= 0$$

where σ denotes the speed of the discontinuity, and subscripts L and R refer to the left and right states on each side of the discontinuity. It must be recalled that the following standard notations are used throughout the paper : $[\phi] = \phi_R - \phi_L$; $\overline{\phi} = (\phi_R + \phi_L) / 2$. As will be seen hereafter, a similar result holds when investigating the propagation system associated with the extension of the laminar WPS algorithm (Agarwal et Halt, 1994 ; Balakrishnan and Deshpande, 1994 ; Baraille, 1992 ; Buffard, 1993 ; Buffard and Hérard, 1993ab, 1994).

3. AN EXTENSION OF THE WAVE PARTICLE SPLIT ALGORITHM

3.1 Introduction

The key idea is to isolate the conservative flux $((U.n) \ W)$ in the whole convective set (11,12,13,14) and to solve alternatively the socalled "propagation" step :

$$(\rho)_{,t} = 0 \qquad (15)$$

$$(\rho\, U_i)_{,t} + P_{,i} + \frac{2}{3} K_{,i} = 0 \qquad (16)$$

$$(E)_{,t} + (\, U_j\,(\, P + \frac{2}{3} K\,))_{,j} = 0 \qquad (17)$$

$$(K)_{,t} + \frac{2}{3} K\,(\, U_j\,)_{,j} = 0 \qquad (18)$$

and the conservative hyperbolic degenerate system :

$$(\rho)_{,t} + (\rho\, U_i)_{,i} = 0 \qquad (19)$$

$$(\rho\, U_i)_{,t} + (\rho\, U_i U_j)_{,j} = 0 \qquad (20)$$

$$(E)_{,t} + (\, U_j\, E\,)_{,j} = 0 \qquad (21)$$

$$(K)_{,t} + (\, U_j\, K\,)_{,j} = 0 \qquad (22)$$

together with the state law (9). Now, a difficult point dwells in the correct definition of the numerical fluxes to compute the set (19, 20, 21, 22). This has been investigated in detail in (Baraille, 1992 ; Buffard, 1993 ; Buffard and Hérard, 1994). The numerical flux (which accounts for the Roe's averaged velocity $\tilde{u} = \left(\rho_L^{1/2} + \rho_R^{1/2}\right)^{-1} \left(\rho_L^{1/2} u_L + \rho_R^{1/2} u_R\right)$ at each finite volume's interface) is actually the same as in the laminar case (see section 4.3).

3.2. Solutions of the propagation system

It must be first emphasized that the straight counterpart of proposition 2 holds, i.e. :

Proposition 3.2 :

(i)   The non conservative convective subset (15, 16, 17, 18) is a non strictly hyperbolic system. Its eigenvalues are in the three dimensional case :

$$\lambda_1 = -c' \; ; \; \lambda_k = 0 \;\; (k=2 \text{ to } 5) \; ; \; \lambda_6 = c'$$

with :

$$\rho\, c'^2 = (\gamma\text{-}1)\, P + \frac{4}{9} K$$

(ii)   The one dimensional Riemann problem associated with (15, 16, 17, 18) and with the following initial conditions :

$$(\rho_L, \rho_L U_L, E_L, K_L) \text{ if} : x < 0 \;\; ; \;\; (\rho_R, \rho_R U_R, E_R, K_R) \text{ if} : x > 0$$

has a unique solution (focusing on the linear path) if and only if the following holds :

$$U_R - U_L < \; Z_R + Z_L$$

with :

$$Z_i = \int_0^{P_i} (\, \rho_i^{-1/2} \frac{\left((\gamma\text{-}1)\, p + \dfrac{4 K(p)}{9}\right)^{1/2}}{(\gamma\text{-}1)\, p + \dfrac{2K(p)}{3}}\,)\, dp$$

and :

$$\frac{p}{p_i} = \left(\frac{K(p)}{K_i}\right)^{3(\gamma\text{-}1)/2}$$

*Moreover, the **mean** variables ρ, p, K remain positive through rarefaction waves, shocks and contact discontinuities .*

(see appendix for proof). Once more, the following jump condition associated with (18) has been written as :

$$-\sigma[K] + \frac{2}{3}\overline{K}\,[U] = 0$$

In the one dimensional case, the 1 and 4 waves are genuinely non linear and the 2-3 wave is linearly degenerate. It must be emphasized that the right eigenvectors associated with the LD field are the same as the ones occuring within the frame of the whole convection set (11 to 14). The connection between the different states through linearly degenerate and genuinely non linear fields is described in appendix. We also refer to (Hérard et al, 1995) which provides the counterpart of the latter result for the whole set ; it is an easy matter to check that the structure of waves is almost the same in both cases, as might be expected. An important point is that U and (P+2K/3) remain constant through the contact discontinuity in both cases. Once more, the limit case (γ=5/3) naturally arises ; for instance the integral present in proposition 3.2 can be easily integrated retaining this specific value, otherwise not ; even more, the mean pressure and the turbulent kinetic energy vary in the same way in rarefaction waves. Obviously, we focus afterwards on the standard value γ = 7/5, which is smaller than the latter.

4. APPROXIMATE RIEMANN SOLVERS

4.1 General framework

We consider a generic form of the equations which is :

$$\mathbf{W}_{,t} + \sum_{i=1}^{3} (\mathbf{F}_i(\mathbf{W}))_{,i} + \sum_{i=1}^{3} \mathbf{A}_i(\mathbf{W})\, \mathbf{W}_{,i} = $$
$$-\sum_{i=1}^{3} (\mathbf{F}_i^{v}(\mathbf{W}, \nabla\mathbf{W}))_{,i} - \mathbf{S}(\mathbf{W})$$

$$(23.a)$$

with :

$$\mathbf{W}^t = (\rho, \rho U, \rho V, \rho W, E, K) \qquad (23.b)$$

The convective part is on the left hand side and the source and viscous contributions are on the right hand side. We now focus on the numerical implementation of the approximate Riemann solvers for hyperbolic systems in non conservative form (where the convective subset is either the whole convective set (11 to 14) or the propagation subset (15 to 18)). The non-conservative part of the convection system reads in both cases :

$$\left(\sum_{i=1}^{3} \mathbf{A}_i \mathbf{W}_{,i}\right)^t = (0, 0, 0, 0, 0, \frac{2K}{3} \sum_{i=1}^{3} U_{i,i}) \qquad (24)$$

The basic Finite-Volume strategy is the following. The non conservative Roe-type scheme is written :

$$(\mathbf{W}_i^{n+1} - \mathbf{W}_i^{n})\, \Omega_i + \Delta t \sum_{j \in V(i)} \int_{\Gamma_{ij}} \mathbf{F}^{Roe}(\mathbf{W}, \mathbf{n})\, d\Gamma \,...$$
$$...+ \Delta t \sum_{k=1}^{3} (\mathbf{A}_k)_i \int_{\Omega_i} \mathbf{W}_{,k}\, d\Omega = 0 \qquad (25)$$

noting $\mathbf{n}$ the outward normal vector and also :

$$\mathbf{F}(\mathbf{W}, n) = \sum_{i=1}^{3} n_i \mathbf{F}_i(\mathbf{W}) \qquad (26a)$$

$$\left\{ \sum_{k=1}^{3} (A_k)_i \int_{\Omega_i} \mathbf{W}_{,k} \, d\Omega \right\}_6 = \frac{2}{3}(K_i^n) \int_{\Gamma_i} \sum_{k=1}^{3} (U_k^n \, n_k) \, d\Gamma \qquad (26b)$$

Now, the important point is that the correction (or diffusive part) in the flux $\mathbf{F}^{Roe}$ accounts for the whole convection system. The numerical flux in the last integral of (26b) is the centered flux ; this is compulsory to minimize numerical entropy-perturbations.

4.2 Numerical scheme to compute set (11-14)

If we restrict our attention to the set (11 to 14) in the one dimensional case, and introduce :

$$H = \gamma \frac{E}{\rho} + \frac{(1-\gamma)}{2} U^2 \qquad (27)$$

$$\mathbf{F}^t(\mathbf{W}) = (\rho U, \rho U^2 + P + 2K/3, U(E+P+2K/3), UK) \qquad (28)$$

the numerical Roe-type flux will be defined as :

$$\mathbf{F}_{ij}^{Roe} = \frac{1}{2}(\mathbf{F}(\mathbf{W}_i) + \mathbf{F}(\mathbf{W}_j)) - \frac{1}{2}\left|\mathbf{B}(\widetilde{\mathbf{W}_{ij}}(\mathbf{W}_i, \mathbf{W}_j))\right| (\mathbf{W}_j - \mathbf{W}_i) \quad (29)$$

The averaged quantities are :

$$\tilde{\rho} = (\rho_L^{1/2} \rho_R^{1/2}) \qquad (30)$$

$$\tilde{u} = (\rho_L^{1/2} + \rho_R^{1/2})^{-1} (\rho_L^{1/2} u_L + \rho_R^{1/2} u_R) \qquad (31)$$

$$\widetilde{H} = \frac{\rho_L^{1/2} H_L + \rho_R^{1/2} H_R}{\rho_L^{1/2} + \rho_R^{1/2}} + \left(\frac{\gamma}{5} - \frac{1}{3}\right) \frac{(K_L - K_R)(\rho_L - \rho_R)}{\rho_L^{1/2} \rho_R^{1/2}(\rho_L^{1/2} + \rho_R^{1/2})^2} \qquad (32)$$

$$\tilde{k} = \frac{K_L + K_R}{2 \, \rho_L^{1/2} \rho_R^{1/2}} - \frac{3}{10} \frac{(K_L - K_R)(\rho_L - \rho_R)}{\rho_L^{1/2} \rho_R^{1/2}(\rho_L^{1/2} + \rho_R^{1/2})^2} \qquad (33)$$

and the Roe type matrix $\mathbf{B}(\widetilde{\mathbf{W}_{ij}}(\mathbf{W}_i, \mathbf{W}_j))$ is chosen as :

$$\begin{pmatrix} 0 & 1 & 0 & 0 \\ (\gamma-3)\tilde{u}^2/2 & -(\gamma-3)\tilde{u} & (\gamma-1) & \left(\frac{5}{3}-\gamma\right) \\ \begin{array}{c} -\widetilde{H}\tilde{u}+(\gamma-\frac{5}{3})\tilde{k}\tilde{u} \\ +\frac{(\gamma-1)}{2}\tilde{u}^3 \end{array} & \begin{array}{c} \widetilde{H}+(\frac{5}{3}-\gamma)\tilde{k} \\ +(1-\gamma)\tilde{u}^2 \end{array} & (\gamma\tilde{u}) & \left(\left(\frac{5}{3}-\gamma\right)\tilde{u}\right) \\ -5\tilde{k}\tilde{u}/3 & 5\tilde{k}/3 & 0 & \tilde{u} \end{pmatrix}$$

$$(34)$$

The matrix $\mathbf{B}(\widetilde{\mathbf{W}}_{ij}(\mathbf{W}_i, \mathbf{W}_j))$ is such that :

$$\mathbf{F}(\mathbf{W}_j) - \mathbf{F}(\mathbf{W}_i) + [\mathbf{S}]_{IJ} = \mathbf{B}(\widetilde{\mathbf{W}_{ij}}(\mathbf{W}_i, \mathbf{W}_j))(\mathbf{W}_j - \mathbf{W}_i) \qquad (35a)$$

$$[\mathbf{S}]_{ij} = (0, 0, 0, \frac{1}{3}(K_i + K_j)(U_j - U_i)) \qquad (35b)$$

4.3 WPS algorithm

4.3.1 Numerical scheme to compute set (15,16,17,18).
We introduce a modified pressure $P^* = P + \frac{2}{3}K$. In the one dimensional case, the numerical Roe-type flux will be defined as :

$$\mathbf{G}_{ij}^{Roe} = \frac{1}{2}(\mathbf{G}(\mathbf{W}_i) + \mathbf{G}(\mathbf{W}_j)) - \frac{1}{2}\left|\mathbf{C}(\widehat{\mathbf{W}_{ij}}(\mathbf{W}_i, \mathbf{W}_j))\right|(\mathbf{W}_j - \mathbf{W}_i)$$

$$(36)$$

with : $\mathbf{G}^t(\mathbf{W}) = (0, P+2K/3, U(P+2K/3), 0)$. This means that the Roe type matrix $\mathbf{C}(\widehat{\mathbf{W}_{ij}}(\mathbf{W}_i, \mathbf{W}_j))$ is chosen as :

$$\begin{pmatrix} 0 & 0 & 0 & 0 \\ (\gamma-1)\tilde{u}^2/2 & -(\gamma-1)\tilde{u} & (\gamma-1) & \left(\frac{5}{3}-\gamma\right) \\ \begin{array}{c} -\frac{\widetilde{P^*}}{\rho}\tilde{u} \\ +\frac{(\gamma-1)}{2}\tilde{u}^3 \end{array} & \begin{array}{c} \frac{\widetilde{P^*}}{\rho} \\ +(1-\gamma)\tilde{u}^2 \end{array} & (\gamma-1)\tilde{u} & \left(\frac{5}{3}-\gamma\right)\tilde{u} \\ -2\widetilde{K}\tilde{u}/(3\tilde{\rho}) & 2\widetilde{K}/(3\tilde{\rho}) & 0 & 0 \end{pmatrix}$$

$$(37)$$

The matrix $\mathbf{C}(\widehat{\mathbf{W}}_{ij}(\mathbf{W}_i, \mathbf{W}_j))$ satisfies :

$$\mathbf{G}(\mathbf{W}_j) - \mathbf{G}(\mathbf{W}_i) + [\mathbf{S}]_{IJ} = \mathbf{C}(\widehat{\mathbf{W}_{ij}}(\mathbf{W}_i, \mathbf{W}_j))(\mathbf{W}_j - \mathbf{W}_i)$$

$$(38)$$

$[\mathbf{S}]_{ij}^t$ is still given by (35b). The averages now simply read :

$$\tilde{\rho} = (\rho_L^{1/2} \rho_R^{1/2}) \qquad (39)$$

$$\tilde{u} = (\rho_L^{1/2} + \rho_R^{1/2})^{-1}(\rho_L^{1/2} u_L + \rho_R^{1/2} u_R) \qquad (40)$$

$$\frac{\widetilde{P^*}}{\rho} = (\rho_L^{1/2} + \rho_R^{1/2})^{-1}\left(\rho_L^{1/2}\left(\frac{P^*}{\rho}\right)_L + \rho_R^{1/2}\left(\frac{P^*}{\rho}\right)_R\right) \qquad (41)$$

$$\widetilde{K} = \frac{K_L + K_R}{2} \qquad (42)$$

and the numerical celerity c' is computed as indicated below :

$$\hat{c}^2 = (\gamma-1)\frac{\widetilde{P^*}}{\rho} + \frac{2}{3}\left(\frac{5}{3} - \gamma\right)\widetilde{K} \qquad (43)$$

Recall that the eigenvalues of the Roe-type matrix are :

$$\lambda_1 = -\hat{c} \; ; \; \lambda_2 = \lambda_3 = 0 \; ; \; \lambda_4 = \hat{c} \qquad (44)$$

Despite of its simplicity, an interesting advantage of the WPS algorithm is that it does not require any entropy correction at sonic points in GNL fields (see Buffard and Hérard, 1994).

4.3.2 Numerical scheme to compute set (19, 20, 21, 22).
The numerical flux which is used to compute the conservative convection system (19, 20, 21, 22) simply reads (see [4], [5] for details) :

If $U_i . n_{ij} > 0$ or : $U_j . n_{ij} < 0$, then :

$$H (W_i, W_j, n_{ij}) = (U_i . n_{ij}) W_i \quad \text{if} : \widetilde{U}_{ij} . n_{ij} > 0 \qquad (45a)$$

$$H (W_i, W_j, n_{ij}) = (U_j . n_{ij}) W_j \quad \text{if} : \widetilde{U}_{ij} . n_{ij} < 0 \qquad (45b)$$

else if $U_i . n_{ij} < 0$ and : $U_j . n_{ij} > 0$, then :

$$H (W_i, W_j, n_{ij}) = 0 \qquad (45c)$$

endif.

(still noting : $\widetilde{U}_{ij} = (\rho_i^{1/2} + \rho_j^{1/2})^{-1} (\rho_i^{1/2} U_i + \rho_j^{1/2} U_j)$). This simple algorithm enables to preserve the positivity of the mean density and mean pressure (see Buffard, 1993), provided that the following CFL like condition holds :

$$Max_i (\|U\|_i \Delta t) < h \qquad (46)$$

(h stands for the size of the mesh). Moreover, it also enables to preserve the positivity of the turbulent kinetic energy K through the convection step.

5. SAMPLE NUMERICAL RESULTS
Shock tube problems are of course severe test cases which enable to judge the reliability of algorithms. More precisely, we may examine whether the algorithm predicts that the mean velocity and the modified pressure (P+2K/3) remain constant through the contact discontinuity. This is actually an major point since states on each side of a contact discontinuity should be connected in a similar way, focusing on rarefaction waves or shocks either. Restricting to the simple Sod shock tube experiment, a number of significant computations may be performed, only changing the ratio K/P (which is proportional to the square of the turbulent Mach number)on each side of the initial discontinuity ; for instance, we may choose (Figure 1) :`

$$(\rho_L = 1., U_L = 0, p_L = 10^5, K_L = 10^4) \quad \text{if} \; x < 0$$
$$(\rho_R = 0.125, U_R = 0, p_R = 10^4, K_R = 10) \quad \text{if} \; x > 0$$

The mean pressure clearly varies through the contact discontinuity, whereas the modified pressure P* does not. THe numerical behaviour of the mean velocity through the LD field is also fairly good. Four distinct meshes have been used to compute this test case. It should be emphasized that the behaviour of the turbulent kinetic energy K is rather interesting in that case : the shock can be hardly distinguished, due to the difference of magnitude order between the left and right inital states, though the contact discontinuity can be clearly identified. Even more, there is

no occurence of negative computed values of K in that case for instance. The computation of supersonic cases obviously requires introducing an entropy correction at sonic points in rarefaction waves, when using the Roe-type solver ; as mentionned before, this is no longer true when using the WPS algorithm. Figure 2 provides the behaviour of "conservative" variables, when choosing the initial states :

$$(\rho_L = 5., U_L = 0, p_L = 5 \; 10^5, K_L = 5 \; 10^3) \quad \text{if} \; x < 0$$
$$(\rho_R = 0.125, U_R = 0, p_R = 10^4, K_R = 10^2) \quad \text{if} \; x > 0$$

The mesh contains 240 nodes and the CFL number is 0.8 here.

6. CONCLUSION
On the whole, it must be mentionned that, as exepected, approximate Riemann solvers provide numerical results which compare well with those obtained using an exact Riemann solver (see Forestier et al, 1995 ; Louis, 1995) ; moreover, the former are of course much cheaper and easier to implement. These enable to account for non conservative terms in a suitable way, unlike most of the schemes which have been used up to now in the turbulent compressible framework. Another fractional step method, which is based on the entropy inequality connected with the whole system is currently under investigation.

REFERENCES
Agarwal, R.K., Halt, D.W. 1994 "A modified CUSP scheme in wave/particle split form for unstructured grid Euler flows" in *Frontiers of Computational Fluid Dynamics*, D.A Caughey and M.M. Hafez editors, pp. 155-168.
Balakrishnan, N., Deshpande, S.M. 1994 "New upwinding scheme based on the wave particle splitting" in the proceedings of the *2nd European Comput. Fluid Dynamics Conf.*, September 5-8 1994, Stuttgart, Germany.
Baldwin, B.S., Barth, T.J. 1990 "A one equation turbulence transport model for high Reynolds number wall- bounded flows", *NASA TM 102847*.
Baraille, R., 1991 . *PhD thesis*, University Bordeaux I, Bordeaux, France.
Baraille, R., Bourdin, G., Dubois, F., Leroux, A.Y., 1992. "A splitted version of the Godunov scheme for hydrodynamic models" *CRAS Paris* I-314, pp. 147-152.
Buffard, T. 1993 *PhD thesis*, University Paris VI, Paris, France , December 6, 1993.
Buffard, T., Hérard, J.M. 1993a "A conservative splitting scheme to solve Euler equations on unstructured meshes" *CRAS, Paris, II.316*, pp. 575-582 ; 1993b "Euler solvers and fractional step methods" in the proc. of *Finite Elements in Fluids, New trends and Applications*, Part. I, pp. 319-328 ; 1994 "A conservative fractional step method to solve non isentropic Euler equations" EDF report HE-41/94/008/A.
Colombeau, J.F. 1992 "Multiplication of distributions" *Springer Verlag*.
Einfeldt, B., Munz, C.D., Roe, P.L., Sjogreen, B. 1991 "On Godunov type methods near low densities" *J. Comp. Physics*, vol. 92, pp. 273-295.
Forestier, A., Hérard, J.M., Louis, X. 1995 "An investigation of the K-ε and K-R turbulent compressible models" *ASME FED* vol. 224, pp. 155-162.

Goldberg, U.C. 1994 "Towards a pointwise turbulence model for wall-bounded and free shear flows", *ASME FED* vol 184, pp. 113-118.

Hérard, J.M. "Basic analysis of some second moment closures". 1994a) Part I : incompressible isothermal turbulent flows" *Theoretical and Computational Fluid Dynamics*, vol. 6, n° 4, pp.213-233, (1994a). 1994b) Part II : incompressible turbulent flows including buoyant effects" *Coll. Bull. DER 94NB00053*

Hérard, J.M. 1994c "A fractional step method to investigate gas-solid flows", *ASME FED* vol 196, pp. 187-196.

Hérard, J.M. 1995 "An approximate Riemann solver to compute a non conservative hyperbolic system derived from a turbulent compressible model" *EDF report HE-41/95/009/A*, in French.

Hérard, J.M., Forestier, A., Louis, X. 1995 "A non strictly hyperbolic system to describe compressible turbulence" *Coll. Bull. DER 95NB0003* .

Jansen, K. 1994 "Finite element applications to the Reynolds averaged Navier-Stokes equations" *ASME FED* vol. 196, pp. 107-116.

Jansen, K., Johan, Z., Hughes, T.J.R 1993 "Implementation of a one equation turbulence model within a stabilized finite element formulation of a symmetric advective-diffusive system" *CMAME*, vol. 105, pp. 405-433.

Le Floch, P.1988 "Entropy weak solutions to non linear hyperbolic systems under non conservative form" *Comm. in Part. Diff. Eq,* , 13(6), pp. 669-727, (1988).

Le Floch, P., Liu, T.P. 1992 "Existence theory for non linear hyperbolic systems in non conservative form" *CMAP report 254* (to appear in Forum Mathematicum).

Louis, X. 1995.*PhD thesis*, Université Paris VI, Paris, France. July 6, 1995.

Roe, P.L. 1981 "Approximate Riemann solvers, parameter vectors and difference schemes" *Journal of Computational Physics* , vol. 43, pp. 357-372.

Sainsaulieu, L. 1991 " Travelling waves solutions of convective diffusive systems and non conservative hyperbolic systems" *C.R.A.S. Paris, I-312*, pp. 491-494.

Sainsaulieu, L.. 1995a *Thesis*, University Paris VI, Paris, France . March 20 1995.

Sainsaulieu, L.. 1995b "Finite Volume approximation of two-phase fluid flows based on an approximate Roe-type Riemann solver" *Journal of Computational Physics* , vol. 121, pp. 1-28.

Smoller, J..1983 "Shock waves and reaction-diffusion equations" *Springer Verlag* .

Toumi, I. 1992 "A weak formulation of Roe's approximate Riemann solver" *Journal of Computational Physics* , vol. 102, pp. 360-373.

Vandromme, D., Ha Minh, H. , 1986 "About the coupling of turbulence closure models with averaged Navier-Stokes equations", *Journal of Computational Physics* , vol 65, n°2, pp. 386-409.

APPENDIX

We focus here on the propagation step (15,16,17,18) in a one dimensional framework :

$$\rho_{,t} = 0 \tag{A1}$$

$$(\rho U)_{,t} + (P_x + \frac{2}{3} K_x) = 0 \tag{A2}$$

$$E_{,t} + (U(P+2K/3))_x = 0 \tag{A3}$$

$$K_{,t} + \frac{2}{3} K U_x = 0 \tag{A4}$$

(i) The eigenvalues are :

$$\lambda_1 = -c' \quad ; \quad \lambda_2 = \lambda_3 = 0 \quad ; \quad \lambda_4 = c' \tag{A5}$$

still noting : $\rho c'^2 = (\gamma-1) P + \frac{4}{9} K$

(ii) <u>The Riemann invariants read:</u>

1-wave (GNL) :

$$P K^{3(1-\gamma)/2}, \; \rho, \; U + \int^{P} \frac{c'(P, \rho, K(P))}{(\gamma-1)P+2 (K(P))/3} dP \tag{A6}$$

2-3 wave (LD) : $U, P + \frac{2K}{3}$ \tag{A7}

4-wave (GNL) :

$$P K^{3(1-\gamma)/2}, \; \rho, \; U - \int^{P} \frac{c'(P, \rho, K(P))}{(\gamma-1)P+2 (K(P))/3} dP \tag{A8}$$

(iii) <u>Shocks and Contact Discontinuities :</u>
<u>1-shock:</u>
$$z_1 = P_1 / P_L > 1$$
$$\frac{K_1}{K_L} = (\mu + z_1) (\mu z_1 + 1)^{-1}$$
$$U_1 = U_L - 2 \left(\frac{P_L}{(\gamma-1)\rho_L} \right)^{1/2} \frac{(z_1-1)}{(2(z_1+1))^{1/2}} (1 + \frac{2}{3} \frac{K_L}{P_L}(\mu z_1+1)^{-1}(1-\mu))^{1/2} \tag{A9}$$

<u>4-shock:</u>
$$z_2 = P_R / P_2 < 1$$
$$\frac{K_R}{K_2} = (\mu + z_2) (\mu z_2 + 1)^{-1}$$
$$U_2 = U_R - 2 \left(\frac{P_2}{(\gamma-1)\rho_R} \right)^{1/2} \frac{(z_2-1)}{(2(z_2+1))^{1/2}} (1 + \frac{2}{3} \frac{K_2}{P_2}(\mu z_2+1)^{-1}(1-\mu))^{1/2} \tag{A10}$$

<u>Contact Discontinuities</u>
$$P_1 + \frac{2}{3}K_1 = P_2 + \frac{2}{3}K_2 \quad ; \quad U_1 = U_2 \tag{A11}$$

<u>Notation :</u> $\mu = \frac{3\gamma-5}{3\gamma-1}$

The latter parametrization enables to derive proposition 3.2 in a straightforward manner. Both P and K decrease (respectively increase) in a 1-rarefaction wave (resp. a 4-rarefaction wave). 5A7) and (A11) enable to check that states on each side of the contact discontinuity are connected in a similar way. If both left and right values K_L and K_R are set to zero, one retrieves the result detailed in (Buffard, 1993).

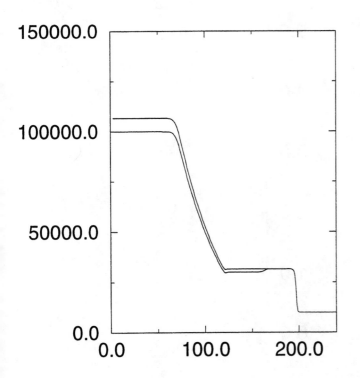

Figure 1a : P and P*

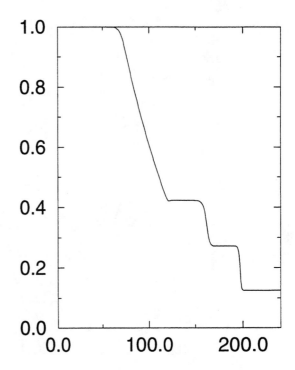

Figure 1c : mean density ρ

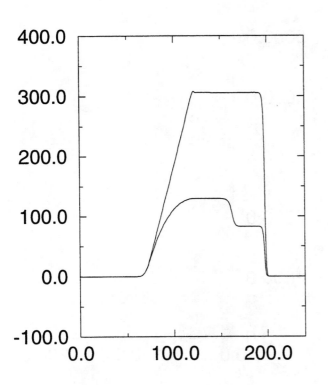

Figure 1b : U and ρU

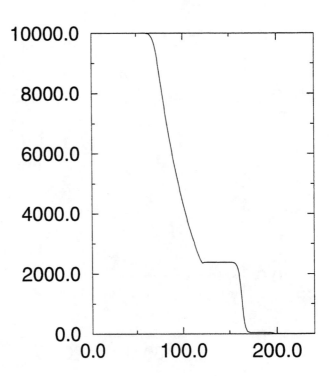

Figure 1d : turbulent kinetic energy K

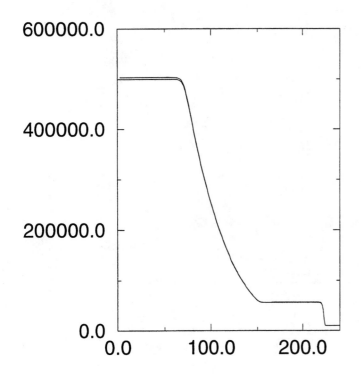

Figure 2a : P and P*

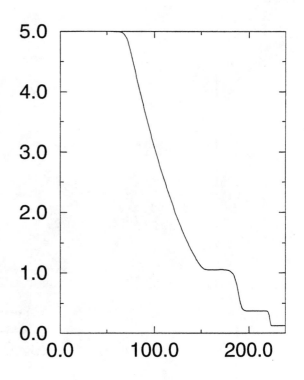

Figure 2c : mean density ρ

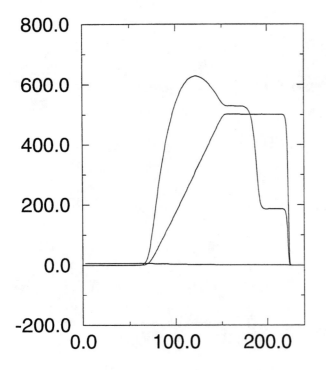

Figure 2b : U and ρU

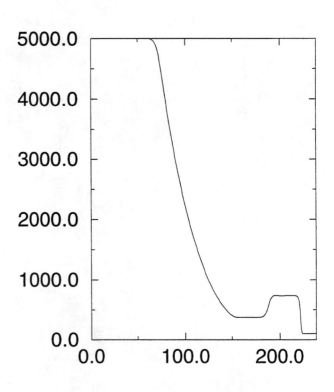

Figure 2d : turbulent kinetic energy K

FED-Vol. 238, 1996 Fluids Engineering Division Conference
Volume 3
ASME 1996

SPURIOUS UNSTEADY SOLUTIONS DUE TO THE QUICK SCHEME IN NUMERICAL SOLUTION OF THE NAVIER-STOKES EQUATIONS

Jeffrey Guoping Li

AG Associates
San Jose, CA 95134

ABSTRACT

The effect of the QUICK scheme on numerical solution of the Navier-Stokes equations was investigated through solving the problem of the flow past a square cylinder contained in a channel. The numerical results show that the original QUICK scheme may introduce spurious solutions to the problem. Two asymmetric periodic solutions are observed at Re = 1000, which have the same Strouhal number and amplitude, but are obtained with different small perturbations. After the QUICK scheme is modified with a simple interpolation limiter, the spurious solutions are suppressed and a single solution is obtained. It is concluded that the QUICK scheme should be used with caution for solving highly convective flows.

1. INTRODUCTION

How to reduce numerical diffusion and maintain numerical stability at the same time is one of the most important issues in computational fluid dynamics (CFD). Many fluid flow and heat transfer problems are either convection-dominated or turbulent. Numerical methods used to solve these problems are required to be stable and to produce small numerical diffusion at high Reynolds numbers. When the grid Reynolds number is larger than two, central difference schemes alone for the convection term usually produce highly oscillating results. Upwind difference schemes are widely used to suppress numerical oscillations in flow calculations.

The QUICK scheme [1] has been proposed to address numerical diffusion and stability problems in the discretization of the convection term. It has many desirable properties and is used mostly in solution of incompressible fluid flow problems. QUICK is a third order upwind scheme. Han et al. [2] used the hybrid and QUICK schemes to calculate various laminar and turbulent flow problems. Their results showed that QUICK is superior to but less efficient than the hybrid scheme [3]. Hayase et al. [4] proposed a rearrangement of the terms in the QUICK scheme to resolve the slow convergence problem. The reorganized QUICK formulation is partitioned into a first order upwind part and a source term part. This modification makes the solution of the momentum equation stable and fast.

While the QUICK scheme is widely used, especially, in numerical heat transfer, it might cause serious problems if it was used without caution. First, QUICK is very restrictive on time step size in explicit flow simulation and is unstable at the inviscid limit. Second, QUICK has no restriction on the magnitude of an interpolated value as long as it is calculated from the quadratic interpolation. For strongly convective flows, QUICK overshoots and undershoots the interpolated value when three interpolating node values have a strong variation. Third, QUICK results in unphysical oscillations when the grid Reynolds number is large. Although some

CFD workers have been aware of these undesirable drawbacks, many others are not.

Because the influence of the QUICK scheme on the numerical solution of flow problems is difficult to analyze analytically, it would be effective to study the scheme by numerically solving a concrete flow problem. The specific problem chosen here is the flow past a square cylinder at Reynolds numbers between 100 and 1000. At moderate Reynolds numbers the flow has regular vortex shedding behind the cylinder with a single mode of oscillation. The unsteady flow at Re = 100 has been widely used as a bench mark test problem. Since this Reynolds number is still relatively low, most numerical methods can pass this test. As the Reynolds number increases, however, the flow undergoes a second order instability and loses the property of the single mode oscillation. We have chosen the flow at Re = 1000 as a bench mark test. At this Reynolds number, the flow is three-dimensional in the transition flow regime. However, since we are interested only in the effect of the QUICK scheme, the influence of three-dimensionality is unimportant to our objective.

2. MATHEMATICAL FORMULATION

Conservation Equations

The unsteady flow past a square cylinder is assumed to be two-dimensional. The fluid is incompressible with constant properties. The governing equations in the Cartesian coordinates are given below in the conservative form:

Continuity:

$$\frac{\partial(\rho u)}{\partial x} + \frac{\partial(\rho v)}{\partial y} = 0 \qquad (1)$$

Momentum:

$$\frac{\partial(\rho u)}{\partial t} + \frac{\partial(\rho uu)}{\partial x} + \frac{\partial(\rho vu)}{\partial y} = -\frac{\partial p}{\partial x} + \mu\left(\frac{\partial^2 u}{\partial x^2} + \frac{\partial^2 u}{\partial y^2}\right) \qquad (2a)$$

$$\frac{\partial(\rho v)}{\partial t} + \frac{\partial(\rho uv)}{\partial x} + \frac{\partial(\rho vv)}{\partial y} = -\frac{\partial p}{\partial y} + \mu\left(\frac{\partial^2 v}{\partial x^2} + \frac{\partial^2 v}{\partial y^2}\right) \qquad (2b)$$

where $\mathbf{x} = (x, y)$ is the Cartesian coordinates, $\mathbf{u} = (u, v)$ velocity, p pressure, ρ density, and μ dynamic viscosity.

Initial and Boundary Conditions

A schematic of the flow configuration is shown in Figure 1 for a square cylinder in a channel with sliding walls. Davis et al. [5] have shown that if the sliding walls are far enough away from the square cylinder, the effect of a uniform velocity boundary condition for the walls can be ignored, and the flow approximates a free stream past a square cylinder. For a better comparison, the same solution domain as in Davis et al. [5] was used. W/d, H/d, and h/d are set to 15, 13, and 4, respectively.

A uniform velocity field u_0 is used as the initial velocity condition for the equation of motion. At the inlet plane the flow has the same constant velocity u_0. Velocity is zero on the surface of the cylinder. The top and bottom channel walls move at the inlet velocity u_0. The boundary condition at the exit plane is a subtle problem. No exact physical boundary condition exists at the outlet because it is artificially cut from the environment. In our calculations, we have ignored the normal velocity gradient and pressure at the exit plane. This approach is equivalent to the modified natural boundary condition.

3. NUMERICAL PROCEDURE

The MAC method [6] is used to solve the governing Navier-Stokes and continuity equations. Improvements are made by using the QUICK scheme, a second order time marching method, and an efficient pressure equation solver. The numerical procedure is briefly presented here and its details can be found in [7-8].

The spatial discretization of the conservation equations involves the diffusion and convection terms. The diffusion term is discretized straightforward by the second order central difference method. The QUICK scheme is used to discretize the convection term. As shown in Figure 2, the velocities at three upwind biased nodes are used to interpolate the unknown velocity at a control volume surface [1]. Let Φ represent velocity component u or v. If $u_{i+1/2} > 0$, Φ_{i-1}, Φ_i, and Φ_{i+1} are identified, respectively, as the upwind node Φ_u, central node Φ_c, and downstream node Φ_d. These three node values are used to interpolate the face value $\Phi_{i+1/2} = \Phi_e$. Using a quadratic interpolation written in the Newton's form, Φ_e is calculated as:

$$\Phi_e = \Phi_c + (x_e - x_c)[\frac{\Phi_d - \Phi_c}{x_d - x_c} + \frac{\frac{\Phi_d - \Phi_c}{x_d - x_c} - \frac{\Phi_c - \Phi_u}{x_c - x_u}}{x_d - x_u}(x_e - x_d)] \quad (3)$$

Similarly, if $u_{i+1/2} < 0$, then Φ_i, Φ_{i+1}, and Φ_{i+2} are identified as Φ_d, Φ_c, and Φ_u respectively and are used to interpolate the face value $\Phi_{i+1/2}$ with the above formulation.

Discretization of the Governing Equations

The discretization of the momentum equation follows the control volume method. If f is used to represent the sum of convective and diffusive momentum fluxes for a control volume, the semi-discretized momentum equation can be written as follows:

$$\frac{du_e}{dt} = \frac{f_u(\mathbf{u})}{\rho} + \frac{1}{\rho \Delta x}(p_P - p_E) \quad (4a)$$

$$\frac{dv_n}{dt} = \frac{f_v(\mathbf{u})}{\rho} + \frac{1}{\rho \Delta y}(p_P - p_N) \quad (4b)$$

Where f_u and f_v are the total diffusive and convective fluxes for u and v respectively.

Integrating the continuity equation over a control volume, the discretized continuity equation has a simple form:

$$u_e - u_w + v_n - v_s = 0 \quad (5)$$

Time Marching Scheme

The semi-discretization of the momentum equation yields a system of ordinary differential equations in time. To study the influence of time marching schemes on flow calculations, we use two explicit integration methods. One is the explicit first order Euler method and the other is a second Runga-Kutta method, or the modified Euler method. Explicit schemes are convenient because the pressure equation needs to be solved only once at each time step and the coefficient matrix of the discrete pressure equation remains the same for all the time steps. This saves the time required to update the matrix in iterative implicit schemes.

Derivation of the Pressure Equation

The pressure equation is derived by substituting the discretized momentum equation into the discretized continuity equation [9-10]. It should be noted that this approach always results in a correct pressure equation without introducing any numerical boundary condition for pressure. Solving the discretized momentum equation, EQ. (4), by the Runge-Kutta method, velocity can be expressed in terms of an intermediate velocity $\hat{\mathbf{u}}$ and pressure gradient:

$$u^{n+c} = \hat{u}^{n+c-1/2} + \frac{1}{\rho \Delta x}(p_P^{n+c-1/2} - p_E^{n+c-1/2}) \quad (6a)$$

$$v^{n+c} = \hat{v}^{n+c-1/2} + \frac{1}{\rho \Delta y}(p_P^{n+c-1/2} - p_N^{n+c-1/2}) \quad (6b)$$

where $c = 1/2$ for the prediction step, and $c = 1$ for the correction step. $\hat{u}^{n+c-1/2}$ and $\hat{v}^{n+c-1/2}$ are defined as:

$$\hat{u}^{n+c-1/2} = u^{n+c-1/2} + c\Delta t \, f_u(\mathbf{u}^{n+c-1/2})/\rho \quad (7a)$$

$$\hat{v}^{n+c-1/2} = v^{n+c-1/2} + c\Delta t \, f_v(\mathbf{u}^{n+c-1/2})/\rho \quad (7b)$$

Substituting EQ. (6) into the discretized continuity equation, the discretized pressure equation is obtained with a form of:

$$a_P p_P^{n+c-1/2} = a_E p_E^{n+c-1/2} + a_W p_W^{n+c-1/2} + a_N p_N^{n+c-1/2} + a_S p_S^{n+c-1/2} + b \quad (8)$$

where b is the divergence of $\hat{\mathbf{u}}^{n+c-1/2}$.

Both the MSI (Modified Strongly Implicit Procedure) and ICCG (Incomplete Cholesky Conjugate Gradient) methods are used to solve the discretized pressure equation. In the ICCG method the preconditioning matrix has the same sparsity as the original pressure coefficient matrix. It is observed in the present calculations that while the MSI and ICCG methods have almost the same convergence speed, the MSI method is insensitive to the singularity of the coefficient matrix of the pressure equation.

4. RESULTS AND DISCUSSION

A domain discretization similar to Davis and Moore [5] was used. Figure 3 shows the computational mesh with 53 times 64 non-uniform nodes in the x and y directions respectively. Dense grid distributions were employed near the cylinder wall. A uniform velocity field was used throughout the calculation domain as the initial velocity condition. The cylinder was then suddenly stopped. The flow became unsteady at high Reynolds numbers after the complete development of the recirculation region behind the cylinder.

The Reynolds number is defined as $\rho u_0 d / \mu$. Time is non-dimensionalized by the characteristic time scale d/u_0. The drag coefficient C_D and lift coefficient C_L are defined as follows:

$$C_D = \frac{F_x}{\frac{1}{2}\rho u_0^2 d}, \quad C_L = \frac{F_y}{\frac{1}{2}\rho u_0^2 d} \quad (9)$$

where F_x and F_y are respectively the total viscous and pressure forces on the cylinder in the x and y directions.

In the current calculations, the Reynolds number was varied between 100 and 1000. Computations at a high Reynolds number were started from a low Reynolds number flow solution, thus reducing the solution time of the initial developing flow. Most of the calculations were performed on a CRAY X-MP/28 computer. A typical run with the 53x64 mesh took one half hour CPU time on the CRAY computer to simulate the evolution of the flow for 60 time scales.

Numerical results

The flow past a square cylinder is complex due to the square cylinder geometry. When Re > 70, the flow is unstable. Periodic vortex shedding occurs behind the cylinder. After the drag and lift coefficients of the square cylinder are averaged over a long time period, the mean drag coefficient, C_D, as a function of the Reynolds number is shown in Figure 4(a), together with the numerical results of Treidler [11] and Davis et al. [5]. The presently calculated C_D is larger at low Reynolds numbers than the predictions of Treidler [11] and Davis et al. [5]. At high Reynolds numbers the current results agree with Davis et al. [5] but not with Treidler [11]. These different results are probably caused by the different discretization schemes used for the convection and unsteady terms.

Figure 4(b) shows the variation of the Strouhal number (S_t = fd/u_0, where f is vortex shedding frequency) with the Reynolds number. The present numerical results are comparable with the experimental data obtained by Davis et al. [5] and Okajima [12], and the numerical results of Davis et al. [5] and Treidler [11]. The scattering in the experimental data might be caused by different experimental conditions. The numerical results show an increasing error with the experimental data when the Reynolds number is larger than 800 at which the real flow is three-dimensional and turbulent [12].

Figure 5 shows the time series of vorticity contours in a vortex shedding period T_s for the flow at Re = 250. Numerical flow visualization is presented in Figure 6. In front of the cylinder a group of particles is released at the grid nodes next to the cylinder. The particle streak lines reveal the fluid motion and clearly show the whole process of vortex shedding. Two symmetric vortices are shed from the upper and lower sides of the square cylinder, and flow out of the solution domain essentially undisturbed.

Time series of C_D and C_L at Re = 250 are shown in Figure 7, and their Fourier transforms are calculated. The regular oscillations of the drag and lift indicate that the flow is periodic at values corresponding to 0.31 Hz for C_D and 0.155 Hz for C_L. The vortex shedding frequency is the basic mode and has the largest power spectrum density. Higher harmonic modes carry a small percentage of the total energy and can be revealed by a log plot.

Effect of discretization schemes for the convection term

In the early stages of this study, the flow was perturbed by imposing a pulse on the velocity component v at x = h on the bottom wall. The velocity pulse had a strength of 1% of the inlet velocity and lasted for one time step. When two pulses with opposite directions were used, two different solutions were obtained for the flow field at Re > 500. It was observed that the two solutions have essentially identical drag coefficients but asymmetric lift coefficients

as shown in Figure 8. Although we doubled the mesh size and used a small time step, these two solutions were still present.

Before these two solutions were observed, the numerical procedure had been successfully applied to calculating the lid-driven cavity flow, the backward facing step channel flow, and the free flow past a square cylinder at low Reynolds numbers [7-8]. These calculations were carried out in steady and unsteady flow regimes where the physical viscosity was dominant and the numerical error due to the discretization of the convection term was relatively small. Since the two spurious solutions occurred at relatively high Reynolds numbers, it is appropriate to consider the effect of the QUICK scheme on the numerical solutions. At high Reynolds numbers, flows in the laminar regime may undergo high order instabilities, marking the transition to three-dimensional and turbulent flows. Therefore, it is important to reduce numerical diffusion in order to obtain a correct solution when physical diffusion is small.

The spurious solutions suggest that the QUICK scheme might introduce non-physical results in calculation of the unsteady laminar flow past a square cylinder at high Reynolds numbers. However, it is not clear why the spurious solutions can be present. Like the central difference scheme, the original QUICK scheme may overshoot or undershoot an interpolated value when the grid Reynolds number (Re_Δ) is large. If $Re_\Delta > 3$, the QUICK scheme may present highly oscillating results.

Schreiber and Keller [13] investigated the spurious solutions in the lid-driven cavity flow simulation. The possibility of spurious solutions is based on a result in algebraic geometry which states that a system of quadratic equations with N unknowns may have 2^N solutions. However, most of the solutions are complex and are not revealed in a real computation. The discretized Navier-Stokes equations are quadratic equations and thus may have multiple solutions. Using central difference methods exclusively on uniform coarse grids (20x20, 40x40, and 50x50), they obtained spurious solutions for the lid-driven cavity flows even at a relatively low Reynolds number Re = 1325, with a 40x40 grid.

Numerical results for the flow past a square cylinder at Re = 1000 are inconsistent in the literature. Davis et al. [5] obtained periodic drag and lift coefficients that are similar to their results for the case of Re = 100. The difference between the two cases is that one more periodic mode exists for Re = 1000. Davis et al. [5] used the QUICKEST scheme for the convection term and the Leith time discretization. Because the pressure term is not included in the Leith scheme, their method is only first order accurate in time integration. Using QUICK in his calculations, Okajima [12] showed the periodic flow results at Re = 1000 with only one mode, indicating large numerical diffusion in his solutions. Arnal et al. [14] used the same QUICK scheme as Okajima [12] but obtained different results that the periodicity is lost even for the flow at Re = 500. Strong cycle-to-cycle variations were observed in their drag and lift coefficients. The discrepancy in these numerical results in the literature shows the difficulty in unsteady flow calculations in the transition flow regime. Unlike steady or unsteady low Reynolds number flow calculations, different methods might present different results for unsteady flow calculations at high Reynolds numbers.

To overcome the difficulty in simulating transition flows, the procedure must be accurate at high Reynolds numbers. The performance of the current numerical procedure was improved in two ways. First, a second order Runge-Kutta method was used for an accurate time integration even though this effort did not eliminate the two spurious solutions. Second, the QUICK scheme was modified to reduce overshoots and undershoots in the presence of sharp velocity variations. The detailed formulation of the enhanced QUICK scheme is presented below. With the limiting mechanism included, the stability of the QUICK scheme is controlled.

For strongly convective flows, QUICK overshoots and undershoots the interpolated value when three interpolating node values have a strong variation. In order to resolve the instability of QUICK, Leonard [15] introduced a limiting mechanism into the QUICK scheme and proposed several modified QUICK schemes which have overall second order accuracy. These schemes are more stable and perform better in the bench mark test of solving the advection equation.

In the modified QUICK schemes, a function ϕ is defined to decide if an interpolated face value is overshot or undershot:

$$\phi(\Phi) = \frac{\Phi - \Phi_u}{\Phi_d - \Phi_u} \qquad (10)$$

When the three node values are monotonic, $0 < \phi_c = \phi(\Phi_c) < 1$.

$\phi(\Phi_e)$ can be obtained by substituting EQ. (3) into EQ. (10):

$$\phi_e = \phi(\Phi_e) \equiv f_Q(\phi_c) \equiv \frac{\Delta x_{ec} \Delta x_{eu}}{\Delta x_{dc} \Delta x_{du}} + \frac{\Delta x_{ed} \Delta x_{eu}}{\Delta x_{cd} \Delta x_{cu}} \phi_c \qquad (11)$$

where $x_{ab} = x_a - x_b$.

The limiting procedure in the enhanced QUICK scheme is used to determine Φ_e from ϕ_e, which is calculated by the following steps:

1) If ϕ_c is not in [0,1], then Φ_c is a local extremum and Φ_e is set to the upwind value Φ_u.

2) Else if $\phi_c < 0.01$, then $\phi_e = 100 f_Q(0.01)$.

3) Otherwise, Φ_e is calculated according to the original QUICK scheme.

With the inclusion of the interpolation limiter for the QUICK scheme in the numerical procedure, the two spurious solutions at Re = 1000 were reduced to one solution. Figure 9 shows the time series of the drag and lift coefficients for the case with Re = 1000. The variations of C_D and C_L are irregular and show a basic vortex shedding frequency. Cycle-to-cycle variations are large. The power spectra of C_D and C_L are also calculated. Compared with the case of Re = 250, high frequency modes have a less spectrum density. A frequency smaller than the vortex shedding frequency is observed in the power spectrum of C_D, which indicates a period doubling. A plot of instantaneous particle streak lines corresponding to this case is shown in Figure 10. The calculated C_D and St are plotted in Figure 4 and are comparable with the other numerical and experimental results. These results verify that the original QUICK scheme may produce spurious solutions to the flow and the interpolation limiter is necessary to obtain physically correct results.

5. SUMMARY

The influence of the QUICK scheme on numerical solution of the Navier-Stokes equations has been investigated by solving the problem of the flow past a square cylinder at Re = 1000 as a numerical experiment. It is shown that the original QUICK scheme may produce spurious solutions to the problem. Two asymmetric periodic solutions are observed at Re = 1000, which have the same Strouhal number and amplitude, but are obtained with different small perturbations. After the QUICK scheme is modified with a simple interpolation limiter, the spurious solutions are suppressed and a single solution is obtained. The numerical results based on the modified scheme are comparable with the experimental results. It is concluded that the QUICK scheme should be used with caution for solving highly convective flows.

ACKNOWLEDGMENT

This work was partially supported by IBM Corp. and the Wong Education Foundation. The author would like to thank his Ph.D advisor Prof. J.A.C. Humphrey for his discussion of the work.

REFERENCES

1. B.P. Leonard, A Stable and Accurate Convective Modeling Procedure Based on Quadratic Upstream Interpolation, Computer Methods in Appl. Mech. and Engr., 19, 59 (1979).
2. T. Han, J.A.C. Humphrey, and B.E. Launder, A Comparison of Hybrid and Quadratic-Upstream Differencing in High Reynolds Number Elliptic Flows, Computer Methods in Appl. Mech. and Engr., 29, 81 (1981).
3. S.V. Patankar, Numerical Heat Transfer and Fluid Flow (McGraw-Hill, 1980).
4. T. Hayase, J.A.C. Humphrey, and R. Greif, A Consistently Formulated QUICK Scheme for Fast and Stable Convergence Using Finite Volume Iterative Calculation Procedure, J. Comp. Phy., 98, 108 (1992).
5. R.W. Davis, and E.F. Moore, A Numerical Study of Vortex Shedding from Rectangles, J. Fluid Mech., 116, 474 (1982).
6. F.H. Harlow and J.E. Welch, Phys. Fluids, 8, 2182 (1965).
7. G. Li and J.A.C. Humphrey, Numerical Modeling of the Confined Flow past a Cylinder of Square Cross-Section at Various Orientations, Int. J. for Num.Methods in Fluids, 20, 1215 (1995).
8. G. Li , Ph.D. thesis, University of California at Berkeley (1993).
9. A. Chorin, A Numerical Method for Solving Incompressible Viscous Flow Problems, J. Comp. Phys., 2, 12 (1967).
10. J.B. Bell, P. Colella, and H.M. Glaz, A Second Order Projection Method for the Incompressible Navier-Stokes Equations, J. Comp. Phys., 85, 257 (1989).
11. E.B. Treidler, An Experimental and Numerical Investigation of Flow Past Ribs in a Channel, Ph. D. thesis, Dept. of Mech. Eng., University of California at Berkeley (1991).
12. A. Okajima, Strouhal Numbers of Rectangular Cylinders, J. Fluid Mech., 123, 379 (1982).
13. R. Schreiber and H.B. Keller, Spurious Solutions in Driven Cavity Calculations, J. Computational Physics., 49, 165 (1983).
14. M. P. Arnal, D. J. Goering, and J. A. C. Humphrey, Vortex Shedding From a Bluff Body on a Sliding Wall, J. Fluid Eng., 113, 384 (1991).
15. B.P. Leonard, Simple High-Accuracy Resolution Program for Convective Modeling of Discontinuity, Int. J. for Num. Methods in Fluids, 8, 1291 (1988).

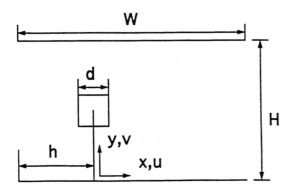

Figure 1 Schematic for the free flow past a square cylinder.

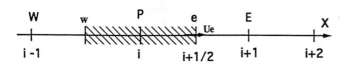

Figure 2 Grid setup for QUICK in the Cartesian coordinates.

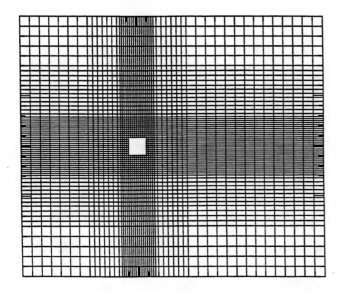

Figure 3 Computational grid (53x64 nodes) for the flow past a square cylinder contained between two sliding walls.

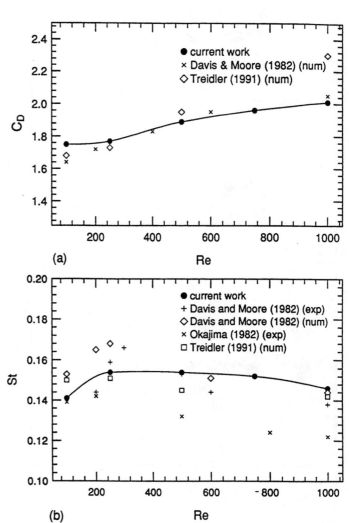

Figure 4 Comparison among the results for free flow past a square cylinder: (a) mean drag coefficient and (b) Strouhal number.

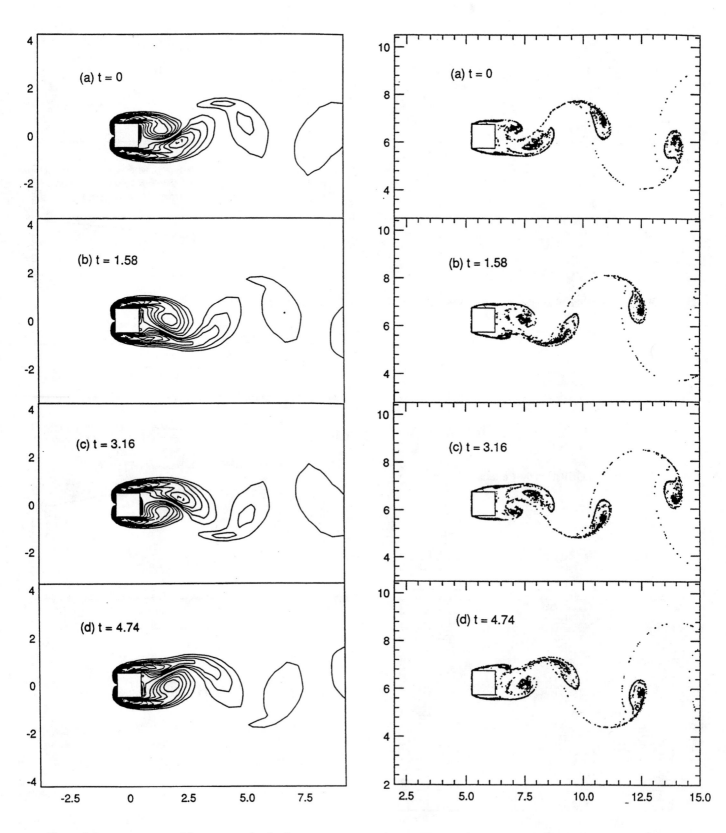

Figure 5 Instantaneous vorticity contours for the flow past a square cylinder at Re = 250.

Figure 6 Instantaneous particle streak lines for the flow past a square cylinder at Re = 250.

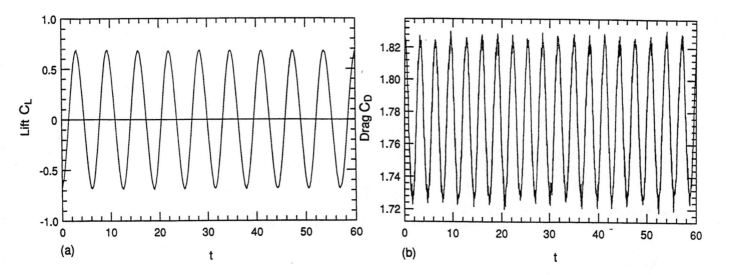

Figure 7 Time series of calculated C_D and C_L for the free flow past a square cylinder at Re = 250.

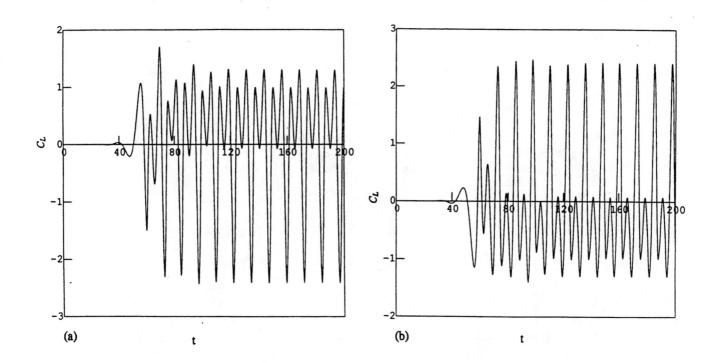

Figure 8 Time series of calculated C_L for the free flow past a square cylinder at Re = 1000 using the original QUICK scheme with different perturbations: (a) $\Delta v/u_0 = 0.01$ and (b) $\Delta v/u_0 = -0.01$.

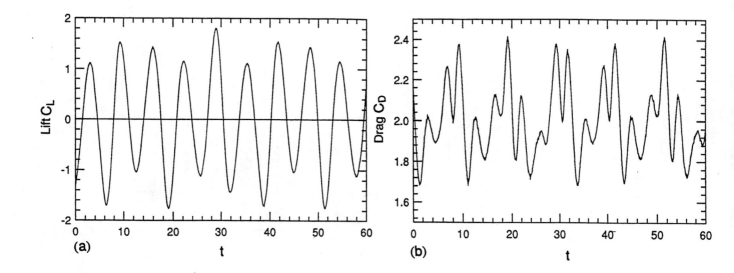

Figure 9 Time series of calculated C_D and C_L for the free flow past a square cylinder at Re = 1000 using the modified QUICK scheme.

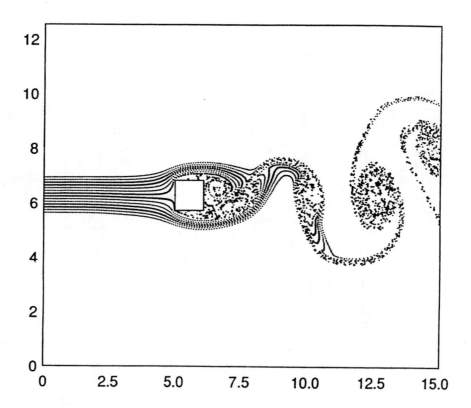

Figure 10 Instantaneous particle streak lines for the flow past a square cylinder at Re = 1000 using the modified QUICK scheme.

204

FED-Vol. 238, 1996 Fluids Engineering Division Conference
Volume 3
ASME 1996

AN ALGORITHM FOR SIMULATION OF TURBULENT FREE SURFACE FLOWS

Natarajan Ramanan, Vahé Haroutunian and Michael S. Engelman
Fluid Dynamics International, Inc.
500 Davis St, Suite 600, Evanston, Illinois-60201

ABSTRACT
Numerical simulation of turbulent free surface flows is an area of significant practical importance. Traditionally, modeling of such flows has been based on fixed mesh methods such as Marker and Cell (MAC) and Volume of fluid (VOF) methods. Though such methods provide good qualitative results, it is often desirable to track the free surface more precisely. In this paper, we present our efforts to extend an algorithm we had developed for laminar free surface flows with capillary effects to simulate turbulent flows. Our approach is based on Galerkin finite element method and includes the effects of interfacial tension in a rigorous fashion. We model the influence of turbulence through a standard two-equation k-ε model. These modifications have been incorporated into FIDAP, a general purpose finite element package. To validate the algorithm, we discuss an application of flow over a circular bump.

INTRODUCTION
Modeling flow in rivers and channels is quite important for studying environmental concerns such as silting, erosion and effluent discharge. Even a casual observation of these flows, reveals the richness and complexity of the flow structure. Such complex flow features are due to variety of reasons. First, due to the large length scales involved, the flows in rivers and channels are turbulent and involve momentum transfer at different length scales. Secondly, these flows contain a free surface that brings in additional physical phenomena such as wave motion, flows due to a gravitational head, breaking waves, etc. The presence of turbulence and free surfaces makes the modeling of these natural flows extremely challenging.

To better understand these flows, idealized models in simpler geometries that are representative of the physics involved are usually constructed. Traditionally, because of the large Reynolds numbers that are characteristic of these problems, one such idealization is to model these as a potential flow[1,2]. However, since the flow is inviscid and irrotational, the model can not predict head loss and flow features such as separation and boundary layers. To include the viscous effects, depth averaged equations are usually solved[3]. The studies of Leschinzer and Rodi[4] take a different approach. They assume that the free surface deformations are small perturbations of the average depth and solve the full Navier-Stokes equations using a two-equation k-ε model.

Lemos[5] has extended the volume of fluid (VOF) approach to turbulent flows. Turbulence is modeled through a two-equation k-ε model. To our knowledge, there is very little study with regard to the proper boundary conditions for k and ε on the free surface. To address this issue, Handler et al.[6] performed a direct simulation of turbulence near a free surface using spectral methods. They observe that while a symmetry condition for k seems to be appropriate, the same is not true of ε. The dissipation rate seems to decrease very sharply near the free surface.

In this paper, we use the Galerkin finite element method to simulate turbulent free surface flows. The algorithm we had developed for laminar free surface flows[7] is applicable for arbitrary surfaces. It also does not require the use of higher order basis functions and can work even with linear elements. Though the effects of capillarity are negligible for external flows such as that presented in this paper, they are included in the equations presented below for completeness.

GOVERNING EQUATIONS
We will restrict our attention to incompressible flow of a Newtonian fluid. The Navier-Stokes equations under such assumptions are :

$$u_{i,i} = 0 \qquad (1)$$

$$\rho(u_{,t} + u_j u_{i,j}) = T_{ij,j} + f_i \qquad (2)$$

In these equations u is the velocity, T the total stress, t the time and f the body force. The fluid density is represented by ρ. The total stress tensor T comprises of the pressure, p and the deviatoric stress τ

$$T_{ij} = -p\delta_{ij} + \tau_{ij} \qquad (3)$$

A constitutive equation is necessary to define the relationship between stress and strain. This can be written for a Newtonian fluid as

$$\tau_{ij} = \frac{\mu}{2}(u_{i,j} + u_{j,i}) \qquad (4)$$

To model turbulence, we incorporate a two-equation k-ε model. In this model, the turbulence field is characterized by two variables, the turbulent kinetic energy, k and the dissipation rate of turbulent kinetic energy, ε. Using dimensional reasoning, a turbulent viscosity can be derived with respect to the aforementioned variables as,

$$\mu_t = c_\mu \rho \frac{k^2}{\varepsilon} \qquad (5)$$

where $c_\mu = 0.09$ is an empirical model coefficient. The k and ε themselves are obtained from the following semi-empirical conservation equations,

$$\rho k_{,t} + \rho u_j k_{,j} = \left(\left(\mu + \frac{\mu_t}{\sigma_k} \right) k_{,j} \right)_{,j} + G - \rho\varepsilon \qquad (6)$$

$$\rho \varepsilon_{,t} + \rho u_j \varepsilon_{,j} = \left(\left(\mu + \frac{\mu_t}{\sigma_\varepsilon} \right) \varepsilon_{,j} \right)_{,j} + c_1 \frac{\varepsilon}{k} G - c_2 \rho \frac{\varepsilon^2}{k} \qquad (7)$$

where,

$$G \equiv -\rho \overline{u_i' u_j'} u_{i,j} \cong \mu_t (u_{i,j} + u_{j,i}) u_{i,j} \qquad (8)$$

is the turbulence shear generation term, $\sigma_k = 1.0$ and $\sigma_\varepsilon = 1.3$ are the turbulent Prandtl/Schmidt numbers of k and ε, $c_1 = 1.44$ and $c_2 = 1.92$ are model constants. The viscosity in the momentum transport is then viewed as a sum of laminar and turbulent viscosity.

The governing equations (1,2,6,7) are subject to Dirichlet conditions on velocity, kinetic energy, dissipation and stress. In addition, the following conditions must be satisfied on the fluid-vapor interface.

$$S_{,t} + u_i S_{,i} = 0 \qquad (9)$$

$$n_i T_{ij} t_j = t_i \sigma_{,i} \qquad (10)$$

$$n_i T_{ij} n_j = -p_0 + \sigma H \qquad (11)$$

where n is the outward pointing normal and t is a tangential direction on the free surface. The free surface is represented by the equation S(x,y,z,t)=0. In the above equations, the ambient pressure is p_0, σ is the surface tension and H the total curvature of the fluid-vapor interface.

NUMERICAL METHOD

Using Galerkin finite element method and the Green-Gauss theorem, the weak form of continuity, momentum, kinetic energy and dissipation transport equations can be written. Since the shape of the free surface is unknown and must be solved for as part of the solution, we proceed with the solution in an iterative fashion. We assume an initial shape of the free surface and solve for the flow-field. The free surface is then updated by satisfaction of kinematic constraint (equation 9). We iterate on this strategy until the free surface and flow field do not change according to our convergence criterion. For the solution of the flow field, we used the segregated algorithm of Haroutunian et al.[8]. To solve this coupled set of transport equations, the segregated algorithm sets up a linear algebraic equation for each degree of freedom. A Poisson type matrix equation is derived for pressure at the discrete level by making use of the momentum equations and the continuity equation.

Free Surface Update

Since the surface tension effects are small in comparison with the viscous or inertial forces the kinematic constraint is used to update the free surface. In this procedure, the normal and tangential stress balance conditions are satisfied during the flow solution. These stress balance conditions enter the momentum equations through the boundary terms of the weak form of momentum equations.

To perform the update, we need to find the new location of the free surface where the kinematic constraint is satisfied in a weighted residual sense. In a weighted sense, the kinematic constraint is then

$$\int_{\Gamma_f} \theta_k (S_{,t} + u_i S_{,i}) \, ds = 0 \qquad (12)$$

where θ is the weight function for free surface deformation. For additional details about the free surface update procedure and remeshing techniques, the reader is referred to Ramanan and Engelman[7].

RESULTS

A rather interesting example of turbulent free surface flow is the flow of water in open channels. It has been observed that the water level can change quite abruptly depending on the terrain on which it flows. This odd behavior is usually explained by classifying the open channel flow based on the Froude number of the upstream flow. In this example, we illustrate the flow over a semi-circular bump under subcritical, supercritical and critical conditions. Though the ratio of the radius of the cylinder and far-field level is the same in all cases, since the size of the separation eddy behind the bump is different for the 3 cases, a different size of the domain is used for each one. For reasons of numerical stability, the simulations are performed with a fixed time step using backward Euler time integration scheme. The height of the water level is fixed at 6.34 cm at the left and the downstream level and shape of the surface are determined as part of the solution. The radius of the cylindrical obstruction is taken to be 3 cm. Open boundary conditions are imposed at the inlet and outlet of the domain. On the free surface, symmetry type of boundary conditions are used for k and ε. A small level of turbulent intensity is prescribed at the inlet through boundary conditions on kinetic energy and dissipation.

For critical flow simulation, a steady velocity profile is established initially on a fixed mesh by imposing a uniform velocity profile at the inlet. This velocity field is then used as an initial condition to the transient simulation. After about 80 time steps, a near-steady solution is approached. Since the flow is subcritical prior to the obstruction, waves (Figure 1) appear ahead of the cylindrical obstruction. The contours of kinetic energy (Figure 2) show that turbulence is generated downstream of the obstruction as the flow accelerates over the cylinder. The turbulent viscosity is measured to be one to two orders of magnitude higher than the laminar viscosity. The inlet Froude number is evaluated to be 0.31 (subcritical) and outlet Froude number comes out to be 2.196 (super-critical). The shape of the surface is compared in figure 3 with experimental data of Forbes[9] and shows a good agreement.

Figure 1: Velocity vector plot (time=10) for critical flow

Figure 2: Turbulent kinetic energy (time=10) contours

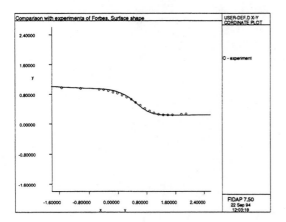

Figure 3: Comparison of free surface shape with experiment

We perform the subcritical flow simulation with a slightly longer domain. According to inviscid theory[10], the flow upstream should be uniform and level and gravity waves should appear and travel downstream of obstruction. Our simulations (figure 4) which were conducted at a high Reynolds number confirm this feature qualitatively. Indeed, a true steady state is never reached as waves appear near the cylindrical obstruction and travel downstream. The flow is subcritical throughout and the only change in the surface is a small dip near the obstruction as it quickly regains the original height of the surface.

Figure 4. Velocity vector plot (time=5) for subcritical flow

We choose an even longer domain for supercritical flow, since the inflow is faster than the last two cases and a large eddy is formed behind the cylinder. The initial inflow velocity is set at 1.42 m/s. We see from figures 7 that the flow is approaching a steady state with no waves on the surface. We notice a small hump near the obstruction and the water level quickly recovers back to its original height. This result is also in qualitative agreement with inviscid theory[10].

Figure 7: Velocity vector plot for supercritical flow (time=1.5)

CONCLUSIONS

In this paper, we have presented our algorithm for simulating turbulent free surface flows using Galerkin finite element method. Unlike the VOF type methods, our approach tracks the free surface and is likely to be more useful for making quantitative comparisons of turbulent flows. The equations have been derived including the capillary effects with the result that they are also applicable when simulating turbulent flows in simulating liquid metal flows in material processing. The method is efficient since it uses a segregated approach to solving each degree of freedom in an iterative manner. The algorithm is surface intrinsic and is applicable for both 2-D and 3-D configurations. We are currently using this approach to solving 3-D turbulent free surface flows in channels.

REFERENCES
1. R.W. Yeung, Ann. Rev. Fluid Mech., Vol. 14, p. 395-442, 1982.
2. J. Crank, "Free and moving boundary problems", Oxford Science Publications, Oxford, England, 1988.
3. A.W. Rastogi and W. Rodi, J. Hydraul.Div. ASCE, Vol. 104, p. 397-420, 1978.
4. M.A. Leschziner and W. Rodi, J. Hydraul. Div. ASCE, Vol. 105, p. 1297-1314, 1979.
5. C.M. Lemos, Intl. J. Numer. Meth. Fluids, Vol. 15, p. 127-146, 1992.

6. R.A. Handler, T.F. Swean, R.I. Leighton and J.D. Swearington, AIAA Journal, Vol. 31, p. 1998-2007, 1993.

7. N. Ramanan and M.S. Engelman, Intl. J. Num. Meth. Fluids, Vol. 22, p. 103-120, 1996.

8. V. Haroutunian, M.S. Engelman and I. Hasbani, Intl. J. Num. Meth. Fluids, Vol. 17, p. 323-348, 1993.

9. L.K. Forbes, J. Eng. Math., Vol. 22, p. 3-13, 1988.

10. H. Lamb, "Hydrodynamics", Dover Publications, New York, 1945.

FED-Vol. 238, 1996 Fluids Engineering Division Conference
Volume 3
ASME 1996

COUPLING FLOW SOLVERS AND GRIDS THROUGH AN EDGE-BASED ADAPTIVE GRID METHOD

Marie-Gabrielle Vallet [*][†]   **Julien Dompierre** [†‡§]   **Yves Bourgault** [§]

Michel Fortin [¶]   **Wagdi G. Habashi** [§]

[*] Institut des Matériaux Industriels, 75 boul. de Mortagne, Boucherville, (QC), Canada, J4B 6Y4.

[†] Centre de Recherche en Calcul Appliqué, 5160 Boul. Décarie, Montréal, (QC), Canada, H3X 2H9.

[‡] CRM, Université de Montréal, C. P. 6128, succ. Centre Ville, Montréal, (QC), Canada, H3C 3J7.

[¶] GIREF, Département de Mathématiques et Statistique, Université Laval, Ste-Foy, (QC), Canada, G1K 7P4.

[§] CFD Laboratory, Dept. of Mechanical Engineering, ER 301, Concordia University, 1455 de Maisonneuve W., Montréal, (QC), Canada, H3G 1M8.

ABSTRACT

A mesh adaptation process is presented that is a combination of $h-$methods and $r-$methods performing local optimization of a mesh to equally distribute an error estimate criterion. Emphasis is placed on mesh anisotropy, hence a criterion is developed by integrating the error field along the edges of the mesh. The adaptation step and the overall loop mesher/solver are shown to converge well and give excellents results. The approach is validated on external flow configurations.

KEY WORDS: edge-based error estimator, interpolation error, unstructured mesh, mesh adaptation, anisotropy, h-method, r-method, spring analogy, mesher-solver coupling, solver independency.

1 INTRODUCTION

The advantages of adapting meshes for compressible flow computations are well known. As flow variables present regions of rapid or abrupt variations whose locations are not known *a priori*, adaptive mesh methods with *a posteriori* local error estimators are the most logical way to optimally compute such complex flows. Moreover, these flows involve features with strong unidirectional gradients, such as shocks and boundary layers, whose features are best captured, without excessive refinement, by directional adaptation.

Most local estimators tend to evaluate an element-wise error measure, such as the solution gradient, and the strategy is normally to refine elements where such gradients are large. In the case of piecewise linear approximations, however, second derivatives are a more justified indicator (D'Azevedo and Simpson, 1989). For multi-dimensional problems, the gradient is a vectorial quantity and the second derivatives form the Hessian matrix. Hence the norm or the determinant has to be taken in order to recover an error measure on each element. Unfortunately, by doing that, the direction of the error is lost: in fact, the adaptation can only be *isotropic* as long as the estimator consists of a single value per element.

Currently, directional adaptation is obtained either by repositioning the nodes (see Hawken et al. (1991) for a review of $r-$methods on structured grids and Palmerio (1988) for an $r-$method on unstructured meshes) or by an improvement of the refinement method where the refinement template is chosen with respect to the tensorial estimator itself or some other information (Körnhuber and Roitzsch, 1990, Apel and Lube, 1995, Zienkiewicz and Wu, 1994). Unfortunately, the local error indicator differs from one adaptive technique to another. This may be a reason why only few studies tend to combine various techniques.

The approach suggested in this paper defines a local error estimate on the edges of the mesh, instead of within the elements. Several optimization techniques can then be simultaneously utilized to equidistribute a unique local error estimator (Fortin et al., 1995), independent of whether a finite element or a finite volume solver is used.

The estimator is derived in the next section. Four different operators performing the local optimization of the mesh are described in §3. They are combined into an iterative mesh adaptor tending to equidistribute the edge-based error estimator. In §4, the coupling of the mesher with the flow solver is discussed. The mesh adaptation step then appears as an optimization problem, solved along with the Navier-Stokes equations. Section 5 shows the convergence of the coupled problem towards a mesh and a solution which are not dependent on the discretization scheme of the Navier-Stokes equations.

2 AN EDGE-BASED ERROR ESTIMATOR

The error on a flow variable u, approximated on a given mesh by a function u_h, is the scalar field $E = (u - u_h)$. An approximation of E can be obtained by computing the difference $E_h = (\tilde{u}_h - u_h)$ where $\tilde{u}_h$ is a more accurate discretization of the same variable. In the case of piecewise linear approximations, $\tilde{u}_h$ must be at least a piecewise quadratic function. One of the smallest approximation spaces for E_h is generated by "bump" functions, i.e. piecewise quadratic functions, with vanishing values at vertices. This choice corresponds to adding a purely quadratic correction to u_h and assuming that it is an indicator of the local error. Naturally, this must not be done through the hierarchical computation of the quadratic approximate solution but through a simplified version.

Once E_h has been recovered, a local error estimator is obtained by local integration: integration over elements gives an estimate of the element error, while integration over edges estimates the error along edges. It can be easily seen that both vanish simultaneously if the error field is in the approximation space presented above. This means that the estimator over edges is as good a control of the error everywhere as the more classical estimator per element.

To approximate the error field, first consider a one-dimensional problem. With piecewise quadratic approximations, the error is written on each element as

$$E_h(x) = \frac{(x - x_i)(x_{i+1} - x)}{2h_i^2}\phi_i, \quad \forall x \in e_i =]x_i, x_{i+1}[\quad (1)$$

and ϕ_i must approach the second derivative of u, for $u_h + E_h$ being a quadratic approximation of u. Second derivatives of a piecewise linear function can be recovered either by local reconstruction, projection or variational recovery (see Dompierre et al. (1995) for the method used in this work and Zienkiewicz and Zhu (1992) for a more classical one). Once u'' has been recovered, the error field E_h is known and the root-mean-square value of E_h over an element e_i is a good local error estimator (Peraire et al., 1987)

$$E_i = \left(\frac{1}{h_i}\int_{e_i} E_h^2(x)\,dx\right)^{1/2} = c\,h_i^2\,|u''|_{e_i} \quad (2)$$

Mesh adaptation may then be carried out by equidistributing the error over the elements, so that the adaptation process is guided by the requirement that the local spacing has to verify

$$h_i^2\,|u''|_{e_i} = \text{constant} \quad (3)$$

An extension of the previous analysis to multi-dimensional problems is obtained by adding a quadratic correction to recover all the second derivatives of the solution. In order to construct an edge error estimator, the root-mean-square value is taken on edges. It can be noted that the restriction of quadratic functions to an edge of the mesh has the same shape as the one-dimensional ones. The previous analysis still holds, with $u''|_{e_i}$ replaced by the second derivative of u in the direction of the edge e_i. An adapted mesh can then be defined as one which equally distributes the error estimator on the edge, i.e.

$$h_i^2\left|\frac{\partial^2 u}{\partial \alpha_i^2}\right|_{e_i} = \text{constant} \quad (4)$$

where h_i denotes the length of the edge and α_i its angle.

3 MESH OPTIMIZATION TECHNIQUES

To adapt a mesh with all edges having approximately the same value of the error estimator, the following approach is used: from an existing mesh and a description of the domain boundaries, the mesh optimization library *modifies* iteratively this mesh. All the modifications to the mesh are local. These local operations are: adding a node, removing a node, moving a node and swapping an edge. Modifying an existing mesh may be cheaper than generating a new one, especially when there are few differences between the initial mesh and the adapted one. In the following the operations involved are discussed.

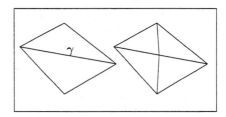

Figure 1: Edge refinement.

Firstly, the mesh is refined by sweeping over all edges and by carrying out local modifications where needed. If the edge error estimate $e(\gamma)$ is greater than E_{max}, then this edge is cut by introducing a new node and two new edges. See Fig. 1.

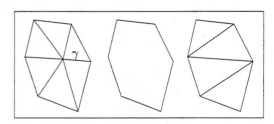

Figure 2: Edge coarsening.

Secondly, the mesh is coarsened by sweeping over all edges and by carrying out local modifications where needed. If the edge error estimate $e(\gamma)$ is lower than E_{min}, then one of the two nodes of the edge is removed, creating a "hole" in the mesh. This hole is then remeshed by some triangulation process. See Fig. 2.

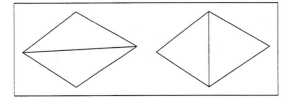

Figure 3: Node reconnection.

Thirdly, edge-swapping is a classical procedure for building the Delaunay triangulation which maximizes the minimum of the angles. An edge between two triangles is a diagonal of a quadrilateral (see Fig. 3). One has to choose between its two diagonals to get the "best" triangles. Maximizing the minimum of

$$\text{shape}(\triangle) = 27 \left(\frac{r}{p}\right)^2 = 27\frac{(p-a)(p-b)(p-c)}{p^3} \quad (5)$$

over the two possible configurations is a way to build an equilateral mesh. Here, p, r, a, b and c stand for the half-perimeter, the radius of the inscribed circle and the lengths of the edges of the triangle, respectively. While this does not lead exactly to the so-called Delaunay triangulation (Vallet, 1992), this criterion has the advantage of depending only on the edge lengths. In the present optimization process these lengths are taken to be the edge-based error estimates so that a mesh is built having all edge errors approximatively the same.

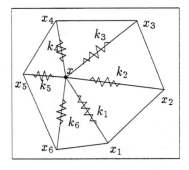

Figure 4: Node displacement

Finally, node displacement is used in order to get a smoother mesh. It is a standard part of many mesh generation codes. The simplest version of node movement, for which the nodes are re-localized at the center of their neighbors, would destroy the previous adaptation efforts. To avoid that, one has to include the error estimates in the procedure. Another way of moving nodes is to make an analogy with a network of springs (Gnoffo, 1982, Gnoffo, 1983, Nakahashi and Deiwert, 1987, Baruzzi, 1995). For moving a node x, all other nodes are supposed to be fixed and all the edges around this node are assimilated to springs. See Fig. 4. The node x is then displaced to minimize the energy of this spring network. The coordinates of x are then the solution of the following minimization problem:

$$\min_{x \in \mathbf{R}^2} E(x) = \min_{x \in \mathbf{R}^2} \sum_{i=1}^{n} (x_i - x)^2 k_i(x), \quad (6)$$
$$\text{with } k_i(x) = e(x_i - x)/\|x_i - x\|,$$

where $k_i(x)$ is the spring constant between x and x_i, $e(x_i - x)$ is the error estimate of the edge $\overline{x\,x_i}$ and $\|x_i - x\|$ is its Euclidean length. This problem is equivalent to finding a point x that is the root of

$$\sum_{i=1}^{n} F_i(x) = \sum_{i=1}^{n} (x_i - x)k_i(x) = 0 \quad (7)$$

where by Hooke's law, $(x_i - x)k_i(x)$ is the force $F_i(x)$ related to the edge $\overline{x\,x_i}$. This method works well by itself and needs only some small modifications to work in combination with other optimization techniques. See Dompierre et al. (1995) for more details.

Node displacement is the more powerful tool in the current optimization strategy. It can be used solely when the mesh topology has to be kept unchanged, such as with structured grids or unstructured grid with a fixed number of nodes, and it greatly improves the mesh quality when combined with other techniques. In fact, all other processes are discontinuous or sporadic: one chooses to do something or not depending on whether a criterion is above a threshold value. Displacement, however, is a continuous adaptive process and it can perform surgical improvements after a discontinuous process.

To conclude this section, there is an analogy between a CFD solver and a mesher. From a mesh (nodes and connectivity between the nodes), a CFD solver finds a solution (ρ, u, v, T, for example) which minimizes the residual of the equations to be solved. From a solution, the current mesher finds a mesh which minimizes the edge error estimate. Adaptation has been traditionally used to improve the mesh, but no one tried to reach the convergence of the mesh. In fact, by letting the remesher converges, a better solution is obtained because the more adapted the mesh is, the more accurate the solution.

4 COUPLING OF THE MESHER WITH A SOLVER

A strongly adapted mesh fits the solution closely and has to be re-adapted as far as the solution changes in an iterative process. The coupling of the solver with the mesher (see also Palmerio (1996)) is done by looping in the following way:

> Given (M_n, S_n), a mesh and a solution on this mesh at step n, the mesher produces a new mesh M_{n+1} and a solution $S_{n+1/2}$, the reinterpolation of S_n on M_{n+1}. A solution S_{n+1} on M_{n+1} is then obtained with the solver starting with $S_{n+1/2}$ as an initial guess. The iteration goes over until convergence is reached.

In this mesher/solver loop, only a mesh file and a solution file are exchanged between the mesher and the solver.

The following points are important when this procedure is applied:

- Instead of converging the solution on intermediate meshes, it is better to do more overall loops with partial resolution on them. Although the above strategy works well mainly for steady flows, quite good results can also be obtained for unsteady flows (with steady shocks), provided a stronger convergence is achieved in the solution steps.

- Many stretched elements must be put in the area of shock waves, to capture them efficiently. As a result, to pass from an adapted solution at a given Re number to an adapted one at another Re number is not a good practice. Adapting the mesh appears like "freezing" the shock wave. A more efficient strategy consists in restarting the computation on a generic mesh. The resolution steps are then achieved by an overuse of artificial viscosity during the first loops and by gradually reducing the amount of artificial viscosity as the mesh converges. In fact, flows over a NACA 0012 airfoil with Re numbers as large as 32000 were adaptively computed this way, with absolutely no artificial viscosity in the final steps demonstrating that a good mesh can lead to solutions requiring no artificial viscosity.

- The choice of the flow variable used to control the mesher is not necessarily obvious. With the variable chosen, one tries to directionally equalize the error for all the areas of variation, for all the variables. The local Mach number appears to be a good choice to track shock waves, as well as boundary layers. A more appropriate choice would be a *scaled* sum of all the variables (Löhner, 1989).

Validating the above strategy is not an easy task. For example, refinement changes the topology of the meshes in a discrete way and no common metric can be used to quantify the convergence of the meshes. We will consider here different ways of looking at the convergence problem in order to lay some foundation to our method, at least from an implementation standpoint.

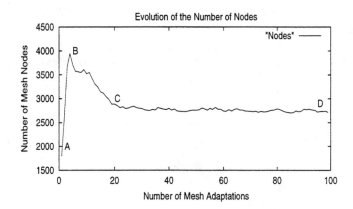

Figure 5: Number of nodes of the mesher as a function of the number of mesh adaptations for the flow over a NACA 0012 at $Ma = 2$ and $Re = 10000$.

The first way to get confidence in the adaptation strategy is a careful monitoring of the looping process. A typical flow over a NACA 0012 airfoil at $Ma = 2$ and $Re = 10000$ is used to illustrate this point. The Fig. 5 shows the number of nodes of the meshes as the overall iteration goes on. An indication of convergence is the convergence of the number of nodes after some remeshing steps. One surprising fact is the increase of nodes followed by a gradual decrease to an asymptotic value. The few first meshes being not so well adapted, the solutions on these meshes are polluted with spurious oscillations. An over-refinement of the meshes results at the beginning, just to correct the solutions. When the solution looks better on the anisotropic grid, the mesher gradually reduces the number of nodes, using all the techniques presented above. Meshes A, B, C and D of Fig. 6 serve as an illustration of these comments.

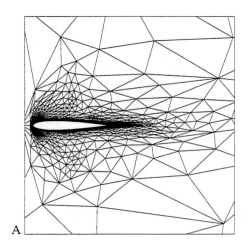

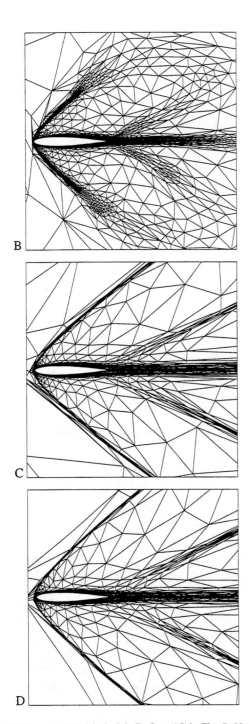

B

C

D

Figure 6: Meshes at step labeled A, B, C and D in Fig. 5. Mesh A with 845 nodes after the first adaptation step, mesh B with 3942 nodes after the fourth adaptation step, mesh C with 2888 nodes after adaptation step 20 and mesh D with 2718 nodes after adaptation step 99.

To demonstrate the accuracy of the solution obtained with these mesh adaptation techniques, Fig. 7 shows the Mach contours for the mesh D of Fig. 6 corresponding to the adaptation step 99. On this figure, the ∆Mach is 0.1.

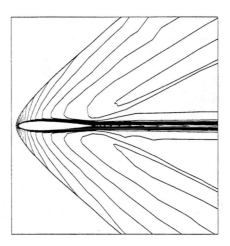

Figure 7: Mach contours for a viscous flow over a NACA 0012 at $Ma = 2$ **and** $Re = 10000$**.**

Figure 8 shows the convergence of the C_p and C_f curves. As expected, the C_f curve takes more mesher/solver iterations to stabilize. Unlike noted in Castro-Díaz et al. (1995), no problem results from a non-uniform distance from the wall of the first layer of points. The same methodology is applied over the computational domain.

Finally, the independence of the final result with respect to the solver used adds to the confidence in the approach. This problem will be addressed in the next section.

5 SOLVER INDEPENDENCY

A point with the current remeshing-resolution strategy is the independence of the final result from the FE solver used i.e. *different solvers give almost the same final result*. One solver may be more efficient in terms of precision and computing time, but the final meshes have the same aspect and nearly the same number of nodes. More than that, the final solutions obtained with the different solvers are all identical, at least for low to moderate Reynolds numbers. As a result, a good solution is more a question of meshers than of solvers.

To justify what has just been asserted, numerical solutions obtained with three different solvers will be presented. All solvers are based on a primitive formulation of the Navier-Stokes equations. The three different solvers are named as follows

P1/(P1-iso-P2): linear elements for density and temperature, P1-iso-P2 elements for the velocity;

P1/P2: linear elements for density and temperature, quadratic elements for the velocity;

Conservative P1/P2: linear elements for temperature, quadratic elements for the velocity and (P1 + bubble) elements for density to ensure local conservation of mass element by element.

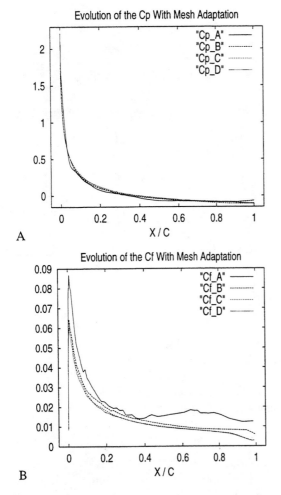

Evolution of the Cp With Mesh Adaptation

A

Evolution of the Cf With Mesh Adaptation

B

Figure 8: Convergence of the C_p (A) and the C_f (B) curves over a NACA 0012 at $Ma = 2$ and $Re = 10000$ for meshes at step labeled A, B, C and D in Fig. 5.

An explicit use of mixed FEM prevents from the addition of extra artificial viscosity to stabilize the pressure at low Reynolds numbers or on adapted meshes. For more details on the solvers, see Boivin and Fortin (1993) and Bourgault (1996).

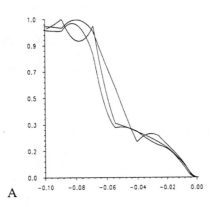

A

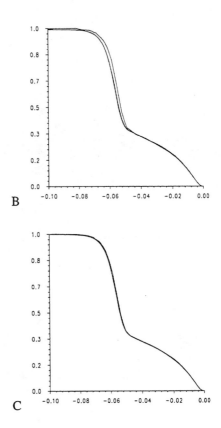

B

C

Figure 9: Cuts of the horizontal velocity component u over a NACA 0012 at $Ma = 2$ and $Re = 500$, given by three solvers: on initial mesh (A), after two remeshing steps (B) and after four remeshing steps (C).

A supersonic flow at $Ma = 2$ over a NACA 0012 was used as a test case. Results are presented at $Re = 500$ because, at such a low Reynolds number, the shock is thick and the convergence behavior is easily seen. The conclusion remains the same at higher Reynolds numbers. Figure 9 presents cuts of the horizontal velocity component in front of the airfoil leading edge before remeshing and after two and four remeshings. Clearly, the viscous shock profiles agree after a few remeshings, although they were different on the initial mesh. The P1/P2 solver converges a bit faster to the correct shock position. Another surprising fact is that mesh adaptation also improves local conservation, as the solution of the conservative method agrees with those of the other schemes.

6 CONCLUSION

An edge-based error estimator was used here to adapt meshes in an anisotropic way. With this uncommon approach to mesh adaptation, different techniques, like mesh refinement, mesh coarsening, nodes movement and edge swapping, were combined to achieve a single goal, i.e. to equidistribute the edge-based error over all the edges. To our knowledge, mesh refinement and node movement, driven by the same criterion has not been attempted before. Moreover, this new way of combining adaptation techniques appears to be convergent for each application of the mesher.

On the basis of computations, we can assert that the coupling of our mesher with a solver gives rise to a convergent process. The solution and the mesh are almost fixed after enough mesher/solver iterations. More than that, the converged solution and mesh are independent of the solver used, be it in type, algorithm or conservation properties. So, using the meshing strategy presented here, one gets closer to justifying the statement: "All the solvers must give the same solution with a fine enough grid, because all of them converge to the same solution of the Navier-Stokes equations."

There are still many questions to be answered. One of them is the quest for a firmer theoretical foundation of the approach. One should also look at ways to adapt meshes for unsteady flows, with moving shock waves and wakes. The development of a 3-D mesher is another extension and the process has already started in Sleiman et al. (1996). The edge based estimator is defined for any dimension, that is the techniques which are still to be improved in 3-D.

ACKNOWLEDGMENTS
The authors would like to thank NSERC and FCAR for Operating and Strategic grants and graduate scholarships under which this work was supported. Thanks are also due to Professor Sylvain Boivin of the Université du Québec à Chicoutimi for his permission to use the P1/(P1-iso-P2) Navier-Stokes solver.

REFERENCES
Apel, T. and Lube, G., 1995. "Anisotropic mesh refinement in stabilized Galerkin methods". Technical Report SPC95-1, TU Chemnitz-Zwickau. (submitted to Nümerische Mathematik).

Baruzzi, G. S., 1995. *A Second Order Finite Element Method for the Solution of the Transonic Euler and Navier-Stokes Equations*. PhD thesis, Concordia University, Montréal, Qc, Canada.

Boivin, S. and Fortin, M., 1993. "A new artificial viscosity method for compressible viscous flow simulations by FEM". *International Journal of Computational Fluid Dynamics*, Vol. 1, pp 25–41.

Bourgault, Y., 1996. *Méthodes des éléments finis en mécanique des fluides: Conservation et autres propriétés*. PhD thesis, Université Laval, Québec, Canada.

Castro-Díaz, M. J., Hecht, F., and Mohammadi, B., 1995. "Anisotropic grid adaptation for inviscid and viscous flows simulations". In *4th International Meshing Roundtable*, pp. 73–85, Albuquerque, New Mexico.

D'Azevedo, E. F. and Simpson, R. B., 1989. "On optimal interpolation triangle incidences". *SIAM Journal on Scientific and Statistical Computing*, Vol. 10, pp. 1063–1075.

Dompierre, J., Vallet, M.-G., Fortin, M., Habashi, W. G., Aït-Ali-Yahia, D., Boivin, S., Bourgault, Y., and Tam, A., 1995. "Edge-base

mesh adaptation for CFD". In *Conference on Numerical Methods for the Euler and Navier-Stokes Equations*, pp. 265–299, Montréal. CRM-CERCA.

Fortin, M., Bourgault, Y., Habashi, W. G., Dompierre, J., and Vallet, M.-G., 1995. "Mesh adaptation for viscous compressible flows". In Morandi Cecchi, M., Morgan, K., Périaux, J., Schrefler, B. A., and Zienkiewicz, O. C., editors, *Ninth International Conference on Finite Elements in Fluids, New Trends and Applications*, pp. 1151–1160, Venezia, Italy. IACM.

Gnoffo, P. A., 1982. "A vectorized finite-volume, adaptive grid algorithm for Navier-Stokes calculation". In Thompson, J. F., editor, *Numerical Grid Generation*, number 9, pp. 819–835, New-York. Elsevier North Holland.

Gnoffo, P. A., 1983. " A finite-volume, adaptive grid algorithm applied to planetary entry flowfields". *AIAA Journal*, Vol. 21, pp. 1249–1254.

Hawken, D. F., Gottlieb, J. J., and Hansen, J. S., 1991. "Review of some adaptive node-movement techniques in finite-element and finite-difference solutions of partial differential equations". *Journal of Computational Physics*, Vol. 95, pp. 254–302.

Körnhuber, R. and Roitzsch, R., 1990. "On adaptive grid refinement in the presence of internal or boundary layers". *Impact of Computing in Science and Engineering*, Vol. 2, pp. 40–72.

Löhner, R., 1989. "Adaptive remeshing for transient problems". *Computer Methods in Applied Mechanics and Engineering*, Vol. 75, pp. 195–214.

Nakahashi, K. and Deiwert, G. S., 1987. "Self-adaptive grid method with application to airfoil flow". *AIAA Journal*, Vol. 25, pp. 513–520.

Palmerio, B., 1988. "A two-dimensional FEM adaptive moving-node method for steady Euler flow simulation". *Computer Methods in Applied Mechanics and Engineering*, Vol. 71, pp. 315–340.

Palmerio, B., 1996. "Coupling mesh and flow in viscous fluid calculations when using unstructured triangular finite elements". *International Journal of Computational Fluid Dynamics*

Peraire, J., Vahdati, M., Morgan, K., and Zienkiewicz, O. C., 1987. "Adaptive remeshing for compressible flow computations". *Journal of Computational Physics*, Vol. 72, pp. 449–466.

Sleiman, M., Tam, A., Robichaud, M. P., Peeters, M. F., Habashi, W. G., and Fortin, M., 1996. "Turbomachinery multistage simulation by a finite element adaptive approach". In *41st ASME Gas Turbine and Aeroengine Congress*, Birmingham, U. K.

Vallet, M.-G., 1992. *Génération de maillages éléments finis anisotropes et adaptatifs*. PhD thesis, Université Pierre et Marie Curie, Paris VI, France.

Zienkiewicz, O. C. and Wu, J., 1994. "Automatic directional refinement in adaptive analysis of compressible flows". *International Journal for Numerical Methods in Engineering*, Vol. 37, pp. 2189–2210.

Zienkiewicz, O. C. and Zhu, J. Z., 1992. "The superconvergent patch recovery and a posteriori error estimates. Part I: The recovery technique". *International Journal for Numerical Methods in Engineering*, Vol. 33, pp. 1331–1364.

FED-Vol. 238, 1996 Fluids Engineering Division Conference
Volume 3
ASME 1996

A STUDY OF MULTIDOMAIN COMPACT
FINITE DIFFERENCE SCHEMES FOR STIFF PROBLEMS

Adrian S. Sabau and Peter E. Raad
Mechanical Engineering Department
Southern Methodist University
Dallas, Texas

ABSTRACT

In this paper, we investigate the applicability of fourth-order and second-order finite difference schemes to problems which admit nonsingular, thin boundary or interior layers. An optimum finite difference scheme is sought based on a thorough study of the convergence and accuracy properties of the classical second-order, and classical fourth-order, compact fourth-order, and mixed second/fourth-order finite difference schemes. The mixed-order finite difference schemes considered result from approximating the first and second derivatives within the nonuniform grid subdomains by the use of either compact or classical fourth-order and second-order schemes. The computational domain is divided into subdomains which are refined independently according to the stiffness of the local solution. In subdomains where high gradients are encountered, the grid points are distributed according to geometric progressions, while in subdomains characterized by a smooth solution, a uniform coarse grid is used. For this study, the Burgers and Reynolds equations are employed as representative boundary layer problems in fluid dynamics.

The results show that all the finite difference schemes considered, both classical and compact, exhibit qualitatively the same rates of convergence. Moreover, the accuracies achieved by the compact schemes are vastly superior. The high-order schemes require larger nonuniform grid ratios, and hence more grid points to resolve the oscillations. However, as the numerically generated oscillations at the interface between the uniform and nonuniform subdomains are eliminated, compact methods are shown to be superior to second-order and fourth-order mixed methods in accuracy, convergence, and computational efficiency for problems with stiff boundary or interior layers.

INTRODUCTION

High-order compact and classical finite difference (FD) methods have been the subject of numerous papers in which they have been successfully applied to problems in fluid dynamics that exhibit moderate gradients over thin interior or boundary layers. However, many nonlinear problems in fluid dynamics exhibit sharp gradients in the dependent variable in thin layers. Example areas include the class of Burgers equations with interior layers (see e.g. Fletcher, 1990), problems in gas dynamics (see e.g. Beam and Warming, 1978), and problems in gas lubrication governed by the Reynolds equation (see e.g. Varghese and Raad, 1994). In order to resolve the gradients that occur in thin layers, nonuniform grids are required in those regions where severe gradients are to be expected (Gresho and Lee, 1981). However, few papers have addressed the applicability of high-order methods to these types of problems which must be solved on nonuniform grids. Also, as indicated by Fletcher (1990), the use of FD approximations of different orders for the diffusive and convective terms may lead to more accurate solutions. Therefore, a number of important questions arise: (a) Are boundary layer solutions more accurate if the convective and diffusive terms are discretized with FD schemes of different order (i.e., using a combination of mixed low- and higher-order FD) within the nonuniform subdomains where large gradients are encountered? (b) Are purely high-order FD schemes appropriate for use in thin boundary layers where large gradients are encountered? (c) If so, is it more advantageous to use classical or compact methods? The goal of this paper is to investigate and clarify these issues. In the following, we review some of the literature in which compact and classical higher-order FD schemes have been used to solve moderately stiff problems, both in the context of uniform and nonuniform grids.

Most of the studies such as the one by Fletcher (1983) have considered a computational grid with uniformly distributed grid points. Warming and Beam (1978) and Lele (1992) have studied the dissipative and dispersive properties of high-order methods in the context of a uniform grid. Adam (1977) tried to improve the efficiency of compact schemes for Burgers equation, and proposed also some compact FD approximations for use near the domain's boundary.

Rubin and Khosla (1977) used spline interpolation to provide compact schemes in a nonuniform mesh. They used a boundary layer problem to test their approach, but did not study the convergence properties of their compact schemes. Aubert and Deville (1983) applied compact schemes to a mapped domain for a Stokes flow problem at moderate values of the Reynolds number, $Re \leq 10^2$.

Fletcher (1990) evaluated on a uniform grid the first and second derivatives of the function $\tanh\left[(x-1)/\varepsilon\right]$ at $x = 0.96$ by use of classical second-order and fourth-order accurate central FD approximations. He considered values of ε equal to 0.2 and 0.05 and varied the uniform spacing from 0.01 to 0.3 which placed (for the upper range of the uniform spacing) at most only one point in the boundary layer region $[1 - \varepsilon, 1]$. Therefore, his conclusion, that "if the gradient is severe enough and the grid coarse enough high-order schemes are not advantageous," may not hold as will be shown below. In addition, as pointed out by De Hoog and Jackett (1985), an assessment of the accuracy of a numerical solution based solely on the order of the local truncation error of the scheme can lead to incorrect conclusions.

The Methodology section presents a one-dimensional implicit scheme based on the Beam and Warming (1978) technique. The scheme is appropriate for high-order FD approximations of conservative equations. Then, the mixed finite difference approximations, which combine classical and compact FD schemes, are introduced. Then, the equations used to test the various methods as well as accuracy and convergence properties of both the classical and the compact FD methods are presented. The results are used to identify the most powerful combination of FD schemes in discretizing the first and second derivatives for boundary and interior layer problems. Finally, a comparison is made between the computational efficiencies of the highest order FD compact method used and the popular second-order classical FD scheme for both the Burgers and Reynolds equations. Tridiagonal compact schemes are found to be not only the most accurate but also the most computationally efficient.

METHODOLOGY

Temporal discretization

A modified scheme based on the Beam and Warming (1978) technique is presented. The methodology was developed in the context of two-dimensional problems. However, to conserve writing, only the one-dimensional case is detailed. Representative two-dimensional results are presented in the discussion on convergence properties. The expense of computing first derivatives is avoided by casting spatially one-dimensional equations in an alternative form, namely:

$$\frac{\partial u}{\partial t} = \frac{\partial F(u,h)}{\partial x} + \frac{\partial^2 G(u,h)}{\partial x^2}. \tag{1}$$

Here $h(x,t)$ is a known function included for the sake of generality. Following the Padé generalized time differencing scheme, the delta form of the unknown variable $u(x,t)$ is written as:

$$\Delta u^k \equiv u^{k+1} - u^k = \sigma_1 \frac{\partial}{\partial t}(\Delta u^k)$$
$$+ \sigma_2 \frac{\partial}{\partial t}(u^k) + \sigma_3 \Delta u^{k-1} \quad , \tag{2}$$

where superscripts $k-1, k, k+1$ refer to the old, current, and new time levels, respectively; $t = (k-1)\Delta t$; and σ_1, σ_2, and σ_3 are constants defined as follows:

$$\sigma_1 = \frac{\zeta \Delta t}{1 + \eta}; \qquad \sigma_2 = \frac{\Delta t}{1 + \eta}; \qquad \sigma_3 = \frac{\eta}{1 + \eta} \quad . \tag{3}$$

Various time differencing formulae can be obtained by choosing appropriate values for ζ and η. In this work, the 3-point backward method is used by setting ζ and η equal to 1 and 0.5, respectively. Solving Eqs. (1) and (2) for Δu^k, the following equation is obtained:

$$\Delta u^k - \frac{\partial}{\partial x}\left[\sigma_1 \frac{\partial F^k}{\partial u}\Delta u^k\right] - \frac{\partial^2}{\partial x^2}\left[\sigma_1 \frac{\partial G^k}{\partial u}\Delta u^k\right] =$$
$$Z^{k-1} + \frac{\partial W^k}{\partial x} + \frac{\partial^2 V^k}{\partial x^2} \tag{4}$$

where the additional functions Z^{k-1}, W^k, V^k are defined as follows:

$$W^k = \sigma_2 F^k + \sigma_1 \frac{\partial F^k}{\partial h}\Delta h^k; \tag{5}$$

$$V^k = \sigma_2 G^k + \sigma_1 \frac{\partial G^k}{\partial h}\Delta h^k; \tag{6}$$

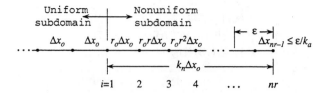

FIG. 1: INTERFACE GRID DISTRIBUTION WITH GRID PARAMETERS Δx_0, k_n, k_a, AND r_0 DEFINED.

$$Z^{k-1} = \sigma_3 \Delta u^{k-1} \quad . \tag{7}$$

Based on Eqs.(4) and (7), we developed a general code in which only the functions $F, G, W,$ and V and the boundary conditions need be defined for a chosen problem.

Discretization of the computational domain

For a problem with boundary or interior layers, the computational domain is divided into two (or more) subdomains with each subdomain discretized with a grid resolution commensurate with the anticipated stiffness of the solution in that subdomain. As shown in Fig. 1, we replace the last k_n uniform spacings with a nonuniform subdomain refined geometrically with a progression ratio $r < 1$ according to the relation:

$$\Delta x_i = r \Delta x_{i-1} , \quad \text{for } i = 2, nr-1 \tag{8}$$

where nr is the number of grid points in the nonuniform subdomain. The first nonuniform spacing is taken to be a fraction r_0 of the uniform grid spacing Δx_0, i.e.,

$$\Delta x_1 = r_0 \Delta x_0. \tag{9}$$

The grid points are distributed in the nonuniform region so that the last spacing is smaller than a corrected boundary layer thickness, namely:

$$\Delta x_{nr-1} \leq \varepsilon / k_a \tag{10}$$

where k_a is an "assurance factor" used to guarantee the placement of at least a few grid points in the thin layer, and ε is the estimated thickness of the boundary layer. For typical stiff problems, where $\varepsilon \ll 1$, Sabau and Raad (1995) obtained the following relation for the nonuniform grid ratio, r:

$$\lim_{\varepsilon \to 0} r = 1 - \frac{r_0}{k_n} \tag{11}$$

Therefore, only r_0 and k_n can be used effectively to control the ratio r so that an appropriate grid distribution can be generated in the nonuniform subdomains.

Spatial differentiation and mixed-accuracy schemes

Two fourth-order accurate FD schemes are used in this paper: one five-point and the other tridiagonal (Lele, 1992); they will be referred to as classical and compact FD schemes (Aubert and Deville, 1983), respectively.

In contrast to classical methods, compact FD schemes for nonuniform grids are not readily obtainable by the use of Taylor series expansions. One rather simple approach for the derivation of high-order compact and classical FD schemes for a nonuniform mesh by means of Legendre interpolation has been presented by Sabau and Raad (1995). For example, the compact fourth-order approximation of the spatial first derivative and compact third-order approximation of the spatial second derivative appear respectively as:

$$\left. \begin{aligned} &\alpha_1 f'(x_{i-1}) + f'(x_i) + \beta_1 f'(x_{i+1}) = \\ &[\rho_1 f(x_{i-1}) + \xi_1 f(x_i) + \tau_1 f(x_{i+1})]/\Delta x_i , \\ &\alpha_2 f''(x_{i-1}) + f''(x_i) + \beta_2 f''(x_{i+1}) = \\ &[\rho_2 f(x_{i-1}) + \xi_2 f(x_i) + \tau_2 f(x_{i+1})]/\Delta x_i^2 . \end{aligned} \right\} \tag{12}$$

Similarly, the corresponding classical fourth-order FD approximations on a nonuniform grid appear as:

$$\left. \begin{aligned} f'(x_i) = &\frac{1}{\Delta x_i}[a_1 f(x_{i-2}) + b_1 f(x_{i-1}) \\ &+ c_1 f(x_i) + d_1 f(x_{i+1}) + e_1 f(x_{i+2})] , \\ f''(x_i) = &\frac{1}{\Delta x_i^2}[a_2 f(x_{i-2}) + b_2 f(x_{i-1}) \\ &+ c_2 f(x_i) + d_2 f(x_{i+1}) + e_2 f(x_{i+2})] . \end{aligned} \right\} \tag{13}$$

In this work, the first and second spatial derivatives in the uniform grid region are both approximated with either second-order or with fourth-order accurate FD schemes, while in the nonuniform region, the first and second spatial derivatives are approximated by the use of combinations of compact fourth-order, and classical second-order and fourth-order approximations.

To illustrate the compact and mixed finite difference discretizations of Eq. (4), the latter is rewritten in general form as:

$$f + (Af)_x + (Bf)_{xx} = Z + W_x + V_{xx}, \tag{14}$$

where $A, B, Z, W,$ and V are identified by comparing Eq. (14) with Eq. (4). In shorthand notation, all finite difference equations, including (12) and (13), can be written as:

$$\left. \begin{array}{l} \mathcal{F}(f') = \mathcal{G}(f) \ , \\ \mathcal{S}(f'') = \mathcal{T}(f) \ , \end{array} \right\} \qquad (15)$$

where $\mathcal{F}$, $\mathcal{G}$, $\mathcal{S}$, and $\mathcal{T}$ are linear operators. For example, the linear operators for the compact fourth-order approximation of the first derivative are:

$$\mathcal{F} = \{\alpha_1, 1, \beta_1\} \quad \text{and} \quad \mathcal{G} = \{\rho_1, \xi_1, \tau_1\}/\Delta x_j \ . \qquad (16)$$

By applying formulae (15) on Eq. (14), one obtains the following final form of the finite difference equation:

$$\mathcal{F}(\mathcal{S}(f)) + \mathcal{S}(\mathcal{G}(Af)) + \mathcal{F}(\mathcal{T}(Bf)) = \mathcal{F}(\mathcal{S}(Z)) \\ + \mathcal{S}(\mathcal{G}(W)) + \mathcal{F}(\mathcal{T}(V)) \ . \qquad (17)$$

The seven combinations of compact and classical FD methods considered are listed in Table 1 along with the linear operators used to discretize the first and second derivatives in the nonuniform subdomains. Compact, classical, and mixed methods are denoted by Cijk, Lijk, and Mijk, respectively. The first numeral index i refers to the order of accuracy of the FD approximations in the uniform region. Compact fourth-order approximations are used in all the methods except for the lowest order method (L221) in which classical second-order approximations are used instead. The second and third indices, j and k, refer to the order of accuracy of the approximations in the nonuniform region of the first and the second spatial derivatives, respectively.

TEST PROBLEMS

Problems governed by the Burgers and Reynolds equations which exhibit boundary or interior layers are employed to study the convergence properties of the multiaccuracy schemes introduced above. In the case of the Reynolds equation of lubrication, an air bearing separating a flat inclined stationary slider from a horizontal translating surface is considered. In the case of the Burgers problem, the stationary shock wave problem is considered.

Burgers equation

The class of Burgers equations are often regarded as qualitatively correct approximations of the Navier-Stokes equations. The modified Burgers problem considered here is that of the stationary shock wave located at $x = 0$. As time progresses, the shock is smoothed by the dissipative term on the right side of the equation:

$$\frac{\partial u}{\partial t} + (u - \alpha)\frac{\partial u}{\partial x} = \nu \frac{\partial^2 u}{\partial x^2}, \qquad (18)$$

TABLE 1: FINITE DIFFERENCE METHODS AND CORRESPONDING LINEAR OPERATORS USED WITHIN THE NONUNIFORM SUBDOMAIN.

FD Methods	first derivative operators	
	$\mathcal{F}$	$\Delta x_i \mathcal{G}$
L221	1	$\{\frac{-r^2}{r+1}, r-1, \frac{1}{r+1}\}$
L441	1	$\{a_1, b_1, c_1, d_1, e_1\}$
M441	$\{\alpha_1, 1, \beta_1\}$	$\{\rho_1, \xi_1, \tau_1\}$
L423	1	$\{\frac{-r^2}{r+1}, r-1, \frac{1}{r+1}\}$
M423	1	$\{\frac{-r^2}{r+1}, r-1, \frac{1}{r+1}\}$
L443	1	$\{a_1, b_1, c_1, d_1, e_1\}$
C443	$\{\alpha_1, 1, \beta_1\}$	$\{\rho_1, \xi_1, \tau_1\}$

FD Methods	second derivative operators	
	$\mathcal{S}$	$\Delta x_i^2 \mathcal{T}$
L221	1	$\{\frac{2r^2}{r+1}, -2r, \frac{2r}{r+1}\}$
L441	1	$\{\frac{2r^2}{r+1}, -2r, \frac{2r}{r+1}\}$
M441	1	$\{\frac{2r^2}{r+1}, -2r, \frac{2r}{r+1}\}$
L423	1	$\{a_2, b_2, c_2, d_2, e_2\}$
M423	$\{\alpha_2, 1, \beta_2\}$	$\{\rho_2, \xi_2, \tau_2\}$
L443	1	$\{a_1, b_1, c_1, d_1, e_1\}$
C443	$\{\alpha_2, 1, \beta_2\}$	$\{\rho_2, \xi_2, \tau_2\}$

where ν is the kinematic viscosity and $\alpha = 0.5$ for the following initial and boundary conditions:

$$u(x,0) = \begin{cases} 1 & \text{if } x < 0 \\ 0.5 & \text{if } x = 0 \ ; \\ 0 & \text{if } x > 0 \end{cases} \qquad (19)$$

$$u(x_L, t) = 1; \qquad u(x_R, t) = 0. \qquad (20)$$

Equation (18) is rewritten in conservative form appropriate for use with Eq. (1):

$$\frac{\partial u}{\partial t} = \frac{\partial}{\partial x}\left(\alpha u - 0.5 u^2\right) + \frac{\partial^2}{\partial x^2}(\nu u). \qquad (21)$$

The left boundary is positioned at $x_L = -2$. When Eq. (21) is solved over the left half of the domain, the solution exhibits a boundary layer near $x_R = 0$. When, on the other hand, Eq. (21) is solved over the entire domain (i.e., with $x_R = 2$), the solution exhibits an interior layer centered around $x = 0$. The lack of smoothness of the initial condition is known to limit the convergence rate. To avoid this problem, the initial condition is replaced by the exact solution at $t = 0.01$ (Fletcher, 1983).

Reynolds equation of lubrication

The Reynolds equation of lubrication is useful as a test model because of its nonlinearity and because of the existence of exact solutions for certain problems that it governs. The dimensionless compressible Reynolds equation appears as (Varghese and Raad, 1995):

$$\frac{\partial}{\partial x}\left(h^3 p \frac{\partial p}{\partial x}\right) = \Lambda \frac{\partial}{\partial x}(ph) + \Lambda \frac{\partial}{\partial t}(ph) \quad (22)$$

where $p(x,t)$ is the bearing pressure, $h(x,t)$ is the bearing clearance, and $\Lambda = 6\mu V L / P_a h_m^2$ is the gas bearing number. The Reynolds equation can be written in conservative form as follows:

$$\frac{\partial u}{\partial t} = \frac{\partial}{\partial x}\left(u + 1.5u^2 h_x/\Lambda\right) + \frac{\partial^2}{\partial x^2}\left(0.5u^2 h/\Lambda\right), \quad (23)$$

where $u = ph$. For a wide wedge gas bearing, the clearance height function $h(x,t)$ is:

$$h(x,t) = h_1 + (1 - h_1)x, \quad (24)$$

where h_1 is the ratio of the leading edge clearance to the trailing edge clearance, and is fixed at 2 in this work. The boundary conditions of ambient pressure appear in dimensionless form as:

$$u(0,t) = h_1, \quad u(1,t) = 1. \quad (25)$$

The pressure exhibits a trailing edge boundary layer of order Λ^{-1}. The bearing number Λ can vary dramatically from 1 to 10^7 since it is proportional to the velocity of the translating surface and inversely proportional to the square of the minimum clearance which in practice can be in the sub-micron range (Varghese and Raad, 1995).

CONVERGENCE PROPERTIES

Sabau and Raad (1995) found that classical and compact fourth-order solutions of the Reynolds and Burgers problems on a nonuniform mesh exhibit numerical oscillations which are initially generated at the interface between the uniform and nonuniform grid regions. The oscillations are eliminated as the nonuniform grid ratio r is increased toward an appropriate value, either by decreasing the interface ratio r_0 or by increasing the length of the nonuniform grid region (i.e., by

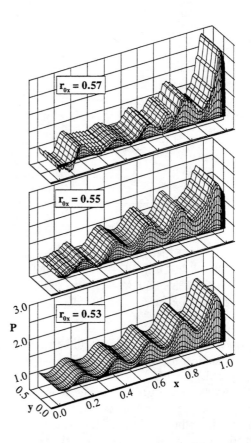

FIG. 2: TWO-DIMENSIONAL STEADY-STATE PRESSURE SOLUTIONS FOR THE REYNOLDS EQUATION WITH A TRAILING EDGE BOUNDARY LAYER THICKNESS EQUAL TO 10^{-6} AND WITH GRID PARAMETERS $r_0 = 0.57$, 0.55, AND 0.53; $\Delta x_0 = 10^{-2}$; $k_n = 3$; AND $k_a = 15$.

increasing k_n), rather than by decreasing the uniform grid spacing Δx_0. An example of how these oscillations are eliminated is shown in Fig. 2 for solutions of the two-dimensional Reynolds problem. They found that these interface oscillations are observed for all mixed FD schemes considered, including classical, compact, and mixed schemes. The same behavior with regard to interface oscillations observed in the one-dimensional cases is observed in their two-dimensional counterparts. For example, in Fig. 2 the oscillations are seen to decrease as the value of r_{0x} is lowered from 0.57 to 0.53. In this paper, we only consider accurate solutions for which the interface oscillations are resolved. Provided the numerically generated oscillations at the interface are mitigated and then eliminated on an appropriate

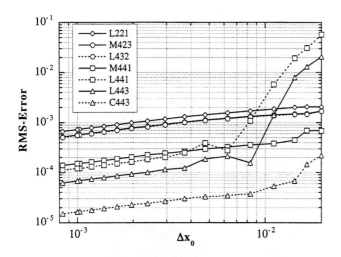

FIG. 3: ROOT-MEAN-SQUARE ERRORS FOR
REYNOLDS PROBLEM WITH THE BOUNDARY
LAYER THICKNESS EQUAL TO 10^{-6} FOR GRID
PARAMETERS $k_n = 6$, $r_0 = 1$, AND $k_a = 15$.

nonuniform grid, compact methods will be shown to be superior to classical low-order and high-order methods in solving problems with boundary or interior layers.

The Reynolds and Burgers problems are used to study the convergence properties of the mixed accuracy schemes introduced above. The Burgers equation is solved first in a one-sided domain with $x_R = 0$ and then in a domain centered about $x = 0$. In the first configuration, the Burgers solutions exhibit a boundary layer and in the second configuration, they exhibit an interior layer. Only steady-state solutions are considered for the Reynolds equation, while for the Burgers equation, the unsteady solutions are considered.

The convergence rates for different combinations of the FD schemes are ascertained from the RMS-norm of the truncation errors defined as:

$$RMS = nt^{-1/2} \left[\sum_{i=1}^{nt} (u_{EXi} - u_{FDi})^2 \right]^{1/2} . \quad (26)$$

where nt is the total number of mesh points in the computational domain, and the indices EX and FD indicate the analytical and computed solutions, respectively. In what follows, the RMS of the error of $(u_{EX} - u_{FD})$ is studied as a function of the uniform spacing Δx_0.

The RMS-errors resulting from the solutions of the nonlinear Reynolds equation by the seven methods are plotted in Fig. 3 versus the uniform spacing Δx_0. We can note that the observed convergence behaviors of the FD schemes do not correspond to the theoretical ones. Instead, the schemes can be grouped according

to their observed levels of accuracy. The overall lowest accuracies are achieved by the L221, M423 and L423 schemes. Higher accuracies are exhibited by the M441, L441, and L443 schemes, and the highest level of accuracy is achieved by the use of C443. Three important points can be made with reference to these results. First, the RMS-error is dependent on the order of approximation of the derivatives in the nonuniform region as evidenced by the behavior of the 221 and 423 schemes compared to the other five. Second, the accuracy appears to be dominated by the approximation order of the first derivative in the nonuniform grid region (denoted by the middle numeral (j)) as evidenced by comparing the 423 and 443 schemes. Finally, the compact higher-order scheme C443 is more accurate than the classical schemes L221 and L443. We must quickly note that (a) for all the results shown, the boundary layer is resolved equally well among the schemes, and (b) the apparent higher *rate* of convergence achieved by the classical methods L441 and L443 at large values of Δx_0 (> 0.005) is misleading because these methods suffer from significant interface oscillations that render the solutions obtained useless. Having eliminated the interface oscillations by a proper choice of k_n and r_0 (Sabau and Raad, 1995), it is noted that all the methods exhibit similar *rates* of convergence with respect to Δx_0, regardless of the formal accuracy of the FD approximations used in each of them.

The overall small rate of convergence observed for all methods can be explained by considering the minimal effect that Δx_0 has on the boundary layer grid distribution. Once the last spacing is fixed (i.e., $k_a \varepsilon$) along with k_n and r_0, the progression ratio r in the nonuniform region is almost constant with respect to the uniform spacing Δx_0 as predicted by Eq. (11). Thus, the grid distribution and consequently the solution within the boundary layer is nearly invariant as Δx_0 is changed. Therefore, because the truncation error is given mainly by the contribution from the nonuniform grid region where large gradients are encountered (Fletcher, 1983), the RMS-error has a small dependence on Δx_0.

Next, the RMS errors of the solutions of Burgers equation for the boundary and interior layer problems are presented. Here, comparisons are made between the accuracy and convergence properties of only the compact and mixed higher-order schemes. At each interface between the uniform and nonuniform grid regions generated for the interior layer Burgers problem, the solution exhibits the same numerical oscillations as for the boundary layer problem. In Fig. 4, the RMS errors are shown for all the mixed high-order accuracy solutions of the boundary and interior layer Burgers

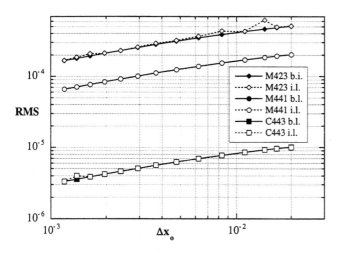

FIG. 4: ROOT-MEAN-SQUARE ERRORS OF COMPACT AND MIXED FD SCHEMES FOR THE INTERNAL (i.l.) AND BOUNDARY (b.i.) LAYER BURGERS PROBLEMS WITH $\nu = 10^{-6}$ FOR GRID PARAMETERS $k_n = 7$, $r_0 = 1$, AND $k_a = 15$.

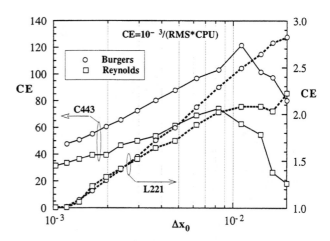

FIG. 5: COMPUTATIONAL EFFICIENCIES FOR BURGERS AND REYNOLDS PROBLEMS WITH A BOUNDARY LAYER THICKNESS EQUAL TO 10^{-6} FOR GRID PARAMETERS $k_n = 6$, $r_0 = 1$, AND $k_a = 15$.

problem at a dimensionless time $t = 0.2$. For the same interface grid distribution, the boundary and interior layer Burgers solutions result in nearly identical RMS errors, with the M423 showing stronger dispersive properties for the interior than for the boundary layer problem. However, the same rate of convergence is attained by all schemes for both the interior and boundary layer Burgers problems (provided that the interface oscillations have been eliminated). As previously seen in the Reynolds problem, the order of approximation of the spatial first derivative in the nonuniform region plays a dominant role in the overall accuracy of the scheme, and the highest levels of accuracy are achieved by the compact higher order scheme C443.

COMPUTATIONAL EFFICIENCY

It was shown in the section above that, for an appropriate grid distribution which does not generate interface oscillations, the fourth-order compact FD schemes result in the smallest RMS errors among all combinations of classical and compact FD schemes considered. Next, an assessment is made of the computational cost associated with the use of the compact C443 and the most popular second-order L221 FD schemes to ascertain their efficiency in solving boundary and interior layer problems. The quantitative measure used to estimate computational performance is the computational efficiency (CE) (Fletcher, 1983) defined by:

$$CE = \frac{k}{CPU * RMS},\quad (27)$$

where RMS is the magnitude of the root-mean-square error, CPU is the time expended by the processing unit, and k is a scaling constant.

Only boundary layer problems are considered since, as previously shown, both the boundary and interior layer problems exhibit the same convergence properties. In Fig. 5, the CE is shown for both Burgers and Reynolds solutions where the boundary layer thickness is of order 10^{-6}. Examination of Fig. 5 indicates that the CE of the fourth-order compact FD scheme is at least one order of magnitude higher than that of the classical second-order FD scheme. When L221 is used for both the Reynolds and Burgers problems, the maximum computational efficiency is attained for the largest Δx_0. With C443, the CE peaks at $\Delta x_0 \simeq 10^{-2}$.

CONCLUSIONS

Solutions of the nonlinear Reynolds and Burgers equations, which exhibit boundary and interior layers, have been used to investigate the accuracy and convergence properties of seven combinations of compact and classical FD schemes. The test problems were solved on a computational grid with adjacent uniform and nonuniform subdomains. The results lead to the surprising observations that all the considered FD methods exhibit qualitatively the same convergence properties. Namely, regardless of the theoretical accuracy of the FD schemes used to approximate the derivatives, the same rate of convergence is exhibited by lower-order classical schemes and higher-order compact schemes. However, the accuracies achieved by the latter schemes are vastly superior.

The computational efficiency of the compact fourth-order FD schemes is at least one order of magnitude higher than that of the classical second-order FD schemes. Therefore, as the numerically generated oscillations at the interface are mitigated and eliminated on an appropriate nonuniform computational grid, compact methods are shown to be superior to classical second-order and fourth-order methods in both accuracy and efficiency for problems with boundary or interior layers.

REFERENCES

Adam Y., 1977, "Highly Accurate Compact Implicit Methods and Boundary Conditions," *Journal of Computational Physics*, Vol. 24, pp. 10-22.

Aubert X., and Deville M., 1983, "Steady Viscous Flows by Compact Differences in Boundary-Fitted Coordinates," *Journal of Computational Physics*, Vol. 49, pp. 490-522.

Beam, R. M., and Warming, R. F., 1978, "An Implicit Factored Schemes for the Compressible Navier-Stokes Equation," *AIAA Journal*, Vol. 16, pp. 393-402.

De Hoog, F., and Jackett, D., 1985, "On the Rate of Convergence of Finite Difference Schemes on Nonuniform Grids," *Journal of the Australian Mathematical Society. Series B, Applied Mathematics*, Vol. 26, pp. 247-256.

Fletcher, C. A. J., 1983, "A Comparison of Finite Element and Finite Difference Solutions of the One- and Two-Dimensional Burgers' Equations," *Journal of Computational Physics*, Vol. 51, pp. 159-188.

Fletcher, C. A. J., 1990, *Computational Techniques for Fluid Dynamics*, Springer-Verlag New York , Berlin, Heidelberg.

Gartland, Jr. E. C., 1989, "Compact High-Order Finite Differences for Interface Problems in One Dimension," *IMA Journal of Numerical Analysis*, Vol. 9, pp. 243-260.

Gresho P. M., and Lee, R. L., 1981, "Don't Suppress the Wiggles They're Telling You Something," *Computers and Fluids*, Vol. 9, pp. 223-253.

Lele, S. K., 1992, "Compact Finite Difference Schemes with Spectral-like Resolution," *Journal of Computational Physics*, Vol. 103, pp. 16-42.

Rubin S. G., and Khosla P. K., 1977, "Polynomial Interpolation Methods for Viscous Flow Calculations," *Journal of Computational Physics*, Vol. 24, pp. 217-244.

Sabau A. S., and Raad P. E., 1995, "On Numerical Oscillations in High-Order Finite Difference Solutions of Boundary Layer Problems on Nonuniform Grids," Numerical Developments in CFD, FED-Vol. 215, pp. 89-96, *ASME Fluids Engineering Summer Meeting*, Hilton Head Island, SC.

Varghese, A. N., and Raad, P. E., 1995, "Surface Texture Effects on Ultrathin Finite-Width Gas Bearings," *ASME Advances in Information Storage Systems*, Vol. 6, pp. 69-96, World Scientific Publishing.

Warming, R. F., and Beam, R. M., 1978, "On the Construction and Application of Implicit Factored Schemes for Conservation Law," *SIAM-AMS Proceedings*, Vol. 11, pp. 85-129.

FED-Vol. 238, 1996 Fluids Engineering Division Conference
Volume 3
ASME 1996

IMPLEMENTATION AND PERFORMANCE OF A DATA PARALLEL ALGORITHM FOR THE DYNAMIC SUBGRID-SCALE STRESS MODEL ON A MASSIVELY PARALLEL COMPUTER

Fady M. Najjar
Thinking Machines Corporation
Bedford, MA 01730

and

Danesh K. Tafti
National Center for Supercomputing Applications(NCSA)
University of Illinois at Urbana-Champaign
Urbana, IL 61801

ABSTRACT

This paper presents the implementation of a data parallel algorithm to perform large-eddy simulations (LES) of turbulent flows. The numerical algorithm is based on a high-order accurate finite-difference procedure. The turbulence closure model uses the dynamic subgrid-scale stress model proposed by Germano et al. (1991). Implementation issues focus on the data parallel programming paradigm using CMFortran which is similar to High Performance Fortran (HPF) standard. The data parallel algorithm makes use of intrinsic HPF functionalities, optimized library routines and detailed array layout directives. Performance studies show that the algorithm has an execution time of $2.3\mu s/\Delta t/grid\ nodes$ for a problem size of 2 million grid points. The data-parallel algorithm is also found to have near perfect scalability . Simulations have been performed for the turbulent channel flow at high Reynolds number, $Re_\tau = 1050$. Results obtained using two test filters (filters A and C) are observed to agree well with experimental measurements.

INTRODUCTION

The advent of massively parallel processing (MPP) architectures provides an enormous opportunity to perform large-scale computations of turbulent flows for complex geometries and at high Reynolds numbers. As turbulence manifests itself in broad range of practical engineering applications, its accurate representation and interpretation represent a major bottleneck in numerical simulations. Computational techniques have been complementing experiments in investigating the fundamental mechanisms of turbulent flow dynamics. A promising approach for turbulence simulations is the Large-Eddy Simulation (LES) concept. This concept decomposes the flow into large resolved scales and subgrid unresolved scales by applying a spatial filter to the velocity vector and pressure fields. Hence, the resolved scales are solved for while the subgrid scales are modeled. Since the computational resources required by LES are not as demanding as Direct Numerical Simulations (DNS), computations can be performed in a more practical range of Reynolds numbers.

However, DNS and LES still fall within the purview of grand challenge applications requiring substantial computational resources and are well suited for scalable massively parallel platforms.

The present study discusses the implementation and performance issues of the dynamic subgrid scale model proposed by Germano et al. (1991) in the data parallel programming environment and how its treatment fits in with the overall Navier-Stokes solution procedure. The programming language used is CMFortran, which is similar to the developing standard of High Performance Fortran (HPF) (Koelbel et al., 1994). The data parallel (SIMD) algorithm is developed on a scalable distributed-memory computer, the CM-5. The Thinking Machines Connection Machine Model 5 (CM-5) is a massively parallel processing platform with a 'Universal Architecture' supporting both SIMD and MIMD computing models. The CM-5 at NCSA currently consists of 512 processing nodes with vector units. This platform provides $64\ GFLOPS$ peak performance for 64-bit floating-point operations and has $16\ GBytes$ of total available memory. Implementation, performance as well as the scalability of the algorithm are described. This paper is organized as follows. Section 2 presents the mathematical formulation including governing equations for the filtered flow field and the dynamic subgrid scale stress model. The fractional-step procedure is also discussed in Section 2. Section 3 presents the data-parallel implementation. Section 4 discusses the performance of the algorithm. Results obtained for the turbulent channel flow at $Re_\tau = 1050$ are described in Section 5. Conclusions and summary are presented in Section 6.

MATHEMATICAL FORMULATION

Filtered Governing Equations

The current numerical procedure solves the time-dependent filtered Navier-Stokes governing equations for an incompressible fluid. The non-dimensionalized mass and momentum equations of the resolved field, written in tensor form, are:

$$\frac{\partial \overline{u}_i}{\partial x_i} = 0 \tag{1}$$

$$\frac{\partial \overline{u}_i}{\partial t} + \frac{\partial}{\partial x_j}\left(\overline{u}_i \overline{u}_j\right) = -\frac{\partial \overline{p}}{\partial x_i} - \frac{\partial \tau_{ij}}{\partial x_j} + \frac{1}{Re}\frac{\partial^2 \overline{u}_i}{\partial x_j \partial x_j} \tag{2}$$

where i and $j = 1, 2$ and 3 correspond to x, y, and z coordinates, respectively; and Re is the Reynolds number. In the above equations, $\overline{u}_i$ is the instantaneous resolved non-dimensional velocity component in the i-direction, $\overline{p}$ represents the non-dimensional pressure, and t is the non-dimensional time. Equations (1) and (2) describe the transport of the filtered velocity (corresponding to the resolved length scales) and contain the contribution of the subgrid-scale stresses which quantify the interaction between the resolved (grid) scales and the unresolved (sub-grid) scales. The subgrid-scale (SGS) Reynolds stresses, τ_{ij}, in Equation (2) are defined as :

$$\tau_{ij} = \overline{u_i u_j} - \overline{u}_i \overline{u}_j \tag{3}$$

and are formulated using the Smagorinsky eddy-viscosity model (Smagorinsky, 1963). As a result, the anisotropic, deviatoric part of the turbulent stress, τ_{ij}, is related to the filtered strain-rate tensor, $\overline{S}_{ij}$, through the following constitutive relation :

$$\tau_{ij}^a = -2\, \nu_t\, \overline{S}_{ij} = -2\, C\, \overline{\Delta}^2\, |\overline{S}|\, \overline{S}_{ij} \tag{4}$$

where $\quad \tau_{ij}^a = \tau_{ij} - \frac{1}{3}\delta_{ij}\tau_{kk}, \qquad \overline{S}_{ij} = \frac{1}{2}\left(\frac{\partial \overline{u}_i}{\partial x_j} + \frac{\partial \overline{u}_j}{\partial x_i}\right),$

$|\overline{S}| = \sqrt{2\,\overline{S}_{ij}\,\overline{S}_{ij}}$ and $(\overline{\Delta})$ is the characteristic subgrid scale energy length scale.

Germano et al. (1991) suggested a dynamic procedure to compute the model constant C in Equation (4). To this end, a second filter, referred to as a test filter and denoted by $\widehat{}$, is applied to the filtered governing equations (Equations 1 and 2) with the characteristic length scale of the test filter being larger than that for the grid filter. Hence, the following closed form for the dynamic subgrid-scale model constant, C, is obtained :

$$C(y,t) = -\frac{1}{2}\frac{\left\langle \mathcal{L}_{ij}^a M_{ij}\right\rangle_{xz}}{\left\langle M_{mn} M_{mn}\right\rangle_{xz}} \tag{5}$$

where $\mathcal{L}_{ij} = \widehat{\overline{u}_i \overline{u}_j} - \widehat{\overline{u}}_i \widehat{\overline{u}}_j$ \hfill (6a)

$$M_{ij} = \left(\alpha_{ij} - \hat{\beta}_{ij}\right) \tag{6b}$$

$$\beta_{ij} = \overline{\Delta}^2 |\overline{S}|\, \overline{S}_{ij}\,;\; \alpha_{ij} = \widehat{\Delta}^2 |\widehat{\overline{S}}|\, \widehat{\overline{S}}_{ij} \tag{6c}$$

In Equation (5), $\langle\;\rangle_{xz}$ represents plane-averaging in the x and z-directions, which are usually homogeneous in particular for the turbulent channel. The averaging procedure applied in Equation (5) represents a smoothing operator to dampen the large local fluctuations in C which are often encountered. Equation (6c) includes the length scales of the grid and test filters, $\overline{\Delta}$ and $\widehat{\Delta}$, defined as follows (Scotti et al., 1993) :

$$\overline{\Delta} = \left(\overline{\Delta}_1\,\overline{\Delta}_2\,\overline{\Delta}_3\right)^{1/3}\,;\; \widehat{\Delta} = \left(\widehat{\Delta}_1\,\widehat{\Delta}_2\,\widehat{\Delta}_3\right)^{1/3} \tag{7}$$

where $\overline{\Delta}_i$ is the grid spacing in the i-th direction and $\widehat{\Delta}_i = \alpha_i \overline{\Delta}_i$. α_i is computed based on the discrete test filter applied. For the Fourier cut-off grid and test filters, $\alpha_i = 2$ was found to be the optimal value from *a-priori* tests for the turbulent channel flow (Germano et al., 1991). It should be noted that when no explicit test filtering is imposed in the i-th direction, $\alpha_i = 1$.

The discrete test filtering operation applied to compute the test-filtered field is summarized as follows :

$$\hat{f}_i = \frac{1}{4}\left(\overline{f}_{i-1} + 2\,\overline{f}_i + \overline{f}_{i+1}\right) \tag{8a}$$

for a three-point explicit test filter (Filter A); and,

$$\hat{f}_i = \frac{1}{256}\left(\overline{f}_{i-3} - 18\,\overline{f}_{i-2} + 63\,\overline{f}_{i-1} + 164\,\overline{f}_i \right.$$
$$\left. + 63\,\overline{f}_{i+1} - 18\,\overline{f}_{i+2} + 63\,\overline{f}_{i+3}\right) \tag{8b}$$

for a seven-point explicit test filter (Filter C). Details for the construction of these test filters and their transfer functions have been presented in Najjar and Tafti (1996). The scaling factor, α, was derived to be $\sqrt{6}$ and 2 for filters A and C, respectively.

Fractional-Step Procedure and Spatial Discretization

The filtered Navier-Stokes equations that include the contribution of the SGS Reynolds stresses are written as :

$$\frac{\partial \overline{u}_i}{\partial t} + \frac{\partial}{\partial x_j}\left(\overline{u}_i \overline{u}_j\right) = -\frac{\partial \overline{P}}{\partial x_i} + 2\,\overline{S}_{ij}\frac{\partial \nu_t}{\partial x_j}$$
$$+ \left(\frac{1}{Re} + \nu_t\right)\frac{\partial^2 \overline{u}_i}{\partial x_j \partial x_j} \tag{9}$$

where $\overline{P}\;\left(\overline{P} = \overline{p} + \frac{1}{3}\delta_{ij}\tau_{kk}\right)$ represents a modified pressure that includes the trace of the subgrid-scale stresses. Equations (1) and (9) are integrated in time with the fractional-step method resulting in the following three steps (Chorin, 1967):

$$\frac{\widetilde{\widetilde{u}}_i - \overline{u}_i^n}{\Delta t} = \left(\frac{3}{2}H_i^n - \frac{1}{2}H_i^{n-1}\right) + \frac{\gamma}{2}\left(\frac{1}{Re} + \nu_t\right)$$
$$\left(\frac{\partial^2 \widetilde{\widetilde{u}}_i}{\partial x_2 \partial x_2} + \frac{\partial^2 \overline{u}_i^n}{\partial x_2 \partial x_2}\right) \tag{10a}$$

$$\nabla \cdot \left(\nabla \overline{\phi}^{n+1}\right) = \frac{1}{\Delta t}\left(\frac{\partial \widetilde{\widetilde{u}}_i}{\partial x_i}\right) \tag{10b}$$

$$\frac{\overline{u}_i^{n+1} - \widetilde{u}_i}{\Delta t} = -\frac{\partial \overline{\phi}^{n+1}}{\partial x_i} \tag{10c}$$

where H_i is given by :

$$H_i = -\frac{\partial}{\partial x_j}\left(\overline{u}_i \overline{u}_j\right) + 2\,\overline{S}_{ij}\left(\frac{\partial \nu_t}{\partial x_j}\right) + \left(\frac{1}{Re} + \nu_t\right)\left(\frac{\partial^2 \overline{u}_i}{\partial x_1 \partial x_1}\right)$$
$$+ (1-\gamma)\frac{\partial^2 \overline{u}_i}{\partial x_2 \partial x_2} + \frac{\partial^2 \overline{u}_i}{\partial x_3 \partial x_3} \tag{10d}$$

with $\gamma = 0$ and 0.5 for the explicit and semi-implicit formulations of the diffusion terms, respectively.

The spatial derivatives in Equations (10a-d) are discretized using high-order accurate approximations on a staggered mesh arrangement. In this context, the advection terms are formulated using a fifth-order upwind biased scheme (Rai and Moin, 1991);

while the viscous terms are discretized using fourth-order accurate central difference stencils. The pressure-Poisson equation has a second-order accurate finite-volume formulation and is solved using 2-D Fast Fourier Transforms and a line solve. Other Krylov-based Poisson solvers have also been implemented as discussed in Tafti (1995a). All interpolation operators utilize sixth-order accurate approximations. More details about these approximations can be found in Tafti (1995b). The computer program has been extensively tested in model problems and direct numerical (DNS) as well as large-eddy (LES) simulations of turbulent channel flow (Tafti, 1995b; Najjar and Tafti, 1996). Details of the subgrid-scale stress model can be found in Najjar and Tafti (1996). Briefly, the computations of the subgrid-scale Reynolds stresses including the strain rate tensor, the turbulent viscosity and the dynamic constant, are done on the scalar nodes so as to minimize averaging between grid points (Mason and Callen, 1986). A sixth-order accurate operator is used to interpolate the staggered variables to the scalar nodes. The first derivatives in the computation of the strain rate tensor are calculated using fourth-order central difference approximations.

Specific steps are needed to incorporate the subgrid-scale Reynolds stresses determined by the dynamic subgrid-scale stress model in the time-stepping procedure. The following steps, performed at every timestep to calculate the resolved velocity and pressure fields, are summarized as :
(i) interpolate the staggered node velocities to the scalar nodes and evaluate the resolved-scale strain rate tensor stresses and its magnitude.
(ii) compute the turbulent viscosity. The sub-steps include :
• evaluate the test-filtered velocity field (Equation 8a or b)
• calculate $\mathcal{L}_{ij}$, M_{ij}, $\mathcal{L}_{ij}^a M_{ij}$, $M_{mn} M_{mn}$ (Equations 6a-c)
• perform planar averaging on $\mathcal{L}_{ij}^a M_{ij}$ and $M_{mn} M_{mn}$.
• calculate $|C|$ (Equation 5) and v_t. $\left(v_t = C \, \overline{\Delta}^2 |\vec{S}| \right)$
• determine the contribution of the subgrid-scale turbulent Reynolds stresses to the filtered Navier-Stokes equations. (Equation 10d)
(iii) solve the momentum equations. (Equation 10a)
(iv) solve the pressure-Poisson equation. (Equation 10b)
(v) update the velocity field. (Equation 10c)

Steps (i)-(ii) represent the DSM algorithm while Steps (iii)-(v) correspond to the fractional-step procedure. Preprocessing steps include the computations of the finite-difference coefficient arrays, the length scales of the grid and test filters (Equation 7).

DATA-PARALLEL IMPLEMENTATION

The key issues in developing a data parallel algorithm are to maintain load balancing and maximize communication efficiency (Olsson and Johnsson, 1990). The major components of the current data parallel algorithm are array layouts and floating point operations, inter-processor communications, and library function calls for the solution of linear systems generated in the semi-implicit treatment of the momentum equations (Equation 10a) and the pressure equation (Equation 10b).

Array Layouts And Floating Point Operations

To take full advantage of the data parallel mode of computation, the finite difference coefficient arrays and the dependent variable arrays have to be conformable. Conformability requires that all the arrays have the same rank and shape and are aligned in memory. In the current context this would require that all arrays be defined as three-dimensional. However, over *400* three-dimensional (3-D) finite-difference coefficient arrays would be required for the high-order formulations of the convective and diffusive terms and the dynamic model. Hence, such an approach results in poor memory utilization. In reality, since the z direction is predominantly assumed homogeneous in turbulent flow simulations, the finite-difference coefficient arrays vary only in the x and y directions and are two-dimensional (2-D). To ensure conformability between the finite difference coefficient arrays and the dependent variable arrays, the finite difference coefficient arrays have a layout of *(:block:procs,:block:procs)* form in x and y and the variable arrays are defined as *(:serial,:block:procs,:block:procs)* in z, x, and y. The periodic dimension (z) is defined as having a *serial* layout, and x and y dimensions are spread across processors using detailed *(:block:procs)* array layout (Thinking Machines Corp., 1994). A *serial* layout directive forces the spanwise dimension to reside in a single vector unit (VU) for each combination of x and y. The *:block* directive corresponds to a block of data local to a vector unit on a given axis and *:procs* corresponds to the number of vector units the axis is spread over. The detailed layout is used as follows :

$$u(:serial, :block=nxb:procs=nxp,$$
$$:block = nyb:procs=nyp, \tag{11a}$$
$$fu(:block=nxb:procs=nxp,$$
$$:block = nyb:procs=nyp) \tag{11b}$$

for 3-D and 2-D arrays, respectively. In Equations (11a-b), u is a 3-D array of size *(nz,nx,ny)* and fu is a 2-D array of size *(nx,ny)*. These compile directives provide better control in array mapping over the *(:news)* layout (Najjar and Vanka, 1994; Tafti, 1994).

In this programming paradigm of detailed array layouts, floating point operations involving 2-D and 3-D arrays are conducted by unrolling the z-axis and utilizing parallelism only in the x-y directions. Hence, computations in the serial (z) direction are performed using the regular 'do-loop' model. For example, the second-order x-component derivative is computed as follows :

$$do \; k = k\_b, k\_e$$
$$d2qdx2(k,:,:) = fu(:,:) * u(k,:,:)$$
$$+ fe(:,:) * uip1(k,:,:) \tag{12}$$
$$+ fw(:,:) * uim1(k,:,:) + ...$$
$$end \; do$$

where *uip1, uim1*, ..., are 3-D arrays with mapping conformable to the shifted array, and *fw, fe*, ... are the corresponding 2-D finite-difference coefficient arrays. This programming paradigm is used through out the computer program. The layout of the 3-D and 2-D arrays is defined as in Equations (11a-b). Although the use of a serial layout reduces the pipe length to the vector unit, the savings in memory usage far outweigh these considerations.

On the other hand, floating point operations between 3-D arrays utilizes the parallelism in all three axis. For example the term $\mathcal{L}_{ij}^a M_{ij}$ is computed as follows :

$$lij\_x\_mij = l11 * m11 + 2 * l12 * m12$$
$$+ 2 * l13 * m13 + l22 * m22 \tag{13}$$
$$+ 2 * l23 * m23 + m33 * m33$$

where *l11, l12*, ..., and *m11, m12*, ..., are 3-D arrays with conforming layout mapping (Equation 11a). In such case, the serial direction contributes to the pipe length on the vector unit.

Inter-Processor Communications

Most of the inter-processor communication costs are due to communications on the axes with *:block:procs* layout, i.e. the x and y directions. In general, there are three types of communication patterns encountered: regular communications, irregular or scatter/gather type of communication and reductions. Regular communication patterns are encountered in computing the finite-difference stencils; while reductions such as sums are used for calculating the dynamic constant. Irregular communication patterns are encountered in multigrid methods and have been presented in Tafti (1994).

Regular communications are the most prevalent in the current algorithm and the least expensive compared to the others. This communication pattern is encountered in calculating finite-difference stencils, e.g. node (k,i,j) requires values from its nearest neighbors, say $(k,i+1,j)$, $(k,i-1,j)$ and so on. In general, for the high-order accurate approximations, values from $(i-3)$ to $(i+3)$ have to be communicated to i for each coordinate direction. Several communication functionalities are provided through CMFortran to access elements of an array along a specific axis. The function *cshift(array, dim, shift)* performs a circular shift of the elements of *array* along the 'parallel' (*:block:procs*) dimension by the amount specified in *shift*. *cshift* implicitly assumes periodicity and wraps around the shift operation. The function *eoshift(array, dim, shift, boundary)* is appropriate when a boundary value (*boundary*) is to be imposed. Initial studies (Najjar and Vanka, 1994) have showed that the ratio of CPU run time for performing *eoshift* over *cshift* can be as high as 7. Hence, the *cshift* operation is also used for non-periodic Dirichlet boundary conditions. To impose the appropriate non-periodic boundary conditions, the finite-difference coefficients are used as arithmetic masks and are set appropriately in the pre-processing stage. The high-order accurate approximation requires the computation of up to *12* array shifts in the x and y (*:block:procs*) directions. Multiple *cshift* operations are performed using the CMSSL polyshift routine, *pshift*. (Thinking Machines Corp., 1993). Communication in the serial (z) direction are performed using the regular 'do-loop' paradigm as shown in the previous section. Further, as a consequence of the present programming paradigm, the periodicity condition of the variable field has to be explicitly applied in the z direction because of its *:serial* nature. For the array axis with *:block:procs* layout, the use of a circular shift implicitly imposes periodicity. However, in a *:serial* dimension the application of periodicity requires buffer elements. This is achieved by padding the array dimension with six nodes (three on either side), hence, defining the z dimension as (k_b-3:k_e+3), where k_b to k_e are the active computational nodes. The three 'fictitious' nodes on either side are a consequence of a seven point stencil used in high-order accurate approximations.

Other communication patterns consist of spread and reduction operations and are applied in step (ii) to compute the dynamic constant. As seen in Equation (5), since planar (zx) averaging is required, this means that 3-D arrays have to be reduced to one-dimensional arrays. This is performed via the reduction functionality, *sum*, as follows :

$$do\ k = k\_b,\ k\_e$$
$$lij\_x\_mij\_avgxz = lij\_x\_mij\_avgxz \qquad (14)$$
$$+ sum(lij\_x\_mij(k,:,:),\ dim=1)$$

$$mij\_sq\_avgxz = mij\_sq\_avgxz$$
$$+ sum(mij\_sq(k,:,:),\ dim=1)$$
$$end\ do$$

where $lij\_x\_mij\_avgxz$ and mij_sq_avgxz are one-dimensional (1-D) arrays of size ny and (*:block=nyb:procs=nyp*) layout. Then, the dynamic constant, a 3-D array variable, is calculated by spreading the 1-D arrays, $lij\_x\_mij\_avgxz$ and mij_sq_avgxz, along the x-direction using the HPF functionality, *spread*, resulting in the following code :

$$lij\_x\_mij\_avg = spread(lij\_x\_mij\_avgxz,1,nx)$$
$$rmij\_sq\_avg = spread(1./mij\_sq\_avgxz,1,nx)$$
$$do\ k = k\_b,\ k\_e \qquad (15)$$
$$cs(k,:,:) = -0.5 * lij\_x\_mij\_avg * rmij\_sq\_avg$$
$$end\ do$$

where $lij\_x\_mij\_avg$ and mij_sq_avg are 2-D arrays of size (nx,ny) and (*:block=nxb:procs=nxp,:block=nyb:procs=nyp*) layout and cs is a 3-D array with (*:serial,. :block=nxb:procs=nxp,:block=nyb:procs=nyp*) layout.

Linear Solvers and FFTs

The discussion in this section pertains to steps (iii) and (iv) in the solution procedure. The semi-implicit treatment of the momentum equations (Equation 10a) results in a system of linear equations and is solved using a penta-diagonal solve. This leads to the following system of equations for each velocity component:

$$A_\varphi \widetilde{\varphi}_{i,j,k} = A_n \widetilde{\varphi}_{i,j+1,k} + A_s \widetilde{\varphi}_{i,j-1,k}$$
$$+ A_{nn} \widetilde{\varphi}_{i,j+2,k} + A_{ss} \widetilde{\varphi}_{i,j-2,k} + rhs_{i,j,k}^{n,n-1} \qquad (16)$$

We encounter two situations depending on whether the elements of the coefficient matrix are two- (function of x and y) or four-dimensional (function of x, y, z and t). The first situation encountered when the DSM algorithm is not activated. Hence, the element arrays are functions only of x and y and are assembled at the pre-processing stage where a factoring operation is performed (see Tafti, 1994). In the second situation, when the dynamic subgrid scale stress model is activated, the diffusion coefficients are functions of the three spatial directions and time by virtue of the inclusion of v_t in Equation (10a). Hence, the element arrays are dynamically allocated at every initiation of the subroutines.

The linear solvers require inter-processor communications along the solve (y) axis for specific array layouts. Thus, to minimize communication costs, the y-axis is given a higher degree of locality over the x-axis. However, full locality of the y axis on the vector unit cannot always be maintained and depends on various factors such as grid resolution, partition size, and memory utilization. In the present implementation, a solution procedure based on pipelined Gaussian elimination is used to solve the linear systems when $nyp=1$; while a method based on substructuring with Cyclic Reduction is used for $nyp>1$. It should be noted that the second strategy involves more floating point operations (depending on layout) with increased communication costs (Thinking Machines Corp., 1993).

The pressure-Poisson solver (Equation 10b) takes full advantage of the two periodic dimensions (for the present test model of the turbulent channel flow) by applying a 2-D FFT in the x and z directions, with a line solve in the inhomogeneous (y)

direction (see Tafti 1994 for more details). This results in the following system of equations:

$$\left[A_{py} + \frac{4}{\Delta x^2} sin^2\left(\frac{2\pi}{L_x}\frac{k_x}{2}\Delta x\right) + \frac{4}{\Delta z^2} sin^2\left(\frac{2\pi}{L_z}\frac{k_z}{2}\Delta z\right)\right]\hat{p}_j^{n+1}$$
$$- A_n\hat{p}_{j+1}^{n+1} - A_s\hat{p}_{j-1}^{n+1} = -\frac{1}{\Delta t}\left(\frac{\partial\widetilde{\widetilde{u}}}{\partial x} + \frac{\partial\widetilde{\widetilde{v}}}{\partial y} + \frac{\partial\widetilde{\widetilde{w}}}{\partial z}\right)_j \quad (17)$$

where $\hat{p}$ is the Fourier coefficient of the discrete pressure field and is a function of the x and z wavenumbers, k_x and k_z. The steps of the pressure-Poisson solver can be summarized as follows. First, a forward FFT is applied to the right-hand-side of the pressure-Poisson equation. Second, a complex system of linear equations is solved using a tri-diagonal solver. Third, an inverse FFT is applied to obtain the new pressure field. Since FFTs are performed along the x and z axes, this results in irregular communication patterns along these axes. As the z axis is already defined locally to each vector unit through the *(:serial)* layout, all communications pertaining to the FFT in the z-direction are local to a vector unit. However, since the x axis with *(:block=nxb:proc=nxp)* layout is spread out across processors, heavy communication costs are incurred. This introduces conflicting requirements between the linear solve and the FFT procedure, one of each requires data locality in y and the other in x. For best computational efficiency, the y axis has to be local to the vector unit during the line solve step while the x axis has to be local to the vector unit during the FFT step. One approach to satisfy these conflicting requirements is to switch the mapping layout of the array axes as the algorithm evolves. This approach requires *4* mapping shifts which would incur heavy communication costs resulting in poor computational efficiency. It should be noted that this procedure has been successfully implemented by Najjar and Vanka (1994) for a direct solver based on eigenvalue decomposition with Discrete Fourier Transform. For this method, the incurred communication overheads do not contribute significantly to the computational costs. However, in the present approach, it was found that maintaining the locality of the y axis over the x axis gave better overall performance.

Steps of DSM Algorithm

The highlights of the data-parallel algorithm for the dynamic subgrid scale stress model (DSM) are summarized as follows :
(a) field variables including velocity, pressure, the dynamic constant and turbulent viscosity, are 3-D arrays defined as (nz, nx, ny) with a *(:serial, :block=nxb:procs=nxp,:block = nyb:procs=nyp)* layout.
(b) finite-difference coefficient arrays are two-dimensional of size (nx, ny) with layouts *(:block=nxb:procs=nxp,:block = nyb:procs=nyp)* conforming to the array layout of the field variables. These coefficient arrays are constructed in the pre-processing stage. Significant reduction in memory utilization is achieved.
(c) stencil operations are performed through *cshift* routine.
(d) Computational code blocks utilizing 3-D field variables and 2-D finite-difference coefficients use do loops structure in the *:serial z* axis.
(e) Computations between three-dimensional arrays as in step (ii) are performed on the full array without serial do-loops.
(f) Periodicity in the *serial* layout is applied explicitly through 'buffer' nodes.

(g) Locality of the y axis is given priority for highest efficiency of the linear solvers.
(h) *sum* and *spread* intrinsic function calls are used for planar averaging in step (ii).
(i) CMSSL line solver routine is used in step (iii).
(j) CMSSL FFT with linear solvers are used in step (iv). For more general class of problems Krylov-based methods such CG, CGS, BICGSTAB, and GMRES are used.

PERFORMANCE

The performance of the data-parallel algorithm described in Section 3 is evaluated in a model problem, the turbulent channel flow. The operating system (OS) is CMOST V7.3 final patch 7 and the code is compiled with CMF2.1.1-2 and linked to the CM Scientific Subroutine Library, CMSSL 3.2. Calculations are performed with *64*-bit precision. The timings reported correspond to *cm _elapsed_time* using *cm_timer_start* and *cm_timer_stop* functionalities.

Table 1 summarizes representative CPU times and GFLOP rate for the Navier-Stokes solver on a *32*-processor CM-5 partition. The 3-D arrays have a size of *64x64x64* and a detailed layout of *(:serial,:block=nxb:procs=nxp, :block=nyb:procs=nyp)* with $nxb = 1$, $nxp = 64$, $nyb = 32$ and $nyp = 2$. These timings are shown for computations performed without activating the DSM algorithm, referred to as 'LES No Model', i.e. steps (iii)-(v), as well as simulations with LES using filter A (Equation 8a) and filter C (Equation 8b). It is observed that in the 'LES No Model' calculations the momentum equations (step iii) account for *80%* of the CPU requirement. This is because, the direct solution of the pressure equation for the turbulent channel flow problem does not contribute substantially to the CPU requirements. Further for the DSM calculations, it is found that there is factor of four increase in the CPU time for steps (i-iii) compared to step (iii) for 'LES No Model' computations. The increase in CPU time in step (iii) in the DSM calculations is due to the larger overhead in factoring and solving the penta-diagonal line solver at each time step. Further, it is seen that computations with Filter C are a factor of *1.6* more expensive than those with Filter A. This is a result of the higher communication costs entailed in calculating the test filtered field. The modest FLOP rates varying from *0.1 GFLOPS* to *0.22 GFLOPS* are a result of the small problem size. Table 2 summarizes similar representative CPU times and GFLOP rate on a *256*-processor CM-5 partition for a problem size of *64x256x128*. The FLOP rates are seen to increase varying from *0.7 GFLOPS* to *1.4 GFLOPS*.

Figure 1 shows the CPU timings in $\mu s/\Delta t/grid\ node$ for a problem size of *64³* on various CM-5 partitions. It is observed that the 'LES No Model' run has CPU time varying from *4.6* to *1.6 µs/Δt/grid node*; while the simulations with the DSM algorithm result in an increase in CPU time by a factor of approximately four. In general, the CPU time is seen to decrease linearly (on a log scale) with increase in number of processors. It is important to note that the increase in CPU time in using the dynamic model is greatly exaggerated in turbulent channel flow as a result of the direct solution procedure used for the pressure equation. For more general problems with complex boundary conditions, we have to resort to iterative solvers for the pressure equation and in such instances, the time spent in the dynamic model procedure would be a much smaller percentage of the total.

The parallel efficiency of the algorithm is evaluated by computing the speed-up factor. The speed-up factor, σ_a, is defined as the ratio of the algorithm performance on a partition of size N over the algorithm performance for a reference partition of size N_r and is computed as $\sigma_a = (CPU)_{N_r} / (CPU)_N$. Figure 2 presents the speed-up factors against processor ratio for a problem size of 64^3 nodes with the 32-processor partition taken as reference, i.e. $N_r = 32$. Also shown is the theoretical limit defined as the processor ratio (N/N_r). At low processor ratio (N/N_r), the speed-up factor is approximately 1.4, close to the theoretical limit of 2. However, as the number of processors is increased, the speed-up factor becomes 1.9 for $(N/N_r) = 4$. The processor utilization efficiency decreases because of the increased communication costs and the loss in vectorization efficiency. It is observed that the parallel efficiency, η, decreases from 70% to 47%. The scalability of the algorithm is assessed by running a fixed number of nodes per processor and increasing the partition size. Figure 3 presents the scaled CPU time in $\mu s/\Delta t$/grid nodes for a problem size of 8192 nodes per processor. The partition size varies from 32 to 128 processing nodes. This corresponds to increasing the problem size from 64^3 to $64 \times 256 \times 128$ nodes. The slope rate of approximately unity testifies to the high scalability of the present algorithm.

TYPICAL RESULTS FOR LES OF TURBULENT CHANNEL FLOW

Numerical simulations are performed for the turbulent channel flow at high Reynolds number, $Re_\tau = 1050$. The Reynolds number, Re_τ, is defined as $Re_\tau = u_\tau \delta / \nu$ where u_τ represents the friction velocity $(u_\tau = \sqrt{\tau_w/\rho})$, δ is the channel half-width and ν is the kinematic viscosity. The computational domain size is $\pi/2 \times 5\pi/2 \times 2$ with a mesh resolution consisting of $128 \times 128 \times 96$ nodes in the z, x and y directions, respectively. A uniform grid distribution is applied in the streamwise (x) and spanwise (z) directions. A non-uniform grid distribution based on a geometric progression function with expansion factor of 1.09 is used in the transverse (y) direction. The time step size, Δt, is set as 2.5×10^{-4}. The computations are performed for 7.5 non-dimensional time units; and the statistics are accumulated over for the last 5 time units which represents 3.28×10^8 realizations. Simulations have been performed using test filters A and C and representative results obtained are discussed below.

Figure 4 presents the mean streamwise velocity profiles in wall coordinates for the runs made. Also shown are the experimental data of Wei and Willmarth (1989). It is seen that the mean streamwise velocity compares favorably with the experiments and the log-law profile. Figure 5 plots the distributions of the root mean square (rms) streamwise and cross-stream stress components in wall coordinates. It is observed that the peak of the streamwise stress is overpredicted by the current computations. Results obtained with filter C are seen to be lower than those obtained with filter A. The peak of the streamwise rms for both simulations is computed at 3.0 with its location being at $y^+ = 17.7$. Wei and Willmarth (1989) have measured a peak value of 2.77 at a location of $y^+ = 15.9$. In the channel core, $y^+ > 100$, the present results are observed to underpredict the experimental measurements. As for the rms cross-stream component, the peak

has a value of 0.97 and occurs at $y^+ = 150$ which compares satisfactorily with 1.05 at $y^+ = 150$ as measured by Wei and Willmarth (1989). The distributions of the total turbulent shear stress, $\overline{u'' v''} + (\tau_{12})_{sgs}$, and the subgrid-scale Reynolds shear stress, $(\tau_{12})_{sgs}$, for the two test filters are shown in Figure 6. It is seen that the curves of $\overline{u'' v''} + (\tau_{12})_{sgs}$ agree satisfactorily with the experimental data. Further, the peak of 0.8 occurs at $y^+ = 82$. This compares well with a value of 0.875 at $y^+ = 90$ measured by Wei and Willmarth (1989). The calculated subgrid-scale Reynolds stresses are highest for the simulations with filter A and lowest for those with filter C. The maximum contribution occurs at $y^+ \approx 30$ and varies from 2.2% to 4% of the total turbulent shear stress. Figure 7 shows the profile of the time-mean dynamic constant, $<C>$, in y^+ coordinates. Also displayed as a reference is the square of the Smagorinsky constant with wall correction, $C_{sw}^2 = 0.01 [1 - exp(-y^+/25)]^2$. It is noted that the value of the dynamic constant obtained for filter C is lower than that of filter A. Further, the dynamic constant reaches in the core a plateau value of 0.022 and 0.016 for filters A and C, respectively, corresponding to an equivalent Smagorinsky constant of 0.15 and 0.13. A more general observation is that the dynamic constant asymptotically tends towards zero in the near-wall region.

SUMMARY AND CONCLUSIONS

This paper presents the development and performance of a data-parallel algorithm for a finite-differenced based large-eddy simulation (LES) procedure. The dynamic subgrid-scale stress model (Germano et al., 1991) is applied to compute the subgrid-scale Reynolds stresses. Implementation issues focus on the data parallel programming paradigm using CMFortran which is similar to HPF (Koelbel et al., 1994). The data-parallel algorithm makes use of intrinsic functionalities, optimized library routines and detailed array layout directives on the massively parallel distributed-memory platform, the CM5. Performance studies show that the algorithm has an execution time of $2.3 \mu s/\Delta t$/grid nodes for a problem size of 2 million points. Performance rates of up to $1.4 GFLOPS$ were obtained with the present algorithm. The data-parallel algorithm is also found to have near perfect scalability with increasing partition size. Simulations are performed for the turbulent channel flow at high Reynolds number, $Re_\tau = 1050$. Turbulence statistics are presented for two discrete test filters and show close agreement with experimental measurements.

ACKNOWLEDGMENTS

F.M. Najjar was supported by a Post-doctoral fellowship from NCSA and the Division of Advanced Scientific Computing (DASC) at the National Science Foundation. The computations were performed on the CM-5 at NCSA. The support of these organizations is gratefully acknowledged. The authors would like to thank Prof. T. Wei for providing experimental data on the turbulent channel flow.

REFERENCES

Chorin, A.J., (1967), 'A Numerical Method for Solving Incompressible Viscous Flow Problems', *J. Comp. Phys.*, Vol. 2, 12-26.

Germano, M., Piomelli, U., Moin, P., and Cabot, H., (1991), 'A Dynamic Subgrid-Scale Eddy Viscosity Model', *Phys. Fluids A*, Vol. 3, 1760-1765.

Koelbel, C.H., Loveman, D.B., Schreiber, R.S., Steele, G.L., and Zosel, M.E., (1994), The High Performance Fortran Handbook, The MIT Press, Cambridge, MA.

Mason, P.J., and Callen, N.S., (1986), 'On the Magnitude of the Subgrid-Scale Eddy Coefficient in Large-Eddy Simulations of Turbulent Channel Flow', J. Fluid Mech., Vol. 12, 439-462.

Najjar, F.M., and Tafti, D.K., (1996), 'Study of Discrete Test Filters and Finite Difference Approximations for the Dynamic Subgrid-Scale Stress Model', to appear in Phys Fluids, April.

Najjar, F.M, and Vanka, S.P., (1994), 'Simulations of Unsteady Fluid Flows on the CM-5', ASME Symp on Advances in Comp. Methods in Fluid Dynamics, FED-Vol. 196, 277-285.

Olsson, P., and Johnsson, S.L., (1990), 'A Dataparallel Implementation of an Explicit Method for the Three-Dimensional Compressible Navier-Stokes Equations', Parallel Computing, Vol. 14, 1-30.

Rai, M.M., and Moin, P., (1991), 'Direct Simulations of Turbulent Flow using Finite-Difference Schemes', J. Comp. Phys., Vol. 96, 15-53.

Scotti, A., Meneveau, C., and Lilly, D.K., (1993), 'Generalized Smagorinsky Model for Anisotropic Grids', Phys. Fluids A, Vol. 5, 2306-2308.

Smagorinsky, J., (1963), 'General Circulation Experiments with the Primitive Equations. I The Basic Experiments', Mon. Weather Rev., Vol. 91, 99-64.

Tafti, D.K., (1994), 'Features and Implementation Issues for a High-Order Finite-Difference Algorithm for Direct and Large Eddy Simulations of Incompressible Turbulence on the CM-5', NCSA Preprint 047.

Tafti, D.K., (1995a), 'A Study of Krylov Methods for the Solution of the Pressure-Poisson Equation on the CM-5', ASME/JSME Symp. on Num Dev. in CFD, FED-Vol. 215, 1-8.

Tafti, D.K., (1995b), 'A Study of High-Order Spatial Finite Difference Formulations for the Incompressible Navier-Stokes Equations', NCSA Preprint 031.

Thinking Machines Corporation, (1993), CMSSL for CM Fortran V 3.1.

Thinking Machines Corporation, (1994), CM Fortran Programming Guide V 2.1.

Wei, T., and Willmarth, W.W., (1989), 'Reynolds-number Effects on the Structure of a Turbulent Channel Flow', J. Fluid Mech., Vol. 204, 57-95.

Steps	LES No Model		Filter A		Filter C	
	CPU (s)	GFLOPS	CPU (s)	GFLOPS	CPU (s)	GFLOPS
(i)	-	-	0.387	0.574	0.371	0.599
(ii)	-	-	1.337	0.685	2.536	0.707
(iii)	1.181	1.700	2.753	0.651	2.793	0.642
(iv)	0.280	1.223	0.274	1.249	0.282	1.214
(v)	0.055	1.030	0.058	0.976	0.051	1.111
Overall	1.516	1.380	4.809	0.706	6.033	0.708

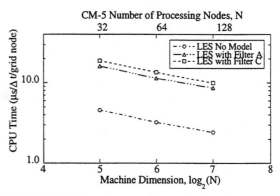

FIGURE 1. CPU timings for problem size of 64³ nodes on various CM-5 partitions.

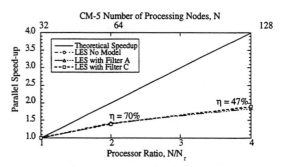

FIGURE 2. Parallel speed-up and efficiency for problem size of 64³ nodes with N_r = 32.

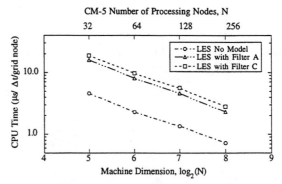

FIGURE 3. Scaled CPU time on various CM-5 partitions. Problem size is fixed to 8192 nodes/processing element.

Table 1. Representative Timings and GFLOPS for 64³ grid on 32-processor CM-5 partition.

Steps	LES No Model		Filter A		Filter C	
	CPU (s)	GFLOPS	CPU (s)	GFLOPS	CPU (s)	GFLOPS
(i)	-	-	0.286	0.097	0.286	0.097
(ii)	-	-	1.238	0.093	1.980	0.113
(iii)	0.958	0.220	2.437	0.095	2.437	0.095
(iv)	0.192	0.195	0.191	0.195	0.192	0.195
(v)	0.041	0.173	0.041	0.173	0.041	0.173
Overall	1.191	0.215	4.193	0.100	4.954	0.107

Table 2. Representative Timings and GFLOPS for 64x256x128 grid on 256-processor CM-5 partition.

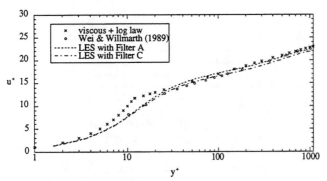

FIGURE 4. Distribution of the time-mean streamwise velocity in wall coordinates for the turbulent channel flow at $Re_\tau = 1050$.

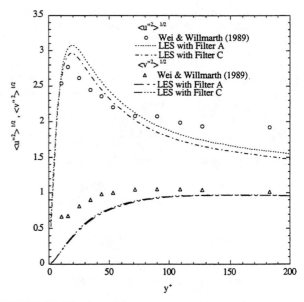

FIGURE 5. Distribution of the rms streamwise and cross-stream stresses in wall coordinates for the turbulent channel flow at $Re_\tau = 1050$.

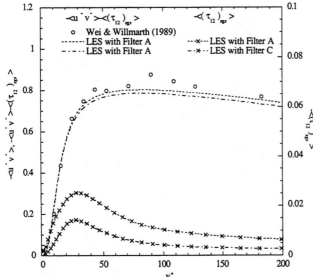

FIGURE 6. Distribution of the mean turbulent and sub-grid scales shear stresses in wall coordinates for the turbulent channel flow at $Re_\tau = 1050$.

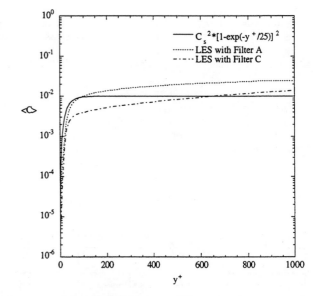

FIGURE 7. Distribution of the time-mean dynamic constant in wall coordinates for the turbulent channel flow at $Re_\tau = 1050$.

FED-Vol. 238, 1996 Fluids Engineering Division Conference
Volume 3
ASME 1996

APPLICATION OF A NEW INCOMPRESSIBLE FLOW ALGORITHM TO FLOWS IN A VARIETY OF SHEAR-DRIVEN CAVITY CONFIGURATIONS

Michael C. Wendl
School of Medicine
Washington University
Saint Louis, Missouri

Ramesh K. Agarwal
Department of Aerospace Engineering
Wichita State University
Wichita, Kansas

ABSTRACT

A recently developed incompressible flow algorithm by the authors is applied to study flows inside a variety of lid-driven cavity configurations. The new algorithm is based upon the pressure correction approach, but employs a regular grid finite-volume arrangement instead of the usual staggered grid arrangement. The pressure equation is derived such that effects which promote the well-known checkerboard instability are minimized. A relevant compatibility constraint on pressure is satisfied by Neumann boundary conditions obtained using a vector identity. Implemented in a second-order-accurate finite-volume code, the algorithm has been evaluated and validated by computing benchmark shear-driven cavity flows. Several geometric variations of the classical lid-driven square cavity flow are currently considered, for example parallelogram and elbow-shaped cavities. In a parallelogram shaped driven cavity, it is shown that the primary eddy in the "posterior" version is similar to both the "anterior" version examined by several previous investigators and to the classical square cavity flow. However, major differences exist in the secondary flow structure including a very strong oblong-shaped eddy in upstream corner region and no eddy at the downstream corner. In another variation, that of flow in an elbow-shaped cavity, bulk flow near the lid is again similar to that of the square cavity, but the flow pattern in the lower region of the cavity is significantly different. A large counter-rotating eddy occupies most of this region in conjunction with a long "finger" of the primary flow that wraps around it at the outer radius of the elbow.

INTRODUCTION

Recirculating flow is a major area of study in fluid mechanics. There are many familiar examples of such flows both in nature and in a wide variety of industrial applications. Two of the most widely quoted and studied examples of such flows are the separation at the step expansion in a duct (internal flow) and the immediate wake behind a bluff body (external flow). Such flows are often steady and usually exhibit a complex circulating flow pattern with closed streamlines. Perhaps the most extensively examined model problem typifying the recirculating flow is the lid-driven square cavity case. First studied in detail by Burggraf (1966), it is a confined flow in which the domain is bounded by four walls, one of which translates in its own plane. The resulting shear forces induce a variety of steady recirculating flow patterns depending upon the Reynolds number. It is important both as a physical model and as a benchmark for computational fluid dynamics (CFD) algorithms. The literature on this problem is extensive and the computational results are available for a wide range of Reynolds numbers (Ghia et al., 1982).

Recently, several geometrically more complex variations of the driven square cavity problem have been considered. These cases include triangular (Ribbens et al., 1994), circular sector (Rosenfeld et al., 1991, Kim and Benson, 1992), parallelogram (Peric, 1990, Karki and Monghia, 1990, Joshi and Vanka, 1991, Demirdzic et al., 1992, Zeng and Wesseling, 1993), and L-shaped (Zeng and Wesseling, 1993) configurations. Like the square cavity, these geometries can serve as important benchmark problems for the ever increasing number of CFD codes that are based on generalized coordinates. Overall flow patterns in these configurations are similar in the sense that there are one or more recirculation "cells" whose strength, size, shape, and location depend upon the Reynolds number and the specific geometry. The focus of this paper is the application of a recently-developed CFD code by the authors (Wendl and Agarwal, 1995) to computing the flow inside two geometric variations of the shear-driven square cavity configuration, namely the parallelogram, and the elbow-shaped cavity.

SOLUTION APPROACH AND NUMERICAL METHOD

Let the cavity region, Ω, be confined by a closed boundary, Γ. The fluid motion in Ω is governed by the continuity equation and the incompressible Navier-Stokes equations:

$$\frac{\partial u_i}{\partial x_i} = 0 \tag{1}$$

$$\frac{\partial u_j}{\partial t} + \frac{\partial u_i u_j}{\partial x_i} = -\frac{\partial P}{\partial x_j} + \frac{1}{\text{Re}} \frac{\partial^2 u_j}{\partial x_i \partial x_i} \tag{2}$$

In Equations (1) and (2), non-dimensional flow variables are the orthogonal velocity components, u_j, and the pressure, P, and the dimensionless independent variables in space and time are x_j and t, respectively. The only non-dimensional parameter is the Reynolds number in Equation (2), $\text{Re} = U_0 d / \nu$, where U_0 and d are characteristic velocity and length scales and ν is the kinematic viscosity. Dirichlet boundary conditions for velocity components are prescribed on Γ. All components of velocity are identically zero on all the walls except for the moving wall, at which the lateral velocity component is set to a value corresponding to the desired Reynolds number.

Because the cavity geometries being considered do not conveniently lend themselves to any of the standard coordinate systems, a generalized coordinate formulation is employed to obtain solutions (Wendl and Agarwal, 1995). The numerical algorithm is based on the pressure correction method (Harlow and Welch, 1965), but employs a non-staggered arrangement of the flow variables on the grid (Abdallah, 1987, Wendl, 1994). Non-staggered grid schemes have several advantages for complex geometries including easy application of boundary conditions and a single control volume per cell which enables straightforward finite-volume discretization of the flow equations.

The pressure Poisson equation is derived by taking the divergence of the momentum Equations (2) and simplifying using the continuity Equation (1):

$$\frac{\partial}{\partial x_i} \frac{\partial P}{\partial x_i} = -\frac{\partial}{\partial x_i} \frac{\partial u_j u_i}{\partial x_j} \tag{3}$$

An additional boundary condition on Γ is required for Equation (3) because the system is raised by an order as a result of the divergence operation. A Neumann boundary condition can be derived from Equation (2) in conjunction with the identity for the Laplacian of a vector:

$$\frac{\partial P}{\partial x_i} = -\frac{\partial u_j u_i}{\partial x_j} - \frac{\varepsilon_{iml}}{\text{Re}} \frac{\partial}{\partial x_m} \left[\varepsilon_{ljk} \frac{\partial u_k}{\partial x_j} \right] \tag{4}$$

The symbol ε_{iml} in Equation (4) is the permutation tensor. Elliptic effects in the governing Equations (1) and (2) are essentially diverted into Equations (3) and (4) which replace and satisfy the continuity Equation (1). This formulation has the desirable properties of satisfying the integrability constraint while exhibiting adequate ellipticity properties in the moderate Reynolds number range for which the current example flow problems will focus on (Armfield, 1991).

The standard finite-volume technique is employed to obtain the discrete equations (Deese and Agarwal, 1988). Convective terms are differenced using a third-order upwinding discretization while viscous and pressure terms are central differenced to second-order accuracy. Because the temporal variable is used merely as an iteration parameter to obtain the steady-state solution, it is differenced using the Euler explicit scheme. Therefore, only a few iterations are performed on the pressure Poisson system at each cycle. Two or three iterations prove to be sufficient to filter out highly oscillatory modes using the SOR method with an over-relaxation factor of 1.8. Time stepping continues until a steady distribution of the flow variables is realized. A CFL number of 0.6 was found to be adequate in maintaining numerical stability. Details of the numerical method are described in Wendl and Agarwal (1995).

Grid generation for the current example problems was accomplished using algebraic methods (Anderson et al., 1984) and the computed solutions were examined with a widely-available flow visualization software package (Walatka et al., 1991). All the computations were performed on a Hewlett-Packard HP-735 scalar workstation.

EXAMPLE PROBLEMS AND RESULTS

Two specific geometric variations of the basic square cavity problem are considered. Though some limited results have been reported in the literature for similar cases, neither of these configurations has been treated thoroughly so far.

The first geometric variation is obtained by skewing the top portion of the square cavity laterally while holding the bottom fixed resulting in a parallelogram as shown in Figure 1. The local coordinates, ξ and η, are skewed and follow the shape of the cavity. The ξ coordinate is coincident with the horizontal x axis while the η coordinate forms an angle θ with the vertical y axis. The characteristic dimension is the width which can be taken as unity, $d = 1$, without loss of generality. The height is also taken as unity making the length of the sloped walls $cos^{-1}\theta$. For this geometry, it is natural to use parallelogram-shaped control volumes of skew angle θ to discretize the cavity. Smooth variation of control volume size from the walls to the center of the cavity is obtained using Roberts transformations (Anderson et al., 1984), with the smallest volumes being placed near the boundaries.

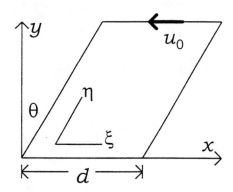

FIGURE 1: SCHEMATIC OF THE PARALLELOGRAM CAVITY

At a Reynolds number of 100, previous studies for a square cavity have shown that a pair of secondary corner vortices exist in addition to the primary eddy (Ghia et al., 1982). It is interesting to determine what effects the skewing has on this flow pattern. For the most part, work on the parallelogram geometry has focused on the "anterior" version, *i.e.* where movement of the top lid originates from the front of the cavity at $(x,y) = (tan\ \theta, 1)$ and proceeds in the $+x$ direction. Karki and Mongia (1990) and Joshi and Vanka (1991) have examined this variation, but report only the results regarding convergence rates of their algorithms. Peric (1990) and Demirdzic et al. (1992) provide a more in-depth treatment giving results for several skew angles at Re = 100. Behavior of the primary eddy near the lid is shown to be similar to that of the square cavity. The main difference is that the bottom region is dominated by a single large secondary vortex with several tertiary eddies piling up in the acute-angle corner. Zeng and Wesseling (1993) show that results are qualitatively similar at lower Reynolds numbers.

To complement these studies, the "posterior" version is treated here in which the lid motion is in the opposite direction, *i.e.* originating from $(x,y) = (tan\ \theta + 1, 1)$ and moving in the $-x$ direction. To the authors knowledge, this version has not been treated previously in the literature. The skew angle is taken as $\pi/8$. A grid containing 124 x 124 control volumes is employed with a Roberts clustering factor of 1.3 to pack higher density at the boundaries. Streamline (Fig. 2) and vorticity (Fig. 3)

distributions derived from the results give insight into the flow pattern. Like the "anterior" version, the primary eddy is qualitatively similar to that of the square cavity. The single secondary eddy, however, is quite different from both the "anterior" parallelogram and square cavity cases. It has an oblong shape and its limiting streamline nearly bisects the acute-angle corner. A closer inspection (Fig. 4) reveals that its strength is of order 10^{-4}, about ten times stronger than the secondary eddy in the "anterior" version computed by Demirdzic et al. (1992). It is also stronger than the secondary eddies of strength 10^{-5} and 10^{-6} shown by Ghia et al. (1982) in the square cavity. Furthermore, unlike the square cavity, there is no eddy in the opposite bottom corner for this version of the parallelogram flow.

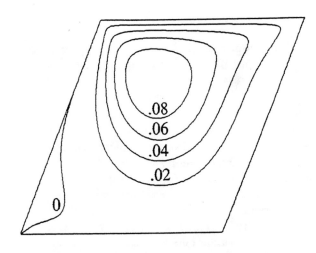

FIGURE 2: STREAMLINE DISTRIBUTION FOR FLOW IN THE PARALLELOGRAM

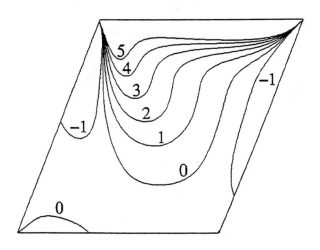

FIGURE 3: VORTICITY DISTRIBUTION FOR FLOW IN THE PARALLELOGRAM

235

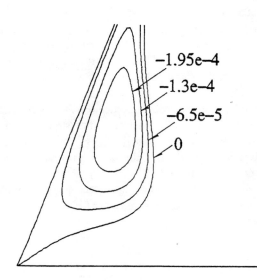

FIGURE 4: SECONDARY EDDY STRUCTURE FOR FLOW IN THE PARALLELOGRAM

For a quantitative comparison to the square cavity flow, the horizontal velocity component along a line proceeding from the midpoint of the lid to the midpoint of the bottom plane is shown in Figure 5. Results are compared to the exact numerical values from Table I of Ghia et al. (1982) for the square cavity. It is evident that the bulk flow is very similar to that of the square. Minor differences are that the center of the main eddy in the skewed cavity is slightly lower and the velocity extrema are not as great. It is expected that the differences would increase with increasing skew angle and Reynolds number.

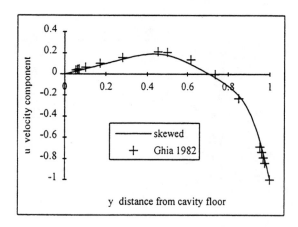

FIGURE 5: VELOCITY COMPARISON FOR PARALLELOGRAM AND SQUARE CAVITIES

A second variation of the square cavity configuration is obtained by holding the base fixed while stretching vertically and then twisting the top plane about the depth-wise axis by an angle of $\pi/2$ resulting in an "elbow" configuration (Fig. 6). To the authors knowledge, this cavity geometry has not been treated in the literature. The translating face is the left extreme of the elbow which moves downward in the -y direction. The length of this face is taken to be unity, $d = 1$, and all other dimensions are given relative to it. Unlike the parallelogram, the (ξ, η) local coordinates are not fixed relative to the (x, y) axes, but rotate following the shape of the elbow. Body-conforming orthogonal control volumes are generated to discretize the geometry. For a Reynolds number of 100, 80 volumes in the radial direction and 200 volumes in the azimuthal direction are employed.

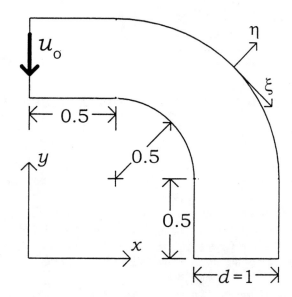

FIGURE 6: SCHEMATIC OF THE ELBOW-SHAPED CAVITY

Streamline (Fig. 7) and vorticity (Fig. 8) distributions are useful once again in visualizing the fluid motion. In the neighborhood of the moving lid, the flow pattern looks remarkably similar to that of the square cavity. Strength of the primary eddy is also approximately of the same magnitude. A large secondary eddy stands further down the elbow occupying over half the total cavity area. It has a very high strength of order 10^{-3}. An unusual feature is the long finger of primary flow which reaches all the way down to the bottom of the elbow.

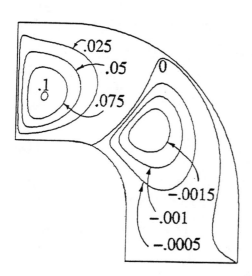

FIGURE 7: STREAMLINE DISTRIBUTION FOR FLOW
IN THE ELBOW-SHAPED CAVITY

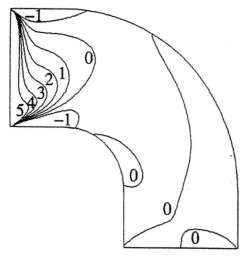

FIGURE 8: VORTICITY DISTRIBUTION FOR FLOW
IN THE ELBOW-SHAPED CAVITY

Figure 9 shows quantitative data in the form of the velocity components plotted along a line connecting $(x,y) = (0.5, 1)$ to $(x, y) = (0.5, 2)$. The primary eddy can be clearly inferred from the two components. Comparison to the corresponding region in the square cavity flow is made for the azimuthal velocity component using exact numerical data from Table II of Ghia et al. (1982). Once again, the bulk flow near the moving lid is similar to the flow in the square cavity. However, in this case, the velocity extrema are slightly greater than those for the square cavity.

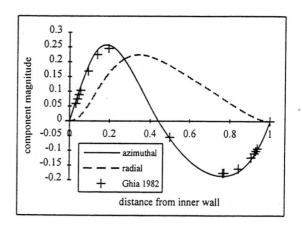

FIGURE 9: VELOCITY COMPARISON FOR ELBOW-
SHAPED AND SQUARE CAVITIES

CONCLUSION

Two novel variations of the classical shear-driven cavity problem have been examined using a recently developed Navier-Stokes algorithm for incompressible flow. The pressure-based non-staggered grid finite-volume algorithm is found to be accurate, robust, and efficient. Computed results show that the bulk flow for parallelogram and elbow cavity shapes at Re = 100 are qualitatively similar to the fluid motion in the square cavity, particularly near the moving lid. However, major differences exist in the secondary flows. The "posterior" version of the parallelogram case differs significantly in the flow pattern from both the square and the "anterior" parallelogram version studied previously by various investigators. An oblong secondary flow eddy exists near the acute-angle bottom corner while no eddy appears in the opposite corner. The elbow cavity geometry exhibits a very strong secondary eddy below the primary one, in conjunction with a long "finger" of the primary flow reaching down to the bottom of the cavity.

REFERENCES

Abdallah, S., 1987, "Numerical Solutions for the Incompressible Navier-Stokes Equations in Primitive Variables Using a Non-Staggered Grid", *Journal of Computational Physics*, **70**, 182-202.

Anderson, D.A., Tannehill, J.C., and Pletcher, R.H., 1984, "Computational Fluid Mechanics and Heat Transfer", Hemisphere.

Armfield, S.W., 1991, "Finite Difference Solutions of the Navier-Stokes Equations on Staggered and Non-Staggered Grids", *Computers and Fluids*, **20**, 1-17.

Burggraf, O.R., 1966, "Analytical and Numerical Studies of the Structure of Steady Separated Flow", *Journal of Fluid Mechanics*, **24**, 113-151.

Deese, J.E., and Agarwal, R.K., 1988, "Navier-Stokes Calculations of Transonic Viscous Flow About Wing/Body Configurations", *Journal of Aircraft*, **25**, 1106-1112.

Demirdzic, I., Lilek, Z., and Peric, M., 1992, "Fluid Flow and Heat Transfer Test Problems for Non-Orthogonal Grids: Benchmark Solutions", *International Journal for Numerical Methods in Fluids*, **15**, 329-354.

Ghia, U., Ghia, K.N., and Shin, C.T., 1982, "High-Re Solutions for Incompressible Flow Using the Navier-Stokes Equations and a Multigrid Method", *Journal of Computational Physics*, **48**, 387-411.

Harlow, F.H., and Welch, J.E., 1965, "Numerical Calculation of Time-Dependent Viscous Incompressible Flow of Fluid with Free Surface", *Physics of Fluids*, **8**, 2182-2189.

Joshi, D.S., and Vanka, S.P., 1991, "Multigrid Calculation Procedure for Internal Flows in Complex Geometries", *Numerical Heat Transfer B*, **20**, 61-80.

Karki, K.C., and Mongia, H.C., 1990, "Evaluation of a Coupled Solution Approach for Fluid Flow Calculations in Body-Fitted Co-Ordinates", *International Journal for Numerical Methods in Fluids*, **11**, 1-20.

Kim, S.-W., and Benson, T.J., 1992, "Comparison of the *SMAC*, *PISO* and Iterative Time-Advancing Schemes for Unsteady Flows", *Computers and Fluids*, **21**, 435-454.

Peric, M., 1990, "Analysis of Pressure-Velocity Coupling on Nonorthogonal Grids", *Numerical Heat Transfer B*, **17**, 63-82.

Ribbens, C.J., Watson, L.T., and Wang, C.-Y., 1994, "Steady Viscous Flow in a Triangular Cavity", *Journal of Computational Physics*, **112**, 173-181.

Rosenfeld, M., Kwak, D., and Vinokur, M., 1991, "A Fractional Step Solution Method for the Unsteady Incompressible Navier-Stokes Equations in Generalized Coordinate Systems", *Journal of Computational Physics*, **94**, 102-137.

Walatka, P.P., Plessel, T., McCabe, R.K., Clucas, J., and Elson, P.A., 1991, "FAST User's Manual", NASA RND Report 91-011.

Wendl, M.C., 1994, "A Pressure-Based Finite-Volume Time-Stepping Algorithm for the Numerical Simulation of Incompressible Flows", *Ph.D. Dissertation*, Washington University.

Wendl, M.C., and Agarwal, R.K., 1995, "A New Pressure-Based Finite-Volume Time-Marching Algorithm for Incompressible Flow Simulation", in *Numerical Developments in CFD-1995*, Proceedings of the ASME Symposium, FED-Vol. 215, 47-54.

Zeng, S., and Wesseling, P., 1993, "Numerical Study of a Multigrid Method with Four Smoothing Methods for the Incompressible Navier-Stokes Equations in General Coordinates", Copper Mountain Conference on Multigrid Methods '93.

FINITE ELEMENT APPLICATIONS IN FLUID DYNAMICS

Introduction

Manoranjan N. Dhaubhadel
Ford Motor Company
Dearborn, Michigan

The 1996 ASME Symposium on Advances in Finite Element Applications in Fluid Dynamics is the fifth in the series sponsored by the ASME Fluids Engineering Division. The symposium is intended to provide an annual forum for presentation of recent advances in finite element simulation of fluid dynamics problems. The topics in this year's volume include flow through multi-hole nozzle for DI diesel engine, underhood thermo-fluids simulation, modeling of two-phase flow in vacuum-degassing of steel, free convection in vertical channels with backward-facing step, flow through multiple channel honeycomb monolithic structure, laminar backward-facing step flow, oil-water settling process, implementation of one point quadrature in finite element CFD code, heat transfer prediction in cooled turbine blades, thermal simulation of spent nuclear fuel canister, free surface flows with merging and breakup and application of MEI finite elements to store separation.

I gratefully acknowledge the efforts of Dr. Michael S. Engelman and Dr. Wagdi G. Habashi as co-organizers of the symposium.

We express our appreciation to the authors for their contributions. We hope that the symposium will be seen as a window on the current advances in finite element applications in fluid dynamics.

FED-Vol. 238, 1996 Fluids Engineering Division Conference
Volume 3
ASME 1996

THEORETICAL INVESTIGATION ON NEEDLE TIP DEVIATION OF A MULTIHOLE V. C. O. NOZZLE FOR D.I. DIESEL ENGINE

Luigi Fiorentino, Domenico Laforgia
Istituto di Macchine ed Energetica
POLITECNICO DI BARI
70125 BARI
ITALY

Abstract

A 3-D analysis of the flow through a multihole V.C.O. (Valve Covered Orifice) nozzle for D.I. Diesel Engine has been carried out. The analysis was performed by means of a finite element code. The nozzle comprises five injection holes.

Aims of the analysis were:

• the investigation of the pressure drops along the conical clearance between the needle and the nozzle;

• the evaluation of the energy losses in the injection holes;

• the disclosure of the velocity profile at the injection hole outlets.

• the differences of flowrate for each hole with geometrical asymmetries.

A second investigation has been made on a needle tip deviation, evaluating again the pressure drops, the energy losses and the velocity profiles in the same location and the flowrate differences for each hole. This kind of investigation is the first step of a more complete spray analysis and provides to better the theoretical knowledge of this kind of nozzle.

Nomenclature

h	needle lift (mm)
k	turbulent kinetic energy (m^2/s^2)
μ	fluid viscosity (kg/ms)
p_1	inlet pressure (Pa)
p_2	outlet pressure (Pa)
ρ	fluid density (kg/m^3)
ψ	area restriction coefficient
K	cavitation coefficient
Lw	energy losses (J/mc)
ε	turbulent kinetic energy dissipation rate (m^2/s^3)

Introduction

There are few studies on the fluid flow through a V.C.O. nozzle due to the fact that they were only recently introduced in D. I. Diesel engines.

Bruni et al. [1, 2] started the investigation achieving interesting results with a bidimensional simulation of the fluid flow. They assumed no cavitating fluid and no reciprocal interactions in the flow towards the holes, obtaining the following results:

- the energy losses in the clearance between the nozzle body and the needle surface are negligible when the needle lift is high, and they increase as the needle lift decreases, as it was noted theoretically [3];

- the flow towards the holes outlets is strongly asymmetrical and the same asymmetry in the flow was found at the outlet surface;

- the losses increase if the offset angle between the cone axis and the hole axis increases due to the increasing of the flow deflection;

- the hole inclination influences the efflux characteristics, and, as a consequence, the spray. A bigger deviation of the flow causes the shift of the geometric point of the velocity median along the outlet section of the hole and reduces the contraction coefficient. The efflux global coefficient increases when the deviation of the hole axis becomes smaller.

Iiyama et al. [5] recently made a numerical analysis of a V.C.O. nozzle by means of CFD with a very simple schematization with needle tip deviation. The nozzle presented five holes symmetrically displaced. The results showed a tangential flow into the clearance between the nozzle body and the needle surface.

Object of the present investigation is the CFD study of the behavior of the 3-D model of an asymmetric five-hole nozzle (Fig. 1), varying the needle lift and the needle tip deviation. A comparison between numerical and some experimental results completes the study. The computational investigation has been performed using Ansysc 5.0 ode [5, 6].

A model with centered needle tip has been developed first, then, a second model with deviated needle tip has been created.

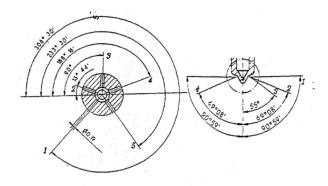

Fig. 1 - The 5 hole nozzle

CENTERED NEEDLE TIP MODEL

Model setup

A preliminary series of different models in terms of mesh has been developed. In Fig. 2 the model at 0.20 mms of needle lift is shown. The figure presents only the mesh representing the clearance between the nozzle body and the needle surface. The mesh of each hole is also clearly represented. The model presents a mesh made of 49474 nodes and 43180 elements.

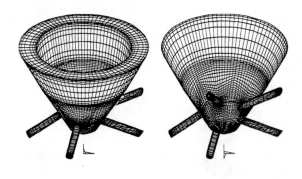

Fig. 2 - Model with 49474 nodes and 43180 elements presented at 0.2 mm of needle lift

Such a model was analyzed using a standard oil (ρ=815 kg/m^3, μ=0.003 kg/ms) and a cavitation number less than 1, where such a number is defined as follows:

$$K = \frac{p_1 - p_2}{p_2}$$

As for the removed part of the sac, preliminary computations suggested to produce negligible errors with respect to the model with the whole sac.

The simulations were performed setting a pressure of 40 MPa at the nozzle inlet surface and of 30 MPa at the hole outlets. The result is a cavitation number which is low enough to avoid cavitating behavior of the nozzle.

The whole simulation has been repeated varying the needle lift in the range of 0.05÷0.20 mms by steps of 0.025 mms. No needle deviation was considered in this first part of the investigation.

Some algorithms have been arranged for the calculation of the following parameters:
- single hole flow rate;
- total energy at each hole outlet;
- total energy entering the nozzle;
- total energy in the restricted sections of each hole.

As for the flow rate, the first step has been the definition of a path between the central node of the hole and each node at the external part of the nozzle (there are 24 elements in this part). As a second step, the velocity integral was calculated along that path, that is to say, the area of the quadrilater combined with each velocity of the path line. The barycenter of the quadrilater was calculated with respect to the needle axis and the volume of the cylinder obtained turning this surface of 15 degrees (360:24). This result expresses the volumetric flow rate flowing from one element of the circular surface of the nozzle. Repeating the calculation for each element of the entire section, and summing up all the results, the global flow rate was obtained.

As for the total energy, the calculation of the total pressure in any circular section is similar to the one of the flow rate, where the rotation of the surfaces is carried out both on the square of velocity and on the pressure.

Being holes No. 2 and No. 4, holes No. 1 and No. 5 symmetrical, only holes No. 1, 2 and 3 were considered in the discussion of results.

The velocity profile and pressure profile maps (Fig. 3), and the velocity vectorial diagrams (Fig. 4) are presented here only for the needle lift of 0.20 mms. The figures show that for hole No. 1, flow reduction is the largest considering the flow deflection entity, it is moderate in hole No. 2 and negligible in hole No. 3, where the flow seems influenced by the flowing back from the sac.

This trend is moreover confirmed by the pressure profiles of hole No. 3, which are almost symmetrical near the hole inlet. Fig. 4 shows how the axis inclination modifies the velocity profiles at the outlet and, consequently, the spray shape development, as already noted in [1] and [7]. It can be seen that hole No. 1 presents the most asymmetrical profiles due to the largest flow deviation.

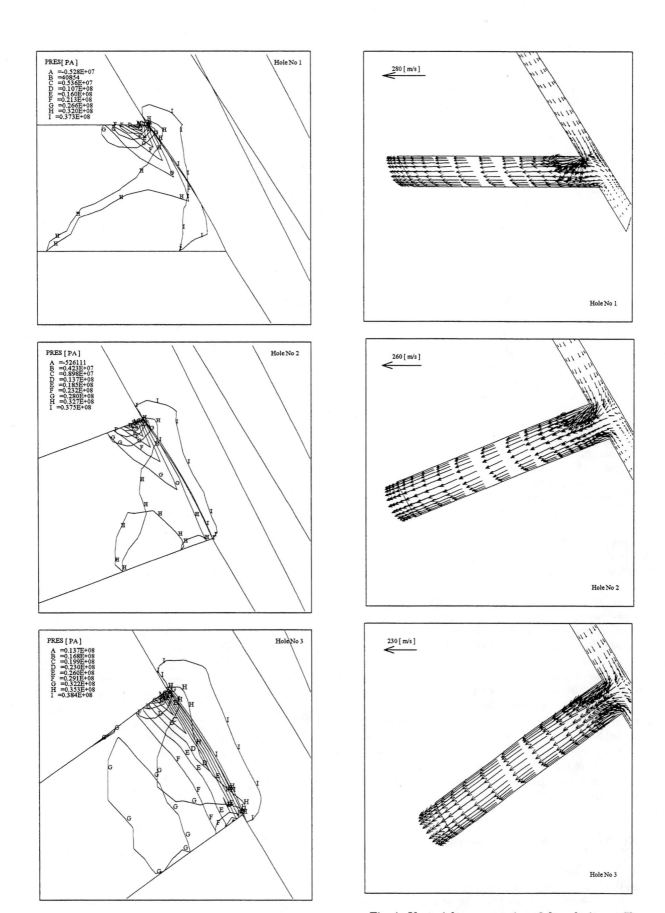

Fig. 3 - Maps of pressure profiles for each hole of the nozzle

Fig. 4 - Vectorial representation of the velocity profiles for each hole of the nozzle

Fig. 5 shows the predicted flow rates for each hole at different needle lifts. The curves are shifted upwards as the hole inclination decreases. The phenomenon is due to the energy losses upstream of the holes and inside them.

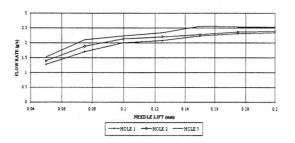

Fig. 5 - The predicted flow rate

The most relevant hypothesis, to prepare the energy losses computing files, was the assumption that the hole inlet area is the whole strip situated in the clearance between the nozzle body and the needle surface. This is a new approach and differs completely from [1] and [3]. According to this new approach the following energy losses could be calculated:

a) energy loss at the needle seat;
b) energy loss due to the change of direction;
c) energy loss in the injection holes;
d) global energy losses;
e) global energy available for each hole.

The results are shown in Fig. 6 for each hole of the nozzle and it can be noted that:

• when the lift is small, the flow through the needle seat is approximately laminar, then the losses become relevant, due to the viscous forces prevailing; with the increase of the lift this effect diminishes its importance due to the flow turbulence;

• the losses due to the change of direction in the needle seat proceed according to the needle seat losses, and this is evident considering the influence of the needle lift; obviously, these losses are never equal to zero;

• the losses into the holes increase as the lift increases, but the rate of change is small, so that the curves become flat as the lift reaches the highest values; this result confirms that the area restriction coefficient ψ varies with the lift and tends to a constant value, the experimental one; that is to say, it tends to the value computed without the needle;

• because of the different energy losses a different flow rate for each hole has been predicted according to the experimental results [8].

Conclusions for the centered needle tip analysis

From the needle lift parametric model, the following considerations can be made:

• the flow streams towards the holes are not yet reciprocally influenced when the needle is centred on the main nozzle axis;

• the flow at the hole inlet is influenced by the flowing back from the sac (in particular for the hole No 3), so that it is important to consider the whole strip at the hole inlet when computing the losses;

• when the lift is small the flow through the needle seat is approximately laminar, therefore, the losses become not negligible due to the viscous forces prevailing;

• a different flow rate can be noted among the five holes due to the different losses and, then, related to the asymmetry of the nozzle holes. This result points out that the spray will be affected by the same asymmetry and, consequently, the whole combustion process will be affected as well.

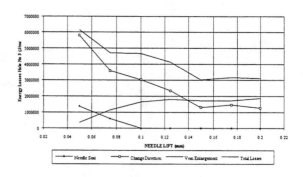
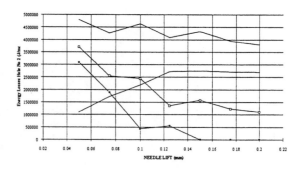
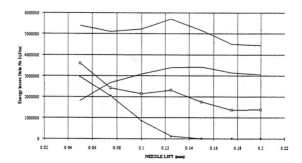

Fig. 6 - Energy losses for each hole of the nozzle

DEVIATED NEEDLE TIP MODEL

Model Setup

The mesh construction is substantially identical to the case of model with centered needle. The deviation of the needle from the principal axle of the nozzle, was obtained freeing the mesh of the centered needle from the rest of the mesh moving it of the desired deviation in the desired direction. The final mesh adopted was made of 48468 nodes and 43120 elements (Fig. 7).

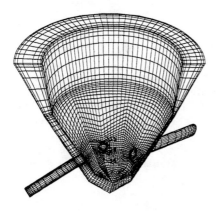

Fig. 7 - The deviated needle tip model

The time of execution of each calculaton has been roughly up to the 30 hours of CPU for a 486/66 computer.

The whole investigation has been carried out considering a needle deviation toward holes No.1 and No. 5 in the plane of symmetry of the nozzle, and the simulations were performed setting pressures at 40 MPa at the nozzle inlet surface and at 30 MPa at the hole outlets.

The choice of a series of lift-deviations couples to depict completely the behavior of the nozzle has been a difficult task, considering the meshability of the model to the different needle lifts. The equation:

$$deviation = 1.25 * h^2$$

appeared to give the best results and it has been adopted for all the simulations. The final lift-deviation diagram is reported in Fig.8.

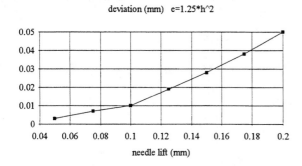

Fig. 8 - The lift vs the needle tip deviation

The hypothesis of varying the needle deviation with the lift was determined by the need of exploring a wider range of deviation possibilities than a mere computation with a single constant deviation.

As already said, the deviation of the needle, in agreement with the results of Damiani et al.[8], is directed towards the holes No. 1 and No. 5, that presented sprays characterized by strong anomalies during the experimental investigation.

Discussion of results

Considering the nozzle symmetry, the presentation of results will be limited only at holes No. 1, No. 2 and No. 3, given that no differences can subsist for holes No. 4 and No. 5 which are symmetrical to holes No. 2 and No. 1, respectively, as shown in Fig. 9.

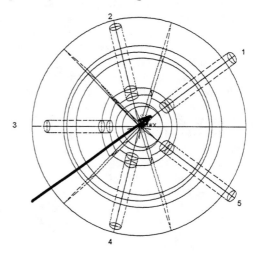

Fig. 9 - Holes numbering

From the curves of Figure10, it is manifest that holes No. 2, No. 3 and No. 4 present a flow rate larger than holes No. 1 and No. 5. However, such differences appear less important than it could be imagined. The needle deviation does not seem to affect so much the flow rate of each hole as the different hole inclinations do. In Figure 11, the curves represent the momentum through the five holes, and clearly show significant differences, affecting obviously the spray penetration.

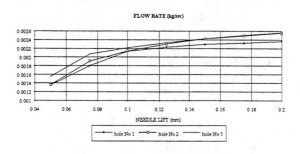

Fig. 10 - Flow rate

245

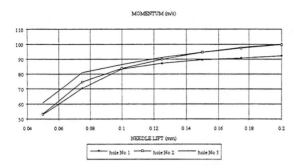

Fig. 11 - Momentum

As for the energy losses in the needle seat, shown in Figure 12, the parabolic curve, which has been selected to link the needle lifts and the deviations, minimizes the differences resulting in apparent contrast with the results of Guglielmotti [3], who showed that narrowing the needle seat an increase of the losses should be predicted. In effect, there is no real contrast with such theoretical and experimental results because the diction "energy losses in the needle seat" means, in our case, more exactly the energy at the inflow section of the hole. In fact, the needle seat, in the direction of the needle deviation, does not practically feed anymore the holes No. 1 and No. 5 from the top. The holes are fed sideways and from the lower part of the nozzle by some flowing back of fuel coming from the mini sac. This effect produces a slight reduction of the losses for change of direction at the holes No. 1 and No. 5. Furthermore, having for each lift about the same ammount of energy at the inlet section of each hole, the study of the fluid dynamic behavior of the nozzle, may be carried out analyzing only the flow inside each hole.

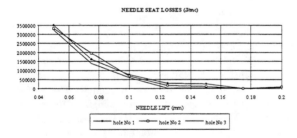

Fig. 12 - Needle seat losses

From Figure 13, it is evident that the holes No. 1 and No. 5 show a lower loss of energy due to the change of direction. This evidence confirms that such holes cannot be fed only from the top of the nozzle, but essentially from the sides or from the lower part of the mini sac, where the geometry of the nozzle permits to feed the two holes even better than the holes No. 2, No. 3 and No. 4. The feeding of holes No. 1 and No. 5 might come from the side in which the needle seat becomes wider. This was not revealed by the analysis of the nozzle with centered needle and could be explained as follows: the fluid, entering mostly laterally (Fig.17), could bump against the hole walls causing a

strong restriction of the vein and a swirl (Fig.18), probably affecting the development of the spray at the outlet.

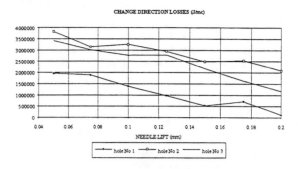

Fig. 13 - Change direction losses

The graphic in Fig.14 seems to confirm such hypothesis. The re-enlargement of the vein is substantial proved for the holes No. 1 and No. 5 affected by the highest energy losses, while the flow in the holes No. 2, No. 3 and No. 4 assumes the typical paths of a symmetrical feeding in tick wall. Finally, Figs. 15 and 16 show the trends of the total losses and of the available energy for the three holes.

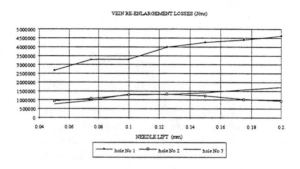

Fig. 14 - Vein enlargement losses

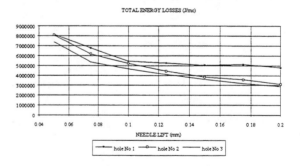

Fig. 15 - Total energy losses

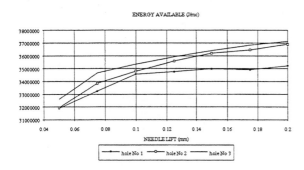

Fig. 16 - Energy available

Conclusions

The analysis of the nozzle with deviated needle has provided interesting results for the comprehension of some anomalies disclosed by the experiments. Although certain conclusions cannot be absolute and generalized to all the possible situations, because of the unpredictability of the needle deviation, some general rules can be extrapolated.

It is conceivable to suppose that the increase of the angle of the spray at the outlet could be generated by the swirl that the fuel acquires prevailing in holes No. 1 and No. 5.

Holes No. 2, No. 4 and, partially, No. 3 should have a less wide but surely more penetrating spray than holes No. 1 and No. 5. Generally speaking, it can be said that, if the spray coming from a hole presents unordinary forms with multiple tips, probably that hole is asymmetrically fed.

In presence of a deviation of the needle, the natural feeding of the nozzle does not occur anymore and the differences in flow rate, losses and energy found in the centered needle simulation can be compensated or increased affecting the flow field and the spray. In the investigated nozzle, the holes No. 1 and No. 5 seem to be fed sideways and from the mini sac.

Different flow rates have been noted for each hole due to the asymmetry of the nozzle holes and the simulated deviation of the needle. This results points out that the spray can be affected by the same asymmetry and, consequently, the combustion process will be affected as well.

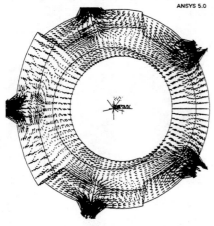

Fig. 17 - The flow towards to the five holes

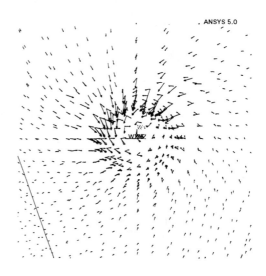

Fig. 18 - The swirl motion inside hole 1 towards to the direction indicated in fig. 9

Acknowledgements

The authors wish to thank Dr. M. Ricco, Director of ELASIS - Bari, for the financial support.

References

[1] Bruni, G. and Laforgia, D.: "Study of the Flow Field of a Multihole V.C.O. Nozzle and Effects on Spray", Fluid Mechanics and Heat Transfer in Spray, FED-Vol. 178/HTD Vol. 270, ASME 1993, p. 173-181.

[2] Fiorentino L.,Laforgia D.,Bruni G.,Fiore A.:"3-D Analysis of the Flow Through a Multihole V.C.O. nozzle for D.I. Diesel Engine",SAE Techichal Paper,No.950058

[3] Guglielmotti, A.: "Ulteriori note sul coefficiente di efflusso dei polverizzatori Sacless", Technical Report, Magneti Marelli, Bari, 1989.

[4] Iiyama, A., Matsumoto, Y., Kawamoto, K. and Ohishi, T.: "Spray Formation Improvement of V.C.O. Nozzle for D.I. Diesel Smoke Reduction", IMechE Seminar on Diesel Fuel Injection Systems, 1992.

[5] Flotran Theoretical Manual, Compuflo, 1992.

[6] Flotran User's Manual, Compuflo, 1992.

[7] Andoh, H. and Shiraishi, K.: "Influence on Injection and Combustion Phenomena by Elimination of Hole nozzle Sac Volume", SAE Technical Papers, No. 860416

[8] Campanella, R., Laforgia, D., Ficarella, A. and Damiani, V.: "Spray Characteristics of 5-Hole V.C.O. Nozzle of a Diesel Electro-Injector", SAE Technical Paper, No. 940192.

**FED-Vol. 238, 1996 Fluids Engineering Division Conference
Volume 3
ASME 1996**

"Underhood Thermo-fluids Simulation for a Simplified Car Model"

M. N. Dhaubhadel* and T. S. Shih
Ford Motor Company, Dearborn, MI
* Consultant

Abstract:

Thermo-fluids modeling of the underhood region in an automobile is crucial in designing the underhood components and maintaining operating temperatures at a desirable level. Because of numerous electronic components packed under the hood and the external aerodynamic shape and size requirements, the underhood region in todays automobiles tends to be more and more crowded. In the present study, thermo-fluids simulations of a box car with a simplified Y-shaped engine block under the hood is carried out. A commercial finite element code FIDAP is employed to solve the Reynold's averaged equations with the standard k-ε model for turbulence closure. Mesh sensitivity analysis is carried out with three different mesh sizes. Results in terms of flow distributions are presented and compared with experimental results. The computed flow field matches the experimental data in overall features. The flow rates through the underhood exits differ somewhat from the experimentally generated values, owing possibly to differences in the computational and experimental conditions. It is observed that a box car model is suitable for testing a CFD code quickly because it has the needed underhood features without the immense complexity of the actual underhood components.

Introduction:

Underhood thermal protection is an important aspect in vehicle development. An extensive amount of CFD work for underhood thermal management can be found in the literature [1-9]. Higher output engines, tighter packaging and smaller engine compartments have rendered the thermal and flow predictions all the more important. Because of immense advances in computers and computational techniques, CFD has become a viable technology for analyzing complex flows in complicated geometries like

the underhood of a car. Use of CFD in the early design stages can significantly reduce the amount of prototyping thereby reducing cost and design cycle time. CFD analysis also provides a better understanding of the thermal and flow details in the complex flow passages. To obtain such detailed thermal and flow data from tests for complicated geometries can be prohibitively expensive when possible.

Modeling a full scale underhood geometry is time consuming and expensive. In order to establish a methodology to quickly obtain thermo-fluids distribution in an underhood environment, a simplified car model called the "box car" is considered. The geometry of the box car is simple but the flow field generated in the underhood region is complex, resembling somewhat the flow field under the hood of actual cars. This allows quick testing of CFD codes in their ability to simulate the underhood flow.

The geometry of the box car used in the analysis is shown in Figure 1. To allow easy modeling, the box car is designed to have planar surfaces with a Y-shaped engine block attached to the sides of the underhood by a shaft. Air enters the engine compartment through a grille hole and exits at four holes located on the hood floor. Exit flow through the floor holes allows interaction of the underhood flow with the flow in the underbody region of the box car. Although the geometry is simple, the box car has features essential to generate a complex flow similar in many ways to that found in real cars in terms of separation and recirculations.

Governing Equations:

The Reynolds averaged equations for incompressible turbulent flow with the standard k-ε model for turbulence closure [10] along with the energy equation are solved by applying a

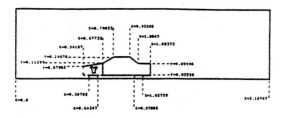

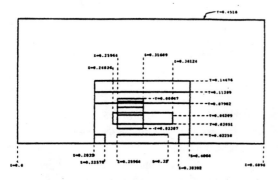

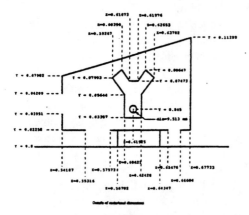

Figure 1. Geometry of the simplified box car

finite element method. The body force term in the z-momentum equation consists of the buoyancy term and all other body forces are assumed zero.

Boundary conditions:

Uniform velocity and temperature conditions are imposed at the inlet. The wind tunnel walls are treated as slip surfaces at constant ambient temperature. All other surfaces are treated as no slip adiabatic walls except the engine block which is considered to have a constant temperature. k and ε values are prescribed at the inlet. Logarithmic law of the wall is imposed for the boundary elements of no-slip walls. Natural or stress free boundary conditions are automatically imposed at the exit because of the finite element formulation. The inlet Reynolds number with respect to the car width (0.2032 m) is $2.4e^{05}$.

Numerical model:

The standard Galerkin formulation of the governing equations leads to the following discrete algebraic system:

$$[k]\{x\}=\{b\},$$

where k is the coefficient matrix and x is the vector of unknowns (u,v,w,t,k and ε) and b is the right hand side vector. The system is nonlinear because of the contributions from the convective terms in the governing equations. The algebraic system is solved using a segregated approach [11,12] with iterative linear equation solvers for both symmetric (Conjugate Residual Method) and nonsymmetric (Conjugate Gradient Squared Method) systems.

Results and discussions:

Figure 2 shows a typical mesh used in the analysis with 8-noded (tri-linear) brick elements with 144,000 nodes. Under the hood in the engine compartment, the mesh is made finer in an attempt to capture the details of the flow. Three mesh sizes with 118,100 nodes, 134,100 nodes and 144,000 nodes were studied and it was found that the calculated flow rates through the grille and the floor holes for the two finer meshes differed by less than 1 percent for each hole indicating grid independent solution within one percent of the average flow rate.

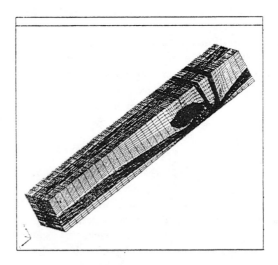

Figure 2. Typical mesh used for the box car in a wind tunnel

Figure 3a shows the velocity field across the central plane which cuts through the domain vertically from the center of the inlet to the center of the exit. Figure 3b shows the blow up of the velocity in the underhood region. Well defined recirculation regions can be observed in the upper left and lower right corners. This pattern matches with experimental data shown in Figure 3c. The lower left side exhibits slightly different flow pattern compared to the experimental data. However, since the flow is three dimensional in general, any recirculation bubble should first be confirmed with flow visualization (numerical) or velocity plots in other planes. The back side of the engine block does not seem to get good flow for cooling.

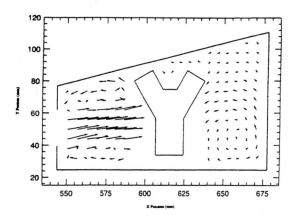

Figure 3c. Experimental velocity field across the central plane

Figure 4a shows the velocity vectors across a vertical plane passing through the centers of the driver side floor holes. The flow field is seen to be very different from the experimental data shown in Figure 4b. Results with other CFD codes [1] which are not presented here, also indicated similar differences with the experimental data for the plane under consideration. The experiment was recently repeated under carefully controlled conditions and the new experimental results indicate that the numerical results are accurate. Because of 'proprietary' reasons, the new experimental data could not be shown here. The computed flow field appears reasonable with flow going out through the floor exits.

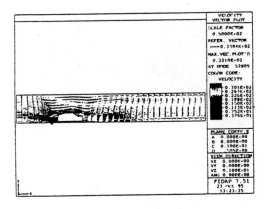

Figure 3a. Velocity field across the central plane

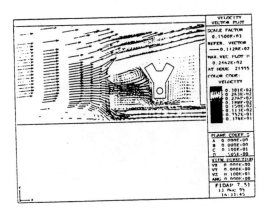

Figure 3b. Velocity field in the underhood region

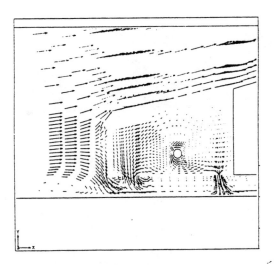

Figure 4a. Computed velocity field on the plane through the driver's side holes

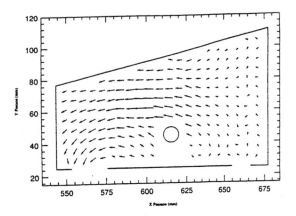

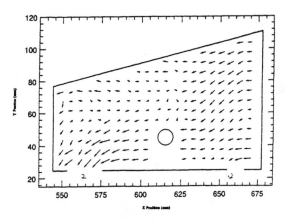

Figure 5b. Experimental velocity vectors on the
plane through the passenger's side hole

Figure 4b. Experimental velocity field on the
plane through the driver's side holes

Figure 5a shows the velocity vectors across a
vertical plane passing through the centers of the
passenger side floor holes. Again as with the
driver side plane, the computed flow field does
not match the old experimental data shown in
Figure 5b. The computed velocity field
resembles one shown in Figure 4a for the driver
side plane.

Figures 6 and 7 show the pressure distributions
across the central plane and the plane through
the floor holes on the driver side. The pressure is
maximum near the grille area because of the
impinging flow as to be expected. Pressure is
more or less uniform in the underhood region
except for near the floor holes and the hood
walls where high gradients are seen.

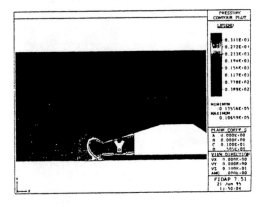

Figure 6. Pressure distribution across the central
plane

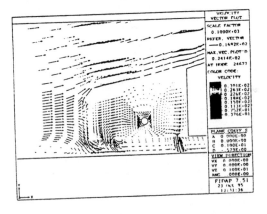

Figure 5a. Computed velocity vectors on the
plane through the passenger's side
holes

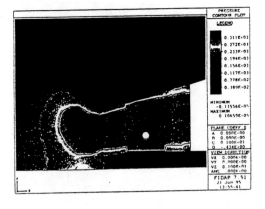

Figure 7. Pressure distribution across the plane
through the driver's side holes

Figure 8 shows the temperature distribution across the central plane. The convective heat transfer to the outgoing air at the floor exits is not as pronounced as one would like to see and can be increased by increasing the flow into the engine compartment.

Figure 9 shows the computed flow rates through the four floor holes for the three different mesh sizes compared with the measured values. The difference between the flow rates for the two finer meshes is within one percent. On the other hand the (old) experimental flow rates differ from the computed ones significantly and again this may be due to experimental conditions being susceptible. The computed flow rates are seen to match the recent new experimental data very well (within 5 percent).

The CFD predicted flow patterns match fairly well with the newly obtained experimental data. The flow rates through the underhood openings predicted by CFD also match well with the latest experimental data.

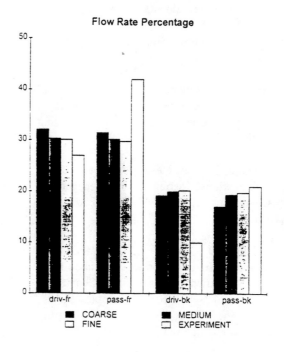

Figure 9. Computed flow rates through the floor holes along with the old measured values

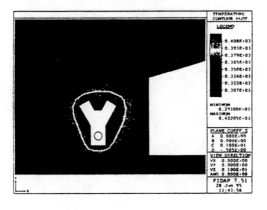

Figure 8. Temperature distribution across the central plane

Conclusions:

A simplified box car model is found to be suitable for quickly testing a CFD code.

CFD is a powerful tool for predicting velocity and temperature distribution in an underhood environment. CFD results present insight into the details of the flow field which can lead to design improvements.

References:

1. Dhaubhadel, M. N., Kumar, K and Shih, T. S. "Evaluation of Commercial CFD Codes for Underhood Cooling," Ford VSCAE TMD Report, February 1995.

2. Aoki, K., Hanaoka, Y. and Hara, M., "Numerical Simulation of Three Dimensional Engine Compartment Air Flow in FWD Vehicles," SAE Paper No. 900086.

3. Katoh, N., Ogawa, T. and Kuriyama, T, "Numerical Simulation on the Three Dimensional Flow and Heat Transfer in the Engine Compartment," SAE Paper No. 910306.

4. Ninoyu, M., Kameyama, J., Doi, H. and Oka H., "Prediction Method of Cooling System Performance," SAE Paper No. 930146.

5. Ashmawey, M., Berneburg, H., Hartung, W. and Werner, F., "A Numerical   Evaluation of the Thermal Effects of the New V6 Engine on the Underhood   Environment of the 1993 Opel Vectra," SAE Paper No. 930295.

6. Shimonosono, H, Shibata, Y. and Fujitani, K., "Optimization of the Heat Flow Distribution in the Engine Compartment," SAE Paper No. 930883.

7. Bauer, W., Ehrenreich H. and Reister H., "Design of Cooling Systems with   Computer Simulation and Underhood Flow Analysis using CFD," IMechE Paper No. C496/042/95.

8. Winnard, D., Venkateswaran, G. and Barry, R. E., "Underhood Thermal   Management by Controlling Air Flow," SAE Paper No. 951013.

9. Shack, D., Bernal, L. amd Shih, G., "Experimental Investigation of Underhood Flow in a Simplified Automobile Geometry," Proceedings of 'Separated and Complex Flows', Joint ASME/JSME Fluids Engineering Conference, Hilton Head Island, SC 1995.

10. Dhaubhadel, M. N.,"Oscillating Flows in Fluid Tuned Vibration Isolators," Advances in Finite Element Analysis in Fluid Dynamics 1992, Eds. M. N. Dhaubhadel, M. S. Engelman and J. N. Reddy, ASME FED-Vol 137, 1992.

11. Haroutunian, V., Engelman, M. S. and Hasbani, I.,"Three Segregated Finite Element Solution Algorithms for the Numerical Solution of Incompressible Flow   Problems," Advances in Finite Element Analysis in Fluid Dynamics 1991, Eds. M. N. Dhaubhadel, M. S. Engelman and J. N. Reddy, ASME FED-Vol 123, 1991.

12. Engelman, M. S., FIDAP User's Manual, Version 7.5, Fluid Dynamics International, 1995.

254

FED-Vol. 238, 1996 Fluids Engineering Division Conference
Volume 3
ASME 1996

MATHEMATICAL MODELING OF TWO-PHASE FLUID FLOW IN VACUUM-DEGASSING OF STEEL

Bulent Kocatulum
Bethlehem Steel Corporation
Research Department
Bethlehem, Pennsylvania 18016
U.S.A.
Telephone : 610-694-2319
Fax : 610-694-2981

ABSTRACT

A three-dimensional, steady state model of the continuous-circulation vacuum-degassing process has been developed. The model consists of two vessels : the ladle which holds the steel and the degasser which is dipped into the steel bath in the ladle through its two cylindrical snorkels. When vacuum is applied in the degasser the steel rises into the degasser through the snorkels since the bath surface in the ladle is exposed to the atmosphere. The circulation of steel through the degasser is obtained by injecting argon gas into one of the snorkels.

The governing two-phase flow equations were solved using the commercial program FIDAP. The Lagrangian approach was used for the flow of dispersed gas phase. The model was used to investigate the effects of gas flow rate, injection port location and bubble size on the flow field and on the circulation rate of steel. Comparisons to actual circulation rates showed good agreement.

NOMENCLATURE

C_D - Drag coefficient
D_b - Bubble diameter
V_b - Volume of bubble
V_E - Volume of element
f - Body force
g - Acceleration due to gravity
k - Turbulent kinetic energy
p - Pressure
q - Argon flow rate
t - Time
t_t - Turnover time

u - Liquid velocity
u_b - Bubble velocity

Greek Symbols

Δ - Height of near-wall element
ε - Dissipation rate of turbulent kinetic energy
ϕ - Source term for momentum equation
κ - Von Karman constant
μ - Molecular viscosity
μ_t - Turbulent viscosity
ρ - Liquid density
ρ_b - Bubble density
τ - Bubble relaxation time

INTRODUCTION

The "RH", or continuous-circulation, vacuum degassing process is employed in the steel industry to reduce dissolved gases, and reach ultra-low carbon levels in liquid steel which are required for high formability of the final product.

As illustrated in Fig. 1, this vacuum degassing process involves two refractory-lined vessels: the ladle which holds the molten steel, and the degasser in which pressures as low as 1 torr are applied. The degasser has two snorkels extending from its bottom. Steel flows up into the degasser and then back down through these snorkels.

At the start of the process the degasser is lowered into the liquid steel in the ladle until the snorkels are immersed to a sufficient depth. A low pressure is then applied in the degasser. Since the ladle surface is exposed to atmospheric pressure steel rises into the lower part of the degasser. Argon gas is injected into one of the

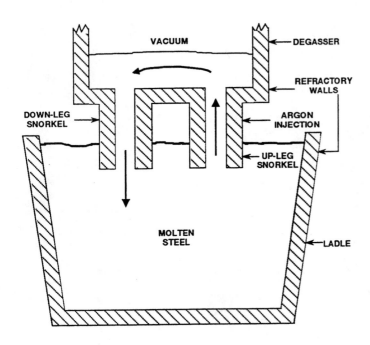

Figure 1. Schematic of Vacuum-Degassing Process

snorkels (the up-leg snorkel) through a series of ports. This causes the steel to flow upwards through the up-leg snorkel, circulate through the degasser and return to the ladle through the other snorkel (the down-leg snorkel). The process continues until the carbon and hydrogen contents are reduced to acceptable levels.

The efficiency of the degassing process depends on the circulation rate of steel. As such, it has been the subject of numerous investigations. Nakanishi et. al. (1975a) used a radioactive tracer to obtain a correlation between the circulation rate and argon flow rate. Seshadri and De Souza Costa (1986) injected nitrogen into a water model in their experiments and concluded that the circulation rate increases as the gas injection ports are lowered towards the bottom of the up-leg snorkel. Numerical investigations were undertaken to study the mixing in the ladle during degassing using two-dimensional (Nakanishi et. al., 1975b; Sano and Mori, 1983) and three-dimensional (Tsujino et. al., 1989; Szatkowski and Tsai, 1991) models.

In the present study a three-dimensional model was developed to simulate the recirculating flow in the degasser operated at Bethlehem Steel Corporation's Burns Harbor plant. The model was used to investigate the effects of argon flow rate on the steel circulation rate and the level of hydrodynamic activity in the entire system.

MATHEMATICAL FORMULATION

The flow of molten steel in the vacuum-degassing process is inherently three-dimensional and turbulent. The Reynolds number based on the snorkel diameter is of the order of 10^6. The free surface in the vacuum vessel is significantly deformed by the erupting bubbles. The current numerical model was developed based on the following assumptions:

- Heat transfer effects are negligible, thus the entire system is isothermal.

- The flow is steady, turbulent, incompressible and Newtonian.

- The free surfaces at liquid-air and liquid-vacuum interfaces remain flat.

- Monosize spherical bubbles are assumed to form at a distance from the wall.

- Bubble growth and coalescence are neglected.

The system has a vertical plane of symmetry passing through the centerlines of both snorkels. Thus, only one-half of the system is modeled.

Liquid Phase Equations

Conservation of mass:

$$\nabla \bullet \mathbf{u} = 0 \tag{1}$$

Conservation of momentum:

$$\rho\,(\mathbf{u} \bullet \nabla \mathbf{u}) = -\nabla p + \rho\,\mathbf{f} + \nabla \bullet \{(\mu + \mu_t)\,[\mathbf{u} + (\nabla \mathbf{u})^T]\} + \phi \tag{2}$$

where f is the body force, ϕ is the momentum transfer from the gas phase, and μ_t is the turbulent (or eddy) viscosity defined by :

$$\mu_t = c_\mu\,\rho\,k^2 / \varepsilon \tag{3}$$

where k and ε are the turbulent kinetic energy and its rate of dissipation, respectively, and are obtained from the solutions of the well-known transport equations of the k - ε model (Launder and Spalding, 1974) with the following standard constants :

$$c_\mu = 0.09 \qquad \sigma_k = 1.00 \qquad \sigma_\varepsilon = 1.30 \qquad c_1 = 1.44 \qquad c_2 = 1.92$$

Gas Phase Equations

The motion of each bubble is obtained by solving the Lagrangian trajectory equation under the influence of interphase drag and buoyancy forces, which can be written as :

$$\rho_b\,(\,d\mathbf{u}_b / dt\,) = \rho_b\,(\mathbf{u} - \mathbf{u}_b\,) / \tau + (\rho_b - \rho\,)\mathbf{g} \tag{4}$$

The subscript b refers to bubbles and τ is the bubble relaxation time, defined by :

$$\tau = 4\,\rho_b\,D_b^2 / (3\,\mu\,C_D\,Re_b\,) \tag{5}$$

where Re_b is the bubble Reynolds number defined by :

$$Re_b = D_b \mid u - u_b \mid \rho / \mu \qquad (6)$$

The drag coefficient is obtained from the power-law model:

$$C_D = 24 \{ 1 + 0.15 (Re_b)^{.687} \} / Re_b \qquad (7)$$

Interphase Momentum Exchange

The momentum exchange between the gas phase and the liquid phase is quantified by means of the Particle Source in Cell (PSIC) method (Crowe et. al., 1977). The trajectories of bubbles are combined into the source term for the momentum equation of the liquid phase. The continuum and the Lagrangian equations are solved consecutively. The process of iteration is continued until equilibrium is attained between the solutions of the two phases.

If n_j is the number of bubbles per unit time traversing the j'th trajectory and δt_j is the residence time of a particle on the j'th trajectory with respect to element E, then the j'th contribution to the momentum transfer source to element E is:

$$\phi(E) = (n_j / V_E) \int_{\delta t_j} \{ 3\mu C_D Re_b V_b (u - u_b) / (4D_b^2) \} dt \qquad (8)$$

where V_E is the volume of the element and V_b is the volume of the bubble.

Boundary Conditions

Zero velocities are applied on all solid boundaries. The normal component of velocity is set to zero on the plane of symmetry and on both free surfaces. Stress free boundary conditions are applied to the remaining variables on the free surfaces. The near-wall modeling methodology (FIDAP 7.0 Theory Manual, 1993) is used to model the effects of viscosity on the turbulence field in the viscous sublayer along the walls. The reason for using the near-wall methodology is that the standard k-ε model is of the high Reynolds number type and therefore cannot be used in the near-wall regions. This approach employs a single layer of elements along solid boundaries in which specialized shape functions, based on universal near-wall profiles, are used to capture the sharp variations of the mean flow variables. The k and ε equations are not solved in the layer of near-wall elements, instead the variation of turbulent viscosity is modeled using van Driest's mixing-length approach. The following boundary conditions for k and ε are applied at the top of special near-wall elements:

$$\partial k / \partial n = 0 \qquad (9)$$

$$\varepsilon = \{ k (c_\mu)^{0.5} \}^{1.5} / (\kappa \Delta) \qquad (10)$$

where κ is the von Karman constant with a value of 0.41 and Δ is the element height.

The gas bubbles are released into the solution domain at eight prescribed locations near the up-leg snorkel wall with zero initial velocity. The bubbles are assumed to leave the system when they reach the free surface in the vacuum vessel.

Solution Procedure

The computational domain is discretized into a finite element mesh, shown in Fig. 2, consisting of 16,961 nodes and 14516 eight-node linear brick elements. The mesh is graded so as to make element size smaller along the walls where steep gradients of solution variables are expected. The governing equations are solved by using version 7.51 of the commercial finite element code FIDAP. The segregated algorithm (FIDAP 7.0 Theory Manual, 1993) was used to solve the nonlinear system of matrix equations arising from the finite element discretization of flow equations. In this approach each conservation equation is solved separately in a sequential manner. Since the formation of a global system matrix is avoided, the storage requirements of the segregated approach are substantially less than that of the fully-coupled solution algorithm.

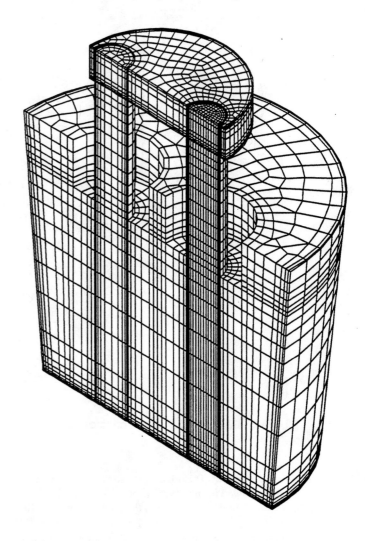

Figure 2. The Finite Element Mesh of the Ladle-Degasser System

Table 1. Dimensions and Material Properties

Ladle Base Diameter	3.82 m
Ladle Side Wall Angle	5°
Liquid Height in Ladle	3.44 m
Snorkel Inner Diameter	0.56 m
Snorkel Outer Diameter	1.27 m
Snorkel Penetration into Ladle	0.66 m
Degasser Diameter	2.27 m
Liquid Height in Degasser	4.88 m
Steel Density	7000 kg/m³
Steel Viscosity	0.00385 kg/m-s
Argon Density (@ 1 atm and 1867 K)	0.26 kg/m³

RESULTS AND DISCUSSION

Table 1 summarizes the geometric dimensions and material properties. Figure 3 shows the computed bubble trajectories. Bubbles are released into the computational domain from 8 ports around the circumference of the up-leg snorkel on a staggered arrangement at two vertical locations. The effect of liquid phase turbulence on the bubble trajectories is neglected. The trajectories are bent near the free surface due to the turning liquid flow. Figure 4 presents the velocity vectors for the flow field computed under the base conditions. It is seen that the highest velocities occur close to the up-leg snorkel wall where the bubble trajectories are located.

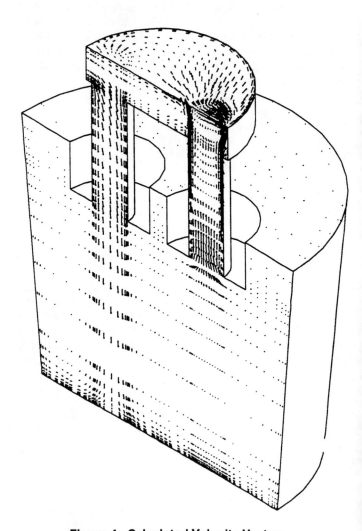

Figure 4. Calculated Velocity Vectors

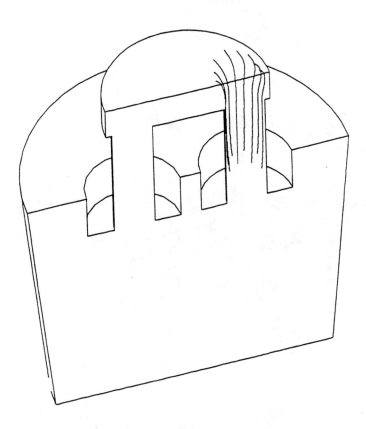

Figure 3. Calculated Bubble Trajectories

Relaxation factors of 0.15-0.20 and streamline upwinding technique were employed to maintain numerical stability. Iterations are continued until the relative change in the norm of each solution variable between two consecutive iterations was less than 10^{-3}. Number of iterations to reach convergence was in the range of 300-600. The computation time was approximately 132 CPU seconds per iteration on a DEC Alpha 200/233 Station.

Parameters Influencing the Circulation Rate

In actual operation, the argon jet injected into the steel disintegrates into bubbles after a short distance of penetration. Since the injection of the gas jet into the liquid bath could not be simulated, a parametric study was carried out by varying the normal distance from the wall at which the bubbles are released into the computational domain. Then computed circulation rates are compared to the range experienced at the Burns Harbor plant. As shown in Fig. 5, when the bubbles are released at a distance of 25 mm from the wall the resulting circulation rate agrees very well with the plant experience. The circulation rate starts to decrease after reaching a peak value at a bubble release distance of 100 mm, suggesting that the efficiency of the momentum transfer from the bubbles to the liquid phase has a maximum and starts to drop as the bubble trajectories converge toward the centerline of the snorkel and get closer to each other.

In practice the circulation rate is controlled by the rate of gas injection. This is illustrated in Fig. 6 where the circulation rates computed by the model as a function of gas injection rate are compared to those calculated using the correlation by Kuwabara et. al. (1987). The agreement is excellent at lower gas flow rates. It should be noted that the above-mentioned correlation was developed based on data at flow rates lower than 2 Nm^3/min which helps explain the gradual divergence of the two curves with increasing gas flow rate.

The effect of bubble diameter was investigated and found to be insignificant regarding the circulation rate as well as the mean values of the speed and the turbulent kinetic energy, as shown in Table 2. This indicates that although the drag force is higher in the case of larger bubbles, it is balanced by the much larger number of smaller bubbles for a given gas flow rate.

The effect of height at which the gas injection ports are located on the up-leg snorkel wall was also investigated. As tabulated in Table 3, the circulation rate as well as the mean values of the speed and the turbulent kinetic energy increase as the ports are moved towards the bottom of the snorkel. This is in agreement with the conclusion of Seshadri and De Souza Costa (1986) and can be directly related to the fact that more time is available for momentum transfer before the bubbles escape the system.

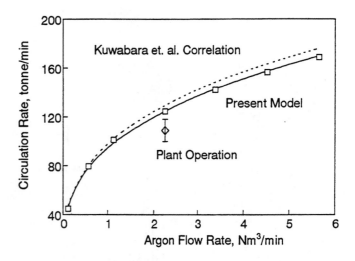

Figure 6.   Comparison of Model Results to Kuwabara et. al. Correlation

Table 2. Effect of Bubble Diameter

Bubble Diameter, mm	Circulation Rate, tonne/min	Speed*, m/s	Turbulent Kinetic Energy*, kg-m^2/s^2
4	124.4	0.2030	0.0240
5	124.6	0.2029	0.0239
8	126.8	0.2051	0.0240
10	125.6	0.2031	0.0237
12	124.6	0.2010	0.0231
15	123.7	0.1993	0.0224

* Volume-averaged mean value.

Table 3. Effect of Injection Port Location

Port Locations*, m	Circulation Rate, tonne/min	Speed*, m/s	Turbulent Kinetic Energy*, kg-m^2/s^2
2.8 and 3.0	141.9	0.2302	0.0292
3.2 and 3.4	124.6	0.2029	0.0239
3.6 and 3.8	106.9	0.1738	0.0192
4.0 and 4.2	73.5	0.1209	0.0118

* Snorkel bottom is at 2.78 m.

* Volume-averaged mean value.

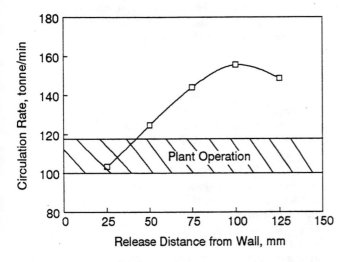

Figure 5.   Variation of Circulation Rate with Bubble Release Distance

Flow in the Ladle

One of the critical issues in the vacuum-degassing process is the degree of mixing in the ladle. Figure 7 shows the path lines for fluid particles which were initially located across the cross-section of the up-leg snorkel near its bottom. It is observed that after circulating through the degasser the stream coming out of the down-leg snorkel

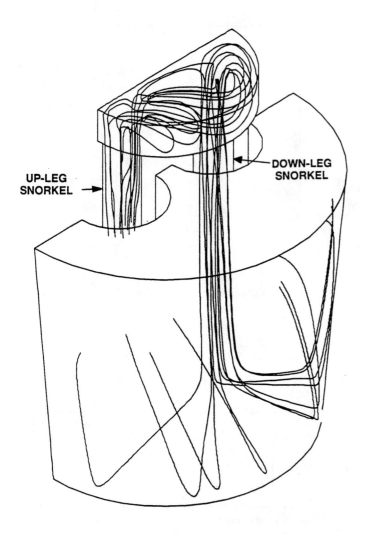

UP-LEG SNORKEL

DOWN-LEG SNORKEL

Figure 7. Calculated Paths for a Series of Fluid Particles Initially Located near the Bottom of Up-leg Snorkel

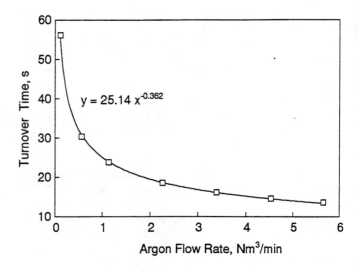

$$y = 25.14\ x^{-0.362}$$

Figure 8.   Variation of Turnover Time with Argon Flow Rate

$$t_t = 25.14\ *\ q^{-0.362} \qquad (12)$$

where t_t is the turnover time in seconds and q is the argon flow rate in Nm³/min.

CONCLUSION

A three-dimensional two-phase flow model of the vacuum-degasser operated at Bethlehem Steel Corporation's Burns Harbor plant was developed to simulate the recirculating flow of steel driven by argon injection. The circulation rate of steel calculated from the flow field agreed well with the plant experience and also with experimental investigations reported in literature.   The results indicate that the two-phase flow model proves to be a useful tool in simulating real-world processes. As a consequence of the encouraging results, the model is currently being used to study alternate potential designs for the vacuum-degassing process.

REFERENCES

Crowe, C. T., Sharma, M. P., and Stock, D. E., 1977, "The Particle-Source-In Cell (PSI-Cell) Model for Gas-Droplet Flows", *ASME Journal of Fluids Engineering,* Vol. 99, pp. 325-332.

Kuwabara, T., Mori, K., Saitou, Y., Mimura, M., Tanaka, T., and Umezawa, K., 1987, "Measurement and Estimation of Circulation Flow Rate during RH Treatment", *Transactions of The Iron and Steel Institute of Japan,* Vol. 27, No. 8, p. B202.

Launder, B. E., and Spalding, D. B., 1974, "The Numerical Computation of Turbulent Flow", *Computational Methods in Applied Mechanics and Engineering,* Vol. 3, pp. 269-289.

Nakanishi, K., Szekely, J., and Chang, C. W., 1975a, "Experimental and Theoretical Investigation of of Mixing Phenomena in the RH-Vacuum Process", *Ironmaking and Steelmaking,* Vol. 2, pp. 115-124.

hits the bottom of the ladle and moves radially outwards to the ladle wall, moves up along the wall and finally turns towards the up-leg snorkel. There is no evidence of by-pass flow between the snorkels which supports the conclusion reached by Tsujino et. al. (1987) who modeled the single-phase flow in the ladle by treating the snorkel openings as the inlet and the exit boundaries.

The most critical region in terms of mixing is that part of the ladle enclosed by the ladle wall, the free surface of the ladle, the snorkel walls and the horizontal plane passing through the bottom of the snorkels. The turnover time for the molten steel contained in this region is obtained by dividing the volume of the region by the flow rate of material into and out of the region. The turnover time is plotted as a function of argon flow rate in Fig. 8. The relationship between the two variables is quantified by the following correlation :

Nakanishi, K., Fuji, T. and Szekely, J., 1975b, "Possible Relationship Between Energy Dissipation and Agitation in Steel Processing Operations", *Ironmaking and Steelmaking,* Vol. 2, pp. 193-197.

Sano, M. and Mori, K., 1983, "Fluid Flow and Mixing Characteristics in a Gas-Stirred Molten Metal Bath", *Transactions of The Iron and Steel Institute of Japan,* Vol. 23, pp. 169-175.

Seshadri, V. and De Souza Costa, S. L., 1986, "Cold Model Studies of R. H. Degassing Process", *Transactions of The Iron and Steel Institute of Japan,* Vol. 26, pp. 133-138.

Szatkowski, M., and Tsai, M. C., 1991, "Turbulent Flow and Mixing Phenomena in RH Ladles: Effects of a Clogged Down-Leg Snorkel", *Iron and Steelmaker,* Vol. 18, No. 4 pp. 65-71.

Tsujino, R., Nakashima, J., Hirai, M., and Sawada, I., 1989, "Numerical Analysis of Molten Steel Flow in Ladle of RH Process", *ISIJ International,* Vol. 29, No. 7, pp. 589-595.

FIDAP 7.0 Theory Manual, 1993, Fluid Dynamics International, Evanston, Illinois.

FED-Vol. 238, 1996 Fluids Engineering Division Conference
Volume 3
ASME 1996

NUMERICAL INVESTIGATION OF FREE CONVECTION HEAT TRANSFER IN VERTICAL CHANNELS WITH BACKWARD-FACING STEP

R. K. Sahoo*, A. Sarkar** and V. M. K. Sastri
Department of Mechanical Engineering
Indian Institute of Technology
Madras - 600 036

**Department of Mechanical Engineering
Jadavpur University
Calcutta - 700032

ABSTRACT

Free convective heat transfer for laminar, two dimensional flow in a vertical channel with a backward-facing step on the heated plate with isothermal boundary conditions has been numerically analyzed. The results compare favorably with the existing numerical results for a plane channel as well as for a backward-facing-step. The velocity distribution shows starved flow situations after the step for a Rayleigh number of 10^3 and higher for a step size of 50% of the plate spacing for asymmetric heating. For a step size of 25% of the plate spacing such situations were observed for Rayleigh numbers of more than 2000. Recirculation starts to disappear as the straight wall temperature approaches the inlet fluid temperature for a step size of 50% of the plate spacing.

INTRODUCTION

For every 10 $^{\circ}$C rise in temperature in electronic circuits there is a decrease in reliability by as much as 50%. It is essential therefore, to analyze the heat transfer as well as the fluid flow characteristics in electronic circuits for better thermal control [1]. Cooling by free convection in the vertical channel configuration is of interest in electronic packaging because of its simplicity and reliability.

A brief review of the literature on free convection in vertical channels with different boundary conditions is given by Peterson and Ortega (1990). Acharya and Jang (1988) have analyzed buoyancy-induced-convection heat transfer in a staggered vertical channel with boundary layer approximations. For a single vertical plate with protrusions like backward-facing step or a horizontal constriction, experimental results are reported by Misumi and Kitamura (1989, 1990). They found the flow to be three-dimensional when the sizes of the protrusions exceeds a certain limit. As far as practical situations are concerned, the electronic circuitry geometry is much more complex than to the simple plane channel geometries. To have accurate results for such complex flow situations, the analysis of 2-D elliptic flow and energy equations is required. For such situations very little information is available on buoyancy - assisted - flows (1985). An experimental study of natural convection by Sparrow and Ruiz (1988) provides correlations for Nusselt numbers for divergent, convergent and parallel channels. The effect of a semicircular obstruction on the average Nusselt number in a plane channel at different locations is given by Said and Krane (1990). Recently, separated flow has attracted a lot of attention for its significant influence on heat transfer performance of devices. Baek et al. (1990) through their experimental and numerical investigations showed that for mixed convection, starved flow situations are found when Rayleigh numbers exceed a certain value. Further, the flow becomes turbulent for higher values of Grashof numbers. A similar analysis with a backward-facing step is carried out by Lin et al. (1990) for mixed convection in buoyancy assisted conditions.

The present numerical study is concerned with a backward-facing step on one wall of a parallel plate

---

* Research Scholar, State University of New York at Stony Brook, Stony Brook, USA channel, with symmetric as well as asymmetric heating, for a Rayleigh number range of 10^2 to 10^4. A finite element primitive variable formulation with mass balance iterative scheme [10] is used to determine the velocity, temperature and average Nusselt number characteristics. The effect of different step sizes is considered.

MATHEMATICAL FORMULATION

The physical model is as shown in Fig. 1. For the analysis, considering the flow to be laminar, two-dimensional, incompressible, constant thermo-physical properties and Boussinesque approximations to be valid for free convection, the governing equations in non-dimensional form can be written as :

Equation of continuity:

$$\frac{\partial U}{\partial X} + \frac{\partial V}{\partial Y} = 0 \tag{1}$$

X-momentum equation:

$$U\frac{\partial U}{\partial X} + V\frac{\partial U}{\partial Y} = -\frac{\partial P}{\partial X} + \frac{1}{A}\left[\frac{\partial^2 U}{\partial X^2} + \frac{\partial^2 U}{\partial Y^2}\right] \tag{2}$$

Y-momentum equation:

$$U\frac{\partial V}{\partial X} + V\frac{\partial V}{\partial Y} = -\frac{\partial P}{\partial Y} + \frac{1}{A}\left[\frac{\partial^2 V}{\partial X^2} + \frac{\partial^2 V}{\partial Y^2}\right] + \theta \tag{3}$$

Energy equation:

$$U\frac{\partial \theta}{\partial X} + V\frac{\partial \theta}{\partial Y} = \frac{1}{A.Pr}\left[\frac{\partial^2 \theta}{\partial X^2} + \frac{\partial^2 \theta}{\partial Y^2}\right] \tag{4}$$

The non-dimensional parameters in the above equations are defined as

$$U = \frac{u}{u_0}, \quad V = \frac{v}{u_0}, \quad X = \frac{x}{s}, \quad Y = \frac{y}{s}$$

$$\theta = \frac{T-T_\alpha}{T_w-T_\alpha}, \quad P = \frac{p-p_\alpha}{\rho\, u_0^2}$$

u_0 = characteristic velocity = $\sqrt{\beta\,.g(T_w-T_\alpha)s}$,

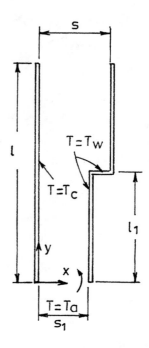

Fig. 1: Physical model considered for analysis

where $A = \sqrt{Gr_s} = \sqrt{Ra_s/Pr}$

Boundary conditions for the problem are specified as follows:

$$\left.\begin{array}{c} U = V = 0 \\ \\ \theta = \theta_c \end{array}\right\} \text{ for } X = 0 \text{ and } 0 \leq Y \leq L$$

$$\left.\begin{array}{c} U = V = 0 \\ \hline \theta = 1 \end{array}\right\} \begin{array}{l} \text{for } X = X_1 \text{ and } 0 < Y < L_1 \\ \text{for } X = 1 \text{ and } L_2 < Y \leq L \\ \text{for } 1 > X > X_1 \text{ and } Y = L_1 \end{array}$$

$$\left.\begin{array}{c} P = -0.5F^2 \\ V = F \\ \theta = 0 \end{array}\right\} \text{ for } 0 < X \leq 1 \text{ and } Y = 0, \text{ and}$$

$$P = 0.0 \qquad \text{for } 0 < X < 1 \text{ and } Y = L$$

where, $\quad X_1 = \frac{s_1}{s}, \quad L_1 = \frac{l_1}{s}$.

Assuming a uniform velocity at the inlet the pressure is calculated at the inlet by Bernoulli's equation: $p(0) = -0.5\rho u^2$, which in non-dimensional form becomes $-0.5\, F^2$, where F is the adjusted inlet average non-dimensional velocity which is taken care by iterative mass balance scheme[10]. Pressure is calculated based on Bernoulli's equation. At the outlet, though it is necessary to specify boundary conditions for velocity (U,V) and temperature, they are not explicitly enforced (except p=0). Boundary conditions for U,V and T are taken care of by natural boundary conditions.

The flow rate is not being fixed at the inlet. A flat velocity as an average velocity at inlet is assumed and is adjusted iteratively to match the conservation of mass, which is taken care of by iterative mass balance scheme for the inlet and outlet. Moreover the plate spacing is small enough to assume such a profile. It is also found from literature that the inlet velocity profile hardly affects the heat transfer rate.

The following values are considered for the analysis:

$$\left. \begin{array}{l} L_1 = 5.0 , \ X_1 = 0.9 \\ L_1 = 5.0 , \ X_1 = 0.75 \\ L_1 = 5.0 , \ X_1 = 0.5 \end{array} \right\} \text{with } L = 10 \text{ and } \theta_c = 0, 0.5, 1$$

For the plane channel problem all the boundary conditions remain the same. The calculation of the heat flux and the Nusselt number on the hot wall are determined as given below :

From energy balance,

$$-K \frac{\partial T}{\partial X}\Big|_{x=x_1(\text{say})} = h(T_w - T_a)$$

Applying this near the hot wall taking average for the whole channel length and non-dimensionalising :

$$\overline{Nu} = -\frac{1}{L} \left| \left[X_1 \int_0^{L_1} \left(\frac{\partial \theta}{\partial X} \right)_{x=x_1} dY + \int_{L_1}^{L} \left(\frac{\partial \theta}{\partial X} \right)_{x=1} dY \right] \right| \tag{5}$$

whereas, for the plane channel it is

$$\overline{Nu} = \frac{1}{L} \left| \int_o^L - \left(\frac{\partial \theta}{\partial X} \right)_{x=1} dy \right| \tag{6}$$

FINITE ELEMENT FORMULATION AND SOLUTION PROCEDURE

The solutions of the non-dimensional equations (1) to (4) are obtained by considering a finite element primitive variable formulation with an eight-noded quadratic quadrilateral, having four variables U,V,P and θ at the corner nodes while only U,V, and θ are considered at the intermediate

nodes to avoid the spurious pressure rise. The simultaneous equations are solved by Frontal Solver given by Hood (1976). As far as the solution technique is concerned, Newton-Raphson method is employed with the iteration form as given below:

$$\xi^{K+1} = \xi^K - [J]^{-1} R^K$$

where, K, is the iteration count and, R, is residual vector given by,

$$R = \left[R_u{}^T R_p{}^T R_v{}^T R_\theta{}^T \right]^T ,$$

$$\xi = \left[U^T P^T V^T \theta^T \right]^T \quad \text{and}$$

J, is the Jacobian Matrix $= [J] = \dfrac{\partial R}{\partial \xi^T}$

For the final results the residues are neglected when the largest of all the residues reaches a value of 5×10^{-5}

RESULTS AND DISCUSSION

Grid Independence

In order to make the results grid-independent both uniform and non-uniform grids (with finer meshes near the walls, entrance and exit region and the step) are considered. The maximum number of elements considered for final results are 300 because of computational limitations. The results are considered to be grid-independent when the maximum variation in the $\overline{Nu}$ is within $\pm 1 - 2\%$.

For backward-facing step problem the whole computational domain is divided into three sub-domains in order to discretize it into different elements. However, care is taken to match the element connectivities of the adjacent elements of different sub-domains.

Results are obtained for air (Pr = 0.71) for different sizes of backward-facing steps as well as for a plane channel with three different cold wall temperatures for a Rayleigh number range of 10^2 to 10^4.

For validation, the program was run for a plane channel problem for different values of Ra_s with Pr = 0.71. A comparison of the present results (plane channel) with the existing numerical as well as experimental results are shown in Fig. 2. The results for asymmetric heating show a variation of 6% (for $Ra^* = 10^3$) to 23% (for $Ra^* = 10$) from the

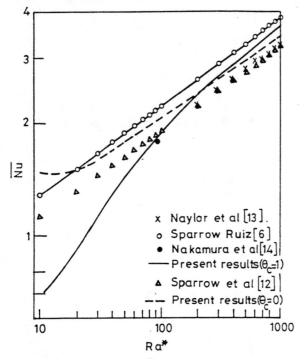

Fig. 2: Variation of $\overline{Nu}$ with Ra* for plane channel (comparison of the present results with existing results)

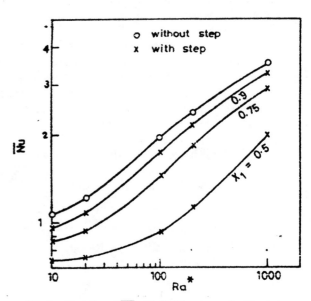

Fig. 4: Variation of $\overline{Nu}$ with Ra* for step and without step, $\theta_c = 0.5$

experimental correlations given by Sparrow et al. (1984). However for symmetric heating the present results are found to agree well with the experimental correlations by Sparrow and Ruiz (1988) and numerical results by Naylor et al.(1991) and Nakamura et al. (1982).

Heat Transfer Rates

The heat transfer rate can be compared by calculating $\overline{Nu}$ as given in equations 5 and 6. To compare the results with those for plane channel,

Ra* is considered instead of Ra$_s$. The Figs. 3,4 and 5 show that, though there is a proportionate drop in $\overline{Nu}$ (34 to 36%) for higher Ra* (10^2 to 10^3), for Bf. 905$_0$ the drop is only 18% for lower Ra* (10 to 20). However for $\theta_c = 0.5$ and 1.0 the $\overline{Nu}$ has more drop (about 58% for Ra* = 10 and Bf. 505$_1$). This shows $\overline{Nu}$ is dependent on $\left| \frac{\partial \theta}{\partial X} \right|$, plate spacing, and plate spacing before the step. Further because of starved flow situation (with $\theta_c = 0$), more air flows near the hot wall, thus the cooling of the hot plate remains unaffected. Smaller values of $\overline{Nu}$ are obtained for symmetric heating and lower Ra*,

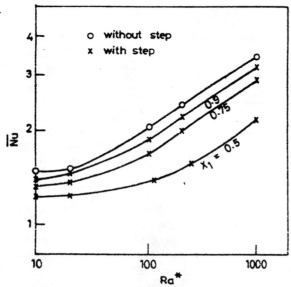

Fig. 3: Variation of with $\overline{Nu}$ with Ra* for step and without step $\theta_c = 0.0$

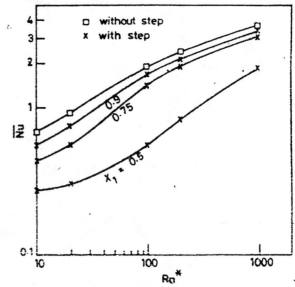

Fig. 5: Variation of $\overline{Nu}$ with Ra* for step and without step $\theta_c = 1.0$

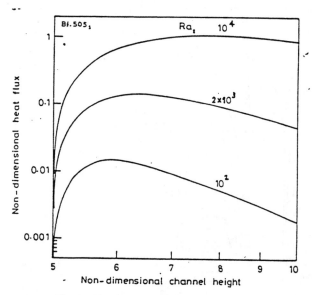

Fig. 6: Variation of local heat flux with channe
height after step

because of the rise of the average fluid temperature and low flow rate compared to higher Ra* cases. For Ra* of 10 and 20 the variation in $\overline{Nu}$ is very small as the step size increases irrespective of the cold wall temperature. It is also found that the portion ahead of the step can be considered independent of the portion on the downstream side of the step. The behaviour of the local heat flux (non-dimensional) near the hot wall after the step shown in Fig. 6 illustrates that, with decreasing Ra_s, there is a drop

in heat flux though initially it increases. For Ra_s = 100 and 200, the values are very small. (not shown in figure).

Temperature and Velocity Distributions

The isotherms shown in Figs. 7 to 9, indicate that for asymmetric heating the temperature distribution is linear towards the outlet irrespective of the step size. For symmetric heating, however, with the increase in step size, the fluid attains maximum temperature within a small height. For the case of Bf. 505_1, it is found that all the isotherms 0.1 to 0.9 are confined to the region before the step. This type of behaviour is also found for other Ra*.

The velocity distributions given in Fig. 10 shows, for Bf. 905_0 no recirculation zone either over the step or near the cold wall. In fact, the maximum velocity occurs near the hot wall when results are compared to the symmetric heating case. The flow is developing throughout. The difference in V_{max} values at different Y-values shows a decreasing trend with the increase of the step size. A study of the case of Bf. 505_0 shows a prominent zone of reversed flow near the cold plate where absolute velocity is negative. It is further noticed that for Bf. 505_1, the zone of recirculation is more above the backward-facing step compared to asymmetric heating. With θ_c or step size approaching zero this zone starts vanishing, thus for step size = 0 no such phenomena are found. (comparable with the case

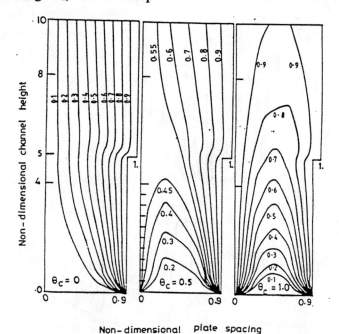

Fig. 7: Isotherms for θ_c = 0, 0.5, 1.0 step position 0.9 5

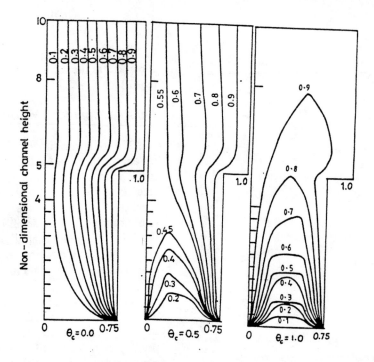

Fig. 8: Isotherms for $\theta_c = 0, 0.5, 1.0$ step position 0.75, 5

of a plane channel). An analysis by Lin et al. [9] shows such a behaviour with mixed condition. This phenomenon is more prominent for $Ra_s = 10^4$ (Not shown in figure). The disappearance of the zone of recirculation above the backward-facing step and appearance of a zone of separation near the cold wall with θc approaching zero has been described as the shifting of main zone of recirculation from hot wall to cold wall. Such phenomenon with a very small

magnitude is also observed even with $Ra_s < 10^3$ for Bf . 505_o.

The following inferences can be drawn based on the above results . For steps of different sizes at the middle of the channel a smaller zone of recirculation appears above the step for larger step sizes and symmetric heating. For smaller step sizes, the zone of recirculation which would have occurred is counterbalanced by the small horizontal

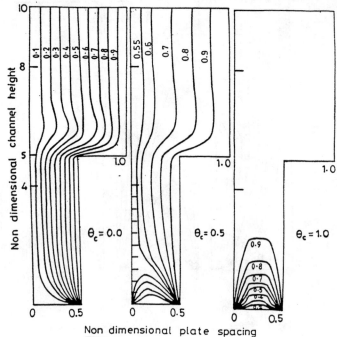

Fig. 9: Isotherms for $\theta_c = 0.0$, 1.0 step position 0.5, 5

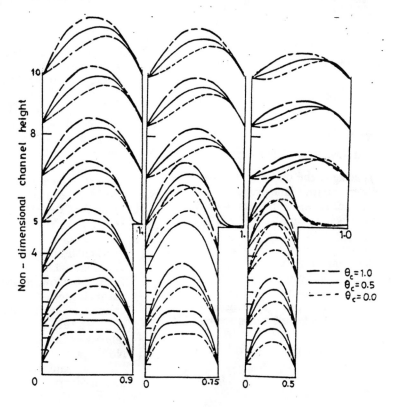

Fig. 10: Non-dimensional velocity (abs.) at different locations

heated step, whereas for larger step sizes the heat transfer from the step is not enough to do so. For asymmetric heating, reversed flow is found near the cold wall.

CONCLUSION

From the solutions of the Navier-Stokes and energy equations for a vertical channel with a backward-facing step it can be concluded that :

For higher Ra*, (10^2 to 10^3) there is a proportionate drop in $\overline{Nu}$, for a channel with a backward-facing step compared to plane channel with asymmetric heating result. With the increase in step size or θ_c (from 0 to 1) there is more drop in $\overline{Nu}$ from plane channel results for lower Ra* compared to higher Ra*.

The zone of recirculation becomes more prominent for symmetric heating compared to asymmetric heating or for more temperature difference between the walls.

The zone of recirculation starts shifting towards the plane wall for larger temperature differences (asymmetric heating) between the plates, thus

approaching a case of starved flow situation for asymmetric heating.

The starved flow situation is more prominent as the step size increases or for higher Rayleigh numbers when fluid is drawn in from the top.

NOMENCLATURE

Bf.905	Backward-facing step at (0.90,5)
Bf.755	Backward-facing step at (0.75,5)
Bf.505	Backward-facing step at (0.50,5)
F	Non-dimensional adjusted inlet velocity in Y direction at Y = 0, u/u$_o$
Gr$_s$	Grashof Number, $\dfrac{s^3 g \beta (T_w - T\alpha)}{\nu^2}$
h	Heat Transfer Coefficient
k	Fluid Thermal Conductivity
l	Plate or channel height
l$_1$	Position of backward facing step from the bottom end
L	Non-dimensional plate or channel height
L$_1$	Non-dimensional backward-facing step position
$\overline{Nu}$	Average Nusselt number on the hot wall
Nu$_L$	Local Nusselt number
p	Pressure
pα	Ambient Pressure

P	Nondimensional pressure, $\dfrac{p - p_\alpha}{\rho\, u_0^2}$
Pr	Prandtl number $\dfrac{\nu}{\alpha}$
Ra	Rayleigh number, Pr. Gr_s
Ra*	Modified Rayleigh number, $\dfrac{Ra_s}{L}$
s	Plate spacing at the outlet for backward facing step and for plane channel
s_1	Plate spacing at the inlet for the backward facing step
T	Fluid temperature
T_w	Hot wall temperature
T_α	Inlet fluid temperature
T_c	Cold wall temperature
u,v	x,y component velocities
X	Non-dimensional plate spacing at the outlet for the backward-facing step and for plane channel
X_1	Non-dimensional plate spacing at the inlet for the backward-facing step
Y	Non-dimensional channel or plate height
u_0	Characteristic velocity, $\sqrt{\beta \cdot g (T_w - T_\alpha) \cdot s}$
U,V	Non-dimensional x,y component velocities
x,y	x,y coordinates
X,Y	Non-dimensional x and y coordinates

Greek Symbols

α	Thermal diffusivity
β	Thermal expansion coefficient of fluid
θ	Non-dimensional temperature
θ_w	Non-dimensional hot wall temperature
θ_c	Non-dimensional cold wall temperature
ν	Kinetic viscosity of fluid
ρ	Density of fluid

Subscripts

α	Ambient condition
w	Hot wall condition
c	Cold wall condition
o	Non-dimensional cold wall temperature is 0
5	Non-dimensional cold wall temperature is 0.5
1	Non-dimensional cold wall temperature is 1.0

REFERENCES

1. G. P. Peterson, A. Ortega, 1990, Thermal control of electronic equipment and devices, Advances in Heat Transfer, Academic press, Vol 20.

2. S. Acharya, D. S. Jang, 1988, Buoyancy-induced-convection Heat Transfer in a Staggered Vertical Channel, Num. Heat Trans., Vol.13, pp 515-526.

3. T. Misumi, K. Kitamura, 1989, Natural convection heat transfer in the separation region of a backward-facing step, Heat Trans. Jap. Res., Vol.18, No.1, pp 32-44.

4. T. Misumi, K. Kitamura, 1990, Natural convection heat transfer from a vertical heated plate with a horizontal partition plate, Heat Trans. Jap. Res., Vol.19, No.3, pp 57-72.

5. W. Aung, Y. Yener, 1985, Research directions in natural convection Natural Convection Fundamentals and Applications Hemisphere Washington D.C.

6. E. M. Sparrow, R. Ruiz, 1988, Experiments on natural convection in divergent vertical channels and correlations of divergent, convergent, and parallel-channel Nusselt numbers, Int. Jl. Heat Mass Trans., Vol.31, No.11, pp 2197-2205.

7. S. A. M. said, R. J. Krane, 1990, An analytical and experimental investigation of natural convection heat transfer in vertical channels with a single obstruction, Int. Jl. Heat Mass Trans., Vol.33 ,No. 6, pp 1121-1134.

8. B. J. Baek, B. F. Palaski, T. S. Chen, 1990, Mixed convection in an asymmetrically heated vertical parallel duct flow, Proc. of the 9th. Int. Heat Trans. Conf. Jerusalem, Vol.2, pp 369-374.

9. J. T. Lin, B. F. Armaly, T. S. Chen, 1990, Mixed convection in buoyancy-assisting, vertical backward-facing step flows, Int. Jl. Heat Mass Trans., Vol.33, No.10, pp 2121-2132.

10. R. K. Sahoo, A. Sarkar, V. M. K. Sastri, 1991, Free convective flow in a vertical channel - A finite element study, Proc. of the 7th Int Conf. for Num. Meth. in Laminar and Turb. Flow, Vol-VII, part-I, pp 155-164.

11. P. Hood, 1976, Frontal solution program for unsymmetric matrices, Int. Jl. Num. Meth. in Engg., Vol.10, pp 379-399.

12. E. M. Sparrow, G. M. Chrysler, L. F. Azevedo, 1984, Observed flow reversals and measured-predicted Nusselt numbers for natural convection in a one-sided heated vertical channel, Jl. Heat Trans., ASME, Vol.106, No.2, pp 325-332.

13. D. Naylor, J. M. Floryan, J. D. Tarasuk, 1991, A numerical study of developing free convection between isothermal vertical plates, Jl. Heat Trans., ASME, Vol.113, August, pp 620-626.

14. H. Nakamura, A. Yutaka, T. Naitou, 1982, Heat transfer by free convection between two parallel flat plates, Num. Heat Trans., Vol.5, pp 95-106.

FED-Vol. 238, 1996 Fluids Engineering Division Conference
Volume 3
ASME 1996

NUMERICAL SIMULATION OF NEWTONIAN FLUID FLOW THROUGH A

MULTIPLE CHANNEL HONEYCOMB MONOLITHIC STRUCTURE

Maher M. Shariff
Department of Mechanical Engineering
Vanderbilt University
Nashville, TN 37240

Hussein J. Hussein
Department of Mechanical Engineering
Vanderbilt University
Nashville, TN 37240

Kenneth A. Debelak
Department of Chemical Engineering
Vanderbilt University
Nashville, TN 37240

John W. Williamson
Department of Mechanical Engineering
Vanderbilt University
Nashville, TN 37240

ABSTRACT

A major geometrical factor for obtaining uniform velocities inside the small channels of monolithic honeycomb structures has been determined numerically. A finite element code (FIDAPv7.51) was employed to solve the conservation laws for mass and momentum. The flow is assumed to be steady, incompressible, and isothermal. Wall porosity of the structure is neglected. Air flow is assumed for all simulations. A uniform velocity of 1.0 cm/s is imposed at the inlet of the structure. The channels of the structure are relatively small, and consequently have small hydraulic diameters. Each channel has a calculated Reynolds number of less than 900; therefore, the flow is laminar. The solution indicates that the container geometry plays a major role in producing uniform velocity profiles within the apparatus. Results obtained using the finite element code were in close agreement with experimental work performed under similar conditions.

NOMENCLATURE

D	characteristic diameter
D_h	hydraulic diameter
L	characteristic length
P	pressure
r, z	cylindrical polar coordinates
Re	Reynolds number
t	time
u_r, u_z	cylindrical polar velocity component
U	characteristic velocity
V	velocity of fluid
μ	dynamic viscosity of fluid
ρ	density of fluid
$(\ )^*$	dimensionless variable

INTRODUCTION

Coated honeycomb structures are commonly employed in automotive catalytic converters. These structures are made of ceramic materials and contain straight, square channels of millimeter dimensions. The extruded ceramic structure, as mentioned by Gulati (1991), has high surface area based on its geometry, low thermal inertia and thermal expansion and low heat capacity. The structure may be coated by submerging the substrate into a slurry container containing the catalyst; or by drawing the slurry into the substrate by

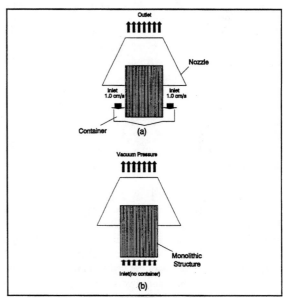

Fig.1 The physical model (a) with container
(b) without container

means of vacuum pressure imposed at the nozzle outlet, see Fig. 1. During coating, the ceramic structure is positioned in a circular container containing the slurry. Slurries are thixotropic, non-newtonian fluids, Kolb et al (1993). In manufacturing, some problems such as uneven coating thickness, insufficient coating at some sections, and clogging have been reported.

This paper presents a numerical simulation of air flow through a multiple channel structure. Uniform velocity profiles will likely increase our ability to achieve a uniform coating of the slurry. It is anticipated that several parameters contribute to the non-uniformity of these flow fields, namely container clearance, pressure drop across the monolith, vacuum time, etc. The objective of this work is to determine geometries that will produce uniform velocity profiles throughout the ceramic, honeycomb structure. Two axisymmetric models were constructed using a finite element code (FIDAPv7.51), developed by Fluid Dynamics International of Evanston, Illinois.

NUMERICAL SIMULATIONS

Both models of the ceramic structure contain fifty six axisymmetric channels that are 0.1 centimeter in diameter and 15.2 centimeters in height. The flow is assumed to be steady, incompressible and isothermal. Wall porosity of the structure is neglected. Air flow is assumed for all simulations.

Container Geometrical Configuration

The first model was constructed in units of centimeters, with an imposed inlet velocity of 1.0 cm/s. The substrate is positioned inside a circular container with a nominal clearance of 0.2 cm. The container geometry was modified several times to determine an optimum configuration that will produce uniform velocity profiles throughout the system. The following convention was utilized to show the effects of each modification on the velocity profiles across the fifty six channels, as well as the pressure drop along the length of each channel of the monolithic structure. The ratios indicated below, are ratios of the container clearance at the centerline to the container clearance at the outer edge of the structure. Three container clearance ratio cases were tested, (i) container clearance ratio 1:1, (ii) container clearance ratio 5:1, (iii) container clearance ratio 1:2.

Comparison with an air flow experiment

In this simulation, a uniform pressure distribution was imposed at the outlet of the nozzle. This was done to determine whether it will produce uniform velocities within the channels of the substrate. For this reason, a second model was constructed with the same number of channels as the first one. This model was constructed in a non-dimensional form with a characteristic length, L = 0.1 cm, and characteristic velocity of the flow, U=12.25 m/s.

Reynolds number was calculated, based on each channel's hydraulic diameter.

$$Re_h = \frac{\rho U D_h}{\mu} \qquad (1)$$

The following dimensionless variables were used, White (1991),

$$z^* = z/L, \quad r^* = r/L, \quad u_z^* = u_z/U, \quad u_r^* = u_r/U, \quad P^* = P/\rho U^2$$

Now, we can solve the non-dimensional conservation equations: namely the continuity equation, in vector form,

$$\nabla \cdot V = 0 \qquad (2)$$

and the momentum equation in vector form,

$$\frac{\partial V}{\partial t} + V \cdot \nabla V = -\nabla P + \frac{1}{Re_h} \nabla^2 V \qquad (3)$$

The density, ρ, is assigned a value of 1.0, and the viscosity, $\mu = 1/Re_h = 1.22 \times 10^{-3}$, FIDAP (1993).

RESULTS AND DISCUSSION

Figs. 2 and 3 present streamlines and a pressure contour plot for case (iii) with clearance ratio of 5:1.
This geometry produces the desired uniform velocity profiles. In addition, two types of line plots were generated

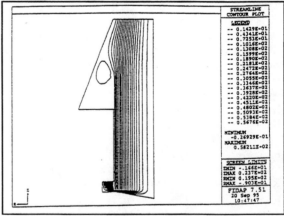

Fig. 2 Streamline contour plot, case (iii) ratio 5:1

for each of the three cases mentioned before. Velocity plot across the channels of the structure, see Fig. 4 (a,b,c), and

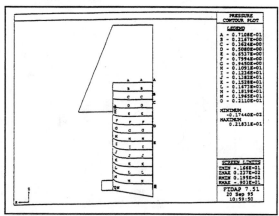

Fig.3   Pressure contour plot, case (iii) ratio 5:1

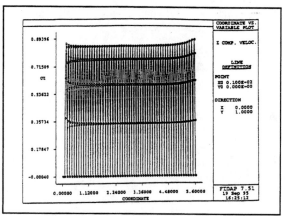

Fig.4 Velocity line plot (c) ratio 5:1

pressure drop along the channels of the structure, see Fig. 5 (a,b,c). Velocities plotted here are in units of centimetrs per second [cm/s], and pressures are in units of grams per centimeter per square seconds [g/(cm-s^2)].

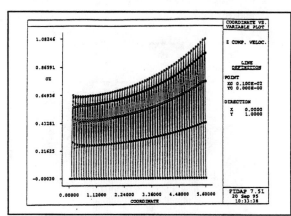

Fig.4 Velocity line plot (a) ratio 1:1

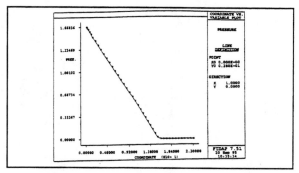

Fig. 5 Pressure line plot (a) ratio 1:1

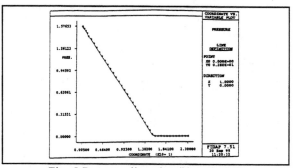

Fig. 5 Pressure line plot (b) ratio 1:2

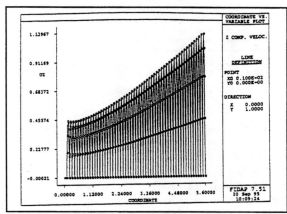

Fig.4 Velocity line plot (b) ratio 1:2

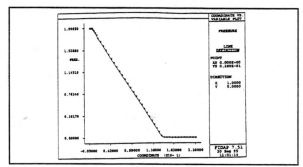

Fig. 5 Pressure line plot (c) ratio 5:1

The results for the non-dimensional model were obtained, by assigning a dimensionless pressure drop, $\Delta P^*=8.93$, based on the following equation,

$$\Delta P^* = \frac{\Delta P}{\rho U^2} = \frac{96}{Re_h}\frac{L}{D}(\frac{1}{2}) \qquad (4)$$

A scale factor was applied to each of the non-dimensional parameters; for velocity the scaling factor was U=12.25 m/s, and for the pressure the factor was ρU^2=180.1 Pa. Figs. 6, 7 show streamline contour, and pressure contour plots for the system with no container present underneath the monolithic structure.

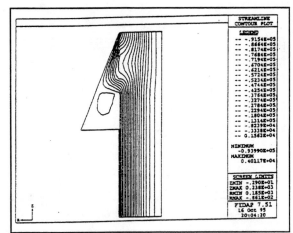

Fig. 6 Streamline contour plot for air flow without the container

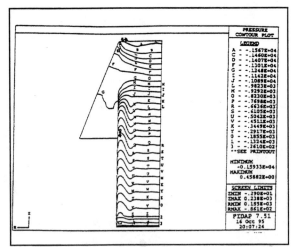

Fig. 7 Pressure contour plot for air flow without the container

A pressure line plot, showing the pressure drop along one channel at location 2.8 cm in the radial direction is

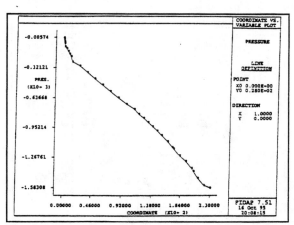

Fig. 8 Pressure line plot along a channel 2.8 cm from the centerline.

presented in Fig. 8. Negative values obtained for the pressure drop, indicate vacuum conditions within the substrate.

Velocity profiles at two different locations, are shown in Figs. 9 and 10, for each of the fifty six channels associated with the monolithic structure. Fig. 9 shows the profiles at location 10 cm along the axis of the channels.

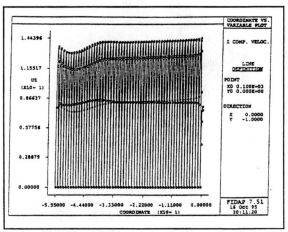

Fig. 9 Velocity profiles at point 10 cm in the z-dir, for each channel within the monolith.

Figure 10, shows the profiles 0.1 cm before the inlet of the channels (i.e. same location where the hot wire measurements were taken). The experimental work mentioned before was performed under similar conditions as the second numerical model. The hot wire measurements were performed by Aderounmu (1994). He measured velocities beneath the monolithic structure without a container. His results are shown in Fig. 11 for comparison. The experimental hot wire measurements of air flow within the apparatus and the numerical simulation performed using the finite element code, are in close agreement with each other, see Figs. 10 and 11.

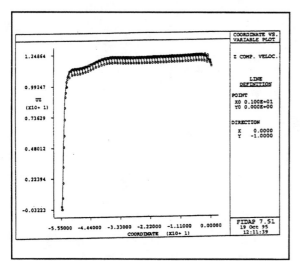

Fig. 10 Velocity profiles at point 0.1 cm, before the inlet of the channels

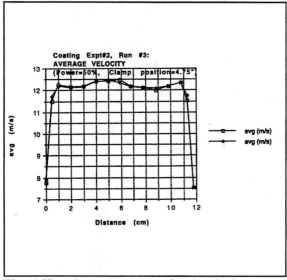

Fig. 11 Hot wire measurements for air velocity 0.1 cm, before the inlet of the monolith

CONCLUSIONS

In this work, the effects of varying container geometries on the uniformity of velocity profiles was investigated using the finite element code, FIDAP. The simulation was successful; it predicted an optimum container clearance ratio of 5:1. This ratio produced the desired velocity profile throughout the monolithic structure. In addition streamline plots determined the exact location of the vortex forming inside the nozzle.

The second part of the simulation involved imposing a niform pressure distribution at the outlet of the nozzle. The numerical results produced by FIDAP, as well the hot wire experiment indicate that the nature of the vacuum pressure imposed, does not affect the uniformity of the velocity profiles.

The comparison between the hot wire experiment and the simulation conducted using FIDAP, produced very close results with each others. The finite element code generated solutions for velocity variations, as well as pressure drops in crucial regions within the monolithic structure. These results can be utilized in future experimental and numerical work.

REFERENCES

Aderounmu, O., Personal contact

Fluid Dynamics International, *FIDAP Theory Manual, Revisions 7.0*, Evanston, IL, 1993.

Gulati, Suresh T., *Ceramic Converter Technology for Automotive Emission Control*, SAE Paper #910371, 1991.

Kolb, W. Blake, A. A. Papadimitriou, R. L. Cerro, D. D. Leavitt, and J. C. Summers, *The Ins and Outs of Coating Monolithic Structures*, Chemical Engineering Progress, February 1993.

White, F. M., *Viscous Fluid Flow* (2nd Edn), p. 82. McGraw-Hill, New York, 1991.

FED-Vol. 238, 1996 Fluids Engineering Division Conference
Volume 3
ASME 1996

LAMINAR BACKWARD-FACING STEP FLOW USING THE FINITE ELEMENT METHOD

Barbara T. Kornblum
Lawrence Livermore National Laboratory
University of California
Livermore, California

Rose C. McCallen
Lawrence Livermore National Laboratory
University of California
Livermore, California

Mark A. Christon
Sandia National Laboratory
Albuquerque, New Mexico

Wolfgang Kollmann
Department of Mechanical and
Aeronautical Engineering
University of California, Davis
Davis, California

ABSTRACT

Laminar, incompressible flow over a backward-facing step is calculated using a finite element spatial discretization with a piecewise continuous pressure approximation and an explicit time marching algorithm. The time-accurate evolution to steady state is demonstrated for both two-dimensional (2D) and three-dimensional (3D) simulations. This approach is shown to accurately predict the lengths of the recirculation zone on the top wall and at the step for various meshes and domain lengths, for a Reynolds number of 800 based on the average inlet velocity and twice the inlet channel height. The instantaneous and steady-state results are investigated. The steady-state solutions are evaluated by comparison to published numerical and experimental results.

INTRODUCTION

The finite element method (FEM) has been used by Gartling (1990) to obtain an accurate solution for *steady* 2D incompressible flow over a backward-facing step, with the intention to provide benchmark data in a format that can be used for testing and evaluation of outflow boundary conditions. However, Gartling (1990) did not investigate the effect of the outflow boundary conditions on the initial transient flow evolution, the effects of the computational channel length, or mesh grading at walls. Neither did he attempt any 3D simulations and thus, did not investigate possible out-of-plane effects. Using a spectral method, Kaiktsis et al. (1991) found 3D transient structures for laminar flow over a backward-facing step at Re = 800. Armaly et al. (1983) has published experimental data for a backward-facing step with the same expansion ratio as was modeled by Gartling (1990).

In this paper, we consider variations in the overall flow behavior due to the computational channel length in both the streamwise and cross-stream (out-of-plane) directions, as well as mesh size, mesh grading at walls, and the magnitudes of particular numerical parameters. Results indicating the separation and reattachment locations of the recirculation zones in the steady-state solution are presented for both 2D and 3D simulations. The homogeneous natural boundary conditions (zero traction), which arise directly from the FEM formulation, are applied at the exit plane, and we show the sensitivity of the flow solution to the location of this outflow boundary condition. Periodic boundary conditions were used on the lateral boundaries in the 3D simulations.

GOVERNING EQUATIONS AND NUMERICAL METHOD

In our investigation, the time-dependent incompressible Navier-Stokes equations are solved using an FEM approach. The incompressible Navier-Stokes equations are:

$$\nabla \bullet u = 0 \qquad (1)$$

$$\frac{\partial u}{\partial t} + u \bullet \nabla u = -\nabla P + \upsilon \nabla^2 u + f \qquad (2)$$

where $u = (u_1, u_2, u_3)$ is the velocity, $P = p/\rho$ where p is the pressure and ρ is the density, υ is the kinematic viscosity, and f is the body force.

Our FEM approach is similar to that developed by Gresho et al. (1984). The computer code HYDRA (Christon 1995) is used to calculate the results presented here. Unlike the original investigations of Gresho et al. (1984), HYDRA allows for the use of unstructured meshes with one-point integration, hourglass stabilization, and balancing tensor diffusivity (BTD) for explicit time integration.

Using the Galerkin finite element method, the discretized continuity and momentum equations can be written in matrix form as

$$C^T u = 0 \qquad (3)$$

$$M_L \dot{u} + [K + A(u)]u + Cp = F \qquad (4)$$

where u is the nodal velocity vector, p is the pressure vector, M_L is the lumped-mass matrix, K is the diffusivity, $A(u)$ is the advection operator, C is the gradient operator, and F is the user-supplied natural boundary condition. For more details see Gresho (1984) and Christon (1995).

In this study, the discrete pressure Poisson equation is solved in place of the continuity equation (3), so that continuity and momentum are decoupled and an explicit time-integration scheme is used. The discrete Poisson equation for pressure is an approximation of the continuous Poisson equation. The continuous Poisson equation is derived by taking the divergence of the momentum equation and applying the continuity equation (1). The analogous discrete Poisson equation is derived by multiplying the matrix form of the momentum equation (4) by $C^T M_L^{-1}$, and since $\frac{d}{dt}(C^T u) = 0$, we obtain

$$C^T M_L^{-1} Cp = C^T M_L^{-1}(F - [K + A(u)]u) \qquad (5)$$

where the coefficient matrix $C^T M_L^{-1} C$ is a discrete approximation of the Laplacian operator. Thus, the final discretized equations in matrix form are (4) and (5).

To reduce computational cost, a lumped mass matrix is employed and the coefficient matrices are generated using one-point Gaussian quadrature. The Q1P0 element formulation is used which provides bilinear velocity support in 2D and trilinear support in 3D with piece-wise constant pressure. The pressure Poisson equation is solved directly with a parallel-vector row solver (Storaasli et al. 1990) and an explicit forward Euler time integration scheme is used for the velocity solution.

An additive correction (diffusivity) to the diffusion matrix balances the negative diffusion induced by explicit Euler time integration (i.e., balancing tensor diffusivity (BTD), Gresho et al., (1984)). Also, an hour-glass correction is added to the one-point quadrature diffusion matrix to damp any zero energy modes that may be present because of the reduced integration scheme (Goudreau and Hallquist, 1982, and Gresho et al., 1984). To reduce the computational effort in the evaluation of the advection term we use a 'centroid advection velocity' simplification as was done by Gresho et al. (1984).

PROBLEM DEFINITION

For the backward-facing step geometry, no-slip boundary conditions are imposed on the step and the upper and lower channel walls, a parabolic velocity profile is specified at the channel inlet, and zero natural boundary conditions are imposed at the channel outlet (Fig. 1). The Reynolds number (Re=UH/υ) of 800 is based on the channel height of $H = 1.0$ and the average inlet velocity of $U = (2U_{max})/3 = 1.0$ where $U_{max} = 1.5$ in a parabolic profile. The step height is one half of the channel height (0.5H). Three different channel lengths, L = 12, 15, and 30, were investigated in 2D. For the 3D simulations, we considered L = 12, out-plane-width W = 1, and enforced periodic boundary conditions on the lateral boundaries (Fig. 2).

The periodic boundary conditions cause a singularity in the pressure matrix which introduces spurious pressure modes and causes the pressure results to display a checker board pattern on the upper and lower no-slip channel walls. We eliminated these modes by using a zero traction boundary condition in the x_3-direction along a single line of nodes on the bottom wall (Fig. 2). This action produces very small x_3-direction velocities, u_3, for the traction nodes on the bottom wall, but their magnitude is machine zero and thus, the no-slip condition is satisfied.

RESULTS

We report numerical results for our 2D and 3D investigations in tabular form to enable precise comparisons. Contour pictures are included for qualitative evaluation. Time evolution of the flow is demonstrated with time-histories plots. Our video tape with animations of both 2D and 3D time-accurate simulations is complete and will be shown during our July 1996 presentation.

Convergence and Comparison Criteria

We used the points where the flow separates and reattaches for comparison in our parameter studies. These separation and reattachment points define the lengths of recirculation zones on the top and bottom walls. The distance l_1 is the length of the major recirculation zone on the bottom wall measured from the step. The lengths l_2 and l_3 are the separation and reattachment positions on the top wall. We determined these lengths by examining the vorticity along the upper and lower walls of the channel. The flow separates or reattaches where the shear stress is zero and for 2D results the vorticity is zero when the shear stress is zero. We found the locations of zero vorticity by interpolating between grid points where the vorticity changed sign. This technique also applied when analyzing our 3D cases because the results were perfectly 2D.

Spatial convergence of our solutions is demonstrated from consistent separation and reattachment positions calculated with various mesh sizes. As the mesh was refined, the amount of change in the solution diminished. The converged solutions also exhibit smooth velocity profiles in high velocity gradient regions.

Temporal convergence was determined by examining time-histories of velocity at several point locations in the flow. In addition, the invariance of the flow's total kinetic energy $KE = u^T M_L u$ demonstrates a time-converged solution by evaluation of a global quantity. A steady solution is achieved well before the simulation time of 400, which is the point in time that we chose to evaluate l_1, l_2, and l_3.

Steady-State Solution

Our 2D and 3D simulations evolve to a steady-state solution for Reynolds number of 800 (Figs. 3, 4, and 5), contrary to the results of Kaiktsis et al. (1991), who was not able to obtain a steady solution in 2D or 3D at this Reynolds number. Our 3D simulation results are identical to our 2D results. They converge to a steady solution which does not exhibit 3D structures. Figure 6 shows the time history of the global kinetic energy which helps demonstrate time convergence. Local velocity time histories (Figs. 7 and 8) at selected point locations also show that time convergence to a steady state has been well achieved.

The streamfunction contours in Fig. 3 and the pressure contours in Fig. 4 capture the well-known character of the backward-facing step for the steady-state 2D solution. Results of 3D simulations are more difficult to display without the use of color. We have chosen isosurfaces of pressure to demonstrate the steady-state 3D solution in black and white (Fig. 5) because isosurfaces of the quantities vorticity or velocity would overlap and prevent details from being seen.[1] It is clear that the 3D pressure isosurfaces of Fig. 5 have no variation in the x_3 direction and are identical to the 2D results in Fig. 4.

We were able to shorten the channel length by a significant amount which reduced the size of the computational domain and thus the computational resources required to obtain a good solution. In Table 1, solutions are compared for three different channel lengths having the same uniform element size. These solutions are essentially identical because the results vary by less than one element size. The positions of the steady-state recirculation zones are relatively insensitive to the channel lengths studied here. This result reflects the ability of the homogeneous natural boundary condition to capture the steady-state outflow condition.

In Table 2, we compare our solutions for a channel length of 12, with different field discretizations including selected results from our investigation of graded meshes and out-of-plane 3D effects. Our only attempt to optimize the distribution of the elements in the graded meshes was to use the simple rule of grading finer in wall regions. We found very little change in the solution until we moved to meshes with coarse x_1 discretization. Results for our coarsest mesh (Case H) are only 3% different from our finest mesh (Case C) even though the finest has 18 times more elements. We found no difference in the solutions in going from 2D to 3D while keeping the same mesh in the $x_1 \times x_2$ plane, and we found no variation in the 3D results for different x_3-direction mesh sizes.

Generally, the calculated lengths l_1, l_2, and l_3 are in good agreement with Gartling (1990), even though Gartling used higher order approximations (9 node elements) than that used in our approach (4 node elements in 2D). Experimental results from Armaly et al. (1983) were estimated from figures in the paper and are included in Table 2. As other investigators have found, numerical simulations do not exactly agree with experiment.

The solution was not affected by the chosen time step size, as long as the time step remained below the Courant limit. This also means that the solution was insensitive to BTD because BTD is proportional to time step size. The test that was performed to evaluate the influence of time step on the solution involved decreasing the time step by factors of 1.5 and 3 on our finest mesh (Case A) and applying our steady-state spatial convergence criteria. In addition, we found no effect on the reattachment positions for a factor of ten variation in the hourglass coefficient.

---

1. We will use color pictures and animation during our presentation.

Transient Phenomena

Our investigation of the flow evolution exhibits a transient pressure fluctuation when the initial vortex reaches the exit of the computational domain at L = 12. The exiting vortex causes an abrupt change in the outlet flow, and the outflow boundary conditions must quickly adjust from what is essentially a zero pressure condition at the exit plane to the low pressure vortex so that the homogeneous natural boundary condition is satisfied. The pressure fluctuation lasts approximately 10 time units. It affects the entire flow field instantaneously, because of the effective infinite sound speed for incompressible flow. This feature, which is purely a computational phenomenon, is clearly seen in our 2D and 3D animations of pressure results.

Computational Resources

All of the cases documented in this report were run on a Silicon Graphics Power Indigo 2 Workstation using the parallel-vector row solver (Storaasli et al. 1990) for the pressure Poisson equation in HYDRA (Christon 1995). Table 3 summarizes the computational resources required to run each case. Memory requirements are dominated by the pressure Poisson equation and correlate with the matrix half-bandwidth. The element cycle time represents the number of microseconds (μsec) required to advance the solution of one element through one time step. Total run time is the CPU time necessary to compute the steady-state solution at time = 400.

There is a strong correlation between total storage (memory) required and matrix bandwidth, with additional storage requirements based on number of elements. As the element count and bandwidth decreased, so did memory. There also exists an obvious correlation between the element cycle time and the bandwidth. Cases A, B, and C in Table 3 have the same bandwidth and virtually identical cycle times. The total run time for these cases, however, is proportional to the element count.

We have included this information to demonstrate the significant reduction in computational resources that we achieved by cutting the domain from L = 30 to L = 12, and in using coarser, graded meshes.

CONCLUSIONS

The finite element method with a piecewise continuous pressure approximation and an explicit time marching algorithm accurately solves the backward-facing step problem at a Reynolds number of 800. Using homogeneous natural boundary conditions allows for a significant reduction in the length of the computational domain, and grading at the walls reduces the overall mesh size. These factors contribute to a reduction in the resources required to obtain converged results.

Both 2D and 3D simulations evolve to the same steady-state solution with the 3D simulation exhibiting no 3D structures. Although the periodic boundary conditions used in the 3D simulations can cause pressure modes, we eliminated them by the use of zero traction boundary conditions in the out-of-plane direction along the center line of the bottom wall.

During the flow evolution, a pertubation in the pressure solution occurs when the initial vortex exits the computational domain. This is due to the abrupt imposition of a strong vortex on the outflow homogeneous natural boundary condition.

This benchmark problem also provided an excellent opportunity to demonstrate the ability of state-of-the-art workstations to solve problems that were formerly relegated to main frame computers.

ACKNOWLEDGMENT

We are grateful to Michael Loomis from the Computations Department at LLNL for creating the 2D and 3D flow animations.

We would also like to thank Lucy Dobson for the skillful preparation of this document.

REFERENCES

Armaly, B.F., Durst, F., Pereira, J.C.F., Schonug, B. 1983, "Experimental and Theoretical Investigation of Backward Facing Step Flow", *Journal of Fluid Mechanics*, Vol. 127, pp. 473-496.

Christon, M., 1995, "HYDRA: A Finite Element Computational Fluid Dynamics Code," LLNL document UCRL-MA-121344.

Gartling, D.K., 1990, "A Test Problem for Outflow Boundary Conditions - Flow Over a Backward-Facing Step," *International Journal for Numerical Methods in Fluids*, Vol. 11, pp. 953-967.

Goudreau, G.L. and Hallquist, J.O., 1982, "Recent Developments in Large-Scale Finite Element Lagrangian Hydrocode Technology," *Computational Methods in Applied Mechanics and Engineering,* Vol. 33, pp. 725.

Gresho, P.M., Chan, S.T., Lee, R.L., and Upson, C.D., 1984, "A Modified Finite Element Method for Solving the Time-Dependent, Incompressible Navier-Stokes Equations. Part1: Theory," *International Journal for Numerical Methods in Fluids*, Vol. 4, pp. 557-598.

Kaiktsis, L., Karniadakis, G., and Orszag, S.A., "Onset of Three-Dimensionality, Equilibria, and Early Transition in Flow over a Backward-Facing Step," *Journal of Fluid Mechanics*, Vol. 231, pp. 501-528.

Storaasli, O.O., D.T. Nguyen, T.K. Agaruwal, "A Parallel-Vector Algorithm for Rapid Structural Analysis on High-Performance Computers," NASA Technical Memorandum 102614, April, 1990.

DISCLAIMER

Table 1. Comparison of 2D results for three different channel lengths using uniform element size $\Delta x_1 = \Delta x_2 = 0.0125$.

run no.	channel length, L	element count	l_1	l_2	l_3
A	30	128,000 [*]	6.03	4.90	10.37
B	15	96,000	6.03	4.90	10.37
C	12	76,800	6.03	4.91	10.35

[*] mesh was uniform for $0 < x_1 < 15$, then graded 1:2 for $15 < x_1 < 30$ as in Gartling (1990).

Table 2. Comparison of results for 2D and 3D simulations with channel length of 12.

run no.	run dim.	Δx_1 min.	Δx_1 max.	Δx_2 min.	Δx_2 max.	Δx_3	x_1 mesh	x_2 mesh	x_3 mesh	element count	l_1	l_2	l_3
C	2D	.0125	n/a	.0125	n/a	n/a	960	80	n/a	76,800	6.03	4.91	10.35
D	2D	.0167	n/a	.0167	n/a	n/a	720	60	n/a	43,200	5.99	4.91	10.31
E	2D	.0250	n/a	.0250	n/a	n/a	480	40	n/a	19,200	5.90	4.91	10.22
F	2D	.0125	.025	.0125	.0250	n/a	482	44	n/a	21,208	5.94	4.82	10.32
G	2D	.0250	.050	.0250	.0417	n/a	340	32	n/a	10,880	5.80	4.82	10.18
H	2D	.0167	.178	.0208	.0417	n/a	124	34	n/a	4,216	5.83	4.76	10.21
I	3D	.0167	.178	.0209	.0417	.167	124	34	6	25,296	5.83	4.76	10.21
J	3D	.0167	.178	.0209	.0417	.100	124	34	10	42,160	5.85	4.76	10.21
Gartling (1990): L=30 with 32,000 9-node elements											6.10	4.85	10.48
Armaly et al. (1983): we estimated these results from figures in the paper											7.0	5.3	9.4

Table 3. Use of Computational Resources

run no.	run dim.	element count	memory (MWords)	1/2 band width	elem. cycle time (μ sec)	total run time(hrs.)
A	2D	128,000	16.87	82	27.5	54.
B	2D	96,000	12.65	82	26.6	40.
C	2D	76,000	10.12	82	26.4	32.
D	2D	43,200	4.84	62	21.8	15.
E	2D	19,200	1.77	42	16.1	4.8
F	2D	21,208	2.04	46	17.2	5.7
G	2D	10,880	0.92	34	13.0	2.2
H	2D	4,216	0.36	36	8.5	0.6
I	3D	25,296	7.21	215	69.1	26.
J	3D	42,160	17.82	359	94.2	61.

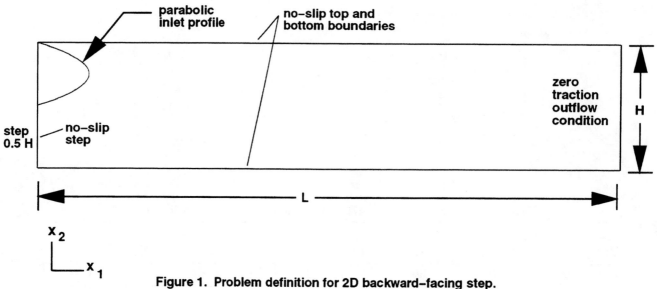

Figure 1. Problem definition for 2D backward-facing step.

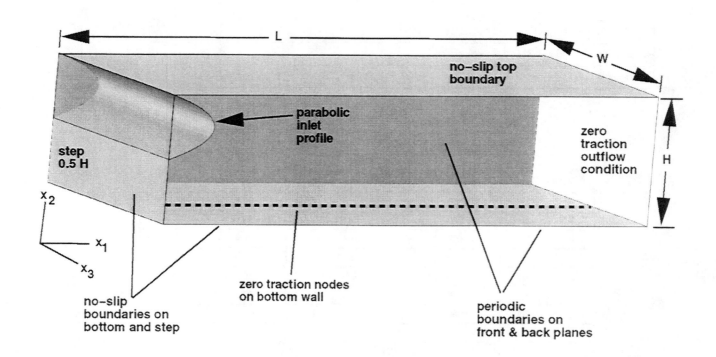

Figure 2. Problem definition for 3D backward-facing step.

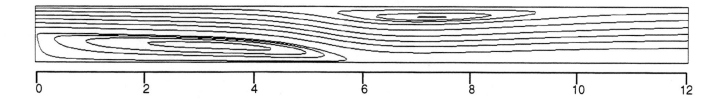

Figure 3. Streamfunction contours for 2D steady-state solution in channel length 12.

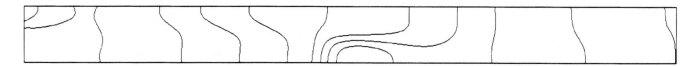

Figure 4. Pressure contours for 2D steady-state solution in channel length 12.

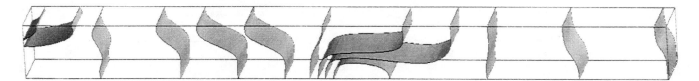

Figure 5. Pressure isosurfaces for 3D steady-state solution in channel length 12.

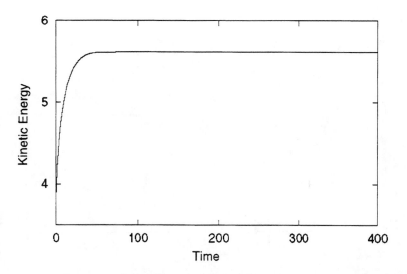

Figure 6. Total kinetic energy of the flow for Case A.

Node Locations:

node	x1	x2
3301	1.0	−0.25
16421	5.0	−0.25
36101	11.0	−0.25

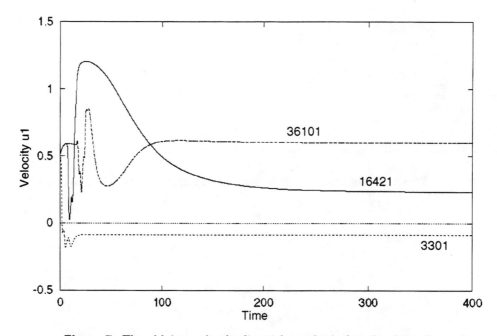

Figure 7. Time history of velocity u1 for selected nodes from Case A.

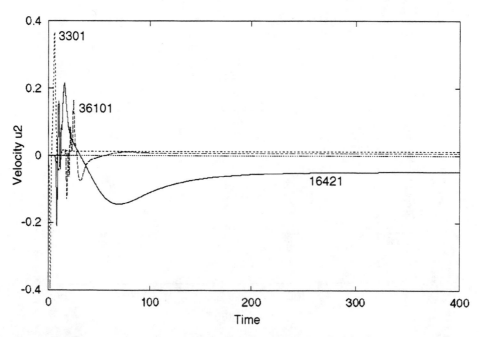

Figure 8. Time history of velocity u2 for selected nodes from Case A.

FED-Vol. 238, 1996 Fluids Engineering Division Conference
Volume 3
ASME 1996

PRELIMINARY MODEL OF AN OIL-WATER SETTLING PROCESS USING FIDAP

Michael A. Langerman
Associate Professor
South Dakota School of Mines and Technology
Mechanical Engineering Department
501 E. St. Joseph St.
Rapid City, South Dakota 57701-3995

Matthew J. Meiners [1]
Graduate Student

Warren Rice
McTighe Industries, Inc.
P.O. Box 928
Mitchell, South Dakota 57301

ABSTRACT

Remediation of oil and/or other oleophilic liquid contaminated sites of the types generated by private and government agency activities is an important ecological concern for this country. One means of wastesite remediation is diluting the oil with water and pumping the mixture to a settling apparatus for final disposition of the separated liquids. The success of this remediation method, however, is greatly influenced by the difference in specific gravity between the dispersed and continuous phases and also upon the size and design of the separator. This study presents results from a preliminary investigation into obtaining better separator designs through a better understanding of the flow fields within the separator. It is shown that the FIDAP finite-element code is an appropriate tool for assessing the effects of the flow field on the resulting oil droplet trajectory. Various separator internal components are modeled, and the results indicate that these components significantly increase the efficiency of the separation process, although more research is required.

INTRODUCTION

The activities of the government and private industry result in the generation of large amounts of wastewater comprising dispersions of oil or other oleophilic materials often emulsified within the continuous water phase. This wastewater almost always requires treatment to separate the oil from the water, sometimes for economic reasons alone, but usually to meet the requirements for waste disposal set by law and regulations. To meet environmental standards for wastewater refinement, the effluents discharged into publicly owned water treatment systems must contain less than 50 ppm (parts per million) oil or equivalently 50 mg of oil per liter mixture. Effluents discharged into surface waters typically are held to a 10-15 ppm standard. In cleanup, the objective is to recover the oil and to produce a clarified water stream.

Background

Where large volumes of wastewater are present, the most common treatment processes include settling, flotation, and centrifugation (Foreman, Hadermann, and Trippe, 1989). In the settling process, the success of separating the oil from the water is dependent upon the difference in specific gravity between the water and the oil, the droplet size of the dispersed liquid phase, and the size and design of the separator. A common settling apparatus used in industry is the shell-type oil-water separator (Figure 1). As an oil and water mixture enters the separator, through the inlet standpipe, the action of gravity and buoyancy forces causes the lighter oil component, with a specific gravity typically between 0.7 and 0.9, to rise to the upper region of the tank, while the heavier water component settles to the bottom. As the water exits through the outlet standpipe at the bottom of the separator, the oil is skimmed off the top.

Presently, these separators are sized based upon one of two simplified mathematical models (Arnold and Sikes, 1986; and Arnold and Koszela, 1990) and/or empirical results often obtained from site specific field tests (Rice,1992). Their performance is often enhanced by the addition of coalescers, such as corrugated plates or oleophilic mediums, although the reasons why these components improve the separation process are generally unknown. Nevertheless, the settling process in separators of the type shown in Figure 1 tends to work well as long as the dispersed oil droplet diameters are 50 μm or larger but becomes significantly less efficient with smaller droplet diameters (Tramier, 1985).

---

[1] Present address: Hughes Christensen, Houston, TX.

Flotation processes are commonly used to strip dispersed oil droplets from water but require introduction of air either by induction through the action of a rotor or dissolution where the aqueous stream is contacted with air at high pressure causing air to dissolve in the liquid. In either method, some system pressure control is required, which limits the practical application of the flotation process for the treatment of many oil-water mixtures.

The efficiency of centrifuges or hydrocyclones is dependent primarily upon the density difference between the oil and the water and by the droplet size, with the larger droplets (diameters of 50 μm or larger) more readily separated than the smaller droplets. Consequently, the efficiency of separation is similarly limited as with the settling process. In addition, however, all centrifugation processes require a relatively high energy input for adequate separation. Sufficient power input is needed to develop the centrifugal forces, through the mechanical rotation of the fluid, to effect a sufficient separation of the two liquid phases.

Of the three treatment processes discussed, the settling process is the most practical in terms of separation efficiency and cost. A brief discussion of the methods used to design separators used in the settling process is presented below.

Current Separator Design Methodologies

As seen in Figure 1, the interior of the separator may contain a variety of components including standpipes, baffles, and flow diverters. These components are used to improve the efficiency of the separator. The inlet flow diverter is used to break up the flow and allow the heavier materials, such as sludge or dirt, to settle more rapidly at the bottom. The sludge baffle prevents the build up of sludge from plugging the outflow standpipe. The inlet standpipe allows the influent to be injected in the upper region of the vessel, while the outlet standpipe entrance is located near the bottom where the mixture contains less oil.

Currently, sizing of oil/water separators is generally based upon one of two simple theories (Arnold and Koszela,1990); the first is called rise-time theory and the second is called retention-time theory. As its name suggests, the rise-time theory predicts the time required for an oil droplet to rise to the surface. It is based upon a force balance between gravity, buoyancy and drag (assuming Stoke's flow, i.e., Re1, where Re is the Reynolds number). The velocity of the oil particle predicted from the rise-time theory is (Meiners, 1995):

$$V_r = \left(\frac{1}{18\mu}\right)(\gamma_w - \gamma_0)d_0^2$$

where w is the specific weight of the water, o is the specific weight of the oil, is the viscosity of the water, d o is the diameter of the oil particle and V r is the rate of rise of the oil particle. The time for the particle to rise to the surface is then obtained and the separator length is sized, assuming uniform internal flow, to provide a fluid residence time within the separator greater than or equal to the calculated droplet rise-time. The problem, however, is that the flow is not uniform, in fact, the fluid flow pathlines can be quite complex depending upon the internals within the separator. Even with no internal components obstructing the flow paths, the flow

recirculates in the upper regions of the separator (Meiners, 1995) Experts in the field of separator manufacturing believe a bette understanding of the details regarding the fluid flow field i necessary for obtaining optimal separator designs (McTigh Industries, 1995).

The retention-time theory is similar to the rise-time theory The main difference is that the droplet rise-time is determine experimentally rather than analytically. A series of "batch tests" i conducted on a fixed ratio of an oil and water mixture. Oil an water are vigorously mixed and allowed to equilibrate. After mixing ceases, the oil will begin to separate, rising to the top with the wate settling on the bottom. The height of the oil-water interface i measured and plotted versus time. A typical plot of this result i shown in Figure 2 (Arnold and Koszela, 1990).

As indicated in Figure 2, the height of the oil-water mixture interface asymptotically approaches its premixed value. The time required to reach the point labeled "emulsion" in Figure 2 is then used in sizing the separator in the same manner as discussed above. If the water contains only stable emulsions of oil, separation will no occur at all, regardless of the time allowed. Other treatment processes must then be incorporated.

Separator designs based upon the retention-time theory can account for specific oil/water mixture ratios and be correlated in-situ for specific tasks. This method, therefore, may result in more appropriate separator sizes for site specific applications than might be obtained applying the rise time theory. The authors, however, could find no data correlating the experimental results to field test results.

It should be noted that there are available studies of specific separator designs, such as conducted by Zeevalkink and Brunsmann, 1983, for parallel plate separators, but of those found, all contained very simplified mathematical models. In the Zeevalkink and Brunsmann study, the theoretical basis assumed uniform flow in the tank and a uniform overflow rate (inlet flow divided by the tank horizontal cross-sectional area). The effect of nonuniform velocity profiles on the accumulated time a particle is within the vessel was accounted for by assuming laminar, parabolic flow within the tank and by a qualitative assessment of friction near the walls of the separator. Recent results obtained (Langerman and Meiners, 1995) have indicated that the flow patterns are much more complex than assumed by Zeevalkink and Brunsmann.

To summarize, where large volumes of wastewater are present, the most common treatment processes are settling, flotation, and centrifugation. Of the three, the settling process is the most practical in terms of separation efficiency and cost. However, a lack of understanding of the governing flow phenomena occurring within the oil/water separator excludes applying modern design methodologies for obtaining an optimal engineering design. Case in point are recent comments obtained from an experienced field engineer (Rice, 1992) regarding corrugated plate packs used in separators, "they seem to increase the efficiency of separation but we don't know why?" Consequently, an investigation was conducted to assess modeling the flow fields within the separator. Preliminary results obtained are discussed below.

RESULTS

Lately, manufactures of oil/water separators have recognized the need for application of sophisticated computational methods for analyzing separator design performance (McTighe Industries, 1995). This need led to recent research (Langerman and Krause, 1995) that investigated the feasibility of modeling the separator settling process using the FIDAP finite-element code (Fluid Dynamics International, 1993). The code was applied to a simplified but similar flow geometry. The model conditions consisted of 2-dimensional flow between surfaces representative of the surfaces in a 190 liter (50 gallon) separator. Figure 3 shows a cross-sectional view of the model separator geometries. Two geometries were used in order to assess the effects that the separator internal components have on the resulting trajectories of oil droplets. Model A has no internal components whereas Model B includes, a sludge baffle, a flow diverter, and standpipe. A mesh refinement study (Meiners, 1995) found that 1824 biquadratic finite elements was sufficient to model the separators and capture phenomena of significance. This resulted in 24 elemets across the separator channel and 76 elements along the length of the separator.

The model fluid used in this study was water at 20 C. The inlet and outlet flow boundary conditions were set at 0.189 liter/s (3 gpm). The flow was assumed to be isothermal. Streamline contour plots were obtained for both models and are shown in Figure 4. Results in Figure 4 indicate the complex flow patterns involved within these simplified separator geometries.

In FIDAP the equation of motion of an oil particle is given as

$$\frac{d\vec{V}_r}{dt} = \frac{(\rho_0 - \rho_w)\vec{g}}{\rho_0} + \frac{(\vec{V}_r - \vec{V}_f)}{\bar{\tau}}$$

where arrowed terms indicate vectors, τ in the second term on the right hand side contains the drag force information and V_f the water velocity. The first term on the right hand side contains the buoyancy force. If an oil droplet is being carried by horizontal flow, the water flow direction is orthogonal to the buoyancy force. In a downward water flow, the effective V_r is reduced due to the water flow acting in the opposite direction as the buoyancy force. Conversely, in an upward water flow, V_r is maximized due to the water flow acting in the same direction as the buoyancy force.

Figure 5 presents three oil particle paths obtained from FIDAP for Models A and B. In Figure 5, for Model A, two of the oil particles were carried to the outlet and only one was successfully separated from the water. In Figure 5, for Model B, only one particle escaped to the outlet while two particles were successfully separated. Although these results track only 3 particles, the trend is apparent and indicates that the internal components in Model B do influence the success of the process.

In Figure 6, the pathline of a 120 mm oil particle (ρ_0 =700 kg/m3) is superimposed upon a streamline contour plot obtained from Model B. Results in this figure show clearly the oil particle path in relation to the flow field and the effect of the particle buoyancy.

In summary, these preliminary FIDAP model results show the trend effect of typical separator components on the flow field solutions obtained. The flow fields, in turn, have a significant effect on the path and velocity of the oil particle. The direction of the flow at a given location can either increase or decrease the effective V_r, thus altering the net efficiency of the separation process.

CONCLUSIONS

Most oil/water separators are sized based upon one of two simple mathematical developments: a "retention time" or a "rise time" development. Neither approach, however, is able to represent the complex flow fields that occur within these separator and the accompanying effect on the oil droplet trajectory.

The results presented indicate that CFD codes can be used as an appropriate tool for assessing the performance of oil/water separators. Although preliminary data obtained indicate that the internal components of the separator affect the process efficiency, more research is needed before these effects can be quantitatively categorized.

REFERENCES

Arnold, K. E. and Koszela, P. J., 1990, "Droplet-Settling vs. Retention-Time Theories for Sizing Oil/Water Separators," SPE Production Engineering, Vol. 5, pp. 59-64.

Arnold, K. E. and Sikes, C. T., 1986, "Droplet-Settling Theory Key to Understanding Separator Size Correlations," Oil and Gas Journal, Vol. 84, pp. 60-64.

Fluid Dynamics International (FDI), 1993, FIDAP User Manuals, Rev. 7, 1 st ed.

Langerman, M. A. Meiners, M., 1995, "A Finite Element Investigation of Oil/Water Separator Design,"Third Annual ASME Region VII Graduate Student Technical Conference, North Dakota State University, Fargo, North Dakota.

Langerman, M. A., Krause W. B., 1995, McTighe Industries Oil-Water Pumping Station, Project #235, Final Report, South Dakota Governor's Office Of Economic Deverlopment, May 1995.

Meiners, M., 1995,"An Investigation of Oil-Water Separator Design Theories," Master of Science Thesis, South Dakota School of Mines and Technology.

McTighe Industries, 1995, Letter, Tim Burke, president, to Dr. M. A. Langerman, Associate Professor, South Dakota School of Mines and Technology, Rapid City, SD.

Rice, Warren, 1992, Performance Tests at Dallas Naval Air Station, Dallas ,TX, McTighe Industries, Contract N62467-90-C-0525.

Tramier, B., 1985, "Water Treatment Technology," Institute for Petroleum Technology Papers, IP 84- 011.

Zeevalkink, J. A., and Brunsmann, J. J., 1983, "Oil Removal From Water In Parallel Plate Gravity- Type Separators," Water Resources, Vol. 17, No. 4, pp. 365-373.

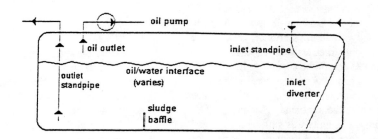

Figure 1. Schematic of a typical cylindrical tank separator.

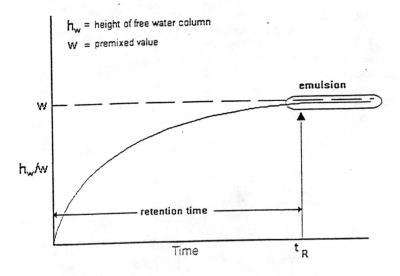

Figure 2. Retention time plot.

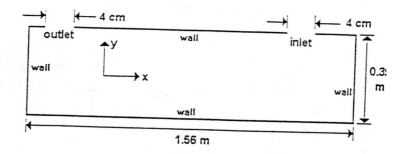

Geometry used for OWS Model A

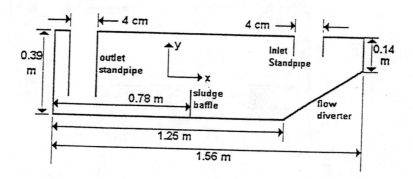

Geometry used for OWS Model B

Figure 3. Separator models.

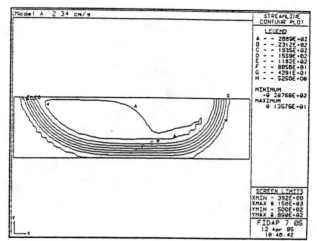

Streamline contour plot for OWS Model A

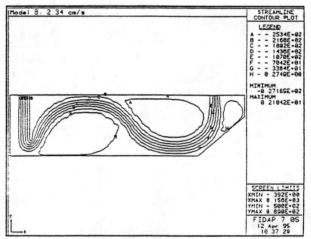

Streamline contour plot for OWS Model B

Figure 4. Streamlines.

290

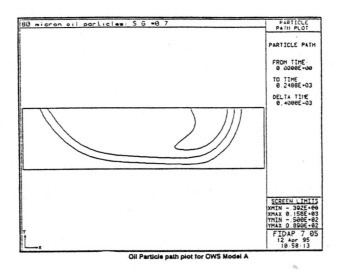

Oil Particle path plot for OWS Model A

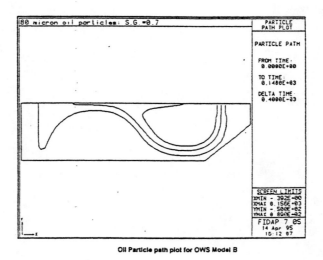

Oil Particle path plot for OWS Model B

Figure 5. Oil particle trajectories.

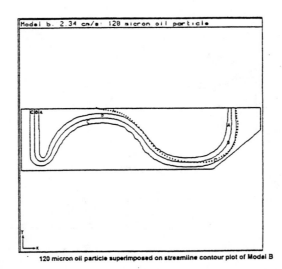

120 micron oil particle superimposed on streamline contour plot of Model B

Figure 6. Oil particle pathline.

FED-Vol. 238, 1996 Fluids Engineering Division Conference
Volume 3
ASME 1996

IMPLEMENTATION OF ONE-POINT QUADRATURE
IN A FINITE ELEMENT CFD CODE

M. Tabatabai, D. Metzger, R.Sauvé

Advanced Systems Technologies
Ontario Hydro Technologies
Toronto, Ontario M8Z 5S4 Canada

ABSTRACT

The use of one-point quadrature integration greatly enhances the computational efficiency of finite element solutions. The procedure is particularly useful when applied to explicit schemes. One-point quadrature integration may, however, produce spurious modes if applied without hourglass stabilization. This paper discusses the application of an efficient hourglass control method to the Galerkin formulation of the conservation of momentum equations. Bilinear shape functions are used for both pressure and velocities, and integration is performed using a one-point quadrature. Hourglass control terms can increase the order of integration up to two-point quadrature. This approach allows a highly vectorized formulation for velocity equations. The proposed hourglass control method has been previously applied to three-dimensional solid elements and its effectiveness and computational efficiency have been established in solid mechanics modelling. Stability problems associated with explicit solvers are overcome by modifying the diffusivity matrix using a balancing tensor. In this work, details of the finite element approach and solution methodology are presented, and the hourglass correction terms corresponding to the diffusion and convection terms in the momentum equation are constructed.

INTRODUCTION

The computational effort required for solving large problems using implicit CFD methods can render such solutions prohibitively expensive. An explicit finite element scheme, used with a lumped mass matrix and one-point quadrature integration, is a cost-effective alternative to the implicit approach. This approach, however, suffers from the distortions caused by the hourglass mode introduced by one-point quadrature integration. A number of correction techniques for addressing this problem exist. Metzger and Sauvé [1] discussed some of the corrections and then presented the complete three-dimensional formulation and application of the unified hourglass control theory, developed by Liu et al. [2]. They demonstrated the advantage of applying this more mathematically accurate correction method to the approximate methods in several solid mechanics applications. In this paper, the theoretical framework of a finite element code being developed using an explicit

scheme is discussed and results from a number of benchmarking studies are also presented.

MATHEMATICAL FORMULATION

The general form of the mass and momentum conservation equations are as follows

$$\dot{\rho} + (\rho u_i)_{,i} = 0 \qquad (1)$$

$$\rho \, \dot{u}_i + (\rho \, u_j) \, u_{i,j} = (\sigma_{ij})_{,j} + f_i \qquad (2)$$

Where ρ is density, u_i, the velocity components, σ_{ij}, the stress and f_i is the contribution from external and body forces. Using the definition of the bulk modulus of elasticity, k, the ratio of the pressure stress to the volumetric strain $k = \partial P/(\partial \rho/\rho)$, the continuity equation yields an equation for pressure, which is valid for both compressible and incompressible flows

$$\dot{P} + u_i P_{,i} + k \, u_{i,i} = 0 \qquad (3)$$

The stress term in equation (3) includes contributions from two sources, hydrostatic pressure and first or higher rate of deformation

$$\sigma_{ij} = -P\delta_{ij} + \sigma'_{ij} \qquad (4\text{-a})$$

for Newtonian fluids, using Stoke's hypotheses, equation (4-a) can be written as

$$\sigma_{ij} = -P\delta_{ij} + \mu \, (\, u_{i,j} + u_{j,i} - \frac{2}{3}\delta_{ij}u_{k,k} \,) \qquad (4\text{-b})$$

where μ is the viscosity of the fluid and δ_{ij} is the Krönecker delta.

The Galerkin finite element discretization method is applied to the conservation equations using the following expansions for pressure and velocities in each element

$$P(x,t) = \lfloor N \rfloor \{ P^{(e)} \} \qquad (5)$$

$$u_i(x,t) = \lfloor N \rfloor \{ u_i^{(e)} \} \qquad (6)$$

Superscript $^{(e)}$ in the above equations indicates values at elements and $\lfloor \ \rfloor$ and { } denote row and column matrices, respectively. In the above equations N is a piecewise bilinear shape function. Note that with one-point quadrature N becomes constant for both pressure and velocity. However, as will become evident later, the introduction of the hourglass control terms, restores the linear order of the velocity shape function.

After applying the Galerkin method to the weak form of the conservation equations, the discretized forms of the equations for each element become

$$\frac{M}{\rho} \{\dot{P}_i\} + k Q^T \{u_i\} + C \{P_i\} = \{ 0 \} \qquad (7)$$

$$M \{\dot{u}_i\} + (C + K) \{u_i\} - Q \{P_i\} = \{F_i\} \qquad (8)$$

In the above equations, coefficient matrices M, Q, K, C and F_i are defined as

$$M = \int_\Omega \rho \, N \, N^T \, d\Omega \qquad (9\text{-}a)$$

$$Q = \int_\Omega B \, N^T \, d\Omega \qquad (9\text{-}b)$$

$$K = \int_\Omega B^T \, D \, B \, d\Omega \qquad (9\text{-}c)$$

$$C = \int_\Omega \rho \, u_{n_j} N \, B^T \, d\Omega \qquad (9\text{-}d)$$

$$F_i = \int_\Omega N f_i \, d\Omega + <\text{boundary conditions}> \qquad (9\text{-}e)$$

where N and B are the shape factor and gradient matrices and D is the constitutive matrix.

The mass matrix, M, in equation 9-a is lumped by row averaging to produce a diagonal matrix. The nonlinearity in the momentum conservation equation is eliminated by using the average convective velocity $(u_n)_i$ at the centroid of each element in calculating the convection matrix (9-d). Appropriate treatment of boundary conditions is essential in obtaining proper solution to problems. The formulation used by Yagawa, et al. [3] was used in the present method. This approach allows proper implementation of both pressure and traction boundary conditions.

SOLUTION

The approach used in solving the discretized conservation equations will be discussed. Note that bi-linear shape functions are used for both velocity and pressure. One-point quadrature integration scheme is used for each element, effectively making the shape functions constant. Introduction of hourglass terms, discussed in a later section, will restore the linear form of the velocity shape function.

Continuity Equation

The general discretized form of the continuity equation(7), is

$$\frac{M}{\rho} \frac{\Delta P}{\Delta t} = -k Q^T (u_i^t + \beta \Delta u) - C (P_i^t + \beta \Delta p) \qquad (10)$$

Where $\beta=0$ corresponds to a fully explicit, $\beta=1$ to a fully implicit and $\beta=.5$ to a semi-implicit discretization scheme. Equation (10) can be written as follows to provide an equation for pressure

$$\left(\frac{M}{\rho} + \beta\Delta t \, C + k\beta^2\Delta t^2 Q^T M^{-1} Q \right) \Delta P = \\ - [k\Delta t \, Q^T (u_i^t + \beta \Delta u')] - (\Delta t \, C \, P) \qquad (11)$$

In the above equation, $\Delta u'$ is obtained from the momentum conservation equation using the information at time t (as discussed in the next section). For an incompressible fluid, the fully implicit formulation yields a consistent Poisson equation for pressure, which has been used by Gresho, et al. [4]. The present approach considers a more general form of the pressure equation and could be viewed as an *exact* penalty method approach.

In an incompressible fluid, the fully explicit continuity equation can be written as

$$\Delta P = -\rho \, k \, \Delta t \, M^{-1} \, Q^T u_i^t \qquad (12)$$

This equation can be solved very efficiently (using the lumped mass matrix).

If the explicit scheme is used for a compressible case, the balancing tensor term (BT), presented in a later section, must also be applied in the continuity equation

$$\Delta P = \Delta t \, \rho \, M^{-1}\{-k \, Q^T u_i^t - C \, P + <balancing \, Tensor>\} \qquad (13)$$

For an implicit solution to the pressure equation a dynamic relaxation algorithm is used. This approach, which is explained in detail by Sauvé and Metzger in [5], involves treating equation (11) as the steady state solution to the following equation; which is analogous to a critically damped wave equation discussed in [5].

$$M'\Delta\ddot{P}^t + C'\Delta\dot{P}^t + K'\Delta P = F_{ext}^t \qquad (14\text{-}a)$$

where in equation 14, F_{ext}^t is the right hand side of equation (11) and K' represents the terms in the parentheses in that equation, M' and C' are arbitrary mass and damping matrices. By choosing an appropriate diagonal mass matrix M', critical damping matrix $C=2\omega M'$ (where ω is the undamped natural frequency of the equation) and time step for the dynamic relaxation Δt_{dr}, the solution to the steady state case of equation (14-a), i.e.

$$K'\Delta P = F_{ext}^t \qquad (14\text{-}b)$$

is obtained. A summary of the steps used in the dynamic relaxation approach is provided in [5].

Momentum Equation

Using a fully explicit time discretization approach, the momentum equation yields

$$u_i^{t+\Delta t} = u_i^t + \Delta t\, M^{-1}\, [F_i - (C + K)\, u_i^t + Q\, (P^t + \beta \Delta P)] \quad (15)$$

or

$$\Delta u = \Delta u' + \beta\, \Delta t\, M^{-1}\, Q\, \Delta P \quad (16\text{-a})$$

where

$$\Delta u' = \Delta t\, M^{-1}\, [F_i - (C + K)\, u_i^t + Q\, P^t] \quad (16\text{-b})$$

Using a lumped mass matrix, the above formulation can be computed via a highly vectorized algorithm. At the beginning of each iteration $\Delta u'$ is calculated using the information at time t. The continuity equation is solved next. If dynamic relaxation is used for solving the pressure equation, $\Delta u'$ is also used in this stage of calculations in equation (11). Once the pressure increment is calculated, the velocity increment is modified using equation (16).

Note that when pressure is calculated from an explicit scheme, equation (12), there should not be a makeup term for the velocity increment. However, an ad hoc procedure, involving fully explicit ($\beta=0$) pressure equation, with $\beta=1$ in equation (16), can improve time step requirements and speed up the convergence in some problems significantly.

The spurious pressure mode, discussed in [6] and [7], is also observed in the solutions reached by the present approach. This mode can be treated by a simple smoothing procedure.

Balancing Tensor

The advantages associated with the forward time differencing come with a price in terms of the stability of the solution. This would make the explicit scheme, in its original form, unsuitable for advection dominated flows. In order to take advantage of the elegance and simplicity of an explicit scheme, the issue of these instabilities must first be resolved. The procedure used to address this problem was that proposed by [8], and implemented by [4]. As explained in these works, a judicious examination of the conservation equations can reveal that the stability problems associated with the convection terms in an explicit solver can be overcome through modifying the diffusivity term by

$$\alpha'_{i,j} = \frac{\Delta t}{2}\, u_i\, u_j \quad (17)$$

Note that the present scheme is superior to other more conventional diffusivity correction schemes such as Lax-Wendroff method [9] where the correction term is $0.5\, u^2_{i,i}\Delta t$. The advantage is due to the contribution of the off-diagonal terms in the $u_{i,j}$ matrix to the stability of the solution.

In the present work, the balancing tensor corrections are added to the diffusivity matrix D, equation (9.c), before the hourglass correction is applied. Therefore, the balancing tensor is also corrected for errors associated with hourglass modes. This is important in convective dominated flows.

Hourglass Correction

The derivation of the hourglass control terms for the two-dimensional case will now be presented. Details of the derivation for the convective terms will be given. The derivation for the diffusion terms can be obtained similarly.

The expression for the convective component C in two-dimensions is

$$C = C_{11} + C_{22} \quad (18)$$

where

$$C_{11} = \int_\Omega \rho\, N\, u_n\, N_x^T\, d\Omega \quad (19)$$

$$C_{22} = \int_\Omega \rho\, N\, v_n\, N_y^T\, d\Omega \quad (20)$$

The derivation of the hourglass correction term for C_{11} is shown. The derivation for C_{22} would be identical. From the Gaussian quadrature rule (in two- dimensions)

$$C_{11} = \frac{\rho\, A}{4}\, u_n\, \Sigma\, w_i\, w_j\, N\, (r_i, s_j)\, N_x^T\, \Big|_{i,j} \quad (21)$$

where A is the area of the element, i and j correspond to the number of integration points in the x and y direction respectively, $w_{i,j}$ are the Gauss weighting factors in the x and y directions and (r_i, s_j) are the coordinates of the integration points.

We now use (2x2) Gauss quadrature with weighting factors of 1, and sampling points at $(\zeta,\eta)=(\pm\sqrt{(\alpha/3)},\pm\sqrt{(\alpha/3)})$,

$$C_{11} = \frac{\rho\, A}{4}\, u_n \sum_{d\zeta, d\eta = \pm\sqrt{\alpha/3}} N(d\zeta, d\eta)\, u_n\, b_1^T(d\zeta, d\eta) \quad (22)$$

In order to enable two-point quadrature, using a only centroidal data, the following Taylor expansion approximations are used

$$N(d\zeta, d\eta) = N(0,0) + \frac{\partial N}{\partial \zeta}\Big|_{0,0} d\zeta + \frac{\partial N}{\partial \eta}\Big|_{0,0} d\eta \quad (23)$$

$$B(d\zeta, d\eta) = B(0,0) + \frac{\partial B}{\partial \zeta}\Big|_{0,0} d\zeta + \frac{\partial B}{\partial \eta}\Big|_{0,0} d\eta \quad (24)$$

Substituting the above two relations in the equation for C_{11}

$$C_{11} = \frac{\rho\, A\, u_n}{4} \sum_{d\zeta, d\eta = \pm\sqrt{\alpha/3}} [N_0 + N_{,\zeta} d\zeta + N_{,\eta} d\eta\,] \\ u_n\, [\, b_{1_0}^T + b_{1,\zeta}^T d\eta + b_{1,\eta}^T d\eta\,] \quad (25)$$

Using the vectors s, ζ and η, where $s^T=[1\ 1\ 1\ 1]$, $\zeta^T=[-1\ 1\ 1\ -1]$ and $\eta^T=[-1\ -1\ 1\ 1]$, the expression for C_{11} is

$$C_{11} = \frac{\rho\, A\, u_n}{4}\, [\, sb_1^T + \frac{\alpha}{3}\, (\, \zeta b_{1,\zeta}^T + \eta b_{1,\eta}^T\,)\,] \quad (26)$$

and similarly for C_{22},

$$C_{22} = \frac{\rho A V_n}{4} [\ sb_2^T + \frac{\alpha}{3} (\ \zeta b_{2,\zeta}^T + \eta b_{2,\eta}^T)\ ] \qquad (27)$$

In the above equations the terms inside the bracket with the $\alpha/3$ factor are the hourglass correction factors for the convective terms C. Similarly the diffusion matrix K can be found

$$K = A\ B^T(0,0)\ D\ B(0,0) + \frac{\alpha A}{3} [B_{,\zeta}^T DB_{,\zeta} + B_{,\eta}^T DB_{,\eta}] \qquad (28)$$

Note that in the above formulation the balancing tensor is included into the D matrix. The hourglass correction terms, second and third terms of the right hand side of equation (27), therefore, are implemented on the balancing tensor as well. It should be emphasized that the above analysis is exact, (i.e., no higher order hourglass terms are neglected).

Stability and Accuracy

For a pure diffusion problem, the solution is conditionally stable with the well-known stability limit of

$$\Delta t \le \frac{\Delta x^2}{2\alpha} \quad [\ or \quad \Delta t \le 1 / [\sum_1^n \frac{2\alpha_i}{\Delta x_i^2}]\ in\ n\ dimensions\ ] \quad (29)$$

where Δx is the size of the smallest element in the domain.

A pure convection problem (i.e. $\alpha=0$) is unstable unless balancing tensors are used. The stability limit of the solution (in one dimension) with the balancing tensor is

$$c\ (= u\ \frac{\Delta t}{\Delta x}) \le 1 \qquad (30)$$

where c is the Courant number of the smallest element.

Another constraint on the time scale is introduced by the choice of k in the fully explicit solution to the pressure equation. Although k is a physical quantity (i.e., the bulk modulus) for steady state solutions, we need not be too concerned with its actual value. Using a smaller value than the bulk modulus of the fluid under study, signifies a fluid more compressible than the actual fluid. Once the steady state is reached, however, the effect of compressibility is irrelevant. Attention must be paid to ensure that the speed of sound in the fluid, c_s is larger than the velocity scale of the flow. Violation of this results in the pressure wave in the flow not traveling fast enough downstream. This condition states that the Courant number based on the speed of sound c_s should be less than 1, or

$$\Delta t \le \frac{\Delta x}{c_s} \qquad (31)$$

Spacial accuracy of the solution with hourglass control correction is second order. The temporal accuracy is also second order when balancing tensor is introduced.

TEST PROBLEMS

A number of classic benchmark problems have been solved, and a brief discussion of the results is presented in this section.

Figure 1 shows the velocity vectors obtained from the simulation of a simple flow between stationary walls at Re=1000. A plug velocity profile at the inlet and prescribed pressure at the exit defined the remaining boundary conditions of the problem. Note the removal of the hourglass mode when the hourglass control is applied.

Figure 1: Velocity in Flow Between Parallel Plates
(a) With Hourglass Correction $\alpha = 1$
(b) Without Hourglass Correction

The numerical grid used to model the flow past a circular cylinder is shown in figure 2. The model is similar to that used in [4]. Boundary conditions for this flow were defined as a constant velocity at all the exterior boundaries except at the exit where a constant pressure was specified. At Reynolds numbers smaller than about 50 the model produces laminar symmetric wakes. At higher Reynolds numbers, vortex shedding is observed. Figure 3 shows a time sequence of streamline distributions at Re=200. Note that, considering the sequence in figure 3 corresponds to approximately half the shedding cycle, the Strouhal number of shedding is about 0.17. Comparison of drag coefficients, C_D, from the present analysis with a number of other experimental and computational studies is provided in Table 1.

Table 1: Comparison of Drag Coefficients

Re	C_D	Reference	Re	C_D	Reference
25	2.	present	100	2	present
25	2.	[12] experimental	100	1.3	[12] experimental
25	2.26	[11] computational	100	1.76	[11] computational
50	2	present	200	2	present
50	1.5	[12] experimental	200	1.2	[12] experimental
50	1.81	[11] computational	200	1.76	[11] computational
50	1.71	[13] computational			

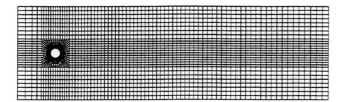

Figure 2: Grid Used for Flow Past a Cylinder

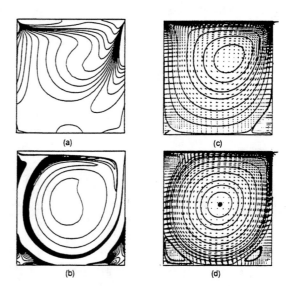

Figure 4: Vorticity Contours at (a) Re=400, (b) Re=500 Velocity Vectors and Streamlines for (c) Re=400, (d) Re=5000

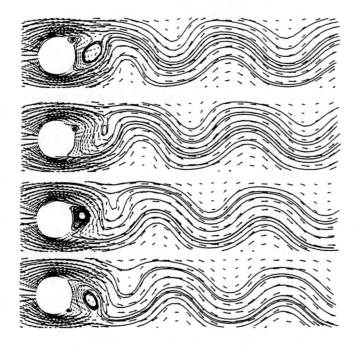

Figure 3: Sequence of Streamlines and Velocity Vectors Showing the Vortex Shedding at Re=200

Table 2: Comparison Between Extremes and Their Corresponding Location

	Re=1000			Re=5000		
	Present Work	[11]	[13]	Present Work	[11]	[13]
u_{min} (x=0)	-.375	-.375	-.383	-.43	-.426	-.436
y	.174	.16	.172	-.426	-.426	-.43
v_{min} (y=.5)	-.516	-.516	-.516	-.563	-.563	-.554
x	.41	.466	.406	.456	.406	.453
v_{max} (y=.5)	.362	.362	.371	.421	.419	.436
x	-.34	-.34	-.344	-.425	-.426	-.422

At Re=60, drag coefficients of 1.77, 1.44, 1.57, .04, 1.343 have been obtained in a study using a number of commercial codes [16].

The flow in a cavity with a moving lid was predicted at three different Reynolds numbers, i.e., Re=400, 1000 and 5000. Figure 4 shows the velocity vectors and streamline and vorticity contours for Re=400 and 5000. A qualitative comparison with studies presented in [11] and [15] indicates agreement between the shapes and sizes of the primary and secondary vortices. Figure 5 shows the normalized u velocity at center of the cavity. The predicted velocities compare well with the computational work of Ghia, et.[13]. Table 2 shows the comparison between various extremes predicted by the present code and those of [11] and [13].

The flow between backward facing step is also modelled in accordance with the geometry in the experimental work of Armaly et al.[10]. The boundary conditions are again specified as a plug inlet velocity and fixed exit pressure. The velocity vector and stream function distribution in the expansion region of the flow is shown in figure 6. Comparison between the reatachment lengths for this configuration is given in Table 3. The under-evaluation of x_1 and x_4 at higher Reynolds number has been reported by other computational schemes as well, [10] and [16]. The under-evaluation of x_1 and x_4 at higher Reynolds number has been reported by other computational schemes as well, [10] and [16].

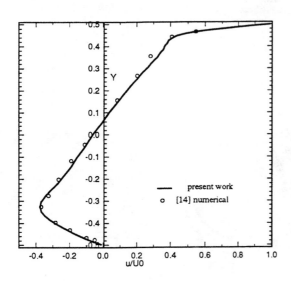

Figure 5: U$_1$ Velocity Profile Along Vertical Centreline at Re=1000

Table 3: Normailized Re-attachment Lengths

Re=200	Present	[10]	Re=1000	Present	[10]
x$_1$/s	~5	5	x$_1$/s	~12	16.3
Re= 450			x$_4$/s	~10	13.5
x$_1$/s	~8	9.5	x$_5$/s	~20	21.7
x$_4$/s	~8	7.6			
x$_5$/s	~11	11.3			

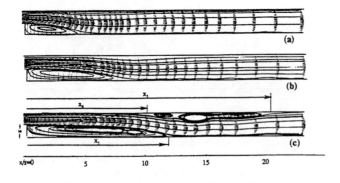

Figure 6: Velocity Vectors and Streamlines at (a) Re=200, (b) Re=450 & (c) Re=1000

REFERENCES

[1] Metzger, D.R. and Sauvé, R. G. , "Three-Dimensional Hourglass Stabilization for One-Point Quadrature Finite Elements", ASME PVP Journal, Vol. 265, 1994.

[2] Liu, W.K., Ong, J.S.J., Uras, R.A., "Finite Element Stabilization Matrices - A Unified Approach", Computer Methods in Applied Mechanics and Engineering, Vol. 53, pp. 13-46, 1985.

[3] Yagawa, G., Eguchi, Y., "Comparison Between the Traction and Pressure-Imposed Boundary Conditions in Finite Element Flow Analysis", International Journal for Numerical Methods in Fluids, Vol.7, pp. 521-532, 1987.

[4] Gresho,P.R., Chan, S.T., Lee, R.L. and Upson, G.D,. "A Modified Finite Element Method For Solving the Time-Dependent, Incompressible Navier-Stokes Equations. Part 1: Theory", International Journal for Numerical Methods in Fluids, Vol. 4, 1984.

[5] Sauve, R.G., Metzger D.R., "Advances in Dynamics Relaxation Techniques for Nonlinear Finite Element Analysis", ASME PVP Journal, Vol. 117, pp. 170-176, 1995.

[6] Sani, R.L., Gresho, P.M., Lee, R.L., Griffiths, D.F., " The Cause and Cure (?) Of the Spurious Pressure Generated by Certain FEM Solutions of the Incompressible Naviour-Stokes Equations", Parts 1, International Journal for Numerical Methods in Fluids, Vol.1, pp. 17-43, 1981.

[7] Sani, R.L., Gresho, P.M., Lee, R.L., Griffiths, D.F., Engelman, M., " The Cause and Cure(?) Of the Spurious Pressure Generated by Certain FEM Solutions of the Incompressible Naviour-Stokes Equations, Parts 2", International Journal for Numerical Methods in Fluids, Vol.1, pp. 171-204 1981.

[8] Dukowicz, J.K., Ramshaw, J.D., "Tensor Viscosity Method for Convection in Numerical Fluid Dynamics", J. Computational Physics, Vol.32, pp. 71-79, 1979.

[9] Fletcher, C.A.J., "Computational Techniques for Fluid Dynamics", Springer-Verlag, Vol. 1, Second Edition, pp. 299-305, 1991.

[10] Armaly, B.F., Durst, F., Pereira, J.C.F., Schönung, B., "Experimental and Theoretical Investigation of Backward-facing Step Flow", Journal of Fluid Mechanics, Vol.127, pp. 473-496, 1983.

[11] Gresho,P.R., Chan,S.T., Lee R.L. and Upson, G.D. , "A Modified Finite Element Method For Solving the Time-Dependent, Incompressible Navier-Stokes Equations. Part 1: Theory", International Journal for Numerical Methods in Fluids, Vol. 4, 1984.

[12] Jordan, S. and Fromm, J., "Oscillatory Drag, Lift, and Torque on a Circular Cylinder in a Uniform Flow", Phys. Fluids, 15 (1972)

[13] Ghia, U., Ghia, K. And Shin, C., "High-Re Solutions for Incompressible Flow Using the Navier-Stokes Equations and a Multi-grid Method", Journal of Computational Physics, 48, 1982.

[14] Gresho, P., Lee, R. Upson, C., "FEM Solution of the Naviour Stokes Equations for Vortex Shedding Behind a Cylinder: Experiments with the four-node Element", Advances in Water Resources, $, 1981.

[15] Ramaswamy, B., Jue, T.C., Mead, A.J. and Akin,J.E. , "Computation of Complex Fluid Flows Using a Semi-Implicit Finite Element Method", Recent Advances and Applications in Computational Fluid Dynamics, FED-Vol. 103, ASME, 1991.

[16] Freitas, C.J., Perspective: Selected Benchmarks from Commercial CFD Codes", Journal of Fluids Eng., Vol. 17, 1995.

FED-Vol. 238, 1996 Fluids Engineering Division Conference
Volume 3
ASME 1996

A Finite Element Method for Heat Transfer Prediction in Cooled Turbine Blades

J.-M. Zhou[*], M.P. Robichaud[*], M.F. Peeters[*] and W.G. Habashi[* **]
* CFD and Performance Applications Department,
Pratt & Whitney Canada, Longueuil, Quebec, Canada
and
** CFD Lab, Department of Mechanical Engineering,
Concordia University, Montreal, Quebec, Canada

Abstract

This paper presents heat transfer numerical predictions of turbine blade external and internal heat loads. A 180° bend coolant passage and the VKI linear turbine cascade are chosen for code validation and the predicted flows and heat transfer are compared with experimental data. For the 180° bend, the predicted heat transfer and pressure losses along the passage compare favorably with the experimental data. For the linear turbine cascade, the predicted isentropic Mach number distribution and the heat transfer coefficient along the blade agree well with the measurement. It is found, however, that the grid near the leading edge of the blade needs substantial refinement to capture physical phenomena such as flow transition. In addition, further improvement of turbulence models suitable for near-wall flow resolution is suggested.

Nomenclature

Ec	: Eckert number
G	: turbulence generation
K	: thermal conductivity
M	: Mach number
P	: pressure
Pr	: Prandtl number
Re	: Reynolds number
T	: temperature
U	: velocity components
W	: weight function
h	: heat transfer coefficient
k	: turbulence kinetic energy
l_m	: turbulence length scale
q	: heat flux
t	: time
x	: coordinates
ε	: turbulence dissipation rate
κ	: von Karmann constant
ρ	: density
μ	: viscosity
λ	: viscous dissipation

1. Introduction

Turbine blade cooling is widely used in high-performance engines to achieve higher power at lower specific fuel consumption. Determination of the external heat load on the blade/vane and of the local heat transfer in internal cooling passages is extremely important in predicting blade metal temperatures and impacts directly upon blade life and the amount of cooling air needed.

Current cooling design methodology in the industry has been mostly based on experimentally measured heat transfer data in test rigs. Such study of the cooling performance for model situations is costly and time consuming, and even more so for real blade and platform geometries. Thus, the situation calls for a computational tool capable of simulating such flows and heat transfer and accurately quantifying the effects of parametric changes on the process. In addition, such a CFD tool enables designers to assess the effect of individual heat transfer enhancement mechanisms, such as the inclusion of ribs (trip-strips), pedestals, end bends, blade rotation effects, impingement and film cooling. Eventually, such a tool provides an integrated multi-disciplinary approach for the thermal-structure analysis of blade and platform cooling.

The present work presents predictions of the flow and heat transfer in the coolant passages and around a turbine blade. The methodology shown can be applied to external heat load analysis and internal cooling scheme designs. In the following, the heat transfer calculation method of the present CFD code (NS3D) will be described. A 180^0-turn coolant passage without ribs, as well as a VKI transonic linear turbine cascade are used to carry out the flow and heat transfer validation. They are representative of the internal cooling and external heat loading, respectively. The predicted pressure and heat transfer coefficients are compared with the experimental data [1-2].

2. Numerical Formulation

The unsteady, compressible Reynolds-averaged conservation equations of mass, momentum and energy can be written in non-dimensional form as:

$$\frac{D\rho}{Dt} = \varepsilon \frac{\partial^2}{\partial x_i \partial x_i}\left[P - \hat{P}\right] \tag{1}$$

$$\frac{D}{Dt}[\rho U_i] = -\frac{\partial P}{\partial x_i} + \frac{1}{Re}\frac{\partial}{\partial x_j}\left[\mu_{eff}\left(\frac{\partial U_j}{\partial x_i} + \frac{\partial U_i}{\partial x_j}\right)\right] \tag{2}$$

$$\frac{D}{Dt}[\rho C_p T_0] = Ec\frac{\partial P}{\partial t} + \frac{1}{Re\,Pr}\frac{\partial}{\partial x_j}\left[K_{eff}\frac{\partial T}{\partial x_j}\right]$$

$$+\frac{Ec}{Re}\frac{\partial}{\partial x_j}\left[\mu_{eff}U_k\left(\frac{\partial U_j}{\partial x_k} + \frac{\partial U_k}{\partial x_j}\right)\right] \tag{3}$$

where U_i (i=1,2,3) are the velocities, P is the pressure, and T_0 is the total temperature. The term on the right-hand-side of the continuity equation is a pressure dissipation term to provide the necessary link between the continuity and momentum equations to avoid the well-known checkerboarding or odd-even decoupling effect. It is set in second order form to represent a 4th-order dissipation as the difference between two Laplacians, where P is calculated at the nodes and $\hat{P}$ is a coarser grid nodal pressure obtained by averaging at each node the pressure values from the nearest Gaussian points of connected elements. On a uniform grid this can be shown to be identical to the use of staggered grids for such a term.

This system of equations is solved by a Finite Element Newton-Galerkin approach [3-4], with the main characteristics of the code being:

1) Domain discretization by multi-block structured hexahedral grids,
2) Equal order interpolation is used for all variables,
3) Newton linearization of the governing equations, for fast and reliable convergence,
4) A parallel iterative algorithm to solve the continuity and momentum equations equations in a fully-coupled way.

Turbulence is modeled by the two-equation k-ε model:

$$\mu_{eff} = \mu + \mu_t, \qquad \mu_t = c_\mu \rho Re \frac{k^2}{\varepsilon} \tag{4}$$

$$\frac{D}{Dt}[\rho k] = \frac{1}{Re}\frac{\partial}{\partial x_j}\left[\frac{\mu_{eff}}{\sigma_k}\frac{\partial k}{\partial x_j}\right] + G + \rho\varepsilon \tag{5}$$

$$\frac{D}{Dt}[\rho\varepsilon] = \frac{1}{Re}\frac{\partial}{\partial x_j}\left[\frac{\mu_{eff}}{\sigma_\varepsilon}\frac{\partial\varepsilon}{\partial x_j}\right] + c_1\frac{\varepsilon}{k}G - c_2\rho\frac{\varepsilon^2}{k} \tag{6}$$

Near-wall turbulence is represented by a logarithmic velocity profile:

$$\frac{U}{U_\iota} = \frac{1}{\kappa}\ln\left(Ey^+\right) \qquad y^+ > 30,$$

$$\frac{U}{U_\iota} = y^+ \qquad y^+ < 30 \tag{7}$$

and the Van Driest mixing length damping function

$$\mu_t = \frac{\rho l_m^2}{Re}\left[\left(\frac{\partial U_i}{\partial x_j} + \frac{\partial U_j}{\partial x_i}\right)\frac{\partial U_i}{\partial x_j}\right]^{1/2}$$

$$l_m = \kappa y\left[1 - \exp\left(-\frac{y^+}{A}\right)\right] \tag{8}$$

is used for the momentum and energy integration in near-wall elements to dispense with ineffective wall functions. The boundary conditions for k and ε are set based on the standard wall function approach to be:

$$k = \frac{C_\mu^{-1/2}\tau_w}{Re\,\rho}, \quad \varepsilon = C_\mu^{3/4}\frac{k^{3/4}}{\kappa y} \tag{9}$$

3. Thermal Boundary Conditions and Heat Flux Calculation

Details will be given here only of the boundary conditions for temperature and heat flux. After integration by parts, the weak form of the Galerkin weighted residual formulation of the energy equation (3) can be written in terms of the total temperature T_0, as:

$$\iiint_V \left\{ \rho C_p \left(\frac{DT_0}{Dt} - Ec \frac{\partial P}{\partial t} \right) \right\} W dv =$$

$$- \iiint_\Gamma \left\{ \frac{K_{eff}}{\text{Re Pr}} \frac{\partial T}{\partial x_i} + \frac{Ec}{\text{Re}} U_i \left(\frac{\partial U_i}{\partial x_j} + \frac{\partial U_j}{\partial x_i} \right) \right\} \frac{\partial W}{\partial x_i} dv$$

$$+ \iint_S \left\{ \frac{Ec}{\text{Re}} \mu_{eff} U_i \left(\frac{\partial U_i}{\partial x_j} + \frac{\partial U_j}{\partial x_i} \right) \right\} W n_i ds$$

$$+ \iint_S \left\{ \frac{1}{\text{Re Pr}} q_i \right\} W n_i ds$$

(10)

where q_i (i=1,2,3) are the heat fluxes, and W is the weight function. For walls, two types of boundary conditions are considered:

1) The heat flux through the wall is imposed. In this case, the last surface integral in equation (10) is evaluated based on the given heat flux values,

2) The wall temperature is imposed and hence no surface integration need be evaluated.

In the case of specified wall temperatures, the heat flux values, needed for the calculation of the heat transfer coefficient, are accurately determined in a post-processing exercise. Instead of using one-sided temperature gradients to determine q, a global and consistent post-processing approach is utilized [5]. Once the temperature is obtained the heat flux is considered the unknown in Eq. (10), which is recast as:

$$\iint_{CS_{WALL}} \frac{1}{\text{Re Pr}} q_n W dS =$$

$$\iiint_V \left\{ \rho Cp \left(\frac{DT_0}{Dt} - Ec \frac{\partial P}{\partial t} \right) \right\} W dv$$

$$+ \iiint_V \left\{ \frac{K_{eff}}{\text{Re Pr}} \frac{\partial T}{\partial x_i} + \frac{Ec}{\text{Re}} U_i \left(\frac{\partial U_i}{\partial x_j} + \frac{\partial U_j}{\partial x_i} \right) \right\} \frac{\partial W}{\partial x_i} dv$$

$$- \iint_S \left\{ \frac{Ec}{\text{Re}} \mu_{eff} U_i \left(\frac{\partial U_i}{\partial x_j} + \frac{\partial U_j}{\partial x_i} \right) \right\} W n_i ds$$

(11)

and assembled only for elements with a surface on a wall. In this case one assumes the weight function $W = \Gamma_m$, and the normal heat flux $q_n = \sum_k (\Gamma_k q_k)$, with m including only wall nodes and k only wall elements. This method has been shown to be consistent with the Finite Element approximation, i.e. if the computed heat fluxes were to be re-imposed as boundary conditions, the same temperature field as the original Dirichlet problem would be obtained.

4. Results

The proposed method has been applied to the prediction of the pressure losses and heat transfer coefficients in a smooth coolant passage and on a 2-D vane cascade. The two cases represent internal cooling and external heat loading, respectively.

4.1 180 -degree bend

The geometric parameters of the 180°-turn coolant passage without ribs [1] shown in Figure 1 are summarized as follows:

Inlet width (W1) / outlet width (W2) = 0.67
Passage thickness (D) / (W1+W2) = 0.2
Bend height (H) /(W1+W2) = 0.5
Split thickness (d) /(W1+W2) = 0.1

Computations have been carried out for the following condition:

$$\mathrm{Re}_D = \frac{\rho U_{in} D_h}{\mu} = 53{,}000 \quad \text{with} \quad D_h = \frac{2W_1 D}{W_1 + D}$$

Inlet total temperature = 538 °R
Heated wall surface temperature = 581.4 °R

The computational grid has 60,000 nodes, with refined mesh near the wall so that the wall elements have an average of y^+ of about 20-40. At inlet, the mass flow and total temperature are imposed. At exit, a constant static pressure is given, along with zero streamwise gradient for all other variables. Adiabatic wall conditions are assumed for the inlet and exit sections. Constant temperature is imposed on the wall surface in the test region. The heat transfer coefficient $h = q_w/(T_w - T_{ref})$ and the Nusselt number $Nu = hD/k$ are calculated by using, as reference temperature, the mass-averaged static temperature at the stations along the passage. This is consistent with the use of a fluid bulk temperature in the experiments. Since only the mean heat flux was measured on each of 17 wall surface segments along the passage (indicated in Figure 1), the predicted local heat fluxes are integrated over the same wall surface segments for comparison.

From the computations, it is found that there is a major recirculation region after the turning and a small separation bubble at the first corner, with heat being trapped in these regions. At the passage turn, significant secondary flows are present, formed by a pair of symmetrical vortices. These vortices are found not to be stable and this unsteadiness prevented a "steady" solution. The instability of the secondary flow and its effect on the pressure loss and heat transfer could be further studied by solving the unsteady equations, but requires larger computational resources. Thus, to permit convergence, the computations were carried out only on one half of the geometry, with symmetry imposed. The heat flux distribution on the wall surfaces is found to be rather non-uniform, especially around the bend surfaces. The peak occurs on the surfaces on which the flow impinges after turning, and also where strong secondary flows occur.

Figure 2 compares the predicted heat transfer coefficient distributions with the experimental data. The overall heat transfer coefficient distribution along the passage is well predicted. The heat transfer coefficient distributions can also be compared with the experiments separately on the upper and side wall surfaces. It is found (Figure 3) that they are well predicted on all walls, but slightly overpredicted on the side bend surface. Because of the significant variation of both the flow pattern and the heat flux on the bend surfaces, due to impingement and to the secondary flows, it is difficult to investigate the cause of this overprediction using the available global measurements.

The pressure loss across the bend is analyzed for the condition of adiabatic wall and compared with the experimental data [1]. Figure 4 shows the normalized local static pressure profiles on the outer wall surfaces. It can be seen that the prediction agrees well with the experimental data. The maximum static pressure appears on the side bend surface due to the flow impingement after turning. The static pressure reaches the minimum in the region of flow separation after turning and recovers after the flow reattaches.

4.2 VKI Linear Turbine Cascade

The geometric parameters of the the VKI linear turbine cascade [2] are summarized as follows:

c:	67.65 mm,	g/c:	0.85,
γ:	55 °,	o/g:	0.2597,
γ_{LE}/c:	0.061,	γ_{TE}/c:	0.0105.

Computations have been carried out for the following conditions:

Inlet:

$$T_0 = 736.2\,^oR \quad P_0 = 26.82\,\mathrm{psi}$$

$$P = 26.49\,\mathrm{psi} \quad M = 0.15$$

$$\mathrm{Re} = 2.7098 \times 10^5$$

Free stream turbulence = 0.8%,
Incidence angle = 0°

Outlet:

$$M = 0.84 \quad \mathrm{Re} = 1.1352 \times 10^5$$

Wall:

Surface temperature $= T_w = 536''R$

The computational domain includes inlet, outlet and periodic and wall surfaces. The computational grid consists of 30 nodes between blades and 130 nodes in the streamwise direction, with 80 nodes on the blade itself (Figure 5). For accurate heat transfer calculations, the grid near the wall is refined so that the near-wall elements have an averaged y^+ value between 20 and 40. The heat transfer coefficient is defined as: $h=q_w/(T_w-T_\infty)$, where T_∞ is the total temperature at inlet.

At inlet, the mass flow (based on the measured flow velocity and fluid density), total temperature and turbulence quantities (based on a turbulence intensity 0.8% and pitch g) are imposed. On the exit plane, a constant static pressure is given, along with zero streamwise gradient for all other variables. Constant temperature is imposed on the blade surfaces. The predicted major flow parameters reached an over-all good agreement when compared with the experimental data at outlet as shown in Table 1.

Figure 6 compares the predicted heat transfer coefficient profiles with the experimental data. They are in good overall agreement, except in the region near the leading edge of the suction side. This is probably due to flow turbulence transition and strong adverse pressure gradient, which are not modelled by the present k-ε turbulence model. From the prediction, it is found that the flow Mach number is supersonic in a very small region near the trailing edge of the pressure side, which creates a local discontinuity of the flow pressure. The oscillation of the total temperature near the shock wave is damped by the added artificial dissipation terms. This has resulted in underpredicting the static temperature near the wall, thus resulting in unphysical negative heat flux near the shock wave region.

The flow calculation without heat transfer is carried out and compared with the experimental data. Figure 7 compares the predicted isentropic Mach number profiles with the experimental data. The predicted isentropic Mach number distribution on both the pressure side and the suction side

agrees very well with the measured data. From the prediction, it is found that the flow separates near the trailing edge of the suction side. This can be clearly shown from the isentropic Mach number profiles.

5. Conclusions

The present method shows promise to become an efficient tool for heat transfer prediction of turbine blade cooling. The code gives insight into the flow and heat transfer characteristics involved in the coolant passage and turbine blade external heat load, thus benefiting the blade cooling design process for high performance turbines. For the 180°-bend coolant passage, the main features of the flow and heat transfer have been well detected through the computation. The predicted overall and local heat transfer coefficients, and the local static pressure distribution along passages, have compared favorably with the experimental data.

For the VKI cascade, the predicted isentropic Mach number distributions on pressure and suction sides agree well with the measured data. The prediction of heat transfer coefficient gives overall good agreement with the experiment, except in the region near the leading edge of the suction side. This probably is due to the flow turbulence transition which is not adequately modelled by the present k-ε turbulence model, rendering further improvements necessary.

Acknowledgment

The authors would like to thank Drs. A. Riahi and J.W. Quick of Pratt & Whitney Canada for their useful suggestions and discussions. The authors also would like to thank Dr. W.S. Ghaly of Concordia University for his initial programming of the energy equation while at Pratt & Whitney Canada.

References

[1] D. Metzger et al., "Pressure Loss through Sharp 180 Deg Turns in Smooth Rectangular Channels," *ASME 84-GT-154*, 1984.

[2] T. Arts, M. Lambert de Rouvroit, and A.W. Rutherford, "Aero-Thermal Performance of a Two Dimensional Highly Loaded Transonic Turbine Nozzle Guide Vane," *ASME 90-GT-358*, 1990.

[3] W.S. Ghaly, W.G. Habashi, M.F. Peeters, P.Q. Gauthier and M.P. Robichaud, "Finite Element Solution of Viscous Compressible Flows in Gas Turbine Components", Proceedings of the 4th International Symposium on Transport Phenomena and Dynamics of Rotating Machinery, Honolulu, April 1992, pp. 641-651.

[4] W.S. Ghaly, W.G. Habashi and M.F. Peeters, "Assessment of a Finite Element Solution Method for Viscous Compressible Flows in Gas Turbines", Proceedings of the 2nd European Computational Fluid Dynamics Conferences, (Volume on Invited Lectures and Special Technological Sessions), September 1994, pp. 221-229.

[5] P.M. Gresho and R.L. Lee, "The Consistent Galerkin FEM for Computing Derived Boundary Quantities in Thermal and/or Fluid Problems," *International Journal for Numerical Methods in Fluids*, Vol. 7, 1987, pp. 371-394.

[6] C. Vuillez and B. Petot, "New Methods, New Methodology, Advanced CFD in the SNECMA Turbomachinery Design Process," AGARD LS-195, 1994.

Parameters	Experiment	Prediction	Error
Outlet Mach number	0.84	0.82	2.2%
Outlet static temperature (°R)	644.0	625.9	2.8%

Table 1: Comparison of flow parameters.

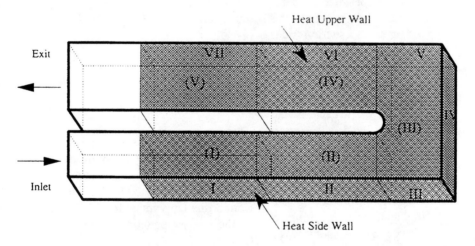

Figure 1: Typical configuration of a cooling passage, with measurement regions indicated.

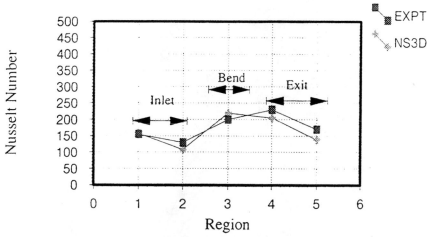

Figure 2: Overall Nusselt number distributions along a blade cooling passage (Re=53,000).

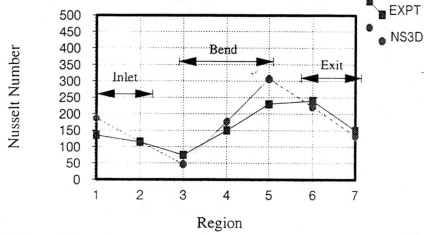

Figure 3: Side-wall Nusselt number distributions along a blade cooling passage (Re=53,000).

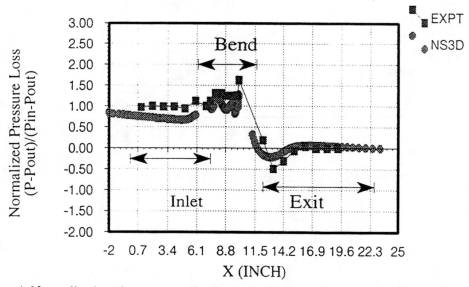

Figure 4: Normalized static pressure distributions along a blade cooling passage (Re=53,000).

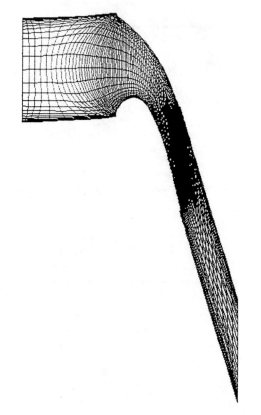

Figure 5: Computational grid for the VKI turbine cascade.

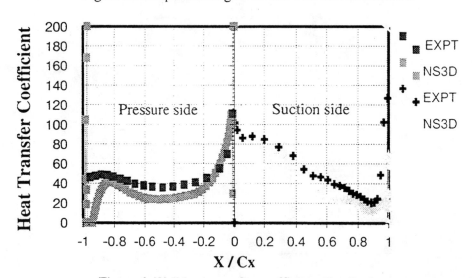

Figure 6: Wall heat transfer coefficient distributions.

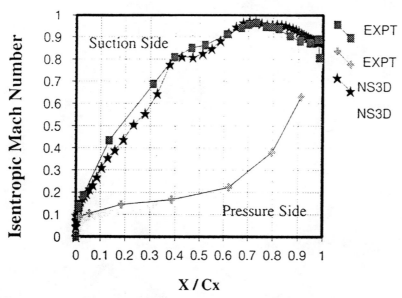

Figure 7: Wall isentropic Mach number distributions.

FED-Vol. 238, 1996 Fluids Engineering Division Conference
Volume 3
ASME 1996

Three-Dimensional Thermal Analysis Simulation of Spent Nuclear Fuel Canister using FIDAP

Davoud A. Eghbali

Savannah River Technology Center
Westinghouse Savannah River Company
Savannah River Site
Aiken, South Carolina

ABSTRACT

Dry storage studies have been initiated by the Experimental Thermal-Fluids (ETF) group of Westinghouse Savannah River Site to develop heat transfer technology for interim storage of foreign research reactor spent nuclear fuel assemblies awaiting final disposition. The computational fluid dynamics computer code FIDAP (version 7.5) has been utilized to model a 3-dimensional thermal analysis of four typical assemblies stored inside a canister. This report provides detailed FIDAP predictions and benchmarks against the test data using the experimental database obtained from the integral canister experiment conducted in the Thermal-Fluids Laboratory of Savannah River Site (SRS). Close comparison of the computational results with the experimental data provide verification that the code can be used to predict reasonably accurate thermal behavior as a result of conduction and convective heat transfer of a typical spent nuclear fuel canister while stored in a dry storage facility.

NOMENCLATURE

c_p specific heat
g gravity
Gr Grashof number
h enthalpy
k thermal conductivity
L characteristic length
P pressure
Pr Prandtl number
q''' heat generation
Ra Rayleigh number
T_w wall temperature
T_∞ ambient temperature

u velocity component in x-direction
y velocity component in y-direction
w velocity component in z-direction
ρ dynamic density
β volume expansion coefficient
μ viscosity
ν kinematic viscosity
Φ viscous dissipation

SUMMARY

The computational fluid dynamics computer code FIDAP, a finite-element code, has been utilized to model a 3-dimensional thermal analysis of four spent nuclear fuel assemblies inside a canister. The purposes of these simulations are: 1) to evaluate the relative effects of conduction and convection heat transfer modes on the resultant temperature and velocity fields inside the canister using Helium as fill gas and, 2) to benchmark the code using an experimental database obtained from the integral canister experiment conducted at SRS. In the experiment, the heated canister (instrumented) accommodates four Material Test Reactor (MTR) fuel assemblies with 100 watts decay heat each, and is surrounded by four full and two half unheated dummy canisters (uninstrumented) inside a wind tunnel. Heat flux sensors were located around the canister at a 22.5° azimuthal angle and at three axial locations (top, middle, bottom) for measuring the heat flux. The experimental heat transfer coefficients around the canister wall, obtained using these heat flux sensors, were used as boundary conditions for simulation, while the top and bottom of the canister were assumed to be insulated. Other measured variables included temperature distribution inside the canister at various locations, air velocity inside the wind tunnel, and the wind tunnel inlet temperature.

Due to the computer resources limitation only one fourth of the heated canister was modeled. Two symmetry boundary planes (x-z and y-z) were assumed in modeling the canister, i.e, the normal component of the velocity to these planes was constrained to be zero while the parallel components were left free. Also, within the fuel can, a no-slip velocity boundary condition was applied to all surfaces. The internal radiation heat transfer between the surfaces was not included in the model, as the evaluation of the radiation view factors (the fraction of the diffusively distributed radiant energy leaving one surface that reaches a second surface) for such a complex geometry would significantly increase the CPU time and make the convergence more difficult to obtain.

For conduction heat transfer simulation, the gas entities inside the canister are treated as solids and the 3-dimensional energy equation with volumetric heat generation source is solved for temperature distribution of the canister. Simulation of convective heat transfer inside the canister requires the 3-dimensional mass, momentum, and energy equations with volumetric heat generation source to be solved for temperature as well as gas velocity distribution inside the canister. As expected, the results indicate that the conduction heat transfer inside the canister is the dominant mode, and the internal natural convection as a result of temperature gradient between the fuel surface and the can wall becomes more significant as the thermal conductivity of the gas surrounding the fuel assemblies is decreased.

The code predictions of the canister temperature distribution are in reasonable agreement with the obtained experimental data. Conduction simulation with Helium as the fill gas predicted a ΔT of 78°C inside the canister which represents the difference between the maximum (fuel) and minimum (canister wall) temperatures. Addition of convective heat transfer to the model decreased the maximum temperature by 4°C.

INTRODUCTION

Dry storage studies have been initiated by the ETF group to develop heat transfer technology for interim storage of spent nuclear fuel while awaiting final disposition. The objective of this study is to perform, using the Finite Element Computer Code FIDAP (version 7.5), scoping thermal analysis calculations for the spent nuclear fuel integral canister experiment which was conducted in the TFL. These simulations are: 1) to determine how well FIDAP can predict the temperature distribution inside the canister given the fuel element's power generation rate, the heat transfer coefficient around the canister wall, and the thermal properties of the canister components and, 2) to evaluate the relative effects of conduction and convection heat transfer modes on the resultant temperature and velocity fields using Helium as fill gas. The uniqueness of this modeling is that a full-scale thermal analysis experiment of the canister was conducted to obtain an experimental database. In the experiment, the heated canister (instrumented) accommodates four MTR fuel assemblies with 100 watts decay heat each, and is surrounded by four full and two half unheated dummy canisters (uninstrumented) inside a wind tunnel. The effect of dummy canisters was to create a prototypic velocity profile distribution around the heated canister. The following variables were measured during the canister integral test: The heat flux distribution around the canister at 22.5° azimuthal angle and at three axial locations (top, middle, bottom); the temperature distribution at various locations on the fuel surfaces, can and canister walls, and canister top and bottom plates; and the air velocity inside the wind tunnel, and the wind tunnel inlet temperature. Using the experimental database, the code was benchmarked to be used for future prediction of

temperature distribution inside the canister given a set of boundary conditions.

The canister outer diameter and length are 40.64 and 91.44 cm, respectively, and are filled with Helium gas. The sealed fuel can is located inside the canister and is designed to accommodate four fuel assemblies; the fuel can will be filled with Helium gas. Figure 2 presents a 2-dimensional radial schematic cross section of a prototypic fuel assembly. Due to the limited computer resources only a quarter sector of the test canister was modeled. Two symmetry boundary planes (x-z and y-z) were assumed in modeling the canister, i.e, the normal component of the velocity to these planes was constrained to be zero while the parallel components were left free. This assumption, however, neglects the effect of internal temperature gradient caused as a result of variant heat transfer coefficient around the canister, on the resultant temperature and velocity distributions. A no-slip velocity boundary condition was applied to all surfaces within the fuel can. The two-dimensional schematics of the quarter sector model are presented in Figures 3 and 4.

The grid plate entity is a stainless-steel plate with a thickness of 0.32 cm, which extends from top to bottom and has an open (flow passage) slot at the top and near the bottom to allow buoyancy driven flow circulation (see Figure 4). The can and canister wall thickness are 0.48 and 0.34 cm, respectively. The gap between the can and the canister wall has a thickness of 0.84 cm and is modeled as a solid entity using the thermal conductivity of the fill gas. The 0.32-cm gap between the fuel and the grid plate is modeled as a solid entity using the thermal conductivity of the fill gas. A three-dimensional schematic of the quarter sector model of the enclosed canister, including the buoyancy driven flow path, is shown in Figure 5. Figure 6 presents a 2-dimensional axial schematic of a prototypic fuel assembly which is composed of eight regions. Regions 1 and 8 are 1.27-cm stainless-steel plates which connect the fuel assemblies to the fuel can. Regions 2 and 3 are the fuel assembly support leg and regions 4, 6, and 7 are the gas space. The fuel region (5) consists of distributed electrically heated and unheated plates joined through a thermal resistance. The open slots for buoyancy-induced flow circulation are located at regions 3 and 7. All fuel assembly regions, except 3 and 7 (flow slots), are modeled as solid entities, and the equivalent effective thermal conductivity of each region is calculated and utilized for the simulations. The effective thermal conductivities of the canister components are given in Table 1.

The internal radiation heat transfer between the surfaces was not included in the model, as the evaluation of the radiation view factors (the fraction of the diffusively distributed radiant energy leaving one surface that reaches a second surface) for such a complex geometry would significantly increase the CPU time and make the convergence more difficult to obtain. Furthermore, the 2-

dimensional analysis of the canister [6] indicated that the presence of the radiation effect in the model had only a small effect on the temperature distribution and almost no effect on the maximum temperature; this is due to the fact that with such small heat generation the dominant mechanisms for heat transfer are the conduction and convection.

The steady circulation of the fill gas inside the fuel can, induced by combined presence of fluid density gradient and a body force (thermal instability), enhances the heat transfer rate. The density gradient within the fluid is due to a temperature gradient between the fuel surface and the can wall. The problem assumes steady state flow of incompressible fluid, with density variation only in the term, according to the Boussinesq approximation.

For conduction heat transfer simulation, the generated heat inside the fuel region is conducted through the solid and gas regions and convected to the ambient temperature of 23°C through the canister surface using radially variable heat transfer coefficients (see Table 2) obtained from the integral experiment. The conduction/convection simulation is based on conduction of internally generated heat through the solid and gas layers, natural convection inside the gas layer, and convection of heat to the ambient temperature of 23°C through the canister surface using the same heat transfer coefficient. The top and bottom of the canister are assumed to be insulated.

FIDAP MODELING AND SOLUTION METHOD

This simulation was mainly conducted for the emperature distributions as a result of heat conduction through the canister as well as the buoyancy-driven flow field induced by the temperature gradient within an enclosed canister. A typical flow and temperature profiles under a natural convection mechanism near a heated wall are illustrated in Figure 1. Temperature decreases rapidly due to the convective cooling effect within a boundary layer region, as shown in the illustration. The boundary layer flow is a buoyancy-induced motion resulting from body forces acting on density gradients which, in turn, arise from temperature gradients in the fluid. The gravitational body force is oriented in the negative z-direction for the present analysis. The governing equations for natural convection employed in FIDAP under Cartesian coordinate system are shown below.

Continuity equation,

$$\frac{\partial \rho}{\partial t} + \frac{\partial (\rho u)}{\partial x} + \frac{\partial (\rho v)}{\partial y} + \frac{\partial (\rho w)}{\partial z} = 0 \qquad (1)$$

Momentum equation in tensor notation,

$$\rho \left\{ \frac{\partial u_i}{\partial t} + u_j \frac{\partial u_i}{\partial x_j} \right\} = \frac{\partial \sigma_{ij}}{\partial x_j} - \rho g_z \qquad (2)$$

where the variables with the subscript (i, j, or k) = 1, 2, or 3, correspond to those of the x-, y-, or z-direction, respectively. σ_{ij} is the stress tensor and ρg_z is the body force term.

$$\sigma_{ij} = -\left\{ P + \frac{2}{3} \mu \frac{\partial u_k}{\partial x_k} \right\} \delta_{ij} + \mu \left\{ \frac{\partial u_i}{\partial x_j} + \frac{\partial u_j}{\partial x_i} \right\} \qquad (3)$$

where

$$\delta_{ij} = (1 \text{ for } i=j, \ 0 \text{ for } i \neq j)$$

Energy equation,

$$\rho \frac{Dh}{Dt} - \frac{\partial}{\partial x} \left\{ k \frac{\partial T}{\partial x} \right\} - \frac{\partial}{\partial y} \left\{ k \frac{\partial T}{\partial y} \right\} - \frac{\partial}{\partial z} \left\{ k \frac{\partial T}{\partial z} \right\} - \frac{DP}{Dt} - \Phi - q''' = 0 \qquad (4)$$

where Φ is the viscous dissipation term, h is the enthalpy, and q''' is the heat generation source term. The viscous dissipation term in not included in the present model. For the present analysis, the Boussinesp approximation was used for the consideration of buoyancy-driven natural convection. It is a two-part approximation in that it neglects all variable property effects in the governing equations and it approximates the density difference term with a simplified equation of state, that is, the gravity term in the z-direction, ρg_z in eq. (2) is replaced by the following equation:

$$\rho g_z \rightarrow \rho \left\{ 1 - \beta (T - T_\infty) \right\} g_z \qquad (5)$$

where β is thermal expansion coefficient. The non-dimensional quantities, Prandtl number (Pr), Grashof number (Gr), and Rayleigh number, (Ra) are given respectively as follows:

$$Pr = \frac{\mu c_p}{k} \qquad (6)$$

$$Gr_z = \frac{g \beta L^3 (T_w - T_\infty)}{\nu^2} \qquad (7)$$

$$Ra = \frac{\rho^2 \beta g c_p \Delta T L^3}{\mu k} \qquad (8)$$

where L is the characteristic length, β is the thermal expansion coefficients, μ is the dynamic viscosity, and ν is the kinematic viscosity. The Gr is the parameter that describes the ratio of buoyancy to viscous forces and for the present analysis it is equal to 1.4e7.

Two quarter-models with different mesh densities of around 43000 and 78000 elements were developed to simulate the conduction and convection heat transfer modes. The effect of doubling the mesh density on the resultant temperature and velocity fields inside the canister was insignificant. The 2- and 3-dimensional mesh plots of the 43000-element model which was used for the simulations, along with the exact number of elements, are given in Figures 7 and 8, respectively.

The segregated iterative finite element scheme, along with conjugate gradient square and conjugate residual iterative methods, is used for the numerical solutions of the three-dimensional mass, momentum, and energy equation inside the canister. For segregated solver, the norm of relative error (‖Ui-Ui-1)/Ui‖, Ui is the solution vector) is computed separately for each degree of freedom being solved; three components of velocity, temperature, and pressure. Convergence is considered to be obtained when all of these norms are simultaneously less than the specified tolerance which was set to be 1e-4 for these simulations.

Dynamic relaxation and upwinding schemes were employed in conjunction with upper and lower relaxation factors. These schemes then dynamically compute the relaxation/upwinding factors during the course of nonlinear iterations. The default upper and lower relaxation factors and upwindings were used in these simulations, and are given in Reference 2. The solution converged after 100 iterations with the upwinding factors followed by 50 iterations with upwinding factors removed.

RESULTS AND DISCUSSIONS

The temperature distribution contours at different axial planes inside the canister simulating the difference between conduction and conduction/convection heat transfer are presented in Figures 9 and 10. Addition of convective heat transfer to the model, decreases the minimum temperature by 3 °C and the maximum temperature by 4°C. The natural convection flow inside the canister tends to change the temperature distribution as heat is removed from the fuel region and carried upwards as a result of density gradient. The flow is then directed towards the cooler region (can wall) of the canister by the top flow passage slot and moves downwards due to fluid body (gravity)

force. Comparison of Figures 11 and 12 shows the development of temperature boundary layer on the fuel surface as a result of buoyancy-induced flow. The velocity vector of this plane, indicating the flow patterns, is given in Figure 13.

The fuel assembly centerline temperature profiles predicted by both conduction and conduction/convection models is presented in Figure 14. The velocity profile at mid-plane (z=45.7 cm) in the y-direction is given in Figure 15. The experimental database was used to benchmark the code. The fuel centerline temperature comparison between the experimental data and the code predictions is presented in Figure 16. The following factors may have attributed to the difference between the experimental and FIDAP's prediction of the fuel centerline temperature profile: First, the model assumes a perfect contact (zero thermal contact resistance) at each interface between canister components; the temperature drop across these interfaces may be appreciable due to poor contact as a result of surface roughness effects. Secondly, the simulation results are based on one fourth of the heated canister for which the effect of variant heat transfer coefficient around the canister wall on the resultant temperature distribution is neglected. Thirdly, more accurate effective thermal conductivities, specifically in the fuel support leg region, would result in closer simulation predictions to the experimental results.

CONCLUSIONS

FIDAP (version 7.5) was successfully utilized to model and analyze a 3-dimensional thermal analysis and buoyancy-induced flow behavior inside a spent nuclear fuel canister. Conduction simulation predicted a ΔT of 78°C (difference between the maximum and the minimum temperatures) inside the canister, and an addition of convective heat transfer to the model decreased the maximum temperature by 4 °C. Figure 16 indicates a reasonable agreement between the experimental data and FIDAP's prediction of the centerline temperature profile. The results of this study indicate that FIDAP may be used for future thermal analysis prediction of canisters of similar configuration.

Table 1
Effective Thermal Conductivity of Canister
Components

Entity	K (w/m-C)
1	17.2
2	17.2
3	24.7
4	20.8
5	34.6
6	20.8

Table 1 continued
Effective Thermal Conductivity of Canister
Components

7	0.519
8	17.2
Gap	0.172
Canister Wall	17.2
Fuel Can Wall	17.2
Grid Plates	17.2

Table 2
Heat Transfer Coefficient around the Canister

Azimuthal Angle	h (w/m^2-C)
0	13.2
22.5	10.4
45	8.6
67.5	10.4
90	13.2

REFERENCES

FIDAP Theory Manual 1993, Fluid Dynamics International, Inc.
FIDAP Update Manual 1995, Fluid Dynamics International, Inc.
Incropera, F.P., Dewitt, D.P., "Fundamentals of Heat Transfer", 1981.
Eckert., E.R.G., Drake., R.M., "Heat and Mass Transfer", 1959, 2nd Edition.

FIGURES

Figure 1. Typical Temperature and Velocity Profile in
Natural Convection Flow

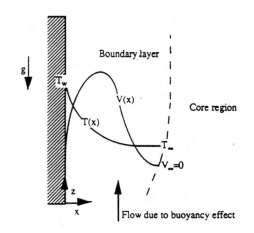

Figure 2. 2-D Schematic of Canister Cross Section

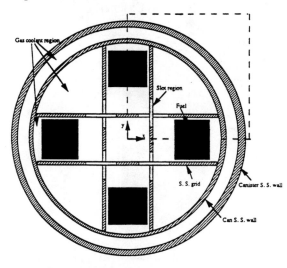

Figure 3. 2-D Schematic of Canister Quarter Model

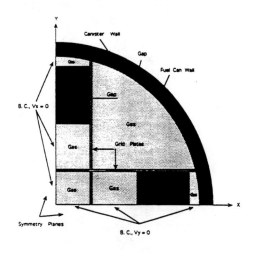

Figure 4. 2-D Schematic of Flow Channel at
Top and Bottom

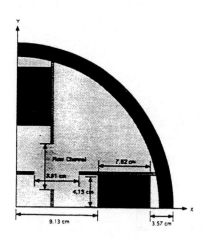

Figure 5. 3-D Schematic of Enclosed Canister with Gas Flow Channel

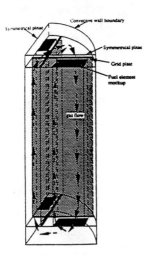

Figure 8. 3-D Mesh Grid for Quarter Canister Model

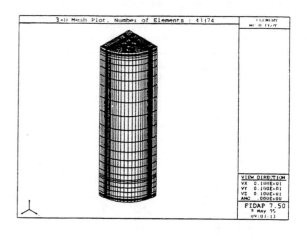

Figure 6. 2-D Axial Schematic of a Prototypic Single Fuel Assembly Component

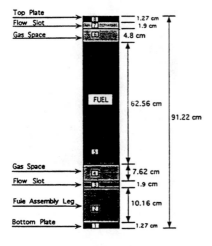

Figure 9. Temperature Contours at six levels inside the Canister (Conduction)

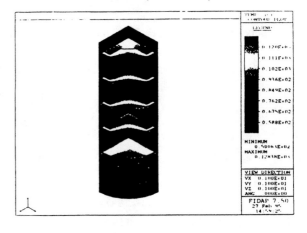

Figure 7. 2-D Mesh Grid in x-y Plane of Quarter Canister Model

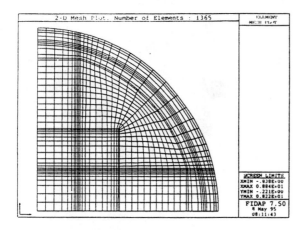

Figure 10. Temperature Contours at six levels inside the Canister (Conduction/Convection)

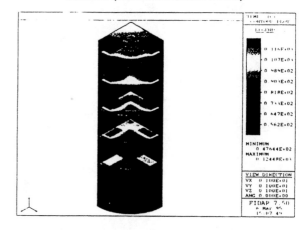

Figure 11. Temperature Contour at an axial plane inside
the Canister (Conduction)

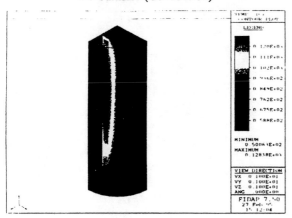

Figure 12. Temperature Contour at an axial plane inside
the Canister Showing Temperature Boundary Layer
Development at the Fuel Surface
(Conduction/Convection)

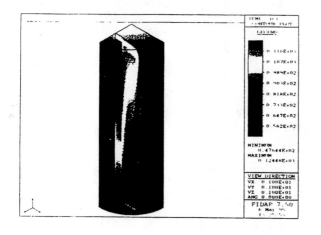

Figure 13. Velocity Vector at an axial plane showing the
Flow Patterns

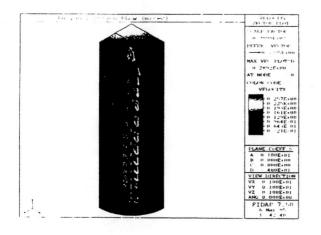

Figure 14. Fuel Assembly Centerline Temperature

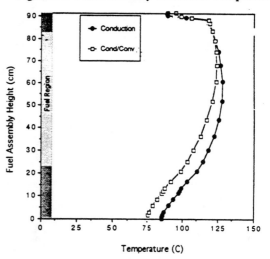

Figure 15. Velocity Distribution at Mid-Plane
(x=10.2 cm, z=45.7 cm)

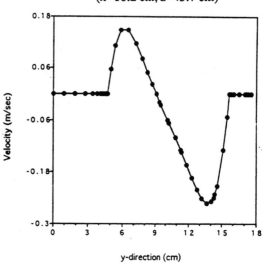

Figure 16. Fuel Assembly Centerline Temperature
Comparison

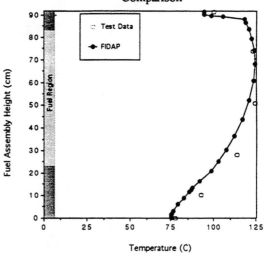

FED-Vol. 238, 1996 Fluids Engineering Division Conference
Volume 3
ASME 1996

A Finite Element Method for Free Surface Flows with Merging and Breakup

J. Rosenberg and M. S. Engelman
Fluid Dynamics International
500 Davis St., Suite 600
Evanston, IL 60201

Summary

A numerical method is presented which provides the means to model transient free surface flows of arbitrary shape and deformation. The method represents a powerful tool in simulating complex phenomena including interface merging and breakup. The Navier-Stokes equations are treated within the context of a Galerkin finite element method. Free interfaces are characterized by a volume-of-fluid (VOF) type representation. Interfaces are resolved using a new reconstruction method that can be applied to meshes of arbitrary topology. A unique flux limiting method is also developed to address the advection of the fluid volume. The overall scheme has been implemented in the general purpose fluid dynamics analysis package FIDAP (Engelman, 1993), and has been applied successfully to various flow problems over a broad range of conditions. Several validation examples are presented, and comparisons with previous experimental and computational results are made wherever possible.

The Numerical Method

Application of the Galerkin method to the equations for the isothermal motion of an incompressible fluid results in the following:

$$\int_V \nabla \cdot \mathbf{u} \varphi_m \, dV = 0 \ , \tag{1}$$

$$\int_V \rho \left(\frac{\partial}{\partial t} \mathbf{u} + \mathbf{u} \cdot \nabla \mathbf{u} - \mathbf{g} \right) \psi_j \, dV$$
$$+ \int_V (\nabla \tau - p \mathbf{I}) \cdot \nabla \psi_j \, dV \tag{2}$$
$$= \int_A \sigma \cdot \mathbf{n} \psi_j \, dA \ .$$

Here, ρ, $\mathbf{u}$, $\mathbf{g}$, τ, and p are the density, velocity vector, gravitational acceleration, stress tensor, and pressure. The symbols ψ_j and φ_m refer to the shape functions for velocity and pressure. The term $\sigma \cdot \mathbf{n}$ is the traction force across the computational boundary.

The fluid volume is represented by a characteristic marker concentration f. The value of f is unity within the tracked fluid and zero outside. Steep gradients in the marker concentration represent free surface locations. The advection of the marker concentration is governed by

$$\frac{\partial}{\partial t} f + \mathbf{u} \cdot \nabla f = 0 \ . \tag{3}$$

Sharp interfaces are maintained by insuring sharp gradients in f. This requires special treatment of the advective term in Equ. (3), which is achieved under the framework of a volume-of-fluid (VOF) type tracking method fully described in Engelman (1993). For a given time step, the volume tracking method determines a new fluid boundary based upon a calculated velocity field. On the basis of the computed fluid boundary, the finite element method is used to predict kinematics. Thus, Equs. (1-3) are resolved at each time step to predict the evolution of the flow.

The solution of Equ. (3) stems from a mass balance around each element. The rate of change of an elemental marker concentration is proportional to the net flow rate of fluid into the element:

$$V_i \frac{\partial}{\partial t} f_i = \sum_k Q_{ik} \; , \qquad (4)$$

where V_i is the total volume of element i, and Q_{ik} is the flow rate into element i across side k. The flow rate Q_{ik} is evaluated as the following integral along element side k:

$$Q_{ik} = \alpha_k \int_k \mathbf{u} \cdot \mathbf{n} \, dS \; . \qquad (5)$$

Here, $\mathbf{n}$ is the normal vector pointing into element i. The factor α_k represents a fractional area over which fluid is allowed to cross. The fraction α_k is determined from the marker concentrations of the elements sharing side k. Solution of Equs. (4-5) alone does not guaranty marker concentrations between zero and unity. In a process analogous to flux limiting (Hirt and Nichols, 1981), small adjustments are made to the fractions α_k such that

$$0 \le \alpha_k \le 1 \; \text{for all } k,$$
$$\text{and } 0 \le f_i \le 1 \; \text{for all } i. \qquad (6)$$

An implicit Euler method is used to integrate the temporal derivatives in Equ. (2), while Equ. (3) is integrated with an explicit scheme. Using a sub-cycling strategy, multiple explicit time steps for marker concentration are performed for a single implicit velocity step.

Collapse of a Water Dam

In this example, a rectangular column of water is initially at hydrostatic equilibrium between two vertical walls. The column measures L units wide by $n^2 L$ units high, as shown in Fig. 1. The right wall is removed, and the water is allowed to flow under the force of gravity. Experimental results for this problem are reported in Martin and Moyce (1952) for various values of L and n. Previous simulation results can be found in both Nichols and Hirt (1971) and Hirt and Nichols (1981).

Two cases are considered here for the purposes of comparison, namely $n^2=1$ and $n^2=2$, with $L=2.25$ inches in both cases. Three meshes of varying refinement are used in each case. The meshes for the $n^2=1$ case have 784, 1474, and 3192 elements, respectively. For $n^2=2$,

the meshes used have 1232, 2204, and 5016 elements. Results are shown in Fig. 2. Agreement with the experiments is good for the meshes considered. The position of the leading edge of the water is plotted as a function of time in a dimensionless form as in Martin and Moyce (1952). Briefly, the leading edge position x is scaled by the dimension L. The value of time is scaled by the factor $(n^2 g/L)^{-1/2}$, where g is the gravitational acceleration.

It is reported in Martin and Moyce (1952) that is was not possible to record the exact time when fluid motion began. To compensate for this effect, the simulation time counter here is shifted by a bias value t_o. The value of t_o is determined by matching the experimental and simulation results at a dimensionless front position of 1.44. The value obtained for t_o for the cases $n^2=1$ and $n^2=2$ is 2.12×10^{-2} and 2.02×10^{-2} seconds, respectively.

Turbulent Filling of a Tank

In this example, a 0.121 m diameter tank is filled with water from a 0.0121 m tube at the bottom. The Reynolds number based upon the tube diameter and average inlet velocity is 2500. Turbulence is simulated using a k-ε model. Both experimental and simulation results for this geometry are reported in Abdullah and Salcudean (1990).

Initially, the fluid is a rest with the free surface at a height of 0.4 m above the bottom of the tank. At $t=0$, flow begins from the inlet tube. Two meshes having 585 and 992 elements, respectively, are used here. Typical results are shown in Figs. 3 and 4. There are some quantitative differences between the simulation and experimental results, especially at early times. The simulations predict a strong initial bulging of the free surface at the axis of symmetry. This curvature is present in the experiments but not to the degree as seen here. This initial bulge is most probably a result of the initial rearrangement of the velocity field at startup. This bulge decreases quickly with time.

Three-Dimensional Mold Filling

In this final example, a three-dimensional mold is filled with fluid under creeping flow conditions. The geometry is shown in Fig. 5. The fluid enters the mold from the two annular regions at the bottom, and is driven by an applied pressure. The pressure applied at the left inlet is twice that applied to the right. Three meshes having 1888, 5304, and 8464 elements, respectively, are used here. Results at various dimensionless times are shown in Figs. 6 and 7. In Fig 7., the comparison of free surface shapes for the three meshes shows that the results are fairly insensitive to mesh refinement. This example illustrates the ability of the method to predict the merging of free surfaces in three-dimensions.

Conclusions

The numerical method presented here is capable of modeling transient free surfaces of arbitrary shape and deformation. The method is applied successfully to several flow problems exhibiting complex free surface motion. The simulation results presented are in good agreement with previous experimental and computational results.

Acknowledgments

The authors wish to thank A. Gooding, I. Hasbani, and V. Haroutunian for their assistance and valuable suggestions during the course of this work.

References

Abdullah, Z., and Salcudean, M., 1990, "Free Surface Flow During the Filling of a Cylinder", *Int. J. Numer. Meth. Fluids*, **11**, 151-168.

Engelman, M. S., 1993, *FIDAP Theoretical Manual*, Version 7.0, Fluid Dynamics International (FDI).

Hirt, C. W., and Nichols, B. D., 1981, "Volume of Fluid (VOF) Method for the Dynamics of Free Boundaries", *J. Comp. Phys.*, **39**, 201-225.

Martin, J. C., and Moyce, W. J., 1952, "An Experimental Study of the Collapse of Liquid Columns on a Rigid Horizontal Plane", *Philos. Trans. Roy. Soc. London Ser. A*, 312-324.

Nichols, B. D., and Hirt, C. W., 1971, "Improved Free Surface Boundary Conditions for Numerical Incompressible-Flow Calculations", *J. Comp. Phys.*, **8**, 434-448.

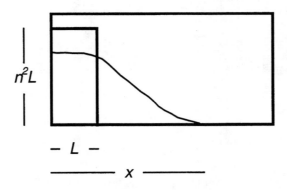

Figure 1. Schematic of the water dam.

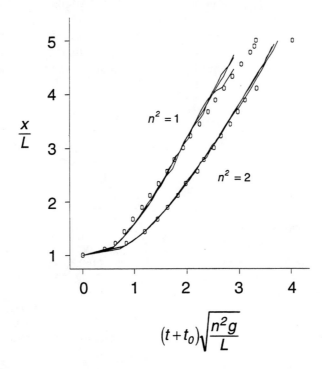

$$\left(t + t_0\right)\sqrt{\frac{n^2 g}{L}}$$

Figure 2. The position of the leading edge versus time for the collapse of the water dam. Experimental results (Martin and Moyce, 1952) are shown as open circles, and simulation results for all meshes are shown in solid lines.

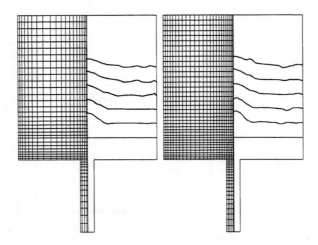

Figure 3. Free surface positions for dimensionless times of 0, 200, 400, 600, 800, and 1000. The meshes used are shown on the left.

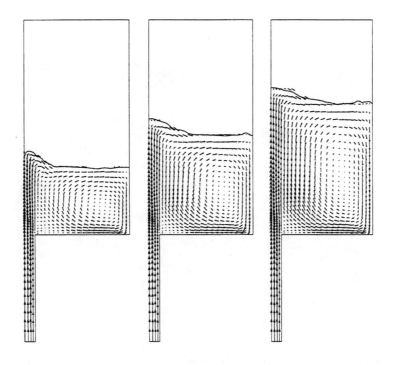

Figure 4. Velocity field within tank at dimensionless times of 300, 600, and 900.

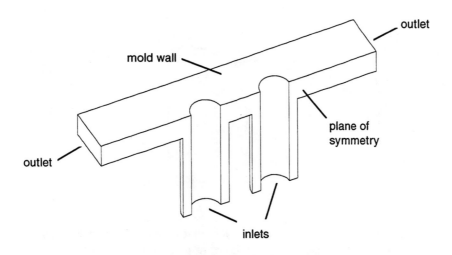

Figure 5. Schematic of mold filling problem.

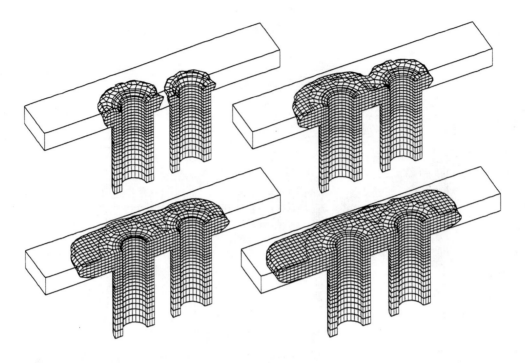

Figure 6. Free surface shapes at dimensionless times of 0.5, 1.0, 1.5, and 2.0. Results shown are for the mesh of intermediate refinement.

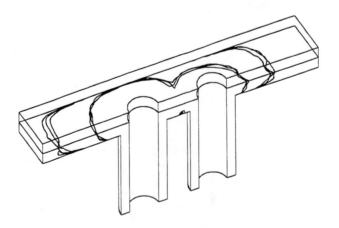

Figure 7. Free surface shapes along a horizontal cutting plane at dimensionless times of 1.0 and 2.0. The three meshes used to produce the results have 1888, 5304, and 8464 elements, respectively.

FED-Vol. 238, 1996 Fluids Engineering Division Conference
Volume 3
ASME 1996

Application of MEI Finite Elements to a Store Separation

Amir A. Mobasher

Ounyoung Park
Edward L. Bernstein
Department of Engineering Technology
Alabama A&M University
Normal, AL 35762

ABSTRACT

One of the most hazardous phenomenon that should be considered during the design and testing of military aircraft, is store separation. Often, when a store (bomb) is released from the aircraft to the free stream, the store moves upward, resulting in structural damage to the aircraft. This phenomenon which has not been well addressed up to this date, is believed to be caused by the shock-wave boundary-layer interaction between the aircraft body and the store.

In this study, an adaptive mixed explicit-implicit (MEI) Taylor-Galerkin methodology that solves the fully coupled Navier Stokes system of equations is introduced. This methodology has proved successful in dealing with shock-wave boundary-layer interaction problems. The algorithm is based on the general family of Taylor-Galerkin finite element methods which have a second order accuracy both in temporal and spatial domains.

The objective of the present study is to investigate the shock-wave boundary-layer interactions occurring in the store separation. The MEI methodology is first validated by means of shock-wave impinging on a flat plate. It is shown that the present formulation predicts the primary features of the flow field quite accurately. The MEI method is then extended to analyze the store separation problem. It is shown that under certain conditions, the pressure differential between the upper and lower sections of the moving store causes a net upward movement of the store.

INTRODUCTION

The computer simulation of the aerodynamically interacted relative motion of two rigid bodies under supersonic flow field, such as the aircraft store separation problem, is one of the most complicated problems in computational fluid dynamics. This problem is of practical importance because aerodynamic interactions can cause the released store to impact upon, and possibly damage, the aircraft. The development of a numerical code for this type of problem would therefore be of considerable benefit in the design of store and release mechanisms with the possibility of cost reduction of the flight tests.

Lohner et al (1987,1989) demonstrated how this type of problem can be simulated by using a single unstructured triangular mesh and an explicit finite element based solution algorithm with local mesh regeneration whenever it is necessary. In practice, it is found that many computational steps can be performed before a mesh regeneration is required, and this reduces both the computational demands and the problems associated with conservation of the physical variables. However, these results only show the location of a moving body at certain time period but does not show the practical problem that caused by the body moving upward. Dougherty and Kuan (1989) considered a specific two-dimensional configuration in which the motion of a falling body is prescribed in a compressible inviscid flow field. The numerical solution is obtained by forming a structured computational mesh for the wing section and then employing an overlapping structured mesh which follows the motion of the body by a finite difference technique.

Explicit forms of finite element methods have been the subject of intense studies in the past few years. The most popular forms of these methods, the Taylor-Galerkin finite element, has been proposed by Donea (1984) for the solution of hyperbolic partial differential equations and later, it was modified to the two-step Lax Wandroff type explicit method by Zienkiewicz et al (1985), Bay (1988), and Oden (1989); they applied their methods to supersonic inviscid and viscous problems. Despite the definite advantages of explicit schemes, such as speed of convergence, the main disadvantage is the limited size of computational steps due to the very small CFL number. Implicit methods, on the other hand, have very large memory requirements but are not subject to any restrictions on CFL number.

Hughes and Tzduyar (1984) developed an implicit finite element algorithm for both supersonic and subsonic flows with the SUPG method; Hughes (1990) et al extended it to viscous compressible flows. An implicit/explicit scheme based on the Taylor-Galerkin finite element method was developed by Hassan et al (1990). Recently Tworzydlo et al (1992a) formulated an adaptive implicit/explicit finite element method for the solution of compressible flow problems in the Cartesian coordinate system; Tworzydlo et al (1992b) extended it to axisymmetric problems. In this algorithm the implicitness or the amount of the damping is controlled by four parameters known as the implicitness parameters. Therefore, depending on the nature of the problem, the appropriate choice of these parameters may vary the methodology in a range from fully explicit to fully implicit.

In the present study, a mixed explicit/implicit Taylor-Galerkin finite element scheme is utilized to predict the inverse movement of the falling store for certain conditions. The method moves a portion of the mesh rigidly with the store and uses local mesh regeneration, whenever the modified geometry makes this necessary. The implicit/explicit method is applied to some two-dimensional inviscid and viscous laminar compressible flows.

GOVERNING EQUATIONS

The most general form of the Navier-Stokes equations for compressible flow is written as:

$$\frac{\partial U}{\partial t} + \frac{\partial F_i}{\partial x_i} + \frac{\partial G_i}{\partial x_i} = B \qquad (1)$$

where

$$U = \left\{ \begin{array}{c} \rho \\ \rho u_i \\ \rho E \end{array} \right\}, F_i = \left\{ \begin{array}{c} \rho u_i \\ \rho u_i u_j + p\delta_{ij} \\ \rho E u_i + p u_i \end{array} \right\} \qquad (2a,b)$$

$$G_i = \frac{1}{Re} \left\{ \begin{array}{c} 0 \\ -\tau_{ji} \\ -\tau_{ji} u_j + q_i \end{array} \right\}, B = \left\{ \begin{array}{c} 0 \\ 0 \\ 0 \\ 0 \end{array} \right\} \qquad (2c,d)$$

where t is the time, u_i are x-y components of the velocity, ρ is the density, p the pressure, μ is the molecular viscosity, τ_{ij} is the molecular stress tensor defined by:

$$\tau_{ij} = 2\mu_L \left(S_{ij} - \frac{1}{3}\frac{\partial u_k}{\partial x_k}\delta_{ij} \right) \qquad (3)$$

with

$$S_{ij} = \frac{1}{2}\left(\frac{\partial u_i}{\partial x_j} + \frac{\partial u_j}{\partial x_i} \right) \qquad (4)$$

and μ_L is the viscosity of the fluid. The term q_j is the heat flux vector defined by:

$$q_i = \left(\frac{\mu_L}{Pr_L} \right) C_p \frac{\partial T}{\partial x_i} \qquad (5)$$

with Pr_L as the laminar Prandtl number and C_p is the specific heat at constant pressure. E is the stagnation energy defined by,

$$E = e + \frac{1}{2}u_i u_i \qquad (6)$$

FINITE ELEMENT FORMULATION

The conservative form of the governing equation for compressible viscous turbulent flows is written as:

$$\frac{\partial U}{\partial t} = -\frac{\partial F_i}{\partial x_i} - \frac{\partial G_i}{\partial x_i} B \qquad (7)$$

where U , F, G and B are the conservative variables, conservative inviscid flux, viscous flux, and source terms respectively. Since $U=U(x,t)$, $F=F(u)$ and $G=G(u, u_{,j})$ following Chung (1992) we may write the following relations for F and G:

$$\frac{\partial F_i}{\partial x_i} = a_i \frac{\partial U}{\partial x_i}$$

$$\frac{\partial G_i}{\partial x_i} = b_i \frac{\partial U}{\partial x_i} + c_{ij} \frac{\partial U_{,j}}{\partial x_i} \qquad (8)$$

Where a_i, b_i and c_{ij} are the Jacobians associated with the inviscid and viscous fluxes.

$$a_i = \frac{\partial F_i}{\partial U}, \quad b_i = \frac{\partial G_i}{\partial U}, \quad c_{ij} = \frac{\partial G_j}{\partial U_{,i}} \qquad (9)$$

The residual representing the mixed implicit/explicit methodology in terms of the conservative variables, fluxes and the Jacobian of the flux terms is given by:

$$R = U^{n+1} - U^n + \Delta t \left(\frac{\partial F_i}{\partial x_i} + \frac{\partial G_i}{\partial x_i} - B \right)^n$$

$$+ s_1 \Delta t \left(a_j \frac{\partial \Delta U^{n+1}}{\partial x_j} - \Delta B^{n+1} \right)$$

$$+ s_3 \Delta t \left(b_j \frac{\partial \Delta U^{n+1}}{\partial x_j} + c_{ji} \frac{\partial^2 \Delta U^{n+1}}{\partial x_j \partial x_i} \right)$$

$$- 0.5 s_2 \Delta t^2 (a_j a_i + b_j a_i) \frac{\partial^2 \Delta U^{n+1}}{\partial x_j \partial x_i}$$

$$- 0.5 s_4 \Delta t^2 (a_j b_i + b_j b_i) \frac{\partial^2 \Delta U^{n+1}}{\partial x_j \partial x_i}$$

$$- 0.5 \Delta t^2 \left\{ \begin{array}{l} (a_j + b_j) \dfrac{\partial}{\partial x_j} \left(\dfrac{\partial F_i}{\partial x_i} + \dfrac{\partial G_i}{\partial x_i} - B \right)^n \\ + \dfrac{\partial B^n}{\partial t} \end{array} \right\}$$

$$(10)$$

$$+ O(\Delta t^3)$$

Here s_1, s_2, s_3 and s_4 are the implicitness parameters associated with the scheme with $0 \leq s_i \leq 1$. For $s_i = 0$ the scheme is explicit and for $s_i \neq 0$ the scheme is implicit. A special case, where all the s parameters are set to 0.5 produces the Crank Nicholson scheme.

The Galerkin finite element formulation of the above relation is obtained by taking the inner product of the residual R and interpolating function F and integrating over the domain, Ω.

$$\int_\Omega R(U, F_j, G_j, B_j) d\Omega = 0 \qquad (11)$$

where

$$U(\underline{x},t) = \Phi_\alpha(\underline{x}) U_\alpha(t)$$
$$F(\underline{x},t) = \Phi_\alpha(\underline{x}) F_\alpha(t)$$
$$G(\underline{x},t) = \Phi_\alpha(\underline{x}) G_\alpha(t) \qquad (12)$$
$$B(\underline{x},t) = \Phi_\alpha(\underline{x}) B_\alpha(t)$$

The compact form of this formulation is given by the following relationship:

$$(A_{\alpha\beta} \delta_{rs} + B_{\alpha\beta rs}) \Delta U_{\beta s}^{n+1} + N_{\alpha r}^{n+1} = H_{\alpha r}^n + N_{\alpha r}^n \qquad (13)$$

Here α, β are the indices associated with the global node and r,s are the indices associated with the individual equations. Each of the matrices $A_{\alpha\beta}$, $B_{\alpha\beta rs}$, $N_{\alpha r}^{n+1}$, $N_{\alpha r}^n$ and $H_{\alpha r}^n$ are defined as follows:

$$A_{\alpha\beta} = \int_\Omega \Phi_\alpha \Phi_\beta d\Omega$$

$$B_{\alpha\beta rs} = \int_\Omega \{ \Delta t[-s_1 \quad a_{jrs} \Phi_{\alpha,j} \Phi_\beta$$
$$- s_3(b_{jrs}\Phi_{\alpha,j}\Phi_\beta + c_{jirs}\Phi_{\alpha,j}\Phi_{\beta,i})]$$
$$+ \frac{1}{2}\Delta t^2 [s_2(a_{jrq}a_{isq} + b_{jrq}a_{isq})\Phi_{\alpha,j}\Phi_{\beta,i}$$
$$+ s_4(a_{jrq}b_{isq} + b_{jrq}b_{isq})\Phi_{\alpha,j}\Phi_{\beta,i}]\}d\Omega$$

$$N_{\alpha r}^{n+1} = \int_\Gamma \{ \Delta t[-s_1 \quad a_{jrs}\Phi_\alpha^* \Phi_\beta^* - s_3(b_{jrs}\Phi_\alpha^*\Phi_\beta^*$$
$$+ c_{jirs}\Phi_\alpha^*\Phi_{\beta,i}^*)]$$
$$+ \frac{1}{2}\Delta t^2 [s_2(a_{jrq}a_{isq} + b_{jrq}a_{isq})\Phi_\alpha^*\Phi_{\beta,i}^*$$
$$+ s_4(a_{jrq}b_{isq} + b_{jrq}b_{isq})\Phi_\alpha^*\Phi_{\beta,i}^*]\}n_j \Delta U_{\beta s}^{n+1} d\Gamma$$

$$N_{\alpha r}^n = -\int_\Gamma [\Delta t \, \Phi_\alpha^* \Phi_\beta^* (F_{\beta r}^n + G_{\beta r}^n)$$
$$- \frac{1}{2}\Delta t(a_{jrs} + b_{jrs})\Phi_\alpha^*\Phi_{\beta,i}^*(F_\alpha^n + G_\alpha^n)]n_j d\Omega$$

$$(14)$$

$$H_{\alpha r}^n = \int_\Omega \{ \Delta t[\Phi_{\alpha,j}\Phi_\beta (F_{\beta r}^n + G_{\beta r}^n) + \Phi_\alpha \Phi_\beta B_\beta]$$
$$- \frac{1}{2}\Delta t^2(a_{jrs} + b_{jrs})[\Phi_{\alpha,j}\Phi_{\beta,i}(F_{\beta\alpha}^n + G_{\beta s}^n)]\}d\Omega$$

$$+ 0.5\Delta t^2 \int_\Omega \frac{\partial B^n}{\partial t} d\Omega$$

The last term appearing in the equation (10) is a time dependent source term and is a function of U and $U_{,j}$. In this formulation Φ indicates the interpolating functions associated with the flux terms inside the domain and the '*' denotes the interpolating function associated with the terms on the boundary. Here U represents the unknowns and u, v represent the x and y components of the velocity vector respectively.

APPLICATIONS

In this study first the present formulation is tested by considering the problem of an oblique shock impinging on a flat plate and then the methodology is applied to a two dimensional store separation problem. The results are discussed below.

Oblique Shock Impinging on a Flat Plate

The first case considers the reflection of an oblique shock from a flat plate. This problem is particularly useful for understanding the physics of the shock wave reflected from a surface. The computations are performed with a mixed explicit/implicit algorithm. The finite element mesh used initially for this problem consisted of 20 nodes along the axial direction and 20 nodes along the vertical direction spaced in a geometric progression. An adaptive procedure (Peraire et al, 1987) was used to refine the mesh in the regions where the flow variables had high gradients (Figure 1a). The initial conditions for this problem are those corresponding to a Mach 3.0 flow coinciding with a wedge located at a distance of $5\delta_0$ from the flat plate at an angle of 13 degrees from the horizontal axis. Inlet boundary conditions are fixed and correspond to the initial conditions for each time step. At the wall, the no-slip conditions are imposed and at the exit plane the gradients of the flow variables are set to zero.

The physics of this problem is as follows: the incoming shock wave, called the incident shock, disturbs the fluid particles underneath the laminar boundary layer formed at the plate. This phenomenon causes eddies to develop, pressure to arise, and consequently the laminar boundary layer to thicken. The interaction of the shock wave with the boundary layer forms a secondary boundary layer. In this region, called the separation region, the flow recirculates causing skin friction to develop in the negative direction with an adverse pressure gradient. The physics of the separation bubble causes the flow field to develop three shock wave regions. Upstream from the incident shock the curvature is concave upward causing compression waves to develop and coalesce into a stronger shock. Downstream from the incident shock the curvature is concave downward causing an expansion wave to develop. Further downstream

the curvature changes to concave upward and compression waves again develop. These features of the flow field are illustrated in detail in Figure 1b.

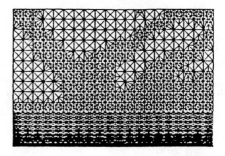

(a)

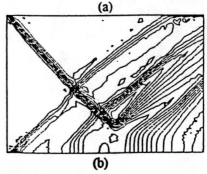

(b)

Fig. 1. Shock wave boundary layer interaction; a. Adapted grid; b. Pressure contours.

Comparison with Experimental Results

An oblique shock impinging at an angle of 32.6° upon a developing laminar boundary layer on a flat plate is considered. For this case, the free stream Mach number is 2 and the Reynolds number, based on the free stream velocity and distance from the leading edge of shock impingement point, is 2.96×10^6. The variation of static pressure along the surgace of the plate is compared with the experimental onservation of Hakinen et al (1959) in Figure 2. The experimental and computational values compare favorably.

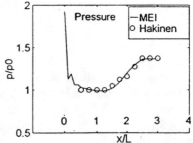

Fig. 2. Comparison of experimental and computed values for static pressure

EXAMPLES

A two-dimensional simulation was made of the store separation from an aircraft wing under both subsonic and supersonic conditions. The geometry considered in this study is shown in Figure 3.

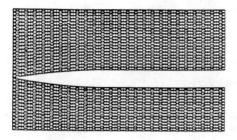

Fig. 3. Mesh used for store simulation

Here the lower surface of the wing is approximated by a horizontal wall. The front part of the store is described by the equation, $y = K\sqrt{x}$ where K is a constant, and the whole size of the store is scaled based on the gap H between the wing and the store. The computation starts from a fixed distance while the Mach number of the free stream varies at the steady state condition. The angle of attack is chosen to be zero. Analyses were made for four different values of the parameter H/d, where d is the diameter of the store. For each value of H/d, the pressure on the surface of the store was calculated for Mach numbers varying from 0.5 to 3.0. Results are shown for H/d = 2 and 4 and for Mach numbers ranging from 1.2 to 3.0 in Figures 3 and 4. The mesh size used in this calculation varied from 2000 to 3500 elements, depending on the value of H/d. For Mach numbers in the subsonic and lower supersonic ranges, the pressure on the lower surface of the store was consistently less than the pressure on the upper surface. However, for Mach numbers greater than 2, a region of pressure reversal developed on the lower surface. As shown in Figures 4a,b and 5a,b, an upward pressure is exerted on the forward section of the lower surface, causing a rotational motion upon release which may cause the store to impact on the wing.

CONCLUSION

A finite element algorithm has been devised for simulating store separation problems in two dimensions. It was found that at higher Mach numbers the pressure on a portion of the lower surface of the store is higher than on the upper surface and may cause unstable rotation upon release of the store with the possibility of structural damage to the aircraft. Further modifications to the code are planned to improve the simulation including a more realistic description of the store as a blunt body shape, extension to three dimensional and time dependent problems, and a more detailed description of the moving boundary conditions.

REFERENCES

Bay, K. S. et al, 1988, "A New Finite Element Approach for Prediction of Aerothermal Loads," *Progress in Inviscid Flow Computations*, AIAA paper 85-1533.

Chung, T. J., 1992, Lecture Notes, Department of Mechanical Engineering, University of Alabama in Huntsville.

Donea, J., 1984, "A Taylor-Galerkin Method for Convective Transport Problems," *International Journal of Numerical Methods in Engineering*, Vol. 20, pp. 101-119.

Dougherty, F. C. and Kuan, J., 1989, "Transonic Store Separation using a Three-Dimensional Chimera Grid Scheme," *AIAA Paper* 89-0637.

Hakinen, R. J., Greber, I., Trilling, L., Abarbanel, S. S., 1959, "The Interaction of an Oblique Shock Wave with a Laminar Boundary Layer," *NASA Memo* 2-18-59.

Hassan, O., Morgan, K., and Peraire, J., 1990, "An Implicit Finite Element Method for High Speed Flows," *AIAA Paper* 90-0402.

Hughes, T .J. R. and Tezduyar, T .E., 1984, "Finite Element Methods for First Order Hyperbolic Systems with Particular Emphasis on the Compressible Euler Equations," *Computer Methods in Applied Mechanics and Engineering*,, Vol. 45, pp. 217-284.

Hughes, T .J. R., Franca, L. P., Harari, I., Mallet, M., Shakib, F., and Spelce, T. E., 1990, "Finite Element Method for High-Speed Flows: Consistent Calculation of Boundary Flux," *AIAA Paper* 87-0556.

Lohner, R., 1989, "Adaptive Remeshing for Transient Problems," *Computational Methods in*

Applied Mechanical Engineering, Vol. 75, pp. 195-214.

Lohner R., Morgan, K. Peraire, J. and Vahdati, M., 1987 "Finite Element Flux-Corrected Transport (FEM-FCT) for the Euler and Navier-Stokes Equations," *International Journal of Numerical Methods in Fluids*, Vol. 7, pp. 1093-1109.

Oden, J. T. et al, 1988, "Adaptive Finite Elements Methods for High Speed Compressible Flows," *Finite Elements in Fluids*, Vol. 7, Wiley-Interscience, pp. 223-240.

Peraire, J., Vahdati, M., Morgan, K. and Zienkiewicz, O. C., 1987, "Adaptable Remeshing for Compressible Flow Computations," *Journal of Computational Physics*, Vol. 72, pp. 449-466.

Tworzydlo, W. W, Oden, J. T., and Thornton, E. A., 1992a," Adaptive Implicit/Explicit Finite Element method for Compressible Viscous Flows," *Computer Methods in Applied Mechanics and Engineering*, Vol. 95, pp. 397-440.

Tworzydlo, W. W, Huang, C. Y., and Oden, J. T., 1992b, "Adaptive Implicit/Explicit Finite Element methods for Axisymmetric Viscous Turbulent Flows with Moving Boundaries," *Computer Methods in Applied Mechanics and Engineering*, Vol. 97, pp. 245-288.

Zienkiewicz, O. C., Lohner, R., Morgan, K., and Peraire, J., 1985, "High Speed Compressible Flow and Other Advection Dominated Problems of Fluid Dynamics," *Finite Elements in Fluids*, Vol. 6, Wiley-Interscience, pp. 41-88.

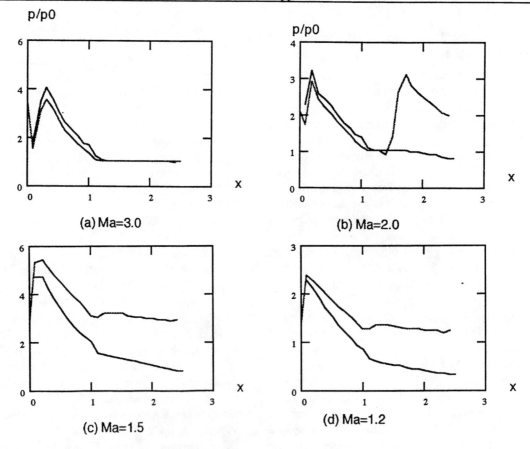

Figure 4. Pressure Profiles on the Surface of a Store for various Mach Numbers. ____ Upper Surface, ... Lower Surface. h/D=2.0, (a) Ma=3.0, (b) Ma=2.0, (c) Ma=1.5, (d) Ma=1.2

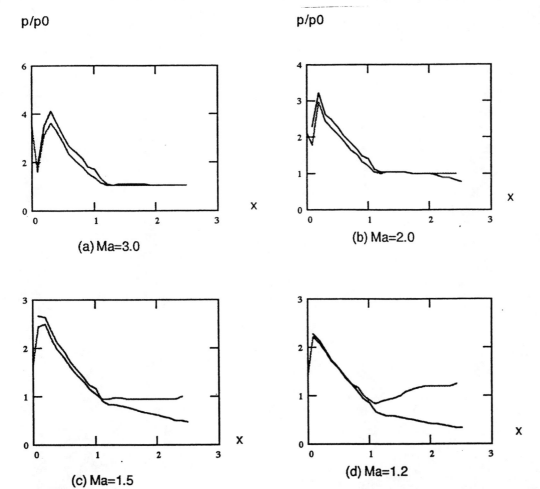

Figure 5. Pressure Profiles on the Surface of a Store for various Mach Numbers. ____
Upper Surface, ... Lower Surface. h/D=4.0, (a) Ma=3.0, (b) Ma=2.0, (c) Ma=1.5, (d)
Ma=1.2

FED-Vol. 238, 1996 Fluids Engineering Division Conference
Volume 3
ASME 1996

ADVANCES IN NUMERICAL MODELING OF FREE SURFACE AND INTERFACE FLUID DYNAMICS

Introduction

Peter E. Raad
Southern Methodist Univ.
Dallas, Texas

Grétar Tryggvason
Univ. of Michigan
Ann Arbor, Michigan

Tom T. Huang
David Taylor Model Basin

Bala Ramaswamy
Rice University
Houston, Texas

Mutsuto Kawahara
Chuo University
Tokyo, Japan

Deepak Ganjoo
ANSYS, Inc.

The keynote address and twenty papers that follow make up the Second Forum on Advances in Numerical Modeling of Free Surface and Interface Fluid Dynamics and were presented at the 1996 Fluids Engineering Division Summer Meeting, held in San Diego, California, July 7–11, 1996. The forum was sponsored by the Coordinating Group for Computational Fluid Dynamics of the ASME Fluids Engineering Division.

The goal of the Forum remained one of providing a platform for presenting results and exposing recent developments in the numerical simulation of fluid dynamics problems characterized by the existence of a free surface or interfaces. However, the scope of the Second Forum was expanded to encompass finite element techniques in addition to the finite difference and volume methods addressed in the First Forum. Of special interest were papers that dealt with improvements in the methodology of solving free surface and interface fluid flow problems, including for example, sloshing, bubble tracking, breaking and spilling waves, droplet impingement, thin-films, flows with large surface deformations, and wave-structure interactions.

The Forum has now doubled in size in its second year; a fact that, while very gratifying to the organizers, more importantly demonstrates the interest in this challenging area of CFD. Researchers from industry, government, and academia have assembled a body of high-quality work, as the reader will observe, that spans all of the topics mentioned above.

Many individuals have contributed to the success of this effort and deserve our gratitude. On behalf of my co-organizers, I extend many thanks to Professor Hugh W. Coleman for his support and to Dr. Edwin P. Rood and Professor Ramesh Agarwal for backing the project from its onset. I also extend my most sincere gratitude to Ms. Peggy King at SMU on whose unselfish help I have greatly relied.

FED-Vol. 238, 1996 Fluids Engineering Division Conference
Volume 3
ASME 1996

A FINITE AMOUNT ABOUT FINITE DIFFERENCE METHODS FOR FREE-SURFACE FLOWS -- YESTERDAY, TODAY & TOMORROW

ABSTRACT

Robert L. Street, M. ASME

Environmental Fluid Mechanics Laboratory
Stanford University
Stanford, CA 94305-4020

INTRODUCTION

In a real sense this is a talk that many in the audience could easily give. As they say in the current jargon, " we have been there, done that, are doing that, and hope to be doing that for awhile!" Let us begin by agreeing to talk about the unsteady flow beneath a free surface of a viscous incompressible fluid. I shall trace some history, talk about what is being done now, and comment on potential developments and/or where current efforts are leading us. Given the time available and my own biases, this will not be an historian's account; I have had to make choices about emphasis and could not be complete in my coverage. Thus, those whose work is not herein discussed should not feel slighted, it is only that their work did not fit in this small painting by this amateur artist!

HISTORICALLY SPEAKING

Using a third of a century ago as the target of our time machine, we land in Los Alamos and find the Marker-and-Cell [MAC] method about to burst into flower [i.e., publication in 1965]. That method is a starting point for this talk. Its bases, its improvements, and its progeny are discussed here historically in two sections:

The Marker-and-Cell Method

Other Branches of the Tree

Here we see some other methods that have similarities to MAC but are not causally related.

Then we move on to comment about some important conceptual issues that are driven by applications, to review some of today's interesting code implementations, to look into the crystal ball for the future, and to reach some conclusions.

CONCEPTUAL ISSUES

Over time a number of conceptual issues have arisen and interesting approaches have been taken. In the next sections, some of the most interesting and/or successful resolutions to these are put forward.

Treatment of the free surface

The Coordinates -- To Map or not to Map?

Variable Placement -- Are you together or separated for conservation?

Solution of the Pressure Poisson Equation -- Fast or Simple or both?

TODAY'S CODES

It is worth spending a significant part of our time looking at some representative codes that are in use today. I have grouped these into those that are clearly MAC derivatives and others.

MAC Today

Here we report on codes that are MAC-based and derivative codes that have significant new features such as the MIC method.

Other Branches of the Tree

Here we report on some innovative codes that use parts of the concepts in MAC or SUMMAC, for example, and one of the more general projection methods that uses two pressure equations derived from the Helmholtz decomposition.

We take a moment as well to peek into the domain of the ocean modelers to see their insights to free-surface problems.

THE CLOUDY CRYSTAL BALL

Let us look deeply into the crystal ball! There are techniques that can both advance our work and not threaten our current practices, or not!!!

The Role of Large Eddy Simulation

Large eddy simulation [LES] has become a major technique in engineering and geophysical flows, yet while the mathematical and physical bases for it are clear, the modeling is at best "teenage" and certainly not mature. We look at the state of play.

The Role of Parallel Processing

The Navier-Stokes equations, which are at the heart of our methods, are notoriously bad performers on the current favorite parallel machines, those with distributed memory. Is the saving grace to be found in message passing?

Recognition of Other Methods

It would be unfair and unwise to move on without noting some important successes in the domains of (i) unstructured grids, and (ii) finite elements.

CONCLUSIONS

Wherein we feel good about moving into the future.

FED-Vol. 238, 1996 Fluids Engineering Division Conference
Volume 3
ASME 1996

FREE SURFACE MIXING WITH HEAT TRANSFER

Dani Fadda
Ph.D. Candidate

Peter E. Raad
Associate Professor

Mechanical Engineering Department
School of Engineering and Applied Science
Southern Methodist University
Dallas, Texas

ABSTRACT

This study investigates the thermal mixing phenomenon as external rocking excitations are applied to a container partially filled with a thermally non-homogeneous fluid. The aim of this work is to determine the effects of the rocking frequency on thermal mixing. Numerical results show that optimum mixing is achieved while rocking at the wave natural frequency of the tank where the free surface displacements are greatest. At this optimal frequency, the strong mixing is observed to be highly concentrated in the area near the free surface.

INTRODUCTION

This work investigates the heat transfer within an incompressible fluid in a partially filled container. The left half of the fluid is initially warmer than the right half, and the container is thermally insulated. This initial configuration is inherently unstable since the fluid is likely unable to resist overturning. When the tank is stationary, buoyancy drives the warmer fluid above the colder fluid while heat transfer brings the two fluids into thermal equilibrium. The magnitude of the resulting flow velocities and the mixing speed depend on the fluid properties, container dimensions, and initial temperature difference between the hot and cold fluids. The physics are governed primarily by a balance between buoyancy, inertial, and diffusive forces, or in other words, by natural convection, with dissipative effects, both viscous and thermal, acting as stabilizing forces. It is therefore beneficial to introduce the Rayleigh number (Ra), which is the ratio of buoyancy to diffusive forces, and serves as a stability indicator in these types of problems. At the high Rayleigh number considered in this work, buoyancy generates inertia forces that cause the fluid to rotate. The fluid therefore oscillates in the tank and as thermal equilibrium is approached the oscillations die down.

To investigate a method of enhancing the heat transfer, an external horizontal rocking motion is imposed on the container at specified frequencies, and the effects of the external rocking excitations on the speed and the characteristics of thermal mixing are observed. A wave natural frequency of the tank is calculated from the dispersion relation for the linearized water-wave formulation. The calculated frequency is approximately one order of magnitude greater than the highest frequency of the buoyancy-induced oscillations. This wave natural frequency is found to cause optimal thermal mixing. The effect of external rocking on enhancing the thermal mixing is seen to be highly concentrated in a region close to the free surface.

Flows induced by buoyancy effects have been studied for a variety of problems. Some examples of these problems have been reported in the literature. De Vahl Davis and Jones (1982), Patterson and Imberger (1980), and Lage and Bejan (1991) discussed fluid flow in a full rectangular enclosure subject to differentially heated isothermal side walls. Fu and Shieh (1991) studied the effects of vertical vibrations on the convection in a similar cavity. Trevisan and Bejan (1987) studied fluid flow in a rectangular enclosure subject to heat and mass transfer from the vertical sides. Farrow and Patterson (1993) and Trevisan and Bejan (1986) analyzed the effects of solar heating on water in a lake. Lage and Bejan (1993) investigated the thermal resonance in an enclosure with one isothermal vertical wall and the other vertical wall subject to an oscillating heat flux. Zhang and Bejan (1987) studied the horizontal heat and mass transfer in an porous enclosure.

NOMENCLATURE
Nondimensional Variables

Ra $\qquad$: Rayleigh Number $= \dfrac{\beta L^3 \Delta T g_y}{\nu \alpha}$

Pr $\qquad$: Prandtl number $= \dfrac{\nu}{\alpha}$

Dimensional Variables

a $\qquad$: Amplitude of oscillation for the tank, m

C   : Specific heat, J/Kg K
f   : Frequency of oscillation, Hz
f*   : Natural frequency of the tank, Hz
g_x : Sinusoidal forcing body force function, m/s^2
g_y : Gravitational acceleration, m/s^2
H   : Fluid depth, m
k   : Thermal conductivity, W/m K
L   : Container length, m
n   : The wave number, m^{-1}
p   : Pressure potential function, s^{-1}
t   : Time, s
T   : Temperature, K
ΔT : Scale for the temperature = T_{hot} - T_{cold}, K
u, v   : Fluid velocities in the x and y directions, m/s
U, V   : Scales for the fluid velocities u and v, m/s
x, y   : Horizontal and vertical spatial coordinates, m

Subscripts

hot, cold : Correspond to the initial highest and lowest temperatures

Greek

α : Thermal diffusivity = $k/\rho\,C$, m^2/s
β : Coefficient of thermal expansion, K^{-1}
μ : Dynamic viscosity, Kg/m s
ν : Kinematic viscosity, 1/s^2
π : Constant = 3.14159
ρ : Fluid density, Kg/m^3
ρ_o : Reference fluid density, Kg/m^3
σ : Thermal standard deviation from the mean temperature of the fluid, K
Θ : Temperature scale = $\dfrac{T - T_{cold}}{T_{hot} - T_{cold}}$

PHYSICAL MODEL

A water tank shown in Fig. 1 is considered in this study. All four walls of the tank are impermeable and thermally insulated.

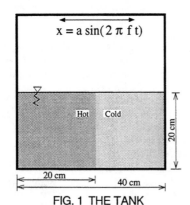

$$x = a \sin(2 \pi f t)$$

FIG. 1 THE TANK

Two liquid bodies at different temperatures are initially placed side by side in the enclosure with a very thin, impermeable and adiabatic partition separating them. The two fluid bodies have identical volumes and physical properties. The temperature of the left half is higher than that of the right half.

At the beginning of the simulation, the thin partition is removed instantaneously without disturbing either side of the fluid. During the course of the simulation, the two fluid bodies merge and become one thermally non-homogeneous fluid body. Heat exchange starts immediately after the partition is removed and buoyancy-induced flow is observed.

For a specified frequency, f, the tank rocks horizontally according to the relation $x = a \sin(2 \pi f t)$. The rocking amplitude, a, is 1 cm and frequencies up to two times the wave natural frequency of the tank are considered. The fluid considered has the physical properties of a molten Aluminum alloy (AL13). The initial temperatures T_{hot} and T_{cold} of the hot and cold fluid bodies are 1373 K and 933 K, respectively, resulting in an initial temperature difference of 440 K. The Rayleigh number (Ra) for this case is 10^9, and the Prandtl number (Pr) is 10^{-2}. The non-dimensional numbers are defined as:

$$Ra = \frac{\beta\,L^3\,\Delta T\,g_y}{\nu\,\alpha} \quad \text{and} \quad Pr = \frac{\nu}{\alpha}.$$

With both temperature limits higher than the solidification temperature of this Aluminum Alloy, no solidification takes place in the process of mixing.

The wave natural frequency f* of the tank is computed by solving the dispersion relation for the linearized water-wave formulation (Stoker, 1957).

$$f^* = \left[\frac{1}{2\pi}\,g_y\,n\,\tanh(n\,H) \right]^{1/2}$$

where n ($= \dfrac{\pi}{L}$) is the wavenumber for the lowest mode solution.

THE NUMERICAL METHOD

A new method, SMMC-E, is developed and used in this work. This method is an extension of the Surface Marker and Micro Cell (SMMC) discussed in Chen et al. (1995), Johnson et al. (1994), and Raad et al. (1995). SMMC is a numerical method designed for the simulation of free surface fluid flow. The new SMMC-E couples the energy equation to the momentum equations solved in the SMMC method, allowing the simulation of heat transfer in free surface fluid flow.

The basic idea in the SMMC-E is that the computational domain is divided into cells which define three different regions: a full region (completely full of fluid and not neighboring the free surface), an empty region (evacuated and also not neighboring the free surface), and a surface region (separating the full and empty regions). As the fluid flows, the full, empty, and surface cells (and consequently the three regions) are redefined according to the motion of the free surface, which in turn is dependent on the computed velocity field in the full region.

As this method assumes that one or more fluid bodies flow in an otherwise evacuated or obstructed cavity, the empty region is identified and excluded from all flow computations. The following is a brief description of the governing equations, the solution methodology, and the boundary conditions.

Methodology

The governing equations are solved only in the full region, where the fluid momentum is computed by a direct solution of the full Navier-Stokes equations, coupled with the continuity equation. In two spatial dimensions, these equations appear as:

$$\rho \left(\frac{\partial u}{\partial t} + u\frac{\partial u}{\partial x} + v\frac{\partial u}{\partial y} \right) = -\frac{\partial p}{\partial x} + \mu \left(\frac{\partial^2 u}{\partial x^2} + \frac{\partial^2 u}{\partial y^2} \right) + \rho\, g_x$$

$$\rho \left(\frac{\partial v}{\partial t} + u\frac{\partial v}{\partial x} + v\frac{\partial v}{\partial y} \right) = -\frac{\partial p}{\partial y} + \mu \left(\frac{\partial^2 v}{\partial x^2} + \frac{\partial^2 v}{\partial y^2} \right) + \rho\, g_y$$

$$\frac{\partial u}{\partial x} + \frac{\partial u}{\partial y} = 0$$

The heat transfer is computed by a solution of the energy equation below coupled with the above momentum and continuity equations:

$$\frac{\partial T}{\partial t} + u\frac{\partial T}{\partial x} + v\frac{\partial T}{\partial y} = \alpha \left(\frac{\partial^2 T}{\partial x^2} + \frac{\partial^2 T}{\partial y^2} \right)$$

The transient momentum equations represent a balance of (from left to right) inertia, pressure, viscous, and gravitational forces. The Oberbek-Boussinesq approximation is introduced to link the momentum equations to the energy equation. With this approximation, the fluid density appearing only in the gravitational terms is considered to vary with the temperature according to the following relation:

$$\rho = \rho_o\, (1 + \beta\, T).$$

A projection method is used to solve the momentum equations along with the mass conservation equation on a rectangular, Eulerian, staggered grid. The first step in this method is a computation of tentative velocities from the momentum equations in the absence of all pressure terms. While the absence of the pressure terms does not affect the vorticity of the flow, the continuity equation is normally not satisfied. The buoyancy terms in this first step are computed by using the current (or most recent) temperature field. An incompressibility deviation function is calculated from the tentative velocity field, yielding local measures of the non-satisfaction of the continuity principle for each control volume in the Eulerian mesh. The computed incompressibility deviation function is then used as the non-homogeneous source term in a pressure Poisson equation to calculate a pressure correction field. Finally, the tentative velocities are corrected by the use of the gradients of this pressure field, resulting in velocities that satisfy both the momentum and continuity equations without affecting the vorticity field.

After advancing the velocity field a small interval in time, the energy equation is solved by the control volume method described by Patankar (1980) in order to update the temperature field. The new temperature field is then used to compute new velocity fields, and the cycle continues for a predefined period of time.

The Free Surface Boundary Conditions

An accurate description of the free surface and appropriate free surface boundary conditions are required to correctly advance the solution of the momentum and energy equations in time. Since the fluid flows in an otherwise evacuated computational domain, the free surface boundary conditions are zero pressure on the free surface and no heat flow across the free surface. The implementations of the zero pressure boundary condition have been discussed in the SMMC method literature cited above.

Thermally insulating the free surface is done by setting the temperature of every surface grid point equal to the temperature of the closest grid point in the full region. If more than one full grid point neighbors the surface grid point, the surface temperature is set equal to the average of all relevant points.

It is useful to note that if the free surface is horizontal and stationary, then this treatment will boil down to the nonporous adiabatic wall boundary condition described by Patankar (1980). This treatment eliminates all heat transfer to the empty region by keeping the full fluid region insulated.

RESULTS

Eleven cases are considered for the analysis of the effects of the rocking frequency on heat transfer. The first case is for a stationary tank while the ten other cases correspond to ten different frequencies up to two times the natural frequency of the tank.

The computational domain considered for all the cases consists of a 40x40 Eulerian grid, and thus 1600 cells. Since half of the domain is full, half (or 800) of the cells are initially wet. At the beginning of the simulation, the horizontal free surface passes through 40 of these cells making them surface cells. The other 760 cells are fully immersed in the fluid. As the free surface moves the total number of surface cells changes. Since the fluid volume is constant, the number of fully immersed cells also changes accordingly.

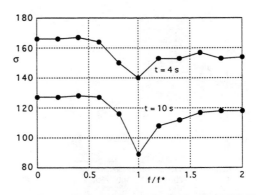

FIG. 2 DEPENDENCE OF THE STANDARD DEVIATION OF THE TEMPERATURE FIELD ON THE ROCKING FREQUENCY

Since the objective of this work is to investigate the effects of sloshing on the mixing speed, it is useful to track an indicator of the speed of mixing. One such indicator is the standard deviation, σ, of the temperature field from the mean temperature ($= \frac{T_{hot} + T_{cold}}{2}$), which is 1153K. At the beginning of each simulation, σ is equal to 220 K ($= \Delta T/2$) since the two fluid bodies are initially at the extreme temperatures T_{hot} and

T_{cold}. The standard deviation decreases with time and vanishes if the simulation runs long enough to allow the temperature field to reach the average of T_{hot} and T_{cold}. For all the frequencies considered, the calculated values of σ are plotted in Fig. 2 at $t = 4$ s and $t = 10$ s.

The results in Fig. 2 point to the existence of a minimum in σ at the natural frequency of the tank. The point of minimum σ corresponds to the case of maximum thermal interaction in the enclosure. After 10 seconds of rocking at the natural frequency, the reduction in the value of σ from the stationary case is a significant 30%. Further comparisons between the stationary and natural frequency cases are given below with more emphasis on physical quantities such as temperature.

The temperatures of the fully immersed cells are sorted in descending order and plotted in Figs. 3 (a) and (b) versus a cell counter. Figures 3 (a) and (b) correspond to a stationary tank and a tank rocking at its natural frequency, respectively. The curves plotted in these two figures are at times $t = 0$, 4, and 10 s.

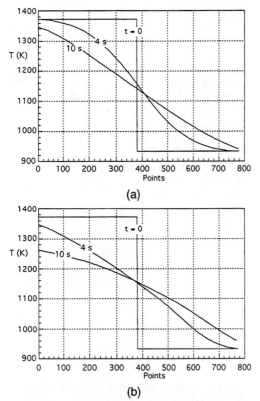

FIG. 3 THE SYSTEM ENERGY LEVEL WITH (a) NO SLOSHING, AND (b) SLOSHING AT THE NATURAL FREQUENCY

At time $t = 0$ s, Figs. 3 (a) and (b) indicate that all the fully immersed grid points are at the extreme temperatures of T_{hot} and T_{cold}. As time passes, less points maintain the extreme temperatures as heat is transferred in the fluid. In the stationary tank, Fig. 3 (a) shows that the maximum and minimum temperatures in the fluid are seen to decrease and increase, respectively. Figure 3 (b), on the other hand, shows that rocking at

the natural frequency has a more pronounced effect in decreasing the maximum temperatures than in increasing the coldest temperatures. A closer look at the physics of the heat transfer in these two cases is presented below.

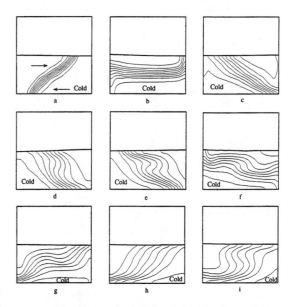

FIG. 4, ISOTHERMS WITH NO EXTERNAL ROCKING AT T = 1 S THROUGH T = 9 S

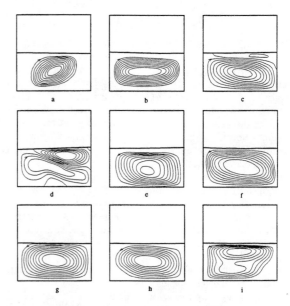

FIG. 5, STREAM LINES WITH NO EXTERNAL ROCKING AT T = 1 S THROUGH T = 9 S

STATIONARY CONTAINER

For the stationary container, the isotherms and stream function are plotted in Figs. 4 and 5, respectively. The (a) through (i) parts of these two figures correspond to nine different times, one second apart, starting at a time equal to one second from the beginning of the simulation. The isotherms plotted in Fig. 4 (a) through (i) have the same equally spaced values between T_{hot} and T_{cold}.

Figure 4 (a) and 5 (a) show the isotherms and the streamlines, respectively, one second after the starting time of the simulation. The isotherms show that the colder fluid is starting to flow under the warmer fluid and the streamlines indicate a clockwise fluid motion in the container. Two seconds after the starting time of the simulation, Fig. 4 (b) shows that the fluid is close to a stable buoyancy position where the colder fluid is under the warmer fluid. This figure indicates that the buoyancy forces in the fluid no longer exert a destabilizing rotating moment.

Figures 5 (b) through (d) show that the majority of the fluid turns in the clockwise direction for the first four seconds of the simulation. Examining the isotherms in Figs. 4 (b) through (d) indicates that this continued clockwise fluid rotation is against the fluid buoyancy. The continued rotation beyond the stable point is a result of an inertial flywheel effect that was built in the fluid body due to the rocking which imparts destabilizing inertial forces on the fluid system. This inertia effect vanishes after four seconds from the start of the simulation as indicated by Figs. 4 (d) and 5 (d) when the buoyancy and dissipative forces counterbalance the inertia forces. At this point in time, a counterclockwise rotation is seen in the streamlines of Figs. 5 (e) through (h) lasting for the next four seconds. Figures 4 (e) through (h) show the corresponding isotherms to the streamlines of Figs. 5 (e) through (h) for the time interval between t = 5 s and t = 9 s. The results in these figures (Figs. 4 (e) through (h)) indicate that the fluid passes through a buoyantly stable state shown in Fig. 4 (f) at a time equal to six seconds. This state is again not maintained due to an inertia effect that sustains the fluid rotation. The counterclockwise rotation is terminated at a time equal to eight seconds (Figs. 4(h) and 5(h)) when the fluid inertia is again counterbalanced by the buoyancy and dissipative forces. Figures 4 (i) and 5 (i) indicate that a new clockwise rotation is expected, and more oscillations about the stable buoyant position are anticipated.

The isotherms in Fig. 4 show some symmetry about the center point of the fluid region. This symmetry is due to the fact that only small displacements in the free surface occur. It is also observed from Fig. 4 that the colder fluid is at all times further away from the free surface than the warmer fluid.

ROCKING CONTAINER

When the container rocks at the natural frequency f*, the amplitude the free surface displacements are seen to increase dramatically. As the fluid sloshes, the average temperatures of the fluid in the right and left halves of the tank are computed. A non-dimensional average temperature, Θ, is defined as:

$$\Theta = \frac{(T - T_{cold})}{(T_{hot} - T_{cold})}$$

Initially, Θ for the left and right halves of the tank are 1 and 0, respectively. Θ is plotted in Fig. 6 versus time. The points in Fig. 6 represent the case of rocking at the natural frequency and the solid line is a smooth fit of these points. The

dashed line in Fig. 6 represents the stationary container case. The periodic nature of this line indicates the presence of buoyancy-induced temperature oscillations in the left and right halves of the container.

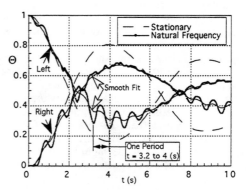

FIG. 6 THE AVERAGE TEMPERATURES OF THE LEFT AND RIGHT HALVES OF THE FLUID CONTAINER, ROCKING AT THE NATURAL FREQUENCY

Comparing the trends of the solid and dashed lines in Fig. 6 leads to the observation that the fluid buoyancy-induced oscillations in Θ remain strongly evident when external rocking is applied. The effects of external rocking are exhibited as small amplitude oscillations superimposed over the buoyancy-induced oscillations. Furthermore, external rocking is seen to decrease both the amplitude and the frequency of the buoyancy induced oscillations in Θ.

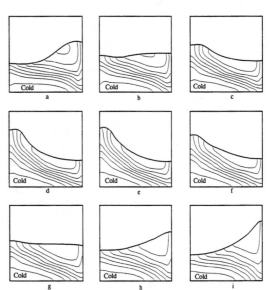

FIG. 7 ISOTHERMS FOR THE CASE OF ROCKING AT THE NATURAL FREQUENCY AT T = 3.2 S THROUGH T = 4 S

It is interesting to note that the small amplitude oscillations are superimposed over the buoyancy-induced oscillations mainly in the colder half of the container. Examining one period of the external rocking motion, say between t = 3.2 s and t = 4.0 s, the results in Fig. 6 indicate that the left half of the container is colder than the right half. The average temperature of the colder half is seen to oscillate in this small period of time while the temperature of the warmer half is fairly steady. Figure 7 shows the isotherms at nine steps within this time period.

The coldest isotherm in Fig. 7 remains in the left region between t = 3.2 s and 4 s. The presence of this isotherm in the left half of the container keeps the average temperature of the left half of the tank colder than that of the right half. Next, examining the warmest isotherm, one observes that the region occupied by the warmer fluid moves back and forth between the two halves of the tank as the fluid body sloshes. The motion of this warmer fluid affects the average temperature of the cold half dramatically while having a mild influence on the average temperature of the warmer half. The net result of the sloshing motion is enhanced thermal mixing in the fluid. The inertial mixing, however, appears to be highly concentrated in the warmer, lighter fluid which is closest to the free surface.

CONCLUSIONS

The focus of this work is on the effects of external rocking on the mixing of a thermally non-homogeneous free surface fluid. Analysis of the simulation results at different frequencies shows that rocking at the wave natural frequency of the tank leads to optimum mixing. Analysis of the heat transfer with no rocking and that with rocking at the tank natural frequency leads to the following primary conclusions:

(1) In the absence of external rocking, the fluid in the tank oscillates about a buoyantly stable state. Beginning initially with a buoyantly unstable state, the fluid oscillations are stabilized over time by thermal and viscous dissipation forces that counteract progressively weaker buoyancy and inertia forces. When an external high frequency rocking motion is imposed on the tank, a new fluid sloshing response is observed, superimposed over the buoyancy-induced oscillations. The new external sloshing motion does not eliminate the buoyancy oscillations, but instead, decreases the frequency of the buoyancy-driven oscillations while enhancing the heat transfer within the fluid.

(2) The buoyancy-induced oscillations cause slight displacements in the free surface of the fluid. The rocking action at the natural frequency of the tank, on the other hand, results in dramatic free surface displacements. These dramatic displacements are observed to cause strong sloshing and mixing in the fluid. The effects of the sloshing on the mixing are maximum in the fluid layers that are closer to the free surface. In those layers, a region of strong thermal mixing exists while less mixing is observed in locations far from the free surface. Only a mild response to the external rocking is observed at the bottom of the tank.

ACKNOWLEDGMENTS

The authors wish to thank the Mechanical Engineering Department at Southern Methodist University for the support that made this project possible.

REFERENCES

Chen, S., 1991, "The SMU Method: A Numerical Scheme for Calculating Incompressible Free Surface Fluid Flows by the Surface Marker Utility," Ph.D. Dissertation, Mechanical Engineering Department, Southern Methodist University.

Chen, S., Johnson, D. B., and Raad, P. E., 1995, "Velocity Boundary Conditions For the Simulation of Free Surface Fluid Flow," *Journal of Computational Physics*, Vol. 116, pp. 262-276.

De Vahl Davis, G. and Jones, J. P., 1983, "Natural Convection in a Square Cavity: A Comparison Exercise," *International Journal For Numerical Methods in Fluids*, Vol. 3, pp. 227-248.

Farrow, D. E. and Patterson, J. C., 1993, "On the Stability of the Near Shore Waters of a Lake When Subject to Solar Heating," *International Journal of Heat and Mass Transfer*, Vol. 36, No. 1, pp. 89-100.

Fu, W. S. and Shieh, W. J., 1992, "A Study of Thermal Convection in an Enclosure Induced Simultaneously by Gravity and Vibration," *International Journal of Heat and Mass Transfer*, Vol. 35, No. 7, pp. 1695-1710.

Johnson, D. B., Raad, P. E., and Chen, S., 1994, "Simulation of Impacts of Fluids Free Surfaces with Solid Boundaries," *International Journal for Numerical Methods in Fluids*, Vol. 19, pp. 153-176.

Lage, J. L. and Bejan, A., 1991, "The Ra-Pr Domain of Laminar Natural Convection in an Enclosure Heated from the Side," *Numerical Heat Transfer*, Vol. 19, part A, pp. 21-41.

Lage, J. L. and Bejan, A., 1993, "The Resonance of Natural Convection in an Enclosure Heated Periodically from the Side," *International Journal of Heat and Mass Transfer*, Vol. 36, N0. 8, pp. 2027-2038.

Patterson, J. and Imberger, J., 1980, "Unsteady Natural Convection in a rectangular cavity," *ASME Journal of Fluid Mechanics*, Vol. 100, part 1, pp. 65-86.

Raad, P. E., Chen, S., and Johnson, D. B., 1995, "The Introduction of Micro Cells to Treat Pressure in Free Surface Fluid Flow Problems," *ASME Journal of Fluids Engineering*, Vol. 117, pp. 683-690.

Stoker, J. J., 1957, "Water Waves," pp. 37-54.

Trevisan, O. V. and Bejan A., 1986, "Convection Driven by the Nonuniform Absorption of Thermal radiation at the Free Surface of a Stagnant Pool," *Numerical Heat Transfer*, Vol. 10, pp. 483-506.

Trevisan, O. V. and Bejan A., 1987, "Combined Heat and Mass Transfer by Natural Convection in a Vertical Enclosure," *ASME Journal of Heat Transfer*, Vol. 109, pp. 104-112.

Zhang, Z. and Bejan, A., 1987, "The Horizontal Spreading of Thermal and Chemical Deposits in a Porous Medium," *International Journal of Heat and Mass Transfer*, Vol. 30, No. 11, pp. 2289-2303.

FED-Vol. 238, 1996 Fluids Engineering Division Conference
Volume 3
ASME 1996

COMPUTATIONS OF FILM BOILING

Damir Juric
Department of Mechanical Engineering and Applied Mechanics
The University of Michigan
Ann Arbor, Michigan

Grétar Tryggvason
Department of Mechanical Engineering and Applied Mechanics
The University of Michigan
Ann Arbor, Michigan

ABSTRACT

Results are presented from direct numerical simulations of film boiling. The fully coupled, time-dependent Navier-Stokes and energy equations are solved using a two-dimensional finite-difference/front-tracking method. Large interface deformations, topology change, latent heat, surface tension and unequal material properties between liquid and vapor phases are included in the simulations. In film boiling a vapor layer adjacent to an upward facing, flat, heated surface undergoes a Rayleigh-Taylor instability, with subsequent pinch off and rise of a vapor bubble. Vaporization of the liquid at the liquid-vapor interface continually replenishes the vapor lost due to bubble departure. The hot vapor from regions near the wall is convected up into the bubble and is carried upward into the ambient fluid as the bubble breaks off and rises. Heat transfer results are compared with a correlation of experimental data.

INTRODUCTION

Fluid flow combined with phase change is an important part of the power generation process. The high heat transfer rates typical of boiling are used to extract energy from solar, fossil and nuclear fuels. Designers of energy generation systems for spacecraft must deal with the added complication of handling low boiling point cryogenic fluids in the absence of gravity. The main feature which categorizes flows with phase change is the behavior of the interface separating the phases. For example, boiling of a liquid from a solid heated surface can be described by three regimes: Nucleate,

Transition and Film. The interface geometry and dynamics determine to a large extent the heat transfer rates in these three boiling modes. Nucleate boiling is characterized by individual vapor bubble formation at distinct sites on the heated surface. Heat transfer is mainly through contact between the heated surface and the liquid. High heat fluxes are possible at relatively low surface temperatures due to rapid mixing associated with bubble formation. In transition boiling, bubble formation is rapid enough that a vapor blanket begins to cover the heated surface. In film boiling, the subject of interest in this study, a layer of vapor completely blankets the heated surface. The vapor is constantly depleted by break off and rise of vapor bubbles and is replenished by vaporization of liquid at the liquid-vapor interface. The vapor layer acts as an insulator thereby lowering the heat transfer rate and increasing the heater surface temperature. Normally, it is desirable to operate close to the peak nucleate boiling heat flux. However, in processes where the heat flux is the controllable variable such as in nuclear reactor operation or in electrically heated applications, exceeding this critical heat flux can be dangerous. The process immediately jumps to the film boiling regime where heater damage can occur due to the high surface temperatures.

Efforts to understand the processes involved in boiling have focused mainly on simple numerical and analytical models of vapor bubble dynamics. Due to the complexity of the full liquid-vapor phase change problem, an assumed interface shape along with various assumptions concerning surface tension, fluid viscosity and vapor phase velocity and temperature are usually incorporated. Lord Rayleigh (1917) formulated a simplified equation of motion for inertia controlled growth of a spherical vapor bubble. Rayleigh's analysis was extended by, among others, Plesset and Zwick (1952), Mikic et al. (1970), Dalle et al. (1975) and Lee and Merte (1993) to include thermal and surface tension dominated growth regimes. In recent numerical work, Lee and Nydahl (1989) compute hemispherical bubble growth in nucleate boiling from inception through departure. Patil and Prusa (1991) numerically study the thermal diffusion controlled growth of a hemispherical bubble as well. The numerical solution of the full phase change problem with fluid flow is particularly difficult due to the coupling of the mass, momentum and energy transport with the interface dynamics and since interphase mass transfer results in discontinuous velocities at the phase boundaries. Welch (1995) has made significant progress in using a two-dimensional, moving mesh, finite volume method to solve the mass, momentum and energy equations for liquid-vapor flows with phase change. However, his method is restricted to flows with only small distortion of the liquid-vapor interface.

Juric and Tryggvason (1995) have recently developed a numerical technique for fluid flow with phase change that has enabled the simulation of problems with relatively complex motion of the boundary separating two (or more) fluids. The method is based on a finite difference approximation of the Navier-Stokes and energy equations and an explicit tracking of the phase boundary. It is an extension of techniques already developed for multifluid flows without phase change by Unverdi and Tryggvason (1992a, 1992b). The multifluid code has been used to investigate the collision of drops (Nobari et al. 1993, Nobari and Tryggvason, 1994), thermal migration of drops (Nas and Tryggvason, 1993) and the evolution of several bubbles (Esmaeeli et al., 1995). For problems without fluid flow we have used the method to simulate the dendritic solidification of pure materials as well as binary alloys (Juric and Tryggvason, 1996a, 1996b).

In this paper we present the mathematical formulation we use for the full liquid-vapor phase change problem. The effects of interphase mass transfer, latent heat, surface tension and unequal material properties between liquid and vapor phases are included. Results from two-dimensional simulations of film boiling from an upward facing flat surface in a horizontally periodic domain demonstrate the ability of the front-tracking method to easily handle large interface deformations and topology change.

FORMULATION

We write the governing equations for the phase change problem for both phases simultaneously while carefully accounting for the jumps in material properties and the mass, force and energy sources at the interface. Note that in two-phase flow, additional terms appear in these equations due to the phase change and the fact that the interface is no longer a material interface. The fluid velocity at the interface and the interface velocity are unequal. This single field, local instant formulation incorporates the interface jump conditions into the governing equations as sources which act only at the interface. Kataoka (1985) shows that this single field representation is equivalent to the local instant formulations of Ishii (1975) and Delhaye (1974). They formulate the phase change problem in terms of local instant variables for each phase with appropriate jump conditions at the moving phase interface. These local instant formulations form the basis for formulations using various types of averaging.

The momentum equation is written for the entire flow field and the surface tension forces are inserted at the interface as body forces which act only at the interface. In conservative form this equation is

$$\frac{\partial}{\partial t}(\rho \mathbf{u}) + \nabla \cdot (\rho \mathbf{u} \mathbf{u})$$

$$= -\nabla P - \rho \mathbf{g} + \nabla \cdot \mu (\nabla \mathbf{u} + \nabla \mathbf{u}^T) + \mathbf{F} . \qquad (1)$$

The notation follows customary convention: $\mathbf{u}$ is the fluid velocity field, P is the pressure, ρ is the density and μ is the viscosity. $\mathbf{F}$ is a source term which accounts for forces acting on the interface

$$\mathbf{F} = \int_{\mathcal{A}} \mathbf{f} \delta (\mathbf{x} - \mathbf{x}_f) \, d\mathcal{A} . \qquad (2)$$

$\mathbf{f}$ is the surface tension normal to the interface,

$$\mathbf{f} = \sigma \kappa \mathbf{n} \qquad (3)$$

where σ is the surface tension and κ is twice the mean curvature.

The conservation of mass equation for a fluid with a volume expansion at the interface due to phase change is

$$\nabla \cdot \rho \mathbf{u} = M \qquad (4)$$

where

$$M = \int_{\mathcal{A}} m \delta (\mathbf{x} - \mathbf{x}_f) \, d\mathcal{A} \qquad (5)$$

and m accounts for mass transfer across the interface due to the phase change

$$m = (\rho_1 - \rho_2) \mathbf{V} \cdot \mathbf{n} . \qquad (6)$$

$\mathbf{V} = (d\mathbf{x}_f/dt)$ is the interface velocity and $\mathbf{n}$ is the normal to the interface. Note that this formulation of Eq.(4) is equivalent to the customary statement of the conservation of mass principle. The subscript 1 will refer to the vapor phase and 2 to the liquid phase.

The energy equation is

$$\frac{\partial}{\partial t}(\rho c T) + \nabla \cdot (\rho \mathbf{u} c T) = \nabla \cdot K \nabla T + Q \qquad (7)$$

where c is the specific heat, K is the thermal conductivity and

$$Q = \int_{\mathcal{A}} q \delta (\mathbf{x} - \mathbf{x}_f) \, d\mathcal{A} . \qquad (8)$$

q is the energy source due to liberation or absorption of latent heat, L, at the interface

$$q = \rho_1 L (\mathbf{V} - \mathbf{u}_1) \cdot \mathbf{n} . \qquad (9)$$

$\mathbf{u}_1$ is the vapor phase fluid velocity at the interface. In this equation L takes into account unequal specific heats:

$$L = L_o + (c_2 - c_1) T_v . \qquad (10)$$

L_o is the customary latent heat measured at the reference equilibrium vaporization temperature, T_v.

The interface temperature condition that must be satisfied on the phase boundary is derived by Alexiades (1993):

$$T_f - T_v - \frac{\sigma T_v}{\rho_2 L_o} \kappa + \frac{T_v}{L_o} \left(\frac{1}{\rho_2} - \frac{1}{\rho_1} \right) (P_v - P_\infty)$$

$$- (c_2 - c_1) \frac{T_v}{L_o} \left[T_f \ln \frac{T_f}{T_v} + T_v - T_f \right] = 0 , \qquad (11)$$

where $T_f = T(\mathbf{x}_f(t))$ is the interface temperature, P_∞ and P_v are the ambient pressure and the pressure at the interface in the vapor respectively.

A key feature of the front-tracking method is the material indicator function which is used to advect the material property fields. From the known position of the interface, we construct an indicator function, $I(\mathbf{x})$, that has the value 1 in the vapor phase and 0 in the liquid phase. This function allows us to evaluate the values of the density, viscosity, specific heat and thermal conductivity fields at every location by

$$\rho(\mathbf{x}) = \rho_2 + (\rho_1 - \rho_2) I(\mathbf{x}) , \qquad (12)$$

$$\mu(\mathbf{x}) = \mu_2 + (\mu_1 - \mu_2) I(\mathbf{x}) , \qquad (13)$$

$$c(\mathbf{x}) = c_2 + (c_1 - c_2) I(\mathbf{x}) , \qquad (14)$$

$$k(\mathbf{x}) = k_2 + (k_1 - k_2) I(\mathbf{x}) . \qquad (15)$$

It is important to note that integration of Eqs.(1), (4) and (7) across the interface directly yields the correct jump conditions in the local instant formulation for two-phase systems given by Delhaye (1974) and Ishii (1975) with the assumptions that the interface is thin and massless and that the bulk fluids are incompressible. However, we allow for volume expansion at the interface in the conservation of mass, Eq.(4), but neglect the volume expansion term in the constitutive shear relation in the momentum, Eq.(1). In the energy equation, viscous dissipation and kinetic energy contributions from the product of the fluid velocity at the interface and the interface velocity are neglected. Contributions to the energy equation from interface stretching are usually small compared with the latent heat and are neglected. Thermocapillary effects are also neglected.

The details of the numerical technique for multifluid flows without phase change are described by Unverdi and Tryggvason (1992a,1992b) and for solidification problems without fluid flow by Juric and Tryggvason (1996a). The finite difference/front-tracking method used to solve the system of Navier-Stokes and energy equations presented in this section is provided in a previous paper by Juric and Tryggvason (1995).

RESULTS

In these simulations we follow the evolution of an unstable vapor layer below a liquid layer which is below another vapor layer. The computations are performed in a 10x30 box with a grid resolution of 50x150. The domain is periodic in the x-direction. To allow for vaporization we let fluid exit at the top boundary where we specify the ambient pressure to be zero. The temperature field is initially zero everywhere with a heat flux, q_w, applied to the rigid bottom wall.

The physics of the phase change problem is governed by

$$\rho_1, \ \rho_2, \ \mu_1, \ \mu_2, \ c_1, \ c_2, \ K_1, \ K_2, \ L_o, \ \sigma, \ T_v, \ g, \ q_w .$$

If we scale temperature by $\rho_1 L_o / \rho_2 c_2$ and choose appropriate length and time scales $l_d = (\mu^2/g\rho^2)^{1/3}$ and $\tau = (\mu/\rho g^2)^{1/3}$ respectively, the 9 resulting dimensionless parameters are the Prandtl number, $Pr = c_2 \mu_2 / k_2$, the Bond Number, $Bo = (g\mu^4/\rho\sigma^3)^{1/3}$, the nondimensional wall heat flux, $q^* = q_w \rho_2 c_2 l_d / K_2 \rho_1 L_o$, the Nusselt number, $Nu = q_w l_d / K_1 (T_w - T_v)$, and a capillary parameter, $d_o = \rho_2 c_2 \sigma T_v / \rho_1^2 L_o^2 l_d$. Note that the Nusselt number is not set beforehand but is determined by the calculation of the wall temperature, T_w. In addition to these we must specify the 4 ratios of the material properties between the liquid and the vapor.

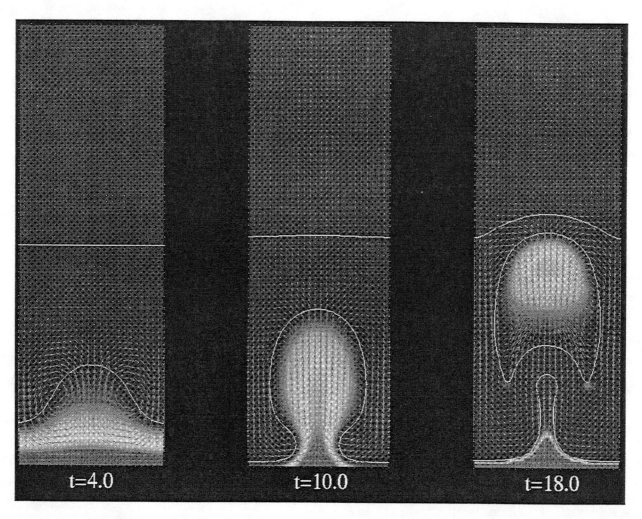

Figure 1: Film boiling simulation at three different times. The solid white lines are the liquid-vapor interfaces, the arrows represent velocity vectors and are plotted only at every fourth grid point. The temperatures are shown as shades of gray where the hottest regions are near the bottom wall and the coolest regions are in the liquid which remains nearly isothermal. A Rayleigh-Taylor instability forms with subsequent pinch off and rise of a vapor bubble. The bubble carries heated vapor up into the ambient liquid. The calculation is in a 10x30 box with grid resolution 50x150. $\rho_2/\rho_1 = 10$, $\mu_2/\mu_1 = 10$, $K_2/K_1 = 10$, $c_2/c_1 = 1$, $Pr = 1$, $q_w = 0.5$, $B_o = 1$, $d_o = 0.002$

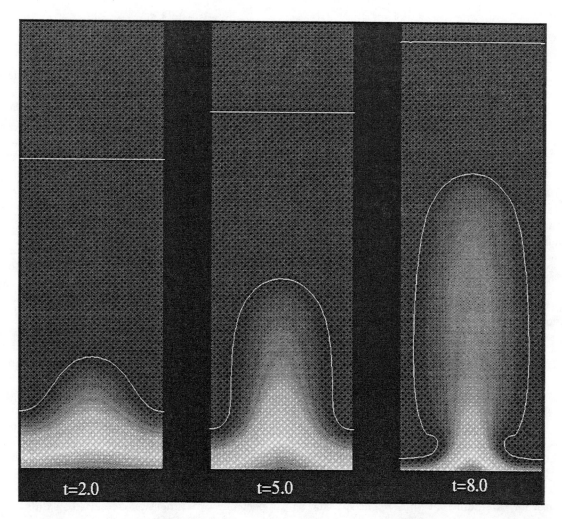

Figure 2: Film boiling simulation for three different times with the density of the liquid 100 times that of the vapor. The amount of vapor in the growing bubble near the bottom wall increases due to vaporization of liquid at the lower interface. Since the low density vapor takes up more volume, the fluid above it is pushed upwards and the upper interface moves passively upward with the fluid. The parameters are the same as in figure (1) except $\rho_2/\rho_1 = 100$, $\mu_2/\mu_1 = 40$, $K_2/K_1 = 20$, $q_w = 10$, $B_o = 0.05$.

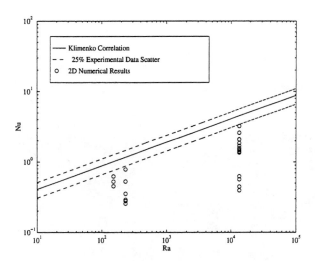

Figure 3: Comparison of heat transfer results from two-dimensional numerical simulations against a correlation by Klimenko (1981). For each of the three numerical runs at three different Rayleigh numbers the average Nusselt number along the heated bottom wall is plotted at different times. Two-dimensional simulations are in good agreement but consistently lower than 3-D experiments. Higher 3-D values are expected since heat flow is not confined to a plane and on average the height of the vapor layer above the heated wall would be lower and thus the heat transfer would be higher in 3-D than in 2-D.

The simulation in figure (1) was run with the following parameters:

$$\frac{\rho_2}{\rho_1} = 10, \quad \frac{\mu_2}{\mu_1} = 10, \quad \frac{K_2}{K_1} = 10, \quad \frac{c_2}{c_1} = 1,$$

$$Pr = 1, \quad q_w = 0.5, \quad B_o = 1, \quad d_o = 0.002$$

and is shown for three different times. The interfaces are plotted as the solid white lines while the arrows represent velocity vectors and are plotted only at every fourth grid point. The temperatures are shown as shades of gray where the hottest regions are near the bottom wall and the coolest regions are in the liquid which remains nearly isothermal. In the first frame of the figure the liquid vapor interface begins to exhibit a Rayleigh-Taylor instability with the formation of counterrotating vortices. Cold liquid is forced down toward the bottom wall and hot vapor is pushed up into the forming bubble. The interface then pinches together and in the last frame the separated bubble rises toward the upper interface carrying with it some of the hot vapor from the heated wall.

Vaporization of the liquid at the liquid-vapor interface continually replenishes the vapor lost due to bubble departure. This is seen more easily in the simulation shown in figure (2) where the density ratio and the wall heat flux are higher. The parameters are the same as in the previous figure except

$$\frac{\rho_2}{\rho_1} = 100, \quad \frac{\mu_2}{\mu_1} = 40, \quad \frac{K_2}{K_1} = 20,$$

$$q_w = 10, \quad B_o = 0.05 .$$

The amount of vapor in the growing bubble near the bottom wall is continually increasing due to vaporization of liquid at the lower interface. Since the low density vapor takes up more volume, the fluid above it is pushed upwards. Note that there is no vaporization at the upper interface. This interface simply moves passively upward with the fluid on either side of it. The fact that the upper interface does move upward is a good indicator that mass transfer is taking place across the lower interface.

In figure (3) we compare heat transfer results from our two-dimensional simulations against a correlation by Klimenko (1981) on a plot of the Nusselt vs. Rayleigh numbers. Klimenko found that his correlation holds within 25% for many different fluids. The open circles represent the numerical results for three different runs at three different Rayleigh numbers. For each of the three runs the average Nusselt number along the heated bottom wall is plotted at different times. Thus we see a range of values for one run which represents the increasing and decreasing heat transfer from the wall as the height of the vapor layer adjacent to the wall decreases or increases with time. The experimental results would naturally give values averaged over the heated area as well as averaged in time. Our 2-dimensional numerical results are consistently lower than the values from 3-dimensional experiments. However we would expect our two-dimensional results to exhibit lower heat transfer for several reasons. In three dimensions the heat flow is not confined to a plane. There are also more bubbles rising from many various points on a heated surface. On average the height of the vapor layer above the heated wall would be lower and thus the heat transfer would be higher in 3-D than in 2-D.

CONCLUSIONS

A two-dimensional front-tracking/finite-difference technique has been used to simulate film boiling. We demonstrate the break off and rise of a bubble from an unstable liquid-vapor interface. Heat transfer results are in good agreement with experimental results within the limitations of the two-dimensional calculations.

ACKNOWLEDGMENT

This work was supported in part by NSF Grant CTS-9503208 and by NASA Graduate Student Fellowship NGT-51070.

BIBLIOGRAPHY

Alexiades, V., and Solomon, A. D., 1993, *Mathematical Modeling of Melting and Freezing Processes* (Hemisphere, Washington, D.C.), p. 92.

Dalle Donne, M., and Ferranti, M. P., 1975, "The Growth of a Vapor Bubble in Superheated Sodium", *Int. J .Heat and Mass Transfer*, Vol. 18, pp. 477-493.

Delhaye, J. M., 1974, "Jump Conditions and Entropy Sources in Two-Phase Systems. Local Instant Formulation", *Int. J. Multiphase Flow*, Vol 1, pp. 395.

Esmaeeli, A., Ervin, E. A., and Tryggvason, G., 1995, "Numerical Simulations of Rising Bubbles and Drops," to appear in *Proceedings of the IUTAM Conference on Bubble Dynamics and Interfacial Phenomena*, J.R. Blake. ed.

Ishii, M., 1975, *Thermo-Fluid Dynamic Theory of Two-Phase Flow,* Eyrolles, Paris.

Juric, D., and Tryggvason, G., 1995, "A Front-Tracking Method for Liquid-Vapor Phase Change," in *Advances in Numerical Modeling of Free Surface and Interface Fluid Dynamics*, FED-Vol. 234, ASME, pp. 141-148.

Juric, D., and Tryggvason, G., 1996a, "A Front-Tracking Method for Dendritic Solidification," *J. Comp. Phys*, Vol. 123, pp. 127-148.

Juric, D., and Tryggvason, G., 1996b, "Directional Solidification of Binary Alloys using a Front-Tracking Method," in preparation.

Kataoka, I. 1985, "Local Instant Formulation of Two-Phase Flow", Technical Report Institute of Atomic Energy, Kyoto University, Kyoto, Japan, Vol. 203, pp. 1-33.

Klimenko, V. V., 1981, "Film Boiling on a Horizontal Plate - New Correlation," *Int. J. Heat and Mass Transfer*, Vol. 24, pp. 69-79.

Lee, H. S., and Merte, H., 1993, "Spherical Bubble Growth in Liquids with Initial Uniform Superheat", Report No. UM-MEAM-93-06, Dept. of MEAM, U. of Michigan, July 1993, to Nasa Lewis Research Center, Cleveland, OH, NASA Contract No. NAS3-25812.

Lee, R. C., and Nydahl, J. E., 1989, "Numerical Calculation of Bubble Growth in Nucleate Boiling from Inception through Departure", *J. Heat Transfer*, Vol. 111, pp. 474-479.

Mikic, B. B., Rohsenow, W. M., and Griffith, P., 1970, "On Bubble Growth Rate", *Int. J. Heat and Mass Transfer*, Vol. 13, pp. 657-666.

Nas, S., and Tryggvason, G., 1993, "Computational Investigation of Thermal Migration of Bubbles and Drops", *Proceedings ASME Winter Annual Meeting, AMD 174/FED 175 Fluid Mechanics Phenomena in Microgravity*, D.A. Siginer et al., ed., pp. 71-83.

Nobari, M.R., Jan, Y.-J., and Tryggvason, G., 1993, "Head on Collision of Drops - A Numerical Investigation", submitted to *Phys. of Fluids A*.

Nobari, M.R., and Tryggvason, G., 1994, "Numerical Simulations of Drop Collisions", AIAA Technical Report, AIAA 94-0835.

Patil, R. K., and Prusa, J., 1991, "Numerical Solutions for Asymptotic, Diffusion Controlled Growth of a Hemispherical Bubble on an Isothermally Heated Surface", *Experimental/Numerical Heat Transfer in Combustion and Phase Change*, ASME HTD, Vol. 170, pp. 63-70.

Plesset, M. S., and Zwick, S. A., 1952, "A Nonsteady Heat Diffusion Problem with Spherical Symmetry", *J. Appl. Phys.*, Vol. 23, p. 95.

Rayleigh, 1917, "On the Pressure Developed in a Liquid During the Collapse of a Spherical Cavity", *Phil. Mag.*, Vol. 34, pp. 94-98.

Unverdi, S. O., and Tryggvason, G., 1992a, "Computations of Multi-fluid Flows", *Physica D*, Vol. 60, pp. 70-83.

Unverdi, S. O., and Tryggvason, G., 1992b, "A Front-Tracking Method for Viscous, Incompressible, Multi-fluid Flows", *J. Computational Physics*, Vol. 100, pp. 25-37.

Welch, S. W. J., 1995, "Local Simulation of Two-Phase Flows Including Interface Tracking with Mass Transfer," *J. Comp. Phys.*, Vol. 121, pp. 142-154.

FED-Vol. 238, 1996 Fluids Engineering Division Conference
Volume 3
ASME 1996

A Fully-Implicit Multigrid Driven Algorithm for Time-Resolved Non-linear Free-Surface Flow on Unstructured Grids

Biing-Horng Liou, Luigi Martinelli and Antony Jameson

Department of Mechanical and Aerospace Engineering
Princeton University
Princeton N.J. 08544
U.S.A.

Abstract

A fully-implicit multigrid method has been developed for the computation of time dependent free surface flow. The method uses the generalized artificial compressibility approach to couple the incompressible Euler equations and continuity equation in a hyperbolic manner which allows several techniques for convergence acceleration to be implemented. Two grid adaption strategies are used to capture wave motions as well as wavemaker's oscillations. Comparisons are made between these two techniques and experimental data of the flow field around a NACA 0012 airfoil placed beneath an initially calm free surface. Transient solutions of a wavemaker oscillating horizontally are also presented to validate the new method.

Introduction

For decades, considerable work has been directed towards the study of nonlinear free surface flows not only to gain new insights into the problem but also because of the practical importance in ship hydrodynamics. However, even with the new generation of computers, two major difficulties still remain which make the development of efficient and accurate free surface flow solvers a challenging task.

One difficulty is the continuous evolution of the physical domain caused by the free surface deformation. Thus the need to adapt the mesh is inevitable. There are two viable approaches. The first one makes use of a kind of spring mechanism or transformation to shift the grids [8, 19]. However, this method fails when the waves start to overturn. Moreover, the numerical discretization on such meshes results into inaccuracies because the approximation does not take into account mesh-point rearrangement and grid distortion.

This problem is prevented by the second approach which deletes and inserts points while the simulation progresses. Both methods are implemented in our work and the results are compared.

The other major difficulty, which is common to any incompressible flows not just free surface flows, is the enforcement of a solenoidal velocity field, as it is required by the continuity equation. Lack of a pressure evolution term precludes the straightforward application of efficient time-marching algorithms which are available for hyperbolic problems. One of the approaches to circumvent this difficulty is to introduce a pseudo-temporal evolution term for the pressure in the continuity equation as in the well-known artificial compressibility method of Chorin [9]. This transforms the governing equations into a hyperbolic system at the expense of time accuracy. However, the time accuracy can be recovered by augmenting spatial residuals in the momentum equations with the discretized time derivatives, and by driving these modified residuals to zero at each mesh point and every time step. This generalized artificial compressibility approach ensures a direct coupling between the velocity and pressure fields upon convergence of the *pseudo-transient* at each time step. The use of this strategy for incompressible flow has been originally proposed by Rogers and Kwak [15]. A similar approach has also been used by Miyaka et al. [16] using an explicit, up to a second order accurate discretization in time, rational Runge-Kutta scheme for the subiterations. A very efficient method, which couples a second order accurate backward differencing of the temporal derivatives and a very efficient finite-volume multigrid strategy, has been described and validated in [1, 12, 13] for both two-dimensional Euler and Navier-Stokes equations on structured quadrilateral meshes. The method has been also implemented and validated for the solution on unstructured grids of both incompressible and compressible flow on oscillating airfoil by Lin [6]. In the present algorithm, fast convergence to a steady state of the pseudo-transient is achieved by making use of a multigrid technique originally developed by Jameson for compressible flow [1], and adapted by Hino, Martinelli and Jameson [8] for steady free-surface calculations on triangular grids. Details on the space discretization can be found in reference [5] and a comprehensive study of the artificial compressibility method for unstructured grids is given in [10]. The A-stable discretization in time allows the stability constraint on the physical time step to be relaxed, while standard convergence acceleration techniques such as local pseudo-time stepping and residual averaging are applied to the pseudo-transient iteration. Also, to alleviate the stiffness effects stemming from the unsteady source terms included in the residuals, a point-implicit five-stage Runge-Kutta scheme is constructed following the guidelines given in [4]. Finally, the range of the characteristic wave speeds associated with the hyperbolic pseudotransient problem is optimized for better convergence by employing a suitable form of the local preconditioning [11, 13].

Discretization of the Governing Equations

Governing Equations

Consider a general two-dimensional homogeneous incompressible inviscid free surface flow problem. Let the reference length, velocity and density be L_0, U_0 and ρ_0. The dimensionless Cartesian velocity components and dimensionless pressure are denoted by u, v and $\hat{p}$ respectively. Let $p = \hat{p} + \frac{1}{F^2}$ be the pressure minus the hydrostatic part, where the Froude number $F = \frac{U_0}{\sqrt{gh}}$, h is height of the free surface, and g is the gravitational acceleration. The dimensionless governing equations which consist of the continuity equation and the time-dependent momentum equation are

$$\frac{d}{dt} \int_{V(t)} dV + \int_{S(t)} (\mathbf{u}_r \cdot \mathbf{n})\, dS = 0 \qquad (1)$$

and

$$\frac{d}{dt} \int_{V(t)} \mathbf{u} dV + \int_{S(t)} \mathbf{u}(\mathbf{u}_r \cdot \mathbf{n})\, dS = -\int_{S(t)} p\mathbf{n} dS \qquad (2)$$

where $\mathbf{u}$ is the velocity measured with respect to an inertial reference frame, $\mathbf{u}_r = \mathbf{u} - \mathbf{u}_b$ is the velocity of the fluid relative to the control surface with velocity $\mathbf{u}_b$, and $\mathbf{n}$ is the unit normal. Note that the time rate of volume change in equation (1) is of importance. In semi-discrete form, equations (1) and (2) become

$$\frac{d}{dt}[\mathbf{T}_{ij} V_{ij}] + \mathbf{R}(\mathbf{w}_{ij}) = 0$$

where $\mathbf{T}_{ij} = \mathbf{w}_{ij} \cdot \mathbf{I}^m + \mathbf{K}$, $\mathbf{I}^m = diag\,[0, 1, 1]$ is the modified identity, $\mathbf{K} = [1, 0, 0]$, $\mathbf{w}_{ij} = [p, u, v]$ and residual $\mathbf{R}(\mathbf{w}_{ij})$ is obtained by approximating convective fluxes with central difference in space plus a third order artificial dissipation term to prevent an odd-even decoupling. A backward difference discretization in time considered here is of the form

$$\frac{d}{dt} = \frac{1}{\Delta t} \sum_{q=1}^{k} \frac{1}{q} [\Delta^-]^q, \quad \Delta^- = (\cdot)^{n+1} - (\cdot)^n$$

In particular, dropping the subscripts i, j for clarity, for a second order discretization in time, one obtains

$$\mathbf{R}^*(\mathbf{w}) = \frac{1}{\Delta t}(q_1 TV + q_2 \mathbf{T}^n V^n + q_3 \mathbf{T}^{n-1} V^{n-1}) + \mathbf{R}(\mathbf{w}) = 0$$

where $\mathbf{q} = (3/2, -2, 1/2)$ and $\mathbf{R}^*(\mathbf{w})$ is the augmented residual. In order to perform time resolved calculation, generalized artificial compressibility approach is used, which results in a system of coupled O.D.E.'s to be solved to convergence at each time step

$$\frac{d\mathbf{w}V}{dt^*} + \mathbf{P}_r \cdot \mathbf{R}^*(\mathbf{w}) = 0 \qquad (3)$$

where the preconditioning matrix is $\mathbf{P}_r = diag\,[\Gamma^2, 1, 1]$ and $\Gamma^2 = \max\,(0.25, u^2 + v^2)$. A point-implicit, k-stage Runge-Kutta method which can be cast as

$$\mathbf{w}^{(0)} = \mathbf{w}^n$$
$$\cdots$$
$$\mathbf{w}^{(i)} V^{n+1}\left(1 + \alpha_i q_1 \frac{\Delta t^*}{\Delta t} \mathbf{I}^m\right) = \mathbf{w}^{(i-1)} V^{n+1}$$
$$-\alpha_i \Delta t^* \left[\mathbf{R}^{*(i-1)} - \frac{1}{\Delta t} q_1 \mathbf{w}^{(i-1)} \cdot \mathbf{I}^m V^{n+1}\right]$$
$$\cdots$$
$$\mathbf{w}^{n+1} = \mathbf{w}^{(k)}$$

where $\mathbf{w}^n$ is the value of $\mathbf{w}$ after n pseudotime steps, is applied to drive equation (3) to steady state in pseudotime t^*. Once a "steady-state" is reach, $\mathbf{R}^*(\mathbf{w}) = 0$ is satisfied and one step in real time has advanced.

Several efficient techniques are employed to accelerate convergence at each time step. The most important one is the multigrid scheme, which also uses separately generated meshes. The details of the multigrid scheme can be found in [5, 7]. Another is called the local time stepping technique which allows each control volume to be advanced in pseudo time by its own maximum local pseudo time step. Residual averaging is also an effective method to increase the pseudo time step by collecting information from residuals at neighboring points [7]. These techniques are performed on the subiterations and do not affect time accuracy. Note that equation (3) can also be used to obtain a steady state solution when Δt approaches infinity, and $\mathbf{R}^*(\mathbf{w}) = \mathbf{R}(\mathbf{w})$. In this paper both steady and unsteady flow problems will be examined.

Boundary Conditions

A free-slip condition on the solid bodies is implemented as

$$\mathbf{u}_r \cdot \mathbf{n} = 0 \qquad (4)$$

which states that there is no normal flow through the bodies.

The free surface condition consists a dynamic and a kinematic condition. The former states the continuity of normal stress on the air-liquid surface. For an inviscid flow, and neglecting the surface tension, this is expressed as

$$\hat{p} = p_0, \qquad \text{at} \qquad y = h$$

or

$$p = p_0 + \frac{h}{F^2}, \qquad \text{at} \qquad y = h \qquad (5)$$

where p_0 is the atmospheric pressure which is assumed to be constant. The latter condition describes that the free surface is a material surface and can be written as

$$\frac{\partial h}{\partial t} + u_r \frac{\partial h}{\partial x} - v = 0, \qquad \text{at} \qquad y = h \qquad (6)$$

This time-marching equation for the wave height must be solved together with the bulk flow equations. Thus, a pseudotime derivative term must be added to implement the dual time stepping method described earlier.

For the steady flow calculations, additional boundary conditions are needed at the far field boundaries because of the truncation of the computational domain. Thus, a wave dumper is imposed on equation (6) near the downstream numerical boundary to prevent reflection of waves to the domain as described in [8, 20]. A uniform flow with an undisturbed free surface is imposed at the inflow: $u = 1, v = 0, p = 0, h = 0$. Also at the bottom, a deep water approximation is applied and the pressure is set to the unperturbed value $p = 0$. At boundary nodes, all the other flow quantities are obtained by using one-sided control volumes.

Grid Generation And Grid Adaption

A computational mesh is necessary to discretize the governing equations in space. Ultimately, the quality of the mesh determines the accuracy of a numerical solution. Several methods have been proposed to generate unstructured meshes. Among them, a Delaunay triangulation technique is used in the present work. The Delaunay triangulation is defined such that no points lie inside the circumcircle of any triangle; it is easy to implement, and it is unique.

The method used to generate the mesh is based on an initial triangulation of the boundary points followed by the insertion of new points inside the domain according to a prescribed rule. Details on grid generation using Dealunay triangulation can be found in reference [14].

Two grid adaption techniques are used. One is the so called spring method which uses a spring mechanism to deform the mesh nodes. This method ignores remeshing procedure and therefore takes into account only mesh deformations. When the mesh distorts too much, the accuracy of the numerical solution will suffer. For this reason, another technique is implemented. In this second approach points are inserted in the domain when better resolution is required while existing points are deleted when they lie outside the domain. Thus, with this grid adaption strategy, the mesh quality can be guaranteed.

Results

Steady Flow Solver

We consider a uniform flow past a NACA0012 airfoil placed beneath the water. The characteristic length, velocity, and density are chosen as the chord length of the airfoil, the distant upstream velocity, and the density of the fluid respectively. The Froude number is 0.567 while the submergence c which is the distance between the center of the airfoil and the undisturbed free surface is either 1.034 or 0.951, as in the experiments of Duncan [17]. This problem is computed to assess both the efficiency and the accuracy of the multigrid solver, as well as to evaluate an alternative strategies of mesh rearrangement including the point insertion/deletion method described earlier. Such a remeshing strategy is more general than the spring method originally employed by Hino et al. [8] and may allow in the future to follow waves past the overturning.

Figure 1a shows the grid corresponding to the final converged solution for $c = 1.034$, while figure 1b and 1c present comparisons of the wave elevations computed by using the two mesh movement strategies. The experimental data from reference [17] are also plotted. The computed waves are in phase with the one measured although there are slight difference in amplitude between the two. This indicates the level of accuracy that is achieved by our discretization method. The two adaption strategies perform equally well for the deeper submergence case, $c = 1.034$. However, for the shallower one, $c = 0.951$, the adaption method gives better accuracy than the spring method as it can be seen in figure 1c. This is due to the excessive mesh stretching exhibited by the spring method which impairs the accuracy of the computed solution for large amplitude waves. The convergence history plots of the root mean square error of the divergence of the velocity presented in figures 2a and 2b show that the multigrid scheme converges the velocity field to satisfy the continuity equation (solenoidality condition) to machine accuracy.

Unsteady Flow Solver

We consider a fluid in a finite rectangular tank with a vertical piston wavemaker at one end which corresponds to the experiment of [18]. The characteristic length, velocity, and density is set as the initial depth of the water H, $\sqrt{gH}$, and the fluid density. The nondimensional length of the tank is 20 in this study and the origin of the axis is fixed at the initial point of the intersection between wavemaker and unperturbed free surface. The horizontal velocity of the piston wavemaker $U(t)$ is prescribed as the following Fourier series

$$U(t) = \sum_{n=1}^{72} U_n cos(\omega_n t - \theta_n) \qquad (7)$$

The amplitudes U_n, frequencies ω_n, and phase θ_n are tabulated in [18].

For this case it is found that 10-25 multigrid cycles are sufficient to make the velocity field solenoidal within a tolerance of 10^{-5} for each physical time step.

The free surface profiles at several different locations, i.e. x=3.17, 5.00, 6.67, 8.33, 10.00, and 12.17, are compared with linear theory. Figure 3 shows that our unsteady solver is able to capture the trend of the wave motion. Moreover, the computed solutions are in better agreement with the experimental data reported in the literature [18]. This is not surprising since we are accounting for most of the nonlinearity of the problem. More specifically, on a 296×16 mesh, when the computed wave height at x=3.17, t=25 is compared to the experiments, we find that:

	Δt	h
computation	0.10	-0.6239
computation	0.05	-0.6662
linear theory		-0.7197
experiments		-0.667

Thus, the error is less than 6% .

Conclusions

A fully-implicit multigrid solver has been developed for the solution of time resolved non-linear surface wave propagation problems. Good performance and accuracy is demonstrated in comparison with experimental evidence and linear theory. The proposed algorithm is quite flexible, and can be extended to both 3-Dimensional flows, and more complex viscous flow problem. Moreover, the method can be applied to problems which require the solution of the flow equations coupled with either a mathematical model of the structure and/or the motion of a body. Thus, we believe that this method will evolve into a viable tool for the simulation of non-linear "seakeaping" problems.

REFERENCES

[1] Jameson, A., "Time Dependent Calculations Using Multigrid, with Applications to Unsteady Flows Past Airfoils and Wings," AIAA Paper 91-1596, June 1991.

[2] Mitty, T. J., *Development of a Delaunay-Based Adaption Scheme with Applications to Complex Three-Dimensional Rotational Flows*, Ph.D. Thesis, Department of Mechanical and Aerospace Engineering, Princeton University, January 1993.

[3] Baker, T. J., "Automatic Mesh Generation for Complex Three-Dimensional Regions Using a Constrained Delaunay Triangulation," *Engineering with Computers*, Vol. 5, pp. 161–175, 1989.

[4] Melson, N. D., Sanetrik, M. D., and Atkins, H. L., "Time-Accurate Navier-Stokes Calculations with Multigrid Acceleration," Presented at the Sixth Copper Mountain Conference on Multigrid Methods, Copper Mountain, Colorado, April 1993.

[5] Mavriplis, D., *Solution of the Two-Dimensional Euler Equations on Unstructured Triangular Meshes*, Ph.D. Dissertation, Department of Mechanical and Aerospace Engineering, Princeton University, 1987.

[6] Lin, P.T., *Implicit Time Dependent Calculations for Compressible and Incompressible Flows on Unstructured Meshes* , Master Thesis, Department of Mechanical and Aerospace Engineering, Princeton University, 1994.

[7] Jameson, A., "Multigrid Algorithms for Compressible Flow Calculations," MAE Report 1743, October 1985, also in the Proceedings of the Second European Conference on Multigrid Methods, in Lecture Notes in Mathematics, Vol. 1228, edited by Trottenburg, U., and Hackbusch, W., Springer-Verlag, pp. 166–201, 1986.

[8] Hino, T., Martinelli, L., and Jameson, A., "A Finite-Volume Method with Unstructured Grid for Free Surface Flow Simulations," Sixth International Conference on Numerical Ship Hydrodynamics, Ship Research Institute, Tokyo, Japan, August 1993.

[9] Chorin, A. J., "A Numerical Method for Solving Incompressible Viscous Flow Problems," *Journal of Computational Physics*, Vol. 2, pp. 12–26, 1967.

[10] Dreyer, J. J., *Finite Volume Solutions to the Steady Incompressible Euler Equations on Unstructured Triangular Meshes*, Master's Thesis, Department of Mechan-

ical and Aerospace Engineering, Princeton University, June 1990.

[11] Rizzi, A. and Eriksson, L., "Computation of Inviscid Incompressible Flow with Rotation," *Journal of Fluid Mechanics*, Vol. 153, pp. 275–312, 1985.

[12] Belov, A., Martinelli, L., and Jameson, A., "A Novel Fully Implicit Multigrid Driven Algorithm for Unsteady Incompressible Flow Calculations," to be presented at the Second European Computational Fluid Dynamics Conference, Stuttgart, Germany, September 1994.

[13] Belov, A., Martinelli, L., and Jameson, A., "A New Implicit Algorithm with Multigrid for Unsteady Incompressible Flow Calculations," AIAA Paper 95-0049, AIAA 33rd Aerospace Sciences Meeting, Reno, Nevada, January 1995

[14] Baker, T.J., "Three Dimensional Mesh Generation by Triangulation of Arbitrary Point Sets," *AIAA 8th CFD conference*, pp. 255-270, 1987.

[15] Rogers, S.E. and Kwak, D., "Upwind Differencing Scheme for the Time-Accurate Incompressible Navier-Stokes Equations," AIAA Journal, Vol. 28, No. 2, 253-262, 1990.

[16] Miyaka, T., Sakamoto, Y., Tokunaga, H., and Satofuka, N., "Numerical Solution of Incompressible Flow Using Two-Step, One-Stage Runge-Kutta Time Intergration Scheme ," Presented at the 1st European Computational Fluid Dynamics Conference, Brussels, Belgium, 7-11, September, 1992.

[17] Duncan, J.H., "The Breaking and Non-Breaking Wave Resistance of a Two-Dimensional Hydrofoil ," Journal of Fluid Mechanics, Vol. 126, pp. 507-520, 1983.

[18] Dommermuth, G.D., Yue, D.K.P., *et al.*, "Deep-Water Plunging Breakers: A Comparison Between Potential Theory and Experiments ," Journal of Fluid Mechanics, Vol. 189, pp. 423-442, 1988.

[19] Haussling, H.J. and Van Eseltine, R.T., "Finite-Difference Methods for Transient Potential Flow with Free Surface ," 1st International Conference on Numerical Ship Hydrodynamics , pp.295-313, 1975.

[20] Israeli, M. and Orszag, S.A., "Approximation of Radiation Boundary Conditions," Journal of Computational Physics, Vol. 41, pp. 115-135, 1981.

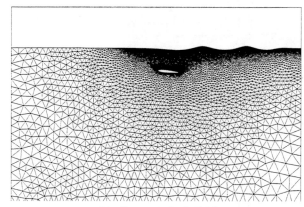

1a: Computationl Grid

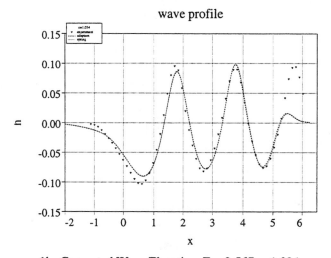

1b: Computed Wave Elevation, F = 0.567 c=1.034

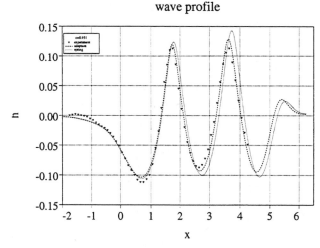

1c: Computed Wave Elevation, F = 0.567 c=0.951

Figure 1: Steady State Calculation of Wave Pattern over a NACA0012 Airfoil . Dot Line Spring Method, Dash Line Adaption Method.

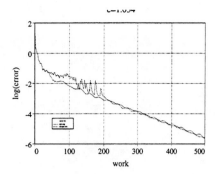 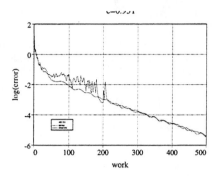

2a: Convergence History for c=1.034   2b: Convergence History for c=0.951

Figure 2: Convergence History. Dot Line Spring Method, Dash Line Adaption Method.

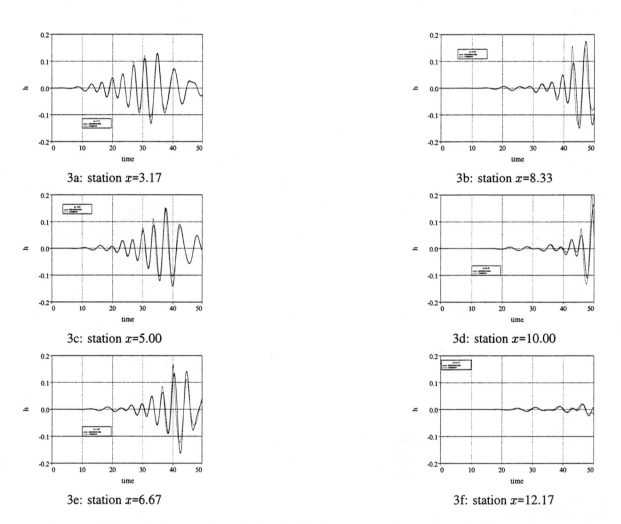

3a: station x=3.17   3b: station x=8.33

3c: station x=5.00   3d: station x=10.00

3e: station x=6.67   3f: station x=12.17

Figure 3: Wave Elevation vs Time. Dashed line Non-Linear calculation, Solid Line Linear Theory.

FED-Vol. 238, 1996 Fluids Engineering Division Conference
Volume 3
ASME 1996

AN ADAPTIVE LEVEL SET APPROACH FOR INCOMPRESSIBLE

TWO-PHASE FLOWS

Mark Sussman
Ann S. Almgren
John B. Bell
Phillip Colella
Louis H. Howell
Michael Welcome

Center for Computational Sciences and Engineering
Lawrence Berkeley National Laboratory
Berkeley, CA

ABSTRACT

In Sussman et al. (1994), a level set method was formulated for solving incompressible two-phase flow with surface tension. In the level set approach, the interface is represented as the zero level set of a smooth function; this has the effect of replacing the advection of density, which has steep gradients at the interface, with the advection of the level set function, which is smooth. In addition, the interface can merge or break up with no special treatment. We maintain the level set function as the signed distance from the interface in order to robustly compute flows with high density ratios (1000:1) and stiff surface tension effects. In this work, we couple the level set scheme to an adaptive projection method for the incompressible Navier-Stokes equations, in order to achieve higher resolution of the interface with a minimum of additional expense.

LEVEL SET METHOD

The numerical computation of incompressible flows consisting of two immiscible fluids, such as air and water, presents many problems at the interface of the two fluids. Steep density gradients along with topological changes such as merging and fragmentation of fluid mass are typically difficult to handle in numerical computation. Furthermore, the free surface boundary conditions due to surface tension and viscous effects can be difficult to impose. Several approaches have been proposed for this problem, such as front-tracking, boundary integral methods, and volume-of-fluid schemes. See, e.g., Unverdi and Tryggvason (1992), Lundgren and Mansour (1991), Brackbill et al. (1992), and the reference cited therein for a discussion of these other approaches. Here we describe the level set method as combined with an adaptive projection method. In the level set formulation, the interface is implicitly represented as the zero level set of a smooth function ϕ; thus merging and breaking up of the interface are handled naturally since the level set function does not become ill-defined during a topology change (Osher and Sethian, 1988). In our implementation of the level set method, ϕ is the signed distance from the interface for all time, thus quantities such as the gradient of ϕ and the curvature can be accurately computed using high-order schemes. Since the interface need never be explicitly reconstructed, implementations of level set schemes are relatively easy to program and easily generalizable from two to three dimensions. Problems involving gas bubbles, water drops, and wave growth due to wind have been computed using the level set scheme on a single grid (Sussman et al., 1996), (Marcus et al., 1995).

ADAPTIVE ISSUES

The level set method lends itself well to being computed on an adaptive grid. For problems with interfaces it is natural to refine around the interface; the refinement criterion can then easily be defined in terms of the level set function, which is also the distance from the interface. Since most of the vorticity in these flows is concentrated on or near the interface, refinement around

*Support for this work was provided by the Applied Mathematical Sciences Program and the HPCC Grand Challenge Program of the DOE Office of Mathematics, Information, and Computational Sciences under contract DE-AC03-76SF00098.

the interface should yield not only finer resolution of the interface itself but also reduced numerical diffusion of the velocity field. In this work, we present results from calculations of bubbles and drops on an adaptive grid in order to demonstrate the fine-scale structure revealed by the improved resolution due to adaptivity. We have tried three versions of the adaptive method; each has its advantages and disadvantages. The first two versions (methods A and B) are based on the Crank-Nicholson schemes presented by Almgren et al. (1993) and Almgren et al. (1996). Unlike method A, method B includes the functionality for doing a MAC projection and a viscous solve. Both methods A and B adapt in time as well as space (sub-cycling). The last version (method C), does *not* adapt in time. Because one does not adapt in time, we can take advantage of multi-level projection schemes (Howell and Bell, 1994) which solve on the coarse and fine grids simultaneously. This allows one to ensure that the divergence-free criterion is satisfied across the coarse-fine grid interface without doing special sync-project operations. Instead of a Crank-Nicholson scheme as the underlying advection algorithm, we use a second order Runge-Kutta method along with second order ENO (Sussman et al., 1996). Inherent in the Runge-Kutta method is that we also do two projections per time-step; instead of a "level-project" and a "mac-project", we do two "multi-level-projects". The projections used in all three methods above are based on the approximate projection (Almgren et al., 1996).

NUMERICAL FORMULATION

At each time step we solve the following dimensionless evolution equations for the velocity $\vec{u}$, pressure gradient ∇p and the level set function ϕ,

$$\phi_t = -\vec{u} \cdot \nabla \phi \tag{1}$$

$$\vec{u}_t = -\frac{1}{\rho}\nabla p + \vec{F}(\vec{u}, \phi) \tag{2}$$

$$\nabla \cdot \vec{u} = 0$$

where

$$\vec{F}(\vec{u}, \phi) = -\vec{u} \cdot \nabla \vec{u} + \frac{\hat{y}}{Fr} + \frac{\nabla \cdot (2\mu D)}{R\rho} - \frac{\kappa(\phi)\nabla H(\phi)}{W\rho}$$

$$\kappa(\phi) = \nabla \cdot \frac{\nabla \phi}{|\nabla \phi|}$$

$$H(\phi) \equiv \begin{cases} 1 & \text{if } \phi > 0 \\ 0 & \text{if } \phi < 0 \\ 1/2 & \text{if } \phi = 0 \end{cases}$$

$$\rho(\phi) = H(\phi) + (\rho_2/\rho_1)(1 - H(\phi)) \tag{3}$$

$$\mu(\phi) = H(\phi) + (\mu_2/\mu_1)(1 - H(\phi))$$

The dimensionless parameters used are Reynolds number ($R = \frac{\rho_1 L U}{\mu_1}$), Froude number ($Fr = \frac{U^2}{gL}$) and Weber number ($W = \frac{\rho_1 L U^2}{\sigma}$).

The method used to update the velocity and pressure is a variable density extension of the approximate projection method described by Almgren et al. (1996). A projection method is a fractional step scheme in which a discretization of (2) is first used to approximate the velocity at the new time, then an elliptic equation for pressure, which results from taking the divergence of (2), is used to impose the divergence constraint on the new velocity and to update the pressure. Briefly, we may rewrite (2) as:

$$\vec{u}_t + \frac{1}{\rho}\nabla p = \vec{F}(\vec{u}, \phi).$$

The resulting equation for pressure is then

$$\nabla \cdot (\frac{1}{\rho}\nabla p) = \nabla \cdot \vec{F}$$

The divergence of the surface tension term as it appears in (2) is ill-defined; we rewrite this term as:

$$\frac{1}{\rho}\kappa(\phi)\nabla H(\phi) \equiv \frac{1}{\rho}\nabla(\kappa H) - \frac{1}{\rho}\nabla(\kappa)H$$

The first term on the right hand side can be incorporated in the pressure gradient term; the remaining term is now well-defined.

Note that the level set approach differs from a standard variable density projection method in that the quantity advected is ϕ, which is smooth at the air/water interface, rather than ρ, which initially is discontinuous across the interface. The density is then defined by (3). In (Sussman et al. 1994), a redistancing operation was presented for maintaining the level set function as the signed distance from the zero level set; improvements to this operation are presented later by Sussman et al. (1996). The operation involves an iteration at each time step to drive $|\nabla \phi|$ everywhere to 1. This redistancing operation is necessary for problems with large density ratios and surface tension.

SINGLE-GRID DISCRETIZATION

The basic components of the discretization involve:

- computing force term $\vec{F}(\vec{u}, \phi)$

- computing level-set advective term $\vec{u} \cdot \nabla \phi$

- projection: decomposing $\vec{F}$ into two components, $\vec{u}_t$ and $\nabla p/\rho$.

- redistance operation; drive $|\nabla \phi|$ to one.

356

We shall give our interface a thickness $\varepsilon = O(\Delta x)$ on which density, viscosity, and surface tension will be dependent. Our resulting Heaviside function is:

$$H_\varepsilon(\phi) = \begin{cases} 0 & \text{if } \phi < -\varepsilon \\ \frac{1}{2}[1 + \frac{\phi}{\varepsilon} + \frac{1}{\pi}\sin(\pi\phi/\varepsilon)] & \text{if } |\phi| \le \varepsilon \\ 1 & \text{if } \phi > \varepsilon \end{cases}$$

There are some algorithmic differences for the first three steps between the Crank-Nicholson and Runge-Kutta schemes.

Crank-Nicholson Approach

In this method, one "predicts" the values of the edge velocities at time $t^{n+1/2}$ in order to solve the momentum equation:

$$\frac{\vec{u}^* - \vec{u}^n}{\Delta t} = \frac{-\nabla p^{n-1/2}}{\rho^{n+1/2}} + \vec{F}^{n+1/2}$$

where

$$\vec{F}^{n+1/2} = -(\vec{u} \cdot \nabla \vec{u})^{n+1/2} + \frac{\hat{y}}{Fr} +$$
$$\frac{\nabla \cdot (2\mu^{n+1/2}(D^n + D^*))}{R\rho^{n+1/2}} + \frac{(\nabla\kappa(\phi^{n+1/2}))H(\phi^{n+1/2})}{W\rho^{n+1/2}}$$

In order to ensure that the predicted edge velocities are numerically divergence-free,

$$u^{n+1/2}_{i+1/2,j} - u^{n+1/2}_{i-1/2,j} + v^{n+1/2}_{i,j+1/2} - v^{n+1/2}_{i,j-1/2} = 0,$$

one applies the MAC projection. The MAC projection is used since the original time-centered edge quantities were approximated using a lagged pressure gradient. The values $\rho^{n+1/2}$ are computed as $\rho(\frac{\phi^{n+1}+\phi^n}{2})$ where:

$$\frac{\phi^{n+1} - \phi^n}{\Delta t} = -(\vec{u} \cdot \nabla \phi)^{n+1/2}$$

Once we have computed $\vec{u}^*$, we apply the following projection step to find $\vec{u}^{n+1}$:

$$\frac{\vec{u}^{n+1} - \vec{u}^n}{\Delta t} = \vec{P}_{\rho^{n+1/2}}(\frac{\vec{u}^* - \vec{u}^n}{\Delta t})$$
$$\frac{\nabla p^{n+1/2}}{\rho^{n+1/2}} = \frac{\nabla p^{n-1/2}}{\rho^{n+1/2}} + (I - \vec{P}_{\rho^{n+1/2}})(\frac{\vec{u}^* - \vec{u}^n}{\Delta t})$$

Runge-Kutta Approach

The following steps are performed for the second order Runge Kutta method that we shall use; details can be found in Sussman et al. (1996):

1. $\vec{F}^n = -(\vec{u} \cdot \nabla \vec{u})^n + \frac{\hat{y}}{Fr} +$

$$\frac{\nabla \cdot (2\mu^n D^n)}{R\rho^n} + \frac{(\nabla\kappa(\phi^n))H(\phi^n)}{W\rho^n}$$
$$\frac{\tilde{\vec{u}}^* - \vec{u}^n}{\Delta t} = \vec{F}^n \tag{4}$$

2. $\dfrac{\phi^* - \phi^n}{\Delta t} = -(\vec{u} \cdot \nabla \phi)^n$

$$\rho^{n+1/2} = \rho(\frac{\phi^* + \phi^n}{2})$$

3. $\dfrac{\vec{u}^* - \vec{u}^n}{\Delta t} = \vec{P}_{\rho^{n+1/2}}(\dfrac{\tilde{\vec{u}}^* - \vec{u}^n}{\Delta t}) \tag{5}$

4. $\dfrac{\tilde{\vec{u}}^{n+1} - \vec{u}^n}{\Delta t} = \vec{F}^* \tag{6}$

5. $\dfrac{\phi^{n+1} - \phi^n}{\Delta t} = -\dfrac{1}{2}((\vec{u} \cdot \nabla \phi)^* + (\vec{u} \cdot \nabla \phi)^n) \tag{7}$

$$\rho^{n+1/2} = \rho(\frac{\phi^{n+1} + \phi^n}{2})$$

6. $\dfrac{\vec{u}^{n+1} - \vec{u}^n}{\Delta t} = \dfrac{\vec{P}_{\rho^{n+1/2}}(\vec{F}^*) + \vec{P}_{\rho^{n+1/2}}(\vec{F}^n)}{2} \tag{8}$

Redistance Operation

We perform a "redistance" update on ϕ^{n+1}. Given $\phi^{n+1,(0)} \equiv \phi^{n+1}$ as initial data, we solve the equation

$$d_\tau = \text{sign}(\phi^{n+1,(0)})(1 - |\nabla d|) \tag{9}$$

for $\tau = 0$ to $\tau = \alpha\Delta x$ where $2\alpha\Delta x$ is the thickness of our interface. The new solution $\phi^{n+1,(\alpha)} = d(\alpha\Delta x)$ will represent the signed distance from the zero level set of $\phi^{n+1,(0)}$ for points within $\alpha\Delta x$ of the interface. We use a new constraint, described in Sussman et al. (1996), for improving the accuracy of the above operation. We rewrite (9) as:

$$d_\tau + \vec{w} \cdot \nabla d = \text{sign}(\phi^{n+1,(0)}) + \lambda H'(\phi) \tag{10}$$

where $\vec{w}$ is a unit normal pointing away from the zero level set,

$$\vec{w} = \text{sign}(\phi^{n+1,(0)})\frac{\nabla d}{|\nabla d|}$$

and λ is chosen to satisfy the constraint,

$$\partial_\tau \int_\Omega H(d) = \int_\Omega H'(d)d_\tau = 0.$$

We let our new ϕ^{n+1} value be $\phi^{n+1,(\alpha)}$.

ADAPTIVE MESH REFINEMENT

The adaptive strategy is based on a mesh structure analogous to that used for hyperbolic conservation laws by Berger and Colella (1989). In this approach fine grids are recursively embedded in the coarse grid until sufficient resolution is obtained. An error estimation procedure automatically determines where the solution resolution is inadequate, and grid generation procedures dynamically create rectangular fine grid patches in these regions. In our problems, the criterion for refinement is based on ϕ; one level of refinement is based on the zero level set of ϕ and further levels of refinement are based on the curvature of ϕ. We shall be experimenting with 3 variations of the adaptive algorithm. The Crank-Nicholson variation (methods A and B) adapts in time as well as space ("sub-cycling"). The Runge-Kutta variation (method C) adapts only in space ("no sub-cycling") and makes use of the multi-level solver for computing the projection (Howell and Bell, 1994).

Sub-Cycling; Methods A and B

In (Almgren et al., 1993), (Almgren et al., 1996), projection methods for solving variable density incompressible flow on an adaptive mesh are presented. We modify these adaptive methods by replacing the advection of ρ with that of ϕ and adding a redistance step. Our approach to adaptive refinement uses a nested hierarchy of grids with simultaneous refinement of the grids in both space and time. The integration algorithm on the grid hierarchy is a recursive procedure in which coarse grids are advanced, finer grids are advanced multiple steps to reach the same time as the coarse grids and the fine and coarse grid data are then synchronized. Let $r(\ell)$ be the refinement ratio between levels ℓ and $\ell+1$. The algorithm can most easily be described recursively; to advance level ℓ, $0 \leq \ell \leq \ell_{max}$ the following steps are taken:

1. Advance level ℓ in time as if it is the only level. Supply boundary conditions for $\vec{u}, p$, and ϕ from level $(\ell-1)$ if level $\ell > 0$, and from the physical domain boundaries.

2. If $\ell < \ell_{max}$

   - advance level $(\ell+1)$ $r(\ell)$ times with time step $\Delta t^{\ell+1} = \frac{1}{r(\ell)} \Delta t^{\ell}$. Use boundary conditions for $\vec{u}, p$, and ϕ from level ℓ, and from the physical domain boundaries.

   - Synchronize the data between levels ℓ and $\ell+1$, and interpolate corrections to higher levels if $\ell + 1 < \ell_{max}$.

3. if $\ell = 0$, perform a multi-level re-distancing step.

The synchronization step requires averaging down of the fine data onto the coarse grid and performing a "sync projection" (and a "macsync projection" for method B) to enforce the divergence condition on the composite grid. The multi-level redistancing operation maintains ϕ as a smooth distance function even across coarse/fine grid boundaries. The sync projection involves the solution of elliptic equations on the coarser grid; details of the sync projection are presented by Almgren et al. (1993) and Almgren et al. (1996). Details of the multi-level redistancing operation are described below.

No Sub-Cycling; Method C

In (Howell and Bell, 1994), a projection method for solving incompressible flow on an adaptive mesh is presented. The approach is to use a nested hierarchy of grids with refinement of the grids only in space and not in time. The advantage is that one does not need to worry about a sync-correction step at the end of a coarse grid step. We use the multi-level projection described by Howell and Bell (1994) in which the pressure is solved for on the coarse and fine grids simultaneously in a way that ensures that the velocity field is divergence-free across a coarse/fine grid boundary. In our computations here, we use a modified version of the multi-level projection which computes an "approximate projection" as opposed to an "exact projection" (Almgren et al., 1996). If we assume that we have a total of $\ell_{max} + 1$ levels at time T, then the time step on all the grids will be $\Delta t = \Delta t^{\ell_{max}}$. The algorithm is described as follows:

1. for all levels ℓ, $0 \leq \ell \leq \ell_{max}$, solve equations (4) and (5).

2. average down fine grid data of $\tilde{\vec{u}}^*$ and ϕ^* onto the underlying coarse grid.

3. perform multi-level projection step

4. Compute second "loop" of the Runge-Kutta method, equations (6) through (8), in same manner as the first three steps above.

5. perform a multi-level re-distancing step.

Multi-Level Re-distance Step

We assume that the thickness of the interface is $2\alpha\Delta x_0$ where Δx_0 is the cell width on the coarsest grid. We solve (9) for $\tau = 0$ to $\tau = \alpha\Delta x_0$. The time step on the coarsest grid is $\Delta\tau_0 = \Delta x_0/2$. We use the same approach as described in the "sub-cycling" section above for solving (9). For each coarse grid step on level ℓ, we perform $r(\ell)$ steps on the level $\ell + 1$. Afterwards, data from level $\ell + 1$ is averaged down onto data at level ℓ.

NUMERICAL EXAMPLES

Our computations will be performed on a two-dimensional axisymmetric $r - z$ grid; we will be testing the behavior of our adaptive scheme on spherical bubbles and drops.

Tests With Sub-Cycling (methods A and B)

In figure 1, we display a rising gas bubble ($W = 200$, $R = \infty$, $\frac{\rho_2}{\rho_1} = 1/1000$) in liquid. The coarse grid has 16×32 cells and the effective fine grid has 512×1024 cells. We compare our result to the same problem done using a single-grid Runge-Kutta scheme with 120×240 cells. This problem has also been done using the boundary integral method, and the results of the boundary integral are very similar (up until pinch off) with our results (Sussman et al., 1996). For this first problem we used method A (sub-cycling turned on, sync-project turned off). With adaptivity, we were able to recover the fine scale behavior during pinch off, with considerably less computational effort than if we had computed with the fine grid covering the whole domain. In figure 2 (first plot), we compute a gas bubble with no surface tension or viscous forces and a $1/10$ density ratio. The coarse grid had 32×64 cells and the effective fine grid had 128×256 cells. We used method B (sub-cycling, sync-project, macsync-project all turned on) for computing this problem. We have found, for problems requiring greater surface tension effects and/or 1:1000 density ratios, that methods A and B fail. If we were to turn on the sync-project option for method A, we would not have been able to compute at the 1000:1 density ratio that we did. This is currently work in progress, since the failure may not be due as much to the algorithmic design as it is due to failure in the multigrid solve (computing the projection). We are able to compute these problems using methods A or B on a single grid. One direction for getting methods A and B to work for a wider range of problems is to use alternate linear algebra solvers such as the conjugate gradient method with multigrid as a preconditioner.

Tests Without Sub-Cycling (method C)

For the rest of our tests, we use method C (no sub-cycling, multi-level solve, Runge-Kutta method). We are able to compute a wider range of problems using this method; albeit, we still have failure for some problems during the composite multigrid solve. In figure 2 (middle plot), we display a rising gas bubble with large surface tension effects ($W = 20$, $R = \infty$ & $\frac{\rho_2}{\rho_1} = 1/1000$).

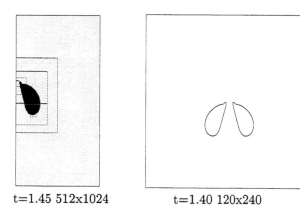

t=1.45 512x1024   t=1.40 120x240

Figure 1: Rising inviscid air bubble in water $W = 200$

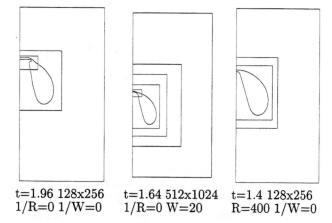

t=1.96 128x256   t=1.64 512x1024   t=1.4 128x256
1/R=0 1/W=0   1/R=0 W=20   R=400 1/W=0

Figure 2: Spherical gas bubbles in liquid; first bubble has density ratio of 10:1, last two have density ratios of 1000:1

The effective fine grid has 512×1024 cells. The results here compare favorably with the boundary integral method (Lundgren and Mansour, 1990). In figure 3, we compute effects of a 1cm radius spherical water drop falling against the bottom of the domain ($W = 0.0135$, $R = 3.130$, $\frac{\rho_2}{\rho_1} = 1000/1$ & $\frac{\mu_2}{\mu_1} = 100/1$). The extra force due to surface tension keeps the drop relatively spherical until it hits the surface, where we can resolve the spray coming off of the ground. The effective fine grid contains 64×256 grid points.

Convergence Check. We perform a convergence check on a viscous gas bubble ($W = \infty$, $R = 400$ & $\frac{\rho_2}{\rho_1} = 1/1000$) as shown on the far right of figure 2 by computing the relative error on successively finer effective mesh sizes. The interfacial thickness is also allowed to approach zero as $O(\Delta x_{fine})$. The relative error be-

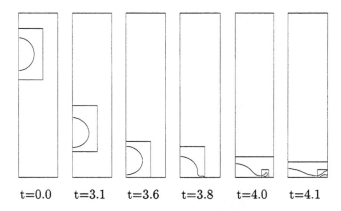

t=0.0   t=3.1   t=3.6   t=3.8   t=4.0   t=4.1

Figure 3: Falling 1cm spherical water drop in air; density ratio 1000:1, 64×256, $R = 3.13$, $W = 0.0135$

tween the coarse (c) and the fine grid (f) at time t is defined to be $E_t \equiv \int_\Omega |H(\phi_c(t)) - H(\phi_f(t))| d\Omega$. Thus, the error is the volume of the region in which the level set function on the coarse grid is not the same sign as on the fine grid. In Table 1 we display the relative errors E_t and volumes $V_t \equiv \int_\Omega (1 - H(\phi(t)) d\Omega$ for the adaptive problem. The initial volume for all problems is $V_{0.0} = 4.189$. We find an order of accuracy of about 1.4 even through pinch off (about $t = 1.4$).

We also ran the convergence study on single non-adaptive grids at the same effective resolution as above and obtained comparable rates and errors. When we compared the fine single-grid results to the fine adaptive results we found the error to be less than half of the error between the fine and medium-fine grids; thus our adaptive solution appears to be converging to the "right" solution. It took about 4 times longer for the single-grid code (fine grid) to reach $t = 1.6$ than for the adaptive code (with the same effective fine grid).

Table 1: Convergence study on adaptive grid

Δx_{fine}	$V_{1.2}$	$E_{1.2}$	$V_{1.4}$	$E_{1.4}$	$V_{1.6}$	$E_{1.6}$
3/32	4.13	N/A	4.10	N/A	4.05	N/A
3/64	4.15	0.090	4.14	0.113	4.11	0.148
3/128	4.17	0.031	4.16	0.043	4.15	0.058
order		1.5		1.4		1.4

References

[1] Almgren, A.S., Bell, J.B., Colella, P. & Howell, L.H., *An Adaptive Projection Method for the Incom-pressible Euler Equations*, Proceedings of the 11th AIAA Computational Fluid Dynamics Conference, Orlando, July 6–9, 1993.

[2] Almgren, A.S., Bell, J.B., Colella, P., Howell, L.H. & Welcome, M.L., *A Conservative Adaptive Projection Method for the Incompressible Navier-Stokes Equations in Three Dimensions*, in preparation.

[3] Almgren, A.S., Bell, J.B. & Szymczak, W.G., *A numerical method for the incompressible Navier-Stokes equations based on an approximate projection*, to appear in SIAM J. Sci. Comput., **17**:2, (1996).

[4] Berger, M.J. & Colella, P., *Local Adaptive Mesh Refinement for Hyperbolic Partial Differential Equations*, J. Comp. Phys., 82, pp. 64-84 (1989).

[5] Brackbill, J.U., Kothe, D.B., and Zemach, C., *A Continuum Method for Modeling Surface Tension*, J. Comp. Phys., 100, pp. 335-353, (1992).

[6] Chambers, D., Marcus, D. & Sussman, M., *Relaxation Spectra of Surface Waves*, Proceedings of the 1995 International Mechanical Engineering Congress and Exposition, November 1995.

[7] Howell, L.H. & Bell, J.B., *An Adaptive-Mesh Projection Method for Viscous Incompressible Flow*, prepared for submittal to SIAM Journal on Scientific Computing, 1994.

[8] Lundgren, T.S. and Mansour, N.N., *Vortex ring bubbles*, J. Fluid Mech., 224, 177 (1991).

[9] Osher, S. and Sethian, J.A., *Fronts Propagating with Curvature-Dependent Speed: Algorithms Based on Hamilton-Jacobi Formulations*, J. Comp. Phys., 79,1, pp. 12-49, (1988).

[10] Sussman, M., Smereka, P., & Osher, S.J., *A level set approach for computing solutions to incompressible two-phase flow*, J. Comp. Phys., 94, 146-159 (1994).

[11] Sussman, M., Fatemi, E., Smereka, P., and Osher, S.J., *An Improved Level Set Method for Incompressible Two-Phase Flows*, to appear, Journal of Computers and Fluids (1996).

[12] Unverdi, S.O. and Tryggvason, G., *A Front-Tracking Method for Viscous, Incompressible, Multi-fluid Flows*, J. Comp. Phys., 100, pp. 25-37, (1992).

FED-Vol. 238, 1996 Fluids Engineering Division Conference
Volume 3
ASME 1996

THREE-DIMENSIONAL, NONLINEAR, VISCOUS WAVE INTERACTIONS
IN A SLOSHING TANK

Ben R. Hodges

Robert L. Street

Environmental Fluid Mechanics Laboratory
Department of Civil Engineering
Stanford University, Stanford, CA 94305-4020

ABSTRACT

A numerical simulation method for the unsteady, incompressible, Navier-Stokes equations applied to viscous free-surface flows has been developed and tested on three-dimensional (3D) and two-dimensional (2D) nonlinear, finite-amplitude standing waves in a rectangular domain. Results are presented for a 3D simulation of two monochromatic waves that are initially superposed at a 90 degree angle. A comparison of 3D simulation results with 2D results provides a basis for analyzing nonlinear wave-wave interaction effects. Viscous damping effects are compared with theory, and wave-wave interactions are analyzed by decomposing into separate nonlinear effects.

NOMENCLATURE

a	wave amplitude
d	depth
$d1, d2$	diagonal symmetry planes
e_{ij}	rate-of-strain tensor
g	gravity
h	wave height
k	wave number
n_j	unit normal vector
p	pressure
t_i	unit tangent vector
t	time
T	theoretical wave period
w	vertical velocity
Δ	(or delta) a portion of surface deformation attributable to nonlinear wave-wave interaction
η	(or eta) surface deformation from quiescent level
ν	kinematic viscosity
ω	wave frequency

INTRODUCTION

This is the second conference paper documenting the development of a numerical simulation code for viscous, nonlinear free-surface problems. The first paper, Hodges et al. (1994), provides a literature review, detailed explanation of the numerical method, and validation of the method for two-dimensional (2D) nonlinear surface waves. This paper demonstrates the ability of the method to simulate a three-dimensional (3D) free-surface problem with viscous and nonlinear effects.

NUMERICAL METHOD

Our approach has been to work with second-order accurate numerical schemes that can be implemented efficiently on a single processor of a vector machine. The foundation of our method is a non-staggered grid, finite-volume method in boundary-fitted curvilinear coordinates developed by Zang et al. (1994), which traces its lineage to the time-splitting method of Kim and Moin (1985). The numerical method solves the unsteady, incompressible, Navier-Stokes equations on a three-dimensional domain where the coordinates and equations in physical space are mapped into a cube in computational space. The equations in computational space are more complex, but their discretization is simplified. As the free surface moves with each time step, a new mapping is calculated so that the free surface remains coincident with a boundary in computational space. The free surface is advanced using a curvilinear space formulation of the kinematic boundary condition that does not require the wave to be single-valued in physical space (Hodges et al. 1994). Currently, limitations of computational memory, computational time, and the unsolved problems associated with wave-breaking prevent us from simulating multi-valued waves. Discretization of the kinematic boundary condition is through the space-implicit, time-explicit method of Chan and Street (1970). The free-surface dynamic boundary conditions for this simulation are: (1) the zero tangential stress condition:

$$e_{ij}\, t_i\, n_j \;=\; 0 \qquad (1)$$

where e_{ij} is the rate of strain tensor and t_i and n_j are the unit tangent and unit normal vectors, respectively; and (2) constant surface pressure (p):

$$p \;=\; 0 \qquad (2)$$

It is planned that future simulations will include both the surface tension and surface-normal viscous effects that are neglected in equation (2).

Further details of our numerical method and two-dimensional validation simulations can be found in Hodges *et al.* (1994). Complete details of the three-dimensional method are to appear in Hodges (1996).

SIMULATION SET-UP

The problem solved is liquid sloshing in a square tank. The initial free surface position is computed from two identical standing waves that are linearly superposed at a 90 degree angle. Each individual wave is monochromatic, nonlinear, and of finite amplitude (using a second-order approximation from Wiegel, 1964). This provides the initial free surface shape shown in Figure (1). The simulation grid contains $32 \times 32 \times 32$ grid cells (for clarity, only one-quarter of the grid cells on the surface are shown). In all figures in this paper, the horizontal coordinates are non-dimensionalized by the lowest mode wavelength, while the surface deformation (η or eta, measured from still free-surface level) is non-dimensionalized by the combined amplitudes of the two superposed waves.

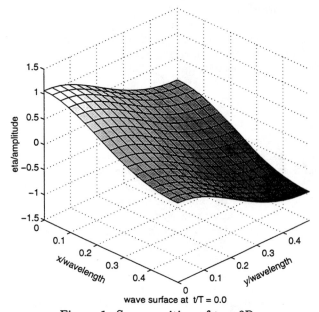

Figure 1: Superposition of two 2D waves

The simulation domain is one-half of a wavelength in length and breadth and one-tenth of a wavelength in depth ($50\,cm \times 50\,cm \times 10\,cm$). The depth of the simulation was chosen in conjunction with the viscosity of the fluid ($7.32 \times 10^{-5}\,m^2/s$) so that the free-surface boundary layer could be resolved using five grid cells without requiring excessive computational time or memory. While the viscosity is still significantly larger than that of water, it is approximately one-fifth of that used in the recent linearized free-surface simulations of Borue *et al.* (1995).

The initial velocity field is the irrotational solution at the maximum displacement of a standing wave (*i.e.* zero for all velocity components). At the start of the simulation, the upper surface is set free and is allowed to evolve in response to the nonlinear kinematic and dynamic boundary conditions as applied to the Navier-Stokes equations. Each of the superposed waves has the following initial characteristics: the wave number (k) is 6.28 $1/m$, the wave Reynolds number ($\omega/\nu\,k^2$) is approximately 2000, the wave ak is 0.0314, the wavelength is 100 cm, and the individual component wave amplitude is 0.5 cm. The frequency (ω) of the component waves is 5.86 rad/sec, as computed from the dispersion relation (Wiegel, 1964):

$$\omega^2 \;=\; gk\,tanh\,(kd) \qquad (3)$$

where g is gravity, d is the depth, and k is the wave number.

The combination of the two waves has a sloshing amplitude of 1.0 cm along a diagonal axis of 70.7 cm. Since the initial conditions are a linear superposition of the two waves, we expect that the primary oscillation of the system should be at the same frequency as the individual waves until the nonlinear interactions have had enough time to act upon the system. However, we should see some nonlinear effects occurring at wavelengths equal to the diagonal axis and twice the diagonal axis. These dimensions have wave k values of 8.89 $1/m$ and 4.44 $1/m$, respectively. The system ak based on the diagonal sloshing is 0.04. From the dispersion relation, we might expect nonlinear effects occurring at frequencies of 7.87 and 4.26 rad/sec, corresponding to the two primary diagonal modes.

The sidewall and bottom boundary conditions are free-slip (no boundary layer). This is appropriate for this simulation since the presence of sidewall boundary layers would obscure the free-surface viscous effects which we seek to capture.

SIMULATION RESULTS

The simulation was carried out for approximately twelve wave periods (4700 time steps). For analysis, we ran an additional simulation of viscous 2D sloshing of one of the monochromatic component waves. Both the 3D and the 2D simulations oscillated with a primary period equal to the theoretical period (for a 2D finite-amplitude standing wave) with an uncertainty of 0.25%. The uncertainty was not surprising since the wave period was not evenly divisible by the simulation time step. There was no perceptible increase or decrease of the period over the course of the simulation, so we can conclude that the duration of the simulation was insufficient for nonlinear interactions to have any significant effect on the overall period of the sloshing. This is a reasonable result. The waves are in linear superposition to the first order, therefore it should require a relatively large number of wave periods for the higher-order nonlinear terms to have a large-scale effect on the dispersion relation.

The effect of wave-wave interactions on the surface deformation (Δ) in the 3D simulation is defined by subtracting the wave surface (η_{2D}) formed from a 90 degree superposition of two of the 2D monochromatic simulations from the wave surface of the 3D (η_{3D}) simulation:

$$\Delta^{[total]} \equiv \eta_{3D} - \eta_{2D} \qquad (4)$$

Since the simulation of the 2D component wave is also nonlinear, this approach removes the nonlinear interactions of each wave with itself, leaving only the interactions between the two waves. Figure (2) shows a plot of the difference between the 3D wave and the superposition of the 2D waves after nine periods have been simulated. This is the total nonlinear effect of wave-wave interactions on the surface deformation (which we will call the "surface deformation effect"). For this point in time ($t/T = 9.015$), the surface wave shape is essentially the same as shown in Figure (1). In Figure (2), the overall surface deformation effect of the nonlinear interactions is less than 4% of the wave amplitude in either direction. Over the duration of the simulation, the maximum difference between the superposed 2D waves and the 3D simulation was about 7% of the wave amplitude. However, at the end of the simulation, the nonlinear effects on the surface deformation were still increasing and would likely continue to increase for some time as resonant modes for the domain are excited (for a discussion of gravity wave resonance, see Phillips, 1974). If the simulation were continued, we expect

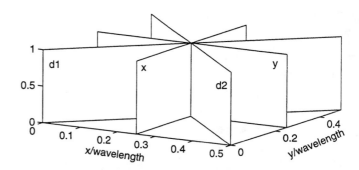

Figure 3: Symmetry/asymmetry planes

the nonlinear effects to eventually reach a zero growth rate or a stable oscillation as energy is exchanged between resonant wave modes.

To provide a better quantitative understanding and analysis of the nonlinear wave-wave interactions, we can decompose the total nonlinear effects (Figure 2) using symmetries and asymmetries around four cutting planes illustrated in Figure (3). These planes can be identified by the following axes:

$d1$ the main diagonal axis along which the overall sloshing is approximately symmetrical

$d2$ the secondary diagonal axis along which the overall sloshing is asymmetrical

x an axis where x/wavelength = 0.25

y an axis where y/wavelength = 0.25

The asymmetrical component of the surface deformation ($\Delta^{[a]}$) at a point (p) about a cutting plane (c_1) is defined as:

$$\Delta_p^{[a:c_1]} \equiv \frac{1}{2}\left(\eta_p - \eta_i^{[c_1]}\right) \qquad (5)$$

where η_p is the surface deformation at point p, and $\eta_i^{[c_1]}$ is the surface deformation of the image point of p relative to the cutting plane c_1. The symmetrical component of the surface deformation ($\Delta^{[s]}$) is defined as:

$$\Delta_p^{[s:c_1]} \equiv \frac{1}{2}\left(\eta_p + \eta_i^{[c_1]}\right) \qquad (6)$$

It follows that $\Delta_p^{[a:c_1]} + \Delta_p^{[s:c_1]} = \eta_p$. If we substitute $\Delta_p^{[s:c_1]}$ for η_p and the image point of $\Delta_p^{[s:c_1]}$ with respect to a second cutting plane (c_2) for $\eta_i^{[c_1]}$, then equations (5) and (6) become:

$$\left(\Delta_p^{[s:c_1]}\right)_p^{[a:c_2]} = \frac{1}{2}\left\{\Delta_p^{[s:c_1]} - \left(\Delta_p^{[s,c_1]}\right)_i^{[c_2]}\right\} \qquad (7)$$

$$\left(\Delta_p^{[s:c_1]}\right)_p^{[s:c_2]} = \frac{1}{2}\left\{\Delta_p^{[s:c_1]} + \left(\Delta_p^{[s,c_1]}\right)_i^{[c_2]}\right\} \qquad (8)$$

Using further recursions of equations (7) and (8) about each of the cutting planes decomposes the surface into sixteen components. The sum of the sixteen components is equal to the original

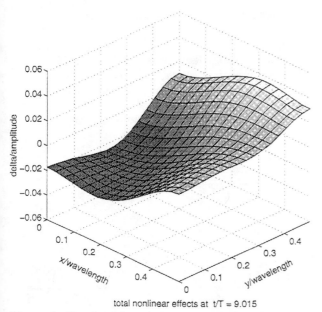

Figure 2: Total surface deformation (3D - superposed 2D)

surface deformation. Fortunately, it turns out that only seven of the components are of any significance (with deformations larger than 0.1% of the wave amplitude). By recombining some of the seven significant components, five decomposed nonlinear effects can be defined:

1. Symmetry along both diagonal planes ($d1$ and $d2$) with asymmetry on the x and y planes (Figure 4).
2. Symmetry on only one diagonal plane (Figures 6 and 7).
3. Symmetry on all planes (Figure 9).
4. Symmetry on x and y planes, with asymmetry on both diagonal planes (Figure 10).

The first of these components (Figure 4) can be seen as two standing waves (one along each diagonal) with wavelengths equal to the the diagonal dimension of the domain. We will call this the "vertical velocity nonlinear effect" for reasons that will be apparent in due course. The second two effects (Figures 6 and 7) are diagonal sloshings with the longest wavelength equal to twice the diagonal dimension of the domain. The third and fourth effects are higher mode waves in the x and y directions that have wavelengths equal to the domain length. In the case of Figure (9), the higher mode waves are in phase so that their crests and troughs coincide in the center. In Figure (10), the higher mode waves are out of phase in the center of the domain.

To understand the development of the nonlinear effects, it is useful to examine a time history of the root-mean-square (RMS) of the deformation components. Figures (5), (8), and (11) provide this data for the various nonlinear terms. Note that the RMS graphs show two peaks for each period of a deformation component. However, in the case of the vertical velocity effect (Figure 5), the second peak is so small as to be almost non-existent.

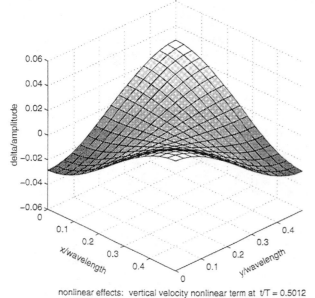

nonlinear effects: vertical velocity nonlinear term at $t/T = 0.5012$

Figure 4: Symmetry across both diagonal planes

ANALYSIS

Vertical velocity nonlinear effect

Figures (4) and (5) provide the data for the "vertical velocity nonlinear effect." This component of the nonlinear effects has five major characteristics:

1. Unlike the other nonlinear effects, the oscillations of the vertical velocity effect are not symmetrical about the still free-surface level (the plane $delta = 0$ in Figure 4). In Figure (5), we see evidence of this in the large RMS peak followed by a very small (almost non-existent) peak. Figure (4) shows the shape of the vertical velocity effect at the top of a large peak. At the top of a small peak, the deformation effect is nearly flat, but is non-zero.

2. The effect shows no significant growth rate. This is consistent with the attribution of the effect to the vertical velocity. We would not expect to see large changes in the vertical velocity terms since such changes would require either rapid growth or rapid damping of the waves.

3. The frequency of the effect is approximately 1.25 times the frequency of the 2D wave, or about $7.33\,rad/sec$. This is in reasonable agreement with the theoretical value of $7.87\,rad/sec$ for a standing wave with a wavelength of the domain diagonal (which appears to be the longest wavelength in Figure 4).

4. This is initially the dominant nonlinear effect, but in the sixth period of the 3D wave combination, it is superseded by the nonlinear sloshing effects along the main diagonal ($d1$). By the eleventh period, the nonlinear sloshing effects along the minor diagonal ($d2$) are also larger than the vertical velocity effect (see Figure 8 for the sloshing effects).

5. In general, this effect shows a decrease in 3D free-surface height (relative to the combination of the 2D waves) at the corners of the main sloshing diagonal ($d1$) and an increase in height along the minor diagonal ($d2$) corners.

This phenomena is attributable to the Navier-Stokes' vertical velocity nonlinear term ($w\,\partial w/\partial z$, where w is the vertical velocity and z is the vertical coordinate). The nonlinear vertical velocity term is included in the superposed component waves, but its 3D effect is different from the sum of the effects of the

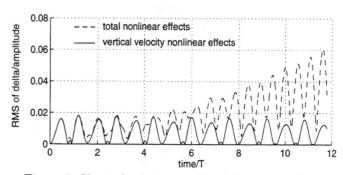

Figure 5: Vertical velocity surface deformation effects

2D component waves, since:

$$(w_1 + w_2) \frac{\partial}{\partial z} \left(w_1 + w_2 \right) \neq w_1 \frac{\partial w_1}{\partial z} + w_2 \frac{\partial w_2}{\partial z} \qquad (9)$$

where the subscripts 1 and 2 indicate the monochromatic waves in the x and y directions, respectively. We note that if $w_1 = w_2$ then the nonlinear term on the left-hand side of equation (5) is twice as big as the nonlinear term on the right-hand side. Thus, if the velocity field is linearly superposed to the first order, then the vertical velocity nonlinear terms at the $d1$ corners of the 3D simulation will be approximately twice that of the superposed waves (or four times that of a single wave). For example, in the first half-period of the sloshing, along the vertical line at the corner $(0,0,z)$ we have $w < 0$ and $\partial w/\partial z < 0$, while at the corner where $(0.5, 0.5, z)$ we have $w > 0$ and $\partial w/\partial z > 0$. It follows that in the Navier-Stokes equations, along the line of $(0,0,z)$, the nonlinear term is accelerating the free surface downward; while along the line of $(0.5, 0.5, z)$, the nonlinear term is retarding the upward motion of the free surface. This is exactly the effect illustrated in Figure (4). Note that in the corners of the $d2$ diagonal the w_1 and w_2 terms are approximately equal and in opposite directions. Therefore, effect of the nonlinear term in the 3D simulation is close to zero, whereas the nonlinear terms in a superposition of the 2D simulations are of the same sign and will accumulate rather than cancel. Thus, the 3D simulation has less damping in the corners of the $d2$ diagonal than there is in the 2D nonlinear waves, resulting in the surface deformation effect being positive at these corners. Again, this is clearly shown in Figure (4).

Diagonal sloshing

Sloshing effects along the main ($d1$) and minor ($d2$) diagonals are illustrated in Figures (6), (7), and (8). The sloshing along the main diagonal exhibits the most rapid growth rate of any of the nonlinear effects. The frequency of the diagonal sloshings is approximately 0.94 times the frequency of the 2D wave, or about $5.5\,rad/sec$. While this is significantly greater than the theoretical value of $4.26\,rad/sec$ for a wavelength of twice the domain diagonal, it is qualitatively correct in that it shows a lower frequency than the 2D wave. Much as the primary 3D sloshing is composed of two 2D waves, each of the 3D nonlinear diagonal sloshing effects could be further decomposed into 2D waves in the x and y directions. Heuristically, one might expect the decomposed waves to follow the dispersion relation and oscillate at the same rate as the main sloshing. Therefore, it is significant that these components are oscillating at a slower rate than the primary sloshing. This indicates that the nonlinear effects are moving the system away from a superposition of two x and y waves, transforming it into a combination of waves along the $d1$ and $d2$ axes. Such waves have a longer primary wavelength and a lower frequency. It is obvious from Figure (8) that the nonlinear diagonal sloshing effects were still in a period of rapid change when the simulation was stopped. It is likely that a longer simulation would show a further decrease of the frequency and continued growth of the diagonal nonlinear terms.

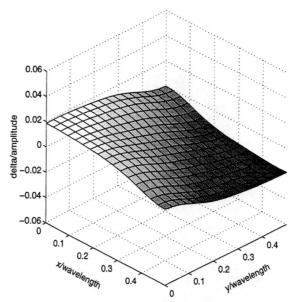

nonlinear effects: secondary sloshing along major diagonal axis at $t/T = 9.642$

Figure 6: Symmetry along main diagonal

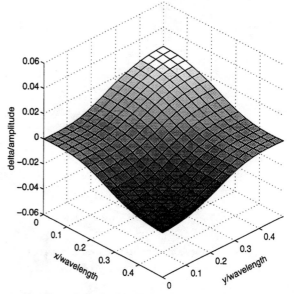

nonlinear effects: secondary sloshing along minor diagonal axis at $t/T = 9.642$

Figure 7: Symmetry along minor diagonal

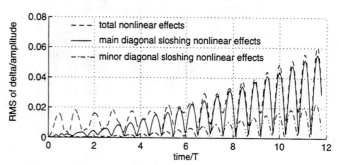

Figure 8: Diagonal sloshing surface deformation effects

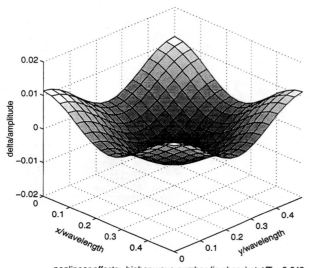

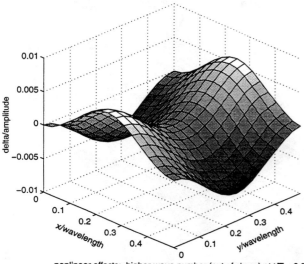

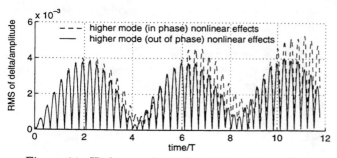

Higher order modes

Surface deformations produced at higher modes in the x and y directions are illustrated in Figures (9) (10) and (11). These nonlinear effects are an order of magnitude smaller than the other effects and do not seem to have a significant growth rate. For all practical purposes, they play a very minor role in the wave interactions. It is interesting to note that Figure (11) shows the existence of several similar waves that are slightly out of phase so as to produce standing wave groups in the higher modes. This is probably due to reflection effects from the free-slip boundaries of the simulation.

Viscous effects

To analyze the viscous effects, we compare the maximum crest-to-trough wave height (as a function of time) to the viscous-damping theory of Lamb (1945), art. 348-349:

$$h(t) = h(0) e^{-2\nu k^2 t} \qquad (10)$$

where $h(t)$ is the wave height as a function of time. Figure (12) shows the results for the 2D monochromatic sloshing, the 3D sloshing, and Lamb's theory. For purposes of comparison, the theory is shown for the k of the 2D superposed waves, as well as for the k for diagonal waves based upon the diagonal length and twice the diagonal length.

As shown in Figure (12), the 2D results are in excellent agreement with the theory, while 3D results and theory are in reasonable agreement, given that we are taking some liberties in applying the theory to the 3D case. Lamb's derivation is based on an energy argument for a steady, linear, 2D monochromatic wave which is characterized by a single wave number, while we are applying it to a nonlinear 3D case that has at least three significant wave numbers with effects that are time-dependent. Despite this, our results are fairly consistent with Lamb's theory. However, we should be careful not to attribute the entire

Figure 9: Symmetry with all planes

Figure 10: Symmetry with x and y planes

Figure 11: Higher mode surface deformation effects

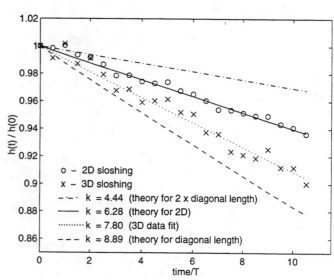

Figure 12: Change in maximum crest-to-trough height

change in the maximum wave height in the 3D simulation to viscous attenuation. A heuristic argument can be made that the individual deformation components should follow the damping theory and, therefore, the total damping should be the sum of the damping of the components. A brief review of the magnitudes of the nonlinear terms in Figures (5) and (8) and the difference in wave height between the 3D simulation and theory in Figure (12) shows that application of equation (10) to the nonlinear terms cannot account for all of the reduction in wave height. A better explanation is that a significant portion of the change in the wave height is caused by the nonlinear terms redistributing the wave energy away from the crests and troughs. For example, from Figure (7), the nonlinear sloshing effect along the minor diagonal ($d2$) has an amplitude of 3% of the combined wave amplitude. This alone could account for most of the difference between the damping theory and the 3D change in wave height.

CONCLUSION

This paper has demonstrated the ability of the numerical method to capture viscous and nonlinear effects in a 3D free-surface Navier-Stokes wave simulation. Comparisons have been made to the viscous damping theory of Lamb (1945) with reasonable agreement. The nonlinear wave-wave interactions have been decomposed into component effects that deform the 2D monochromatic waves of the initial conditions. Unfortunately, we have not found any laboratory experiments in the literature which would provide a suitable basis for direct validation of the 3D wave-wave interactions. This would perhaps be an interesting task that could provide a standard validation method for free-surface simulations, much as laboratory measurements of the lid-driven cavity flow have provided for turbulent flow simulations. We hope to provide further validation of the numerical method at a later date through simulations of progressive water waves and comparisons to laboratory data.

ACKNOWLEDGMENT

The support of the Fluid Dynamics Program, Mechanics and Energy Conversion Division, Office of Naval Research, through Grant N00014-94-1-0190 [Program Officer: Dr. E.Rood] is gratefully acknowledged.

REFERENCES

Borue, V., Orszag, S.A. and Staroselsky, I., 1995, "Interaction of surface waves with turbulence: direct numerical simulations of turbulent open-channel flow," *J. Fluid Mech.* Vol. 286, pp. 1-23.

Chan, R.K.-C., and Street, R.L., 1970, "SUMMAC - A numerical model for water waves," Technical Report 135, Stanford University, 155 pages.

Hodges, B.R., Street, R.L., and Zang, Y., 1994, "A method for simulation of viscous, non-linear, free-surface flows," *20th Symp. on Naval Hydrodynamics*, preprint volume W1 through Th5, pp. 247-265.

Hodges, B.R., 1996, *Numerical simulation of free-surface flows,* Ph.D. thesis, Department of Civil Engineering, Stanford University, Stanford, CA, to appear.

Kim, J., and Moin, P., 1985, "Application of a Fractional-Step Method to Incompressible Navier-Stokes Equations," *J. Comp. Physics*, Vol. 59, pp. 308-323.

Lamb, H., 1945, *Hydrodynamics*, 6th ed., Dover Publications.

Phillips, O.M., 1974, "Wave Interactions," in *Nonlinear Waves*, ed. S. Leibovich and A.R. Seebass, Cornell University Press, pp. 186-211.

Wiegel, R.L., 1964, *Oceanographical Engineering*, Prentice-Hall, Inc.

Zang, Y., Street, R.L. and Koseff, J.R., 1994 "A Non-staggered Grid, Fractional Step Method for Time-Dependent Incompressible Navier-Stokes Equations in Curvilinear Coordinates," *J. Comp. Physics*, Vol. 114, pp. 18-33.

FED-Vol. 238, 1996 Fluids Engineering Division Conference
Volume 3
ASME 1996

FLOW OVER A CYLINDRICAL CONTAINMENT DIKE

Adrian S. Sabau and Peter E. Raad
Mechanical Engineering Department
Southern Methodist University
Dallas, Texas

ABSTRACT

In this paper, a free surface numerical technique is validated by comparing numerical and experimental results of cylindrical flows involving impact between a fluid and a solid obstacle. Numerical simulations are presented for an axisymmetric, high-speed flow during which impacts occur and the free surface changes shape dramatically. The numerical results of a flow over a dike possess the same open dome-like fluid structures observed in experiments, thus providing strong validation for the numerical technique. The manner in which the fluid surges over a given dike depends strongly on the prescribed fluid height. Different overflow fluid structures that lead to large overspills are identified.

INTRODUCTION

Storage tanks and their impounding dikes, which are often required to contain any accidental spillage, are usually cylindrical and the volume capacity of the dike region is approximatively equal to that of the tank. As a result of a sudden rupture or collapse of a tank, the contained fluid flows under the influence of gravity, impacts the containment dike, and spills over it. Although a global investigation of the process has been made experimentally by Greenspan and Johansson (1981), a better understanding of the water-solid impact on a cylindrical structure is required to investigate the ensuing physics which are important to dike design.

Abdullah and Salcudean (1990) studied the free surface flow during the filling of a cylinder with water. They proposed an efficient method for the simulation of axisymmetric flows. However, in their method, free surfaces can only be a function of the axial coordinate. Sabau and Raad (1995) showed that even in the most recent codes, the deficiencies associated with the implementation and application of boundary conditions preclude an accurate treatment of impact.

In Sabau and Raad (1995), the authors presented a new Volume of Fluid method with improved Boundary Conditions (VOFBC) based on RIPPLE (Kothe et al., 1991). In VOFBC, new procedures are implemented for the assignment of boundary conditions at the free surface or along solid boundaries for velocities, pressure, and VOF function. Also, the new technique incorporates the most recent advances in impact treatment (Johnson et al., 1994; Cooker and Peregrine, 1995). The free surface is represented by a set of line segments fitted within each surface cell by knowing the surface orientation and volume of fluid fraction F (Ashgriz and Poo, 1991). The interface is advected by the use of a volume conservation constraint algorithm (Youngs, 1982). For two dimensional problems in Cartesian coordinates, these procedures were validated against experimental results (Sabau and Raad, 1995).

In this paper, these procedures are generalized to handle axisymmetrical flow configurations as a step toward the simulation of fully three-dimensional impact on solid structures. The calculation of velocities is improved by assigning the velocity boundary conditions according to the same principles stated in Raad et al. (1995) and Chen et al. (1995); namely, (a) the velocity information, which captures the momentum history of the fluid that has entered the surface cell, is used in all assignment steps, and (b) the boundary conditions at a solid boundary have to be considered only after the fluid touches the boundary. Experimental and numerical results of flow over a cylindrical containment dike, during which impact occurs, are used to demonstrate the effectiveness of the improved VOF method.

METHODOLOGY

In this Section, we give a succinct presentation of the VOFBC method which is used for numerical simulations. More details about this VOF method are shown

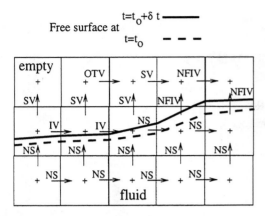

Figure 1. Velocity flags near free surface

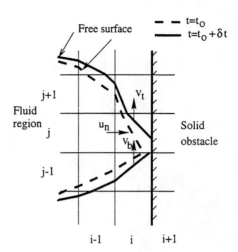

Figure 2. Impact identification

in Sabau and Raad (1995), where simple modifications are pointed out that have to be made in the computational cycle of VOF methods in order to handle the high-speed fluid impact on solid structures.

Velocity boundary conditions at the free surface

In VOFBC, free surface velocity boundary conditions are treated in detail by the use of procedures similar to those introduced by Chen et al. (1995, 1996). The procedures were developed in the context of a marker and cell method and have been shown to lead to significant improvements over previous methods, providing very accurate results (Raad et al., 1995). It is especially worth mentioning that the assignment of tentative velocities has been improved considerably since the velocities are assigned to take into account the momentum history of the fluid, and not merely to satisfy continuity as in the classical application of boundary conditions.

For a more efficient and systematic application of velocity boundary conditions, a velocity flag $\mathcal{F}$ is introduced. The velocity flag is used to compute or assign the tentative and final velocities, and is updated every time cycle after the interface reconstruction is completed. The velocities are classified in the following five types according to the placement of the fluid in their control volumes at the current time level (Fig. 1):

a) Navier-Stokes velocity (NS): velocity (inside the fluid) on a face shared by two nonempty cells.

b) Internal velocity (IV): velocity (outside the fluid region) on a face shared by nonempty fluid cells.

c) Surface velocity (SV): velocity on a face shared by a nonempty cell and an empty cell.

d) Outside tangential velocity (OTV): velocity between two empty cells which themselves are adjacent to nonempty cells.

e) New fluid internal velocity ($NFIV$): velocity between a new fluid cell and a nonempty cell.

Treatment of Impact

Instead of pressure, we use as a variable the pressure impulse, which is a preferable physical quantity to model during impact since the time scale at impact is very small (Johnson et al., 1994; Cooker and Peregrine, 1995). The pressure impulse is defined as follows:

$$P^{k+1} \equiv P(r, z, t^{k+1}) = \int_{t^k}^{t^{k+1}} p(r, z, t)\, dt \ , \quad (1)$$

where superscripts k, and $k+1$ refer to the current and new time levels, respectively.

Figure 2 presents a typical impact situation where the fluid interface is shown at $t = t_0$ and $t = t_0 + \delta t$. Impact is identified when the fluid is *actually* touching the solid boundary at the end of computational cycle $t = t_0$ after the new interfaces have been determined (Sabau and Raad, 1995). Thus, the velocity flag $\mathcal{F}_{ij}$ indicates that impact is occurring on the right face of cell (i, j). The tentative velocities are computed at $t = t_0 + \delta t$ and $\widetilde{U}_{ij}$ is assigned as a tentative surface velocity, i.e. its flag is set to SV, because its flag $\mathcal{F}_{ij}$ indicates an impact on its face. Then, the pressure Poisson equation is solved subject to the impact boundary condition (Johnson et al., 1994; Cooker and Peregrine, 1995):

$$\frac{\partial P^{k+1}}{\partial r} = \rho^k \widetilde{U} \ . \quad (2)$$

Next, the velocity flag $\mathcal{F}_{ij}$ is set to indicate a regular contact (as opposed to impact) between the fluid and the obstacle. The velocity flag is also used when setting the boundary conditions at a solid obstacle for both the pressure and the fluid volume fraction F so that the fluid does not sense the obstacle before the fluid actually strikes the obstacle surface.

Computational cycle

Considering that the velocities are classified in different types according to the fluid placement in their control volumes, and including the impact treatment, the VOFBC computational cycle is:

1. Compute only tentative NS velocities $\tilde{\vec{V}}$:

$$\frac{\tilde{\vec{V}} - \vec{V}^n}{\delta t} = -\nabla\left(\vec{V} \cdot \vec{V}\right)^n + \frac{1}{\rho^n}\nabla \cdot \vec{\tau}^n + \vec{g} \quad (3)$$

2. Assign tentative internal (IV), surface (SV), and new fluid ($NFIV$) velocities $\tilde{\vec{V}}$ by using procedures described in detail by Chen et al. (1995, 1996).

3. Calculate the pressure impulse P^{k+1}:

$$\nabla \cdot \left[\frac{1}{\rho^k}\nabla P^{k+1}\right] = \nabla \cdot \tilde{\vec{V}} , \quad (4)$$

with the following impact pressure boundary conditions:

$$\frac{1}{\rho^k}\frac{\partial P^{k+1}}{\partial n} = \vec{n} \cdot \tilde{\vec{V}} , \quad (5)$$

where $\vec{n}$ is the unit normal to the obstacle.

4. Reflag impact velocity flags into obstacle flags, and reset the impact velocities to zero.

5. Compute final NS, $NFIV$, and IV velocities:

$$\vec{V}^{k+1} = \tilde{\vec{V}} - \frac{1}{\rho^k}\nabla P^{k+1} \quad (6)$$

6. Assign final surface (SV) velocities, $\vec{V}^{k+1}$:

$$\nabla \cdot \vec{V}^{k+1} = 0 , \quad (7)$$

7. Assign U^{k+1} and V^{k+1} outside tangential velocities (OTV) equal to the value of the nearest respective NS velocities.

8. Advect the F function.

9. Reconstruct the interface.

10. Identify impact and set velocity flags $\mathcal{F}$.

SIMULATION RESULTS AND DISCUSSION

Greenspan and Johansson (1981) presented experimental results of the surge front of a cylindrical fluid column that collapses under the influence of gravity and subsequently impacts a containment dike. After impact, the fluid piles up and pours over the dike while a bore returns toward the region of initial collapse, all in less than 1 s. The problem is characterized geometrically by the radius R and initial height H of the fluid column, and the height a, radius r, and inclination angle θ of the dike. In this work, we will present results only for $R=9.53$ cm (3.75 in), $r=22.86$ cm (9 in), and $\theta=60°$.

In order to validate VOFBC for axisymmetric problems, results of numerical simulations are compared with the experimental results presented by Greenspan and Johansson (1981). Then, the overflow structures, formed by the fluid after impact, are investigated for different initial heights H of the fluid column.

In Figs. 3 (a) and (b), we present the experimental and simulation results, respectively, for an initial fluid column $H=29.21$ cm (11.5 in) and a dike height $a=5.1$ cm (2 in). Because the time sequence for the experiment is not reported, the figures representing the results of the VOFBC simulation are arranged to correspond visually with the pictures of the experiment. The first two frames in Figs. 3 (a) and (b) show the fluid before impact at times $t=0.05$ s and 0.11 s, respectively. As a result of impact, high impulsive pressures are generated and the fluid piles straight up on the dike as shown in frames 3. The pile is formed by the leading front of the fluid cylinder that collapsed. The fluid momentum is directed in the vertical direction after impact. The momentum of the remainder of the fluid behind the front not only is smaller, but it is now able to develop radially out since the region in front of the dike is now filled with water. The arriving fluid, therefore, pushes the mid-section of the initial pile outwardly, while the head of the pile is collapsing under the influence of gravity. The outcome of these two actions is the formation of an open, dome-like shape observed in frame 4 of both the numerical and experimental results. As seen in frames 5, the open-dome finally collapses under the influence of gravity and folds on itself. In frames 6, the formation of a spike is observed as the bore returns toward the center.

Greenspan and Johansson (1981) found that, for a fixed dike inclination, the total fluid overspill is essentially determined by the ratio of the heights of the dike and initial fluid column, a/H. In Table 1, the experimental (Q_{EX}) and numerical (Q_{VOF}) spillage fractions are listed for comparison. The spillage fraction is defined as the fraction of the initial fluid volume that flows over the dike. The dike height is fixed at $a=3.8$ cm (1.5 in) and the initial height H of the fluid cylinder is varied. The disagreement observed at the smaller values of a/H is due, based on the authors experience from the two-dimensional cases, to the inappropriate application of pressure boundary conditions. Indeed, in VOFBC the free surface pressure condition is applied at the cell center of a surface cell instead of being prescribed right

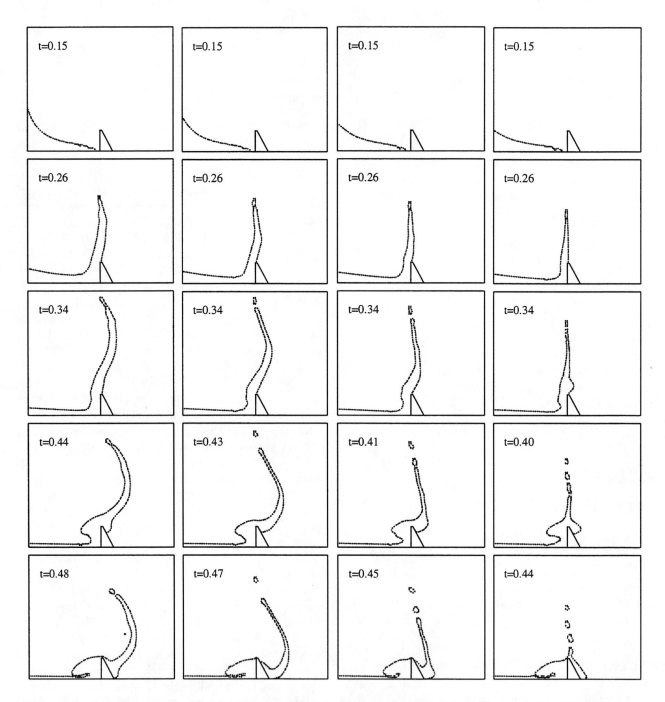

Figure 3. Radial cross-sections of numerical results at selected times (Columns 1 through 4 for H=21.9, 17.8, 15.2, 12.7 **cm, respectively)**

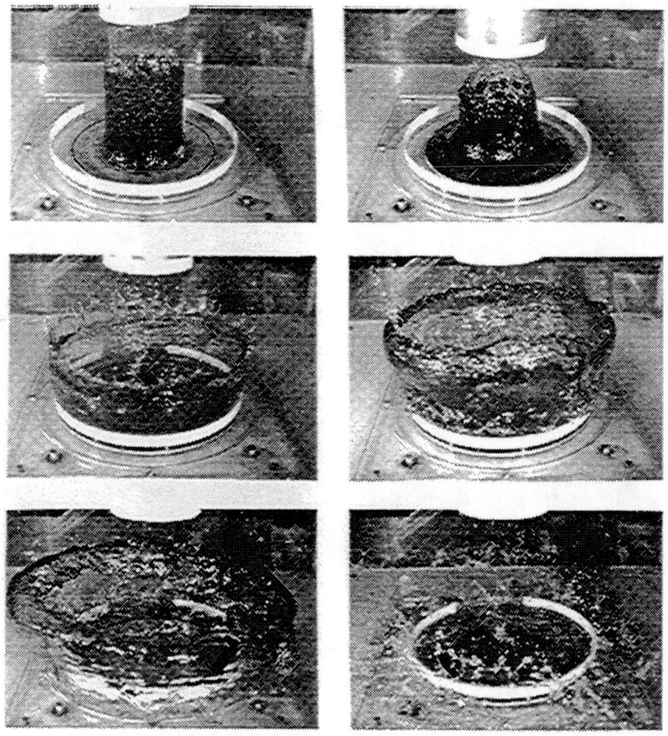

(b) VOFBC simulation results

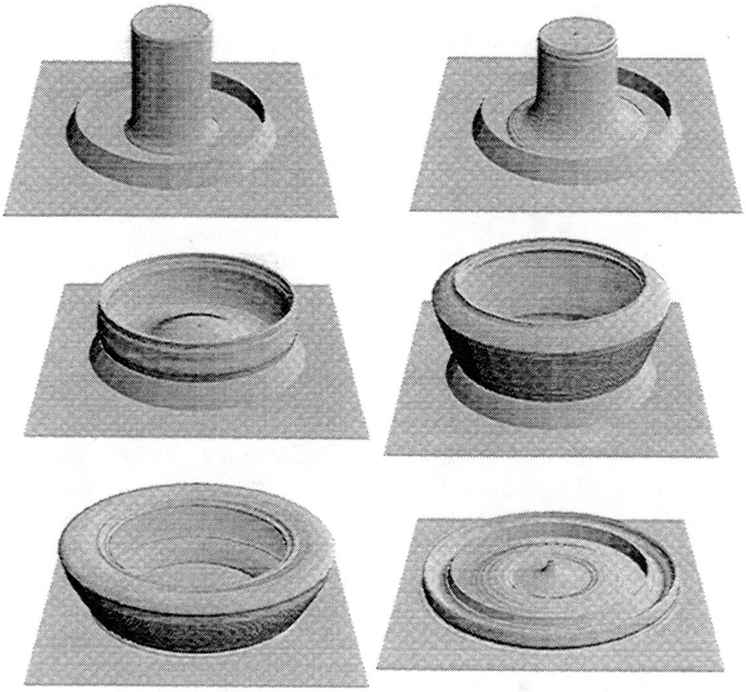

Figure 4. Flow over a containment dike (H=29.21 cm, a=5.1 cm)

Table 1. Experimental and numerical spillage fractions for a dike with $a=3.8$ cm

a/H	Q_{EX}	Q_{VOF}
0.174	0.50	0.58
0.214	0.42	0.53
0.250	0.35	0.47
0.300	0.26	0.30

on the free surface. Thus, the overflow, which is in fact a thin fluid column that undergoes large deformations over a short period of time, is not accurately modeled. The implementation of the pressure boundary condition at the free surface for axisymmetric problems is in progress and further results will soon be available.

The four columns of frames shown in Fig. 4 correspond to initial fluid heights of 21.9, 17.8, 15.2, and 12.7 cm, respectively. We present the results in a radial cross-section in order to capture details not easily seen in a three-dimensional plot. As shown in Fig. 4, the manner in which the fluid surges over the dike, whose height is fixed, varies dramatically with the initial fluid height. In the second row of frames at a time $t=0.26$ s, one observes a direct relationship between the initial water cylinder height and the height and thickness of the rising pile. The larger momentum generated by the higher initial fluid height is responsible for the thickness of the jet that emerges after the first impact with the dike. As previously mentioned, the momentum of the fluid behind the leading front (which itself makes up the pile) strikes the mid-section of the pile and pushes it radially out, creating in the process the arch-like shape observed in the experimental results of Fig. 3. Meanwhile, the head of the pile, which is higher than any subsequently arriving fluid can reach, continues to move along a vertical path. Then, as observed in rows 3 and 4, the entire pile is pushed outwardly, resulting in a significant amount of spillage. The case shown in column 4 which corresponds to the shortest initial fluid height exhibits a different behavior. Here, the momentum of the fluid behind the leading front is not significant enough to carry the fluid pile over the dike. Instead, any spillage is simply due to the initial pile collapsing on itself and onto the dike, with part of the fluid falling on each side of the dike. Finally, in the fifth row of frames, we are able to observe the touchdown of the fluid as well as the formation of a bore on the left side of the dike. This bore will result in sloshing in the dike region, but no additional spillage takes place for the cases considered.

CONCLUSIONS

Numerical simulations by the use of new VOF method are presented for an axisymmetric, high-speed flow involving impact and significant free surface deformations. The numerical results of an axisymmetric flow over a dike indicate that the numerical technique can faithfully simulate the physical flow and capture important details such as the open, dome-like fluid structures observed in the experiments. The manner in which the fluid surges over a given dike depends strongly on the initial fluid height. A physical interpretation is given for observed impact and overflow processes which result in large overspills.

REFERENCES

Abdullah, Z., and Salcudean M., 1990, "Free Surface Flow during the Filling of a Cylinder," *International Journal for Numerical Methods in Fluids*, Vol. 11, pp. 151-168.

Chen, S., Johnson, D.B., and Raad, P.E., 1995, "Velocity Boundary Condition for the Simulation of Free Surface Fluid Flow," *Journal of Computational Physics*, Vol. 116, pp. 262-276.

Chen, S., Johnson, D.B., Fadda, D., and Raad, P.E., "The Surface Marker and MicroCell Method," To be submitted to Journal of Fluid Mechanics (1996).

Cooker, M.J., and Peregrine, D. H., 1995, "Pressure-impulse theory for liquid impact problems," *Journal of Fluid Mechanics*, Vol. 297, pp. 193-214.

Greenspan, H.P., and Johansson, A.V., 1981, "An Experimental Study of Flow over and Impounding Dike," *Studies in Applied Mathematics*, Vol. 64, pp. 211-223.

Greenspan, H.P., 1993, Personal communication.

Johnson, D.B., Raad, P.E., and Chen, S., 1994, "Simulation of impacts of Fluid Free Surfaces with Solid Boundary," *International Journal for Numerical Methods in Fluids*, Vol. 19. No. 2, pp. 153-176.

Kothe, D. B., Mjolsness, R. C., and Torrey, M. D., 1991, *RIPPLE: A Computer Program for Incompressible Flows with free surfaces*, Los Alamos National Lab., LA-10612-MS, Los Alamos, NM.

Raad, P.E., Chen, S., and Johnson, D.B., 1995, "The Introduction of Micro Cells to Treat Pressure in Free Surface Fluid Flow Problems," ASME *Journal of Fluids Engineering*, Vol. 117, pp. 683-690.

Sabau, A.S., and Raad, P.E., 1995, "On Two-Dimensional Water-Solid Impact with VOF Methods," ASME *Winter Annual Meeting*, San Francisco, CA, November 1995, FED-Vol. 215, pp. 89-96.

FED-Vol. 238, 1996 Fluids Engineering Division Conference
Volume 3
ASME 1996

DYNAMICS OF POLYDISPERSE BUBBLY
FLOWS IN PERIODIC DOMAINS

Asghar Esmaeeli
Department of Mechanical Engineering and Applied Mechanics
The University of Michigan
Ann Arbor, Michigan

Grétar Tryggvason
Department of Mechanical Engineering and Applied Mechanics
The University of Michigan
Ann Arbor, Michigan

ABSTRACT

Dynamics of polydisperse bubble clouds is investigated. A front tracking/finite difference technique is used to solve the full Navier-Stokes equations for the flow inside and outside deformable bubbles. The evolutions of two, two-dimensional system of bidisperse bubbles with the the same equivalent nondimensional numbers are studied and the statistics of the flow (i.e. rise velocity, liquid Reynolds stresses, etc.) are compared to an equivalent monodisperse bubble cloud. Results from one fully three-dimensional simulation of four bubbles are also presented.

INTRODUCTION

Mixture of gas bubbles or liquid drops in another liquid or gas occurs in many physical processes. Heat transfer through boiling, cloud cavitation in hydraulic systems, and bubble driven circulation systems used in metal processing operations, are a few such examples. The literature on the dynamics of a single bubble or a drop is vast. While experimental results are available for almost all regions of the parameter space, numerical results are mostly confined to the two limiting cases of low Re number (creeping flow) and high Re number (potential flow). The numerical simulations of Youngren & Acrivos (1975), Rallison (1981), Dandy & Leal (1989), Ryskin & Leal (1984) are a few examples of previous studies of a single bubble.

In practical problems where many bubbles or drops move together, it is the collective behavior of the bubbles or the drops that is of interest. In the limits of zero and infinite Reynolds number the Navier-Stokes equations can be simplified and boundary integral techniques used to simulate the motion of deformable particles. The work of Zhou & Pozrikidis (1993, 1994) on the interactions of two-dimensional drops and Manga & Stone (1993) on the three-dimensional interactions of two drops are a few examples in the Stokes flow limit, and the work of Sangani & Didwania (1993) and Smereka (1993) are examples of the inviscid flows. In the intermediate Reynolds number it is necessary to solve the full Navier-Stokes equations. The literature is limited to the papers by Feng *et al.* (1994, 1995), who studied rigid particles, and Unverdi & Tryggvason (1992) and Esmaeeli & Tryggvason (1996a, b, c) for the deformable particles.

All the previous studies were done for monodisperse flows where the particles have the same equivalent diameters. In real physical problems, the particles may be of different sizes. The problem becomes more complicated as a result of the introduction of additional parameters.

To the best of our knowledge, the problem of unsteady interactions of deformable particles of different sizes at intermediate Reynolds number has not been addressed previously. There is, however, a relatively modest body of literature about the interactions of two rigid particles of different sizes. The analytical papers of Batchelor (1982, 1983) and Cox (1990) for the interactions of rigid polydisperse spheres in Stokes flow and the numerical work of Kumaran and Koch (1993a, b) in potential flows are a few examples.

The focus of the current study is on the long time evolution of two- and three-dimensional polydisperse bubbly flows in the intermediate Reynolds number.

FORMULATION AND NUMERICAL METHOD

The governing equations are solved using the finite difference/front tracking technique developed by Unverdi and Tryggvason (1992). The method was inspired by Peskin's computation of flow in the heart (1977) but is more general since it is capable of solving viscous multi-fluid problems with large differences in the material properties of the different fluids.

Consider a domain consisting of two different immiscible fluids with different material properties. Rather than writing the Navier-Stokes equation separately for each of the fluids, we use a formulation which is valid for the entire flow field and takes the jump in properties across the interface into account. The momentum equations in conservative form for such a flow are:

$$\frac{\partial \rho \overline{u}}{\partial t} + \nabla \cdot \rho \overline{u}\overline{u} = -\nabla p + \nabla \cdot \mu(\nabla \overline{u} + \nabla \overline{u}^T) + \qquad (1)$$

$$(\rho_0 - \rho)\mathbf{g} + \oint \sigma \kappa \mathbf{n}\delta(\mathbf{x} - \mathbf{x}^f)ds$$

In the above equation $\overline{u}$ is the velocity, p is the pressure, ρ is the density, μ is the viscosity field, σ is the surface tension coefficient, κ is the curvature, and $\mathbf{n}$ is the unit vector normal to the interface (from liquid to gas). $\delta(\mathbf{x} - \mathbf{x}^f)$ is a delta function which is zero everywhere except at the interface where $\mathbf{x} = \mathbf{x}^f$. ds is an area (length) element over interface in three (two) dimension. Here, ρ_0 is the average density, and $\rho_0 g$ is a force to prevent uniform acceleration of the whole flow field in the direction of gravity, when we use periodic boundary condition in that direction. If the bubble density is zero, then the momentum is all due to the ambient fluid and this would lead to no net motion of the ambient flow. Here, the bubble density is not exactly zero, but since it is much smaller than the density of the ambient fluid, and the bubbles are relatively small, the net flow is almost zero.

We take each fluid to be incompressible, so:

$$\nabla \cdot \overline{u} = 0. \qquad (2)$$

The above equations are supplemented by equations of state for the fluids:

$$\frac{D\rho}{Dt} = 0; \qquad \frac{D\mu}{Dt} = 0, \qquad (3)$$

as well as initial and boundary conditions. Here, $\frac{D\rho}{Dt}$ is the substantial derivative. Inside each fluid the density

and viscosity are constant but there are jumps in these properties across the interface.

The above equations are solved using a projection method on a fixed, regular, staggered grid. The equations are discretized using a conservative, centered difference scheme for the spatial variables and an explicit second order time integration method. In addition to the Eulerian grid, there is another grid which is used to represent the interface. This grid is not structured and is used to keep the density and the viscosity stratification sharp and to calculate surface tension. At each time step information must be passed between the front and the stationary grid. To determine density and viscosity at every point in the flow field we solve a Poisson equation which is obtained by spreading the gradients of these parameters (which approximates a delta function) onto the grid points.

The controlling parameters for the dynamics of a bubble rising in a periodic domain are: the density of the outer and the inner fluid, ρ_o, ρ_i; viscosity of the outer and inner fluid, μ_o, μ_i; gravity, g; the equivalent diameter of the bubble, d_e; the surface tension coefficient, σ; and a length scale representing the size of the periodic domain, L. Nondimensionalization of the above variables leads to the following nondimensional numbers: the Morton number, $M = g\mu_o^4/\rho_o\sigma^3$; the Eötvös number, $Eo = \rho_o g d_e^2/\sigma$; the density ratio, $\lambda = \rho_i/\rho_o$; the viscosity ratio, $\gamma = \mu_i/\mu_o$; and the void fraction, $(\alpha \sim (d_e/L)^n)$ ($n = 2$ or 3 in two or three dimensions). When we present our results, d_e, $\sqrt{d_e g}$, and $\sqrt{d_e/g}$ are used as length, velocity, and time scale. For the bubble rise velocity, we use $\mu_o/\rho_o d_e$ as a velocity scale giving a Reynolds number.

RESULTS

It is, perhaps, of fundamental interest in the analysis of polydisperse flows whether it is possible to define an equivalent monodisperse system. Or, in other words, if it is possible to characterize the dynamics of such flows by using equivalent properties. Here, we examine this possibility for equivalent parameters defined as follows:

$$\alpha_e = \frac{1}{A_b}\sum_{i=1}^{N} a_i, \qquad (4)$$

and

$$Eo_e = \frac{\sum_{i=1}^{N} Eo_i a_i}{\sum_{i=1}^{N} a_i} \qquad (5)$$

where A_b is the area (volume) of the computation box, a_i is the area (volume) of each bubble in two- and three-dimensions, Eo_i is the individual Eötvös number of the bubble, and N is the number of bubbles. In order to address the above question we have done several two- and three-dimensional simulations.

Figure 1 shows sixteen frames from one of these simulations. The frames are equispaced in time. The first frame (top left hand corner) shows the initial positions of the bubbles. Initially the bubbles were put in four rows and their positions were perturbed randomly. To make it easier to follow the interaction of the bubbles, one row is colored black. The bubbles are of two different sizes and their nondimensional numbers are $Eo_1 = 2$, $\alpha_1 = 0.0785$, and $Eo_2 = 3$, and $\alpha_2 = 0.1177$. Here, the void fraction for each species is simply the ratio of the area of that species to the area of the computation domain. The Morton number is $M = 10^{-5}$ and the ratio of material properties are $\lambda = 0.1$ and $\gamma = 0.1$. The equivalent parameters as defined above are $Eo_e = 2.56$ and $\alpha_e = 0.1962$. The size of the domain is $x/d_m = 8.0$, and $y/d_m = 8.0$ and the resolution is 288×288 grid points. Here, $d_m = 0.5$ is the diameter of the bubbles in a monodisperse flow with similar equivalent properties. The rest of the frames show the evolution of the bubbles and the streamlines. Initially, the velocity is zero everywhere. As a motion starts, the initial configuration starts to break up because the bubbles rise with different velocities. When a bubble leaves the periodic domain on one side, its periodic counterpart enters the domain from the other side (frame 2). By frame 3 little trace remains of the initial setup. The bubbles deform greatly and collisions, pairwise and triplewise interactions, and local clustering can be seen. Although, we do not allow rupturing of the bubbles in the current simulations (to avoid making the problem more complex), we have simulated flows where we allow that to happen (see Esmaeeli 1995 and Esmaeeli *et al.* 1996). Even though the main motion is in the direction of gravity, the bubbles also move in the horizontal direction as a result of their interactions.

Figure 2 shows the rise Reynolds number of the centroid of the bubbles versus time. The Reynolds number is fluctuating and has several local minimums and maximums. The time-averaged Re number is 22.89. It has been shown, for monodisperse systems at intermediate Reynolds number, in Esmaeeli and Tryggvason (1996c) that the decrease in the rise velocity is a result of the tendency of the bubbles to form local side-by-side configurations and the increase in the rise velocity is due to the bubbles lining up in a rising column.

In order to show how the bubbles interact, we show the trajectories of the bubbles in Fig. 3. It is seen that the bubbles have risen through ten periodic boxes in the vertical directions and they have spread over five

periodic boxes in the horizontal direction (the size of each box in is one period).

Figure 4 shows the Reynolds stresses for the continuous phase (liquid) for this flow. In the derivation of the Reynolds stresses we have used the phasic average (see Drew 1983) which is defined as:

$$< \phi_k > = \frac{1}{\alpha_k A} \int \phi X_k dA; \qquad k = 1, 2 \quad (6)$$

where A is the area of the domain, ϕ is a field variable such as $\overline{u}$, α_k is the volume fraction of fluid k, and X_k is a phase function which is 1 if a point is inside phase k and zero otherwise. The velocity field is decomposed in the following way:

$$\overline{u} = < \overline{u} > + \overline{u}'_k, \qquad (7)$$

and the Reynolds stresses are then derived by taking another phasic average of the fluctuation velocities:

$$\mathbf{Re} = < \overline{u}'_k \overline{u}'_k > \qquad (8)$$

The figure shows that the vertical stresses are comparable to the horizontal ones. The cross term is almost zero as expected. It is seen that the vertical and horizontal stresses are correlated with the velocity field, having a peak when the velocity is maximum and a valley when the velocity is minimum.

In order to show how the velocities of the bubbles change with respect to the velocity of their center of mass, we plot the *rms* fluctuations of the bubbles' velocities in Fig. 5. This measure is defined by:

$$\overline{u}_{rms} = \frac{1}{v_s N} \sqrt{\sum_{i=1}^{N} (\overline{u}_i - \overline{u}_0)^2} \qquad (9)$$

In the above equation $\overline{u}_i$ is the velocity of each individual bubble, $\overline{u}_0$ is the velocity of the center of mass of the bubbles, and $v_s = \sqrt{d_m g}$ is the velocity scale. It is seen that this measure has a similar behavior as the vertical and horizontal Reynolds stresses in the liquid. Furthermore, the *rms* fluctuations in horizontal and vertical directions are comparable, as we realized from the trajectories of bubbles.

Next we consider simulations of another bidisperse system of twenty-two bubbles and a monodisperse system of sixteen bubbles with the same Morton number, void fraction, and material properties ratios as the first run. The equivalent Eötvös number for these runs is $Eo_e = 2.360$ which is not exactly the same as in the first simulation. The domain sizes and the resolutions are the same as before. The species Eötvös numbers and void fractions for the bidisperse simulation are $Eo_1 = 2$,

$\alpha_1 = 0.1256$, and $Eo_2 = 3$, and $\alpha_2 = 0.0706$. Figure 6 shows the initial positions of the bubbles in these simulations. An inspection of the bubbles and the flow fields from these simulations (not included here) showed a similar behavior as in Fig. 1. Even though the details of the two flows were not the same at the corresponding times, the general features of the flows (i.e. bubble collision, pairing, clustering, etc.) were similar to those in Fig. 1

Figure 7 compares the rise Reynolds number for these runs and the first run. The time-averaged Reynolds number for theses cases are recorded in table 1. Even though the instantaneous velocities for the bidisperse systems are not identical, the time-averaged Reynolds numbers are very close. The time-averaged Reynolds number of the monodisperse system is 16.2% less than the ensemble average of the Reynolds numbers of the two bidisperse cases. Similarly, Fig. 8 compares the vertical and horizontal Reynolds stresses in the liquid for the above runs. The corresponding time-averaged quantities are recorded in table 1. With the exception of the cross terms (which are almost zero) the Reynolds stresses show a marked difference for the two bidisperse systems. The horizontal and vertical stresses of the first bidisperse system are, however, close to the corresponding values of the monodisperse one.

To start an investigation of the problem in three-dimensional flows, we have done a number of monodisperse simulations. The insight gained by the predictions of these runs, will be used for the analysis of three-dimensional polydisperse flows. Figure 9 shows one of theses simulations. Here, $E = 2$, $M = 10^{-5}$, $\alpha = 0.065$, $\lambda = 0.05$, and $\gamma = 0.05$. The box size is $x/d = 2$, $y/d = 4$, and $z/d = 4$, and the resolution is $34 \times 66 \times 66$. This simulation has run up to $t^* = 18.38$. The bottom frame shows the initial positions of the bubbles. The middle frame shows the bubbles at time $t = 6$, and the last frame shows the bubbles at $t^* = 18.38$. It is seen that the dispersion of the bubbles in the horizontal directions is small. The interactions between the bubbles are not as strong as in the two-dimensional simulations, primarily because of the lower void fraction of the three-dimensional system. However, it is seen that collision takes place frequently. Figure 10 shows the rise Reynolds number of the centroid of the bubbles versus time. Initially the Reynolds number reaches a value comparable to what is found for arrays where the bubbles remain fixed with respect to each other. Here, when the bubbles start to move around freely, the Reynolds number decreases. This phenomenon is similar to what happens in two-dimensional simulations of flows at intermediate Reynolds number and results

in time-averaged Reynolds numbers (both in two- and three-dimension) which are smaller than the Reynolds numbers for the rise of a single bubble in two- and three-dimensions (Esmaeeli & Tryggvason 1996c).

In conclusion, we note that while the results presented here are too limited to give a definite answer to the question posed at the beginning of the paper, namely whether a polydisperse system could be examined in terms of an equivalent monodisperse one, table 1 suggests that it may be true for at least some aspects of the flow. A more thorough investigation is in progress.

ACKNOWLEDGMENT

This work was supported by NSF grant CTS-9503208. We would like to acknowledge constructive discussions with Professor V. Arpaci at the Department of Mechanical Engineering of the University of Michigan.

BIBLIOGRAPHY

Batchelor, G. K., 1982, "Sedimentation in a dilute polydisperse system of interacting spheres. part 1, General theory," J. Fluid Mech., Vol. 119, pp. 379-408.

Batchelor, G. K., 1983, "Diffusion in a dilute polydisperse system of interacting particles," J. Fluid Mech., Vol. 133, pp. 155-175.

Cox, P. G., 1990, "Instability of sedimenting bidisperse suspensions. Int. J. Multiphase Flow," Vol. 16, pp. 617-638.

Dandy, D. S., and Leal, L. G., 1989, "Buoyancy-driven motion of a deformable drop through a quiescent liquid at intermediate Reynolds numbers," J. Fluid Mech., Vol. 208, pp. 161-192.

Drew, D. A., 1983, "Mathematical modeling of two-phase flow," Ann. Rev. Fluid Mech., Vol. 15, pp. 261-91.

Esmaeeli, A., 1995, "Numerical simulations of bubbly flows," Ph.D. Thesis. The University of Michigan, Ann Arbor, MI.

Esmaeeli, A., and Tryggvason, G., 1996a, "An inverse energy cascade in two-dimensional, low Reynolds number bubbly flows," J. Fluid Mech., Vol. 314, pp. 315-330.

Esmaeeli, A., and Tryggvason, G., 1996b, "Direct Numerical Simulations of Bubbly Flows, Part I-Low Reynolds number arrays," Submitted to *J. Fluid Mech.*

Esmaeeli, A., and Tryggvason, G., 1996c, "Direct Numerical Simulations of Bubbly Flows, Part II-Intermediate Reynolds number arrays," In preparation.

Esmaeeli, A., Tryggvason, G., and Arpaci, V., 1996, "Thermal migration of bubbles toward a fluid interface," Accepted for publication in AIChE (Heat Transfer) Symposium Series of 1996 National Heat Transfer Conference (to be held in Houston, Texas, August 3-6, 1996).

Feng, J., Hu, H. H., and Joseph, D. D., 1994, "Direct simulation of initial value problems for the motion of solid bodies in a Newtonian fluid, Part 1. Sedimentation," J. Fluid Mech., Vol. 261, pp. 95-134.

Feng, J., Hu, H. H., and Joseph, D. D., 1995, "Direct simulation of initial value problems for the motion of solid bodies in a Newtonian fluid. Part 2. Couette and Poiseuille flows," J. Fluid Mech., Vol. 277, pp. 271-301.

Kim, I., Elghobashi, S., and Sirignano, W. A., 1993, "Three-dimensional flow over two spheres placed side by side," J. Fluid Mech., Vol. 246, pp. 465-488.

Kumaran, V., and Koch, D. L., 1993, "The rate of coalescence in a suspension of high Reynolds number, low Weber number bubbles," Physc. Fluids A, Vol. 5.

Kumaran, V., and Koch, D. L., 1993, "The effect of hydrodynamic interactions on the average properties of a bidisperse suspension of high Reynolds number, low Weber number bubble," Physc. Fluids A, Vol. 5.

Manga, M., and Stone, H. A., 1993, "Buoyancy-driven interactions between deformable drops at low Reynolds numbers," J. Fluid Mech., Vol. 256, pp. 647-683.

Peskin, C., 1977, "Numerical analysis of blood flow in the heart," J. Comput. Phys., Vol. 25, pp. 220-252.

Rallison. J. M., 1981, "A numerical study of the deformation and burst of a viscous drop in general shear flows," J. Fluid Mech., Vol. 109, pp. 465-482.

Ryskin, G., and Leal, L. G., 1984, "Numerical solution of free-boundary problems in fluid mechanics. Part 2. Buoyancy-driven motion of a gas bubble through a quiescent liquid," J. Fluid Mech, Vol. 148, pp. 19-35.

Sangani, A. S., and Didwania, A. K., 1993, "Dynamic simulations of flows of bubbly liquids at large Reynolds numbers," J. Fluid Mech., Vol. 250, pp. 307-337.

Smereka, P., 1993, "On the motion of bubbles in a periodic box," J. Fluid Mech., Vol. 254, pp. 79-112.

Unverdi, S. O., and Tryggvason, G., 1992, "A front-tracking method for viscous, incompressible, multi-fluid flows," J. Comput Phys., Vol. 100, pp. 25-37.

Youngren, G. K., and Acrivos, A., 1975, "Stokes flow past a particle of arbitrary shape: a numerical method of solution," J. Fluid Mech., Vol. 69.

Zhou, H., and Pozrikidis, C., 1993, "The flow of ordered and random suspensions of two-dimensional drops in a channel," J. Fluid Mech. Vol. 255, pp. 103-177.

Zhou, H., and Pozrikidis, C., 1994, "Pressure-driven flow of suspensions of liquid drops," Phys. Fluids, Vol. 6.

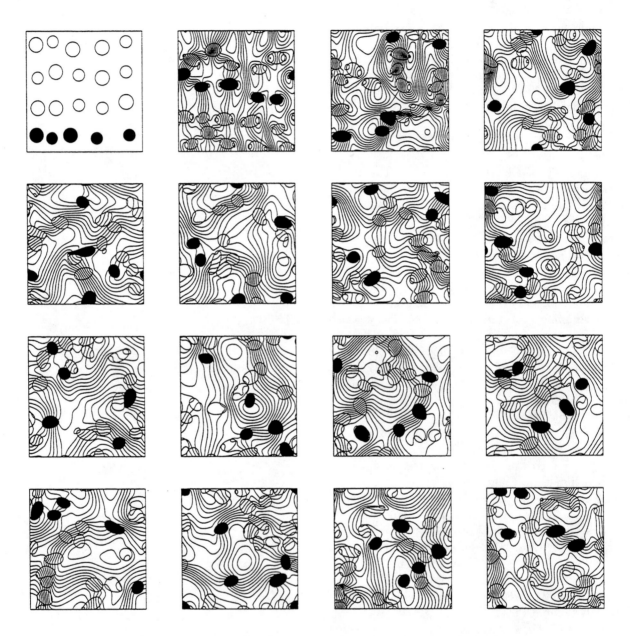

Figure 1: Evolution of a weakly perturbed array of a bidisperse system of twenty bubbles. Here, $Eo_e = 2.56$, $M = 10^{-5}$, $\alpha_e = 0.1962$, $\lambda = 0.1$, and $\gamma = 0.1$. The resolution is 288×288 grid points in a $x/d_m = 8.0$, $y/d_m = 8.0$ box. Time starts from zero and proceeds in equispaced intervals of 7.07.

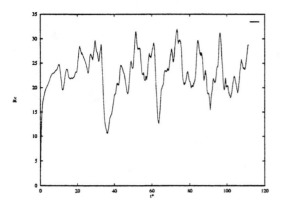

Figure 2: Reynolds number of the centroid of the bubbles versus time.

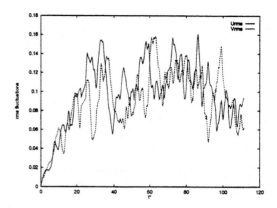

Figure 5: u_{rms} and v_{rms} for the bubbles in the figure 1 versus time.

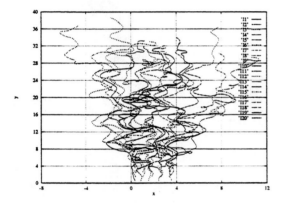

Figure 3: Trajectories of the bubbles in figure 1.

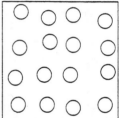

Figure 6: Initial positions of the bubbles in the second bidisperse simulation (left frame) and the monodisperse one (right frame). The box sizes and the resolutions are the same for both cases and are equal to the corresponding ones in figure 1.

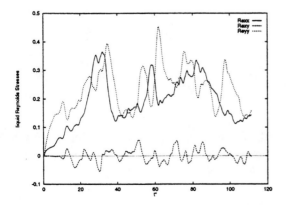

Figure 4: Liquid Reynolds stresses versus time.

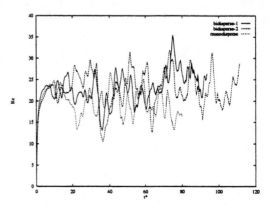

Figure 7: Evolution of the centroid Reynolds numbers versus time.

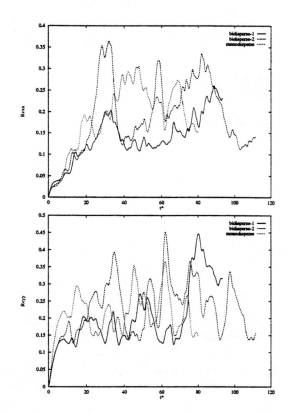

Figure 8: Evolution of the vertical and horizontal Reynolds stresses of the previous runs.

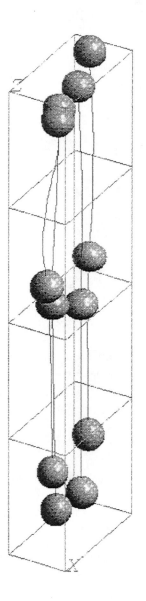

Figure 9: Interactions of four three-dimensional bubbles in a periodic box. Here, $x/d = 2.0$, $y/d = 4.0$, $z/d = 4.0$ and the resolution is $34 \times 66 \times 66$.

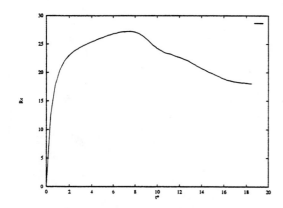

Figure 10: Reynolds number of the centroid of the bubbles in the previous figure versus time.

Simulation	Re	$< u'u' >$	$< u'v' >$	$< v'v' >$
bidisperse-1	22.8987789	0.1834027	-0.0007393	0.2332063
bidisperse-2	22.6680202	0.1241498	-0.0001380	0.1790335
monodisperse	19.5954895	0.1857566	0.0165742	0.2130237

Table 1: Time-averaged statistics for the two-dimensional simulations.

FED-Vol. 238, 1996 Fluids Engineering Division Conference
Volume 3
ASME 1996

AN ADVECTION AND INTERFACE RECONSTRUCTING SCHEME
FOR INCOMPRESSIBLE FLOW CALCULATIONS

José Ronaldo C. de Melo e Angela O. Nieckele
Departamento de Engenharia Mecânica
Pontifícia Universidade Católica do Rio de Janeiro -- PUC/Rio
22453-900 Rio de Janeiro, RJ -- Brazil
Tel: (55-21) 239-0719   Fax: (55-21) 294-9148
e-mail: nieckele@mec.puc-rio.br

ABSTRACT

The present work presents a numerical method for the solution of two-dimensional flow of incompressible and immiscible fluids in the presence of a interface. The conservation equations are discretized by the finite volume method. The interface modeling based on the VOF method, describes the relative amount of the fluids in each control volume by a variable, denominated saturation. Once known the distribution of this quantity, it is possible to construct the interface, when needed.

Several schemes approximate the interface inside a cell by a horizontal or vertical line. The present scheme represents the interface inclination inside a cell by an inclined line. Further, the interface angle is evaluated by a mean angle inside the cell, which is obtained based on its saturation and on the saturation of two adjacent cells crossed by the interface. The use of a mean angle inside the cell results in a more precise method, without the need of very refined mesh. With the present scheme, the interface curvature needed to calculate the capillary pressure can be easily obtained.

To validate the method, the shape and period of an oscillating bubble was examined as well as the initial motion of large spherical bubbles, presenting good results.

INTRODUCTION

Numerical simulation of the flow field of immiscible fluids in the presence of a interface has some difficulties. If a traditional numerical scheme is adopted, the artificial numerical diffusion will rapidly destroy the interface definition. Therefore, several methods have been developed, like boundary element methods (Youngren and Acrivos, 1976), boundary adjustable meshes (Shopov et al., 1992), height functions methods (Mashayek e Ashgriz, 1993), MAC method (Welch et al., 1966) and VOF method (Hirt and Nichols, 1981), among others. The last two methods, instead of following the interface, work with the regions occupied by the fluids, and from this information, the interface is reconstructed.

The VOF method is widely used, due to its simplicity, robustness and versatility. Its main idea is to describe the interface indirectly through the distribution of a scalar variable, called here as saturation, S. The saturation represents the relative fraction of the cell volume, filled with a particular fluid (Fig. 1). In a cell full with the fluid, the variable is equal to 1, in a completely empty it is 0, and in the interface cells, the variable has intermediate values. In any time instant, from the saturation field, the interface position and orientation inside the cell can be determined. This method allows the prediction of great deformations, it can also predicts situations in which the interface breaks or joins. This method also allows the use of the full momentum conservation equations.

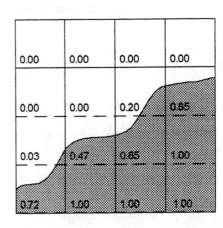

Figure 1. VOF method. A discretized saturation field.

MATHEMATICAL MODELING

The flow field is governed by mass and momentum conservation equations:

$$\partial\rho / \partial t + \mathbf{div}(\rho\,\vec{u}) = 0 \qquad (1)$$

$$\rho\,\frac{D\,\vec{u}}{Dt} = -\mathbf{grad}\,p + \mathbf{div}[\mu(\mathbf{grad}\,\vec{u} + (\mathbf{grad}\,\vec{u})^{T})] + \rho\,\vec{g}$$

where $D\vec{u}/Dt = \partial\,\vec{u}/\partial t + \vec{u}\bullet\mathbf{grad}\,\vec{u}$, D/Dt is the material derivative, $\vec{u}$ and $\vec{g}$ are the velocity and gravity vectors, t is time, p is pressure, ρ e μ are the density and absolute viscosity of the mixture formed by fluid 1 and 2, and are defined as a function of the saturation S

$$\rho = \rho_1(1-S) + \rho_2 S \quad , \quad \mu = \mu_1(1-S) + \mu_2 S \qquad (2)$$

For a system formed by two or more immiscible fluids, the local volumetric fraction of each fluid (saturation) can be employed to model the advection of the interface between them. In this case, the displacement of the interface depends on the local velocities, and it can be determined by the following equations:

$$\frac{\partial S}{\partial t} + \vec{u}\cdot\mathbf{grad}\,S = 0 \quad \mathbf{or} \quad \frac{\partial S}{\partial t} + \mathbf{div}(S\,\vec{u}) = 0 \qquad (3)$$

The second form, is more adequate to the integration by the finite volume method, since it is in a conservative form. However, it is only valid when the fluids are incompressible, that is, when $\mathbf{div}\,\vec{u} = 0$.

NUMERICAL MODELING

The flow field conservation equations were discretized by the finite volume method, utilizing the "power-law" scheme of Patankar (1980), with a semi-implicit time integral. Velocities are stored in a staggered location in relation to all other variables. The pressure-velocity coupling were resolved by the SIMPLEC method of Van Doormal and Raithby (1984). The system of algebraic equations was solved by the line-by-line TDMA algorithm with the block-correction algorithm to accelerate convergence rate (Patankar, 1980).

After solving for the flow, the saturation field is obtained from the actual velocity distribution, but the saturation is treated explicitly

$$S_P(\Delta\forall / \Delta t) = S_P^o(\Delta\forall / \Delta t) + S_W^o u_W - S_E^o u_E + S_S^o u_S - S_N^o u_N \qquad (4)$$

where the superscript P refers to the mean saturation of a cell, and the subscripts w, e, s e n are associated with the cell faces. The saturation is stored at the cell center and appropriate interface advection schemes must be used to obtain its value at the cell faces.

INTERFACE ADVECTION SCHEMES

The most delicate part of the VOF method is related with the scheme adopted to predict the interface advection, that is, the scheme employed to estimate the interface saturation needed by Eq. 3.

Therefore, better results are obtained, if a precise scheme is used to represent the interface inside a cell, as well as to estimate the amount of fluid that crosses each face. A good review of this subjected is presented by Ashgriz and Poo (1991). However, here, only two schemes will be mentioned, the "donor-acceptor" and FLAIR schemes.

The "donor-acceptor" scheme is widely used. It was introduced in the original work about the VOF method (Hirt and Nichols, 1981). The amount of fluid that crosses an interface is based on the saturation of the donor (from which the fluid comes) or acceptor (from which the fluid goes), depending on the saturation of adjacent cells. It is a simple scheme, very easy to implement. Its main limitation is that it does not take into account the interface inclination. The interface is considered either vertical or horizontal. As a consequence, errors are introduced in the prediction of interface advection as well as the capillary pressure, and good results are only obtained with very fine meshes.

The interface inside a cell is represented by an inclined line by FLAIR (Flux Line-Segment Model for Advection and Interface Reconstruction) scheme of Ashgriz and Poo (1991). The interface angle is determined at the cell faces, through which the fluid migrates. Considering two adjacent cells crossed by the interface, it is assumed that it can represented by a straight line based on the cell face angle. The amount of main fluid that crosses the boundary between the cells is based on the boundary saturation and interface inclination. It also depends on the fluid velocity u and time step Δt (shaded area indicated in Fig. 2a). When the fluid migration occurs from a cell with an interface to a full or empty cell, an internal angle obtained as a mean of the donor-cell interface angles is used as the interface inclination.

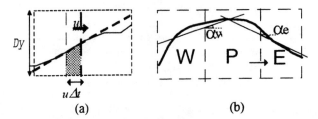

(a)   (b)

Figure 2. Interface angle evaluated at a) cell face,
b) inside cell as mean of face angles.

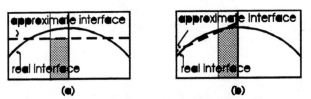

(a)   (b)

Figure 3. Volume of fluid that migrated (shaded area)
based on a) cell face angle, b) internal angle.

The use of the interface angle to evaluate the volume of fluid that crosses the cell faces can underpredict the amount of fluid that migrates (Fig. 3a). With the present scheme, the mean angle inside the donor-cell is always used (Fig. 3b), resulting in a more precise scheme, without the need of a very refined mesh.

INTERFACIAL SHEAR TREATMENT

The treatment of the interfacial forces is accomplished through the integration of the capillary pressure over the interface inside each cell. The capillary pressure is obtained through the Laplace equation (Dullien, 1992) utilizing the interfacial shear σ and the mean curvature interface radius R_{med}

$$P_{cap} = 2\sigma / R_{med} \quad , \quad R_{med} = 2R_p R_{cil} / (R_p + R_{cil}) \quad (5)$$

where R_p is the interface radius in the plane and R_{cil} is the transversal plane radius, when cylindrical coordinates are been used.

Mean Curve Radius

Since the advection method takes into account the interface inclination angle inside the cell, the curvature radius can be precisely calculated.

The method adopted here is based on Liang's (1991) method. Once the interface position is obtained, the coordinates of the end points of the line segment which represents the interface, (x_1, y_1) and (x_2, y_2), can be used to determine the central point of the line segment, as the arithmetic mean of the end points (Fig. 4a). The central point is denominated "water-mark". The interface curvature is obtained as the circular curve adjusted to connect the water-marks of three adjacent cells, crossed by the interface (Fig. 4b). Therefore, the center and radius of the circle are determined (Fig. 5).

In axi-symmetric situations, the curvature center coincides with the symmetry axis. Thus, it can be obtained from the interface inclination angle α, and the distance D_y between the water-mark and the symmetry axis as $R_{cil} = D_y / \cos\alpha$.

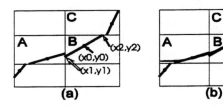

Figure 4. Interface approximated by line segments.
a) central points are the "water-marks".
b) cell B curvature is the circle that passes by the water-marks of the A, B and C cells.

Capillary Pressure Force

The capillary pressure represents a discontinuity in the pressure field, and it is not easy to be numerically treated. Therefore, it is indirectly introduced in the momentum equation by the resulting force obtained by its integration along the interface.

At the present work, the capillary pressure was integrated along the circumference utilized to calculate the curvature radius R_p. For the A cell (Fig. 5), the end points of integration are the center of the arcs between water-marks. The arc length $R_p \beta_1$ and $R_p \beta_2$ can be easily obtained from the distance between each pair of water-marks. The capillary force can be obtained as $F_{cap} = P_{cap} R_p (\beta_1 + \beta_2)$.

Distribution of the Capillary Force in the Staggered Cells. The capillary force is determined at the main mesh, however, its components used to calculate the velocity components u and v, must be displaced to the respective staggered mesh, which overlaps the main mesh.

This distribution can be made proportional to the interface position, that is, it is inversely proportional to the distance between the water-mark and the main control volume face, as suggested by Hirt and Nichols (1980). However, they mentioned in their work, that perturbations in the velocity field can appear near the interface. According to Liang (1991), the capillary force can also be distributed as a function of the mass inside the staggered control volumes, assuming that the control volume with more mass can absorb more of this force. Both approaches were tested in the present work, with equivalent results. The first option was then selected because of the smaller computing effort, and because no perturbation was observed even when fluids with great density and viscosity contrast were tested.

TEST PROBLEMS

Several test problems were tested by Chaves de Melo (1995) to validate the scheme. At the present work two samples were selected to illustrate the performance of the method. The first one is an oscillating bubble in a quiescent medium and the second is the prediction of the initial motion of a large spherical bubble.

Oscillating Elliptic Bubble

The oscillation of a kerosene bubble, immerse in a semi-infinite two-dimensional domain of air is considered. At the initial time instant, the bubble is a quiet ellipse.

Figure 5 illustrates the computational domain, with one of the mesh size tested. A uniform mesh size of 14 x 14 was employed in the core, with an external region with 5 control volumes, having the width equal to the maximum diameter of the ellipse.

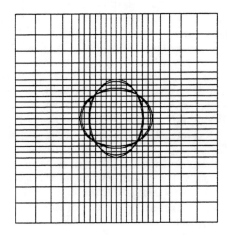

Figure 5. Mesh size of 14 x 14 in the core.
Bubble shape at 0 ms, 80 ms, 220 ms and 300 ms.

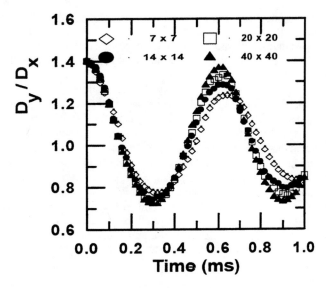

Figure 6. Variation of vertical diameter with time.

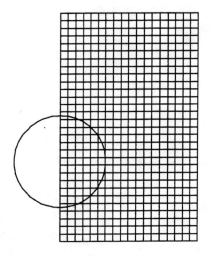

Figure 7. Computational domain. Mesh of 30 x 14.

The diameter ratio of an ellipse can be defined as the ratio of the vertical to horizontal diameter, D_y/D_x. For a small diameter ratio, Fyfe et at, (1988), using a linear theory, obtained that the period of oscillation of an elliptic bubble is $\omega = 6\,\sigma\,/\,(\,\rho_k - \rho_a)\,r^3$, where r is the mean radius of the bubble, ρ_k and ρ_a, are the kerosene and air density. This test was performed using the same properties and geometry of Fyfe et al. (1988) and Liang (1991): $\rho_k = 0.82$ g/cm^3, ρ_a = 0.0013 g/cm^3, σ = 30 dinas/cm, r = 0.0125 cm and diameter ratio equal to 1.4. The viscosities of both fluids was neglected. With these properties, the theoretic period of oscillation is 0.592 ms. Note that the density ratio is equal to 650, therefore this a severe test. Further, since the viscosities are neglected, this is a critical case in relation to the false diffusion, since the mesh Peclet number is infinite.

The period predicted by Fyfe et al. (1988) was equal to 710 ms, with an error of 20%. The results of Liang are much better. With an non-uniform mesh and a uniform core mesh of 14 x 14, the period of oscillation was predicted as 0.600 ms, corresponding to a deviation of 1.4% in relation to theoretic solution. The time step was not informed.

Figure 5 illustrates the present results for the bubble shape, for a mesh of 14 x 14, at the time instants equal to 0, 80, 220 and 300 ms.

Figure 6 represents the diameter ratio (D_y/D_x) of the ellipse as a function of time for different mesh sizes in the core. It can be seen that as the mesh is refined, the solution becomes independent of the mesh size. The effect of the time step Δt on the solution was also investigated. It was observed that the solution was not affected by changing Δt from 10^{-3} ms to 10^{-4} ms, but for a Δt equal to 10^{-2} ms, convergence was not obtained with the finer meshes and small discrepancies were observed for the meshes smaller than 14 x 14. The period of oscillation predicted was 0.640 ms for the 7 x 7 (error = 8.1%). For the mesh size 14 x 14 to 40 x 40, the period obtained varied from 0.607 ms (2.5% of error) to 0.600 ms corresponding to 1.4 %. It can be concluded that, the results obtained can be considered pretty good, even for the course mesh case.

Initial Movement of Spherical Large Bubble

The present test consists on predicting the initial movement of a spherical bubble of air in the water. This problem has been studied by several authors like Bhaga and Weber (1981), Ryskin and Leal (1986) and Nickens and Yannitel (1987), among others. The results are compared with experimental data of Waters and Davidson (1963) and numerical predictions of Bugg and Rowe (1991), utilizing the SOLA-VOF code.

The physical proprieties of the fluids were: absolute viscosity and density of water equal to μ_o = 1 cp and ρ_o = 1 g/cm^3, where the subscript 'o' refers to the external fluid. The air viscosity was neglected and the air density inside the bubble was taken as ρ_b = 0.0012 g/cm^3, with an interfacial shear stress equal to σ = 72.8 dinas/cm. The initial radius of the sphere was 2.972 cm, corresponding to a volume of 110 cm^3. The gravitational acceleration was g = 981 cm/s^2.

Three different mesh sizes were tested: 30 x 18, 40 x 25 and 50 x 30 control volumes in the axial and radial directions. The smallest mesh is illustrated in Figure 7. The length of the computational domain was set equal to 5 R, where R is initial sphere radius. In the radial direction, the domain was set equal to 3 R. A time step equal to Δt = 0,1 ms was adopted in all cases.

The conservation equations were solved in cylindrical coordinates, assuming angular symmetry. The bubble position was maintained fixed in relation to the computational mesh. Therefore, at the end of each time step, a mean bubble velocity was calculated, and this value was subtracted from the whole velocity field. Thus, for the new time step, the bubble mean velocity was zero.

Figure 8 illustrates the axial dimensionless diameter D* defined as the diameter measured along the symmetry axis at each time instant, normalized by the original diameter of the spherical bubble (2 R). The dimensionless time is defined as $t^* = t\,(g/R)^{0.5}$. It can be observed a good agreement between the numerical and experimental results.

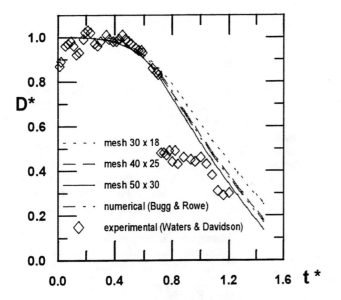

Figure 8. Vertical diameter as a function of time.

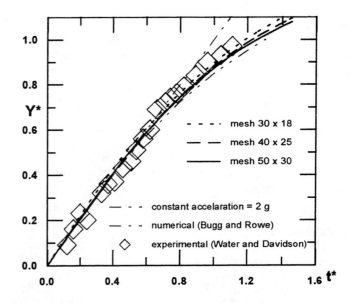

Figure 9. Vertical distance traveled as a function of time.

It can also be noted that, as the mesh is refined the results tend to get closer to the experimental results. The intermediate mesh size results are almost coincident with Bugg and Rowe (1991) data. The mesh size adopted in that work was not informed.

The distance traveled by the bubble since the initial time instant H, can become dimensionless as $Y^* = (H/R)^{0.5}$, and it is plotted in Fig. 9. In this figure, the theoretical displacement, valid for the initial stage of the movement, corresponding to a constant acceleration of 2g is also shown. It can be observed that all results coincide with the constant acceleration prediction, at the initial stages of the movement. Further, it can be said that, for the whole range of experimental data, agreement of the present results with the experiment was good. The dependency of the solution in the mesh size, was again quite small.

Finally, the agreement of the present work is slightly better than the results of Bugg and Rowe (1991).

Figure 10 illustrates the bubble shape at different time instants. Three different stages can be found during the movement of the bubble. The first one is characterized by a constant acceleration equal to 2 g. At the second stage of the movement, the bubble suffers large deformations, with the liquid entraining at the central part of the it, forming a large toroidal bubble, with a very small bubble in front of it. The third stage corresponds to the movement of the bubbles, until they reach constant velocity and shape. Bugg and Rowe (1991) presented the solution of the problem, for the first two stages, and the results are in good agreement with the present ones.

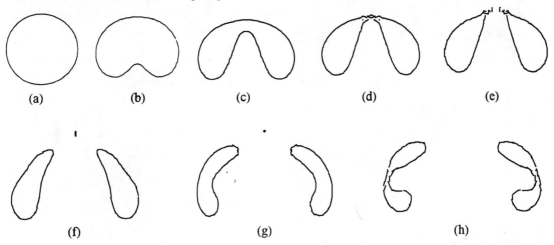

Figure 10. Bubble shape for the following time instants: (a) 0 ms; (b) 50 ms; (c) 80 ms; (d) 90 ms; (e) 100 ms; (f) 150 ms; (g) 200 ms; (h) 250 ms.

CONCLUSION

A numerical scheme to solve immiscible fluid flow was present. Two-dimensional, incompressible fluids were considered. The scheme employed to predict the interface is based on the VOF method. An inclined line inside the cell is used to represent the interface. The inclination angle is based on the mean angle at each face of the interfacial cell. As a result, a better representation of the interface was obtain, allowing a better prediction of the amount of fluid which migrates between cells. It also allows a better specification of the capillary pressure. Two test problems were presented. The agreement with available solution was good, validating the method.

REFERENCES

Ashgriz, N. e Poo, J. Y. , 1991, "FLAIR - Flux Line Segment Model for Advection and Interface Reconstruction", J. Computational Physics, vol. 93, pp. 449-468.

Bhaga, D. e Weber, M.E., 1981, "Bubbles in Viscous Liquids: Shapes, Wakes and Velocities," Journal of Fluid Mechanics, Vol. 105, pp.61-85, 1981.

Bugg, J. D. e Rowe, R. D., 1991,"Modelling the Initial Motion of Large Cylindrical and Spherical Bubbles, "International Journal Numerical Methods Fluids, Vol. 13, pp. 109-129, 1991.

Chaves de Melo, J. R., 1995, "Simulação Numérica de Escoamentos Bifásicos com Interfaces", Master Thesis, Dept. Mech. Eng., PUC-RJ, RJ, Brazil (in portuguese).

Dullien, F. A. L., 1992, "Porous Media - Fluid Transport and Pore Structure," 2nd Ed., Academic Press, Inc.

Fyfe, D. E., Oran, E. S. and Fritts, M. J., 1988, "Surface Tension and Viscosity with Lagrangian Hydrodynamics on a Triangular Mesh," J. Computational Physics, vol. 76, n. 2, pp. 349-384.

Hirt, C. W. e Nichols, B. D., 1980, "Numerical Simulation of Boiling Water Reactor Vent-Clearing Hydrodynamics," Nuclear Sc. Eng., Vol. 73, pp. 196-209.

Hirt, C. W. e Nichols, B. D., 1981, "Volume of Fluid (VOF) Method for the Dynamics of Free Boundaries", J. Computational Physics, vol. 39, pp. 201-225 .

Liang, P. Y., 1991, "Numerical Method for Calculation of Surface Tension Flows in Arbitrary Grids", AIAA J.,vol 29, n. 2.

Mashayek, F. and Ashgriz, N., 1993, "A Height Flux Method for Simulating Free Surface Flows and Interfaces," Intl. J. Numerical Methods in Fluids, vol. 17, pp. 1035-1054.

Nickens, H. V. e Yannitel, D. W., 1987, "The Effects of Surface Tension and Viscosity on the Rise Velocity of a Large Gas Bubble in a Closed, Vertical Liquid-filled Tube," International Journal of Multiphase Flow, Vol. 13, no. 1, pp. 57-69.

Patankar, S. V., 1980, "Numerical Heat Transfer and Fluid Flow", Hemisphere Publishing Corporation.

Ryskin, G. e Leal L. G., 1984, "Numerical Solution of Free Boundary Problems in Fluid Mechanics, Part 2. Buoyancy Driven Motion of a Gas Bubble through a Quiescent Liquid," J. Fluid Mechanics, Vol. 148, pp. 19-35.

Shopov., P. J., Minev, P. D. and Bazhlekov, I. B., 1992, "Numerical Method for Unsteady Viscous Hydrodynamical Problems with Free Boundaries," Intl. J. Numerical Methods, vol. 14, pp. 681-705.

Van Doormaal, J.P. e Raithby, G.D., 1984, "Enhancements of the SIMPLE Method for Prediction Incompressible Fluid Flows", Numerical Heat Transfer, vol. 7, pp. 147-163.

Waters, J.K. e Davidson, J. F., 1963, "The Initial Motion of a Gas Bubble Formed in an Inviscid Liquid, Part 2: The Three Dimensional Bubble and the Toroidal Bubble," Journal of Fluid Mechanics, Vol. 17, pp.321-339.

Welch, J. E., Harlow, F. H., Shannon, J. P. e Daly, B. J., 1966, "The MAC Method: A Computing Technique for Solving Viscous, Incompressible, Transient Fluid Flow Problems Involving Free Surfaces," Los Alamos Scientific Laboratory Report - LA-3425.

Youngren, G. K. and Acrivos, A., 1976,"On the Shape of a Gas Bubble in a Viscous Extensional Flow", J. Fluid Mechanics, vol. 76, pp. 433-442.

FED-Vol. 238, 1996 Fluids Engineering Division Conference
Volume 3
ASME 1996

Numerical Simulation of Nonlinear Wave over Permeable Submerged Breakwater

Tsutomu Sakakiyama

Central Research Institute of Electric Power Industry(Criepi)
Hydraulics Department
1646, Abiko, Abiko-city, Chiba, 270-11, Japan
phone:+81 471 82 1181, fax:+81 471 84 7142,
e-mail:sakaki@abiko.denken.or.jp

ABSTRACT The numerical simulation model has been developed to predict nonlinear wave motions interacting with permeable breakwaters. Effects are included as the porosity, the drag and inertia coefficients. The present model has been verified through comparisons with hydraulic experimental results on the wave decomposition through the permeable submerged breakwater. The simulated results of surface displacements of water wave were in fairly good agreement with the experimental results.

1. INTRODUCTION

A monochromatic water wave passing over a submerged breakwater is decomposed into waves with higher frequencies. Previous works in coastal engineering were based on the potential theory and were restricted to the wave transformation over an impermeable submerged breakwater. The wave energy dissipation due to the interaction between the structure and waves is neglected. Wave transformation over a permeable structure is not simulated so far. The purpose of this paper is to evaluate an ability of the fully nonlinear model which includes the effects of the permeable structure (Sakakiyama and Kajima,1992) for the wave decomposition. An effect of the permeability of the submerged structure on the wave transformation is also investigated performing the experiments and calculation for both permeable and impermeable submerged breakwaters.

2. GOVERNING EQUATIONS

The governing equations of two-dimensional wave motions for incompressible fluid called the porous body model are given as follows (Sakakiyama and Kajima,1992).

$$\frac{\partial(\gamma u_i)}{\partial x_i} = 0, \quad (i = 1,2) \tag{1}$$

$$\frac{\partial(\lambda u_i)}{\partial t} + \frac{\partial(\lambda u_i u_j)}{\partial x_j} = -\gamma\frac{\partial\phi}{\partial x_i} + \lambda g_i - R_i$$
$$+ \frac{1}{\rho}\frac{\partial(\gamma\tau_{ij})}{\partial x_j} \quad (i,j = 1,2) \tag{2}$$

where $\phi = p/\rho$, p is the pressure, ρ the density of the fluid and $\lambda = \gamma + (1-\gamma)C_M$, γ the porosity, C_M the inertia coefficient. The term R_i in the right-hand side of Eq. (2) is the drag force. Taking account of the nonlinearity of the drag force, it is evaluated by the following quadratic equation:

$$R_i = \frac{C_D}{2\Delta x_i}(1-\gamma)u_i\sqrt{u_j u_j} \quad (i,j = 1,2) \tag{3}$$

where C_D is the drag coefficient of permeable structure.

3. BOUNDARY AND INITIAL CONDITIONS

The continuity equation (1) and the momentum equations(2) are numerically solved with the following boundary and initial conditions.

A kinematic boundary condition on the free surface is expressed as:

$$\frac{\partial \eta}{\partial t} + u_S \frac{\partial \eta}{\partial x} = w_S, \qquad (4)$$

where η is the free surface displacement, u_S and w_S are the horizontal and vertical components of the velocity on the free surface η, respectively.

A dynamic boundary condition at the free surface is represented by the following:

$$p = 0 \qquad \text{on} \quad z = \eta. \qquad (5)$$

At bottom boundary, a free slip condition is imposed. When a water depth is uniform, the free slip conditions for the velocity u, w and the pressure p are expressed as follows:

$$\frac{\partial u}{\partial z} = 0, \qquad (6)$$

$$w = 0, \qquad (7)$$

$$\frac{\partial p}{\partial z} = -\rho g. \qquad (8)$$

Equation(8) of the boundary condition on the pressure is led by substituting Eq. (7) into the vertical component of the momentum equation, Eq. (2).

The inflow boundary works as a wavemaker. A perturbation solution for the nonlinear wave theory by Isobe et al.(1978) is used to give the inflow boundary condition for the free surface displacement and the velocity and pressure fields. The wave theory which is applied to the inflow boundary condition depends on the following wave condition:

$$\left.\begin{array}{ll} \text{5th order Stokes wave} & U_S \leq 25 \\ \text{3rd order cnoidal wave} & 25 < \ U_S \end{array}\right\}, \qquad (9)$$

where U_S is the shallow water Ursell parameter:

$$U_S = \frac{g H T^2}{h^2}. \qquad (10)$$

At the outflow boundary Sommerfeld's radiation condition is imposed:

$$\frac{\partial F}{\partial t} + C \frac{\partial F}{\partial x} = 0, \qquad (11)$$

where C is the wave celerity and F denotes the variable η, u, w or p. Equation(11) indicates that the variable F progresses with the phase speed C.

The initial condition is set as the still water state. The surface displacement η at $t = 0$ is null for a whole computational region as well as $u = w = 0$. The pressure p at $t = 0$ is given the hydrostatic pressure.

Simulation method used is the finite difference method which is based on the MAC method(Welch et al.,1966). The dynamic boundary condition on the free surface given by Eq. (5) is exactly satisfied in the iterative process of the pressure computation by applying the "irregular star" method(Chan and Street,1970).

4. EXPERIMENTS

The experiments were carried out to calibrate the present numerical model by using a wave flume(50.0m long, 1.5m deep and 2.0m wide). Figure-1 shows an experimental setup. The surface displacements were measured with ten capacitance type wave gages. The velocity was also measured with eight two-component electromagnetic current meters(EMCM). The wave period were from T=1.0s to 2.2s and the incident wave height H_i=0.045m to 0.065m which are nobreaking waves at on the submerged breakwater.

Figure-2 shows the model submerged breakwater, $0.7h$ high, $2h$ wide at top and $2.7h$ wide at bottom, where $h(=0.20$m$)$ is the water depth at the submerged breakwater. A permeable submerged breakwater (the porosity γ=0.53, CASE P series) as well as an impermeable one(CASE I–10) were used to investigate an effect of the permeability on the wave disintegration.

Table 1 shows the experimental calculation conditions which are nonbreaking waves, where H is the wave height of the progressive wave on the imper-

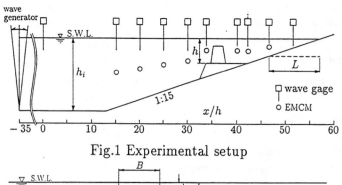

Fig.1 Experimental setup

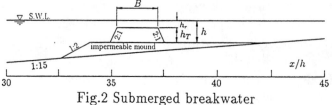

Fig.2 Submerged breakwater

Table 1 Experimental and calculation conditions

CASE	wave period T(s)	wave height H_i(m)	wave height H(m)
P–10	1.0	0.047	0.035
P–15	1.5	0.056	0.058
P–17	1.7	0.054	0.059
P–20	2.0	0.056	0.075
P–22	2.2	0.065	0.089
I–10	1.0	0.047	0.035

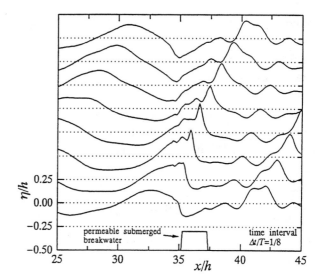

Fig.3 Sequential surface profiles passing over submerged breakwater

meable mound without the submerged breakwaters. The ratio of the progressive wave height H to the water depth h ranges from H/h =0.19 to 0.45 for the wave period from T=1.0s to T=2.2s. Waves break on the submerged breakwaters when H/h is greater than these values.

5. CALCULATION CONDITIONS

The cell dimensions are $\Delta x/h$=1/10 and $\Delta z/h$=1/20 for all the cases. The time increment depends on the wave period as $\Delta t/T$=1/200. The calculation region was set as follows: The incident wave boundary was at x/h=0 as shown in Fig. 1 and the out-flow boundary at the position away from a wave-length from x/h=45.6. A flat bottom is set in the calculation illustrated with the dashed line in Fig. 1 to propagate the transmitted wave by applying Sommerfeld's radiation condition. The inertia and drag coefficients C_M, C_D are given by Sakakiyama(1996).

6. RESULTS

Figure-3 shows the calculated sequential surface profiles for one wave period with the time interval Δt=2T/8 (CASE P–15, T=1.5s and H=0.058m). Both x and z coordinates are normalized with the water depth h at the submerged breakwater. The wave disintegration after passing over the submerged breakwater can be simulated as observed in the hydraulic experiment. When the wave runs on the submerged breakwater, it shows the profile steeping the front surface and becoming more peaked. After the main wave passes the submerged breakwater, a hump of smaller height appears at the rear and trails behind the main wave. This small wave is the second-order free wave with the wave period T_2=T/2. The main wave(first-order wave) deforms as propagating onshore. The third-order wave of which amplitude is much smaller

than that of the secondary wave is catched up and passed by the main wave.

Figure 4 shows the calculated velocity fields at t/T=12.75+1/8 and t/T=12.75+3/8 near the perme-

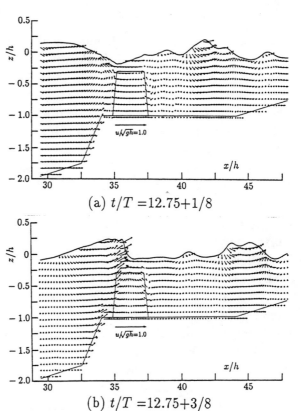

(a) t/T =12.75+1/8

(b) t/T =12.75+3/8

Fig.4 Simulated results of velocity field(CASE P–17)

able submerged breakwater for CASE P–17(T=1.70s). Generating vortex is simulated on the leeside of the permeable submerged breakwater. By applying the potential theory to these simulation, the vortex is not simulated in the calculation of the wave transformation due to the impermeable breakwater. In this calculation, the vortex generated behind the permeable submerged breakwater is caused by the velocity difference between inside the permeable structure and outside.

Figure 5 shows the comparisons between the calculated and measured surface displacements of CASE P–15(T=1.5s) for various positions both on the windward and leeward sides. The displacements obtained at x/h=30 shown in Fig. 5(a) are synchronized at the time of the first crest level. Figures 5(a) and (b) are the surface displacements on the windward side of the permeable submerged breakwater and Figures 5(c) through (e) those on the leeside. On the leeward side, the main wave and the free waves of higher order which were provoked by the wave disintegration over the submerged breakwater propagate with each propagation velocity. Consequently, the surface displacement changes in space. Fig. 5(c) shows the steep wave front and the mild rear of the surface displacements. Then Fig. 5(d) shows the opposite. The surface displacement in Fig. 5(e) is similar to that of Fig. 5(d). The calculated surface displacements are in good agreement with the measured ones at all three positions except that the phase of the surface displacements shift slightly between them. The superposition on the main wave with the secondary and third waves causes the transient wave profiles because they propagate with each wave celerity as free waves. That results in the nonuniform distribution of the transmitted wave height on the leeward side.

Figures 6 and 7 show the comparisons of the surface displacements between the calculation and the experiments for the other wave periods, CASE P–17 and CASE P–22 at each one position on the windward and leeward sides, respectively. As the wave period increases, the number of the disintegrated wave increases. It is observed that at T=1.7s the main and secondary waves are seen in Fig. 6 and in addition to the main and secondary wave, the third-order wave is seen at the longest wave period $T = 2.2$s in Fig. 7. Both the surface displacement and the number of disintegrated waves in the simulation agree with the mea-

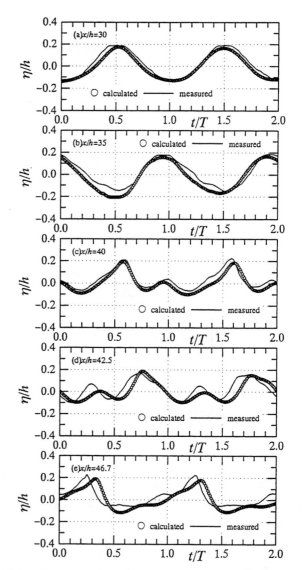

Fig.5 Comparison of surface displacements(T=1.5s)

sured ones.

Fig. 8 shows the comparison between the calculated time history of the velocity and the measured one. The velocity was measured in the middle of the water depth at eight positions where the wave gages were installed. The velocity of the wave component with the higher frequency decreases as the depth increases. The higher frequency components of velocity disappear in the time history, although that is seen in the corresponding surface displacement shown in Fig. 6. The agreement of the calculated with the measured velocity is good except for the difference in the DC component.

Figure-9 shows the surface displacement at three

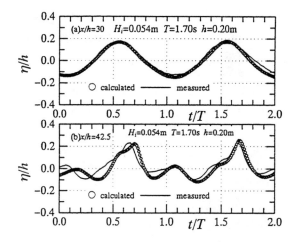

Fig.6 Comparison of surface displacements(T=1.7s)

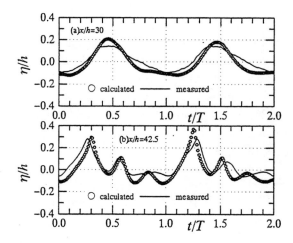

Fig.7 Comparison of surface displacements,(T=2.2s)

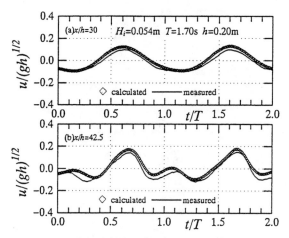

Fig.8 Comparison of velocity time series(T=1.7s)

remarkably compared with the velocity on the offshore side. The vertical profile shows that the wave motion inside the permeable structure is almost in-phase with those outside it. Figures 10 shows that the velocity inside the permeable structure is small.

Figure 11 is the comparison of the velocity field and the surface profile at the same calculated time between due to the permeable and impermeable sub-

location on the submerged breakwater, at the offshore edge, the center and the onshore edge, respectively (CASE P–22, T=2.2s and H=0.089m). Variation of the surface displacement in space shows the development of the wave disintegration.

Figure-10 shows the velocity profiles of the horizontal component at several moments under the water wave motion of the surface displacement in Fig. 9(c). The time interval is $\Delta t/T$=1/8. The dashed line shows the top level of the permeable submerged breakwater. Comparing with the velocity profiles from offshore to onshore side through the center, it is clearly found that the wave dissipates through the permeable structure. The velocity decreases at the center and onshore side

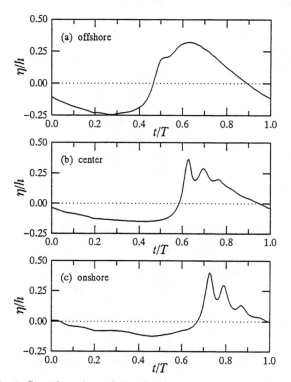

Fig.9 Simulated surface displacement over submerged breakwater

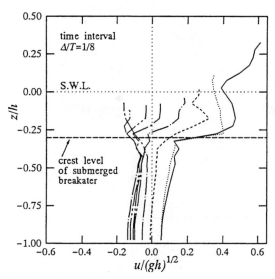

Fig.10 Simulated velocity profiles over submerged breakwater

merged breakwaters (T=1.0s, H=0.035m, CASE P–10 and CASE I–10). The surface profile on the impermeable submerged breakwater becomes steeper than that on the permeable one. It is because the water depth on the impermeable submerged breakwater is shallower than "the effective water depth" of the permeable one. The effective water depth means the

water depth which includes an effect of the porosity in the permeable submerged breakwater on the water depth. The wave passing over the permeable submerged breakwater propagates faster than that passing over the impermeable one. The effective water depth is larger and the wave celerity over the permeable submerged breakwater is greater than that over the impermeable one. The water depth has a stronger effect on the wave celerity than the wave height.

7. CONCLUSION

The wave disintegration passing the permeable submerged breakwater was simulated for various wave periods under the condition of nobreaking wave. The simulated results of the surface displacements and the velocity both on the leeward and windward sides were in fairly good agreement with the experimental results. The velocity profiles in the permeable submerged breakwater were also evaluated with the present model to investigate the effect of the permeability on the wave disintegration. The present numerical simulation model is applicable for the evaluation of nonbreaking wave motion near and in a permeable breakwater with an arbitrary configuration and an impermeable structure.

REFERENCES

Chan,R.K.C. and R.L.Street(1970): A computer study of finite-amplitude water waves, *J. Computational Physics*, 6, pp.68-94.

Isobe,M., H.Nishimura and K.Horikawa(1978): Expressions of perturbation solutions for conservative waves by using wave height, *Proc. 33rd Annu. Conf. of JSCE*, II, pp.760-761(in Japanese).

Sakakiyama,T. and R.Kajima(1992): Numerical simulation of nonlinear wave interacting with permeable breakwaters, *Proc. 23rd Int. Conf. Coastal Engrg., ASCE*, Vol.2, pp1517-1530.

Sakakiyama,T.(1996): Scale effects in experiments on interaction of waves with permeable breakwaters, doctoral dissertation, the University of Tokyo, 192p.

Welch, J.E., F.H. Harlow, J.P. Shannon and B.J.Daly (1966):The MAC method. A computing technique for solving viscous, incompressible, transient fluid-flow problems involving free surfaces, Los Alamos Scientific Laboratory of the University of California, Report LA-3425, 145p.

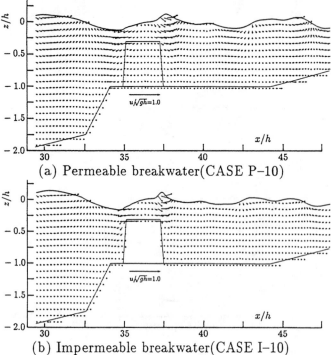

(a) Permeable breakwater(CASE P–10)

(b) Impermeable breakwater(CASE I–10)

Fig.11 Velocity fields around submerged breakwaters

FED-Vol. 238, 1996 Fluids Engineering Division Conference
Volume 3
ASME 1996

A NUMERICAL STUDY ON THE COLLISION BEHAVIOR OF DROPLETS

Albert Y. Tong
Department of Mechanical and Aerospace Engineering
The University of Texas at Arlington
Arlington, TX

ABSTRACT

Numerical simulations of head-on collisions of water droplets at various Weber numbers have been performed. The Navier-Stokes equations are solved by using a finite-volume formulation on a fixed grid by with a two-step projection method. Free surfaces are tracked by a technique called "volume-of-fluid"(VOF). A continuum surface force(CSF) model is used to calculate the surface tension force. Both equal-size and unequal-size droplets have been studied. The results are in agreement with experimental observations.

NOMENCLATURE

$\vec{F}_b$: body force

$\vec{F}_{sv}$: surface volume force

$F(\vec{x}, t)$: fluid fraction

$\vec{g}$: gravitational acceleration

p : pressure

$\vec{V}$: velocity vector

We : Weber number

GREEK SYMBOL

τ : viscous stress

μ : dynamic viscosity

ν : kinematic viscosity

ρ : density

σ : surface tension coefficient

κ : local curvature

(All other symbols are defined where they appear)

INTRODUCTION

Collision dynamics of liquid droplets is one of the most interesting, yet complicated, problems in fluid dynamics. Most of the studies on droplet collisions found in the literature have been experimental. Recently, extensive and systematic studies of the binary collision of liquid droplets for the Weber number range of 1 to 100 and droplet radius on the order of 0.1mm have been performed by Ashgriz et al.(1990) and Jiang et al.(1992). Although different fluid is used, the two studies are quite similar. The objective of the studies is to understand the characteristics of the different types of droplet collisions and to define the boundaries separating them. Their results show that permanent droplet coalescence is favored for small values of Weber number and impact parameter. At larger Weber numbers, two different types of separating collisions, namely reflexive and stretching separations, occur depending on the values of the impact parameter.

Jiang et al.(1992) reports that the collision behavior of hydrocarbon droplets is significantly more complex than that of water droplets. Bouncing collision which does not occur in water droplets, is observed in hydrocarbon droplets. It should also be mentioned that there is a discrepancy in the experimental observations on head-on collisions of water droplets between the two studies. While permanent coalescence is always observed by Jiang et al.(1992), reflexive separation is observed by Ashgriz et al.(1990). More in-depth study is needed to resolve this discrepancy.

The numerical simulation of the collision of liquid droplets is not at all trivial. One of the complexities is modeling the dynamics of a rapidly moving surface. The challenge is that the droplet surface deforms while the values of the field variables are being solved. Another difficulty is the accurate modeling of the surface tension force which has a significant effect on the shape of the free surface.

Recently, a numerical simulation to investigate the motion of inviscid droplets undergoing a large deformation of the free surface has been performed by Murray(1995). The equations of motion are solved by a boundary element method in which the free surface of the droplet is represented by a moving grid. The method is used to simulate the collision of two cylindrical rather than spherical droplets. The way in which surface tension and inertia affect the fluid dynamics of coalescence is examined.

The objective of the present study is to obtain a detailed quantitative simulation of the head-on collision phenomena of liquid droplets. The goal is to gain understanding of the mechanisms that control the outcomes of droplet collisions.

The computer code RIPPLE, developed at Los Alamos(1991), is used with minor modifications in the present study. The code is designed for transient, two-dimensional, incompressible fluid flows with surface tension on free surfaces of general topology. It has been used in a recent study(Holt et al. 1995) by the present author and a co-worker to simulate the normal impact and solidification phenomena of a liquid metal droplet onto a substrate. In that study, an enthalpy-based formulation of the energy equation which includes both convection-diffusion heat transfer and a mushy-region for the phase change was developed and integrated into RIPPLE. The numerical results generated by the modified code were satisfactory enough to prompt this author to use the RIPPLE code in the present study.

A brief overview of the numerical formulation is given next, followed by the Results and Discussion section.

NUMERICAL FORMULATION

For incompressible fluids, the continuity and momentum equations are given by:

$$\nabla \bullet \vec{V} = 0 \tag{1}$$

and

$$\frac{\partial \vec{V}}{\partial t} + \nabla \bullet \left(\vec{V}\vec{V}\right) =$$
$$-\frac{1}{\rho}\nabla p + \frac{1}{\rho}\nabla \bullet \tau + \vec{g} + \frac{1}{\rho}\vec{F}_b \tag{2}$$

respectively. If the fluid is Newtonian, then

$$\tau = 2\mu S, \quad S = \frac{1}{2}\left[\left(\nabla\vec{V}\right) + \left(\nabla\vec{V}\right)^{\mathrm{T}}\right] \tag{3}$$

where S is the rate-of-strain tensor. Combining Eq. 2 and Eq. 3 gives the Navier-Stokes equations which are solved by using a fixed staggered grid. The basic algorithm is the two-step projection method in which a time discretization of the momentum equation is broken up into two steps. In the first step, a velocity field is computed from incremental changes resulting from viscosity, advection, gravity, and body forces. In the second step, the velocity field is projected onto a zero-divergence vector field resulting into a single Poisson equation for the pressure field which is solved by using an incomplete Cholesky conjugate gradient solution technique. The details of the overall solution scheme can be found in Reference 1

Since density and viscosity of air are much less than that of liquid, it is sufficient to neglect the effects of the air and solve the governing equations for the liquid portion only. This will maximize the computational efficiency with very minimal sacrifice on the accuracy of the results.

Free surfaces are tracked by a method pioneered by Hirt and Nichols(1981) called "volume-of-fluid" (VOF). The VOF technique provides a means of following fluid regions through an Eulerian mesh of stationary cells. The basis of the VOF method is the fractional volume of fluid scheme for tracking free boundaries. The governing equation in this method is given by:

$$\frac{DF}{Dt} = \frac{\partial F\left(\vec{x},t\right)}{\partial t} + \left(\vec{V} \bullet \nabla\right)F\left(\vec{x},t\right) = 0 \tag{4}$$

where F is defined whose value is unity at any point occupied by fluid and zero elsewhere. When averaged over a computational cell, it is equal to the fractional volume of the cell occupied by fluid. In particular, a unit value of F corresponds to a cell full of fluid, whereas a zero value indicates that the cell contains no fluid. Cell with F values between zero and one contains a free

surface. In addition to defining which cells contain a boundary, the F function can be used to define where fluid is located in a boundary cell.

A non-conventional approach called "Control Surface Force Method" is used to model surface tension. It interprets surface tension as a continuous, three-dimensional effect across an interface rather than as a boundary value condition at the interface. Interfaces between fluids of different properties (called colors) are represented as transition regions of finite thickness. Across this region there is a continuous variation of the property value of one fluid to the property value of the other fluid. At each point in the transition region, a force density is defined which is proportional to the curvature of the surface of constant property at the point. It is normalized so that the conventional description of the surface tension on an interface is recovered when the ratio of local transition region thickness to local radius of curvature approaches zero.

The volume force used in the modeling of surface tension effects in the CSF method is given by:

$$\vec{F}_b = \vec{F}_{sv} = \sigma\kappa\left(\vec{x}\right)\frac{\nabla\tilde{c}\left(\vec{x}\right)}{[c]} \tag{5}$$

where $\tilde{c}$ is the "color" function and [c] is the normalizing factor. The details of the CSF method is reported in Reference 3.

A large number of head-on collisions of droplets at various velocities have been simulated. Several of the simulations are presented in the next section.

RESULTS AND DISCUSSION

The results of head-on collision of equal-size droplets of 0.1mm radius at 1m/s are shown in Figure 1. Water with $\rho=10^3$ kg/m^3, $\nu=1.004\times10^{-6}$ m^2/s, and $\sigma=7.28\times10^{-2}$ N/m is used. To maximize the computational efficiency of the problem and take advantage of the symmetry of the impacting droplets, the governing equations are solved on a 2-D axisymmetric (cylindrical coordinates) slice that represents one half plane of the computational domain. This slice can be revolved 360 degrees to get the three-dimensional representation of the solution. The droplets are initially lined up vertically and are separated by a small gap. In order to minimize computation, the smallest computational domain which covers the span of the liquid spread during the period of simulation is used. A 80X30 uniform grid is used here. At higher impact velocity, where liquid thinning occurs at the mid-plane, a non-uniform grid with finer grid at the mid plane is used. The first 67 frames of the simulation taken at 0.02ms time interval are shown. The actual time step size for the numerical solution varies and is controlled by a stability criteria required by the numerical scheme. It is always less than 0.001ms.

As reported in Ashgriz et al.(1990) and Jiang et al.(1992), the two droplets collide and form a disk-like drop, the exact shape of which depends on the impact velocity. The disk then contracts radially inward, pushes the liquid out from its center, and deforms into a cylindrically-shaped column. The contraction process is a reflexive action caused by the liquid surface tension. The liquid then oscillates until a spherical droplet is formed.

Simulations for higher values of viscosity and surface tension are also obtained. It is found that with increasing surface tension coefficient, the droplet deformation process oscillates at a higher frequency with a smaller amplitude. The viscosity, and therefore the Reynolds number, is found to have no effect on the outcomes of a collision.

The results for higher impact velocities are given in Figure 2. To conserve space, only selected time frames are shown. Weber numbers corresponding to 1,2,3, and 4 m/s are 2.75, 11, 24.75, and 44 respectively. As velocity (Weber number) increases, the disk shape changes into a torus shape, with decreasing thickness in the center region. The results are in general agreement with the experimental observations of Jiang, et al.(1992).

It is reported in Ashrig et al.(1990) that as the Weber number is increased, a critical condition will be reached , at which point the liquid cylinder formed after the surface reflex, will break into two droplets. Their experimental results show that, for equal size droplets, the onset of reflexive separation is at We=19. At this point two droplets are generated with no satellites. As the Weber number is increased, a satellite droplet is generated in the middle of the two bigger primary droplets. The satellite size grows with the increase in Weber number. As mentioned earlier, this is contrary to what is reported in Jiang et al.(1992) where permanent coalescence always results for water droplets in the parametric range investigated.

No separation is observed in the present numerical study. However, it should be mentioned that at the 4m/s case, which corresponds to Weber number of 44, a small hole is seen at the center in the t=0.18ms frame. It is reported in Ashrig et al.(1990) that a thin film, instead of a hole, is always observed at the center. The numerical mesh used in the present study may not be fine enough to capture the thin film. Thus, the formation of a hole may not be real. The failure to capture the thin film may cause a reduction in surface energy which may lower the strength of the reflexive contraction to the extent that reflexive separation becomes unattainable. More work is needed to clarify this droplet separation issue.

The phenomena of collision of unequal-size is generally more complex than that of equal-size. Simulations at various impact velocities with diameter ratio of 0.75 have been obtained. The results for 2m/s, 5m/s, and 7m/s are shown in Figure 3. Similar to the head-on collisions of equal-size droplets, the liquid in both droplets will coalesce and spread radially in the plane normal to the center-to-center line. This will generate a disk-like droplet which will later contract, forming a liquid column. Unlike the liquid column formed by the collision of equal-size droplets, droplets with different sizes form an asymmetric column. For the 2 and 5 m/s collisions, the combined mass simply shifts upwards and oscillates until a spherical droplet is formed. For the 7m/s case, the liquid column separates into two unequal size droplets in the first reflexive contraction. The initially larger droplet becomes smaller after the collision and vice versa. The numerical results appear to agree well with the experimental observations(Fig.20) of Ashgriz et al.(1990).

In summary, very encouraging numerical results have been obtained in the present study. Further study is still needed to understand the collision dynamics of liquid droplets.

CONCLUSION

Numerical simulations of the head-on collision of water droplets at various Weber numbers have been performed. Both equal-size and unequal-size droplets have been studied. The results are in agreement with experimental observations reported in the literature.

For equal-size droplet collisions, no separation occurs. This may be due to the failure of the numerical solution to capture the thin film in the center region which will lead to a reduction in surface energy. Consequently, the strength of the reflexive contraction may be lowered to the extent that reflexive separation becomes unattainable. Thus, the formation of a hole may not be real. More work is needed to clarify this droplet coalescence/separation issue.

For unequal-size droplet collisions, separation occurs at high impact velocity. The initially larger droplet becomes smaller after the collision and vice versa.

REFERENCES

1. Kothe, D.B., Mjolsness, R.C., and Torrey, M.D., 1991 "RIPPLE, A Computer Program for Incompressible Flows with Free Surfaces," LA-12007-MS, Los Alamos National Laboratory.

2. Hirt, C.W., and Nichols, B.D., 1981 "Volume of Fluid (VOF) Method for the Dynamics of Free Boundaries," J. Computational. Physics, Vol. 39, pp. 201-225.

3. Brackbill, J.U., Kothe, D.B., and Zemach, C., 1992 "A Continuum Method for Modeling Surface Tension," J. Computational Physics, Vol. 100, pp. 335-354.

4. Holt, B.R., and Tong, A.Y., 1995 "Numerical Simulation of A Liquid Metal Droplet Impacting Onto a Substrate," ASME/JSME Thermal Engineering Joint Conference, Vol. 2, pp. 149-156.

5. Holt, B.R., and Tong, A.Y., 1995 "The Normal Incidence Impact and Solidification Phenomena of A Liquid Metal Droplet Onto A Rigid Substrate," FED-Vol. 234, Proceedings of the ASME Fluids Engineering Division, pp. 215-224.

6. Jiang, Y.J., Umemura, A., and Law, C.K., 1992 "An Experimental Investigation on the Collision Behavior of Hydrocarbon Droplets," J. Fluid Mech., Vol. 234, pp. 171-190.

7. Ashgriz, N., and Poo, J.Y., 1990 "Coalescence and Separation in Binary Collisions of Liquid Drops," J. Fluid Mech., Vol. 221, pp. 183-204.

8. Murray, P.E. 1995 "Numerical Simulation of Large Deformation of Invicid Drops," FED-Vol. 234, Proceedings of the ASME Fluids Engineering Division, pp. 241-251.

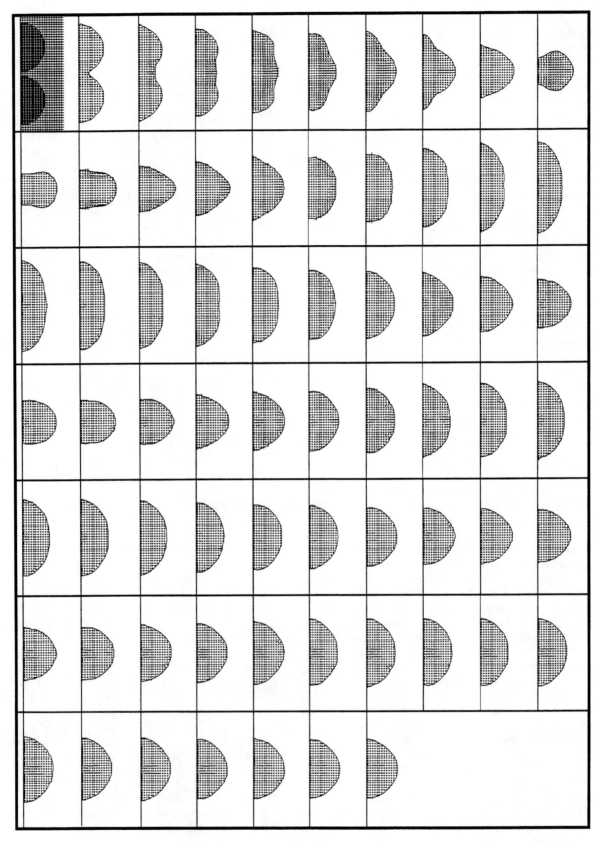

Figure 1. Head-on collision of equal-size drops at 1 m/s
(Frames are taken at 0.02ms time interval)

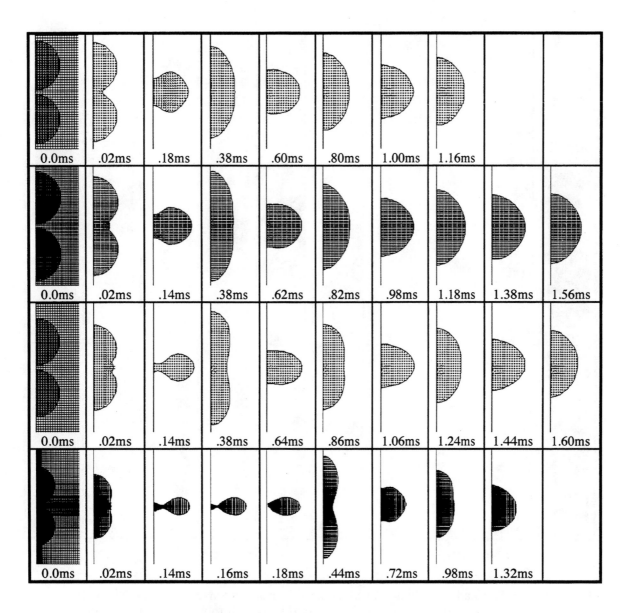

Figure 2. Head-on collision of equal-size drops at various impact velocities
(top row: 1m/s ; second row: 2m/s ; third row: 3m/s ; bottom row: 4m/s)

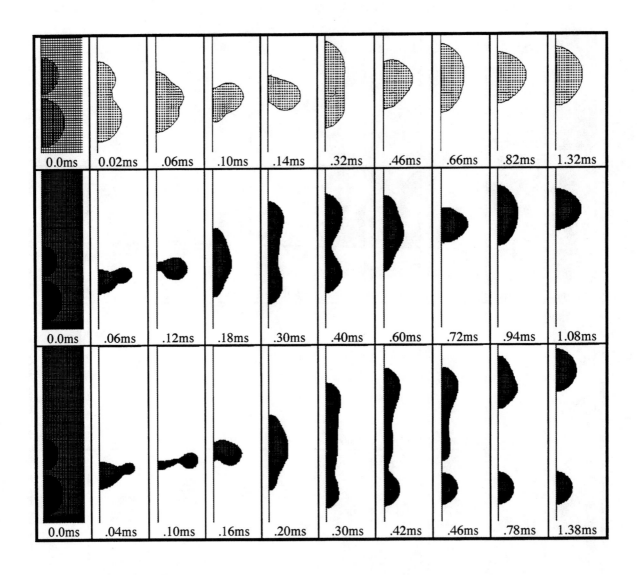

Figure 3. Head-on collision of unequal-size drops at various impact velocities
(diameter ratio=0.75 ; top row: 2 m/s ; middle row: 5 m/s ; bottom row: 7 m/s)

FED-Vol. 238, 1996 Fluids Engineering Division Conference
Volume 3
ASME 1996

A Numerical Scheme for Liquid-Liquid System: Deformation of a Falling Liquid Droplet

H. Zhang,[†] T. Y. Hou[‡] and V. Prasad[†]

[†] *Department of Mechanical Engineering*
State University of New York at Stony Brook
Stony Brook, NY 11794-2300

[‡] *Department of Applied Mathematics*
California Institute of Technology
Pasadena, CA 91125

ABSTRACT

A generalized numerical scheme for problems involving highly deformable free surfaces is developed based on combined level set formulation and multizone adaptive finite volume scheme. The interface is captured by the level set function. The multizone adaptive finite volume algorithm is used to generate grids for irregular domains and make the solution procedure computationally efficient. The resulting scheme is capable of accurate and efficient representation of irregular surfaces, fast tracking of moving interfaces/surfaces between the phases, and deformation, merger and break-up of free surfaces caused by impingement, collision and other phenomena. Four complex problems of liquid-liquid and liquid-solid systems are considered to demonstrate the effectiveness and versatility of this new scheme.

INTRODUCTION

Numerical simulations for processes/systems involving nonplanar moving boundaries and interfaces present a great challenge to numerical analysts and computational scientists. For example, consider the plasma spraying process where droplets with different solid fractions impinge on the substrate to solidate into a deposit (Trapaga and Szekely, 1991; Fukai et al., 1995). Simulation of this process is extremely difficult because the solidifying droplets continually deform and bond together (as well as with the substrate) to form a deposit. Similarly, a numerical analysis of crystal growth process is not an easy task since the dynamics of melt/crystal interface and melt free surface are complex (Prasad and Zhang,

1995). There are two basic approaches for computations of this kind of problem which differ in the types of grids used (Crank, 1984). The first approach is so called "front capturing" based on a fixed uniform or non-uniform grid system. Here, a scale function is introduced into the system of governing equations to define the interface (e.g., a level set function, fractional volume of fluid, etc.) or massless markers are introduced to define the location and trace the movement of the free surface (Harlow and Welch, 1965; Harlow and Amsden, 1971; Chen et al., 1995). This approach is easy to implement and is considered robust for both 2D and 3D calculations. However, the front capturing methods typically introduce numerical viscosity that can diffuse to the interface region, especially when the velocity gradients are large near the interface (Hirt and Nicholes, 1981; Brackbill et al., 1992; Hou, 1995).

The second approach known as "front tracking" tracks the free surfaces or interfaces explicitly or implicitly (Crank, 1984; Glimm et al., 1985; Zhang et al., 1995a, 1995b, 1996). This scheme reduces the numerical diffusion, but has a tendency to smooth out the front shape and its dynamics. Also, the method is successful only if the front profile is simple. When the interface becomes highly branched, the generation of a boundary conforming grid becomes an extremely difficult task. Such special situations may require local surgery of moving grid points (Glimm et al., 1985). Furthermore, in the event of topological changes such as the merger or break-up of interface(s), the tracking methods may fail to continue beyond that point.

A methodology that combines a front tracking scheme

(e.g., MAGG technique) with a fixed grid system (e.g., level set formulation) can prove to be much more robust for moving free surface/interface problems since this algorithm will take full advantage of both the techniques. All of the problems that can be handled either by the MAGG technique or by the level set formulation can be solved much more efficiently by this new method. Also, the false diffusion can be greatly suppressed by using a suitable grid generation. The applicability and effectiveness of this combined scheme is shown here by performing computations for several liquid-liquid and liquid-solid systems. The algorithm has the capability of accurate and efficient representations of irregular surfaces, moving interfaces between the phases, and deformation, merger, and break-up of the free surfaces. It also allows an efficient, adaptive distribution of grids in response to the developing solutions with time.

GOVERNING EQUATIONS

Most free surface problems have enough common features to develop a generalized computational procedure that can take into account most of the relevant transport mechanisms. Here, we consider a liquid-liquid system where one liquid may be in a droplet form and the other as a continuous medium (e.g., a pool). To formulate such problems, the following assumptions are made: (1) the flow is incompressible, laminar and two-dimensional; (2) the fluids are Newtonian; and (3) the thermophysical properties are constant and uniform.

The equations governing the transport of mass and momentum are therefore given by

$$\nabla \cdot \mathbf{u} = 0 \,, \tag{1}$$

$$\rho(\frac{\partial \mathbf{u}}{\partial t} + \nabla \cdot (\mathbf{uu})) = -\nabla P + \rho \mathbf{g} + \nabla \cdot (2\mu \nabla D) + \sigma \kappa \delta(d)\mathbf{n} \,, \tag{2}$$

where $\mathbf{u}$ is the velocity vector, ρ and μ are the discontinuous density and viscosity fields, respectively, and $D = (u_{i,j} + u_{j,i})$ is the deformation tensor rate. The density and viscosity inside the droplet and for the continuous phase are described by ρ_d and μ_d, ρ_c and μ_c, respectively. The last term in Eq.(2) represents surface tension term which is considered to be a force concentrated at the interface. In Eq.(2), σ is the surface tension coefficient, κ is the curvature of the front, δ is the Dirac delta function, d is the normal signed distance to the front, and $\mathbf{n}$ is an unit outward normal vector at the front.

For immiscible liquids, the density and viscosity are governed by (Sussman et al., 1994; Chang et al., 1996)

$$\frac{\partial \rho}{\partial t} + \nabla \cdot (\rho \mathbf{u}) = 0 \,, \tag{3}$$

$$\frac{\partial \mu}{\partial t} + \nabla \cdot (\mu \mathbf{u}) = 0 \,. \tag{4}$$

Level Set Formulation for Interface Capturing

Since ρ and μ change sharply at the front, conventional finite difference schemes incur excessive numerical diffusion and oscillation when solving Eqs. (3) and (4). To avoid that a level set technique is employed to "capture" the interface. The level set formulation (LSF) is similar to the enthalpy method that is widely used for interface tracking in melting/solidification (Crank, 1984). It was first introduced for moving interfaces by Osher and Sethian (1988) and has been further developed by Sussman et al. (1994), Hou (1995) and Adalsteinsson and Sethian (1995). In this scheme, the level set function is denoted as ϕ and the boundary of two fluid interfaces is modeled as the zero set of the smooth function ϕ defined on the entire computational domain. The boundary is then moved by solving a Hamilton-Jacobi type equation on the computational domain. The initial level set function, $\phi < 0$ defines one fluid and $\phi > 0$ defines the other one. The signed distance from the front is used as ϕ in this paper, $\phi = 0$ defining the interface between the two fluids. Note that $\phi = 0$ may define more than one surface depending on continuous or broken interfaces between the two fluids, e.g., a falling droplet broken into two smaller droplets. With the introduction of the level set function ϕ, the momentum equation (2) can be written as:

$$\rho(\frac{\partial \mathbf{u}}{\partial t} + \nabla \cdot (\mathbf{uu})) = -\nabla P + \rho \mathbf{g} + \nabla \cdot (2\mu \nabla D) + \sigma \kappa \nabla \phi \delta(\phi) \,. \tag{5}$$

where ϕ can be solved from

$$\frac{\partial \phi}{\partial t} + \mathbf{u} \cdot \nabla \phi = 0 \,. \tag{6}$$

In Eq.(5), $\delta(\phi)$ is one-dimensional Dirac delta function, and the curvature κ is obtained from

$$\kappa = -\frac{\phi_y^2 \phi_{xx} - 2\phi_x \phi_y \phi_{xy} + \phi_x^2 \phi_{yy}}{(\phi_x^2 + \phi_y^2)^{3/2}} \,. \tag{7}$$

Equation (7) will move the zero level of ϕ exactly as the actual droplet interface moves.

Since ϕ is a smooth function, unlike the fractional function in enthalpy method, porosity in the porous media based approach, and volume of fluid in the VOF method, the equation for ϕ can be solved much more easily. It is also important to note that only the zero level set is physically meaningful. The LSF provides freedom in extending the level set function outside the front. It is also possible to re-initialize the level set function ϕ. This scheme helps preserve mass conservation and keep the thickness of the interface non-diffusive in time. Note that the VOF scheme (Hirt and Nichols, 1981) can be considered as a special case of the level set formulation when the level set function is a step function. However this type of function is difficult to solve and manipulate.

In level set formulation, Eqs. (3) and (4) are replaced by $\rho = \rho_c + (\rho_d - \rho_c)H(\phi)$ and $\mu = \mu_c + (\mu_d - \mu_c)H(\phi)$, where H is the Heaviside (step) function that satisfies $H(x) = 1$ for $x > 0$ and $H(x) = 0$ for $x < 0$. The Dirac delta function and Heaviside function can be expressed as

$$\delta_\epsilon = \begin{cases} (1 + cos(\pi x/\epsilon))/(2\epsilon) & if \; |x| < \epsilon \\ 0 & otherwise \end{cases} \quad (8)$$

$$H_\epsilon = \begin{cases} 0 & if \; x \leq -\epsilon \\ (x+\epsilon)/(2\epsilon) + sin(\pi x/\epsilon))/(2\pi) & if \; |x| < \epsilon \\ 1 & if \; x \geq \epsilon \end{cases} \quad (9)$$

Initially, we set the level set function as a signed distance from the front. In the case of computations for large times, it will not remain a distance function at later times. An iterative procedure to re-initialize the level set function proposed by Sussman (1994) is therefore employed to keep ϕ as a signed distance from the front at all times. This is accomplished by solving the following equation to steady state

$$\frac{\partial \phi}{\partial t} = sgn(\phi_o)(1 - |\nabla \phi|) \quad (10)$$

with the initial condition

$$\phi(\mathbf{x}, 0) = \phi_o(\mathbf{x})$$

where sgn is the sign function. The solution of ϕ will have the same sign and the same zero level set as ϕ_o, and will satisfy $|\nabla \phi| = 1$, and is therefore a distance function from the front.

Another important issue is the mass conservation. Numerical discretization of the level set formulation does not guarantee mass conservation even with the above re-initialization procedure. To overcome this difficulty, Chang et al. (1996) has proposed another re-initialization procedure aimed at preserving the total mass in time. They replace Eq.(10) by

$$\frac{\partial \phi}{\partial t} + (A_o - A(t))(-P + \kappa) = 0$$
$$\phi(\mathbf{x}, 0) = \phi_o(\mathbf{x}) . \quad (11)$$

where A_o is the total mass at $t = 0$, $A(t)$ is the total mass corresponding to the level set function $\phi(t)$, and P is a positive constant, taken as unity in this paper. The surface tension term in Eq.(5) is treated in a similar fashion as that outlined by Brackbill et al. (1992).

The boundary consitions of the level function at solid wall can be written as (Brackbill et al., 1992):

$$\nabla \phi/|\nabla \phi| = \mathbf{n} \, cos\theta + \mathbf{t} \, sin\theta , \quad (12)$$

where $\mathbf{n}$ is the unit wall normal directed into the wall, $\mathbf{t}$ is the unit wall tangent, and θ is the equilibrium contact angle. The value of ϕ at wall can be calculated from the above equation. As soon as the sign of ϕ changes, the material above the wall

changes or the droplet considers touch down to the wall. The surface tension is calculated by a new formulation described by Fukai et al. (1995).

After the level set function is obtained, the entire domain can be treated as a single domain. Regions of various liquids or phases can be distinguished by the level function. Any numerical technique based on either the finite differences, finite volume or finite element can be used to solve the system of equations which comprise continuity equations, Navier-Stokes equations and scale equations for temperature, concentrations and other quantities of interest. All of the LSF based algorithms reported thus far have employed only finite difference methods. The research has generally focused on the development of LSF method and sensitivity of the grid size and other numerical treatments. High order numerical schemes are used in these studies, but the geometry has remained simple.

In this paper, we use the multizone adaptive curvilinear finite volume scheme (Zhang et al., 1993) to solve convection-diffusion equations. The equations for level set formulation, which are hyperbolic in nature, are solved by a high order scheme, ENO (Harten et al., 1987), to reduce numerical diffusion in the free surface. We believe that this type of treatment will be able to preserve the accuracy of the scheme, and will also allow the use of this technique for industrial problems where both phase-change interface(s) and free surface(s) must be considered simultaneously in irregular domains, e.g., thermal spray, welding, and molding processes.

Multizone Adaptive Grid Generation

The multizone adaptive curvilinear finite volume scheme is based on multizone adaptive grid generation (MAGG) and curvilinear finite volume (CFV) discretization. It has been very successful in simulating the transport phenomena associated with complex thermohydrodynamic problems with moving interfaces and free surfaces. The computational domain in this scheme can be permitted to consist of various materials in different phases with significantly different thermophysical and transport properties (Zhang and Prasad, 1995b). This scheme combined with level set method will be immediately capable of solving the systems with simultaneously moving melting/solidification front(s) and free surface(s).

The MAGG scheme is based on constrained variational methods, and minimize a linear combination of integrals that are measures of different grid characteristics. One of the major advantages of this scheme is that it preserves internal interfaces separating various zones/phases and always makes them coincide with a grid line. The scheme allows grids to move adaptively as the solutions progress and/or domains change. By selecting appropriate weighting functions, the grid nodes can be concentrated in the regions of large variations in field variables and by using appropriate grid inertia, the rate of grid movement can be selectively adjusted. The generated grids are smooth and orthogonal in the vicinity of the interface. To our knowledge, both of these characteristics can not be achieved simultaneously by any other formulation.

The general formulation of the MAGG and CFV is presented here in brief. If the general curvilinear coordinates are denoted by ξ^i (i = 1,2) and Cartesian coordinates are denoted as x_r (r = 1, 2), a two-dimensional grid generation system is obtained as Euler-Lagrange equations by minimizing a linear combination of important grid characteristics; namely the smoothness, I_s, orthogonality, I_o, weighted cell area, I_w, and inertia, I_m of the grids given by

$$I = I_s + \lambda_w I_w + \lambda_o I_o + \lambda_v I_v = \iint F \, d\xi^1 d\xi^2 \,. \quad (13)$$

The Euler-Lagrange equations in the transformation space are

$$\frac{\partial}{\partial \xi^1}\frac{\partial F}{\partial (x_i)_{\xi^1}} + \frac{\partial}{\partial \xi^2}\frac{\partial F}{\partial (x_i)_{\xi^2}} - \frac{\partial F}{\partial x_i} = 0 \,, \qquad i = 1, 2. \quad (14)$$

where F is the kernel of the functional which is also referred to as the overall "performance function" of the optimization problem.

This grid generation routine can be formulated for the entire domain with the exception of the zonal interfaces where a grid distribution is obtained by the same variational problem as above subject to the constraints

$$f_k = f_{int,k}(x, y) = 0 \,, \quad (15)$$

where $f_{int,k}$'s are known real-valued functions with respect to arguments x and y which are implicit functions of ξ and η. They define the interfaces for constant ζ_k values, k representing the interface at different locations. The above constrained optimization problems are converted to unconstrained ones by introducing Lagrange multipliers Λ_k (Zhang and Moallemi, 1995a) to form an augmented functional:

$$I = \iint (F + \Lambda_k f_k) d\xi^1 d\xi^2 \,. \quad (16)$$

The Euler-Lagrange equations derived from equation (13) along with constraint (12) provide necessary conditions to determine the grid distribution (x, y) and Lagrange multipliers, Λ_k. The interface position function and its derivatives are determined from a curve fitting procedure in order to preserve its shape, while the grid points move along the interface. The finite difference approximation of the Euler-Lagrange equations in this algorithm are solved by a SOR method to obtain coordinates of the grid points.

Curvilinear Finite Volume Discretization

The CFV scheme employs a flux discretization in the physical domain, that makes it easy for modifications in the physical process models to be incorporated into the computer algorithm. The conservation equations in a generalized coordinate system (ξ^i) (i = 1,2) can be integrated over each finite volume in the computational domain. For a typical primary point P, the integrated equation with $\Delta \xi = \Delta \eta = 1$ can be expressed as:

$$\frac{(r^n Ja \, \rho \, \phi - r_o^n Ja^o \, \rho^o \, \phi^o)_P \, \Delta\xi \, \Delta\eta}{\Delta t}$$
$$+ (\alpha_\xi J_\xi - \beta_\xi J_\eta)_e \Delta\eta - (\alpha_\xi J_\xi - \beta_\xi J_\eta)_w \Delta\eta$$
$$+ (\alpha_\eta J_\eta - \beta_\eta J_\xi)_n \Delta\xi - (\alpha_\eta J_\eta - \beta_\eta J_\xi)_s \Delta\xi +$$
$$= (r^n Ja \, \hat{S})_P \Delta\xi \, \Delta\eta \,, \quad (17)$$

where the superscript o denotes values from the previous time step, α, β are the geometrical coefficient, and J is the flux at a control volume.

Non-staggered grids are used to discretize the governing equations since they are more appropriate for the imposition of interfacial boundary conditions in the case of multiphase systems. However, a non-staggered grid system requires a momentum interpolation method to prevent pressure oscillations instead of a conventional linear interpolation. The solution algorithm for flow calculations in a generalized curvilinear coordinate system is presented in Zhang et al. (1996). It solves a pressure equation to obtain the pressure field and then uses a pressure-correction equation to correct the predicted velocities.

The smoothness function Eq.(12) in the MAGG scheme acts on the interface and in the vicinity of the interfaces, and can smear out the local structure of the interface. Since, the free surface front is usually non-smooth, this restricts the applicability of the MAGG scheme. This is where the LSF provides a great benefit to the MAGG-CFV based scheme. In the combined algorithm, the MAGG is used to generate irregular domains and track melting/solidification front which is smooth. The transport equations are solved by using the multizone adaptive finite volume scheme and the level set function ϕ is solved by the second order ENO scheme. The interface is updated explicitly in this paper. The time step used in the calculation is limited by numerical stability considerations (Hirt and Nichols, 1981).

RESULTS AND DISCUSSIONS

The results presented in this paper demonstrates the effectiveness and robustness of this new formulation. As a first example, a liquid jet impinging over a solid surface with a bump, as shown in Fig. 1, has been considered for numerical simulation. The background of this problem is thermal spray coating and molding processes. However, only an ideal numerical system is considered here rather than the real industrial processes. The MAGG is used to obtain initial grids and follow adaptively the free surface movement. The deformation of the free surface is captured by the level set function. The shape of the free surface is quite smooth in this

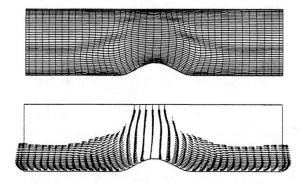

Figure 1: A liquid jet impinging over a solid surface with a bump.

case. Therefore, the adaptivity has been successfully and no interface smear is expected in this case.

A single liquid droplet falling into a pool of the same material (liquid), as shown in Fig. 2, is considered as a second case to demonstrate the capability of the numerical scheme to simulate the merging process. The wavy liquid surface oscillates and finally settles to a stable surface once the kinetic energy has been fully dissipated.

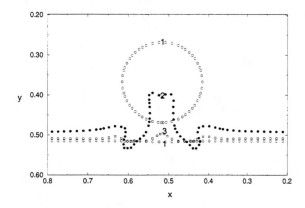

Figure 2: A spherical single liquid droplet falling into a pool of the same material (liquid). The shape of the liquid droplet at various stages of impact and merger with the pool liquid is demonstrated in this diagram: 1 - initial state, 2 - after the droplet has hit the liquid in the pool, 3 - at a later stage.

The third example considers the process of two droplets merging and breaking-up near a solid wall as shown in Fig. 3. No wetting is considered at the bottom surface. The liquid is therefore unable to attach to the bottom. The results show that a large droplet is formed after merger, and this droplet impinges on the solid wall. The droplet then becomes thinner and finally breaks-up in the middle. Two equal size cells are then formed due to the transfer of kinetic energy from vertical to horizontal direction. These two cells oscillate for a while until the energy is fully dissipated.

The fourth example considers the process of one droplet

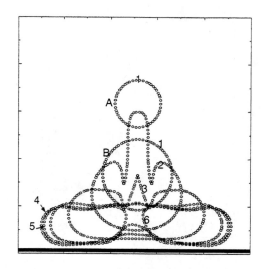

Figure 3: Two spherical droplets (A and B) merging and breaking-up near a solid wall: $\rho_1/\rho_2 = 0.1$, $Re_1/Re_2 = 0.25$. The diagram presents the shape profile at various stages (1,2 ...) of this merger and separation.

impinging on a wet surface, as shown in Fig. 4. The thin liquid film adheres to the bottom and side walls of the container in the beginning of the simulation. As the droplet moves down in the container, the liquid film also falls down. The droplet then merges with the liquid film at the bottom. A deformed free surface is then formed which oscillates until the entire liquid is settled down at the bottom of the container. The simulation is capable of predicting the merger and oscillation processes.

Simulations are performed on IBM SP2 using only one node. For the first problem, approximately one hour of CPU time is required. For the last three examples, approximately 3—4 hours of CPU time is needed to obtain the results presented in this paper.

CONCLUSIONS

A numerical scheme is proposed to combine the multizone adaptive finite volume scheme with the level set formulation. In this new scheme, the grid lines follow the irregular domain based on a multizone adaptive curvilinear finite-volume scheme (a front tracking method) and the free surfaces are modeled by the level set formulation (a front capturing method). The multizone adaptive grid generation technique provides the capability of accurate representation of boundaries which are usually smooth, and the merger and break-up of the interfaces are captured by using the level set formulation. The strength and versatility of this scheme have been demonstrated by four different problems where the free surfaces are highly deformable and in some cases oscillate until the kinetic energy is fully dissipated. The results indicate that the new scheme is fully capable of predicting merger and

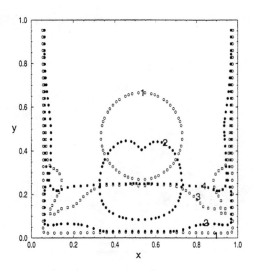

Figure 4: A spherical droplet impinges on wet surfaces (both bottom and side). The diagram presents the shape profile at various stages (1,2 ...) of this impinging process.

break-up of the droplets as well as impingement on the surface. The scheme can be useful to a wide range of industrial problems including thermal plasma coating, welding, crystal growth and molding processes.

ACKNOWLEDGMENTS

This research has been partially supported by ARPA, AFOSR and NSF.

REFERENCES

Adalsteinsson, D., and Sethian, J. A., 1995, "A Level Set Approach to a Unified Model for Etching, Deposition, and Lithography I: Algorithms and Two-Dimensional Simulations," *J. Comput. Phys.*, Vol. 120, pp. 128-144.

Brackbill, J. U., and Saltzman, J. S., 1982, "Adaptive Zoning for Singular Problems in Two Dimensions," *Journal of Computational Physics*, Vol. 46, pp. 342-368.

Brackbill, J. U., Kothe, D. B., and Zemach, C., 1992, "A Continuum Method for Modeling Surface-Tension," *J. Comput. Phys.*, Vol. 100, pp. 335-354.

Chang, Y. C., Hou, T. Y., Merriman B., and Osher, S., 1996, "A Level Set Formulation of Eulerian Interface Capturing Methods for Incompressible Fluid Flows," (submitted to J. Comput. Phys.)

Chen, S., Johnson, D. B., and Raad, P. E., 1995, "Velocity Boundary Conditions for the Simulation of Free Surface Fluid Flow," *J. Comp. Phys.* Vol. 116, pp. 262-276.

Crank, J., 1984, "Free and Moving Boundary Problems," Clarendon Press, Oxford.

Fukai, J., Shiiba, Y., Yamamoto, T., Miyatake, O., Poulikakos, D., Megaridis, C. M., and Zhao, Z., 1995, "Wetting Effects on the Spreading of a Liquid Droplet Colliding with a Flat Surface: Experiment and Modeling," *Phys. Fluids,* Vol. 7, pp. 236-247.

Glimm, J., Klingenberg, C., McBryan, O., Plohr, B., Sharp, D., and Yaniv., S., 1985, "Front Tracking and Two Dimensional Riemann Problem," *Adv. Appl. Math.*, Vol. 6, pp. 259-290.

Harlow, F. H., and Welch, J. E. W., 1965, "Numerical Calculation of Time-dependent Viscous Incompressible Flow of Fluid with Free Surface," *Phys. Fluids*, Vol. 8, pp. 2182.

Harlow, F. H., and Amsden, A. A., 1971, "A Numerical Fluid Dynamics Calculation Method for All Flow Speeds," *J. Comp. Phys.*, Vol. 8, pp. 197-213.

Harten, A., Engquist, B., Osher, S., Chakravarthy, 1987, "Uniformly High-order Accurate Essentially Nonoscillatory Schemes, III," *J. Comput. Phys.*, Vol. 71, pp. 231-303.

Hirt, C. W., and Nichols, B. D., 1981, "Volume of Fluid (VOF) Methods for the Dynamics of Free Boundaries", Journal of Computational Physics, Vol. 39, pp. 201-225.

Hou, T. Y., and Wetton, B., 1992, "Convergence of a Finite Differece Scheme for the Navier-Stokes Equations Using Vorticity Boundary Conditions," *SIAM J. Numer. Anal.,* Vol. 29, pp. 615-639.

Hou, T. Y., 1995, "Numerical Solutions to Free Boundary Problems," *Acta Numerica,* pp. 335-415.

Osher S., and Sethian, J. A., 1988, "Fronts Propagating with Curvature-Dependent Speed: Algorithms Based on Hamilton-Jacobi Formulations," *J. Comput. Phys.*, Vol. 79, pp. 12-49.

Prasad, V., and Zhang, H., 1996, "Challenging Issues in Bulk Crystal Growth Modeling," *Ceramic Transactions,* Vol. 60, pp. 3-36.

Sussman, M., Smereka, P., and Osher, S., 1994, "A Level Set Approach for Computing Solutions to Incompressible Two-Phase Flow," *J. Comput. Phys.*, Vol. 114, pp. 146-159.

Trapaga, G., and Szekely, J., 1991, "Mathematical Modeling of the Isothermal Impingement of Liquid Droplets in Spraying Processes," *Metall. Trans. B*, Vol. 22, pp. 901-914.

Zhang, H., and Moallemi, M. K., 1995a, "A Multizone Adaptive Grid Generation Technique for Simulation of Moving and Free Boundary Problems," *Num. Heat Transfer, Part B,* Vol. 27, pp. 255-276.

Zhang, H., and Prasad, V., 1995b, "A Multizone Adaptive Process Model for Low and High Pressure Crystal Growth," *J. of Crystal Growth*, Vol. 155, pp. 47-65.

Zhang, H., Moallemi, M.K., and Prasad, V., 1996, "A Numerical Algorithm Using Multizone Grid Generation for Multiphase Transport Processes with Moving and free Boundaries," *Num. Heat Transfer, Part B*, Vol. 29 (in press).

FED-Vol. 238, 1996 Fluids Engineering Division Conference
Volume 3
ASME 1996

Numerical Simulation of the Shallow Water Equations

S. Chippada, C. N. Dawson, M. L. Martinez, and M. F. Wheeler
TICAM, Univ. of Texas–Austin

ABSTRACT

Shallow Water Equations (SWE) are widely used in the modeling of tidal fluctuations and circulations in coastal seas, bays and estuaries. The numerical solution of the SWE is not completely straight forward mainly due to the extremely complicated and irregular physical domains (e.g. shore lines and islands), and the strong coupling between the fluid depth and velocities which could lead to spurious spatial oscillations if proper care is not taken in choosing the approximating spaces. The primary focus of our work has been to develop robust and accurate numerical schemes which also have the local conservation property. Local conservation of mass is a very desirable property, especially, if salinity and contaminant transport is to be modeled. We have looked at a numerical formulation based on nonconforming triangular element, and our findings are reported in this paper.

1 INTRODUCTION

Shallow Water Equations (SWE) are used to describe free surface hydrodynamics in vertically well-mixed water bodies with the characteristic length scales in the horizontal direction much greater than the fluid depth. The SWE are obtained by the vertical integration of the three-dimensional Navier–Stokes equations along with the hydrostatic pressure assumption. Most of the naturally occurring fluid flows are turbulent in nature, and a vertical uniform velocity profile is assumed. With this, the three-dimensional free boundary problem reduces to a two-dimensional fixed boundary problem with the primary variables being the horizontal fluid velocities and the fluid depth. The SWE can be used to study many physical phenomena of interest such as, storm surges, tidal fluctuations, tsunami waves, forces acting on off-shore structures, and contaminant and salinity transport (Kinnmark, 1985). Due to their obvious importance, the numerical simulation of the SWE has been widely investigated in the past few years.

The resulting equations obtained from the vertical integration of the Navier–Stokes equations are referred to as the primitive form of the shallow water equations (P-SWE),

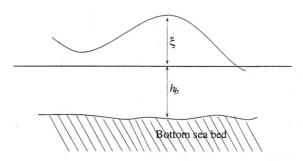

Figure 1: Definition of elevation and bathymetry

and are written as follows:

$$\frac{\partial \xi}{\partial t} + \nabla \cdot (\mathbf{u}H) = 0 \tag{1}$$

$$\begin{aligned}\frac{\partial \mathbf{u}}{\partial t} + \mathbf{u} \cdot \nabla \mathbf{u} + \tau_{bf}\mathbf{u} + f_c \mathbf{k} \times \mathbf{u} + g\nabla\xi & \\ -\frac{1}{H}\nabla \cdot \left[\nu_T H \left(\nabla \mathbf{u} + \nabla \mathbf{u}^T \right) \right] &= 0 \end{aligned} \tag{2}$$

Eqn.1 represents the conservation of mass, and Eqn.2 represents the conservation of momentum in non-conservative form. In the above equations, ξ represents the deflection of the air-liquid interface from the mean sea level, $H = h_b + \xi$ represents the total fluid depth, and h_b is the bathymetric depth (see Fig.1). $\mathbf{u} = (u,v)$ is the depth averaged horizontal velocity field, f_c is the Coriolis parameter resulting from the earth's rotation, $\mathbf{k}$ is the local vertical vector, g is the gravitational acceleration, τ_{bf} is the bottom friction coefficient which is usually computed using either the Manning's or the Chezy's friction law, and ν_T is the depth averaged turbulent viscosity. In addition, to the above described phenomena, often we need to include the effects of surface wind stress, variable atmospheric pressure and tidal potentials (Luettich *et al.*, 1991). The eddy viscosity coefficient ν_T is often computed using a turbulence closure model. However, in most situations the bottom friction dominates lateral diffusion and dispersion, and the parameter ν_T is set to zero in the subsequent discussion. The conservative form of the momentum equation can be derived by combining Eqns.1&2, resulting in:

$$\frac{\partial \mathbf{u}H}{\partial t} + \nabla \cdot \mathbf{u}\mathbf{u}H + \tau_{bf}\mathbf{u}H + f_c \mathbf{k} \times \mathbf{u}H + gH\nabla\xi = 0 \tag{3}$$

Thus the continuity equation (Eqn.1) along with the non-conservative momentum equation (Eq.2) or the conservative momentum equation (Eq.3) represent the shallow water equations system in the primitive form (P-SWE) and are solved, usually numerically, for ξ and $\mathbf{u}$.

2 NUMERICAL MODELING

Due to the extremely complicated and irregular domains encountered in modeling coastal areas, the Finite Element Method (FEM) has been widely used in the numerical modeling of the shallow water equations (e.g., Lynch and Gray (1979), Kawahara et al. (1982), Kinnmark (1985), Navon (1988), Zienkiewicz and Ortiz (1995)). Due to the strong coupling between the elevation ξ and velocity $\mathbf{u}$, the numerical methods based on P-SWE are suspectible to '$2\Delta x$' spatial oscillations which usually manifest themselves in the elevation field. Especially vulnerable are the numerical methods based on the non-staggered grids in the finite difference context and equal order approximations in the finite element context. There exist atleast two other approaches that have been developed over the years to eliminate the spurious spatial oscillations. One is based on the use of staggered grids or mixed interpolation spaces. For example, King and Norton (1978) approximate velocities and elevations through piecewise quadratic and piecewise linear basis functions respectively. The other is based on the reformulation of the first order hyperbolic form of the primitive continuity equation (Eq.1) as a second-order wave equation (Lynch and Gray (1979), Luettich et al. (1991)). If the spurious spatial oscillations are suppressed through careful splitting between the elevation and velocity field, the numerical procedures based on staggered or equal order approximations are generally considered to be more effective from implementation point of view. Hence, a wide variety of numerical procedures have been developed based on the P-SWE and equal order approximations (Kawahara et al. (1982), Szymkiewicz (1993), Zienkiewicz and Ortiz (1995)).

The above discussion illustrates the important role the velocity-elevation coupling has played in the development of numerical algorithms. Although, there are several algorithms already in use by private and state agencies for the modeling of environmental surface flows, there is still room for improvement in the numerical modeling of the shallow water equations. One very important feature missing from most, if not all, of the currently used numerical procedures is the local conservation of mass and momentum. On comparison, numerical models developed for gas dynamics and subsurface flows have placed greater emphasis on the local conservation property. For smoothly varying data and solution with significant physical diffusion, both types of algorithms, namely, that which ensure local conservation and

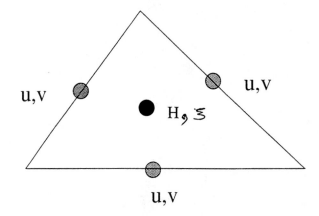

Figure 2: Typical triangular element

that which ensure only global conservation are expected to perform equally well. However, in the event of advection-dominated flows and discontinuous solutions, this is not necessarily true, and the numerical methods based on the local conservation property are expected to perform better. For example, in supercritical flows we could have the formation of hydraulic jumps or bores across which the solution varies sharply. Very often, we are also interested in the transport of thermal energy, salinity, and contaminant. In these cases, we could have concentration fronts, which should be located very accurately. Thus there are many physical situations where the local conservation of mass, momentum and all other scalar transport variables are very important. This is the basic motivation of our research and we have worked towards developing numerical algorithms that conserve all properties locally. The physical domains of interest are often very complex and irregular, and numerical methods based on triangulations are to be preferred.

The numerical method currently being developed by us is based on the P-SWE, and uses triangular elements of the form shown in Fig.2. The elevations are approximated as piecewise constant in the element and are discontinuous across the element edges, whereas the velocities are piecewise linear within each element and only continuous across the mid-points of the element edges. Alternately, the elevations are taken to be existing at the centroid of the element and velocities exist at the mid-points of the edges. This type of mixed finite element velocity-pressure formulation for the Stokes problem has been shown to satisfy the Babuska-Brezzi condition (Thomasset, 1981), and thus does n't lead to spurious modes in the elevation approximation. The major drawback is the increase in unknowns. Usually, there are about three times more edges than vertices in a mesh. However, there are several advantages as well in addition to the fact that it does n't give rise to spurious spatial oscillations. There is no ambiguity associated with the normal direction of an edge unlike in the case of a vertex, and

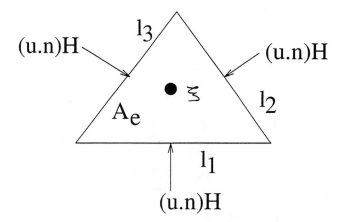

Figure 3: Control volume for elevation

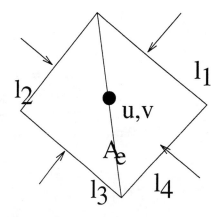

Figure 4: Control volume for velocities

should help greatly in the imposition of boundary conditions. Moreover, in a Galerkin formulation, these spaces lead naturally to a diagonal mass matrix, without the necessity of mass lumping. To our knowledge, this type of nonconforming triangular element has been applied in the numerical solution of shallow water equations only by Hua and Thomasset (1979). This mixed formulation satisfies the continuity equation discretely, but not the momentum equation. Hence, we have local conservation of mass, but not necessarily local conservation of momentum.

To ensure local conservation of both mass and momentum, we formulate the problem in a control/finite volume sense. The control volume for the primitive continuity equation is shown in Fig.3. Knowing the previous time-step elevation (ξ^k) and velocities (u^k, v^k), next time-level elevation (ξ^{k+1}) is computed as follows:

$$\left(\frac{\xi_e^{k+1} - \xi_e^k}{\Delta t}\right) A_e = -\sum_{i=1}^{i=3} [(\mathbf{u} \cdot \mathbf{n}) H]_i^{k+\theta} l_i \quad (4)$$

A_e and l_i are respectively, the area of the element and the length of the edges. $\mathbf{n}$ is the unit normal to the edge pointing out of the element. The parameter θ controls the time level at which the fluxes are computed and for $\theta = 0.5$ we will have second-order accuracy in time. An explicit second-order method in time can be obtained using the second-order Adams-Bashforth scheme, which can be expressed as:

$$F^{k+\frac{1}{2}} = \frac{3}{2}F^k - \frac{1}{2}F^{k-1} + O(k^2), \quad (5)$$

and F in our case is $(\mathbf{u} \cdot \mathbf{n}H)$. The value of H on each edge is choosen to be either the upstream value or the downstream value based on the sign of $\mathbf{u} \cdot \mathbf{n}$, thus resulting in a first-order upwinding scheme.

Things get a little more complicated when it comes to the velocities. Since the velocities lie on the edges, we found it convenient to define the control volume for the velocities

as shown in Fig.4. Thus the two adjacent elements which share the edge form the control volume for the velocity, and we have over-lapping control volumes. We could use the conservative momentum equation (Eq.3) and rewrite it in the integral form. However, the surface elevation gradient term $gH\nabla\xi$, poses a problem and cannot be converted into an integral without giving rise to additional terms involving gradient of the bathymetric depth h_b. Thus, we chose the non-conservative momentum equations (Eq.2) and rewrite the advective terms using the the vector identity ($\mathbf{u} \cdot \nabla\mathbf{u} = \nabla\left(\frac{1}{2}\mathbf{u} \cdot \mathbf{u}\right) - \nabla \times \nabla \times \mathbf{u}$) resulting in the following form after neglecting the viscous terms:

$$\frac{\partial \mathbf{u}}{\partial t} + \nabla\left(g\xi + \frac{1}{2}\mathbf{u} \cdot \mathbf{u}\right) + (f_c + \omega)\mathbf{k} \times \mathbf{u} + \tau\mathbf{u} = 0 \quad (6)$$

The integral form of the above equation is given by:

$$\begin{aligned} \int_A \left(\frac{\partial \mathbf{u}}{\partial t} + \tau\mathbf{u} + (f_c + \omega)\mathbf{k} \times \mathbf{u}\right) dA \\ + \int_\Gamma \left(g\xi + \frac{1}{2}\mathbf{u} \cdot \mathbf{u}\right)\mathbf{n} \end{aligned} = 0 \quad (7)$$

$\omega = \nabla \times \mathbf{u}$ is the fluid vorticity. We need an additional equation to compute the vorticity which is obtained by taking the curl of Eq.6, resulting in:

$$\frac{\partial \omega}{\partial t} + \tau\omega + \nabla \cdot [(f_c + \omega)\mathbf{u}]\, d\Gamma = 0 \quad (8)$$

And the above equation for vorticity can be written in the integral formulation as:

$$\int_A \left(\frac{\partial \omega}{\partial t} + \tau\omega\right) dA + \int_\Gamma (f_c + \omega)\mathbf{u} \cdot \dot{\mathbf{n}}\, d\Gamma = 0 \quad (9)$$

In surface flows governed by the shallow water equations, vorticity is generated by Coriolis acceleration, no-slip boundary conditions, pressure gradient and wind stress terms. The vorticity nodes are taken to be at the mid-points of the edges of the triangle, and hence lie in the same spaces as velocities.

The vorticity equation is discretized in time as follows:

$$\left(\frac{\omega^{k+1}-\omega^k}{\Delta t} + \frac{1}{2}\tau\left(\omega^{k+1}+\omega^k\right)\right)A_e$$
$$+ \sum_{i=1}^{i=4}\left((f_c+\omega)\,\mathbf{u}\cdot\mathbf{n}\right)^{k+\frac{1}{2}}l_i \quad = \quad 0, \tag{10}$$

and, the nonlinear terms are discretized using the second-order Adams-Bashforth scheme. Finally, after computing ξ^{k+1} and ω^{k+1}, the next time-level velocities are calculated as follows:

$$\left[\frac{\mathbf{u}^{k+1}-\mathbf{u}^k}{\Delta t} + \frac{1}{2}\tau\left(\mathbf{u}^{k+1}+\mathbf{u}^k\right)\right.$$
$$\left.+ \frac{1}{2}\left(\left(f_c+\omega^{k+1}\right)\mathbf{k}\times\mathbf{u}^{k+1} + \left(f_c+\omega^k\right)\mathbf{k}\times\mathbf{u}^k\right)\right]A_e$$
$$+ \sum_{i=1}^{i=4}\left(g\xi^{k+1} + \frac{3}{2}\frac{\mathbf{u}^k\cdot\mathbf{u}^k}{2} - \frac{1}{2}\frac{\mathbf{u}^{k-1}\cdot\mathbf{u}^{k-1}}{2}\right)\mathbf{n}l_i \quad = \quad 0 \tag{11}$$

In the above scheme all terms are second-order accurate in time except the elevation gradient $g\xi$. A second-order accurate Crank-Nicholson treatment of this term was found to be unstable in certain problems where the bottom friction term is too small. In the above time discretization, the smoothness comes from the first-order Backward Euler treatment of the elevation gradient term. All the quantities in the above discretization exist at the mid-points of the edges, except the surface elevation term. An average of the surface elevations of the two adjacent elements is assigned to the edge and the numerical formulation as described above treats all advection and surface gradient terms in a conservative fashion. Thus, the numerical scheme described conserves mass, momentum and vorticity locally. Due to the first-order treatment of the surface elevation term in the momentum equation, it is only first-order accurate in time. Globally the scheme is first-order accurate in space, but there exists superconvergent points in the elements, where the procedure is spatially second-order accurate.

To close the system we need boundary conditions and initial conditions. At the open sea boundary the elevation is specified as a function of time.

$$\xi = \hat{\xi}(t), \quad \text{on the sea boundary.} \tag{12}$$

On the land boundary we set the normal velocity to be zero.

$$\mathbf{u}\cdot\mathbf{n} = 0, \quad \text{on the land boundary.} \tag{13}$$

3   TEST RESULTS

We have implemented the numerical procedure described in the previous section on some test problems and the results obtained will be discussed below. The first problem solved is Lynch and Gray (1978)'s quarter-annulus test problem with quadratically varying bathymetry. The geometry and the finite element mesh are shown in Fig.5. A tide with 12.4h period and 1ft amplitude is imposed at the sea boundary. The bathymetry varies quadratically from 10ft at the

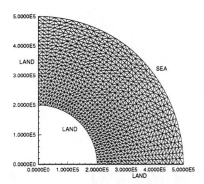

Figure 5: Numerical mesh and boundary conditions for the quarter annulus problem. Lengths are in ft.

inner radius $r_1 = 2\times10^5$ft to 62.5ft at the outer radius $r_2 = 5\times10^5$ft. The bottom friction parameter τ is set to $0.0001s^{-1}$ and the Coriolis parameter is set to zero. The simulations are performed from a cold start with $\xi = 0$ and $u = v = 0$, and the open boundary forcing is gradually applied through a ramp function over a period of four days. The simulation was run for 10.0days and the elevation and velocities were measured at three stations with coordinates $(126697.0, 389933.0)$, $(380238.0, 276259.0)$, and $(218743.0, 71073.0)$ starting from the fifth day. The results obtained are compared with the predictions made by the ADCIRC code which solves the SWE numerically through the use of Generalized Wave Continuity Equation (GWCE) formulation (Luettich et al. (1991)). The accuracy of this procedure has been established through comparisons with several test problems and field data and is used by many state and federal agencies. We find excellent agreement between the present approach and the ADCIRC as seen through Fig.6-7. The elevation and velocity field did not exhibit any spatial oscillations and the accuracy we get is atleast of the same order as that obtained through the wave formulations.

Fluid flow driven by tides around the Bahamas is simulated next. The numerical mesh, geometry and bathymetry is shown in Fig.8. The following tidal forcing with time(t) in hours was imposed at the open sea boundary:

$$\begin{aligned}
\hat{\xi}(t) = &\ 0.075\cos(\tfrac{t}{25.82} + 3.40) + 0.095\cos(\tfrac{t}{23.94} + 3.60) \\
+ &\ 0.100\cos(\tfrac{t}{12.66} + 5.93) + 0.395\cos(\tfrac{t}{12.42} + 0.00) \\
+ &\ 0.060\cos(\tfrac{t}{12.00} + 0.75)\ (meters)
\end{aligned} \tag{14}$$

The bottom friction was imposed using the Chezy-friction law with friction coefficient 0.0001 and the Coriolois parameter was set to $3.19\times10^{-5}s^{-1}$. The simulations were cold started and the tidal forcing are imposed gradually through a ramp function over a period of two days. The elevation and velocities are measured at four different stations whose coordinates

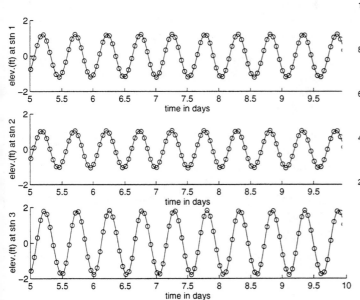

Figure 6: Station recordings of the elevation: present formulation(solid line) and ADCIRC(open circles).

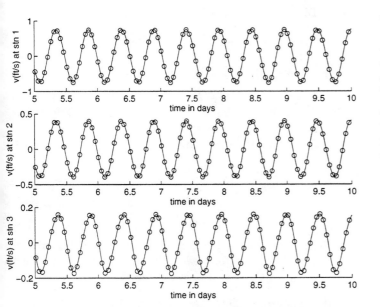

Figure 7: Station recordings of the y-velocity: present formulation(solid line) and ADCIRC(open circles).

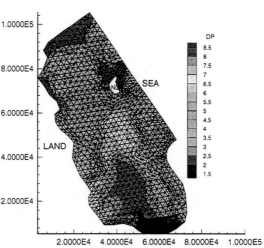

Figure 8: Numerical mesh and the bathymetry for flow around Bahamas Islands. Lengths are in meters.
in meters are: (38666.66, 49333.32), (56097.79, 9612.94), (41262.60, 29775.73), and (59594.66, 41149.62). The results obtained are compared with the predictions made by AD-CIRC and the elevation and x-velocity recordings at the four stations are shown in Fig.9-10. We obtain excellent agreement between both the methods, showing that the present numerical approach has promise.

4 CONCLUSIONS

A numerical procedure based on the P-SWE has been developed that does n't lead to spurious spatial oscillations and conserves mass and momentum locally. This procedure has been compared against the wave formulation of Luettich et al.(1991), and very good agreement is found between both the approaches. There are several aspects in the present formulation that can be improved further and we are currently working on them.

5 ACKNOWLEDGEMENTS

This work was partially funded by the National Science Foundation, Project No. DMS-9408151. The authors thank J.J.Westerink and W.G.Gray for sharing the ADCIRC code and data sets.

References

[1] Hua, B.L., and Thomasset, F., 1979, "Numerical study of coastal upwellings by a finite element method," in

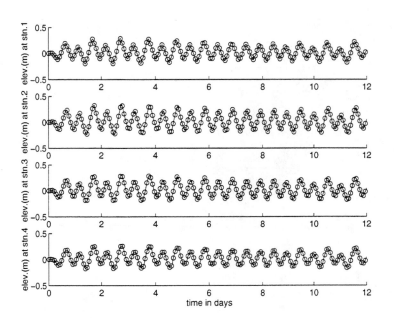

Figure 9: Elevation recordings at four stations: present formulation (soild line) and ADCIRC (open circles).

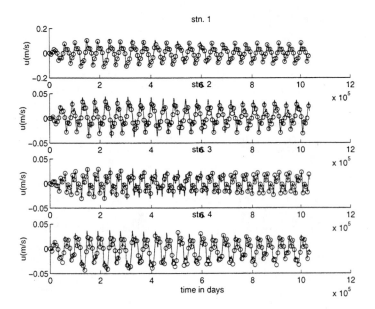

Figure 10: x-velocity recordings at four stations: present formulation (solid line) and ADCIRC (open circles).

Computing Methods in Applied Sciences and Engineering, Proceedings of international symposiums organized by IRIA-LABORIA, 4th symp., 1979, Glowinski, R., and Lions, J. L., eds., North-Holland, Amsterdam.

[2] Kawahara, M., Hirano, H., Tsuhora, K., and Iwagaki, K., 1982, "Selective lumping finite element method for shallow water equations," Int. J. Num. Meth. Engg., 2, pp.99-112.

[3] King, I.P., and Norton, W.R., 1978, "Recent application of RMA's finite element models for two-dimensional hydrodynamics and water quality," in Finite Elements in Water Resources II, C.A. Brebbia, W.G.Gray, and G.F.Pinder, eds., Pentech Press, London.

[4] Kinnmark, I., 1985, "The shallow water wave equations: formulation, analysis and application," Lecture Notes in Engineering, C. A. Brebbia and S. A. Orszag, ed., Springer-Verlag.

[5] Luettich, Jr., R. A., Westerink, J. J., and Scheffner, N. W., 1991, "ADCIRC: An Advanced Three-Dimensional Circulation Model for Shelves, Coasts and Estuaries," Report 1, U.S. Army Corps of Engineers, Washington, D.C. 20314-1000, December 1991.

[6] Lynch, D.R., and Gray, W.G., 1978, "Analytic solution for computer flow model testing," ASCE J. Hydraulic Div., 104, pp.1409-1428.

[7] Lynch, D.R., and Gray, W., 1979, "A wave equation model for finite element tidal computations," Comput. Fluids, 7, pp.207-228.

[8] Navon, I.M., 1988, "A review of finite element methods for solving the shallow water equations," in B.Schreffler and O.C.Zienkiewicz, ed., Computer Modelling in Ocean Engineering, Balkeman, Rotterdam, pp.273-278.

[9] Szymkiewicz, R., 1993, "Oscillation-free solution of shallow water equations for nonstaggered grid," J. Hyd. Engg., 119, No.10, pp.1118-1137.

[10] Thomasset, F., 1981, Implementation of Finite Element Methods for Navier–Stokes Equations, Springer Series in Computational Physics, Springer-Verlag.

[11] Zienkiewicz, O.C., and Ortiz, P., 1995, "A split-characteristic based finite element model for the shallow water equations," Int. J. Num. Meth. Fluids, 20, pp.1061-1080.

FED-Vol. 238, 1996 Fluids Engineering Division Conference
Volume 3
ASME 1996

THREE-DIMENSIONAL INSTABILITIES IN HEATED FALLING FILMS: A FULL-SCALE DIRECT NUMERICAL SIMULATION

S. Krishnamoorthy and B. Ramaswamy

Department of Mechanical Engineering and Materials Science, Rice University, Houston, Texas, USA

S. W. Joo

Department of Mechanical Engineering, Wayne State University, Detroit, Michigan, USA

ABSTRACT

A liquid layer draining on a heated inclined surface is subjected to both thermocapillary and surface-wave instabilities. The combined influence of these two instabilities result in the formation of waves at the interface or breaking of the film. Since these phenomena are highly nonlinear, they can not be analyzed fully using either a linear or a weakly nonlinear analysis; the full system is to be solved. Hence in the present study, we integrate the governing equations for conservation of mass, momentum and energy in three-dimensional form. Through extensive numerical experiments, an instability mechanism for the formation of rivulets in horizontal and vertical layers is examined.

INTRODUCTION

The flow of a liquid film on a solid substrate has many significant engineering applications in material processing, biomedical engineering, nuclear, aerospace and chemical industries. In these flows, the most widely observed phenomena such as the formation of waves on the surface, breaking of stream of liquid into independent rivulets, evaporation and termination of liquid layer at a contact line forming dry spots, are associated with the instability mechanism. Hence, understanding the dynamics of this mechanism will be useful in the in the analysis of heat and mass transfer rates.

A horizontal layer of liquid is subjected to the thermocapillary instability when heated from below. When the layer is tilted, it is subjected to the surface-wave instability (Yih, 1955). When the layer is tilted and heated, both the

instabilities coexist and dictate the dynamics of the ensuing flow in a competitive manner. This combined mechanism has been studied extensively using linear theory (Scriven and Sterlin, 1964; Goussis and Kelly, 1991). Though this analysis gives useful information on critical layer thickness, inclination angle, intensity heating and cut-off wavenumber for instability to occur, it can not follow the dynamics of the flow. Since the instabilities appear in the form of long interfacial waves, weakly nonlinear analysis using long-wave evolution equation (Benney, 1966) are very popular. Several studies on the instability mechanism have been performed (Burelbach et al., 1988; Joo and Davis, 1992; Joo et al., 1996) so far. However toward rupture, the inertial forces become significant and the lubrication type approximation used in the long-wave theory formulation becomes inappropriate to study the nonlinear dynamics of the flow. Hence, the full system of Navier-Stokes equations must be solved.

First, the mathematical formulation is discussed in §2. The numerical scheme is explained in §3. In §4, results from the direct numerical simulation using finite-element method are presented and comparisons with spectral computation of evolution equation are made. Important observations are summarized in §5.

MATHEMATICAL FORMULATION

We consider Newtonian, incompressible, non-volatile, constant property (density ρ, viscosity μ, thermal conductivity k, thermal diffusivity α) liquid kept on a plate maintained at a constant temperature T_w and inclined at an angle β in the streamwise direction. The film is unbounded in both streamwise and spanwise directions. It is thick enough so that the continuum theory is valid. The buoyancy effects and the dynamics of the air above the liquid is neglected. A two-dimensional cross-sectional view of the physical domain is shown in Fig. 1. The heat transfer across the liquid layer and through the interface determines the interfacial temperature T_i. We assume that the surface tension decreases linearly with temperature:

$$\sigma(T) = \sigma_o\left[1 - \gamma(T - T_s)\right], \qquad (1)$$

where σ_0 is the value of the surface tension at the reference temperature T_s and $\gamma(=d\sigma/dT)$ is positive for most common liquids.

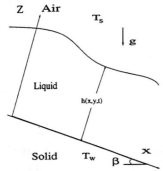

Figure1: Physical configuration of a thin film flowing down a heated inclined plate (two–dimensional sectional view)

The governing equations are time-dependent and three-dimensional conservation laws for mass, momentum and energy. Using mean film thickness d and viscous time d^2/ν, we write the governing equations in an ALE (Arbitrary Lagrangian Eulerian) frame of reference as:

$$\mathbf{u}_{i,i} = 0 \qquad (2)$$

$$\mathbf{u}_{i,t} + (\mathbf{u}_j - \mathbf{g}_j)\mathbf{u}_{i,j} = \sigma_{ij,j} + \mathbf{G}_i \qquad (3)$$

$$\theta_{,t} + (\mathbf{u}_j - \mathbf{g}_j)\theta_{,j} = \frac{1}{P}\theta_{,ii} \qquad (4)$$

where, $\mathbf{u}_i = (u,v,w)$ is the velocity vector, $\mathbf{g}_i = (g_x, g_y, g_z)$ is the grid-point velocity vector, $\theta = (T - T_s)/(T_w - T_s)$ is the nondimensional temperature, i=1,2,3, j=1,2,3, and "$_,$" denotes the partial derivative. Here, $\mathbf{G_i} = (G\sin\beta, 0, -G\cos\beta)$, where $G(=d^3g/\nu^2)$ is the Galileo number that is analogous to the Reynolds number and g is the gravitational acceleration. This parameter is a measure of film thickness. $P(=\nu/\alpha)$ is the Prandtl number and the stress tensor σ_{ij} is expressed as:

$$\sigma_{ij} = -p\delta_{ij} + (\mathbf{u}_{i,j} + \mathbf{u}_{j,i}) \qquad (5)$$

where p is the pressure and δ_{ij} is the Kronecker delta. We use a Cartesian coordinate system $\mathbf{x}_i = (x,y,z)$, with x-axis

directed downstream and the z-axis into the liquid from the bottom plate.

The location of the liquid-air interface ($h(x,y,t)$) is defined by the kinematic equation:

$$h_{,t} + uh_{,x} + vh_{,y} = w. \qquad (6)$$

The normal component of the surface traction is balanced by the capillary force:

$$\sigma_{ij}n_j n_i = 6HS, \qquad (7)$$

where H is the mean curvature of the interface and $S(=\sigma_0 d/3\rho\nu^2)$ is the surface tension number and n_i is the outward normal to the interface. The tangential-stress conditions are:

$$\sigma_{ij}n_j t_i^x = -\frac{2M}{P}\theta_{,i}t_i^x, \qquad (8)$$

$$\sigma_{ij}n_j t_i^y = -\frac{2M}{P}\theta_{,i}t_i^y, \qquad (9)$$

where, $M(=\gamma\Delta T d/2\mu k)$ is the Marangoni number and t_i^x and t_i^y are the orthonormal tangent vectors to the free surface. The energy balance on the interface gives

$$\theta_{,i}n_i + Bi\theta = 0 \qquad (10)$$

where, $Bi(=hd/k)$ is the Biot number and h is the heat-transfer coefficient at the interface.

NUMERICAL SCHEME

The governing equations (2) to (4) along with the boundary conditions are solved using finite-element method based on a projection scheme (Chorin, 1968; Ramaswamy, 1990). Starting with an initial free-surface profile, the first step is to compute an intermediate velocity field by omitting the pressure term from the momentum equations. Since the pressure term is omitted, the intermediate velocity field need not satisfy the incompressibility constraint.

Next, the pressure is calculated from the intermediate velocity field by projecting it on a divergence free space. Using the intermediate velocity field and pressure, we calculate the final velocity field by employing a velocity correction procedure. Then the temperature field is calculated in similar fashion. The next step is to locate the free-surface by solving the kinematic equation. Using the new free-surface height, grid-point velocities are computed and the procedure is repeated.

RESULTS AND DISCUSSIONS

We integrate Eqs.(2) to (4) by posing an initial-value problem. A simple-harmonic disturbance of the form

$$h(x, y, 0) = 1 + 0.1 \cos(k_x x) + 0.1 \cos(k_y y) \qquad (11)$$

is imposed on the free surface at $t=0$, and its evolution is studied in time. Here, k_x and k_y are respectively the streamwise and the spanwise wavenumber of the disturbance such that $k=\sqrt{k_x{}^2 + k_y{}^2}$, and $k_x = k \cos\theta$ and $k_y = k \sin\theta$. The perturbation wavenumber (k) is selected from the long-wave asymptotic (Joo et al., 1992). The integration is performed on one spatial period ($2\pi/k_x, 2\pi/k_y$). The results are presented in terms of free surface shape $h(x,y,t)$ at various time levels and the norms N_x and N_y, which measure respectively the streamwise and spanwise components of the total wave energy. Integration is terminated when the local film thickness becomes less than 1% of the initial mean thickness, at which moment rupture is assumed. Beyond this point intermolecular forces become significant and our governing system will be insufficient for the accurate description of the ensuing physics. When the film does not rupture, we continue the integration until a saturated state is reached by monitoring the Fourier modes of the surface wave.

In Fig. 2., the evolution of a horizontal layer is shown when $G=1$, $S=100$, $Bi=1$, $M=35.1$, $P=7.02$, $k_x=0.05$ and $k_y=0.05$. In this figure, results from both full-scale computation and the spectral computation of long-wave evolution equation are shown. In this case, the free surface is perturbed with a symmetric disturbance ($k_x=k_y$). This causes the trough to lie in the center of the domain surrounded by the crests at the four corners. Since the center of the trough is closer to the bottom plate, it becomes hotter than other locations on the free surface. As a result, the thermocapillary convection sets in and displaces the fluid from the hotter trough to the colder crests. The trough is drawn downward while the crests are pushed upwards. This is shown in Fig. 2(a)&(b) where at $t=500$, all the crests have grown approximately 140% of the initial mean thickness while the the trough has become thinner by almost 30%. As the crest is getting hotter and hotter, the thermocapillarity is enhanced and the downward growing trough manifest itself as a finger. The same phenomena is also predicted by the long-wave evolution equation.

As the trough thins further, it feels the bottom. The plate begins to offer resistance due to the viscous effects and the trough become flat. However, the edges have sharp corner and are subjected to a high capillary pressure. The result is the fluid trapped at the center of the annulus is pushed upward to conserve the mass. This sequence of events is evident from Fig. 2(c)&(d). Beyond $t=1000$, the inertial effects become dominant and the evolution equation ceases to follow the dynamics (Fig. 2(e)&(f)). However, with direct numerical simulation, we observe that the downward growing fingers continue to evolve and finally, at $t=1242$, touch the plate forming a concave dome shaped

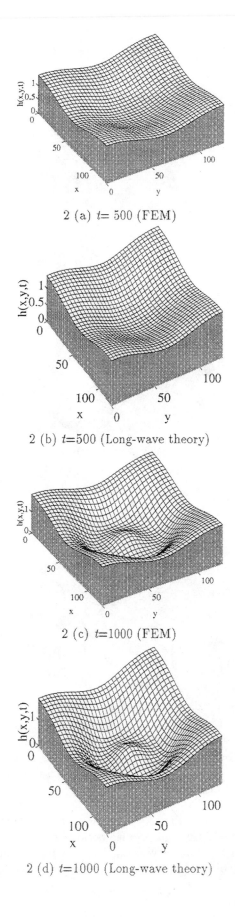

2 (a) $t=500$ (FEM)

2 (b) $t=500$ (Long-wave theory)

2 (c) $t=1000$ (FEM)

2 (d) $t=1000$ (Long-wave theory)

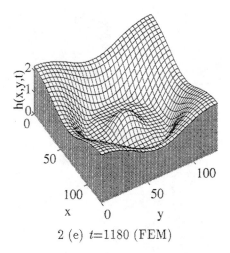

2 (e) $t=1180$ (FEM)

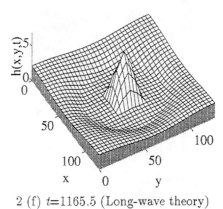

2 (f) $t=1165.5$ (Long-wave theory)

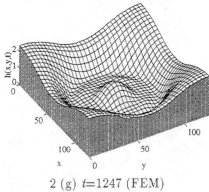

2 (g) $t=1247$ (FEM)

Figure2: $G=1$, $S=100$, $Bi=1$, $M=35$, $P=7$, $k_x=0.05$, $k_y=0.05$, and $\beta=0$. The free-surface shapes from both full-scale computation and the spectral computation of long-wave evolution equations are shown at various time levels indicated. At $t=1242$, the long-wave theory is no longer valid and only result from the full-scale computation is shown.

rivulet as shown in Fig. 2(g). In this particular problem, an axisymmetric rivulet has formed because $k_x=k_y$.

When the film is vertical, both thermocapillary and surface-wave instabilities coexist. Consequently, the flow

may saturate or rupture depending on the dominant mode. In Fig. 3 the evolution of a vertical layer is illustrated when $G=1$, $S=100$, $Bi=1$, $M=35$ and $P=7$. In each figure, the free-surface shapes predicted by both finite-element method and the spectral computation of long-wave evolution equation are shown. In this case also the imposed disturbance is symmetric with $k_x=k_y=0.5$. Initially as the liquid drains, the surface-wave instability dominates (Fig. 3(a)&(b)). As time progresses, the thinning of the liquid layer persists and the thermocapillarity begins to dictate the growth of the layer. The transverse wave is affected by the three-dimensional instability.

In the absence of mean flow in the spanwise direction, the liquid is displaced laterally (Fig. 3(c)&(d)) by thermocapillary instability. This process is similar to the evolution of a heated thin film on a horizontal substrate (Krishnamoorthy et al., 1995). The fingers grow and form a longitudinal rivulet along the centerline of the stream. Beyond $t=950$, all the superharmonics are excited and the long-wave theory fails to follow the dynamics (Fig. 3(e)&(f)). However, with full-scale computation, we can integrate the governing equations all the way to rupture. The final state, $t=1027$, is shown in Fig. 3(g). This simulation confirms Joo et al. (1996) observation that a longitudinal rivulet aligned with the mean flow can form only when both the thermocapillary and surface-wave instabilities are properly balanced and neither of these two instabilities alone has the tendency to develop such pattern. This also explains a mechanism for rivulet formation based on stability analysis. The energy norm of the free-surface evolution is shown in Fig. 4. FEM and long-wave solutions agree very well up to $t=800$, after which the long-wave theory fails to follow the dynamics of the flow.

CONCLUDING REMARKS

In this study, rivulet formation in a thin heated layer under the combined thermocapillary and surface-wave instabilities is studied by integrating the complete system of governing equations using finite-element method. An Arbitrary Lagrangian Eulerian frame of reference is used to facilitated free-surface calculation. It is shown that rivulets form *via* a fingering mechanism as predicted by the long-wave theory. The growth of the fingers is isotropic when the film is horizontal and the imposed disturbance is symmetric. When we tilt the plate, surface-wave instability sets in and a longitudinal rivulets can form only if both thermocapillary and surface-wave instabilities are properly balanced.

ACKNOWLEDGMENT

The authors acknowledge the support for this work provided by the National Science Foundation, under GRANT

No: CTS-9408409. All computations were performed using Cray-YMP computer at North Carolina Supercomputing Center and NASA Lewis Research Center, Cleveland, Ohio.

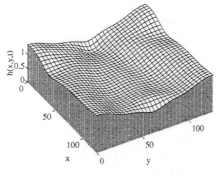

3 (a) t=300 (FEM)

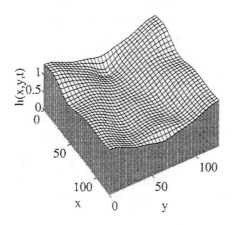

3 (b) t=300 (Long-wave theory)

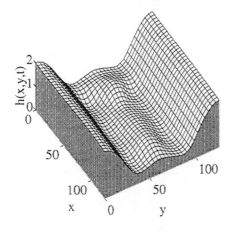

3 (c) t=900 (FEM)

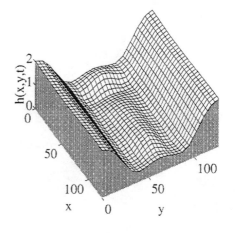

3 (d) t=900 (Long-wave theory)

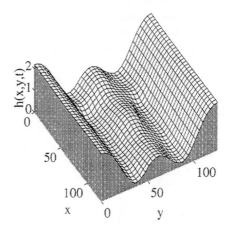

3 (e) t=975 (FEM)

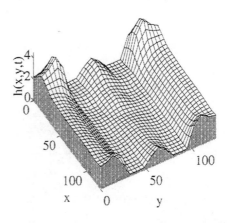

3 (f) t=975 (Long-wave theory)

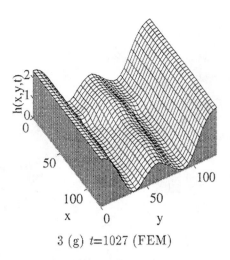

3 (g) $t=1027$ (FEM)

Figure3: $G=1$, $S=100$, $Bi=1$, $M=35$, $P=7$, $k_x=0.05$, $k_y=0.05$, and $\beta=90$. The free-surface shapes from both full-scale computation and the spectral computation of long-wave evolution equations are shown at various time levels indicated. At $t=1027$, the long-wave theory is no longer valid and only result from the full-scale computation is shown.

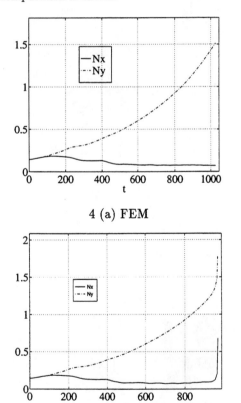

4 (a) FEM

4 (b) Long-wave theory

Figure4: $G=1$, $S=100$, $Bi=1$, $M=35$, $P=7$, $k_x=0.05$, $k_y=0.05$ and $\beta=90°$. The energy norms in the streamwise direction N_x and in the spanwise direction, N_y are compared.

REFERENCES

Benney, D. J., 1966, "Long Waves on Liquid Films", *Journal of Mathematics and Physics*, Vol. 45, pp. 150-155.

Burelbach, J. P., Bankoff, S. G., and Davis, S. H., 1988, "Nonlinear Stability of Evaporating/Condensing Liquid Films", *Journal of Fluid Mechanics*, Vol. 195, pp. 463-494.

Chorin, A. J., 1968, "Numerical Simulation of Navier-Stokes Equations", *Mathematics of Computation*, Vol. 22, pp. 745-762.

Goussis, D. A., and Kelly, R. E., 1991, "Surface Waves and Thermocapillary Instabilities in a Liquid Film Flow", *Journal of Fluid Mechanics*, Vol. 223, pp. 25-45.

Joo, S. W., and Davis, S. H., 1992, "Instabilities of Three-Dimensional Viscous Falling Films", *Journal of Fluid Mechanics*, Vol. 242, pp. 529-547.

Joo, S. W., Davis, S. H., and Bankoff, S. G., 1996, "A Mechanism for Rivulet Formation in Heated Falling Films", *Pending Publication*.

Krishnamoorthy, S., Ramaswamy, B., and Joo, S. W., 1995, "Spontaneous Rupture of Thin Liquid Films Due to Thermocapillarity: A Full-Scale Direct Numerical Simulation", *Physics of Fluids*, Vol. 7, pp. 2221-2223.

Ramaswamy, B., 1990, "Numerical Simulation of Unsteady Viscous Free Surface Flow", *Journal of Computational Physics*, Vol. 90, pp. 396-430.

Scriven, L. E., and Sterling, C. V., 1964, "On Cellular Convection Driven Surface Tension Gradients: Effects of Mean Surface Tension and Surface Viscosity", *Journal of Fluid Mechanics*, Vol. 19, pp. 321-340.

Yih, C. S., 1955, "Stability of Laminar Parallel Flow with a Free Surface", *Proceeding of 2nd US National in Applied Mechanics*, ASME, pp. 623.

FED-Vol. 238, 1996 Fluids Engineering Division Conference
Volume 3
ASME 1996

Free surface flow computation using a fully consistent method

Pompiliu Donescu, Lawrence N. Virgin
Duke University, Department of Mechanical Engineering,
Durham, North Carolina 27708, U.S.A.

ABSTRACT

Free surface flows described by nonlinear equations due to nonlinear boundary conditions written for unknown boundary position are solved using a new implicit, fully consistent method. The proposed algorithm is tested for a couple of hydrodynamic free surface problems studying both the evolution of an initial disturbance and the creation of waves by wave makers and proves to be accurate, computationally efficient and extendible towards the study of floating vessels behavior in waves.

1 Introduction

Free surface phenomena are inherently nonlinear because of the dynamic boundary condition on the free surface and also because of the imposition of the boundary conditions on a boundary whose position is unknown and has to be computed from the kinematic boundary conditions.

Free surface phenomena and large oscillations of structures in fluids have been historically analyzed from two perspectives: (a) assuming small free surface motion with linearized boundary conditions (large structure motions have been studied by Lin & Yue, 1990), or (b) studying large nonlinear waves using explicit integration of the equations of motion starting with the pioneering work of Longuet-Higgins and Cokelet (1976) in a Lagrangian description. Following this work, Sen (1992) developed a method for studying two dimensional fluid structure interaction using an Eulerian-Lagrangian approach in which

no overturning is allowed. The explicit integration typically requires small time steps and cases of growing (sawtooth) instabilities have been reported despite the use of smoothing procedures.

Implicit or semi-implicit procedures have also been developed such as segregated approaches used in FIDAP and by Haack et al. (1993) in which iterations between the computation of the free surface position and the solution of the *linear* boundary element equations for potentials and fluxes are used at each time step until convergence is obtained, or by using weighted residuals for the nonlinear boundary conditions on the free surface (Abe & Kamio, 1993). A different approach adopted by Medina et al. (1991) consists in explicitly considering that the boundary element equations depend on the free surface position and linearizing the integral equations and boundary conditions with respect to the potentials, fluxes and free surface position defined by displacements on preferred directions of motion.

In contrast to previous research, this paper presents a fully consistent formulation based on the use of an implicit scheme (the generalized trapezoidal rule) in which, by applying the boundary element method, both the domain equations and the boundary conditions become *nonlinear* algebraic equations for the free surface position. For these equations the exact Jacobians with respect to potentials, fluxes and position of the free surface are obtained by assembling the elemental contributions, thus allowing the code to be valid in two or three dimensions and to employ different type of elements and boundary conditions.

2 Mathematical formulation of the problem

Based on the assumptions that the fluid is incompressible and inviscid and the motion is irrotational, there exists a velocity potential Φ such that:

$$\nabla^2\Phi = 0 \qquad (1)$$

in the time-dependent fluid volume Ω.

Laplace's equation translated into a boundary integral equation:

$$c\,\Phi = \int_{S_w(t)+S_f(t)} \left(G\frac{\partial\Phi}{\partial n} - \Phi\frac{\partial G}{\partial n} \right) dS \qquad (2)$$

where G is the Green's function and n the unit outer normal is completed by boundary conditions:

- on the fluid-structure interface $S(t)$:

$$\frac{\partial\Phi}{\partial n} = v_n \qquad (3)$$

where v_n is the normal derivative of the structure velocity;

- on the free surface $S_f(t)$:

$$\frac{D\Phi}{Dt} + \frac{p}{\rho} - \frac{1}{2}\|\mathbf{u}\|^2 + gz_1 = 0 \qquad (4)$$

where ρ is the fluid density, $\mathbf{u}$ the fluid velocity and p is the pressure on the free surface, usually taken equal to 0. The motion of the free surface is described by following the fluid particles using:

$$\frac{dx_{1i}}{dt} = u_i = \frac{\partial\Phi}{\partial x_{1i}} \qquad (5)$$

- on the intersection of the free surface with rigid boundaries and at infinity. On the rigid boundaries with a known motion (e.g. a wall or a wave maker) the nodes' position is given parametrically by:

$$\mathbf{x} = \mathbf{f}(\xi, t) \qquad (6)$$
$$\frac{d\xi}{dt} = \mathbf{u}_\xi \qquad (7)$$

where $\mathbf{u}_\xi = \mathbf{g}(\xi, \mathbf{u}, t)$ is the velocity in the direction of the parameter ξ.

3 Numerical solution of the nonlinear free surface problem

3.1 Semi-discrete equations of motion

By spatially discretizing the boundary integral equation (2) and the boundary conditions (3-5) using boundary elements, the semi-discrete equations of motion are obtained as a combination of time dependent algebraic equations and ordinary differential equations:

$$[\mathbf{H}][\mathbf{\Phi}^*] + [\mathbf{G}][\mathbf{q}^*] = [\mathbf{0}]$$
$$\frac{D\Phi_f^*}{Dt} = -gz_f^* + \frac{1}{2}\|\mathbf{u}^*\|^2 \qquad (8)$$
$$\frac{D\mathbf{x}_f}{Dt} = \mathbf{u} = D_x\Phi_f$$
$$\frac{d\xi}{dt} = \mathbf{u}_\xi$$

where $\mathbf{x}_f = (x_f, y_f, z_f)$ and

$$[\mathbf{H}] = \begin{bmatrix} \mathbf{H}_{ff} & \mathbf{H}_{fw} \\ \mathbf{H}_{wf} & \mathbf{H}_{ww} \end{bmatrix}, \quad [\mathbf{G}] = \begin{bmatrix} \mathbf{G}_{ff} & \mathbf{G}_{fw} \\ \mathbf{G}_{wf} & \mathbf{G}_{ww} \end{bmatrix}$$
$$[\mathbf{\Phi}^*] = \begin{bmatrix} \mathbf{\Phi}_f^* \\ \mathbf{\Phi}_w^* \end{bmatrix}, \quad [\mathbf{q}^*] = \begin{bmatrix} \mathbf{q}_f^* \\ \mathbf{q}_w^* \end{bmatrix}$$

In the above equations the * superscript is used for values at the collocation points and if * is missing the quantities are evaluated at the nodes (nodes and collocation points may not be the same). Also the subscript f shows that the variables are on the free surface whereas w refers to the rest of the boundary (walls/wave makers). These equations are completed with: known boundary conditions (i.e. fluxes on the walls and/or wave makers and radiation boundary conditions for infinite domains) and relations used to compute the nodal and collocation points velocity.

3.2 Discretized equations of motion

Using the generalized trapezoidal rule a nonlinear system of $N_{cp} + N_{cp,f} + dN_{n,f} + (d-1)N_{n,w}$ equations is obtained at the new time t_{n+1} for the unknown degrees of freedom:

- $N_{cp} + N_{cp,f}$ potentials $\mathbf{\Phi}^{(n+1)}$ or fluxes $\mathbf{q}^{(n+1)}$ at the collocation points (both at the collocation points on the free surface and only one at the rest of the collocation points);

- $dN_{n,f}$ unknown nodal coordinates $\mathbf{x}_f^{(n+1)}$ on the free surface (and not on rigid bodies); $d = 2,3$ is the number of spatial dimensions;

- $(d-1)N_{n,w}$ unknown nodal parametric coordinates $\xi^{(n+1)}$ for the moving nodes on the rigid bodies.

For simplicity, the superscript * on the potentials and fluxes is no longer used.

This system of equations is then solved using a Newton-Raphson method with line search whose successive iterations at time t_{n+1} (denoted by (m)) involve computing the direction $(\delta\Phi, \delta q, \delta\mathbf{x}_f, \delta\xi)^{(m)}$ from the affine (linearized) model:

$$
\begin{bmatrix}
\mathbf{H}_{fw}^{(m)} & \mathbf{G}_{ff}^{(m)} & \mathbf{H}_{ff}^{(m)} & \mathcal{H}_{fx\xi}^{(m)} + \mathcal{G}_{fx\xi}^{(m)} \\
\mathbf{H}_{ww}^{(m)} & \mathbf{G}_{wf}^{(m)} & \mathbf{H}_{wf}^{(m)} & \mathcal{H}_{wx\xi}^{(m)} + \mathcal{G}_{wx\xi}^{(m)} \\
\mathbf{0} & \mathcal{Q}^{(m)} & \mathcal{D}^{(m)} - \mathbf{I} & \mathcal{D}_{x\xi}^{(m)} \\
\mathbf{0} & \mathcal{F}_{x\xi}^{(m)} & \mathcal{E}_{x\xi}^{(m)} & \mathcal{A}_{x\xi}^{(m)} - \mathbf{I}
\end{bmatrix}
\begin{bmatrix}
\delta\Phi_w^{(m)} \\
\delta\mathbf{q}_f^{(m)} \\
\delta\Phi_f^{(m)} \\
\delta(\mathbf{d}_f, \xi)^{(m)}
\end{bmatrix}
=
\begin{bmatrix}
-\mathbf{H}_{ff}^{(m)}\Phi^{(m)} - \mathbf{H}_{fw}^{(m)}\Phi_w^{(m)} - \mathbf{G}_{ff}^{(m)}\mathbf{q}_f^{(m)} - \mathbf{G}_{fw}^{(m)}\mathbf{q}_w^{(m)} \\
-\mathbf{H}_{wf}^{(m)}\Phi_f^{(m)} - \mathbf{H}_{ww}^{(m)}\Phi_w^{(m)} - \mathbf{G}_{wf}^{(m)}\mathbf{q}_f^{(m)} - \mathbf{G}_{ww}^{(m)}\mathbf{q}_w^{(m)} \\
-\mathbf{C}_f^{(n)} - \mathbf{C}_f^{(n+1)} \\
-\mathbf{C}_{x\xi}^{(n)} - \mathbf{C}_{x\xi}^{(n+1)}
\end{bmatrix}
\tag{9}
$$

In this equation it is taken into account that the boundary element matrices $\mathbf{H}_{ff}, \mathbf{H}_{fw}, \mathbf{H}_{wf}, \mathbf{G}_{ff}, \mathbf{G}_{fw}, \mathbf{G}_{wf}$ depend also on the position of the free surface.

The boundary element equations at the new time t_{n+1} are *linear* with respect to potentials and fluxes but *nonlinear* with respect to the position of the free surface and can be written as:

$$
\mathbf{B}(\mathbf{x}_f^{(n+1)}, \xi^{(n+1)}, \Phi^{(n+1)}, \mathbf{q}^{(n+1)}) \equiv
$$
$$
[\mathbf{H}^{(n+1)}][\Phi^{(n+1)}] + [\mathbf{G}^{(n+1)}][\mathbf{q}^{(n+1)}] = 0 \tag{10}
$$

where the matrices $[\mathbf{H}^{(n+1)}]$ and $[\mathbf{G}^{(n+1)}]$ are obtained by assembling the elemental contributions from eq. (2).

The Jacobian with respect to the free surface position is determined from:

$$
\begin{cases}
\dfrac{\partial H_{ij}^{(n+1)}}{\partial x_{f,kl}^{(n+1)}} = \underset{(e)}{\mathcal{A}} \dfrac{\partial H_{ij}^{(e)(n+1)}}{\partial x_{f,kl}^{(n+1)}} \\[12pt]
\dfrac{\partial H_{ij}^{(n+1)}}{\partial \xi_j^{(n+1)}} = \underset{(e)}{\mathcal{A}} \dfrac{\partial H_{ij}^{(e)(n+1)}}{\partial x_{w,kl}^{(n+1)}} \dfrac{\partial x_{w,kl}^{(n+1)}}{\partial \xi_j^{(n+1)}}
\end{cases}
\tag{11}
$$

and similarly for $\mathbf{G}$.

The discretization of the dynamic boundary condition at each collocation point i on the free surface leads to:

$$
\mathcal{D}_i(\mathbf{x}^{*\,(n+1)}, \Phi^{(n+1)}, q^{(n+1)}) \equiv
$$
$$
(1-\alpha)\,\Delta t \left[-gz_i^{*\,(n)} + \tfrac{1}{2}\left\| \mathbf{u}_i^{*\,(n)} \right\|^2 \right] +
$$
$$
+\alpha\,\Delta t \left[-gz_i^{*\,(n+1)} + \tfrac{1}{2}\left\| \mathbf{u}_i^{*\,(n+1)} \right\|^2 \right] -
$$
$$
-\left(\Phi_i^{(n+1)} - \Phi_i^{(n)} \right) = 0 \tag{12}
$$

where α is the implicitness parameter and Δt is the time step.

The dynamic boundary condition is differentiated with respect to the degrees of freedom resulting in:

$$
\begin{cases}
\dfrac{\partial \mathcal{D}_i}{\partial \Phi_j^{(n+1)}} = \alpha\,\Delta t\, u_{ik}^{*\,(n+1)} \dfrac{\partial u_{ik}^{*\,(n+1)}}{\partial \Phi_j^{(n+1)}} - \delta_{ij} \\[12pt]
\dfrac{\partial \mathcal{D}_i}{\partial q_j^{(n+1)}} = \alpha\,\Delta t\, u_{ik}^{*\,(n+1)} \dfrac{\partial u_{ik}^{*\,(n+1)}}{\partial q_j^{(n+1)}} \\[12pt]
\dfrac{\partial \mathcal{D}_i}{\partial x_{jl}^{(n+1)}} = \alpha\,\Delta t \left(-g\dfrac{\partial z_i^{*\,(n+1)}}{\partial x_{jl}^{(n+1)}} + \dfrac{\partial u_{ik}^{*\,(n+1)}}{\partial x_{jl}^{(n+1)}} \right)
\end{cases}
\tag{13}
$$

(in the above formulae there is no sum over index i).

On the free surface the nodes' motion is described by:

$$
\mathcal{K}_{ik}(\Phi^{(n+1)}, q^{(n+1)}, \mathbf{x}^{(n+1)}) \equiv
$$
$$
(1-\alpha)\,\Delta t\, u_{ik}^{(n)} + \alpha\,\Delta t\, u_{ik}^{(n+1)} - \left(x_{ik}^{(n+1)} - x_{ik}^{(n)} \right) = 0 \tag{14}
$$

where i represents the node number and k is the coordinate number ($k = \overline{1,d}$, d being the number of spatial dimensions).

In this case the Jacobian with respect to the degrees of freedom is:

$$
\begin{cases}
\dfrac{\partial \mathcal{K}_{ik}}{\partial \Phi_j^{(n+1)}} = \alpha\,\Delta t\, \dfrac{\partial u_{ik}^{(n+1)}}{\partial \Phi_j^{(n+1)}} \\[12pt]
\dfrac{\partial \mathcal{K}_{ik}}{\partial q_j^{(n+1)}} = \alpha\,\Delta t\, \dfrac{\partial u_{ik}^{(n+1)}}{\partial q_j^{(n+1)}} \\[12pt]
\dfrac{\partial \mathcal{K}_{ik}}{\partial x_{jl}^{(n+1)}} = \alpha\,\Delta t\, \dfrac{\partial u_{ik}^{(n+1)}}{\partial x_{jl}^{(n+1)}} - \delta_{ij}\delta_{kl}
\end{cases}
\tag{15}
$$

On a rigid wall or wave maker the discretized form of the equations of motion for node i, parametric coordinate k ($k = \overline{1, d-1}$) is:

$$
\mathcal{W}_{ik}(\Phi^{(n+1)}, \xi^{(n+1)}) \equiv
$$
$$
(1-\alpha)\,\Delta t\, g_k(\xi_i^{(n)}, \mathbf{u}_i^{(n)}, t_n) +
$$
$$
+\alpha\,\Delta t\, g_k(\xi_i^{(n+1)}, \mathbf{u}_i^{(n+1)}, t_{n+1}) - \left(\xi_{ik}^{(n+1)} - \xi_{ik}^{(n)} \right) = 0 \tag{16}
$$

The equations of motion (16) depend only on the potentials and parametric coordinates thus their Jacobian is:

$$
\begin{cases}
\dfrac{\partial \mathcal{W}_{ik}}{\partial \Phi_j^{(n+1)}} = \alpha\Delta t\, \dfrac{\partial g_k}{\partial u_{im}^{(n+1)}} \dfrac{\partial u_{im}^{(n+1)}}{\partial \Phi_j^{(n+1)}} \\[12pt]
\dfrac{\partial \mathcal{W}_{ik}}{\partial \xi_{jl}^{(n+1)}} = \alpha\Delta t \left(\dfrac{\partial g_k}{\partial \xi_{jl}^{(n+1)}} + \dfrac{\partial g_k}{\partial u_{im}^{(n+1)}} \dfrac{\partial u_{im}^{(n+1)}}{\partial \xi_{jl}^{(n+1)}} \right) - \delta_{ij}\delta_{kl}
\end{cases}
\tag{17}
$$

Also the non penetration boundary condition becomes the fixed flux boundary condition.

The choice of elements can determine if the velocity is continuous across the inter element boundaries or the nodal velocities may be computed by averaging the elemental velocities at the given node over all elements containing the node:

$$u_{ik} = \frac{1}{n_{e,i}} \underset{(e),i\in(e)}{\mathcal{A}} u_{ik}^{(e)} \qquad (18)$$

The elemental velocities at a node (i.e. the velocities computed from the element data) depend on the elemental potentials and fluxes and nodal coordinates:

$$u_{ik}^{(e)} = u_{ik}^{(e)}(\mathbf{\Phi}^{(e)}, \mathbf{q}^{(e)}, \mathbf{x}_n^{(e)}) \qquad (19)$$

The Jacobian of the nodal velocities with respect to the motion degrees of freedom is computed using eq. (18) by assembling elemental Jacobians:

$$\frac{\partial u_{ik}}{\partial d_j} = \frac{1}{n_{e,i}} \underset{(e),i\in(e)}{\mathcal{A}} \frac{\partial u_{ik}^{(e)}}{\partial d_j^{(e)}} \qquad (20)$$

where d_j is a degree of freedom (potential, flux, nodal coordinate, etc.) and $d_j^{(e)}$ is the corresponding degree of freedom in the element.

4 Examples

The above algorithm has been translated into a computer code and tested for several problems on an IBM Risc/6000-370 (62.5 MHz) using several meshes with continuous and discontinuous linear elements and several time steps.

The first example represents the wave generated in a tank from by the gravitational forces starting from a triangular initial position (Fig. 1). The results agree well with previously published results by Medina et al. (1991) and it has been noticed that accuracy does not degrade when larger time steps are used (Table 1, Fig. 2, 3) thus resulting in a competitive code from the point of view of both speed and accuracy.

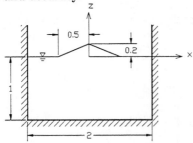

Figure 1: Triangular wave in a tank.

Time step	iter / Δt	CPU time (sec)
0.20	4.28	10.6
0.10	2.94	14.4
0.02	2.00	50.0

Table 1: Run times for the triangular wave.

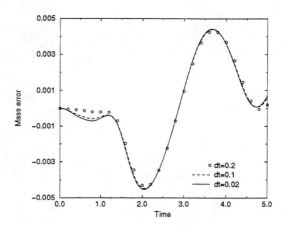

Figure 2: Time evolution of the mass error for the triangular wave.

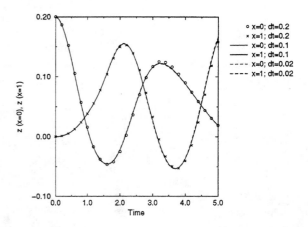

Figure 3: Time evolution of nodes in the center and on the wall.

The second example represents the generation of tsunami waves by the motion of the sea bottom. The tsunami waves (Fig. 4) showing significant nonlinear effects have been studied by initially considering the bottom fixed but a variable flux imposed on it

$$q = -\alpha_0 d_0 e^{-\alpha_0 t} \qquad (21)$$

for impulsive, transition and creeping flows ($\alpha_0 = 5.843, 1.041, 0.046$, $d_0 = 0.010, 0.005, 0.015$ respectively). The results (Fig. 5-7) agree very well with both previously reported results (Medina et al., 1991) and experiments (Hammack, 1973).

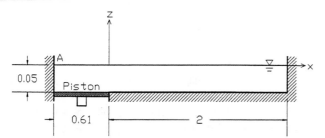

Figure 4: Tsunami generation in a tank by bottom movement.

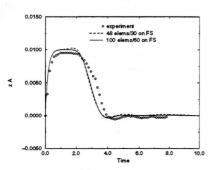

Figure 5: Motion of the surface node at the left wall (A) in impulsive flow.

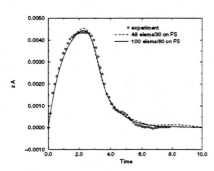

Figure 6: Motion of the surface node at the left wall (A) in transition flow.

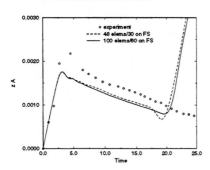

Figure 7: Motion of the surface node at the left wall (A) in creeping flow.

Better agreement (Fig. 8-10) is obtained if the piston is allowed to move following the equation described in Hammack (1973)

$$\zeta = d_0(1 - e^{-\alpha_0 t}) \qquad (22)$$

the only significant difference being in creeping flow when, due to the solid boundary on the end of the tank instead of a dissipative system as used in the experiment, reflected waves return and interact at A (Fig. 4).

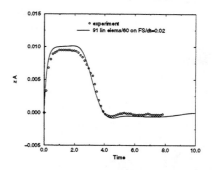

Figure 8: Motion of the surface node at the left wall (A) in impulsive flow with bottom motion.

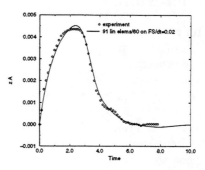

Figure 9: Motion of the surface node at the left wall (A) in transition flow with bottom motion.

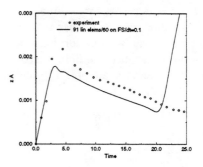

Figure 10: Motion of the surface node at the left wall (A) in creeping flow with bottom motion.

Also an example in which the surface motion could be followed up to overturning has been studied using a mesh with 141 linear elements with 120 on the free surface and a time step $\Delta t = 0.02$ (Fig. 11). At the overturning the initial discretization proved inadequate and it is necessary to rediscretize the domain or to use higher order boundary elements.

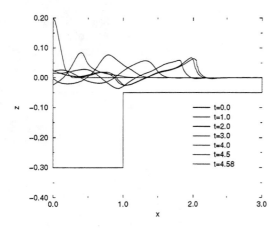

Figure 11: Motion of waves up to overturning.

5   Conclusions

A new, fully consistent (implicit) method for computing nonlinear free surface flows has been developed and tested. The procedure explicitly considers the boundary element equations and the discretized boundary conditions as nonlinear equations of the potentials, fluxes and free surface position at the new time and thus offers both accurate results and the possibility of choosing large time steps. Despite its simplicity in the solution of the nonlinear equations the algorithm is computationally efficient and can further benefit from more sophisticated numerical algorithms.

The presented procedure has its merits in the fact that is both valid in two and three dimensions and it is consistent. The algorithm is further developed by adopting a variable time step, a radiation boundary condition, by remeshing and, because the fluid degrees of freedom are on the boundaries, it is adapted for fluid-structure interaction.

References

Abe, K., and Kamio, T., 1993, "A boundary element formulation with Lagrangian particle description for two-dimensional nonlinear sloshing analysis", Proceedings, 15th International Conference on Boundary Element Methods, Worchester Polytech. Institute, Southampton, Boston, Computational Mechanics Publications, pp. 81-91.

Brebbia, C.A., 1987, "Topics in Boundary Element Research", Vol. 1-3, Springer-Verlag Berlin, Heidelberg.

FIDAP 7.0., 1993, Users Manual. Theory Manual, Fluid Dynamic International.

Haack, C., Schlegel, V., Mahrenholtz, O., 1993, "The interaction of nonlinear gravity waves with fixed and floating structures", Proceedings, 15th International Conference on Boundary Element Methods, Worchester Polytech. Institute, Southampton, Boston, Computational Mechanics Publications, pp. 249-262.

Hammack, J.L., 1973, "A note on tsunamis: their generation and propagation in an ocean of uniform depth", J. Fluid Mech., Vol. 60, pp.769-799.

Lin, W.-M., Yue, D., 1990, "Numerical Solutions for Large-Amplitude Ship Motions in the Time Domain", Eighteenth Symposium on Naval Hydrodynamics : ship motions, ship hydrodynamics, experimental techniques, free-surface aspects, wave/wake dynamics, propeller/hull/appendage interactions, viscous effects, Ann Arbor, Mich., pp. 41-66.

Longuet-Higgins, M.S., Cokelet, E.D., 1976, "The deformation of steep surface waves on water: I. A numerical method of computation", Proceedings, Royal Society of London, Series A, 350, pp. 1-26.

Medina, D.E., Liggett, J.A., Birchwood, R.A., Torrance, K.E., 1991, "A Consistent Boundary Element Method for Free Surface Hydrodynamic Calculations", Intl. J. Num. Meth. Fluids, Vol. 12, pp. 835-857.

Sen, D., 1993, "Numerical Simulation of Motion of Two-Dimensional Floating Bodies", Journal of Ship Research, Vol. 37, pp. 307-330.

FED-Vol. 238, 1996 Fluids Engineering Division Conference
Volume 3
ASME 1996

A PICARD ALGORITHM FOR THE SOLUTION OF UNSTEADY
FREE SURFACE FLOWS

Natarajan Ramanan and Michael S. Engelman
Fluid Dynamics International, Inc.
500 Davis St, Suite 600, Evanston, Illinois-60201

ABSTRACT

An algorithm to simulate unsteady, viscous free surface flows is presented in this paper. A Picard type approach wherein the flow and free surface updates are performed alternatively is utilized to iterate for a solution in every time step. The procedure is intended for large-scale two or three dimensional problems. A surface intrinsic coordinate system which facilitates representation of general free surface shapes is used. Using a Galerkin finite element method (GFEM) and the kinematic constraint as the distinguished condition, a transient algorithm for tracking free surfaces is formulated. It is shown that the effects of surface tension, surface tension gradients and imposition of contact angles can be simulated elegantly within the framework of GFEM. A novel feature of the updates is that the deformations are sought in a direction normal to the current iterate free surface shape with the result the method is ideally suited for use with an automatic mesh generator. A segregated method is utilized to solve iteratively one degree of freedom at a time for the solution of the flow variables. As a result, the memory and disk space requirements are minimal. Sample problems that deal with the wave propagation in falling films, sloshing in containers and coating flows are presented to clearly illustrate the convergence behavior and accuracy of the algorithm. The above approach has also been used with success in modeling turbulent free surface flows.

INTRODUCTION

In an earlier paper[1], we outlined a Picard approach to solution of flows that are characterized by free surfaces and internal interfaces. In this paper, we report our extension of that algorithm for unsteady flows. This algorithm has been implemented in a general purpose finite element code (FIDAP) and tested on a wide range of problems that encompass laminar and turbulent flow regimes. In this regard, we will also outline our experiences with this approach.

Traditionally, the modeling of free surface flows was pioneered by the Marker and cell[2] (MAC) and volume of fluid[3] (VOF) methods that relied on a fixed (Eulerian) mesh. The location of the free surface was inferred by the amount of fill of the cell with the fluid. Such an approach has the inherent disadvantage of approximating the location of the free surface. Besides, simulation of flows with multiple interfaces can not be modeled (to the best of our knowledge) with such an approach. However, these approaches do allow one to study problems that involve break-up and filling of arbitrary containers.

Subsequent to the VOF method, a number of approaches which are based on tracking the interface have been proposed. In the finite volume and finite difference context, a body fitted coordinate system[4] can be used to transform the physical domain to a structured domain where the equations can be integrated. In the finite element context, tracking the free surface simply implies that one has to remesh the domain as the location of the free boundary is modified after an iteration. The equations are then solved in an arbitrary Lagrangian-Eulerian[5] (ALE) where the mesh is moved with a velocity that is different from the fluid velocity. This approach has been used successfully by a number of researchers[5-7] and has become the standard approach to solution of free boundary problems. The main distinguishing factor between the various approaches is how the system of equations are solved and how the location of the free surface is predicted. If one chooses to solve the system of equations together using a coupled solution scheme, such as successive substitution or Newton based techniques, the size and the bandwidth of the matrices will be large as the problem size is increased. When the number of degrees of freedom are large (as is the case in 3-D problems), it is necessary to look for means of reducing the size of the matrix system. Solving the system of equations in an uncoupled fashion is one of the options to allow solution of such large problems on workstations. With this in mind, we have implemented this approach in the context of the segregated (uncoupled) solver in our code. To predict the location of the free surface, we seek a deformation of the free surface in a form that is surface intrinsic and does not make any assumptions about the geometry of the problem.

The convergence of the Picard solver that is presented is here is definitely slower in comparison with the coupled solvers. However, it is more robust and allows one to obtain convergence with a poor or zero initial conditions.

The paper is organized as follows. First the governing equations are presented. Then, we briefly outline the Galerkin finite element method to simulate unsteady free surface flows. Only the extensions to unsteady free surface flows are highlighted here. It should be noted that our approach does not require the use of higher order basis functions and can work well with linear elements. The effects of capillary forces and also the influence of variable surface tension are all modeled in this framework. We conclude the paper with some examples that were modeled to illustrate the convergence of the solver.

GOVERNING EQUATIONS

We will restrict our attention to incompressible flow of a Newtonian fluid. The Navier-Stokes equations under such assumptions are :

$$u_{i,i} = 0 \qquad (1)$$

$$\rho(u_{,t} + u_j u_{i,j}) = T_{ij,j} + f_i \qquad (2)$$

In these equations u is the velocity, T the total stress, t the time and f the body force. The fluid density is represented by ρ. The total stress tensor T comprises of the pressure, p and the deviatoric stress τ

$$T_{ij} = -p\delta_{ij} + \tau_{ij} \qquad (3)$$

A constitutive equation is necessary to define the relationship between stress and strain. This can be written for a Newtonian fluid as

$$\tau_{ij} = \frac{\mu}{2}(u_{i,j} + u_{j,i}) \qquad (4)$$

If turbulence is modeled, we also include a two-equation k-ε model.

The governing equations (1,2) are subject to Dirichlet conditions on velocity and stress. In addition, the following conditions must be satisfied on the fluid-vapor interface.

$$S_{,t} + u_i S_{,i} = 0 \qquad (5)$$

$$n_i T_{ij} t_j = t_i \sigma_{,i} \qquad (6)$$

$$n_i T_{ij} n_j = -p_0 + \sigma H \qquad (7)$$

where n is the outward pointing normal and t is a tangential direction on the free surface. The free surface is represented by the equation S(x,y,z,t)=0. In the above equations, the ambient pressure is p_0, σ is the surface tension and H the total curvature of the fluid-vapor interface. The above equation can be generalized also for cases where interfaces between immisicble fluids are modeled.

NUMERICAL METHOD

The numerical solution of unsteady free surface flows involves three main steps. In the context of the Picard approach, the fluid flow and free surface prediction are performed alternately. To that end, we will first describe the flow solution procedure.

Flow Solution

Using Galerkin finite element method and the Green-Gauss theorem, the weak form of continuity, momentum, kinetic energy and dissipation transport equations can be written. Since the shape of the free surface is unknown and must be solved for as part of the solution, we proceed with the solution in an iterative fashion. We assume an initial shape of the free surface and solve for the flow-field. The free surface is then updated by satisfaction of kinematic constraint (equation 9). We iterate on this strategy until the free surface and flow field do not change according to our convergence criterion. For the solution of the flow field, we used the segregated algorithm of Haroutunian et al.[8]. To solve this coupled set of transport equations, the segregated algorithm sets up a linear algebraic equation for each degree of freedom. A Poisson type matrix equation is derived for pressure at the discrete level by making use of the momentum equations and the continuity equation. For time integration of the equations, we have implemented a backward Euler and a second order accurate trapezoidal scheme[9].

The equations that govern the flow are based on an ALE approach. This step is described next.

The ALE approach

In the ALE approach, the governing equations are solved in an arbitrary frame of reference where the mesh velocity and the fluid velocity are different. The mesh velocity is typically inferred from the remeshing based on the free surface deformation. The consequence of this framework is that the Eulerian time derivative has to be replaced by

$$\frac{\partial z}{\partial t} = \frac{\delta z}{\delta t} - \mathbf{u}_m \cdot \nabla z \qquad (8)$$

where $\partial/\partial t$ is the Eulerian time derivative, $\delta/\delta t$ is the time derivative in the computational region, $\mathbf{u}_m$ is the mesh velocity and z is the variable whose derivative is desired (u,v,T etc.). In the following section, we will briefly describe the procedure to update the free surface motion.

Free Surface Update

The kinematic constraint (equation 5) is used to update the free surface. In this procedure, the normal and tangential stress balance conditions (6-7) are satisfied during the flow solution. These stress balance conditions enter the momentum equations through the boundary terms of the weak form of momentum equations.

To perform the update, we need to find the new location of the free surface where the kinematic constraint is satisfied in a weighted residual sense. In a weighted sense, the kinematic constraint is then

$$\int_{\Gamma_f} \theta_k (S_{,t} + u_i S_{,i}) \, ds = 0 \qquad (9)$$

where θ is the weight function for free surface deformation. For additional details about the free surface update procedure and remeshing techniques, the reader is referred to Ramanan and Engelman[1].

RESULTS

To illustrate the performance of the Picard approach, three problems with different physics are presented below. First, we consider the propagation of a solitary wave in a container. Next, we simulate at the behavior of the free surface in a falling film around an annular cylinder. Lastly, we will show an example of a curtain coating problem that is solved to a steady solution through time integration.

1. Solitary wave propagation

In this example, we study a classical wave propagation problem that was proposed by Laitone[10]. Here, a solitary wave that is created in a water tank is observed in time. The tank is 10 meters deep and 160 meters wide. The amplitude of the wave created is 2 meters. The initial shape of the wave and the velocity profile are assumed to be the same as Ramaswamy and Kawahara[5]. A uniform mesh of 161x11 nodes was used and fixed time steps of 0.02 seconds was used for the time integration. Figures 1 through 3 show the velocity vectors and contours of velocity components in the tank. The side and bottom walls of the tank are assumed to be boundaries where the fluid can freely slip. According to Laitone[10], the crest of the wave is supposed to reach the right wall at time 7.7 seconds and the run-up should be around 4.2 meters. Our simulations indicate (as seen on figure 5) the run-up to be around 4.35 meters at a time of 7.7 seconds.

Figure 1. Initial velocity distribution (t=0)

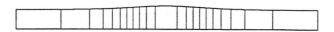

Figure 2. Contours of x component of velocity (t=0)

Figure 3. Contours of y component of velocity (t=0)

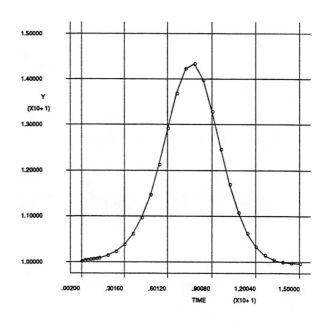

Figure 4. Time history of the water level on the right wall

429

Figure 5. velocity vector plot (t=7.7)

Figure 5 shows the velocity vectors as the wave hits the right wall. At this point, the x component contours (figure 6) show some oscillations. This is mostly due to the coarse mesh that was used in this simulation. The pressure distribution as seen in figure 8 is essentially hydrostatic. After about 15 units, the wave arrives back at the original location, but is now moving to the left (figure 8). This type of a simulation shows that we can use this approach to solution of laminar and turbulent flows in water tanks and open channels. Turbulent open water simulations of such nature are reported in a related paper[11] in this conference.

Figure 6. Contours of x component of velocity (t=7.7)

Figure 7. Pressure distribution (t=7.7)

Figure 8. Velocity vector plot (t=15)

2. Falling films

In this example, we show the application of the Picard solver to a problem that is governed by viscous, gravity and capillary forces. It has been observed that falling films around annular containers can

assume rather non-trivial shapes under certain circumstances. As an example, we model a scenario that was proposed by Bullister et al.[7] Here a flat film of uniform thickness (=h) that is falling under the action of gravity is perturbed with a sinusoidal wave with an amplitude of 0.46 times the thickness of the film. The Reynolds number for the flow is 9.1 and the Weber number ($=\gamma / (\rho h U^2)$) is 16.8. The characteristic velocity, U ($U = \rho g h^2 / 2\mu$) is based on the balance between gravitational and viscous forces. The wave number ($=2\pi h / \lambda$) of the disturbance is 0.07. λ is the wavelength of the disturbance. Under these circumstances, periodic ripples are observed which move at a constant velocity. We simulate this case with periodic boundary conditions at the top and bottom boundaries. Fixed time steps of 0.05 are used with backward Euler time integration. The initial conditions for velocity are those that are appropriate for a full developed film flow. After 101 time steps, we observe ripples that are very similar to those reported by Bullister et al.

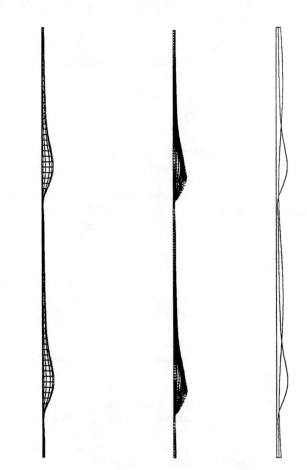

(a)   (b)   (c)

Figure 7. Mesh plot (a), velocity vectors (b) after 101 time steps. Initial and final free surface shapes (c)

3. Curtain coating

In this example, we illustrate the use of the transient approach to obtain a steady solution of a curtain coating process. Here, fluid is issued through a slot of width L, and falls along an incline and then forms a curtain (under the action of gravity) and impinges on a substrate that is moving to the right at a constant velocity, U. Two free surfaces are formed as a consequence. One on the left that forms a dynamic contact line on the substrate, the location of which is also to be determined from the simulation. The free surface on the right forms the top surface of the coated fluid that is carried with the substrate. The curtain falls through a distance of 10L. Using the slot width as the characteristic length and the substrate velocity as the characteristic velocity, three non-dimensional numbers can be formed for this problem. The Reynolds number, Re, capillary number, Ca and the bond number (Bo=$\rho g L^2 / \gamma$). We assume a unit inflow through the slot. For this simulation, we set Re=2.5, Ca=5.0 and Bo=5.0.

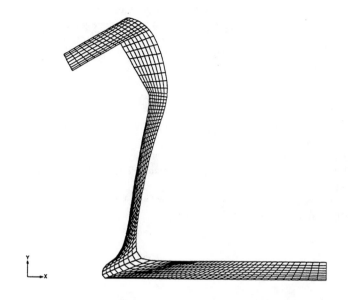

Figure 9. Mesh used for curtain coating

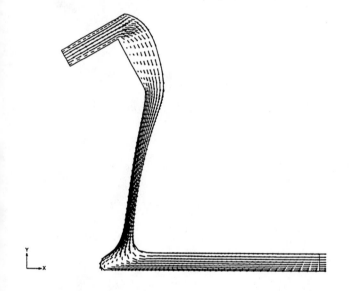

Figure 8. Velocity vectors for curtain coating

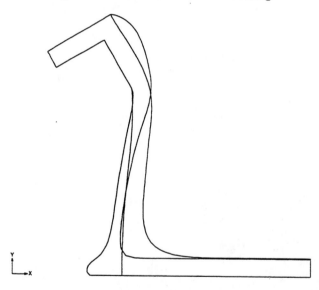

Figure 10: Initial and final positions of the free surfaces

CONCLUSIONS

In this paper, we have presented our algorithm for simulating unsteady free surface flows using Galerkin finite element method. Unlike the VOF type methods, our approach tracks the free surface and is likely to be more useful for making quantitative comparisons for flows that are strongly influenced by the free surface position. The equations have been derived including the capillary effects with the result that they are also applicable when simulating problems that involve surface tension gradients due to the presence of surfactants. The method is extremely efficient since it uses a segregated approach to solving each degree of freedom in an iterative manner. The algorithm is surface intrinsic and is applicable for both 2-D and 3-D configurations.

REFERENCES

1. N. Ramanan and M.S. Engelman, Int. J. Num. Meth. Fluids, Vol. 22, 103-120, 1996.

2. B.D. Nichols and C.W. Hirt, J. Comput. Phys., Vol. 9, 434, 1971.

3. C.W. Hirt and B.D. Nichols, J. Comput. Phys., Vol. 39, 201-225, !981.

4. J. Crank, "Free and moving boundary problems", Oxford Science Publications, Oxford, England, 1988.

5. B. Ramaswamy and M. Kawahara, Int. J. Num. Meth. Fluids, Vol. 7, 1053-1075, 1987.

6. A.A. Johnson and T.E. Tezduyar, Comput. Methods Appl. Mech. Engrg., Vol. 119, 73-94, 1994.

7. E.T. Bullister, L.W. Ho and E. Ronquist, Adv. Finite Element Analysis in Fluid Dynamics, FED. Vol. 137, Proceedings of ASME, 1992.

8. V. Haroutunian, M.S. Engelman and I. Hasbani, Intl. J. Num. Meth. Fluids, Vol. 17, p. 323-348, 1993.

9. M.S. Engelman, FIDAP 7.0 manuals, Fluid Dynamics Intl., Evanston, Illinois, 1993.

10. E.V. Laitone, J. Fluid Mech., Vol. 9, 430-444, 1960.

11. N. Ramanan, V. Haroutunian, and M.S. Engleman, Symposium on Numerical Developments in CFD II, ASME Fluids Eng., San Diego, July, 1996.

FED-Vol. 238, 1996 Fluids Engineering Division Conference
Volume 3
ASME 1996

Simulation of Two-fluid Flows
by the Least-Squares Finite Element Method
Using a Continuum Surface Tension Model

Jie Wu,* Sheng-Tao Yu†and Bo-nan Jiang‡
NASA Lewis Research Center, Cleveland, OH 44135

ABSTRACT

In this paper a numerical procedure for simulating two-fluid flows is presented. This procedure is based on the continuum surface force (CSF) model first developed by Brackbill, et al. (1992). In this approach fluids of different properties are identified through the use of a color function. The interfaces between different fluids are represented as transition regions with finite thicknesses. The interfaces are distinct due to sharp gradients of the color function. The evolution of the interfaces is captured by solving the convective equation of the color function. The surface tension effect is presented in terms of stresses, following the work of Jacqmin (1995). The stresses are defined by the gradient of the color function. In its analytical form, this stress formulation is equivalent to the original CSF model (Brackbill, et al., 1992). Numerically, however, the use of the stress formulation has some advantages over the original CSF model, as it bypasses the difficulty in approximating the curvatures of the interfaces.

The least-squares finite element method (LSFEM) is used to discretize the governing equation systems. The LSFEM has proven to be effective in solving incompressible Navier-Stokes equations and pure convection equations, making it an ideal candidate for the present applications. The LSFEM handles all the equations in a unified manner without any additional special treatment such as upwinding or artificial dissipation.

Various bench mark tests have been carried out for both two dimensional planar and axisymmetric flows, including dam breaking, oscillating and stationary bubbles and the conical liquid sheet in a pressure swirl atomizer.

1 Introduction

Multi-fluid flows exist in many engineering problems. Examples of such flows include injection molding, metal casting,

---

*Institute for Computational Mechanics in Propulsion, Ohio Aerospace Institute

†NYMA Technology Inc.

‡Institute for Computational Mechanics in Propulsion, Ohio Aerospace Institute

crystal growth and spray atomization, etc. At the interface of different fluids, surface tension exists as a result of uneven molecular forces. The interface behaves in a way similar to a thin stretched membrane. The prediction of the evolution of the interface and the treatment of the interface conditions have been a challenging task for numerical simulations.

The pressure jump across the interface is related to the surface tension coefficient σ, the curvature of the interface κ, and the viscous stress tensor τ^v by the Laplace's formulas (Landau and Lifshitz, 1959):

$$(p_1 - p_2 + \sigma\kappa)n_i = (\tau_{1ik}^v - \tau_{2ik}^v)n_k \tag{1}$$

where **n** is the unit normal of the interface, and the subscripts 1 and 2 denote the two different fluids.

Most existing numerical methods for multiphase/free-surface flows fall into two categories : (1) those which use a fixed grid; and (2) those in which the grid deforms in time so that it remains surface-intrinsic. In the first category the computational grid is fixed throughout the calculation. An additional variable is used to identify the interface. Examples of such methods are the Maker and Cell (MAC) method proposed by Harlow and Welch (1965) and the Volume of Fluid (VOF) method by Hirt and Nichols (1981). The MAC method uses massless marker particles which travel with the fluid to trace the fluids and the interface. The VOF method modifies the MAC method by replacing the discrete marker particles with a continuous field variable (color function). This function assigns a unique constant (color) to each fluid and has sharp gradient at fluid interfaces. Numerical methods in this category are sometimes referred to as "front capturing" methods. Such methods possess great flexibility in handling large deformation and topological changes. The most difficult task with the front capturing approach is to accurately identify the interface and to impose the interface condition (1), such as exemplified by the elaborate work of Daly (1969).

For methods in the second category (see, for example, Fritts and Boris, 1979, Fyfe et al., 1988) , which are referred to as "front tracking" methods, imposing the interface condition (1) is easy compared with the first, because the interface always coincides with mesh sides. However, it requires frequent update of the computational mesh which can be a complex and time-consuming procedure. Particularly, it encounters severe difficulty when the flow experiences complex topological changes.

Another approach which can be regarded as a combination of the above is the front-tracking method introduced by Unverdi and Tryggvason(1992). This approach uses a fixed, structured grid to represent the flow field. A separate, unstructured grid is used to represent the interface. The interface is explicitly tracked and kept at a constant thickness of the order of mesh size. This ensures that the interface will not be smeared by the numerical diffusion. Much success has been achieved in solving a variety of two-fluid flow problems using this approach (Nobari and Tryggvason, 1994a, 1994b). The difficulty with this approach is the handling of complex topological changes.

Brackbill, et al. (1992) proposed a continuum approach for modeling the surface tension effect. In this approach the VOF method is used to identify the fluids and the interface. In addition, a continuum surface force (CSF) model is introduced to handle the surface tension force. Instead of treating the interface as a zero-thinkness membrane and imposing the pressure jump condition (1), the interface is now regarded as having a finite thinkness, and the surface tension effect is interpreted as a continuous body force spread across the finite thickness of the interface, which acts as a source term for the momentum equations. By using the CSF model, the surface tension effect is obtained through some differential operators on the spatially continuous color function. The interface condition (1) is implied in the momentum equations. The location of the interface is no longer explicitly required in the calculation. The computer implementation of the CSF model is thus easy compared with other approaches. The CSF model has been used by a number of authors to simulate multi-phase phenomenon involving complex topological changes (Richards, et al., 1994, Lafaurie, et al., 1994).

Jacqmin (1995) derives the CSF model through the analysis of tension energy. He pointed out that the surface tension can be expressed in terms of a stress tensor which is uniquely defined by the gradient of the color function. Let τ_{ij} denote the the stress components in Cartesian coordinate system. They are related to the color function C as :

$$
\begin{aligned}
\tau_{ij} &= -\frac{\sigma}{[C]}\frac{1}{|\nabla C|}\left(\frac{\partial C}{\partial x_i}\frac{\partial C}{\partial x_j} - \delta_{ij}\frac{\partial C}{\partial x_k}\frac{\partial C}{\partial x_k}\right) \\
&= -\frac{\sigma}{[C]}\left(\frac{1}{|\nabla C|}\frac{\partial C}{\partial x_i}\frac{\partial C}{\partial x_j} - \delta_{ij}|\nabla C|\right)
\end{aligned}
\tag{2}
$$

where δ_{ij} is the Kronecker delta and $[C]$ denotes the jump of C across the interface. σ is the surface tension coefficient. In this paper only constant σ will be considered.

The volumetric body force caused by the surface tension is expressed as:

$$
f_i = \frac{\partial \tau_{ij}}{\partial x_j}
\tag{3}
$$

The above formulation for **f** is analytically equivalent to the original CSF model by Brackbill, et al. (1992). τ is also analytically equivalent the "capillary pressure tensor" defined in the work of Lafaurie, et al., (1994). The advantage of using the above formulation instead of the original CSF model or the capillary pressure tensor is that Eqns (2) and (3) do not require the explicit calculation of the normalized gradient term, whose definition is not clear when $|\nabla C|$ approaches zero. In Eqns (2) and (3) both τ and **f** are well defined in the whole domain; and naturally vanish when $|\nabla C|$ becomes zero. An additional advantage of using the stress tensor τ is that it can be regarded as part of the momentum flux. In many numerical procedures τ can be used directly and there is no need to calculate **f**.

In this paper numerical solutions to problems involving two immiscible fluids are sought. A large number of such problems deal with the interaction between some kind of liquid and the air, which are often simplified as free-surface problems. In the free-surface formulation the flow equations are only applied to the liquid, and zero traction is assumed on the interface. In the present calculation such problems are treated as true two-fluid cases. The VOF approach and surface tension model of (2) and (3) are used to simulate two-fluid problems. The LSFEM is used to discretize the governing equation system. The LSFEM has proven to be effective in solving incompressible Navier-Stokes equations and pure convection equations, making it an ideal candidate for the present applications. Some preliminary two dimensional calculations have been reported by Yu et al. (1995). In the next section the governing equations and the discretization procedure will be presented. Some two dimensional and axisymmetric numerical tests will be presented in Section 3. The first test case is a two dimensional dam breaking problem. The numerical results by the present approach are compared with the experimental data and those by other approaches. Good agreements are observed. The second test case deals with an oscillating bubble for both two dimensional and axisymmetric cases. The last test case simulates the formation of a liquid sheet in a pressure swirl atomizer (Simplex nozzle). Finally some conclusions are given in Section 4.

2 The Governing Equations and the Discretization Procedure

The governing equations for the two-fluid problems are the standard Navier-Stokes equations. Incompressibility is assumed for both fluids. In order to use C_0 element in the LSFEM formulation, the governing equations need to be rewritten as a first-order system. Here we choose the following velocity-pressure-vorticity form:

$$\nabla \cdot \mathbf{u} = 0 \tag{4}$$

$$\rho \frac{\partial \mathbf{u}}{\partial t} + \rho (\mathbf{u} \cdot \nabla) \mathbf{u} + \nabla p + \mu \nabla \times \omega$$
$$+ (\nabla \mu \cdot \nabla \mathbf{u} + (\nabla \mu \cdot \nabla) \mathbf{u}) = \mathbf{f} \tag{5}$$

in which ρ is the density, $\mathbf{u}$ is the velocity vector, p is the pressure, ω is the vorticity vector, μ is the dynamic viscosity, and $\mathbf{f}$ is the body force, which generally consists of the surface tension effect given by Eqn (3) and the gravitational force. The terms in the last pair of brackets on the left hand side represents the effect of non-uniform viscosity.

The vorticity ω is defined by the velocity $\mathbf{u}$ as:

$$\omega = \nabla \times \mathbf{u} \tag{6}$$

From the above we immediately have:

$$\nabla \cdot \omega = 0 \tag{7}$$

The above equation system (4-7) has been used by Jiang et al. (1994) in the theoretical analysis of Navier-Stokes equations systems; and has been extensively used as the basis of LSFEM calculations (see, for example, Jiang and Povinelli, 1990 and Tang and Tsang, 1993).

The fluids are identified by the different value of the color function C, which is convected by the flow field:

$$\frac{\partial C}{\partial t} + (\mathbf{u} \cdot \nabla) C = 0 \tag{8}$$

Fluid properties such as the density and the viscosity are assumed to be distributed in the same manner as C, i.e.:

$$\rho = \rho_1 + \frac{\rho_2 - \rho_1}{C_2 - C_1} (C - C_1) \tag{9}$$

$$\mu = \mu_1 + \frac{\mu_2 - \mu_1}{C_2 - C_1} (C - C_1) \tag{10}$$

We use a simple backward Euler finite difference for time discretization. The non-linear terms are linearized using simple substitution. The standard LSFEM procedure (Jiang and Povinelli, 1990) is used for spatial discretization. To ensure time-accuracy, inner iterations are performed within each time step until convergence is reached.

3 Numerical Examples

3.1 A Broken Dam Problem

This problem has been used by many as a test case for simulating free-surface problems. Experimental data for this case are available (Martin and Moyce, 1952). Here the problem is solved as a two-fluid problem involving both the water and air. Zero surface tension and slippery walls (left and bottom sides) are assumed. On the top and right sides zero pressure is imposed. The computational domain is 2 units high and 6 units long. Initially water occupies a 1×1 area at the bottom left corner. The computational mesh consists of 120×40 uniform bilinear quadrilateral elements. The time step is $\Delta t = 0.05$. The gravitational acceleration $g = 1$. The viscosity is set to 3.05×10^{-5} for water (same choice as that by Nakayama and Mori, 1996) and 3.05×10^{-8} for air. the densities for water and air are 1 and 0.001 respectively.

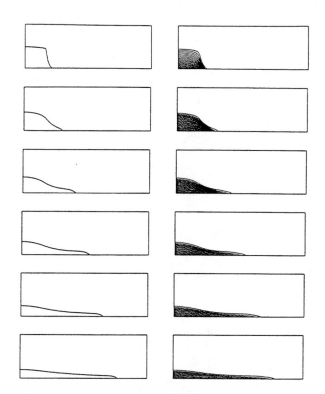

Figure 1: A broken dam, free surface profile and pressure contours. From top to bottom: $t = 0.5, 1.0, 1.5, 2.0. 2.5, 3.0$.

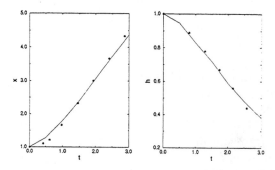

Figure 2: A broken dam, front location and water column height. solid line — calculated results; dots — experimental data.

Figure 1 shows the free surface profile (contour line of density at $\rho = 0.5$ and the pressure contours at different times. The calculated water front location and water column height are compared with the experimental data in Figure 2. It can be seen that the calculated results agree well with the experiments and the calculation by Nakayama and Mori (1996).

3.2 An Oscillating Bubble

In this example the oscillation of a bubble due to surface tension is studied. Both two-dimensional planar and axisymmetric cases are considered. The two dimensional case was simulated Fyfe et al. (1988) using a Lagrangian approach. The computation domain in our calculation is 4×12 units with the symmetry plane/axis along the longer side. Initially the shape of the bubble is elliptical, given by $x^2/4 + z^2 = 1$. The density of the fluid inside and outside the bubble is 1.5 and 0.5 respectively. The dynamic viscosity is 0.01 for both fluids. A time step of $\Delta t = 0.05$ is used in both cases. After the calculation reaches $t = 15.0$, viscosity is increased to 1.0 to allow the solution to converge to steady state. When steady state is reached the sizes of the bubbles are 1.40 and 1.58 respectively, while the theoretical values are 1.41 and 1.59. At steady state, it is verified that the Laplace's formulas (1) for the pressure jump is satisfied.

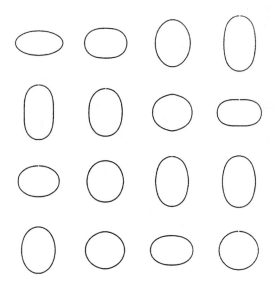

Figure 4: An oscillating bubble, interface profile for axisymmetric case, $t = 0, 1, 2, 3, 4, 5, 6, 7, 8, 9, 10, 11, 12, 13, 14, 40$, respectively

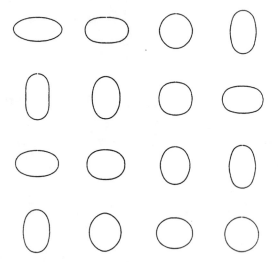

Figure 3: An oscillating bubble, interface profile for two dimensional case, $t = 0, 1, 2, 3, 4, 5, 6, 7, 8, 9, 10, 11, 12, 13, 14, 40$, respectively

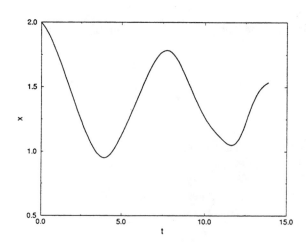

Figure 5: An oscillating bubble, time history of the interface location on the x-axis for two dimensional case

In Figure 3 and Figure 4 the interface shapes at different time are shown for two dimensional and axisymmetric cases respectively. The corresponding time history of the interface location on the x-axis is shown in Figure 5 and Figure 6. The oscillation periods are estimated (based on the first two

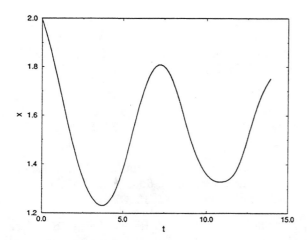

Figure 6: An oscillating bubble, time history of the interface location on the x -axis for axisymmetric case

cycles) to be 7.6 for the two-dimensional case and 7.2 for the axisymmetric case. Theoretical solutions of the periods are available from linear analysis for small amplitudes (see Fyfe et al., 1988 and Nobari and Tryggvason, 1994b for details and references), which for this example are 6.1 for the two-dimensional case and 6.3 for the axisymmetry case. Since in our calculation both nonlinear and viscous effects are present, the theoretical solutions can be used only as references. Our numerical simulation predicts higher values of the oscillation periods than the linear theory, which is consistent with the experience of Fyfe et al. (1988).

3.3   Flow in a Pressure Swirl Atomizer

This example deals with the swirling flow in a pressure swirl atomizer (Simplex nozzle). The computational domain is shown in Figure 7. The liquid comes into the swirling chamber though a number of inlet slots. For the present calculation axisymmetry is assumed. At the inlet values of the liquid density and velocity are prescribed. Slippery boundary conditions are imposed on the portion of the wall which comes into contact with the liquid; and non-slip conditions are imposed elsewhere on the wall. Figure 8 shows the profile of interface. The formation of the conical liquid sheet, which is characteristic of Simplex nozzles, is successfully predicted in this simulation. At this moment no experimental data are available for comparison.

4   Concluding Remarks

In this paper a numerical procedure based on a CSF model and the LSFEM is presented for two-fluid flow problems. Numerical tests carried out on a number of two dimensional planar and axisymmetric flows indicate that this approach

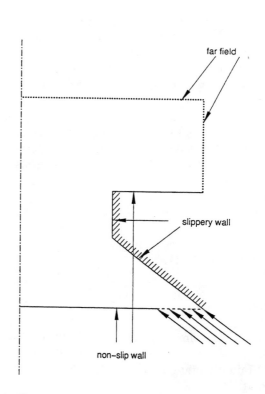

Figure 7: Flow in a pressure swirl atomize, problem definition

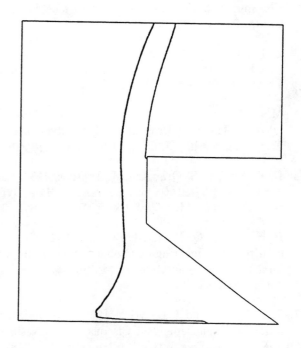

Figure 8: Flow in a pressure swirl atomize, interface profile

is capable of simulating such flow phenomena. The present approach has the advantage in the ability to handle complex topological changes such as the breakup of liquid jets. Another advantage is the ability to handle complex geometrical configurations in practical engineering environment, since the LSFEM is based on totally unstructured grids. Currently the interface is typically spread over $3-5$ grids. Change of interface thickness is also observed in the calculations. The analysis by Haj-hariri et al. (1994) suggests that migration velocity is strongly affected the smearing of interface. Thus to ensure good accuracy of the simulation fine grids have to be used. Improvement of the accuracy of the numerical scheme is expected by introducing higher order discretization schemes in both time and spatial domain. Our test (Yu et al., 1995) indicates that the discontinuity can be modeled within 3 grids, even when the interface undergoes very large deformation due to a highly vortical flow field.

References

[1] A. V. Anilkumar, C. P. Lee and T. G. Wang, 1991, "Surface-Tension-Induced Mixing Following Coalescence of Initially Stationary Drops", *Phys. Fluids A*, **3**, 2587-2591.

[2] J. U. Brackbill, D. B. Kothe and C. Zemach, 1992, "A Continuum Method for Modeling Surface Tension", J. Comp. Phys. , **100**, 335-354.

[3] B. J. Daly, 1969, "A Technique for Including Surface Tension Effects in Hydrodynamic Calculations", J. Comp. Phys. , **4**, 97-117.

[4] M. J. Fritts and J. P. Boris, 1979, "The Lagrangian Solution of Transient Problems in Hydrodynamics using a Triangular mesh", J. Comp. Phys. , **31**, 173-215.

[5] D. E. Fyfe, E. S. Oran and M. J. Fritts, 1988, "Surface Tension and Viscosity with Lagrangian Hydrodynamics on a Triangular Mesh", J. Comp. Phys. , **76**, 349-384,

[6] H. Haj-hariri, Q. Shi and A. Borhan, 1994, "Effect of Local Property Smearing on Global Variables: Implication for Numerical Simulations of Multiphase Flows", *Phys. Fluids*, **6**, 2555-2257.

[7] F. H. Harlow and J. E. Welch, 1965, " Numerical Calculation of Time-Dependent Ciscous Incompressible Flow of Fluid with Free-Surface", *Phys. Fluids*, **8**, 2182-2189.

[8] C. W. Hirt and B. D Nichols, 1981, "Volume of Fluid (VOF) Method for the Dynamics of Free Boundaries', J. Comp. Phys. , **39** , 201-225.

[9] D. Jacqmin, 1995, "Three-Dimensional Computations of Droplet Collisions, Coalescence, and Droplet/Wall Interactions Using a Continuum Surface-Tension Method", AIAA-95-0883

[10] B. N. Jiang, C. Y. Loh and L. A. Povinelli, 1994, "Theoretical Study of the Incompressible Euler Equations by the Least-Squares Method", NASA TM 106535, ICOMP-94-24

[11] B. N. Jiang and L. A. Povinelli, 1990, "Least-squares finite element method for fluid dynamics", Comp. Meth. Appl. Mech. Engng. , **81**, 13-37.

[12] B. Lafaurie, C. Nardone, R. Scardovelli, S. Zaleski and G. Zanetti, 1994, "Modeling Merging and Fragmentation in Multiphase Flows with SURFER", J. Comp. Phys. , **113**, 134-147.

[13] L. D. Landau and E. M. Lifshitz, 1959, *Fluid Mechanics*, Pergammon, New York.

[14] J. C. Martin and W. J. Moyce, 1952, "An Experimental Study of the Collapse of Liquid Columns on a Horizontal Plane", *Philos. Trans. R. Soc. Lond. A*, **244**, 312-324.

[15] T. Nakayama and M. Mori, 1996, "An Eulerian Finite Element Method for Time-Dependent Free Surface Problems in Hydrodynamics", Int. J. Num. Meth. Fluids , **22**, 175-194.

[16] M. R. Nobari and G. Tryggvason, 1994, "Numerical Simulation of Drop Collisions", NASA TM 106751, ICOMP-94-23.

[17] M. R. Nobari and G. Tryggvason, 1994, "The Flow Induced by the Coalescence of Two Initially Stationary Drops", NASA TM 106752, ICOMP-94-24.

[18] J. R. Richards, A. M. Lenhoff and A. N. Beris, 1994, "Dynamics Breakup of liquid-liquid jets", *Phys. Fluids A*, **6**, 2640-2655.

[19] L. Q. Tang and T. T. H. Tsang, 1993, "A Least-Squares Finite Element Method for Time-Dependent Incompressible Flows with Thermal Convection", *Int. J. Num. Meth. Fluids* , **17**, 271-289.

[20] S. O. Unverdi and G. Tryggvason, 1992, " A Front-Tracking Method for Viscous, Incompressible. Multifluid Flows", J. Comp. Phys. , **100**, 25-37.

[21] S. T. Yu, B. N. Jiang, J. Wu and D. Jacqmin, 1995, "A Unified Approach for Simulation Free-Surface Flows by the Least-Squares Finite Element Method ", *Proceedings of the Sixth International Symposium on Computational Fluid Dynamics* Sept. 1995, Nevada, USA

FED-Vol. 238, 1996 Fluids Engineering Division Conference
Volume 3
ASME 1996

NUMERICAL COMPUTATION OF
SURFACE TENSION EFFECTS

David J Burt
Computational Fluid Dynamics Services,
AEA Technology, 8.19 Harwell,
Didcot OX11 0RA, UK

John W J Ferguson
Schlumberger Cambridge Research,
High Cross, Madingley Road,
Cambridge CB3 0EL, UK

Harbi Pordal
AEA Technology, Engineering Software Inc.,
2000 Oxford Drive, Suite 610
Bethel Park, PA 15241, USA

ABSTRACT

A CFD prediction procedure for computing the effect of surface tension forces in two-phase free-surface flows is presented. In order to assess the capability of the model, calculations are carried out for a number of benchmark cases for which published data are available. The cases considered are: a non-equilibrium rod; merging and fragmentation of colliding rods; formation of a droplet at a nozzle; and interaction of a moving fluid-fluid interface with a flat plate. The model, which represents the surface tension effects as volumetric forces across the interface, is implemented in an existing co-located finite-volume formulation. In all of the cases, the calculations compare favourably with the analytical, experimental and numerical results.

NOMENCLATURE

B	body forces	**Greek symbols**	
c	colour function	κ	surface curvature
d	rod diameter	μ	fluid viscosity
F_v	surface tension force	θ_{eq}	equilibrium contact angle
n	normal vector	ρ	fluid density
r	volume fraction	σ	surface tension coefficient
S	gradient of colour function		
U	velocity		
x	position vector		
w	weighting factor		

1. INTRODUCTION

The basic principle of surface tension, that liquid surfaces can behave as if they possess an elastic skin, is a common and familiar phenomenon. Surface tension results in a localised surface force that can act both normal and tangential to a fluid interface. Interfacial motion is, at least, affected by surface tension and can, under certain circumstances, be induced by it (Tritton, 1988).

The study of surface tension is crucial to the understanding of interfacial stability, droplet coalescence and break up, creeping flows, surfactant behaviour, cavitation and many other hydrodynamic processes important to industry.

There are a wealth of methods that attempt to provide a usable modelling tool for the engineer interested in surface tension phenomena. Many take the form of specialised codes that are limited to a reduced range of surface tension problems.

The main objective of the present work is to demonstrate that surface tension effects can be predicted with a general-purpose CFD code. The Continuum Surface Force (CSF) model of Brackbill et al (1992) is implemented in the CFX 4 (formerly CFDS-FLOW3D) code, and is validated against a series of test cases including both free surface flows and wall effects.

The remainder of the paper is divided into three sections. Section 2 outlines the mathematical model and describes the solution procedure. Section 3 describes and discusses the solutions obtained for the various applications, and in Section 4, concluding remarks are made.

2. MATHEMATICAL MODEL
2.1 Surface Tension

This study is concerned with the modelling of two continuous fluid phases (gas/liquid or liquid/liquid) where surface tension forces arise at the interface between the phases and at the juncture of the phase interface with a wall.

The two-phase flow behaviour is predicted using a reduced form of the multi-fluid model (CFDS, 1995), in which it is assumed that the velocities of both phases are identical. This approach is often referred to as the homogeneous multiphase model and is frequently used for the calculation of free surface flows.

In this study, the calculation of the surface tension is based on the Continuum Surface Force (CSF) model proposed by Brackbill et al (1992). This model interprets the surface tension force as a continuous three-dimensional effect across an interface. This effect is modelled as additional gradient forces which arise in the momentum equations at the interface between the phases and where the interface touches a wall. The method is applicable to flows in which the surface tension coefficient is constant and the surface tension force acts normal to the phase interface. This places some limitations on the range of applications for which the model may be used, and in particular precludes the simulation of Marangoni convection.

The governing equations for each phase, α, are conservation of mass,

$$\frac{\partial}{\partial t}(r_\alpha \rho_\alpha) + \nabla(r_\alpha \rho_\alpha U) = 0 \qquad (1)$$

and conservation of momentum,

$$\frac{\partial}{\partial t}(r_\alpha \rho_\alpha U) + \nabla \bullet (r_\alpha \rho_\alpha (U \otimes U) - r_\alpha \mu_\alpha (\nabla U + (\nabla U)^T) = F_v + B_\alpha - \nabla p \qquad (2)$$

where r is the phase volume fraction, ρ is the phase density, U is the fluid velocity, μ is the phase viscosity, B represents additional body forces, ∇p is the pressure gradient force and F_v is the volumetric surface tension force.

The CSF method defines the surface tension force in terms of the gradient of a colour function, c, as follows:

$$F_v(x) = w\sigma\kappa(x)\frac{\nabla c}{[c]} \qquad (3)$$

where σ is the surface tension coefficient, κ is the surface curvature and w is a density weighting factor, w, given by:

$$w = \frac{2(r_1\rho_1 + r_2\rho_2)}{\rho_1 + \rho_2} \qquad (4)$$

Without this weighting factor, convergence difficulties are apparent across interfaces with large density jumps. In the present contribution, the colour function is represented by the first phase volume fraction, such that $c = r_1$ and $[c] = \max(r_1) - \min(r_1) = 1.0$, and surface curvature is given by:

$$\kappa = -(\nabla \bullet \frac{n}{|n|}) \qquad (5)$$

where the normal vector to the free surface, n, is given by the gradient of the volume fraction as follows:

$$n = \nabla c = \nabla r_1 \qquad (6)$$

The curvature, Eq. (5), may also be written in the following form:

$$\kappa = \frac{1}{|n|}\left[\left(\frac{n}{|n|} \bullet \nabla\right)|n| - (\nabla \bullet n)\right] \qquad (7)$$

This latter equation is better suited to cell-centred finite difference discretisation than Eq. (5) as explained in Brackbill et al (1992).

2.2 Wall Adhesion

Wall adhesion is the surface force acting on the fluid interface at the points of contact with the wall. In a static condition the surface force is balanced by a pressure gradient, observed as a surface curvature. A line drawn tangential to the curved surface touching the wall makes an angle with the wall known as the static equilibrium contact angle. In the case of a fluid interface moving along a wall the contact angle may vary as some function of a local variable. In most cases it is sufficient to model the moving interface with a constant dynamic equilibrium contact angle.

A corollary of the free surface making a constant angle at the wall θ_{eq} is that the free surface normal makes an angle θ_{eq} with the wall normal. In the present implementation of the wall adhesion boundary condition, the free surface normal and the colour function at the wall are repeatedly modified until the equilibrium contact angle condition is satisfied. Changing the surface normal at the wall modifies the curvature and introduces an additional force calculated from Eq. (3). This force tends to move the interface towards the desired contact angle and balances the pressure gradient at convergence.

By convention, a phase interface normal to a wall is taken to have an equilibrium contact angle of 90°. The wall is hydrophobic to the first phase when the angle is greater than 90° and hydrophilic when the angle is less than 90°. The gradient of the colour function at some point near the wall is denoted as S, and the wall outward unit normal as $\hat{n}_w$. S is resolved into two components normal and tangential to the wall.

$$S_n = (S \bullet \hat{n}_w)\hat{n}_w \qquad (8)$$

$$S_t = S - S_n \qquad (9)$$

The direction vector S_d for the colour function gradient at the wall is then calculated by applying the boundary condition,

$$S_d = \frac{|S_t|}{\tan\theta_{eq}}\hat{n}_w + S_t \qquad (10)$$

and is normalised so that the colour function gradient at the wall has the same magnitude as S but makes the angle θ_{eq} with the wall unit normal. This is the prescribed boundary condition,

$$S_w = \frac{|S|}{|S_d|} S_d \qquad (11)$$

One further step is to calculate the colour function gradient normal to the wall and to use this to modify the absolute value of the colour function at the wall from a first order Taylor series expansion.

2.3 Implementation

The model is implemented in the CFX 4 general-purpose CFD software, which uses a multi-block co-located cell-centred finite volume approach, in combination with the Rhie-Chow algorithm (Rhie and Chow, 1983). Special treatment of the surface tension forces is included to avoid unphysical checkerboard oscillations of the free surface.

The standard treatment for the transport of the phase volume fraction can produce some numerical diffusion and spreading of the interfacial region. The origins of this diffusivity and a means of limiting it are discussed in Lafaurie et al. (1994). Sharp interfaces are maintained by reconstructing the free-surface at each time step with a surface sharpening algorithm (CFDS, 1995).

3. PRESENTATION AND DISCUSSION OF THE RESULTS
3.1 Preliminary Remarks

The purpose of this section is to demonstrate the ability of the mathematical model to predict surface tension effects for a number of benchmark test cases, for which analytical or published data are available. Four test cases are presented in the following order: a non-equilibrium rod; two colliding rods; droplet formation at a nozzle; and interaction of a moving fluid-fluid interface with a flat plate.

3.2 Non-equilibrium Rod

A simple demonstration of the surface tension model is the non-equilibrium rod test case, in which a square rod of oil responds to unbalanced surface tension forces. Similar examples using structured single-block grids are reported by Brackbill et al (1992) and Lafaurie et al (1994). Here, the example demonstrates the implementation of the surface tension model in unstructured multi-block meshes. The model consists of a 5-block computational mesh of 1040 grid cells, where the central block is initialised as oil of density 790.0 kg/m³, the surrounding region as air of density 1.2 kg/m³, and the surface tension coefficient for the oil/air interface is 0.0236 N/m.

The initial shape of the liquid rod results in large surface tension forces at the high-curvature corners. Figure 1 shows that these forces set the rod into symmetrical oscillation and that damping by viscous forces dissipates the energy of the system until it reaches its lowest energy state, a cylinder.

The calculations are quantitatively in good agreement with the results presented by Brackbill et al (1992) and Lafaurie et al (1994).

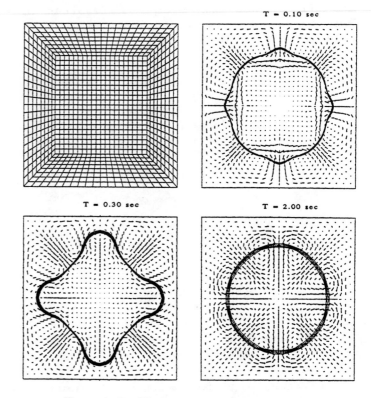

Figure 1: Oscillation of a non-equilibrium rod

In the final equilibrium condition, the predicted pressure difference between the gas and liquid phases is within 2% of that calculated analytically. Also, the so-called 'parasitic' currents mentioned in Lafaurie et al (1994) are evident here, and tend to persist, at very small magnitude, even when the system has passed through 5 seconds of real time and has seemingly attained a steady state.

3.3 Colliding Rods

The second example is taken from Kothe and Mjolsness (1992) and demonstrates water rod coalescence and break up. This shows the competition of inertial and surface tension forces that occurs with different initial conditions.

The computational domain is a square of 10 cm by 10 cm and is discretised as a single block with an 80 by 80 mesh. Two water rods of radius 1.5 cm and density 1000 kg/m³ collide, head on, in air of density 1.2 kg/m³ and with an overlap of 1.33 radii. The surface tension coefficient is 0.0725 N/m. Two simulations are performed with impact velocities of 10 cm/s (Fig. 2) and 15 cm/s (Fig. 3).

The relative magnitude of the surface tension to the inertial forces can be assessed by the dimensionless Weber number, We, defined as follows:

$$We = \frac{\rho \, (\Delta U)^2 d}{2\sigma} \qquad (12)$$

441

where ΔU is the combined impact velocity and d is the rod diameter. Thus, in the two calculations performed in this study, the Weber numbers are respectively: $We \sim 8.3$ and $We \sim 18.6$.

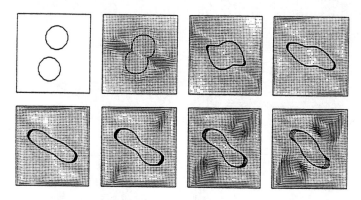

Figure 2: Collision of water rods - $We \sim 8.3$ - frame intervals of 0.1 seconds

Figure 2 shows that for the lower We number case, the inertial forces are not sufficiently strong to overcome the surface tension and the rods coalesce.

For the higher We number case, Fig. 3, the two rods meet, exchange momentum, and then separate again. These results show qualitatively good agreement with those reported by Kothe and Mjolsness (1992), who also found that the rods coalesce at the lower Weber number, and separate at the higher Weber number.

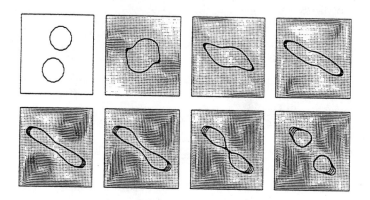

Figure 3: Collision of water rods - $We \sim 18.6$ - frame intervals of 0.1 seconds

In this calculation, the split that ultimately occurs for the high We number case was slightly uneven when the surface sharpening algorithm was used. This is consistent with the results of Kothe and Mjolsness (1992) who observed the same phenomenon for their advection scheme.

3.4 Droplet Formation at a Nozzle

This calculation is based on the experimental work of Thornton et al (1985). A nozzle of 3.31 mm diameter situated at the top of a cylindrical vessel delivers an aqueous phase (water with a density of 1000 kg/m³) at a rate of 0.417 ml/s into an immiscible organic phase, (toluene with a density of 815 kg/m³). The nozzle Reynolds number is $Re \sim 169$ and the surface tension coefficient is specified as 0.034 N/m. The free-surface equilibrium contact angle, θ_{eq}, is 110° as the wall is hydrophobic to the aqueous phase.

The domain is modelled in a two-dimensional cylindrical co-ordinate system using a 4 block mesh of 6800 finite volumes. The domain radius is 40 mm and from the tip of the nozzle it extends to an axial distance of 50 mm. The free surface of the toluene above the nozzle is modelled as a frictionless wall and the exit plane as a pressure boundary.

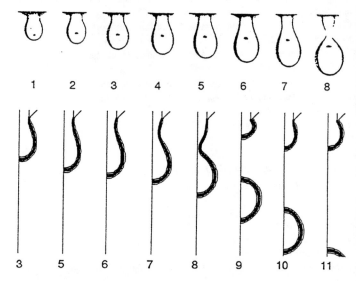

Figure 4: Experimental and computed results of droplet formation at a nozzle - frame intervals of 50 m/s

Figure 4 compares the numerical prediction with a sequence of photographs taken from the experiment at intervals of 50 ms. The droplet produced at the nozzle is seen to grow until such time that the gravity force exceeds the surface tension force. Frames 7 and 8 show the free surface necking and snapping, with the seed of a second droplet forming just behind the first. The experimental data shows an approximately spherical droplet to be produced with a diameter of 7.5 mm with an error band of ± 0.5 mm. From the diameter and the known flow rate of the water, the pulsing frequency of the drop is calculated to be between 0.43 and 0.64 seconds.

For the computed results, the diameter of the separated droplet, measured across the 0.5 volume fraction contour line, is 7.13 mm which gives a pulsing frequency of 0.46 seconds.

Animation of the pulsing droplet produced from the simulation shows the first drop pinching off at 0.76 seconds leaving a residue still attached to the nozzle. This residue grows into a second drop which pinches off at 1.20 seconds giving a predicted pulsing frequency of 0.44 seconds. Estimating the pulsing frequency in this way gives an answer very close to that obtained by direct measurement of the 0.5 volume fraction contour.

In the numerical model, the surface sharpening algorithm is particularly important in preventing numerical diffusion of the volume fraction field which can otherwise lead to false behaviour downstream of the nozzle.

This calculation demonstrates the effectiveness of the model in capturing all of the important features of two-phase flow with surface tension and wall adhesion. Particularly, the diameter of the pendant drop, which is more than twice that of the nozzle, is accurately predicted within the bounds of the measurement errors of ± 7%.

In this case the static equilibrium contact angle is hydrophobic to the aqueous phase. Studies with a hydrophilic wall contact angle show the drop crawling up the outside surface of the nozzle before separating under the influence of gravity.

3.5 Interaction of a Moving Fluid-Fluid Interface with a Flat Plate

The final test case considers wall effects and is based on the analytical results of Billingham and King (1995) which consider the interaction of an infinite, initially straight, interface between two inviscid fluids, advected in an initially uniform flow towards a semi-infinite thin flat plate perpendicular to the interface. Using a similarity solution, they obtain an expression for the position of the moving wall contact line, $y_c(t)$, given by:

$$y_c(t) = U_\infty t - 0.852 \left(\frac{\pi}{2} - \theta_{eq} \right) \left(\frac{\sigma}{\rho_1 + \rho_2} \right)^{1/3} t^{2/3} \qquad (13)$$

where t is time and U_∞ is the uniform flow velocity. The limits of validity of this formulation are explained in Billingham and King (1995).

To compare the results of the numerical surface tension model with this analytical solution, three cases are considered using parameters within the range of validity of the formulation as follows:

case 1: $\sigma = 30$ g/s^2, $\theta_{eq} = 135°$
case 2: $\sigma = 15$ g/s^2, $\theta_{eq} = 135°$
case 3: $\sigma = 30$ g/s^2, $\theta_{eq} = 112.5°$

In all cases $U_\infty = 10$ mm/s, $\rho_1 = 800$ kg/m^3 (fluid initially completely in contact with the plate) and $\rho_2 = 1000$ kg/m^3. The same viscosity is used for both fluids.

Figure 5 shows the shape and position of the interface at 2 second intervals for case 1. The interface profile is in good qualitative agreement with the analytical solution, though, because the computational grid is finite, the capillary wave moving along the

interface away from the plate reaches the domain boundary within 6 seconds.

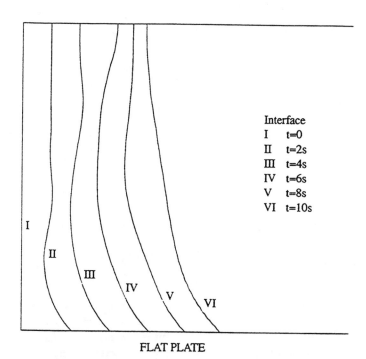

FLAT PLATE

Figure 5: Case 1 - Interface profile at 2 second intervals

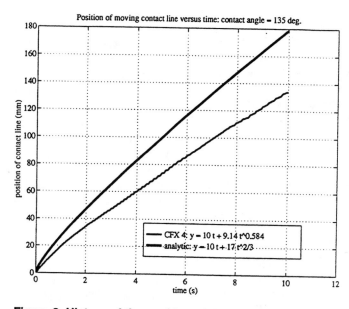

Figure 6: History of the position of the moving contact line

Figure 6 compares the predicted and analytical history of the position of the contact line on the plate for case 1. The agreement between these solutions is good, and shows correct prediction of the trends. For each of the three cases, the numerically predicted contact line position is fitted to the following curve:

$$y_c(t;a_0,a_1) = 10t + a_o t^{a_1} \tag{14}$$

In Table 1, these curves are compared with the analytical solution given by Eq. (13).

case	a_o		a_1	
	$0 < t < 10s$	$0 < t < 2s$	$0 < t < 10s$	$0 < t < 2s$
1	9.2	9.0	0.584	0.707
error	46%	46%	12%	5%
2	8.4	7.9	0.568	0.723
error	38%	42%	15%	8%
3	4.3	4.5	0.735	0.694
error	50%	47%	10%	4%

Table 1: Summary of fitted data

The table shows that good agreement between the analytical and numerical solution is achieved for the exponent, a_1 (with a relative error of between 4% and 15%), whereas the agreement for the coefficient, a_0, is only between 40 and 50%. The correct prediction of a_1 suggests that the form of the similarity solution is accurately predicted by the numerical solution, especially at early times ($t < 2s$) when the capillary wave and far field boundary condition do not interact.

The relatively large difference in the coefficient a_0 may possibly be attributed to the singular nature of the analytic solution at $t = 0$, when the contact line and flat plate first meet resulting in a finite impulsive force and an infinite contact line velocity. It should also be remembered that the agreement between the two solutions is much better than that between the coefficients in the curve fit. To accurately predict this impulsive start, the problem would have to be set up with an initial state given by a very early time solution of the analytic solution found in Billingham and King (1995). However, it is believed that there is more value in numerically solving a non-singular viscous problem, where the only unknown is the contact angle versus contact line velocity.

4 CONCLUSIONS

A numerical model is described which simulates the characteristics of surface tension in free-surface flows and wall adhesion. The prediction procedure is based on the CSF model and is implemented in a general purpose CFD code. A series of test cases shows that the model can predict complex free surface effects such as capillary waves, droplet coalescence, pinching off and break up. It is believed that the verification and validation studies give confidence in the implementation and it is hoped that the generality of the CFD

code will make this work of genuine value to the engineering community.

ACKNOWLEDGEMENTS

The authors wish to thank the following individuals for their ideas and assistance: Dr. Alan Burns, Ian Hamill, Dr. Ian Jones, Dr. Simon Lo and Dr. Nigel Wilkes.

REFERENCES

Billingham, J., and King, A.C., 1995, "The Interaction of a Moving Fluid/Fluid Interface with a Flat Plate," J. Fluid Mech., Vol. 296, pp 325 351.

Brackbill, J.U., Kothe, D.B., and Zemach, C., 1992, "A Continuum Method for Modelling Surface Tension," J. Comp. Phys. Vol. 100, pp 335-354.

CFDS, 1995, "CFX 4.1 Flow Solver User Guide", Computational Fluid Dynamics Services, AEA Technology, Harwell, Oxon, UK.

Kothe, D.B., and Mjolsness, R.C., 1992, "RIPPLE: A New Model for Incompressible Flows with Free Surfaces," AIAA J. Vol. 30, No 11.

Lafaurie, B., Zaleski, S., and Zanetti, G., 1994, "Modelling Merging and Fragmentation in Multiphase Flows with SURFER," J. Comp. Phys. Vol. 133, No 1.

Rhie, C.M., and Chow, W.L., 1983, "Numerical Study of the Turbulent Flow Past an Airfoil with Trailing Edge Separation", AIAA J, Vol. 21 pp 1527-1532.

Thornton, J.D., Anderson, T.J., Javed, K.H. and Achwal, S.K., 1985, "Surface Phenomena and Mass Transfer Interactions in Liquid-Liquid Systems, Part 1: Droplet Forming at a Nozzle," J. AIChE, Vol. 31, No 7, pp 1069 1076.

Tritton, D.J., 1988, "Physical Fluid Dynamics", Oxford University Press, Oxford, 2nd Ed.

FED-Vol. 238, 1996 Fluids Engineering Division Conference
Volume 3
ASME 1996

3-DIMENSIONAL ANALYSIS OF INCOMPRESSIBLE FLOW
AROUND CIRCULAR CYLINDER

Shinji OHTA, Akira MARUOKA,
Hirokazu HIRANO and Mutsuto KAWAHARA

Department of Civil Engineering, Chuo University,
1 − 13 − 27, Kasuga, Bunkyou − ku, Tokyo 112, Japan

ABSTRACT

This paper presents 3-dimensional analysis of incompressible viscous flow by the finite element method. It is known that a lot of computational time and memory are necessary to this calculation. Therefore, the analytical integration formula for 8-node isoparametric is used to calculating coefficient matrix in place of the numerical integration formula. The analytical integration formula can obtain as speed as one-point quadrature and better accuracy than it. And computational memory can be reduced. The governing equation is incompressible Navier-Stokes equation. For numerical example, 3-dimensional flow around circular cylinder is calculated. In this result, 3-dimensional characteristic which can not be obtained in 2-dimensional calculation can be found. The differences between 3-d and 2-d calculations are compared and examined. Also, it is can be confirmed that 3-d results are corresponded with experimental ones. The main purpose of this study is that the necessity and the effect of 3-dimensional analysis are confirmed.

INTRODUCTION

Formerly, if the flow around any structures is calculated by numerical analysis, it has been said to be satisfied by using 2-dimensional analysis. However, it is unnatural to treat an actual phenomenon as 2-dimensional. The flow for 3-dimensional direction (the vertical direction) is existed. As a necessity, it is impossible that 3-dimensional characteristic is researched from 2-dimensional analysis. It is essential to apply 3-dimensional analysis (Tamura, T., 1990). However, 3-dimensional analysis has some serious problems. It is that a lot of computational time and memory are necessary. Recently, the developments of computers have made computational time much speedy, and its memory much large. Therefore, it has been said that 3-dimensional analysis has been possible. However,

in spite of these developments, 3-dimensional analysis has not been yet complete enough.

One of the advantage of the finite element method over other numerical methods is to be more adaptable to arbitrary shapes. On the other hand, disadvantage of the finite element method is that much computational time and capacity of memory are demanded. Especially, 3-dimensional analysis demands much memory, and requires longer time. In case of calculating coefficient matrix, numerical integration formula so-called "Gauss quadrature" have been generally used. Two-point quadrature which is one of the numerical integration is generally used, and it is known that this accuracy is good. However, much memory is required in two-point quadrature. On the other hand, one-point quadrature is one of the ways in which computational time is speeded up. However, it is known that this method causes numerical unstability. Therefore, a certain method which can obtained as speed as one-point quadrature and as good accuracy as two-point quadrature, should be considered.

In this study, calculating coefficient matricis, analytical integration formula (Mizukami, A., 1986) for 8-node isoparametric element is applied. This method makes computational time speedy, and memory reduced. And, this accuracy is better than one-point quadrature. Analytical integration formula means that integration equations are calculated by hand and its results are used against numerical integration formula. For numerical example, 3-dimensional analysis of incompressible flow around circular cylinder is calculated. In case of this calculation, it is known that 2-dimensional results are very different from experimental ones. The reason is considered that the flow for vertical direction is exist. The main purpose of this study is that this flow for vertical direction is researched. Also, comparing with experimental results, it is found that they are corresponded each other. Therefore, it is found that the existence of 3-dimensional characteristic is much effective. And the necessity and the effect of 3-dimensional analysis are discussed. Also, the calculated domain and boundary condition on 3-dimensional analysis are discussed.

BASIC EQUATIONS

Let Ω be a spatial domain, and Γ denotes a boundary of Ω. Basic equations for incompressible flow are expressed as the Navier–Stokes equations. The momentum equation and the continuity equation can be written as:

$$\rho \left(\frac{\partial u_i}{\partial t} + u_j u_{i,j} \right) + p_{,i} - \mu(u_{i,j} + u_{j,i})_{,j} = 0 \quad \text{in} \ \ \Omega \ \ (1)$$

$$u_{i,i} = 0 \quad \text{in} \ \ \Omega \tag{2}$$

where u_i and p are velocity and pressure, ρ and μ are density and dynamic viscosity.

The boundary Γ is divided into two parts Γ_1 and Γ_2. Velocity and pressure gradient are specified on Γ_1, velocity gradient and pressure are specified on Γ_2. Boundary conditions on Γ_1 and Γ_2 can be written as:

$$u_i = \hat{u}_i \quad p_{,i} n_i = \hat{r} \quad \text{on} \ \ \Gamma_1 \tag{3}$$

$$(\mu(u_{i,j} + u_{j,i})) n_j = \hat{s}_i \quad p = \hat{p} \quad \text{on} \ \ \Gamma_2 \tag{4}$$

where $\hat{u}_i$, $\hat{r}$, $\hat{s}_i$, $\hat{p}$ mean prescribed values, n_i is unit outward normal vector to Γ, and δ_{ij} is Kronecker's delta function.

FRACTIONAL STEP METHOD

In this study, the fractional step method (Hayashi, M., 1991) is applied to solved the momentum equation and the continuity equation. Algorithm of the velocity correction method that is one of the fractional step method is explained.

For numerical integration in time, Eqs. (1),(2) can be discretized at n-th time point as follows.

$$\rho \left(\frac{u_i^{n+1} - u_i^n}{\Delta t} + u_j^n u_{i,j}^n \right) + p_{,i}^{n+1} - \mu(u_{i,j}^n + u_{j,i}^n)_{,j} = 0 \tag{5}$$

$$u_{i,i}^{n+1} = 0 \tag{6}$$

where superscript n and Δt are time step number and time increment.

ALGORITHM

1. The intermediate velocity $\tilde{u}_i$ is calculated from the momentum equation which subtracts the pressure p^{n+1} from Eq. (5)

$$\rho \left(\frac{\tilde{u}_i - u_i^n}{\Delta t} + u_j^n u_{i,j}^n \right) - \mu(u_{i,j}^n + u_{j,i}^n)_{,j} = 0 \tag{7}$$

2. The pressure p^{n+1} is calculated by the pressure Poisson equation.

$$\frac{\Delta t}{\rho} p_{,ii}^{n+1} = \tilde{u}_{i,i} \tag{8}$$

3. From Subtracting equation at 1, the velocity u_i^{n+1} is calculated by the velocity correction equation.

$$\rho \left(\frac{u_i^{n+1} - \tilde{u}_i}{\Delta t} \right) + p_{,i}^{n+1} = 0 \tag{9}$$

4. $n \leftarrow n + 1$ and go to 1.

This method is classified as one of the semi–implicit schemes. The Navier-Stokes equations can be transformed into a form in which velocity and pressure can be calculated by independent equations, velocity is solved by the explicit scheme and pressure is solved by the implicit scheme.

The weighted residual formulation is applied to Eqs. (7)–(9), and the conventional Galerkin method is employed for the space discretization. Adding the balancing tensor diffusivity (BTD) term to the advection term, it is one of the artificial diffusion. The finite element equations can be obtained as follows.

$$\boldsymbol{M} \left(\frac{\tilde{u}_i - u_i^n}{\Delta t} \right) + \boldsymbol{K}^n u_i^n + \boldsymbol{S}_{ij}^n u_j^n = 0 \tag{10}$$

$$\boldsymbol{L} p^{n+1} = -\frac{1}{\Delta t} \boldsymbol{G}_i \tilde{u}_i \tag{11}$$

$$\boldsymbol{M} \left(\frac{u_i^{n+1} - \tilde{u}_i}{\Delta t} \right) + \boldsymbol{G}_i p^{n+1} = 0 \tag{12}$$

where the matrices $\boldsymbol{M}$, $\boldsymbol{K}^n$, $\boldsymbol{S}_{ij}^n$ and $\boldsymbol{G}_i$ are mass, advection, diffusion that includes the BTD term, and gradient matrices.

$$\boldsymbol{M} = \int N_\alpha N_\beta d\Omega \quad \boldsymbol{K}^n = \int \rho u_j^n N_\alpha N_{\beta,i} d\Omega$$

$$\begin{aligned} \boldsymbol{S}_{ij}^n &= \left(\int \frac{\Delta t}{2} \rho u_j^n u_k^n N_{\alpha,j} N_{\beta,k} d\Omega \right. \\ &\quad + \left. \int \mu N_{\alpha,k} N_{\beta,k} d\Omega \right) \delta_{ij} + \int \mu N_{\alpha,i} N_{\beta,j} d\Omega \end{aligned} \tag{13}$$

$$G_i = \int N_\alpha N_{\beta,i}\, d\Omega \qquad L = \int \frac{1}{\rho} N_{\alpha,i} N_{\beta,i}\, d\Omega$$

where N_α means linear or multilinear interpolation function.

ANALYTICAL INTEGRATION FORMULA

It is known to use numerical integration formula so-called "Gauss quadrature" for calculating coefficient matrix. Two-point quadrature which is one of the numerical integration is generally used. However, two-point quadrature is required a lot of computational capacity memory. On the other hand, one-point quadrature is one of the ways in which computational time is speeded up. However, it is known that this method causes numerical unstability. Then, this section is summarized analytical integration formula instead of numerical integration formula. This method makes computational time as speedy as one-point quadrature, and capacity of memory much smaller than two-point quadrature.

Let us consider 8-node isoparametric element. The physical (global) coordinates and reference (local) coordinates of node $i(1 \le i \le 8)$ are (x_i, y_i, z_i) and (ξ_i, η_i, ζ_i), respectively. The shape functions are expressed as.

$$N_i = \frac{1}{8}(a_i + b_i\xi + c_i\eta + d_i\zeta + e_i\eta\zeta + f_i\xi\zeta + g_i\xi\eta + h_i\xi\eta\zeta) \quad (14)$$

where

$$
\begin{aligned}
a_i &= [\quad 1, \quad 1, \quad 1, \quad 1, \quad 1, \quad 1, \ 1, \quad 1 \ ] \\
b_i &= [\ -1, \quad 1, \quad 1, \ -1, \ -1, \quad 1, \ 1, \ -1 \ ] \\
c_i &= [\ -1, \ -1, \quad 1, \quad 1, \ -1, \ -1, \ 1, \quad 1 \ ] \\
d_i &= [\ -1, \ -1, \ -1, \ -1, \quad 1, \quad 1, \ 1, \quad 1 \ ] \\
e_i &= [\ -1, \ -1, \ -1, \ -1, \quad 1, \quad 1, \ 1, \quad 1 \ ] \\
f_i &= [\ -1, \ -1, \ -1, \ -1, \quad 1, \quad 1, \ 1, \quad 1 \ ] \\
g_i &= [\ -1, \ -1, \ -1, \ -1, \quad 1, \quad 1, \ 1, \quad 1 \ ] \\
h_i &= [\ -1, \ -1, \ -1, \ -1, \quad 1, \quad 1, \ 1, \quad 1 \ ]
\end{aligned}
$$
$$(15)$$

and (x, y, z) are related to (ξ, η, ζ) by

$$
\begin{aligned}
x &= N_i x_i = \frac{1}{8}(x_i a_i + x_i b_i\xi + x_i c_i\eta + x_i d_i\zeta + x_i e_i\eta\zeta \\
&\quad + x_i f_i\xi\zeta + x_i g_i\xi\eta + x_i h_i\xi\eta\zeta) \\
y &= N_i y_i = \frac{1}{8}(y_i a_i + y_i b_i\xi + y_i c_i\eta + y_i d_i\zeta + y_i e_i\eta\zeta \\
&\quad + y_i f_i\xi\zeta + y_i g_i\xi\eta + y_i h_i\xi\eta\zeta) \\
z &= N_i z_i = \frac{1}{8}(z_i a_i + z_i b_i\xi + z_i c_i\eta + z_i d_i\zeta + z_i e_i\eta\zeta \\
&\quad + z_i f_i\xi\zeta + z_i g_i\xi\eta + z_i h_i\xi\eta\zeta)
\end{aligned}
$$
$$(16)$$

Now, using (16), the Jocobian matrix $\boldsymbol{J}$ can be obtained by one-point quadrature as follow.

$$
[\boldsymbol{J}] = \begin{bmatrix} \frac{\partial x}{\partial \xi} & \frac{\partial y}{\partial \xi} & \frac{\partial z}{\partial \xi} \\ \frac{\partial x}{\partial \eta} & \frac{\partial y}{\partial \eta} & \frac{\partial z}{\partial \eta} \\ \frac{\partial x}{\partial \zeta} & \frac{\partial y}{\partial \zeta} & \frac{\partial z}{\partial \zeta} \end{bmatrix} = \frac{1}{8} \begin{bmatrix} b_i^t x & b_i^t y & b_i^t z \\ c_i^t x & c_i^t y & c_i^t z \\ d_i^t x & d_i^t y & d_i^t z \end{bmatrix}
$$

$$
= \begin{bmatrix} J_{11} & J_{12} & J_{13} \\ J_{21} & J_{22} & J_{13} \\ J_{31} & J_{32} & J_{13} \end{bmatrix} \quad (17)
$$

And, determinant of $\boldsymbol{J}$ can be expressed as follow.

$$
\begin{aligned}
|\boldsymbol{J}| &= (J_{11}J_{22}J_{33} + J_{21}J_{32}J_{13} + J_{31}J_{12}J_{23}) \\
&\quad - (J_{13}J_{22}J_{31} + J_{23}J_{32}J_{11} + J_{33}J_{12}J_{23}) \quad (18)
\end{aligned}
$$

Now, we are ready to give integration formula. For example, the follows are shown how to integrate mass matrix $\boldsymbol{M}$.

$$
\begin{aligned}
\boldsymbol{M} &= \int (N_\alpha N_\beta) d\Omega \\
&= \int_{-1}^{1}\int_{-1}^{1}\int_{-1}^{1}(N_\alpha N_\beta) dx\,dy\,dz \\
&= \int_{-1}^{1}\int_{-1}^{1}\int_{-1}^{1}|\boldsymbol{J}|(N_\alpha N_\beta) d\xi\,d\eta\,d\zeta
\end{aligned}
$$

Considering one-point quadrature.

$$
= |\boldsymbol{J}| \int_{-1}^{1}\int_{-1}^{1}\int_{-1}^{1}(N_\alpha N_\beta) d\xi\,d\eta\,d\zeta \quad (19)
$$

Following equation is integrated and summarized.

$$
\begin{aligned}
&\int_{-1}^{1}\int_{-1}^{1}\int_{-1}^{1}(N_\alpha N_\beta) d\xi\,d\eta\,d\zeta \\
&= \frac{1}{64}\int_{-1}^{1}\int_{-1}^{1}\int_{-1}^{1}(a_i a_i^t + b_i b_i^t\xi^2 + c_i c_i^t\eta^2 + d_i d_i^t\zeta^2 \\
&\qquad + e_i e_i^t\eta^2\zeta^2 + f_i f_i^t\xi^2\zeta^2 + g_i g_i^t\xi^2\eta^2 \\
&\qquad + h_i h_i^t\xi^2\eta^2\zeta^2) d\xi\,d\eta\,d\zeta \\
&= \frac{1}{216}[27a_i a_i^t + 9(b_i b_i^t + c_i c_i^t + d_i d_i^t) + 3(e_i e_i^t \\
&\qquad + f_i f_i^t + g_i g_i^t) + h_i h_i^t] \\
&= \boldsymbol{m} \quad\quad\quad (20)
\end{aligned}
$$

Therefore, mass matrix can be expressed as follow.

$$\boldsymbol{M} = |J|\boldsymbol{m} \quad (21)$$

447

In this point, it can be found that only matrix $|\boldsymbol{J}|$ is depended on the shape of the element. On numerical integration formula, all integration terms are depended on the shape of the element. Therefore, the memory of all coefficient matricis should be ready for total number of element. And, computational capacity of memory is made larger. However, on analytical integration formula, only matrix $|\boldsymbol{J}|$ is kept. The effect of these differences is very large. Also, so using analytical integration, the computer does not have to calculated the integration. Therefore, computational time is made speedy.

NUMERICAL EXAMPLE

For the numerical example, the flow around a circular cylinder is calculated. Formerly, 2-d calculation has been used to this analysis. However, it is known that 2-d results are not corresponded with experimental ones. Therefore, in order to be corresponded with this, 3-d analysis is essential. The Reynolds number is determined from the cylinder diameter D and the uniform inflow velocity U. They are set as $Re = 1000$, 2500 and 10000. The calculated domain is set as $6.5D$ for upstream and cross flow direction, and $20D$ for downstream direction on 2-d mesh. The finite element mesh is shown. Total nodes are 7518 and elements are 7360, and the minimum mesh size is $0.005D$(2-d mesh). Surface of circular is divided 128. Also, another mesh(nod.=10990, ele.=10800) is ready at $Re = 10000$. Surface of circular is divided 160. For vertical direction, these layers numbers are set as follows(Table.1).

Vertical length	$Re = 1000$	$Re = 2500$	$Re = 10000$
$1D$	10		
$2D$	20,40	20	20

Table.1 Layers number on each conditions

The boundary condition is prescribed that consist of uniform velocity for inlet boundary, slip condition for lateral, top and bottom boundary, no-slip around the cylinder, and zero-pressure for outlet boundary. 2-d results are applied to the initial condition of 3-d calculation.

CALCULATION RESULT

Fig.3 shows the time history of $'u, v, w'$ at $1D$ past the cylinder along the center line ($Re = 1000$, 20 layers divided $2D$). It can be found that the velocity $'w'$ for vertical direction is exist and its maximum is from 0.5 to 1.0.

As time passes, the changing situation from 2-d characteristic to 3-d one is found. This is caused by the initial condition (2-d results), and 3-d characteristic is appeared gradually.

Fig.4 shows velocity vector on x-z plane past circular cylinder ($Re = 1000$, 40 layers divided $2D$). It is can be found that the eddy for vertical direction is exist. Therefore, it is considered that this eddy is closely related to 3-d characteristic.

Next, 3-d results are compared with 2-d ones and experimental ones(Fig.5). This figure is drag coefficient and strohal number. 2-d results are different from experimental ones. Comparing with these, 3-d results are nearly corresponded with experimental ones. From these, it is considered that these differences are occurred by the effect of 3-d characteristic, and the necessity of 3-d analysis can be confirmed. At $Re = 10000$, the drag coefficient Cd of 3-d calculation is nearer to experimental result than 2-d one, however the strohal number is different. This reason is considered that this mesh is laugh. Especially, it is necessary for the layer length to make fine.

It is known that the determination of number of vertical layers is important for 3-d analysis. In this study, 10, 20, and 40 layers models are used. Fig.6 shows the time history of drag and lift coefficient at $Re = 1000$ each other. Though 40 layers result is not enough for the calculation times, 3-d characteristic is appeared earlier than 20 and 10 layers one. At 40 layers, this is appeared from $Time = 250$, but at 10 layers, this is appeared from $Time = 320$. Also, 40 layers can obtain more stable flow than 10 and 20 layers. In 20 and 10 layers, the flow is a little unstable, and the convergence time is longer. Also, from the time averaged surface pressure distribution, it can be found that 3-d result is different from 2-d ones(Fig.7). 3-d one is nearly corresponded with experimental one (Scruton, C., 1971).

CONCLUSION

From calculation results, 3-d results which are different from 2-d results can be obtained. This reason is considered that 3-d characteristic is appeared. Also, the flow for 3-dimensional direction (vertical direction) is exist, and it is nearly related to 3-d characteristic. And, 3-d results are corresponded with experimental ones. Therefore, the necessity and the effect of 3-d analysis can be confirmed. Also, it can be confirmed that the determination of the layer number is related very much for this analysis.

The progress of the computer speed for using analytical integration formula is not researched. Because, other methods (numerical integration formula) have not be tried yet. In the future, these differences will be compared. However, it is considered that its memory can be reduced. Therefore, the calculation efficiencies have been progressed.

REFERENCES

Hayashi, M.,Hatanaka, K., and Kawahara, M., 1991, "Lagrangian finite element method for free surface Navier–Stokes flow using fractional step methods," Int. J. Num. Meth. Fluids, Vol.13, pp.805–840.

Mizukami, A., 1986, "Some integration formulas for a four-node isoparametric element," Computer methods in applied mechanics and engineering 59, North-Holland, pp.111–121.

Scruton, C., and Rogers, E. W. E., 1971, "Steady and unsteady wind loading of buildings and structures," Phil. Trans. R. Soc. Lond. A, 269, pp.353–383.

Tamura, T., Ohta, I., and Kuwahara, K., 1990, "On the reliability of two-dimensional simulation for unsteady flows around a cylinder-type structure," Elsevier science publishers B.V..

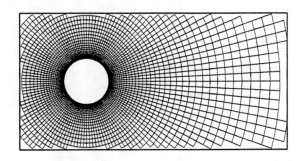
2-d

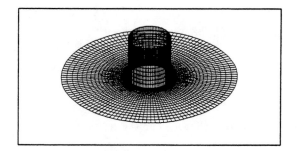
3-d

Fig1. Finite element mesh

end wall : slip

inlet : unform flow

D — cylinder surface : no-slip

1D or 2D

14D

outlet : p=0

26.5D

side wall : slip

Fig.2 Calculation model

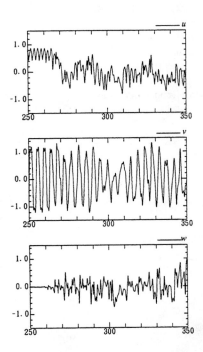

Fig.3 The time history of $'u, v, w'$ at 1D past the cylinder along the center line

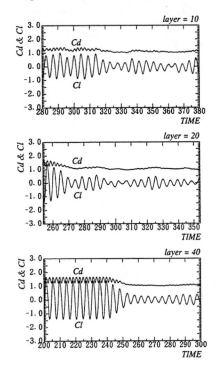

Fig.6 The time history of drag and lift coefficient

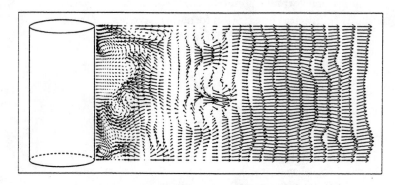

Fig.4 Velocity vector on x-z plane past circular cylinder

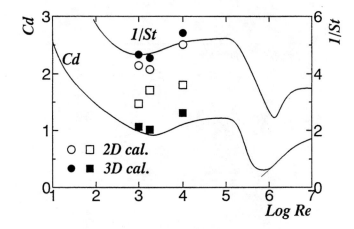

Fig.5 Drag coefficient and strohal number

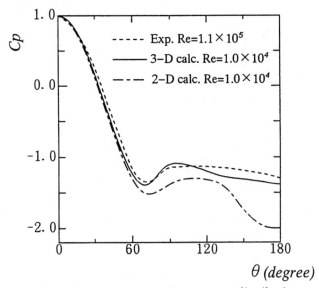

Fig.7 Time averaged surface pressure distribution

FED-Vol. 238, 1996 Fluids Engineering Division Conference
Volume 3
ASME 1996

NUMERICAL ANALYSIS OF RUN-UP ON A CONICAL ISLAND BY FINITE ELEMENT METHOD

Hirokazu KONDO, Toshimitsu TAKAGI,
and Mutsuto KAWAHARA

Department of Civil Engineering, Chuo University,
$1-13-27$, *Kasuga, Bunkyou $-$ ku, Tokyo* 112, *Japan*

ABSTRACT

In this paper, numerical analysis of run-up of solitary waves on a circular island are presented. Shallow-water equations are used as basic equations. Three-step explicit finite element method is employed to solve the equation. A moving boundary scheme is employed to choose wet elements in fixed coordinate of finite element mesh(Umetsu, 1995). Numerical solutions are compared with laboratory experimental data. The laboratory experiments were performed at the US Army Corps of Engineers(Liu, Cho and Fujima, 1994). The results of numerical simulation are good agreements with laboratory experimental data.

INTRODUCTION

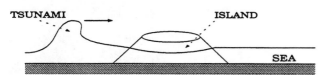

1. Tsunami occurred near Babi island and Okushiri island.

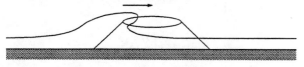

2. Tsunami attacked the front side of these islands.

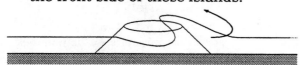

3. After that, tsunami attacked the back side of these islands.

Figure 1:Purpose of this study.

When a submarine earthquake occurs, the bottom of the sea rises and sinks in large area and the upheaval of the surface becomes wave. The wave is expanded into tsunami. In 1992 and 1993, the tsunami attacked some islands. One is Babi Island in Indonesia on December 12, 1992, and the other is Okusiri Island in Japan on July 12, 1993. The tsunami caused a great deal of damage to the back side of these islands. Therefore, this paper presents a numerical procedure of wave run-up on a conical island and comparison between the numerical solutions and the laboratory experimental data.

BASIC EQUATIONS

Non-liner shallow water equations can be written as follows:

$$\dot{u}_i + u_j u_{i,j} + g\zeta_{,i} - A_l(u_{i,j} + u_{j,i})_{,j} = 0 \qquad (1)$$

$$\dot{\zeta} + q_{i,i} = 0 \qquad (2)$$

where u_i is the velocity, g is the gravity acceleration, ζ is the water elevation, A_l is the eddy viscosity and q is the flux of water in unit width

BOUNDARY CONDITION

On the boundary Γ_1 which the water element and the velocities are prescribed:

$$\zeta = \hat{\zeta}_0, u = \hat{u}, v = \hat{v} \qquad On \ \Gamma_1 \qquad (3)$$

On the shore boundary Γ_2 such as the land boundary:

$$u_n = 0 \qquad On \ \Gamma_2 \qquad (4)$$

where $\hat{\ }$ is prescribed value, u_n is outward normal vector.

FINITE ELEMENT EQUATION

The basic equations (1),(2) are discretized by the standard Galerkin finite element method using a linear triangular element to apply the explicit scheme for the time. Finite element equations can be written as follows:

$$M_{\alpha\beta}\dot{u}_{\beta i} + K_{\alpha\beta\gamma j}u_{\beta j}u_{\gamma i} + gH_{\alpha\beta i}\zeta_\beta$$
$$+ A_l(L_{\alpha j\beta j}u_{\beta i} + N_{\alpha j\beta i}u_{\beta j}) = \hat{\Omega}_{\alpha i} \qquad (5)$$

$$M_{\alpha\beta}\dot{\zeta}_\beta + H_{\alpha\beta i}q_{\beta i} = 0 \qquad (6)$$

where each the coefficient matrix can be expressed as:

$$M_{\alpha\beta} = \int_\Omega (\Phi_\alpha \Phi_\beta)d\Omega \ , \ \hat{\Omega}_{\alpha i} = \int_\Gamma (\Phi_\alpha \hat{t}_i)d\Gamma$$

$$K_{\alpha\beta\gamma i} = \int_\Omega (\Phi_\alpha \Phi_\beta \Phi_{\gamma,i})d\Omega \ , \ H_{\alpha\beta i} = \int_\Omega (\Phi_\alpha \Phi_{\beta,i})d\Omega$$

$$L_{\alpha j\beta j} = \int_\Omega (\Phi_{\alpha,j}\Phi_{\beta,j})d\Omega \ , \ N_{\alpha j\beta i} = \int_\Omega (\Phi_{\alpha,j}\Phi_{\beta,i})d\Omega$$

THREE-STEP EXPLICIT FINITE ELEMENT EQUATION

A three-step explicit scheme which is derived from Taylor's series is used for the time integration.

Three-step explicit finite element equations can be written as follows:

<The first time step>

$$\bar{M}_{\alpha\beta}u_{\beta i}^{n+1/3} = \bar{M}_{\alpha\beta}u_{\beta i}^n$$
$$- \frac{1}{3}\Delta t(K_{\alpha\beta\gamma j}u_{\beta j}^n u_{\gamma i}^n + gH_{\alpha\beta i}\zeta_\beta^n$$
$$+ A_l(L_{\alpha j\beta j}u_{\beta i}^n + N_{\alpha j\beta i}u_{\beta j}^n)) \qquad (7)$$

$$\bar{M}_{\alpha\beta}\zeta_\beta^{n+1/3} = \bar{M}_{\alpha\beta}\zeta_\beta^n - \frac{1}{3}\Delta t(H_{\alpha\beta i}q_{\beta i}^n) \qquad (8)$$

<The second time step>

$$\bar{M}_{\alpha\beta}u_{\beta i}^{2(n+1)/3} = \bar{M}_{\alpha\beta}u_{\beta i}^n$$
$$- \frac{1}{2}\Delta t(K_{\alpha\beta\gamma j}u_{\beta j}^{(n+1)/3}u_{\gamma i}^{(n+1)/3} + gH_{\alpha\beta i}\zeta_\beta^{(n+1)/3}$$
$$+ A_l(L_{\alpha j\beta j}u_{\beta i}^{(n+1)/3} + N_{\alpha j\beta i}u_{\beta j}^{(n+1)/3})) \qquad (9)$$

$$\bar{M}_{\alpha\beta}\zeta_\beta^{2(n+1)/3} = \bar{M}_{\alpha\beta}\zeta_\beta^n - \frac{1}{2}\Delta t(H_{\alpha\beta i}q_{\beta i}^{(n+1)/3}) \qquad (10)$$

<The third time step>

$$\bar{M}_{\alpha\beta}u_{\beta i}^{n+1} = \bar{M}_{\alpha\beta}u_{\beta i}^n$$
$$- \Delta t(K_{\alpha\beta\gamma j}u_{\beta j}^{2(n+1)/3}u_{\gamma i}^{2(n+1)/3} + gH_{\alpha\beta i}\zeta_\beta^{2(n+1)/3}$$
$$+ A_l(L_{\alpha j\beta j}u_{\beta i}^{2(n+1)/3} + N_{\alpha j\beta i}u_{\beta j}^{2(n+1)/3})) \qquad (11)$$

$$\bar{M}_{\alpha\beta}\zeta_\beta^{n+1} = \bar{M}_{\alpha\beta}\zeta_\beta^n - \Delta t(H_{\alpha\beta i}q_{\beta i}^{2(n+1)/3}) \qquad (12)$$

The matrix $\bar{M}_{\alpha\beta}$ is the lumped coefficient matrix of the matrix $M_{\alpha\beta}$.

MOVING BOUNDARY TREATMENT

In order to express the moving water boundary at each time step, a technique which is based on a fixed grid approaches. For each triangular element, when h_a, h_b and h_c, are greater than or equal to ϵ_h, such elements are omitted from computation.

For example, water boundary element which is shown in Figure 2(a) is included computation. At the n-th time step, node a and b have water depth but a node c doesn't have water depth or is less than ϵ_h. ϵ_h means minute water depth as a criterion of computational stability. The problem is the boundary condition of dry node c. It must be imposed slip condition on this node. Simply, non slip condition $u_i = 0$ is given on this point, but in this case, including zero velocity to superposing mass matrix velocity power will be going down as showing Figure 2(b).

<Non-slip condition>

$$u_{i(dry)}^n, u_{i(dry)}^{n+1/2}, u_{i(dry)}^{n+1/3} = 0 \qquad (13)$$

To impose as slip condition on the dry node, the computation is carried out using following procedure in each time step.

<Slip condition>

$$u_{i(dry)}^n, u_{i(dry)}^{n+1/2}, u_{i(dry)}^{n+1/3} = \tilde{u}_i \qquad (14)$$

$$\tilde{u}_i = \sum_{l=1}^k u_{il}/k \qquad (15)$$

where k is the number of wet node.

Figure 2(c) shows this procedure. $\tilde{u}_i$ is imposed on dry node as transient value. After this treatment, new values u_i^{n+1} , h_i^{n+1} are calculated by eq(7) - eq(12). This technique is possibly applied to not only the region increasing water level but also that decreasing.

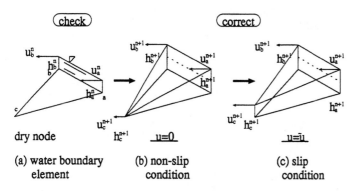

Figure 2:Boundary condition on dry node in water boundary element

NUMERICAL EXAMPLE

A solitary wave can be written as follows:

$$u = \sqrt{gh}\frac{\zeta_0}{h}sech^2(\sqrt{\frac{3\zeta_0}{4h^3}}(x-ct)) \qquad (16)$$

$$\zeta = \zeta_0 sech^2(\sqrt{\frac{3\zeta_0}{4h^3}}(x-ct)) \qquad (17)$$

$$c = \sqrt{gh(1+\frac{\zeta_0}{h})} \qquad (18)$$

where u is a velocity, ζ_0 is a incident wave height, and c is a wave velocity.

The incident wave heights are 0.015(m) in case-A, 0.030(m) in case-B and 0.060(m) in case-C(Figure 3).

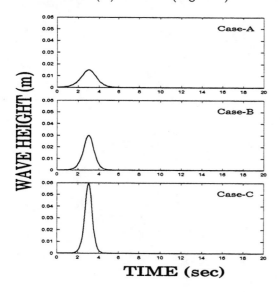

Figure 3: Incident wave heights

Finite element mesh is shown in Figure 8. This mesh consists of 38640 nodes and 78640 elements.
A model of the island is shown in Figure 4.

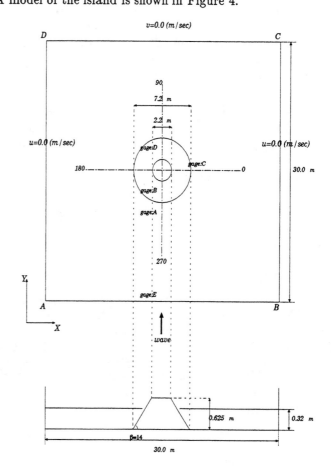

Figure 4: Computation area and a model island

CALCULATION RESULT

The locations of wave gages are shown in Figure 4. Figure 5 shows the comparison of the time history of water elevation at these gages between the experimental data and the numerical results.

Figure 6 shows the water profiles at some instant on the line x=15.0(m).

Figure 7 shows the comparison of the vertical run-up heights around the island between the experimental data and the numerical results.

Both results are in good agreement with each other.

Table.1 shows the ratio of maximum run-up heights to the incident wave heights. Run-up height at the back side of the island is about twice as high as incident wave height.

CONCLUSION

The comparison of the time history of water elevation between the numerical results and the experimental data is in good agreement (Figure 5).

However, the comparison of the vertical run-up heights at the back side of the island in Case-B, C and the front side of the island in Case-C between the numerical results and the experimental data is not in good agreement (Figure 7). Because these error might be influenced by breaking wave.

It is obvious that the run-up heights at the back of the island dose not decrease so much (table.1, Figure 7). This effect may cause a great deal of damage to back of Okushiri Island and Babi Island.

REFERENCES

Philip L.-F. Liu and Yong-Sik Cho and Koji Fujima 1994, "Numerical solutions of three-dimensional run-up on a circular island" International symposium : waves - physical and numerical modeling ,University of British Columbia,Canada.

T.Umetsu, 1995, "A boundary condition technique of moving boundary simulation for broken dam problem by Three-step finite element method" Advances in Hydro-Science and Engineering, Beijing,China.

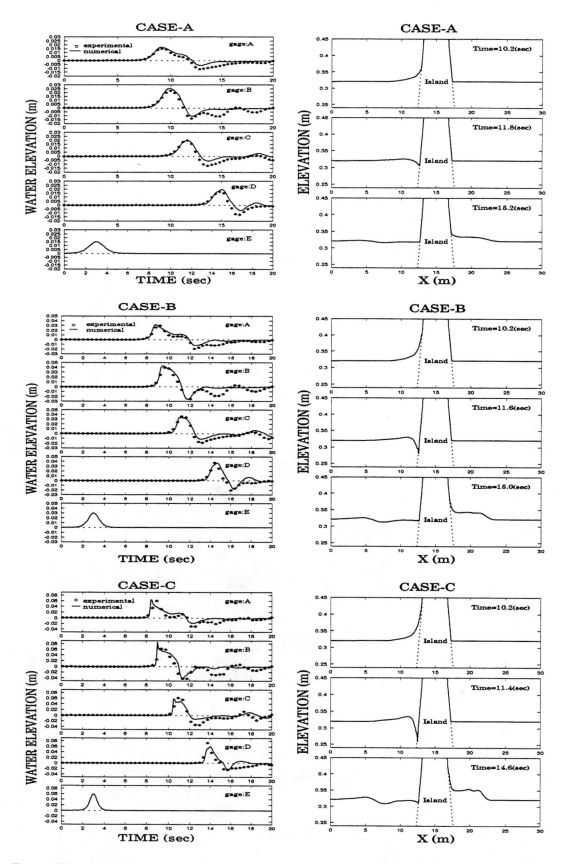

Figure 5:The time history of the water elevation

Figure 6:The water profiles

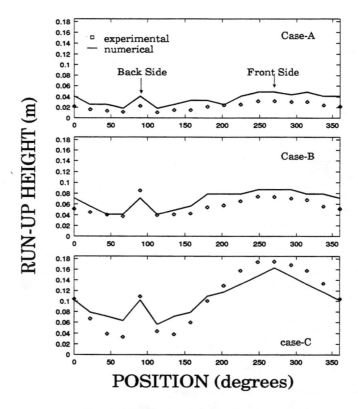

Figure 7:The vertical run-up heights

Figure 8:Finite element mesh

Table.1   Maximum run-up heights at the front side and the back side of the island.

Case	Incident wave heights(m)	Front(m)	Back(m)
A	0.015	0.049	0.041
B	0.030	0.087	0.072
C	0.060	0.163	0.102

FED-Vol. 238, 1996 Fluids Engineering Division Conference
Volume 3
ASME 1996

QUASI-3 DIMENSIONAL NEARSHORE CURRENT SIMULATION

Toshimitsu TAKAGI
Department of Coastal Engineering, INA Corporation,
$1-44-10$, *Sekiguchi, Bunkyou − ku, Tokyo* 112, *Japan*

and

Mutsuto KAWAHARA
Department of Civil Engineering, Chuo University,
$1-13-27$, *Kasuga, Bunkyou − ku, Tokyo* 112, *Japan*

ABSTRACT

This paper presents a quasi 3-dimensional nearshore current model which is combined the finite element method and spectral method. This model is consists of the lateral model and the vertical model, which is derived by using the mode split method. The former model is composed by the finite element method, and the latter model is composed by the spectral method. This model can compute the under tow flow which characterize the 3-dimensional structure of nearshore currents by comparing the computed results with the experimental results in a rectangular channel and a basin(Okayasu,1988,1992). Furthermore, this model can reduce a computational load since the vertical model is used intermittently.

INTRODUCTION

The mass of water carried shoreward by the breaking waves in a surf-zone will be compensated by a seaward return flow close to the bottom. Furthermore if waves are coming obliquely to a coast line, longshore currents are developed. Therefore, in the surf-zone, these currents are fully 3-dimensional flow with a free surface as shown in Fig.1.

Several numerical models of nearshore currents have been developed, introducing the idea of radiation stresses caused by waves. Almost models are based on the shallow water equations which contains the depth mean velocity, namely; the velocity is assumed to be uniform over the depth. Recently, the importance of vertical profiles of velocity field has been recognized, because, for instance in order to estimate the sediment transport, it is necessary to evaluated the velocity close to the bottom accurately.

This paper presents an efficient and economical technique to obtain 3-D velocity profile of wave-induced cur-

rents in the surf-zone by a finite element method. The verification of the present model is carried out, comparing with physical experiment results by Okayasu(1988,1992).

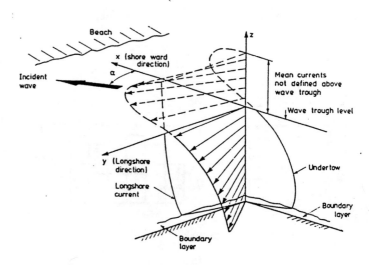

Fig.1 Three-dimensional velocity field in the surf-zone
(Svendsen *et al.*,1989)

GOVERNING EQUATIONS

The governing equations described fluid motion in shallow water can be expressed in the following form, using the notation of Fig.2.

$$\frac{\partial u_i}{\partial t} + u_j u_{i,j} = -g\eta_{,i} + (N_v u_{i,z})_{,z} + F_i \qquad (1)$$

$$\frac{\partial \eta}{\partial t} + \left(\int_{-h}^{\eta} u_i dz\right)_{,i} = 0 \qquad (2)$$

where, $u_i (i = 1, 2)$ are the velocity components at the depth z, η is the free-surface elevation and h is the water depth. F_i is the horizontal eddy viscosity term as follows:

$$F_i = (N_h u_{i,j})_{,j}. \qquad (3)$$

N_v and N_h are the vertical and the horizontal eddy viscosity coefficients respectively.

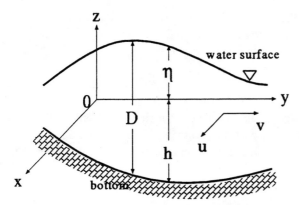

Fig.2 Basic Notation for the Model

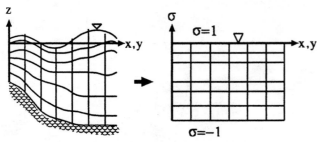

Fig.3 Sigma coordinate

Transforming to a σ coordinate(Fig.3) such as:

$$\sigma = 1 - 2\left(\frac{\eta - z}{h + \eta}\right) = 1 - 2\frac{\eta - z}{D} \qquad (4)$$

where $D = h + \eta$, the governing equations can be expressed as follows:

$$\frac{\partial u_i}{\partial t} + u_j u_{i,j} + \omega u_{i,\sigma} = -g\eta_{,i} + \frac{4}{D^2}(N_v u_{i,\sigma})_{,\sigma} + F_i \qquad (5)$$

$$\frac{\partial \eta}{\partial t} + (Du_i)_{,i} + D\omega_{,\sigma} = 0 \qquad (6)$$

where,

$$\omega(x_i, \sigma, t) = \left\{ u_i \gamma_i - \frac{(1+\sigma)}{D}\frac{\partial \eta}{\partial t} + \frac{2}{D}w \right\} \qquad (7)$$

The velocity field u_i can be considered as the sum of its mean and fluctuation parts as follows:

$$u_i(x_i, z, t) = U_i(x_i, t) + u_i'(x_i, z, t) + \hat{u}_i(x_i, z, t) \qquad (8)$$

where, U_i is the depth and phase averaged velocity, u_i' is the difference between U_i and phase averaged velocity, and $\hat{u}_i$ is the fluctuation velocity caused by wave motion. Fig.4 explains each velocities. Averaging governing equations

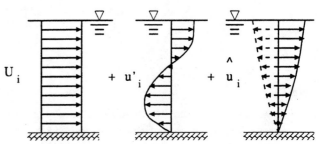

Fig.4 Schematization of velocity field

over the depth and the wave phase, the following equations can be derived:

$$\frac{\partial U_i}{\partial t} + U_j U_{i,j} = -g\eta_{,i} - \frac{1}{D}\left(\int_{-h}^{\eta} u_i' u_j' dz\right)_{,j}$$
$$+ \frac{1}{\rho D}(-S_{ij,j} + \tau_{Si} - \tau_{Bi}) + \bar{F}_i \qquad (9)$$

$$\frac{\partial \eta}{\partial t} + (DU_i)_{,i} = 0 \qquad (10)$$

where, τ_{wi} and τ_{bi} are the components of shear stress on the mean water surface and on the bottom respectively, and S_{ij} are radiation stresses which describe the excess momentum flux caused by the wave motion. If waves are assumed to be of small amplitudes, the radiation stresses can be expressed as follows:

$$S_{ij} = E\frac{c_g}{c}\frac{k_i k_j}{k} + E\left(\frac{c_g}{c} - \frac{1}{2}\right)\delta_{ij} \qquad (11)$$

where $E = \rho g H^2/8$ is the wave energy density, H is the wave height, k is the wave number, c is the wave celerity, c_g is the group velocity, $k_1 = k\cos\alpha, k_2 = k\sin\alpha$, and α is the angle of wave incidence measured counterclockwise from the x-axis. The second term in right hand side of Eq.(9) describe the dispersion caused by the vertical profile of velocity.

MODE SPLITTING METHOD

Applying the the mode split method(Sheng *et al.*,1982), a external and an internal mode models can be derived. The external mode model is a 2-D model, whose governing equations are already described in Eqs.(9)-(11). The equation of the internal mode model is obtained from the residual between Eqs.(5) and (9) as follows:

$$\frac{\partial u_i'}{\partial t} = \frac{4}{D^2}\frac{\partial}{\partial \sigma}\left(N_v \frac{\partial u_i}{\partial \sigma}\right) + C_i \tag{12}$$

where,

$$C_i = \frac{1}{D}\left(\int_{-h}^{\eta} u_i' u_j' dz\right)_{,j} + \frac{1}{\rho D}(\tau_{Bi} - \tau_{Si} + S_{ij,j}) - \bar{F}_i \tag{13}$$

Fig.5 shows the flow chart of the computation. The external mode computation is carried out by the finite element method in conjunction with the internal mode computation by the spectral method.

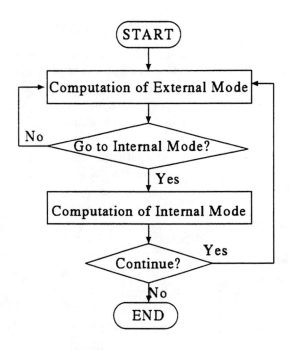

Fig.5 Flow Chart of Computation

Expanding the x and y direction components of velocity u_i' in terms of M depth-dependent function $f_r(\sigma)$ and coefficients $A_{ri}(x_i,t)$ varying with horizontal position and through time, gives

$$u_i'(x_i,\sigma,t) = \sum_{r=1}^{M} A_{ri}(x_i,t)f_r(\sigma). \tag{14}$$

Multiplying Eq.(12) by f_r and integrating it over the depth gives

$$\int_{-1}^{+1}\frac{\partial u_i'}{\partial t}f_r d\sigma = \int_{-1}^{+1}\frac{4}{D^2}\frac{\partial}{\partial \sigma}\left(N_v \frac{\partial u_i}{\partial \sigma}\right)f_r d\sigma + \int_{-1}^{+1} C_i f_r d\sigma \tag{15}$$

Integrating the first term of right hand side in Eq.(15) by parts twice, and applying the boundary conditions on the surface and the bottom such as:

$$\left.N_v \frac{\partial u_i}{\partial \sigma}\right|_{\sigma=+1} = \left.\frac{D}{2}N_v \frac{\partial u_i}{\partial z}\right|_{z=\eta} = \frac{D}{2\rho}\tau_{Si} \tag{16}$$

$$\left.N_v \frac{\partial u_i}{\partial \sigma}\right|_{\sigma=-1} = \left.\frac{D}{2}N_v \frac{\partial u_i}{\partial z}\right|_{z=-h} = \frac{D}{2\rho}\tau_{Bi}, \tag{17}$$

Eq.(15) can be rewritten as follows:

$$\int_{-1}^{+1}\frac{\partial u_i'}{\partial t}f_r d\sigma = \frac{2}{\rho D}\tau_{Si}f_r(+1) - \frac{2}{\rho D}\tau_{Bi}f_r(-1)$$
$$- \frac{4}{D^2}u_{Si}N_v\left.\frac{\partial f_r}{\partial \sigma}\right|_{+1} + \frac{4}{D^2}u_{Bi}N_v\left.\frac{\partial f_r}{\partial \sigma}\right|_{-1}$$
$$+ \frac{4}{D^2}\int_{-1}^{+1}u_i\frac{\partial}{\partial \sigma}\left(N_v\frac{\partial f_r}{\partial \sigma}\right)d\sigma + \int_{-1}^{+1}C_i f_r d\sigma \tag{18}$$

The function f_r can be chosen arbitrarily. Now f_r may be chosen to be eigenfunctions, with corresponding eigenvalues λ of an eigenvalue problem involving the vertical eddy viscosity, of the form

$$\frac{d}{d\sigma}\left[N_v \frac{df_r}{d\sigma}\right] = -\lambda_r f_r. \tag{19}$$

The boundary conditions are

$$f_r|_{+1} = 1, \tag{20}$$
$$N_v f_r' + \beta_1 f_r|_{+1} = 0, \tag{21}$$
$$N_v f_r' + \beta_2 f_r|_{-1} = 0, \tag{22}$$
$$\int_{-1}^{+1} f_r f_k dz = 0, \qquad r \neq k, \tag{23}$$

and

$$f_k(+1) = 1. \tag{24}$$

Considering the boundary conditions yield as follows:

$$\frac{\partial A_{ki}}{\partial t} + \frac{4}{D^2}\lambda_k A_{ki} = \left\{\frac{\tau_{Si}}{\rho D}(2 - a_k) + \frac{\tau_{Bi}}{\rho D}[a_k - 2f_k(-1)]\right.$$
$$+ \frac{4}{D^2}[\beta_1 u_{Si} - \beta_2 u_{Bi}f_k(-1)] - \frac{4}{D^2}\lambda_k U_i a_k$$
$$\left. + \frac{a_k}{D}\left(\int_{-h}^{\eta}u_i' u_j' dz\right)_{,j} + \frac{a_k}{\rho D}S_{ij,j}\right\}\phi_k \tag{25}$$

where, u_{Si} and u_{Bi} are the velocities on the surface and the bottom respectively and

$$a_k = \int_{-1}^{+1} f_k d\sigma, \qquad \phi_k = 1/\int_{-1}^{+1} f_k^2 d\sigma. \qquad (26)$$

Now the following function can be chosen as f_r, which satisfy the boundary conditions.

$$f_k(\sigma) = \cos p_k(1-\sigma) - \frac{\beta_1}{N_v p_k} \sin p_k(1-\sigma) \qquad (27)$$

where

$$p_k = \sqrt{\frac{\lambda_k}{N_v}} \qquad (28)$$

and also p_k can be obtained from the following relationship.

$$\tan 2p_k \equiv \tan \alpha_k = \frac{\beta_2 - \beta_1}{\dfrac{N_v \alpha_k}{2} + \dfrac{\beta_1 \beta_2}{N_v \alpha_k/2}} \qquad (29)$$

NUMERICAL PROCEDURES

In the external mode model, a linear interpolation function based on the three-node triangular finite element is used for the velocity and the water elevation including the water depth. With the Galerkin approach, the finite element equations can be derived from Eqs.(9) and (10) in the form:

$$M_{\alpha\beta} \dot{U}_{\beta i} + K_{\alpha\beta\gamma j} U_{\beta j} U_{\gamma i} + H_{\alpha\beta i} \eta_\beta + E_{\alpha i\beta j} U_{\beta j}$$
$$+ F_{\alpha\beta} U_{\beta j} + R_{\alpha i\beta j} S_{ij\beta} = \hat{\Omega}_{\alpha i} \qquad (30)$$

$$M_{\alpha\beta} \dot{\eta}_\beta + [B_{\alpha\beta\gamma i} + C_{\alpha\beta i\gamma}](h_\beta + \eta_\beta) U_{\gamma i} = 0 \qquad (31)$$

where,

$$M_{\alpha\beta} = \int_V \Phi_\alpha \Phi_\beta dV,$$

$$H_{\alpha\beta\gamma i} = g \int_V \Phi_\alpha \Phi_{\beta,i} dV,$$

$$K_{\alpha\beta\gamma j} = \int_V \Phi_\alpha \Phi_\beta \Phi_{\gamma,j} dV,$$

$$E_{\alpha i\beta j} = N_h \int_V \Phi_{\alpha,i} \Phi_{\beta,j} dV + N_h \int_V \Phi_{\alpha,k} \Phi_{\beta,k} \delta_{ij} dV,$$

$$F_{\alpha\beta} = \frac{C_f \sqrt{u_k u_k}}{\rho(h+\eta)} \int_V \Phi_\alpha \Phi_\beta dV,$$

$$R_{\alpha\beta} = \frac{1}{\rho(h+\eta)} \int_V \Phi_\alpha \Phi_{\beta,j} dV,$$

$$\hat{\Omega}_{\alpha i} = \int_S \Phi_\alpha \hat{t}_i dS,$$

$$B_{\alpha\beta\gamma i} = \int_V \Phi_\alpha \Phi_\beta \Phi_{\gamma,i} dV,$$

$$C_{\alpha\beta i\gamma} = \int_V \Phi_\alpha \Phi_{\beta,i} \Phi_\gamma dV$$

To avoid the time-consuming solution of a simultaneous equation and to acquire numerical stability, the two-step explicit scheme with a lumping technique(Kawahara et al.,1982) is used.
The first step is

$$\overline{M}_{\alpha\beta} U_{\beta i}^{n+1/2} = \widetilde{M}_{\alpha\beta} U_{\beta i}^n - \frac{\Delta t}{2} \{ K_{\alpha\beta\gamma j} U_{\beta j}^n U_{\gamma i}^n + H_{\alpha\beta i} \eta_\beta^n$$
$$+ S_{\alpha i\beta j} U_{\beta j}^n + F_{\alpha\beta} U_{\beta i}^n \} \qquad (32)$$

$$\overline{M}_{\alpha\beta} \eta_\beta^{n+1/2} = \widetilde{M}_{\alpha\beta} U_{\beta i}^n - \frac{\Delta t}{2} [B_{\alpha\beta\gamma i} + C_{\alpha\beta i\gamma}](h_\beta + \eta_\beta^n) U_{\gamma i}^n \} \qquad (33)$$

and the second step is

$$\overline{M}_{\alpha\beta} U_{\beta i}^{n+1} = \widetilde{M}_{\alpha\beta} U_{\beta i}^n - \Delta t \{ K_{\alpha\beta\gamma j} U_{\beta j}^{n+1/2} U_{\gamma i}^{n+1/2}$$
$$+ H_{\alpha\beta i} \eta_\beta^{n+1/2} + S_{\alpha j\beta j} U_{\beta j}^{n+1/2} + F_{\alpha\beta} U_{\beta j} \} \qquad (34)$$

$$\overline{M}_{\alpha\beta} \eta_\beta^{n+1} = \widetilde{M}_{\alpha\beta} \eta_\beta^n - \Delta t [B_{\alpha\beta\gamma i} + C_{\alpha\beta i\gamma}]$$
$$(h_\beta + \eta_\beta^{n+1/2}) U_{\gamma i}^{n+1/2} \qquad (35)$$

where

$$\widetilde{M}_{\alpha\beta} = e M_{\alpha\beta} + (1-e)\overline{M}_{\alpha\beta}. \qquad (36)$$

$\overline{M}_{\alpha\beta}$ denotes the lumped matrix generated by concentrating the non-diagonal element of matrix $M_{\alpha\beta}$ to diagonal one. The parameter e is referred to as the selective lumping parameter, which controls the numerical dumping and numerical stability. This parameter is usually set to be about 0.9.

In descritization of the internal mode model, the central difference scheme to time derivative in Eq.(25) is applied as follows:

$$A_{ki}^{n+1} = \frac{1 - 2\Delta t \lambda_k/D^2}{1 + 2\Delta t \lambda_k/D^2} A_{ki}^n + \frac{\Delta t C_{ki}^n \phi_k}{1 + 2\Delta t \lambda_k/D^2} \qquad (37)$$

where

$$C_{ki}^n = \frac{\tau_{Si}}{\rho D}(2 - a_k) + \frac{\tau_{Bi}}{\rho D}[a_k - 2f_k(-1)]$$
$$+ \frac{4}{D^2}[\beta_1 u_{Si} - \beta_2 u_{Bi} f_k(-1)] - \frac{4}{D^2}\lambda_k U_i a_k$$
$$+ \frac{a_k}{D}\left(\int_{-h}^{\eta} u_i' u_j' dz\right)_{,j} + \frac{a_k}{\rho D} S_{ij,j} \qquad (38)$$

NUMERICAL EXAMPLES

The applicability of the present model to the nearshore currents is tested using the experiment results by Okayasu(1988,1992). The physical experiment was performed in a channel with a 1/20 slope. A incident wave has 5.63 cm height and 2.0 s wave period. The radiation stresses are computed according to a small amplitude theory under the regular wave condition. A vertical eddy viscosity coefficient N_v is assumed to be constant vertically and to have the relation to the total depth D such as $N_v = 0.002D$. Other parameters are assumed as follows: $\beta_1 = 0.00001, \beta_2 = 0.001, C_f = 0.01$ and $\Delta t = 0.05s$. The number of eigenvalue function f_r is 40 and the number of layer for depth is 20. Also the computation of vertical model is carried out every ten steps. Fig.6 shows the vertical profiles of on-offshore velocity. The computed results are in reasonable agreement with the experiments, especially at x=22.4m. However, some differences between both results can be recognized in detail. In the experiment, the return flow is developed under the trough, which means that the neutral position of velocity profile is located at the trough line. On the other hand, in the computation, that is located at almost the center of depth. It seems that these are caused by the profile of the vertical eddy viscosity. Actually, according to the experiments, it is recognized that the eddy viscosity is distributed over the depth.

Next, the verification of this model is performed on a basin which has a 1/20 slope. Fig.7 shows the finite element mesh whose area is almost same as experiments. Fig.8 shows the vertical profiles of velocity components at 4 points indicated in Fig.7 and Fig.9 shows the depth-mean velocity vectors and the velocity vectors on the mean water surface and on the bottom. Under the oblique incident wave, a circulation is developed and the currents on the surface is developed toward oblique onshore. Contrary, the currents on the bottom is developed toward oblique offshore. These tendencies have been measured in the experiment by Okayasu(1992).

CONCLUSION

The quasi 3-Dimensional model for wave-induced currents has been presented. Applying this model to wave induced currents measured in the physical experiment models, the reasonable results can be obtained in reduced computational load. In particular, the 3 dimensional structure of nearshore currents, characterized by offshore currents developed close to the bottom can be obvious by using this model. However, the vertical profiles of velocity over the depth were not agreement with experiment results strictly. Those seems to be caused by the profile of eddy viscosity coefficient over the depth.

REFERENCES

Okayasu,A., T. Shibayama and K. Horikawa,1988, "Vertical variation of undertow in the surf zone", Proc. 21th ICCE., pp.478-491.

Okayasu,A., K. Hara and T. Shibayama,1992, "3-D profile of steady currents in a surf zone under a oblique incident wave", Proc. 39rd Japanese Conf. Coastal Eng.,pp.66-70.(in Japanese)

Kawahara, M., H. Hirano, K. Tsubota and K. Inagaki,1982, "Selective Lumping Finite Element Method for Shallow Water Flow", Int. J. Numer. Meth. Fluids, 2:89-112.

Sheng, Y. P. and H. Lee Butler,1982, "Modeling coastal currents and sediment transport", Proc. 18th ICCE., pp.1127-1148.

Svendsen, I. A. and Lorenz, R. S.,1989, "Velocities in Combined Undertow and Longshore Currents", Coastal Eng., Vol. 13, pp.55-79.

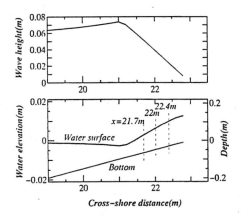

Fig.5 Profiles of wave height and water elevation

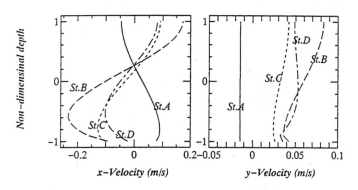

Fig.8 Vertical Profile of Horizontal velocities

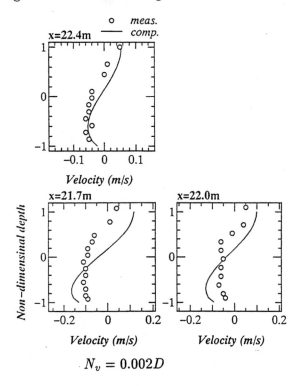

$$N_v = 0.002D$$

Fig.6 Vertical Profile of horizontal velocities

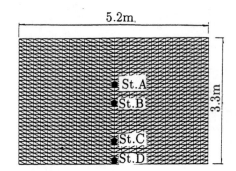

Fig.7 Finite Element Mesh

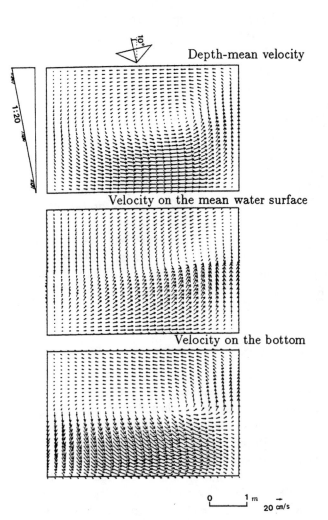

Fig.9 Nearshore Current Vectors

COMPUTATIONAL AEROACOUSTICS

Introduction

A. S. Lyrintzis
Purdue University
West Lafayette, Indiana

O. Baysal
Old Dominion University
Norfolk, Virginia

This part of the volume is a compilation of papers presented at the 1996 Fluids Engineering Division Summer Meeting at the Forum on Computational Aeroacoustics (CAA). This is a continuation of similar forums organized at the 1993 and 1995 meetings (FED Vol. 147 and FED Vol. 219). The Forum has attracted a wide variety of topics from fundamental research to engineering applications. The papers describe work being conducted at universities, government laboratories, and in industry. There is also a contribution from France. The invited lectures were chosen in order to address topics of practical importance. We express our appreciation to the authors for their valuable contributions and for making this forum an important and timely event.

FED-Vol. 238, 1996 Fluids Engineering Division Conference
Volume 3
ASME 1996

Experiences in the Practical Application of Computational Aeroacoustics

Philip J. Morris, Lyle N. Long, Ashok Bangalore,
Thomas Chyczewski, David P. Lockard, Yusuf Ozyoruk
Department of Aerospace Engineering
Penn State University
University Park, PA 16802

Abstract

This paper describes some of the issues that must be addressed in the use of Computational Aeroacoustics (CAA) for the solution of problems of practical importance. Solutions to some of these difficulties are also given. Previous studies have only emphasized the development of algorithms and their application to relatively simple model problems. The particular issues addressed in this paper include: the computational resources required for CAA calculations; grid selection; boundary treatments; equation and algorithm selection; artificial dissipation; Kirchhoff methods; and, post-processing. Examples of computational aeroacoustic calculations are given for ducted fans and jets. The need for three-dimensional, non-linear simulations and the feasibility of such solutions on high performance parallel computers is emphasized.

Introduction

Computational aeroacoustics (CAA) describes the direct calculation of both the aerodynamic sources and the sound they radiate. CAA is distinct from Computational Fluid Dynamics (CFD) in its ability to generate time-accurate compressible flow solutions with minimum dispersion and dissipation errors. The acoustic field, which is the property of interest, may have fluctuation levels that are many orders of magnitude below those in the unsteady flow or source region. Finally, boundary treatments that are non-reflecting and do not generate fictitious numerical acoustic sources must be implemented.

Previous studies of CAA have emphasized algorithm development and numerical methodologies. Often, these new ideas have been validated by comparisons with simple model problems for which an analytic solution exists. Tam (1995) has provided an excellent review of these studies to date; however, as he notes, CAA can not be viewed in isolation from the practical problems that must be solved eventually. It is not productive to seek solutions to model problems whose simplicity avoids the difficult issues that must be addressed in practical applications.

In this paper, we examine some of these issues. These include: the computational resources required for CAA; the choice of grid; boundary treatments; the selection of the appropriate equations and algorithms; and, efficient methods to determine the acoustic far field. Examples are given that elucidate these difficulties and some techniques for their solution are provided. We begin with a discussion of the computational resources. This is related to the grid requirements and the choice of model equations which are described next. Boundary treatments are then discussed. A brief discussion of artificial dissipation is also given. Then, the use of Kirchhoff methods is reviewed. Finally, some post-processing issues are discussed.

Computational Resources

The computational power of high performance computers needs to be exploited in order for realistic CAA calculations to be performed. Parallel computers offer orders of magnitude speed-up over conventional vector processors, at a time when the performance of vector computers is leveling off. In fact, workstations are rapidly approaching the speed of vector computers and massively parallel computers are built from off-the-shelf workstation components. Table 1 compares three parallel computers, from IBM, Intel, and Cray Research. All of these machines look relatively sim-

	IBM SP2 Cornell TC	Intel Paragon Sandia Labs.	Cray T3D Pitt. SCC
Number of Processors	512	1840	512
Processor Type	Power PC RS/6000	Intel I-860	DEC Alpha
Network	High-Speed Switch	Grid	Torus
Total Memory GB	77	38	140
Peak Total Speed Gflop	128	140	77

Table 1: Comparison of Some Current Parallel Computers

ilar at first glance, but the performance and software can be quite different. Achieving more than about 20% of peak on any of these machines on practical applications is quite difficult but not impossible. All of the above machines will eventually run High Performance Fortran (HPF) and Message Passing Interface (MPI) software. These two standards have been agreed upon by virtually all the computer manufacturers. HPF is based on Fortran-90 and adds compiler directives important for parallel processing. In HPF the compiler performs all the complicated parallel processing and message passing automatically. MPI can be used with Fortran-77, Fortran-90, or c and is basically a set of subroutines for message passing. MPI requires that the user decompose the domain manually and handle all of the message passing explicitly. Although there is great freedom to tune a code optimally for a given application, the programmer must take on the responsibility of implementing everything.

One way to address the computer resource requirements is to discuss how many grid points can be modeled, given the memory available. A typical CAA scheme may require roughly 75 floating point numbers (or 600 bytes, in double precision) per grid point. Therefore a 512-processor machine with 256 MB of memory per processor, could store a problem with a grid of 600x600x600 grid points (216 million points). In aeroacoustics simulations, these schemes require roughly 10 grid points per wavelength, which means these large computers could fit roughly 60x60x60 wavelengths (at 3000 Hz, this is roughly 6 m x 6 m x 6 m). Computers even larger than this should be available 2-3 years from now. Also, since these computers and algorithms are meant to be scalable, proportionally smaller problems could be run on smaller computers. For example, a 160-processor SP2 could theoretically hold a problem with roughly 400x400x400 grid points.

Another way to consider what is possible is to estimate the CPU time required. If the scheme requires one mi-

crosecond per cell per time step, then a 600x600x600 grid, and 10,000 time steps, would require 25 days of computer time. The above simulations would therefore require a large computer for many weeks. Clearly these problems are CPU bound, not memory bound. Even if we could fit larger problems on the computer, we may not be able to afford the computer time. Of course, anything we can do to reduce the number of cells required, the number of time steps required, and the mflops sustained per processor would help reduce the CPU time required. If one would like to limit the runs to no more than 24 hours of CPU time, then we would be limited to 8 million (200x200x200) grid points on 512 processors. This would only use 4% of the available memory!

The computational resources CAA requires are not limited to just CPU memory and speed. Mass storage facilities are required to handle the time average numerical solution as well as the numerical solution at many sample times so that a time series analysis can be performed. Modern tape robot facilities are quite effective in storing large quantities of data. The burden of storing the time history of the numerical solution can be reduced by saving only specific locations of interest in the domain and by lowering the time series sampling frequency. Using a reduced sample frequency should not compromise any information since the frequency range of interest is usually relatively low.

Consider a case where a time step Δt of 3.0×10^{-7} seconds is found to be optimum based on the numerical scheme and grid. The highest frequency that can be resolved is given by the Nyquist frequency (see Hardin (1990) for example): $f_N = 1/(2 * \Delta t)$. Thus for the time step of 3.0×10^{-7} seconds, the sample will resolve a frequency up to 1.67 MHZ. This frequency is well above the typical frequencies found in aeroacoustic problems and well above the resolution of practical numerical grids. Based solely on the Nyquist frequency, a good sampling frequency would be once every 32 time steps, which gives $f_N = 52$ kHz. Reducing the sampling frequency has no effect on the resolution of the spectrum since, when applying Fast Fourier Transform (FFT) techniques, the spacing between frequencies of the spectrum (the bin width) is determined by : $BW = 1/(N * \Delta t)$, where N is the number of samples. So, if only 1 in every 32 time steps is saved, N is reduced by a factor of 32, but Δt is multiplied by a factor of 32 so that BW is unchanged.

Selection of Grids

The characteristics of numerical wave propagation depend on the points per wavelength (PPW) and the isotropy of the grid. It is known that the number of grid points per wavelength required to resolve an acoustic wave with a certain degree of accuracy depends on the dissipation and dispersion characteristics of the algorithm. Simple one-dimensional wave calculations could be performed to deter-

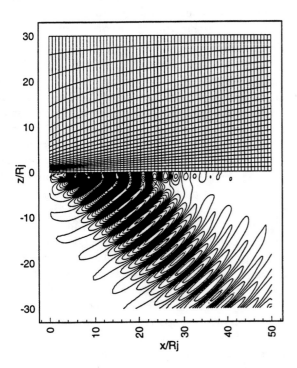

Figure 1: Computational Grid and Perturbation Pressure Contours for a Three-Dimensional, Supersonic Jet Simulation (Every Other Grid Point Shown).

The supersonic jet has a circular nozzle geometry with a jet Mach number of 2.1. The three-dimensional simulations have been performed using stretched Cartesian grids as well as polar grids. Figure 1 shows a cross-section of the grid along the jet axis, and the corresponding perturbation pressure contours are shown in the lower half of the figure. The Mach wave radiation angle is predicted well at 35 degrees to the jet axis. A typical cross-section of a stretched Cartesian grid normal to the jet axis and the corresponding perturbation pressure contours are shown in Figure 2. The perturbation field is expected to be axisymmetric since the mean flow as well as the excited instability mode are axisymmetric in nature. The pressure contours indicate clearly that the anisotropy of the grid distorts the acoustic wavefront in the diagonal direction; hence, the pressure field does not possess azimuthal symmetry. Also, from a points per wavelength (PPW) perspective, the PPW changes along the azimuth resulting in nonuniform dispersion and dissipation in the azimuthal direction. This leads to inaccurate results; hence, stretched Cartesian grids of this type are not suitable for jet noise calculations. This problem of azimuthal nonuniformity may be rectified by the use of polar grids. Figure 3 shows a cross-section of the polar grid normal to the jet axis and the corresponding pressure contours. As expected, the pressure field is axisymmetric. In this case, the PPW do not vary along the azimuth. Also, the coordinate (radial) lines are normal to the acoustic wavefronts. The polar grid has a singularity at zero radius and needs careful treatment; however, a polar grid is recommended for jet noise computations in spite of having this grid singularity.

Boundary Conditions

Non-reflecting boundary conditions are necessary for acoustic simulations since non-physical reflections of waves into the computational domain can alter the solution significantly. These boundaries are in general composed of inflow and outflow boundaries. A set of boundary condition operators, B_m, was constructed by Bayliss & Turkel (1982). When they are applied, the terms of the asymptotic series solutions of the convective wave equation are annihilated to $O(1/d^{2m+1})$ where d is the distance of the boundary point to a reference point in the source region. High order B_m operators are more accurate but are difficult to implement because of their high order temporal and spatial derivatives. Tam & Webb (1993) derived essentially the same operator as the B_1 operator using asymptotic solutions of the linearized Euler equations. Tam and Webb applied the B_1 operator to all of the primitive perturbation variables on inflow boundaries and on the pressure perturbation on outflow boundaries. The linearized Euler equations are used at outflow boundaries for the other perturbation variables. This type of boundary condition

mine the PPW requirements for different finite difference algorithms. However, the isotropy of the grid also plays an important role in capturing the wave in a direction not coincident with the coordinate (grid line) direction. This section illustrates a practical example of a three-dimensional aeroacoustic calculation of an axisymmetric supersonic jet. The generation of the grid for a free jet is relatively simple as there are no body surfaces involved in the domain. Some of the grid types that could be considered to solve the jet problem include uniform/stretched Cartesian grids and polar grids. Uniform Cartesian grids would require an enormous number of grid points for three-dimensional aeroacoustic calculations to resolve all the scales in jet mixing layer as well as the acoustic field. As discussed above, such very large simulations cannot be performed using present day computers. This limitation on the maximum grid size has lead the authors to use stretched Cartesian grids or polar grids for three-dimensional jet calculations. These jet noise calculations are performed by solving the nonlinear disturbance equations on parallel computers using a domain decomposition strategy (see Bangalore, Morris & Long (1996) for details).

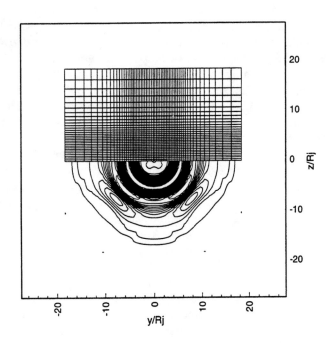

Figure 2: Perturbation Pressure Contours and Stretched Cartesian Grid

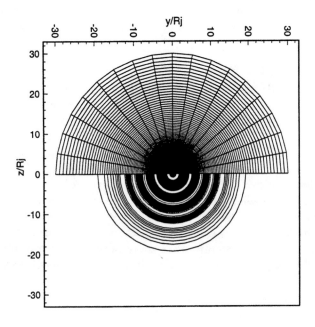

Figure 3: Perturbation Pressure Contours and Polar Grid

attempts to exploit the physics of the problem to simplify the equations in the vicinity of the boundary. Very successful aerodynamic and aeroacoustic simulations using the full Euler equations together with these conditions are reported by Ozyoruk & Long (1996b).

These conditions in general work very well when all of the assumptions are satisfied. Unfortunately, there are many physical situations where they are not. The most obvious involves finite-amplitude effects when a nonlinear flow solver is used in the interior. Relatively large reflections can be caused by finite amplitude waves. One practical solution is to stretch the grid in the vicinity of the boundary to move the boundary farther away from the source and to damp out the waves on large cells. This is useful since the accuracy of the conditions is a function of the boundary point distance d and wave amplitude, as indicated above. Although the condition is somewhat forgiving to errors in the specification of the source point, it is important to have the wave angle correct. For instance, the condition will fail for a plane wave when all wave angles are calculated for a point source with cylindrical or spherical propagation. Difficulties also arise when vorticity or entropy propagates parallel to no-flow boundaries which require the same treatment as inflow boundaries. The presence of vorticity or entropy produces large errors since all waves are assumed to be acoustic.

The numerical implementation of the Bayliss-Turkel/Tam-Webb inflow and outflow conditions usually involves adding cells to the domain where the boundary equations are solved. Some researchers have used three additional cells so that a seven point central difference operator can be used throughout the interior, and the biased operators are restricted to the region where the alternate set of equations which allow outward propagation are solved. Although this is better for stability, there is very little difference in the results for most Euler calculations if only one point is used. Obviously, there is a reduction in the work done in the boundary region. Furthermore, there is an additional complication when nonlinear equations are solved in conservative form in the interior. The conditions are most concisely written for the perturbed variables so that additional bookkeeping is needed when the total variables are used.

Giles (1990) used a different approach to derive approximate, unsteady boundary conditions for two-dimensional problems by performing a Fourier decomposition of the linearized Euler equations. They have been applied to turbomachinery problems by Giles (1990) and have been found to be effective. When implemented with a buffer zone, these conditions have been able to permit nonlinear vortical structures to leave a computational domain with little reflection(see Colonius & Lele (1993)). A drawback of both the asymptotic and Fourier methods is that their derivation employs a set of equations that have been linearized with respect to a reference solution. In many cases the reference solution is not known a priori and must be developed as the equations are integrated. Experimentation with a rectangular jet problem by Chyczewski (1996) suggests that asymptotic and Fourier methods are not capable of establishing a reasonable reference, or time-averaged, solution when the initial condition is a quiescent fluid. For this case the quasi one-dimensional boundary procedure developed by Thompson (1990) has been found to be capable of minimizing reflections. The approach consists of decomposing the full nonlinear Euler equations into modes of definite velocity and specifying nonreflecting conditions for those modes that have a velocity directed into the computational domain. This approach requires special attention in corner regions and also makes implicit assumptions about the wave propagation direction. Recently, Dong (1996) has also investigated modifications to the asymptotic boundary conditions to incorporate variations in the mean flow.

An important consideration for any boundary condition is its effect on the stability of the scheme. Since biased operators must be used, instabilities are likely to develop first in boundary regions. Carpenter, Gottlieb & Arbanel (1993) recently developed a stability analysis for asymptotically large times. This is important for CAA since many time steps are required to reach a periodic steady state and to sample the data. This analysis can verify that a certain set of spatial derivative operators will always be stable.

Selection of Equations

From the preceding sections it is clear that computational resources should be used as efficiently as possible. Thus, the selection of the appropriate equations and algorithms is extremely important. In terms of analysis and coding it is easiest to deal with linearized equations. For some scattering problems this is sufficient. If nonlinear effects need to be included, the Euler equations could be used. Though acoustic phenomena are usually contained within these inviscid equations, many source and propagation effects are associated with viscous effects. With the emergence of parallel computers it has become possible to include more physics in the numerical simulation of aerodynamic noise phenomena. Chyczewski & Long (1996) performed simulations of high speed jet noise using the full, three-dimensional Navier-Stokes equations; however, only the largest scales were resolved and no sub-grid-scale turbulence model was used. Such simulations are appropriate for high speed jet noise where the scales of the energy-containing turbulence structures match those of the acoustic field. For lower speed flows additional scale resolution would be needed, and this would require a finer spatial and temporal resolution.

These approaches provide the researcher with the capability to simulate the effects of nonlinearity, flow-acoustic interactions, and non-uniform background flow; however, the instantaneous solution contains both the aerodynamic as well as the acoustic solution. The basic aerodynamic solution may be identified first, but this process can take as much as 47% of the total solution time (see Chyczewski (1996)) for the initial transients to leave the computational domain. The same higher-order algorithms should be used for the entire calculations. This is because the use of a different algorithm for the averaged flow field could give rise to additional numerical errors that might not be distinguishable from the physical fluctuations. This is one deficiency of the use of the full non-split equations. However, in other cases, such as the ducted fan calculations of Ozyoruk & Long (1996a) and Ozyoruk & Long (1996c), the basic aerodynamic field is equivalent to the steady flow field. Then convergence acceleration techniques, such as the multigrid method can be used to overcome the slow convergence of higher-order schemes to obtain the mean flow field.

An equivalent approach has been used in jet noise simulations by Bangalore et al. (1996). In their calculations, the time-averaged flow is obtained from a Reynolds-averaged Navier-Stokes solution. Then, the nonlinear disturbance equations are solved with the mean flow as source terms. This approach takes advantage of previous advances in turbulence modeling for steady flows, is computationally less intense then DNS or LES simulations, and makes boundary treatments simpler. It is also possible to check whether the turbulent stresses modeled in the RANS solutions are compatible with those calculated from the nonlinear disturbance equations. This provides some additional insight into existing turbulence models and the basis for an iterative turbulence model for complex flows.

In all of these calculations, the use of high-order accurate discretization schemes is essential. These schemes provide the best combination of dissipation and dispersion characteristics with minimal grid requirements. These considerations have been discussed previously (Tam & Webb (1993), among others) and will not be reiterated here.

Artificial Dissipation

Many schemes, such as Runge-Kutta-central-difference or DRP schemes, contain very little dissipation and require the addition of extra terms to damp out spurious high frequency modes and for stability. The spectral characteristics of these terms can be optimized for acoustic applications (see Tam & Webb (1993) for example) by reducing the filter's impact on the resolved frequency range. Nonlinear filter schemes (i.e. dissipation functions that have solution dependent coefficients) have been found to be valuable in some investigations. For example Chyczewski & Long (1996), have developed a dissipation algorithm that supplies second order dissipation in the high flow gradient regions for stability and sixth order dissipation in the smooth regions to damp spurious modes. In supersonic jet noise applications, they have found that the low order dissipation is confined to the shear layer. Thus the acoustic field contains only sixth order dissipation which does not significantly effect the acoustic solution.

Kirchhoff Methods

Formidable computational costs associated with the direct numerical calculation of far-field noise radiation of aeroacoustic problems can be overcome by using far-field extrapolation techniques. One very useful tool has been the Kirchhoff method. Given the time evolution of the acoustic pressure on a surface enclosing the source region, this method provides an integral solution for the far-field noise. The Kirchhoff method assumes that the acoustic field outside this closed surface, called the Kirchhoff surface, is governed by the wave equation. Various forms of the Kirchhoff integral formula have appeared in the literature. Reviews can be found by Lyrintzis (1994) and Farassat (1996). Farassat & Myers (1988) derived a general form of the Kirchhoff formula in the time domain for arbitrarily moving and deforming surfaces using generalized function theory. This formula was used for the far-field predictions of ducted fan noise by Ozyoruk (1995) and Ozyoruk & Long (1996a), Ozyoruk & Long (1996c); jet noise by Chyczewski & Long (1996); and rotorcraft noise by Wissink, Lyrintzis, Strawn, Oliker & Biswas (1996). Due to the assumptions of the Kirchhoff method, some care must be taken in applications. First, the Kirchhoff surface must be chosen such that it encloses any nonlinearities and flow non-uniformities that might be important. Also, the pressure fluctuations over the Kirchhoff surface must be associated only with the acoustic waves. An example where this can be important is the far-field calculation of jet noise by Chyczewski & Long (1996). For jet calculations an open Kirchhoff surface is usually employed so that hydrodynamic fluctuations associated with the convecting eddies can be avoided. Additional restrictions to the choice of the Kirchhoff surface arise from numerical issues, such as the points-per-wavelength requirement of the computational mesh in the neighborhood of the Kirchhoff surface and its distance to the outer boundaries of the domain. No far-field boundary conditions are truly nonreflecting and; therefore, any possible reflections could not contaminate the acoustic solution on the Kirchhoff surface. Since the Kirchhoff formula requires the acoustic solution on the Kirchhoff surface at the retarded times, efficient coupling of it with a near-field flow solver is another important issue. A very efficient numerical implementation of the Kirchhoff formula of Farassat & Myers (1988) can be found in Ozyoruk (1995) and Ozyoruk & Long (1996a) for fixed observers relative to a rigid Kirchhoff surface in rectilinear

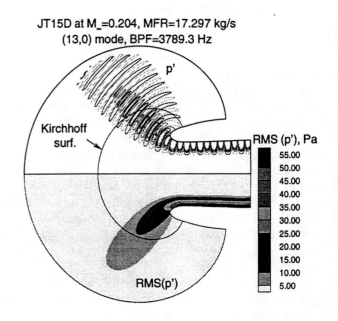

Figure 4: Instantaneous and RMS Acoustic Pressure Contours, and the Kirchhoff Surface. JT1D Inlet. $M_\infty = 0.204$, $MFR = 17.297$ kg/s, BPF= 3789.3 Hz.

motion. This implementation uses a recursive summation approach for the surface integrations and thereby removes the need for the long time histories of the acoustic solution on the surface. An example of the use of the Kirchhoff surface for the far-field prediction of ducted fan noise (Ozyoruk (1995); Ozyoruk & Long (1996a), Ozyoruk & Long (1996c)) is shown in Figure 4. The acoustic contours of the spinning (13,0) mode of the JT15D engine (from Eversman, Parrett, Preisser & Silcox (1985)) and the placement of a Kirchhoff surface used for the far-field predictions are shown. It should be noted that this surface is also open. A general rule for the use of an open Kirchhoff surface in any application is that the far-field contributions of the removed portion of the closed surface be negligible. The corresponding far-field prediction by the Kirchhoff method is shown in Fig. 5 together with the finite element/wave envelope (FE-WE) solution and experimental data of Eversman et al. (1985). Despite the open Kirchhoff surface, the Euler/Kirchhoff predictions are in very good agreement with the other data.

Post-Processing Issues

One of the most valuable tools used to characterize noise is the Fourier transform of a time dependent signal; such as mass flux in the noise source region or pressure in the acoustic field. These transforms are usually obtained using efficient Fast Fourier Transform (FFT) methods. FFT's

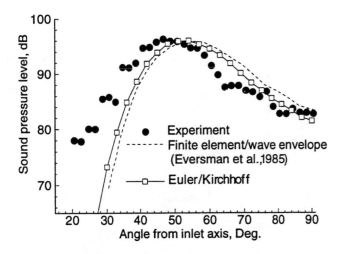

Figure 5: Far-Field Sound Pressure Level of the (13,0) Mode. JT15D Inlet. $M_\infty = 0.204$, $MFR = 17.297$ kg/s, BPF= 3789.3 Hz.

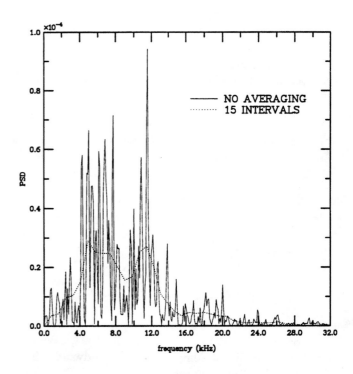

Figure 6: Effect of Ensemble Averaging on a Typical Spectrum in the Jet Shear Layer.

are exact only when there is precisely an integer number of wavelengths of each frequency in the time series. Since the FFT perceives the time series as periodic and infinite, a non-integer number of wavelengths is interpreted as a discontinuity and will produced errors in the spectrum. When dealing with random signals it is impossible to get an integer number of wavelengths and errors are incurred. The impact of these errors, however, can be reduced in a couple of ways. One is to use a window, such as Hanning or Kaiser (see Hardin (1990)), which reduces the relative influence of the samples near the beginning and end of the time series. Another method (which can be used in addition to a window) is to break the entire time sample into many intervals, take the FFT of each interval and average the results. This method does change the bin width, however, since the number of samples (per interval) is changed while keeping a constant Δt. If a low time series sampling frequency is used, only a small number of intervals can be generated, which reduces the effectiveness of the method. Thus the averaging process would compel a sampling frequency that is higher than one based on Nyquist frequency considerations. As an example, consider Fig. 6 which shows a typical spectrum taken from the shear layer of a supersonic jet shear layer simulation. The record length is 2048 time samples. When a single interval of 2048 samples is used, the spectra is very 'spiky' and may lead to incorrect conclusions about the signal. On the other hand, the FFT averaged over 15 intervals is more broadband and is easier to interpret.

Discussion

In this paper we have presented some problems that arise in the application of CAA to practical problems. Solutions have also been provided in most cases. Clearly, additional problems need to be addressed. For example, the application of boundary conditions on curved walls, or the numerical simulation of frequency dependent wall boundary conditions for liner applications, are not discussed here. The authors are addressing these and other issues and they will be reported elsewhere (see Ozyoruk & Long (1996d) for example). In any application, it is the authors' contention that three-dimensional simulations should be performed. Few aeroacoustic phenomena are truly two-dimensional. Methods that are developed for two-dimensional model problems may be elegant and relatively simple, but unless their extension to three-dimensional applications is clear, they will be of limited long-term use. Also, few problems of sound generation as well as radiation are linear. With the availability of high performance, parallel computers, three-dimensional nonlinear simulations are feasible, and should be the emphasis of current and future activities.

References

Bangalore, A., Morris, P. J., and Long, L. N., 1996, "A Parallel Three-Dimensional Computational Aeroacoustic

Method Using Nonlinear Disturbance Equations", AIAA Paper 96-1728.

Bayliss, A., and Turkel, E., 1982, "Far Field Boundary Conditions for Compressible Flow", J. Computational Physics, Vol. 48, pp. 182–199.

Carpenter, M. H., Gottlieb, D., and Arbanel, S., 1993, "The Stability of Numerical Boundary Treatments for Compact High-Order Finite-Difference Schemes", Journal of Computational Physics, Vol. 108, pp. 272–295.

Chyczewski, T. S., 1996, A Time-Dependent, Three-Dimensional, Numerical Study of Supersonic Rectangular Jet Flow and Noise Using the Full Navier-Stokes Equations, PhD thesis, Penn State University.

Chyczewski, T. S., and Long, L. N., 1996, "Numerical Prediction of the Noise Produced by a Perfectly Expanded Jet". AIAA-96-1730.

Colonius, T., and Lele, S. K., M. P., 1993, "Boundary Conditions for Direct Computation of Aerodynamic Sound Generation", AIAA Journal, Vol. 31(9), pp. 1574–1582.

Dong, T. Z., 1996, "A set of simple radiation boundary conditions for acoustics computations in non-uniform mean flows", AIAA Paper-96-0274.

Eversman, W., Parrett, A. V., Preisser, J. S., and Silcox, R. J., 1985, "Contributions to the Finite Element Solution of the Fan Noise Radiation Problem", Trans. ASME, pp. 216–223.

Farassat, F., 1996, "Generalized Functions and Kirchhoff Equations", AIAA Paper 96-1705.

Farassat, F., and Myers, M. K., 1988, "Extension of Kirchhoff's Formula to Radiation From Moving Surfaces", Journal of Sound and Vibration, Vol. 123(3), pp. 451–460.

Giles, M. B., 1990, "Nonreflecting Boundary Conditions for Euler Equation Calculations", AIAA Journal, Vol. 28(12), pp. 2050–2057.

Hardin, J. C., 1990, Introduction to Time Series Analysis, NASA Reference Pub. 1145.

Lyrintzis, A. S., 1994, "Review: The Use of Kirchhoff's Method in Computational Aeroacoustics", ASME Journal of Fluids Engineering, Vol. 116, pp. 665–675.

Ozyoruk, Y., 1995, Sound Radiation From Ducted Fans Using Computational Aeroacoustics on Parallel Computers, PhD thesis, Penn State University.

Ozyoruk, Y., and Long, L. N., 1996a, "Computation of Sound Radiating From Engine Inlets", AIAA Journal, Vol. 34(5).

Ozyoruk, Y., and Long, L. N., 1996b, "A New Efficient Algorithm for Computational Aeroacoustics on Parallel Processors"', Journal of Computational Physics, Vol. 125, pp. 135–149.

Ozyoruk, Y., and Long, L. N., 1996c, "Progress in Time-Domain Calculations of Ducted fan Noise", AIAA Paper 96-1771.

Ozyoruk, Y., and Long, L. N., 1996d, "A Time-Domain Implementation of Surface Acoustic Impedance Boundary Conditions With and Without Flow", AIAA Paper 96-1663.

Tam, C. K. W., 1995, "Computational Aeroacoustics: Issues and Methods", AIAA Journal, Vol. 33(10), pp. 1788–1796.

Tam, C. K. W., and Webb, J. C., 1993, "Dispersion-Relation-Preserving Difference Schemes for Computational Aeroacoustics", J. Computational Physics, Vol. 107(2), pp. 262–281.

Thompson, K. W., 1990, "Time-Dependent Boundary Conditions for Hyperbolic Systems, II", Journal of Computational Physics, Vol. 89, pp. 439–461.

Wissink, A. M., Lyrintzis, A. S., Strawn, R. C., Oliker, L., and Biswas, R., 1996, "Efficient Helicopter Aerodynamic and Aeroacoustic Predictions on Parallel Computers", AIAA Paper 96-0153.

FED-Vol. 238, 1996 Fluids Engineering Division Conference
Volume 3
ASME 1996

From Jet Flow Computations To Far-field Noise Prediction.

J.L. ESTIVALEZES   L. GAMET *

ONERA-CERT-DERMES

2, Av. Edouard BELIN

31055 TOULOUSE Cedex

FRANCE

Abstract

Recent developments in jet acoustics conducted us to implement highly accurate codes with appropriate inflow and outflow boundary conditions. Non-reflexive Boundary Conditions based on a Thompson's like approach were coupled with a 2-4 MacCormack interior scheme. The full time dependent Navier-Stokes equations were solved in a two or three-dimensional case. Subgrid scale modelling is provided by the structure-function model of Lesieur et al. Sufficiently refined unsteady simulations of the near-field of the jet flows will then be used to obtain the far-field pressure at observation positions at large distances, in the outside flow governed by a linear convective wave equation. An integral method based on a Kirchhoff surface integral is proposed to calculate the linear propagation of pressure waves in the far-field.

1 Introduction

Jet noise suppression is one of the challenging tasks in the future supersonic flight transport programs. In a first step, accurate prediction of jet noise, and other noise mechanisms, is an essential prerequisite in order to be able to control or modify flow-generated sounds.

Recent advances in Computational Fluid Dynamics (CFD), and in computer technology, have made some

---

*Ph.D. Student at the ENSAE, 10 Av. Edouard BELIN, 31055 TOULOUSE Cedex

simple aeroacoustics computations plausible, even if direct extension of CFD methods to Computational Aero-Acoustics (CAA) remains difficult, in both the sound generation and sound propagation. In principle, one could directly calculate the sound field by extending the computational domain to the far field. However, this requires storage capabilities and CPU resources that are beyond the currently available ones. Besides, because the acoustic perturbations are usually quite small, the use of non-linear equations could result in errors [12]. Kirchhoff integral method is an alternative to this problem. The basic idea is to restrict the full computation to the near field and to use an acoustic approximation based on a Kirchhoff integral to get the far field. The physical domain is then divided in two parts: the near field, modelled by the full equations, where we perform Large Eddy Simulations (LES) or Direct Numerical Simulations (DNS), and the far field, modelled by a simple wave equation. We present in that paper the current developments undertaken in that direction, and some first results.

2 Numerical algorithm

The full time dependent Navier-Stokes equations of the two or three-dimensional fluid motion are written in a non-dimensional conservative form. For instance, in a three-dimensional cylindrical case we have:

$$\frac{\partial U}{\partial t} + \frac{\partial F}{\partial x} + \frac{\partial rG}{r\partial r} + \frac{\partial H}{r\partial \theta} - \frac{\partial F_v}{\partial x} - \frac{\partial rG_v}{r\partial r} - \frac{\partial H_v}{r\partial \theta} = \mathcal{S}$$

F, G, H are the non-viscous fluxes, F_v, G_v, H_v the viscous contributions, and $\mathcal{S}$ the cylindrical source term.

Equations are solved using a finite volume high order extension of MacCormack's scheme, developed originally by Gottlieb and Turkel [5]. Based on predictor corrector phases, the scheme is explicit, second order accurate in time and fourth order in space. Extension to two or three dimensions and to the solving of the complete fluid motion equations is done through a directional splitting sequence. Boundary conditions are applied at the end of each sweep.

The values of flux vectors at nodes situated two cells outside the computational domain are needed at cells close to the left and right side boundaries for each direction. Third order extrapolations are used to get fluxes at these points outside the computational domain (grid points $N+1$, $N+2$, -2 and -1) at both predictor and corrector stages. Following Thompson [13, 14], a characteristic based Boundary Condition procedure is then used to get the correct boundary values. The approach we used was to linearize the equations and consider one-dimensional characteristic variables normal to the boundary. The boundary treatment is based on the inviscid equations. Giles [2, 4, 3] boundary treatment was also used as a radiation boundary condition in jet flow computations.

A subgrid scale model based on the second order velocity structure function model developed by Lesieur et al. [9, 6] was implemented. This model introduces an eddy-viscosity calculated from a spectral eddy-viscosity obtained from a kinetic energy spectrum local in space, in the 3D simulations. This model was found to be too sensitive to the large scales of motion in the flow field, providing too much eddy-viscosity during the early stages of transition in a shear flow. Therefore, we also implemented the filtered structure function model [1], where a high-pass filter is applied to the resolved velocity field before computing its structure function.

3 Kirchhoff Method

A Kirchhoff integral method was chosen to evaluate the radiated sound from a jet flow. The principle of the method is to first calculate a numerical simulation of the near-field of the jet, using the above numerical method. Pressure in the far field at a given observer position can then be obtained in terms of an integral involving the pressure and its derivatives on a control surface S that surrounds all the non-linear sources. Outside this control surface, the flow is moving at a uniform subsonic speed U_∞, and is governed by the convective wave equation:

$$\nabla^2 \Phi - \frac{1}{c_\infty^2}\left(\frac{\partial}{\partial t} + U_\infty \frac{\partial}{\partial x}\right)^2 \Phi = 0 \qquad (1)$$

where Φ is any quantity satisfying the wave equation. This equation is solved in terms of a Green's function. The solution at an observer point $\mathbf{x} = (x, y, z)$ outside S can be obtained in the final form:

$$\Phi(\mathbf{x}, t) = \frac{1}{4\pi}\iint_{S_0}\left[\frac{\Phi}{r_0^2}\frac{\partial r_0}{\partial n_0} - \frac{1}{r_0}\frac{\partial \Phi}{\partial n_0} \right. $$
$$\left. + \frac{1}{c_\infty r_0 \beta^2}\frac{\partial \Phi}{\partial \tau}\left(\frac{\partial r_0}{\partial n_0} - M_\infty \frac{\partial x_0}{\partial n_0}\right)\right]_\tau dS_0 \qquad (2)$$

The subscript 0 denotes the Prandtl-Glauret coordinate transformation (defined by $x_0 = x$, $y_0 = \beta y$, $z_0 = \beta z$ with $\beta = \sqrt{1 - M_\infty^2}$). r_0 is the distance between the observer position and a point on the surface. $\mathbf{n}_0$ denotes the outward pointing vector normal to the surface. The terms in $[\ ]_\tau$ are to be evaluated at the retarded time $t - \tau$ with:

$$\tau = \frac{r_0 - M_\infty(x - x')}{c_\infty \beta^2} \qquad (3)$$

$\mathbf{x}' = (x', y', z')$ refers to a point on the control surface. The method only requires first order derivatives on the control surface, and so, is easily implemented. It has been recently reviewed by Lyrintzis [7] and applied to jets aeracoustics by Lyrintzis [8] and Soh [11].

In the case of jets, the Kirchhoff surface is taken to be a cylinder, included in the cylindrical calculation domain. On the bases of this cylinder, Kirchhoff's hypotheses are no longer true, since the surface is not in a linear domain. In our calculations, the integration will simply not be performed on the cylinder bases.

4 Jet noise calculations

The simulations presented here show exploratory results of jet noise calculations, on a hot jet at Mach number $M = 2$ and total temperature 1366 K at nozzle exit. This case is taken from the experiments of Seiner and Ponton [10].

For the simulations, we impose inflow velocity of a given momentum thickness and density profiles. Random velocity perturbations of low amplitude are superimposed on the inflow profiles. Once the initial conditions are evacuated, far-field pressure is calculated using Kirchhoff method, at a number of observers situated in a plane including the jet axis and on a circle of radius 80 (R^*) centered on the origin of the domain, at nozzle exit on the jet axis. Kirchhoff's surface is a cylinder of radial and axial dimensions L_{rK} and L_{xK} equal to the domain size (except in the 3D case below).

Preliminary results were obtained with axisymmetric simulations, at $Re = 1000$, on a 40×6 (radii) domain, with 344×120 points. Inflow momentum thickness equals $1/19$. Figure 1 shows OASPL far field acoustic data and Strouhal dependence on angle to jet inlet axis in this case. Numerical data seem to be shifted by 35 dBs. Frequency data exhibit a few points in the low angles that does not make sense, and a large amount of scatter can be seen at large angles. But, the general trend in amplitude and frequency variation seems to be recovered. An instantaneous snapshot of the pressure field is plotted on Figure 2, showing that the flow is dominated by directional Mach wave emissions, in agreement with the experiments.

Further results were then obtained with fully 3D cylindrical LES at $Re = 30000$ for the same case, on a $40 \times 6 \times 2\pi$ domain, with $144 \times 50 \times 40$ points. Inflow momentum thickness equals $1/10$. Figure 3 shows mean velocity variation along the jet axis, and averaged velocity profiles plotted versus the reduced radial coordinate $\eta = (r - r_{1/2})/x$, where $r_{1/2}$ is the radius to half velocity. Figure 4 shows other statistics calculated in cylindrical coordinates. Except $\langle u'w' \rangle$ and $\langle v'w' \rangle$ cross-correlations, the profiles look similar.

OASPL and Strouhal angular dependence on angle to jet inlet axis are shown on Figure 5 in the 3D cylindrical calculation. A better agreement with the experiment can be obtained with a Kirchhoff surface shorter than the total domain axial size (We have not find an explanation to that point). The agreement is better than the one obtained with axisymmetric simulations. The flow field close to the nozzle exit is also dominated by Mach wave emissions (not show here), but the pictures of Figure 6 show the evident three-dimensionality of the flow features downstream.

5 Conclusion

The present paper shows limited but preliminary results of jet flow simulations coupled with a Kirchhoff predictive method, to determine the radiated jet noise. LES of the fully three-dimensional equations shows more promising results than axisymmetric simulations, which can not take into account the three-dimensionality of highly compressible flows.

References

[1] F. DUCROS, P. COMTE, and M. LESIEUR. Large-eddy simulation of a weakly-compressible boundary layer spatially developing over an adiabatic flat plate. In *Proceedings of the International Symposium on Turbulence, Heat and Mass Transfer*. Lisbon, Portugal, August 1994.

[2] M. GILES. Non-reflecting boundary conditions for the euler equations. Technical Report CFDL-TR-88-1, Computational Fluid Dynamics Laboratory, Massachusetts Institute of Technology., 1987.

[3] M. GILES. Non-reflecting boundary conditions for Euler equation calculation. *AIAA journal*, 28(12):2050–2058, 1990.

[4] M. GILES. Non-reflecting boundary conditions for unsteady airfoil calculations. Technical Report CFDL-TR-90-1, Computational Fluid Dynamics Laboratory, Massachusetts Institute of Technology., 1990.

[5] D. GOTTLIEB and E. TURKEL. Dissipative two-four methods for time dependent problems. *Mathematics of Computation*, 30:703–723, 1976.

[6] M. LESIEUR, O. METAIS, X. NORMAND, and A. SILVEIRA-NETO. *Spectral Large Eddy Simulation of Turbulent Shear Flows*, pages 179–192. Boris Galerpin and Steven A. Orszag, Cambridge University Press, 1993.

[7] A.S. LYRINTZIS. Review: The use of Kirchhoff's method in computational aeroacoustics. *Journal of Fluids Engineering*, 116:665–676, 1994.

[8] A.S. LYRINTZIS and R.R. MANKBADI. On the prediction of the far-field jet noise using Kirchhoff's formulation. *AIAA Paper 95-0508*, 1995.

[9] O. METAIS and M. LESIEUR. Spectral large-eddy simulation of isotropic and stably stratified turbulence. *Journal of Fluid Mechanics*, 239:157–194, 1992.

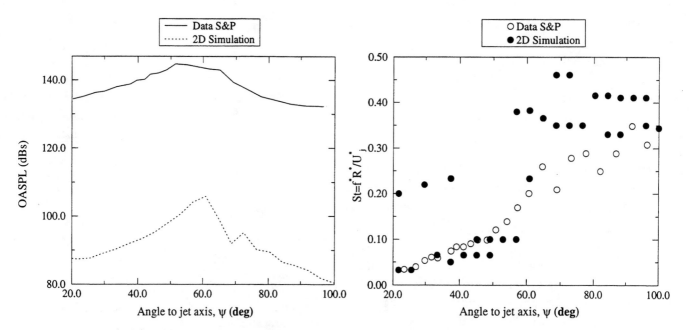

Figure 1: OASPL (left) and dominant Strouhal number (right) versus angle to jet axis in the 2D axisymmetric simulation. $\psi = 0$ corresponds to the jet axis itself.

Figure 2: Instantaneous snapshot of the pressure field in the 2D axisymmetric simulation.

[10] J.M. SEINER and M.K. PONTON. The effects of temperature on supersonic jet noise emission. *DGLR-AIAA Paper 92-02-046*, 1992.

[11] W.Y. SOH. Unsteady jet flow computation towards noise prediction. *AIAA Paper 94-0138*, 1994.

[12] R.W. STOKER and M.J. SMITH. An evaluation of finite volume direct simulation and perturbation methods in CAA applications. *AIAA Paper 93-0152*, 1993.

[13] K.W. THOMPSON. Time dependent boundary conditions for hyperbolic systems I . *Journal of Computational Physics*, 68:1–24, 1987.

[14] K.W. THOMPSON. Time dependent boundary conditions for hyperbolic systems II . *Journal of Computational Physics*, 89:439–461, 1987.

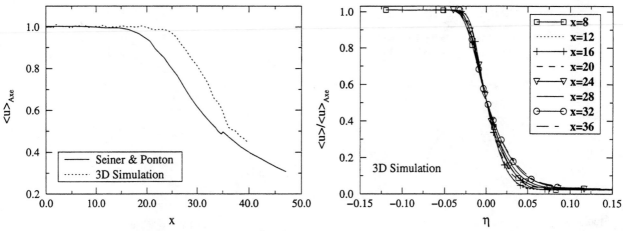

Figure 3: Mean velocity along the jet centerline (left) and averaged velocity profiles (right) as a function of reduced radial coordinate η in the 3D cylindrical simulation.

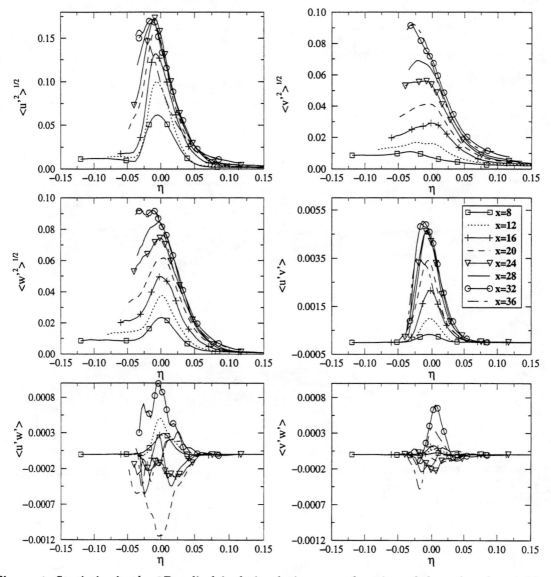

Figure 4: Statistics in the 3D cylindrical simulation, as a function of the reduced variable η.

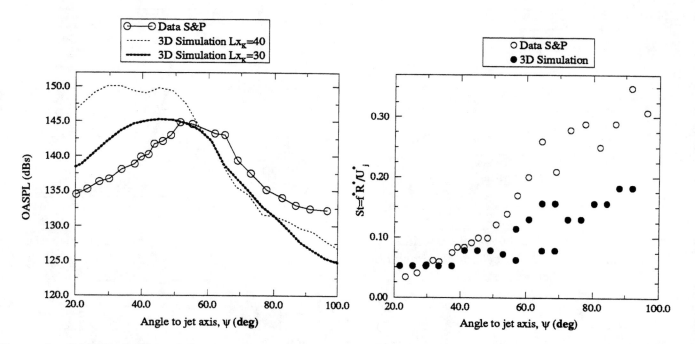

Figure 5: OASPL (left) and dominant Strouhal number (right) versus angle to jet axis in the 3D cylindrical simulation. Two different lengths are used for the Kirchhoff's control surface: $L_{xK} = 30$ and $L_{xK} = 40$. $\psi = 0$ corresponds to the jet axis itself.

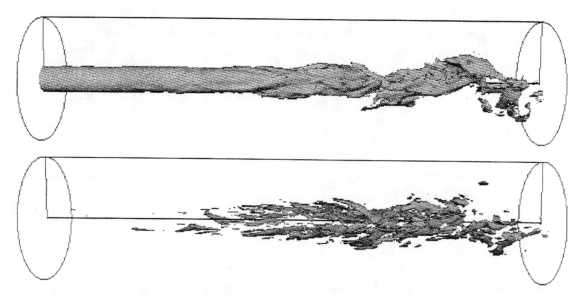

Figure 6: Instantaneous isosurfaces of passive scalar field (isosurface $C = 0.5$) and axial vorticity (green $\omega_x = 0.6$, magenta $\omega_x = -0.6$) in the 3D cylindrical simulation.

FED-Vol. 238, 1996 Fluids Engineering Division Conference
Volume 3
ASME 1996

Numerical Simulation of the Mixing Noise in Turbulent Flows

M. E. Hayder, Y. Zhou and R. Rubinstein
Institute for Computer Applications in Science and Engineering
NASA Langley Research Center
Hampton, VA 23681-0001

Abstract

We present a formulation to simulate the noise generated by turbulence. Theories relating to the construction of the turbulence source terms in the governing equations are also presented. We solve the linearized Euler equations with turbulence source terms to simulate generation and propagation of jet noise.

Introduction

Realiable predictive tools are needed to develop noise suppression technology for flows like those associated with a high speed civil transport plane. Our focus in this study is in the prediction of noise in turbulent flows. In particular we consider an axisymmetric supersonic jet. The current status of jet noise research may be found in the review article by Tam (1995). Direct numerical simulation (DNS) of such a flow field is extremely expensive. In a previous study (Mankbadi et al., 1994), we made large eddy simulations (LES) of this problem. To reduce computational cost, the flowfield was assumed axisymmetric and the simulations were limited to two dimensions. Such LES simulations are also very expensive and routine calculations may not yet be feasible. On the other hand, one can get valuable insights by solving the linearized Euler equations. In this study, we examine one such approach. In our governing equations, we retain contributions due to products of fluctuating velocity components. Such products are important in noise generation. We use a stochastic approach to simulate these terms and they act as sources in our equations. Thus we may be able to account for many accurate features of turbulence, even though we solve the linearized Euler equations. In our development of the source term, we pay special attention to the temporal correlations. In fact, we believe that the temporal correlation is directly responsible for the frequency distribution of the noise energy (Rubinstein and Zhou, 1996). Indeed,

the choice of the two-time correlations that based on local straining or that dominated by large scale sweeping of isotropic turbulence lead to distinctive expressions of the acoustic power (Zhou and Rubinstein, 1996). Our turbulence source not only has the correct inertial range spatial correlation, but also has the desired temporal correlation which is consistent with local strain. Recently Bechara et al. (1993) also employed a stochastic approach to the turbulence source term, and in fact, their turbulence spatial correlation is essentially same as ours. However, their velocity field is frozen in time and the temporal correlation is white, i.e., there is no temporal correlation. At each step, they used a filtering operation which was defined through the mean values of turbulent kinetic energy and dissipation. Although this step leads to a power spectra density of the filter output signal, this filtering procedure clearly is not a desired way to construct temporal correlations. Our turbulence source is more realistic and is an alternative to that of Bechara et al. (1993).

In the next two sections we discuss the governing equations and the numerical model. We then discuss the construction of source terms and present preliminary results.

Governing Equations

We present a formulation to solve the noise field in two steps. In the first step the mean flow field is calculated by solving the Navier Stokes equations for turbulent flows. In the second step the linearized Euler equations with turbulence source terms for noise are solved. The noise source terms are constructed from the turbulence kinetic energy (K) and dissipation rate (ϵ) computed in the first step. Since the first step of our formulation is well known in the computational fluid dynamics and computational aeroacoustic communities, we shall discuss only our formulation in the second step, namely the form of the linearized Euler equations and the noise source terms due to turbulence.

In this study we assume both mean and turbulence flowfield to be axisymmetric. We will examine validity of this assumption in future studies. We linearize the Euler equations in polar coordinated about the mean flow. Variables are split into a time averaged and a fluctuating component, i.e., $\rho = \bar{\rho} + \tilde{\rho}$, etc. In our notation, quantities with "bar" are time averaged and those with "tilde" are fluctuating components. We subtract the mean values from the full compressible Euler equations to obtain the linearized Euler equations. All second order fluctuating quantities except for the velocity products are neglected. Second order velocity products act as the noise source terms in our equations. Thus we have

$$\tilde{Q}_t + (\tilde{F} + \tilde{f})_x + (\tilde{G} + \tilde{g})_r = \tilde{S}$$

where

$$\tilde{Q} = r \begin{pmatrix} \tilde{\rho} \\ \widetilde{\rho u} \\ \widetilde{\rho v} \\ \tilde{E} \end{pmatrix}$$

$$\tilde{F} = r \begin{pmatrix} \widetilde{\rho u} \\ \tilde{p} + 2\widetilde{\rho u}\bar{u} - \bar{\rho}\tilde{u}^2 \\ \widetilde{\rho u}\bar{v} + \widetilde{\rho v}\bar{u} - \bar{\rho}\tilde{u}\tilde{v} \\ (\tilde{p} + \tilde{E})\bar{u} + (\widetilde{\rho u} - \bar{\rho}\tilde{u})\bar{H} \end{pmatrix}$$

$$\tilde{G} = r \begin{pmatrix} \widetilde{\rho v} \\ \widetilde{\rho u}\bar{v} + \widetilde{\rho v}\bar{u} - \bar{\rho}\tilde{u}\tilde{v} \\ \tilde{p} + 2\widetilde{\rho v}\bar{v} - \bar{\rho}\tilde{v}^2 \\ (\tilde{p} + \tilde{E})\bar{v} + (\widetilde{\rho v} - \bar{\rho}\tilde{v})\bar{H} \end{pmatrix}$$

$$\tilde{f} = r \begin{pmatrix} 0 \\ \bar{\rho}(\tilde{u}\tilde{u} - \overline{\tilde{u}\tilde{u}}) \\ \bar{\rho}\tilde{u}\tilde{v} \\ 0 \end{pmatrix} = r \begin{pmatrix} \tilde{f}_1 \\ \tilde{f}_2 \\ \tilde{f}_3 \\ \tilde{f}_4 \end{pmatrix} \quad (1a)$$

$$\tilde{g} = r \begin{pmatrix} 0 \\ \bar{\rho}\tilde{u}\tilde{v} \\ \bar{\rho}(\tilde{v}\tilde{v} - \overline{\tilde{v}\tilde{v}}) \\ 0 \end{pmatrix} = r \begin{pmatrix} \tilde{g}_1 \\ \tilde{g}_2 \\ \tilde{g}_3 \\ \tilde{g}_4 \end{pmatrix} \quad (1b)$$

$$\tilde{S} = \begin{pmatrix} 0 \\ 0 \\ \tilde{p} \\ 0 \end{pmatrix}$$

$$H = \frac{E + \bar{p}}{\bar{\rho}}$$

$$\tilde{p} = (\gamma - 1)[\tilde{E} - (\widetilde{\rho u}\bar{v} + \widetilde{\rho v}\bar{u}) + \frac{1}{2}\tilde{\rho}(\bar{u}^2 + \bar{v}^2)]$$

$$\bar{p} = (\gamma - 1)[\bar{E} - +\frac{1}{2}\bar{\rho}(\bar{u}^2 + \bar{v}^2)]$$

In the above equations p, ρ, u, v, E and H denote the pressure, density, axial and radial velocity components, total energy and enthalpy. Readers can find the linearized Euler equations in absence of noise source terms $\tilde{f}_x$ and $\tilde{g}_r$ in Mankbadi (1994). It is straight forward to extend the above equations for three dimensional flows.

Numerical Model

We use the fourth order MacCormack scheme, due to Gottlieb and Turkel (1976) to solve the linearized Euler equations. This scheme uses predictor and corrector steps to compute time accurate solutions. One sided differences (forward or backward) are used to compute spatial derivatives at each predictor or corrector step. For the present computations, the operator L in the equation $LQ = S$ or equivalently $Q_t + F_x + G_r = S$ is split into two one-dimensional operators and the scheme is applied to these split operators. The predictor step for the one dimension model/split equation $Q_t = F_x + S$ may be written as

$$\bar{Q}_i = Q_i^n + \frac{\Delta t}{6\Delta x}\{7(F_{i+1}^n - F_i^n) - (F_{i+2}^n - F_{i+1}^n)\} + \Delta t S_i$$

and the corrector step as

$$Q_i^{n+1} = \frac{1}{2}[\bar{Q}_i + Q_i^n + \Delta t S_i$$

$$-\frac{\Delta t}{6\Delta x}\{7(\bar{F}_i - \bar{F}_{i-1}) - (\bar{F}_{i-1} - \bar{F}_{i-2})\}]$$

We define L_1 as a one dimensional operator with a forward difference in the predictor and a backward difference in the corrector. Its symmetric variant L_2 uses a backward difference in the predictor and a forward difference in the corrector. This scheme becomes fourth-order accurate in the spatial derivatives when alternated with symmetric variants. For our computations, the one dimensional sweeps are arranged as

$$Q^{n+1} = L_{1x}L_{1r}Q^n$$

$$Q^{n+2} = L_{2r}L_{2x}Q^{n+1}$$

Our linearized Euler code is based on the numerical model developed and used in earlier studies (Hayder et al., 1993; Mankbadi et al., 1994). Discussions of the Navier Stokes version of the code may be found in cites references. The Navier Stokes and the linearized Euler versions of the code share many similarities in numerical treatments. We use characteristic boundary conditions at the inflow. At the outflow we use the asymptotic pressure boundary conditions. We will also use the perfectly absorbing layers (Hu, 1995; Hayder et al., 1996) at the computational boundaries. Such layers are very effective in reducing errors generated at the computational boundaries.

Synthesis of the Noise Source

We compute the noise source terms $\tilde{f}_x$ and $\tilde{g}_r$ using the following stochastic technique. We use a Gaussian random field to synthesize the noise source term. Let us adopt for two point two time velocity correlations according to the following hypothesis

$$Q^{ij}(x, \xi, t, \zeta) = < u^i(x, t) u^j(\xi, \zeta) >$$
$$= Q^0(K(\frac{x+\xi}{2}), \epsilon(\frac{x+\xi}{2}), d, t, \zeta) \qquad (2)$$

where $d = \frac{x-\xi}{2}$. Thus, inhomogeneity enters through the single point descriptiors turbulence kinetic energy (K) and dissipation rate (ϵ) alone. This hypothesis and normality implies that the two point two time velocity products have the following form

$$< u^i(x,t) u^j(x,t) u^k(\xi,\zeta) u^l(\xi,\zeta) > = \tau^{ij}(x,t) \tau^{kl}(\xi,\zeta)$$
$$+ Q^{ik}(x, \xi, t, \zeta) Q^{jl}(x, \xi, t, \zeta)$$
$$+ Q^{il}(x, \xi, t, \zeta) Q^{jk}(x, \xi, t, \zeta)$$

where the two point two time correlations are determined by equation (2). Let us now define a length scale at a point as $\Delta = K^{\frac{3}{2}}/\epsilon$ and the time scale $T = \Delta / K^{\frac{1}{2}}$. Then we assume the fluctuation of velocity at a point to be

$$u^j = \sum_{b,l} A^j_{\mathbf{b}l} e^{i(\vec{y} \cdot \vec{k}_b + \omega_l t)}$$

where $\vec{k}_b = \frac{\pi}{\Delta}\mathbf{b}$ and $\omega_l = \frac{\pi}{T}l$. "A" is a set of Gaussian distributed random vectors which satisfies

$$< A^i_{\mathbf{b}l} A^j_{\mathbf{b}'l'} > =$$
$$\delta(\mathbf{b} + \mathbf{b}') \delta(l + l') \delta_{ij} C_k \epsilon^{\frac{2}{3}} |\vec{k}_b|^{-\frac{11}{3}} e^{-\omega^2/(Kk_b{}^2)}$$

We divide the flowfield into several uncorrelated elements. A central location is chosen at each of the element. We call these locations the source points. Let us now consider an element with the source point at (r^s, x^s). Then using our above formulation we

write velocity fluctuations $\tilde{v}$ and $\tilde{u}$ at any point (r,x) inside the element at any time t as

$$\tilde{v}(r, x, t) = \sum_{m,n,l} \{A^s_{rmnl} cos[\frac{m}{2\pi\Delta^s}(r - r^s)$$
$$+ \frac{n}{2\pi\Delta^s}(x - x^s) + \frac{l}{2\pi T^s}t] + B^s_{rmnl} sin[\frac{m}{2\pi\Delta^s}(r - r^s)$$
$$+ \frac{n}{2\pi\Delta^s}(x - x^s) + \frac{l}{2\pi T^s}t]\} \qquad (3a)$$

$$\tilde{u}(r, x, t) = \sum_{m,n,l} \{A^s_{xmnl} cos[\frac{m}{2\pi\Delta^s}(r - r^s)$$
$$+ \frac{n}{2\pi\Delta^s}(x - x^s) + \frac{l}{2\pi T^s}t] + B^s_{xmnl} sin[\frac{m}{2\pi\Delta^s}(r - r^s)$$
$$+ \frac{n}{2\pi\Delta^s}(x - x^s) + \frac{l}{2\pi T^s}t]\} \qquad (3b)$$

A_r, A_x, B_r and B_x are chosen as

$$A^s_{rmnl} = I^s_{mnl} cos(\theta^s_{mnl}) cos(\psi^s_{mnl})$$
$$A^s_{xmnl} = I^s_{mnl} cos(\theta^s_{mnl}) sin(\psi^s_{mnl})$$
$$B^s_{rmnl} = I^s_{mnl} sin(\theta^s_{mnl}) cos(\phi^s_{mnl})$$
$$B^s_{xmnl} = I^s_{mnl} sin(\theta^s_{mnl}) sin(\phi^s_{mnl})$$

where $\theta(m, n, l)$, $\psi(m, n, l)$ and $\phi(m, n, l)$ are random angles uniform on $[0, 2\pi]$ and

$$I_{mnl} = \alpha \sqrt{\epsilon^{\frac{2}{3}}(\frac{m^2 + n^2}{\Delta^2})^{-\frac{11}{6}} e^{\frac{-(l/T)^2 \Delta^2}{K(m^2 + n^2)}}}.$$

The constant α is determined from the following constraint

$$\overline{\tilde{u}\tilde{u}} = \overline{\tilde{v}\tilde{v}} = \frac{1}{2}\sum_{m,n} I^2_{mnl}|_{l=0} = \frac{K}{3}$$

In the above formulation we have $\overline{\tilde{u}\tilde{v}} = 0$. One may seperate spatial and temporal dependences in equation (3) using trigonometric relations such as $cos(\theta_1 + \theta_2) = cos(\theta_1)cos(\theta_2) - sin(\theta_1)sin(\theta_2)$, etc. Such seperation may result in computationally less demanding implementations. Because $\theta(m, n, l)$, $\psi(m, n, l)$ and $\phi(m, n, l)$ are random angles, there is no correlation of $\tilde{u}$ and $\tilde{v}$ across the elements. However, these angles do not change within a single element, therefore, fluctuating velocity components are correlated within each element.

Test of a Simple Model

This is an ongoing project and we are currently testing various parameters of our source formulation. In this paper we present results with a simplified version of the noise source as a test of our numerical model. In this version, the domain is divided into several elements and $\tilde{u}$ and $\tilde{v}$ at each grid point is defined as

$$\tilde{u} = \sqrt{\frac{4}{3}K}\cos(\frac{\epsilon}{2\pi K}t + \theta^s) \qquad (4a)$$

$$\tilde{v} = \sqrt{\frac{4}{3}K}\sin(\frac{\epsilon}{2\pi K}t + \theta^s) \qquad (4b)$$

where θ^s is a random number uniform in $[0, 2\pi]$, but it is a constant within any element s. In our formulation, any randomness in the field is introduced only at the beginning of the computations. Thus the solution with one set of parameters corresponds to one realization. One may need to calculate the average of several such realizations to determine the correct field.

We consider a supersonic axisymmetric jet for the results presented in this paper. We used a computational domain which is about 56 radii long and 44 radii wide. The mean flow field is shown in figure 1. We plotted only upto 5 radii in the radial direction in order to show the details near the nozzle exit. A snapshot of presure and overall sound pressure level for the simple model [equation (4)] are shown in figures 2 and 3 respectively. These results are for one realization. Source terms $\tilde{f}_x$ and $\tilde{g}_r$ in equation (1) are resposible for the generation of noise. The propagation of noise is influenced by the mean flow field. The time average of the source terms is zero. It is interesting to examine the contours of source terms at a particular time. In figures 4 and 5, we examine three components of the source terms for the simple and the full model [equation (3)] respectively. In these figures snapshots of components $\tilde{f}_2$ or $\bar{\rho}(\tilde{u}\tilde{u} - \overline{\tilde{u}\tilde{u}})$; $\tilde{f}_3$ ($=\tilde{g}_2$) or $\bar{\rho}\tilde{u}\tilde{v}$; and $\tilde{g}_3$ or $\bar{\rho}(\tilde{v}\tilde{v} - \overline{\tilde{v}\tilde{v}})$ are shown. These components for the simple model appear to be very regular except at element boundaries [note that the domain is divided into several uncorrolated elements]. Discontinuities in such fields are the consequence of different values of θ^s across neighboring elements. Similar plots for the full model show considerable amount of randomness. Detailed parametric study and comparisons with experimental data are needed to fully evaluate the potential of our source model. At present we are making these experiments and results of these studies will be presented at the forum.

Acknowledgement

We would like to thank Dr. Abbas Khavaran for providing the mean flow field data used in the calculations in this paper.

References

Bechara, W., Bailly, C. and Lafon, P., 1993, "Stochastic Approach to Noise Modeling for Free Turbulent Flows", *AIAA Journal,* Vol 32, No. 3, pp 455-463.

Gottlieb, D. and Turkel, E., 1976, "Dissipative Two-Four Methods for Time Dependent Problems", *Math. Comput.,* **30**, pp. 703-723.

Hayder, M. E., Turkel, E. and Mankbadi, R. R., 1993, "Numerical Simulations of a High Mach Number Jet Flow", AIAA paper 93-0653, also NASA TM 105985.

Hayder, M. E., Hu, F. Q. and Hussaini, M. Y., 1996, "Towards Perfectly Absorbing Layer as Non-Refecting Boundary", *Presented at the 15th International Conference on Numerical Methods in Fluid Dynamics,* Monterey, CA, June 1996.

Hu, F. Q., 1995, "On Absorbing Boundary Conditions for Linearized Euler Equations by a Perfectly Matched Layer", ICASE report 95-70.

Mankbadi, R. R., 1994, "Transition, Turbulence, and Noise: Theory and Application for Scientists and Engineers", *Kluwer Academic Publishers,* Norwell, MA.

Mankbadi, R. R., Hayder, M. E. and Povinelli, L. A., 1994, "The Structure of Supersonic Jet Flow and Its Radiated Sound" *AIAA Journal,* vol. 32, No. 5, pp 897-906.

Rubinstein, R. and Zhou, Y., 1996, "Frequency spectra of sound radiated by turbulent shear flows", in preparation.

Tam, C. K. W., 1995, "Supersonic Jet Noise", *Annual Review of Fluid Mechanics,* **27**, pp 17-43.

Zhou, Y. and Rubinstein, R., 1996, "Sweeping and straining effects in sound generation by high Reynolds number isotropic turbulence", *Physics of Fluids,* Vol 8, 647.

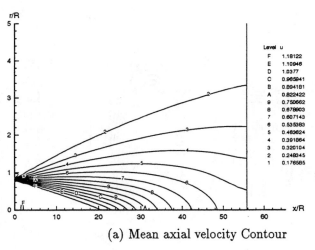

(a) Mean axial velocity Contour

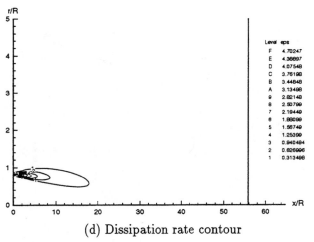

(d) Dissipation rate contour

Figure 1: Mean flow field

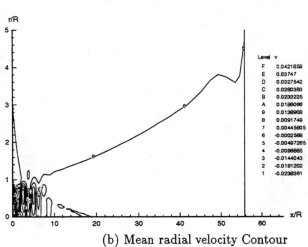

(b) Mean radial velocity Contour

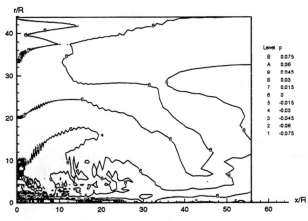

Figure 2: Snapshot of pressure

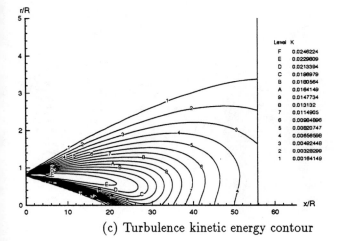

(c) Turbulence kinetic energy contour

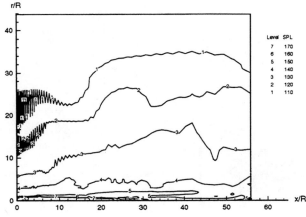

Figure 3: Overall sound pressure level

483

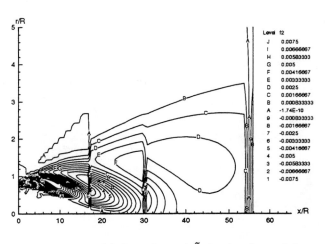

(a) Snapshot of $\tilde{f}_2$ in simple model

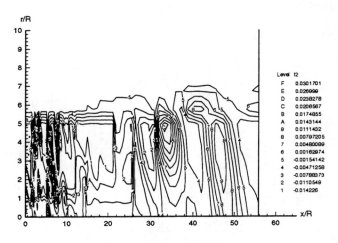

(a) Snapshot of $\tilde{f}_2$ in full model

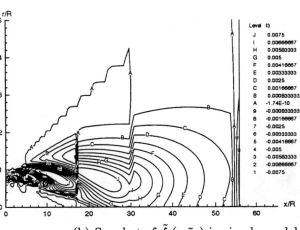

(b) Snaphot of $\tilde{f}_3(=\tilde{g}_2)$ in simple model

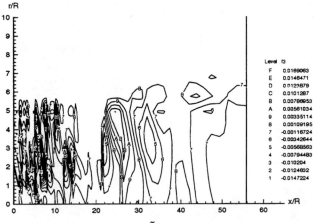

(b) Snapshot of $\tilde{f}_3(=\tilde{g}_2)$ in full model

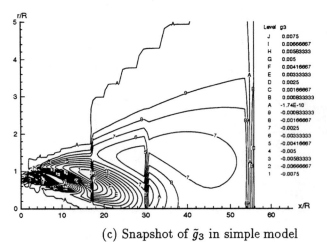

(c) Snapshot of $\tilde{g}_3$ in simple model

Figure 4: Noise source terms for simple model

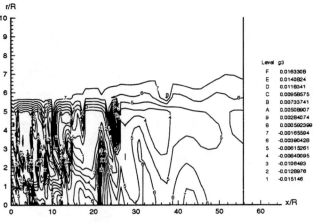

(c) Snapshot of $\tilde{g}_3$ in full model

Figure 5: Noise source terms for full model

FED-Vol. 238, 1996 Fluids Engineering Division Conference
Volume 3
ASME 1996

ACOUSTIC RADIATION FROM OSCILLATING RIGID BODIES IN MEAN COMPRESSIBLE FLOW

Ramesh K. Agarwal
Aerospace Engineering Department
Wichita State University
Wichita, Kansas 67260-0044

Kevin S. Huh
Integral, Inc.
Cambridge, Massachusetts 02138

ABSTRACT

The problem of acoustic radiation from two-dimensional oscillating rigid bodies in compressible mean flow is considered numerically. The acoustic perturbation field is calculated by solving the acoustic equations derived from the unsteady Euler equations by linearizing about a steady mean flow and by assuming a single frequency disturbance. A computational code is developed which is validated by computing the unsteady loads and acoustic radiation due to an oscillating circualr cylinder in compressible flow. Numerical results are compared with the exact analytical solution. Excellent agreement is obtained. The validated code is employed to compute the acoustic radiation from oscillating airfoils in compressible mean flow. Parametric studies are performed by varying the Mach number of the mean flow, the angle of attack and the geometry (thickness and camber) of the airfoil. Conclusions are drawn about the magnitude and phase of acoustic radiation for various Mach numbers, angles of attack, and airfoil geometries.

INTRODUCTION

The determination of unsteady loads on an airfoil/wing due to unsteadiness in the mean flow due to gust, turbulence etc. or due to unsteady motion of the body, for example flutter, is a problem of fundamental importance in aerodynamics. The earliest analytical solutions on gust/airfoil interactions date back to the works of Theodorsen, vonKarman, and Sears among others. These papers dealt with the calculation of unsteady loads on a flat plate due to an impulse or sinusoidal gust in incompressible flow. These solutions are described in most of the books on unsteady aerodynamics, see for example Bisplinghoff and Ashley (1982) and Ashley and Landahl (1984). The introduction of compressibility effects makes the problem substantially more difficult to solve even for a flat plate. Amiet (1974) obtained asymptotic solutions for a compact gust ($K < 1$) where compactness ratio K is defined as the ratio of the airfoil chord to the gust (acoustic) wavelength. Landahl (1981), using a very clever approach was able to obtain solutions for a noncompact gust in compressible flow. There have been several attempts to improve upon these calculations especially in the leading edge and trailing edge regions of the flat plate. However, all these calculations have severe limitations. They cannot account for the effects of airfoil geometry (thickness and camber), high subsonic and transonic Mach numbers, and high angles of attack. The calculation of these effects necessarily requires a numerical solution approach. The authors have recently developed a computational code which has the attributes to compute the unsteady loads and acoustic radiation due to unsteadiness in the flow either due to unsteady motion or due to gust and other unsteady disturbances in the flow. In Agarwal and Huh (1996a) they address the problem of acoustic radiation due to gust/airfoil interaction numerically. The paper illustrates the application and validation of this code by computing the unsteady loads on a flat plate due to a gust in incompressible flow (Sears problem), and unsteady loads and acoustic radiation due to a compact and noncompact gust in compressible flow. In this paper, we employ this code to compute the acoustic radiation from oscillating airfoils in compressible mean flow. Parametric studies are performed by varying the Mach number of the mean flow, the angle of attack and the geometry of the airfoil.

PROBLEM DESCRIPTION

An oscillating body in a compressible fluid medium generates propagating pressure disturbances, and if the frequency of oscillation is within the audible range, we perceive such disturbances as sound. This, in fact, is the basis of classical acoustics - sound generation from unsteady motion of bodies in still media. When an oscillating body also convects in the flow sound is generated as a result of interactions between the propagating pressure waves with the underlying mean flow. This noise generation mechanism is common to many aerospace components such as wings and propellers, for example, wing flutter can create similar sound radiation. Noise generated by such mechanisms often tend to be loud and are important sources of sound. In this paper, we consider sound generation properties of such an unsteady process.

Consider an oscillating airfoil in a steady flow of Mach number M_0 as shown in Figure 1. We assume that the oscillation is purely in the y direction, given by

$$y = e^{i\omega t} \qquad (1)$$

about the mean chord of the airfoil. Also the amplitude of oscillation is sufficiently small such that the complete flow can be thought of as a superposition of linear unsteady perturbation upon a steady mean flow. Then without any loss of generality, we can also assume that the airfoil oscillates with a single frequency ω.

The inviscid wall boundary condition is that the total normal velocity with respect to the airfoil is zero, and since the surface is moving, the boundary condition is

$$\mathbf{U} \cdot \mathbf{n} = \frac{\partial \mathbf{r}}{\partial t} \cdot \mathbf{n} \qquad (2)$$

where $\mathbf{U}$ is the flow velocity, $\mathbf{n}$ is the unit normal vector to the surface, and $\mathbf{r}$ is the surface position vector. Since in general the normal vector is a function of position, $\mathbf{n} = \mathbf{n}(\mathbf{r})$, the boundary condition in Equation (2) is nonlinear.

Ideally, boundary condition (2) should be applied at the instantaneous location of the surface. If the surface moves, the location at which the boundary condition is applied should correspondingly change also. It is, thus, more convenient to rederive the boundary condition so that it is enforced at the fixed mean position. To do this, we linearize the variables about the mean and assume a small amplitude harmonic perturbations as follows.

$$\mathbf{r} = \mathbf{r}_0 + \widetilde{\mathbf{r}} e^{-i\omega t}, \qquad \mathbf{n} = \mathbf{n}_0 + \widetilde{\mathbf{n}} e^{-i\omega t}, \qquad \text{and}$$

$\mathbf{U} = \mathbf{u}_0 + \widetilde{\mathbf{u}} e^{-i\omega t}$, where the subscript $_0$ refers to the steady mean quantity, and $\widetilde{}$ values denote the complex perturbation amplitudes.

Next we expand in Taylor series the velocity $\mathbf{U}$ for small excursions in the surface position,

$$\mathbf{U}(\mathbf{r}) \approx \mathbf{U}(\mathbf{r}_0) + (\mathbf{r} - \mathbf{r}_0) \cdot \nabla \mathbf{U}$$
$$\approx \mathbf{u}_0(\mathbf{r}_0) + \widetilde{\mathbf{u}}(\mathbf{r}_0) e^{-i\omega t} + \widetilde{\mathbf{r}} \cdot \nabla \mathbf{u}_0 e^{-i\omega t} \qquad (3)$$

If we substitute the above equations into the boundary condition in Equation (2), we obtain

$$\mathbf{u}_0 \cdot \mathbf{n}_0 = 0 \qquad (4)$$

for the mean steady boundary condition and,

$$\widetilde{\mathbf{u}} \cdot \mathbf{n}_0 = -\mathbf{u}_0 \cdot \widetilde{\mathbf{n}} - \widetilde{\mathbf{r}} \cdot \nabla (\mathbf{u}_0 \cdot \mathbf{n}_0) - i\omega \widetilde{\mathbf{r}} \cdot \mathbf{n}_0 \qquad (5)$$

as the first-order unsteady boundary condition.

For an oscillating airfoil, $\widetilde{\mathbf{r}} = \mathbf{j}$ and $\widetilde{\mathbf{n}} = 0$ since the airfoil does not rotate. All the terms on the right hand side of Equation (5) are functions of the steady mean solution and are known quantities. However, the second term involves the gradient of the normal mean velocity and must be computed numerically.

A transversely oscillating airfoil is similar to an airfoil subjected to a sinusoidal 'gust'. In fact for a flat plate and infinite wavelength, the two problems become identical. Thus we have used the incompressible gust validation case reported in Agarwal and Huh (1996a) as a check to ensure that the current surface boundary condition (5) is correctly enforced. This is described in a later section under code validation.

CLASSICAL ANALYSIS OF THE AERODYNAMIC PROBLEM

Before we embark on the numerical study, it is useful to first consider the mathematics for the flat plate problem which may illuminate some insights and identify some key parameters.

The linearized Euler equations in a uniform flow of streamwise velocity U_0 can be represented by an equivalent convective form of the wave equation in the perturbation velocity potential ϕ,

$$\phi_{tt} + 2U_0 \phi_{xt} - (c_0^2 - U_0^2)\phi_{xx} - c_0^2 \phi_{yy} = 0 \qquad (6)$$

where c_0 is the sound speed and $u' = \phi_x$ and $v' = \phi_y$ are the acoustic perturbation velocities.

We introduce the following transformations for both dependent and independent variables,

$$(x, y, t, \phi) \leftrightarrow (\xi, \eta, t, \Phi),$$
$$\xi = x, \eta = \beta y$$

and

$$\Phi(\xi, \eta, t) = -i\omega\phi(x, y) e^{-i(\omega t + M_0)}, \qquad (7)$$

where

$$\beta = \sqrt{1 - M_0^2},$$

$$K = \frac{\nu M_0}{\beta^2},$$

$\nu = \dfrac{\omega a}{2U_0}$ is the reduced frequency, ω is the frequency of the oscillation, and a is the characteristic length. We then arrive at,

$$(\widetilde{\nabla}^2 + K^2)\Phi = 0 \qquad (8)$$

with the boundary conditions,

$$\frac{\partial \Phi}{\partial \eta} = -\frac{1}{\beta} e^{-i\nu/\beta^2} \qquad (9)$$

along the body, $-\dfrac{a}{2} < \xi < \dfrac{a}{2}$ and,

$$\Delta\Phi = (\Delta\Phi)_{t.e.} e^{-i\nu/\beta^2} \qquad (10)$$

along the wake, $\xi > \dfrac{a}{2}$. $\widetilde{\nabla}$ is the Laplacian operator computed in the (ξ, η) domain, and $\Delta\Phi$ represents the jump of Φ across the wakeline. The latter boundary condition results from the continuity of pressure in the wake.

The Hemholtz Equation (8) can be solved using the Green's Theorem,

$$\Phi(\xi, \eta) = \frac{1}{2\pi} \oint \left(\Phi \frac{\partial G}{\partial \eta'} - G \frac{\partial \Phi}{\partial \eta'} \right) d\xi'. \qquad (11)$$

The integration is over the body and the wake. The free space Green's function for Equation (8) is

$$G(r) = i\frac{\pi}{2} H_0^{(1)}(Kr) \qquad (12)$$

486

where $r = \sqrt{(\xi - \xi')^2 + (\eta - \eta')^2}$ and $H_0^{(1)}$ is the Hankel function of the first kind zeroth order. An exact solution to Equation (12) requires the enforcement of boundary conditions, but even without such a statement, the nature of the general solution illustrates that the parameter K plays an important role. K is actually a nondimensional parameter based on the ratio of expected length scales. An acoustic length scale is based on the acoustic wavelength,

$$L_{acou} = \overline{\lambda} = \frac{2\pi c}{\omega} \qquad (13)$$

where c is the speed of sound and $\overline{\lambda}$ is an average acoustic wavelength in the domain. The convection length scale is dependent on the geometry of the case, and for now, define it to be a,

$$L_{conv} = \overline{\lambda} = a . \qquad (14)$$

K can then be cast as a simple multiple of the ratio L_{conv} / L_{acou} as

$$K = \frac{vM_0}{\beta^2} = \frac{\pi}{\beta^2} \frac{L_{conv}}{L_{acou}} = \frac{\pi}{\beta^2} \frac{a}{\overline{\lambda}} . \qquad (15)$$

An oscillating flat plate has the second term in the integral Equation (11) equal to zero, and the flat plate can be thought of as a distribution of simple dipoles. At a given point, the sound heard from such collection of dipoles is a function of compressibility and the 'compactness' of the source.

In compressible flows with finite phase speeds, the concept of 'compactness' is an important issue. A compact source is one in which the acoustic length scale is much longer than the body such that an observer 'hears' the distribution of sources in phase, and there are little or no retarded time differences. The differences in 'firing' time $\Delta(t - r/c_0)$ are small such that all the sources can be thought to be grouped as a single dipole firing in phase.

In contrast, a noncompact source is one in which the acoustic length scale is much shorter than the body such that an observer 'hears' the distribution of sources out of phase; he 'hears' the sources closest to him first, and there are large retarded time differences between the sources. In such cases, instead of radiation from a simple dipole we expect a more complicated acoustic field due to a distribution of dipoles over the chord with large differences in phase.

K is a measure of the compactness of the acoustic source. When K is small, it must follow that $L_{conv} \ll L_{acou}$ and the body is essentially compact. Conversely when K is large, $L_{conv} \gg L_{acou}$ and the body is no longer compact.

Note that in an unsteady flow, the condition $M_0 \ll 1$ is not sufficient to guarantee an incompressible flow. We need to require that the acoustic length scale is much longer than the flow length scale, i.e. we need to assure that the source is compact, and so the correct parameterization is $M_0 \ll 1$ and $K \ll 1$.

NUMERICAL SOLVER FOR STEADY MEAN FLOW

For numerical solution of the steady mean flow over an airfoil, a two-dimensional Euler solver is employed (Agarwal and Deese, 1984). It solves the 2-D compressible Euler equations in conservation law form. The numerical method employed is an explicit node-based finite-volume algorithm wherein spatial terms are discretized using a fourth-order compact difference operator while the time integration is carried out using a four-stage explicit Runge-Kutta time-stepping scheme. A sixth-order compact dissipation operator is added to stabilize the algorithm. Variable time stepping and residual smoothing are employed to enhance convergence to steady state. The details of the numerical scheme are given in Agarwal and Huh (1996b). The code is employed to calculate the steady mean flow over airfoils at various Mach numbers and angles of attack.

NUMERICAL SOLVER FOR ACOUSTIC PERTURBATIONS

The governing acoustic equations are derived from the unsteady Euler equations by linearizing about a steady mean flow. These equations are written as a set of first-order partial differential equations in hyperbolic conservation-law form. As a consequence, the well-developed CFD algorithms for the solution of compressible Euler equations are applied for the numerical solution of these equations. However, for wave propagation problems, the requirements of accuracy are substantially different than that for aerodynamics. In the present work, the governing equations are solved both in time- and frequency-domain using the method of lines which decouples the temporal terms from spatial terms. In frequency domain, a pseudo-time variable is introduced. Again, an explicit node-based finite-volume algorithm is developed wherein the spatial terms are discretized using a fourth-order compact dispersion-relation preserving difference operator while the time-integration is carried out using a four stage explicit/point-implicit Runge-Kutta time-stepping scheme. A sixth-order compact dissipation operator is added to stabilize the algorithm. A novel analytic treatment is developed for the implementation of the farfield radiation boundary condition. It is based on the modal analysis of the similarity form of the linearized Euler equations. Analytical relations are derived to insure that there are no incoming modes in the computational domain. For a circular boundary, in the absence of mean flow, this boundary condition is equivalent to exact integral form of the Sommerfeld radiation condition. For cases with mean flow, it is shown that this boundary condition provides an excellent approximation to exact integral boundary condition (Agarwal and Huh, 1995). This approach substantially reduces the size of the computational domain for accurate acoustic field computations. The details of the acoustic perturbation solver are given in Agarwal and Huh (1996b).

CODE VALIDATION

For the purpose of validating the acoustic perturbation solver, we consider a set of two numerical calculations for which there exists an analytical solution. For historical reasons we start the validation with a problem in classical acoustics - acoustic radiation from an oscillating cylinder.

Oscillating Circular Cylinder

Consider a circular cylinder in a quiescent field which oscillates in the x direction with an amplitude of 1 and a frequency of ω as shown in Figure 2.

The surface boundary conditions are that the local normal fluid velocity and the cylinder velocity are the same. In mathematical terms the boundary condition can be expressed using equation (5) as,

$$\widetilde{\mathbf{u}} \cdot \mathbf{n}_0 = -i\omega \widetilde{\mathbf{r}} \cdot \mathbf{n}_0 \qquad (16)$$

where $\widetilde{\mathbf{r}} = \mathbf{i}$, $\mathbf{n}_0$ and $\mathbf{i}$ are the surface unit normal vector and the unit vector in the $+x$ direction, respectively. At the far field we have implemented the specialized no-flow version of the boundary condition as described in Agarwal and Huh (1995).

The runtime parameters were as follows:
- Grid: 129 x 100
- ω: 7.434 ($\lambda = 1$)
- Far-field: 1
- Iters: 800
- $L_2(\delta\rho)$: 4.3 x 10^{-4}

$L_2(\delta\rho)$ is the L_2 norm of the difference in density and is equivalent to the root mean square of the density residual. The residual is normalized such that the first iteration difference is set to 1. The calculations required 800 iterations for 4 orders of magnitude convergence in density. $\omega = 7.434$ corresponds to an acoustic wavelength of 1 and so the domain contains exactly 1 wavelength in all directions.

The exact analytical solution for the acoustic pressure is provided in Dowling and Ffowcs Williams (1983) and it is,

$$\widetilde{p} = \frac{\omega c_0 \cos\theta}{H_0^{(1)''}(\frac{\omega}{2c_0})} H_0^{(1)'}(\frac{\omega r}{c_0}), \qquad (17)$$

where $r = \sqrt{x^2 + y^2}$ and θ is measured counterclockwise sense from the $+x$ axis. In equation (17), $H_0^{(1)'}$ and $H_0^{(1)''}$ denote the first and second derivatives of the Hankel functions of first kind zeroth-order.

Figure 3 and 4 show the amplitude and phase of the computed acoustic pressure, High accuracy in both the amplitude and the phase was found in the entire domain. Figures 5 and 6 show the absolute error of the real and imaginary part of $\widetilde{p}$ when compared with the exact analytical solution $\Re(\widetilde{p})$ and $\Im(\widetilde{p})$ respectively from equation (17). The largest absolute errors of approximately 0.03 for the real part and of approximately 0.04 for the imaginary part are at the far field. The average $L_2(\Delta|\widetilde{p}|)$

was 1.2714 x 10^{-5}, the average $L_2(\Delta\Re(\widetilde{p}))$ was 1.0638 x 10^{-5}, and the average $L_2(\Delta\Im(\widetilde{p}))$ was 1.9656 x 10^{-5}.

In no flow situations, the combination of current numerical scheme and the specialized far field boundary conditions produce highly accurate results.

Oscillating Flat Plate in Incompressible Flow

Consider a flat plate oscillating in an incompressible flow. The transverse oscillation in the y-direction is given by Equation (1). We seek to compute the time-harmonic response of the plate and its surrounding fluid perturbed by the oscillation. The steady base mean flow was computed first, and the following parameters were used:
- Geometry: NACA0001
- Grid: 300 x 150 ('O' topology)
- M_0: 0.1
- α: 0.0
- Far Field Radius: 10 chords
- Iterations: 500
- $L_2(\delta\rho)$: 1.3 x 10^{-4}

M_0 is the free stream Mach number, and α is the angle of attack. The Mach number was purposely chosen to be small so that the simulation would closely resemble an incompressible flow, and a NACA0001 airfoil section was used to model a flat plate.

The mean flow solution was used as an input to the acoustic perturbation solver on an identical grid with the same base Mach number. The run time perturbation parameters were as follows:
- ω: 0.01
- Iterations: 8500
- $L_2(\delta\rho)$: 3.8 x 10^{-4}

$\omega = 0.01$ corresponds to a reduced frequency, $\nu = 0.0425$ and a wavelength of 743 chords. Within a domain of 10 chords the computed solution should correspond closely to that of an incompressible approximation. As was pointed out before, this problem is identical to the incompressible gust problem (Sears problem) for infinte wave length. Figure 7 shows a plot of the difference in the upper and lower surface pressures, $\Delta\widetilde{p}$, along the flat plate. The lines represent the real and imaginary parts of exact $\Delta\widetilde{p}$ which have been obtained from Bisplinghoff and Ashley (1982), and the symbols represent the corresponding computed solutions. The accuracy is good and uniform even at the leading edge where there is a singularity. In terms of the total lift, the analytic solution is $|\widetilde{L}| = 0.3448$ and arg $\widetilde{L} = -82.7$ and the computed solution is $|\widetilde{L}| = 0.3455$ and arg $\widetilde{L} = -88$. The error is approximately 0.2% in amplitude and approximately 5.3% in phase. It appears that the methodology is accurate in predicting the unsteady pressure values and the surface boundary condition is correctly enforced.

The computation required 168 minutes of cpu time on a Cray X-MP for convergence. The time required was large but expected since the Mach number was so low. A low Mach number case is inefficient when integrated by a compressible solver, because the vorticity and acoustic waves travel at very different rates, and the solver must integrate in a CFL limit sense to accommodate the slower moving wave.

These code validation studies indicate that the numerical method is accurate and consistent throughout the domain for incompressible as well as compressible flow conditions.

We have performed extensive parametric studies to determine the effects of the mean flow Mach number, the mean loading, the airfoil thickness, and the angle of attack on the radiated sound field. The results of these studies are summarized below.

PARAMETRIC STUDIES

EFFECT OF THICKNESS

We first consider the effects of thickness on an oscillating airfoil. The currently available theory is based upon the convective wave equation, and the aerodynamic analysis is as presented in the section above. The thickness does not have any effect on the unsteady solution and, we expect the radiation pattern to be a function of the compactness ratio K.

Compact Case

We first consider a compact case in which K is 1.0. We have computed 2 comparison studies for a NACA0001 and a NACA0013 airfoils in which the angle of attack is zero, and we have used a grid of 200 x 100 node points for both computations. Other pertinent parameters are as tabulated below:

Table I: Parameters for $M_0 = 0.7$, NACA0001 and NACA 0013 Airfoils in compact oscillation.

	Case 1	Case 2
M_0	0.7	0.7
M_{max}	0.71	0.98
v	0.729	0.729
K	1.0	1.0
τ	1%	13%
$|\tilde{L}|$	2.18	5.68
W_a	0.46	4.50

In Table I, M_0 = free stream Mach number, M_{max} = Maximum Mach number on the airfoil, v = reduced frequency, K = compactness ratio, τ = airfoil thickness, $\tilde{L}$ = magnitude of lift, and W_a = acoustic power.

The sound radiation due to an oscillating airfoil is a direct function of the thickness. The 13% airfoil has significantly higher total lift (x2.6) and the radiated sound

power (x9.8). The increased sound energy is graphically illustrated in the polar plot of far field directivity D_p shown in Figure 8. The sound amplitude is much higher for the 13% case in all directions, and, in addition, the sound pressure lobes indicate a direct 'tilt' towards the upstream direction for the 13% case.

The radiated sound energy in the oscillating airfoil is a strong function of the thickness, because the source distribution is a function of the mean flow gradient. Consider the surface boundary conditions of equation (5). A large mean velocity gradient in the normal direction at a point translates directly to a large source strength at that point. Thus a thick airfoil which has large mean flow gradients has strong source strengths along the airfoil.

Figures 9 and 10 show the contours of acoustic pressure amplitude in the domain. The 13% airfoil shows increased sound amplitude and a forward tilt in the directivity. Figures 11 and 12 show the contours of acoustic pressure phase in the domain. The constant phase contour lines for the two plots are virtually identical. Evidently the current long wavelength oscillation does not exhibit much diffraction for either thickness cases.

Noncompact Case

A 1% and a 13% NACA0001 airfoils are oscillating such that the compactness ratio K is 3. A grid of 270 x 120 was used for both airfoils and the far field was chosen such that the domain contained approxiamtely 4.5 wavelengths in all directions. The key parameters are tabulated below:

Table II: Parameters for $M_0 = 0.7$, NACA0001 and NACA 0013 airfoils in noncompact oscillation.

	Case 1	Case 2
M_0	0.7	0.7
M_{max}	0.71	0.98
v	2.186	2.186
K	3.0	3.0
τ	1%	13%
$|\tilde{L}|$	7.88	9.16
W_a	11.9	18.0

The 13% airfoil again has a higher lift (+16%) and sound power (+51%) than the 1% airfoil. The large mean flow gradient has increased the surface source strength.

Figure 13 is the polar plot of far field directivity. The sound pressure level is generally higher in all directions for the 13% airfoil, but it is particularly higher in the up and downstream direction.

Figures 14 and 15 show the constant acoustic pressure contours for the two thickness cases. The 13% case exhibits large pressure gradients throughout the domain, particularly near the thick leading edge region. This is as expected since the mean flow gradients are also the greatest in the leading edge region.

The diffraction of sound from the varying mean flow is also illustrated in the pressure phase contour plots of Figures 16 and 17. Both airfoils exhibit some warping of the contour lines which shows that the airfoils are composed of sources 'firing' out of phase. The 13% airfoil also illustrates a complicated phase behavior directly ahead of the airfoil indicating that the forward upstream direction is a region of high diffraction. The acoustic wavelength is much shorter in the upstream direction and is, therefore, more sensitive to small changes in the flow gradients.

In this section we have investigated the effects of thickness on the radiated sound field from an oscillating airfoil. When the oscillating frequency is sufficiently low such that the associated compactness ratio K is 1 or less, the thickness increases the integrated radiated sound energy. This amplification of sound is believed to be the result of an increase in the source specification along the airfoil caused by the gradients in the flow field. The directivity is also slightly altered such that the sound field has a slight tilt towards the upstream direction.

When the oscillating frequency is high and the airfoil is no longer a compact source of sound, the thickness still increases the integrated radiated sound energy, but, in addition, the diffractive effect of the varying mean flow amplifies sound in the upstream and downstream directions and generally increases the complexity of the sound propagation patterns in the forward direction.

The currently available linear theory is unable to incorporate the diffractive effect of the varying mean flow or the increase in the overall sound pressure levels from the thickness. Consequently the linear method would only be applicable if both the thickness of the airfoil and the frequency of oscillation are quite small. We suspect that the constraint of Equation (6) is probably sufficient for the compact case but because of the diffractive effect of the mean flow, the constraint is probably insufficient in the noncompact case.

EFFECT OF ANGLE OF ATTACK

The effect of angle of attack on the radiated sound of an oscillating airfoil is presented in this section. The linear theory based on the convective wave equation considers an airfoil at an angle of attack as an equivalent projected airfoil at zero incidence. Thus according to the linear theory, angle of attack should slightly decrease the amplitude of unsteady lift and the associated acoustic energy.

Compact Case

Consider a thick NACA0024 airfoil oscillating at a reduced frequency of $v = 1$ at 0 and 5.5° angles of attack. The computational domain contains 200 x 100 node points and the far field is approximately a 4 wavelengths away in all directions. The pertinent parameters are tabulated below:

Table III: Parameters for $M_0 = 0.5$, NACA0024 airfoil at $\alpha = 0$ and $\alpha = 5.5°$ in compact oscillation.

	Case 1	Case 2
M_0	0.5	0.5
M_{max}	0.74	1.00
v	1.0	1.0
K	2/3	2/3
α	0	5.5°
$|\widetilde{L}|$	4.53	4.58
W_a	1.71	1.78

There is a small increase in both the amplitude of lift (+1%) and the radiated sound power (+4%) for the $\alpha = 5.5°$ case. Evidently the radiated sound energy is only weakly dependent on the angle of attack for the current case.

Figures 19 and 20 show the contours of acoustic pressure amplitude in the domain. Near the airfoil the $\alpha = 5.5°$ case indicated higher sound pressure levels in the upper region than the lower region, but away from the airfoil the lower region has significantly higher sound amplitudes. Close to the airfoil the leading edge suction effect creates higher sound amplitudes for the upper region. Further away, however, the mean bound vorticity tends to direct sound towards the leading edge in the lower zone and towards the trailing edge in the upper zone, and thus sound amplitude levels are higher in the lower than in the upper region at the far field. Figure 18 clearly illustrates this mean flow diffraction effect. The lower lobe is amplified at the expense of the upper lobe for the 5.5° angle of attack airfoil.

Figures 21 and 22 show the contours of acoustic pressure phase for the two angles of attack cases. Note the rotation of phase lines in the clockwise direction for the 5.5° case; this is an indication of diffraction of sound towards the lower leading edge and the upper trailing edge regions.

Noncompact Case

We consider an oscillating NACA 0024 airfoil in a free steam of $M_0 = 0.5$ with angles of attack of $\alpha = 0$ and $\alpha = 5.5°$. The numerical domain contains 270 x 120 node points and approximately 4 wavelengths in all directions. The pertinent parameters are tabulated below:

Table IV: Parameters for $M_0 = 0.5$, NACA0024 airfoil at $\alpha = 0$ and $\alpha = 5.5°$ in noncompact oscillation.

	Case 1	Case 2
M_0	0.5	0.5
M_{max}	0.74	1.00
v	3.0	3.0
K	1.73	1.73
α	0	5.5°
$|\widetilde{L}|$	7.02	7.64
W_a	11.1	12.6

There is a larger increase in both the amplitude of lift (+8.8%) and the radiated acoustic power (+13.5%) as compared to the compact case. Apparently there is a larger amount of transferred radiated sound energy from the mean flow when the compactness ratio is higher.

Figures 24 and 25 show the contours of acoustic pressure amplitude in the domain. Near the airfoil the $\alpha = 5.5°$ case has higher pressure levels on the upper surface than the lower surface; this is an indication of the leading edge suction effect. Further away from the airfoil the sound amplitude is higher in the lower region than the upper region, and this is an indication of diffraction by the mean bound vortex.

The diffractive effect of the bound vortex is also evident in the far field polar directivity plot of Figure 23. At 5.5° angle of attack there is a significant increase in the lower lobe, and there also appears an additional lobe towards the upstream direction.

Figures 26 and 27 show the contours of acoustic pressure for the two angles of attack cases. Away from the airfoil, the 5.5° case indicates a rotation of phase lines in the clockwise direction. In addition there are many regions of warped phase lines for both figures but particularly for the nonzero angle case; the warping of the phase lines is an indication of gradients in propagation direction, i.e. diffraction.

In the current section we have investigated the effects of angle of attack on the radiated sound field of an oscillating airfoil.

When the frequency of disturbance is compact, the angle of attack modifies the sound propagation direction such that near the airfoil leading edge on the upper 'suction' side of the airfoil is amplified, while in the far field the upstream lower 'pressure' side of the airfoil is amplified. The effects are purely diffractive, and the total radiated sound energy does not seem to be strongly influenced by the angle of attack.

Given a noncompact source of disturbance, the angle of attack similarly changes sound directivity in both the near and the far field, but in addition, there appears a new upstream directed sound lobe at the far field. The total radiated sound energy increases moderately when there is a mean lift.

CONCLUSIONS

We have developed a computational aeroacoustics code and computed the radiated sound of an airfoil oscillating in a compressible mean flow. The code has been validated by computing the unsteady loads on an oscillating flat plate in incompressible flow (Sears problem). For these two cases the numerical results are compared with the exact analytical solutions. Excellent agreement is obtained.

A parametric study of the effects of the thickness and the angle of attack on an oscillating airfoil has been conducted. While we have not conducted enough case studies to conclude general trends, some early indications of the geometric influences have been formulated.

A thick symmetric airfoil at a zero incidence angle in a compact oscillation (K<1) has a significantly higher acoustic energy level than a flat plate case. The symmetry of the problem precludes the mean flow energy transfer

through the wake, and instead, the energy cascade is direct and immediate from the mean flow to the acoustic mode via interactions of the mean flow gradients and the oscillating airfoil. A large mean flow variations in the surface normal direction corresponds to large surface source strengths. The diffractive effect from the thickness is small for the long wavelength case, but there is a distinct upstream tilting of the directivity lobes due to the thick leading edge.

The same airfoil in a noncompact oscillation (K>1) also has higher energy levels than a flat plate though to a lesser degree. The diffraction of sound due to the thickness is much more pronounced for the short wavelength case such that there is an amplification of sound in the zone 90° $< \theta <$ 270°, and moreover, in the directivity plot additional lobes appear in the forward upstream direction.

The linear theory based upon the convective wave equation does not incorporate the diffractive effect of the varying mean flow or the increase in the overall sound energy levels from the thickness. Thus the linear method would only be applicable if both the thickness of the airfoil and the frequency of the oscillation are small. It is expected to be sufficient for the compact case, but because of the diffractive effect of the mean flow, it is probably insufficient in the noncompact case.

A thick symmetric airfoil at an angle of attack in a compact oscillation has only slightly higher energy levels when compared to the same airfoil at zero incidence. Apparently the energy transfer from the vortical wake is insignificant when compared to the direct energy transfer through the thickness contributions. The diffraction of sound from the leading edge suction and the bound vortex effects create a sound field at the far field which has amplified sound pressure levels in the lower 180° $< \theta <$ 270° zone.

The same airfoil in a noncompact oscillation has moderately higher energy levels than the same airfoil at zero incidence. The diffraction of sound from the mean bound vortex dominates at the far field, and there appears amplified pressure levels in the upstream direction.

The linear theory based upon the convective wave equation is unable to predict the diffraction of sound from both the leading edge suction and the bound vortex contributions, and therefore, is ineffective for thick airfoils at an angle of attack.

REFERENCES

1. Agarwal, R.K., and Deese, J.E. 1989, "Computation of Viscous Airfoil, Inlet, and Wing Flowfields," AIAA paper 84-1551.

2. Agarwal, R.K. and Huh, K.S. 1995, "A Novel Formulation of Farfield Boundary Condition for Computational Acoustics," in Computational Acoustic, ASME FED-Vol. 219, pp.35-40.

3. Agarwal, R.K. and Huh, K.S., 1996a, "Acoustic Radiation Due to Gust-Airfoil Interaction in Compressible Flow," AIAA paper 96-1755.

4. Agarwal, R.K. and Huh, K.S., 1989, "A Dispersion-Relation-Preserving Fourth-order Compact Time-

Domain / Frequency-Domain Finite-Volume Method for Computational Acoustics," AIAA paper 96-0277.

5. Amiet, R.K., 1974, "Compressibility Effects in Unsteady Thin Airfoil Theory," AIAA Journal, vol. 12, pp. 252-255.

6. Ashley, M. and Landahl, M., 1989, Aerodynamics of Wings and Bodies, Dover, New York.

7. Bisplinghoff, R.L. and Ashley H., 1982, Principles of Aeroelasticity, Dover, New York.

8. Dowling, A.P. and Ffowcs Williams, J.E., 1983, Sound and Sources and Sound, Chicester, England: Ellis Horwood Limited.

9. Landahl, M., 1981, Unsteady Transonic Flow, Pergamon Press.

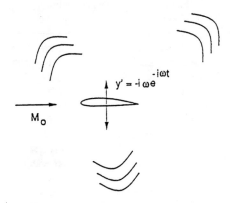

Figure 1. Oscillating Airfoil in Compressible Mean Flow

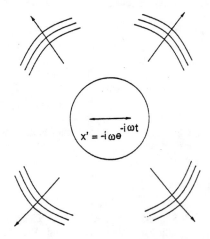

Figure 2. Oscillating Circular Cylinder

Contour of Pressure Amplitude

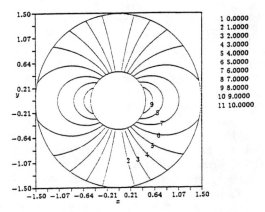

Figure 3. Amplitude of Computed Acoustic Pressure

Contour of Pressure Phase

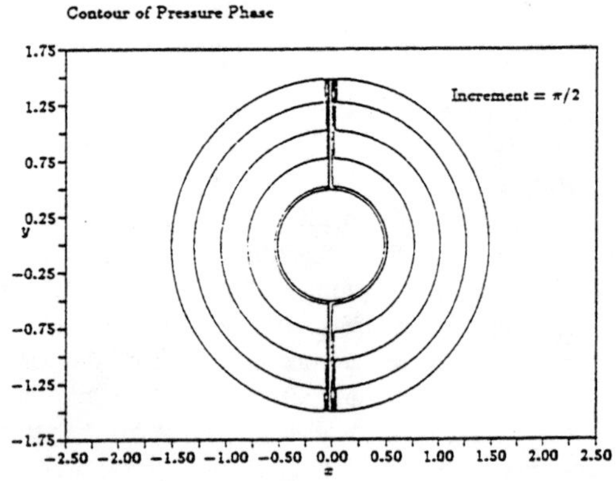

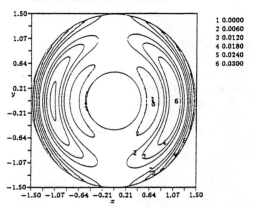

Figure 4. Phase of Computed Acoustic Pressure

Error Contour of Real Part of Pressure

Figure 5. Absolute Value of Error of Real Part of Acoustic Pressure

492

Error Contour of Imaginary Part of Pressure

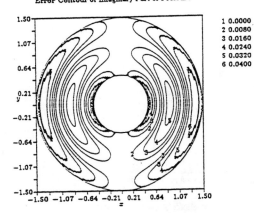

Figure 6. Absolute Value of Error of Imaginary Part of Acoustic pressure

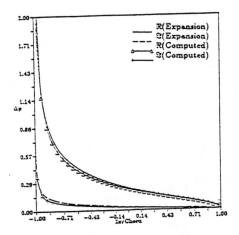

Figure 7. $\nabla \bar{p}$ on the Flat Plate in Incompressible Flow

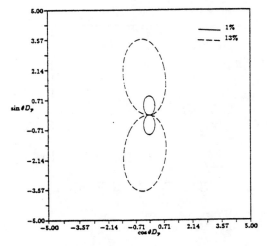

Figure 8. Polar Plot of D_p at the Far Field, $M_0 = 0.7, K = 1.0$

Contour of Pressure Amplitude

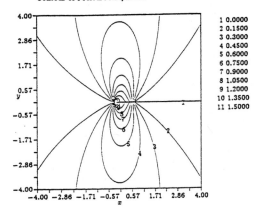

Figure 9. Amplitude of Acoustic Pressure, $M_0 = 0.7, K = 1.0, \tau = 1\%$

Contour of Pressure Amplitude

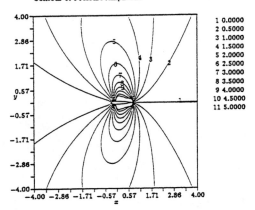

Figure 10. Amplitude of Acoustic Pressure, $M_0 = 0.7, K = 1.0, \tau = 13\%$

Contour of Pressure Phase

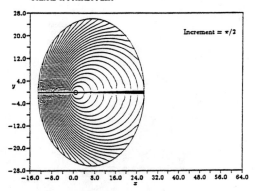

Figure 11. Phase of Acoustic Pressure, $M_0 = 0.7, K = 1.0, \tau = 1\%$

493

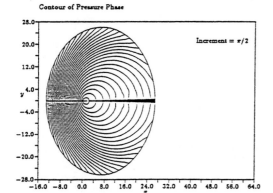

Contour of Pressure Phase

Increment = π/2

Figure 12. Phase of Acoustic
Pressure, $M_0 = 0.7, K = 1.0, \tau = 13\%$

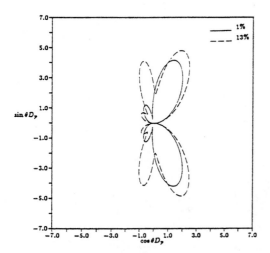

Figure 13. Polar Plot of D_p at the Far Field,
$M_0 = 0.7, K = 3.0$

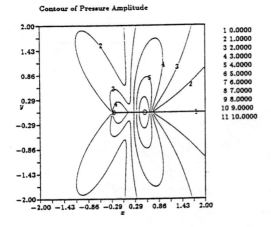

Contour of Pressure Amplitude

1	0.0000
2	1.0000
3	2.0000
4	3.0000
5	4.0000
6	5.0000
7	6.0000
8	7.0000
9	8.0000
10	9.0000
11	10.0000

Figure 14. Amplitude of Acoustic Pressure,
$M_0 = 0.7, K = 3.0, \tau = 1\%$

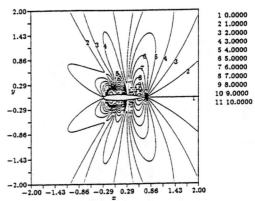

Contour of Pressure Amplitude

1	0.0000
2	1.0000
3	2.0000
4	3.0000
5	4.0000
6	5.0000
7	6.0000
8	7.0000
9	8.0000
10	9.0000
11	10.0000

Figure 15. Amplitude of Acoustic Pressure,
$M_0 = 0.7, K = 3.0, \tau = 13\%$

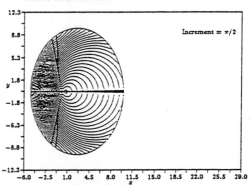

Contour of Pressure Phase

Increment = π/2

Figure 16. Phase of Acoustic Pressure,
$M_0 = 0.7, K = 3.0, \tau = 1\%$

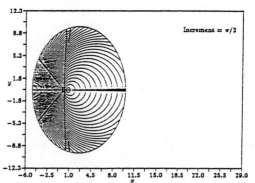

Contour of Pressure Phase

Increment = π/2

Figure 17. Phase of Acoustic Pressure,
$M_0 = 0.7, K = 3.0, \tau = 13\%$

494

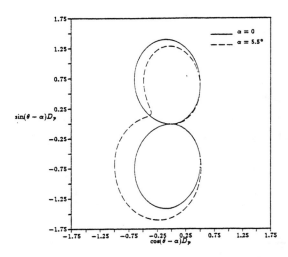

Figure 18. Polar Plot of D_p at the Far Field, NACA0024 airfoil, $M_0 = 0.5, K = 2/3$

Contour of Pressure Amplitude

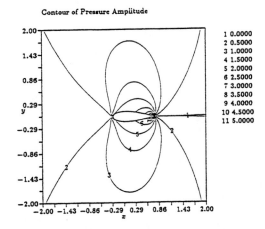

1	0.0000
2	0.5000
3	1.0000
4	1.5000
5	2.0000
6	2.5000
7	3.0000
8	3.5000
9	4.0000
10	4.5000
11	5.0000

Figure 19. Amplitude of Acoustic Pressure, NACA0024 airfoil, $M_0 = 0.5, K = 2/3, \alpha = 5.5^0$

Contour of Pressure Amplitude

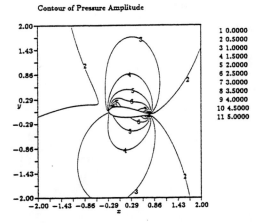

1	0.0000
2	0.5000
3	1.0000
4	1.5000
5	2.0000
6	2.5000
7	3.0000
8	3.5000
9	4.0000
10	4.5000
11	5.0000

Figure 20. Amplitude of Acoustic Pressure, NACA0024 airfoil, $M_0 = 0.5, K = 2/3, \alpha = 5.5$

Contour of Pressure Phase

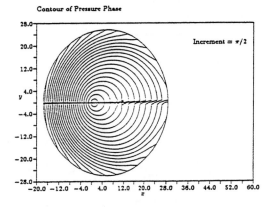

Figure 21. Phase of Acoustic Pressure, NACA0024 airfoil, $M_0 = 0.5, K = 2/3, \alpha = 5.5^0$

Contour of Pressure Phase

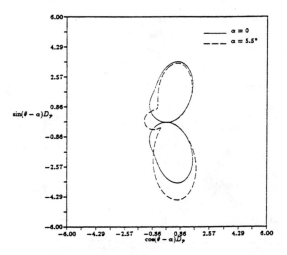

Figure 22. Phase of Acoustic Pressure, NACA0024 airfoil, $M_0 = 0.5, K = 2/3, \alpha = 5.5^0$

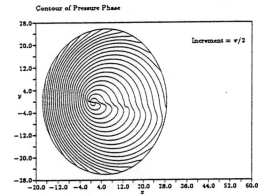

Figure 23. Polar Plot of D_p at the Far Field, NACA0024 airfoil, $M_0 = 0.5, K = 1.7$

495

Contour of Pressure Amplitude

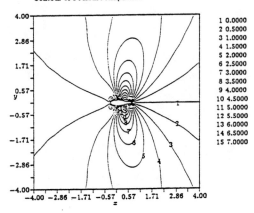

1	0.0000
2	0.5000
3	1.0000
4	1.5000
5	2.0000
6	2.5000
7	3.0000
8	3.5000
9	4.0000
10	4.5000
11	5.0000
12	5.5000
13	6.0000
14	6.5000
15	7.0000

Figure 24. Amplitude of Acoustic Pressure, NACA0024 airfoil $M_0 = 0.5, K = 1.7, \alpha = 0$

Contour of Pressure Phase

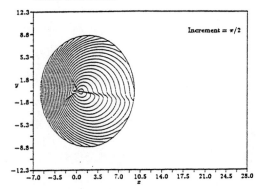

Increment $= \pi/2$

Figure 27. Phase of Acoustic Pressure, NACA0024 airfoil, $M_0 = 0.5. K = 1.7, \alpha = 5.5^0$

Contour of Pressure Amplitude

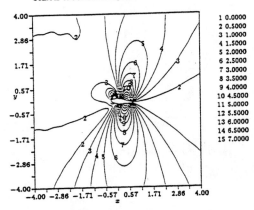

1	0.0000
2	0.5000
3	1.0000
4	1.5000
5	2.0000
6	2.5000
7	3.0000
8	3.5000
9	4.0000
10	4.5000
11	5.0000
12	5.5000
13	6.0000
14	6.5000
15	7.0000

Figure 25. Amplitude of Acoustic Pressure, NACA0024 airfoil, $M_0 = 0.5, K = 1.7, \alpha = 5.5^0$

Contour of Pressure Phase

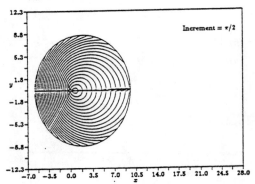

Increment $= \pi/2$

Figure 26. Phase of Acoustic Pressure, NACA0024 airfoil, $M_0 = 0.5, K - 1.7, \alpha = 0$

FED-Vol. 238, 1996 Fluids Engineering Division Conference
Volume 3
ASME 1996

COMPUTATION AND VERIFICATION
OF THE EFFECTS OF FINITE LENGTH FLEXIBLE SEGMENTS
ON ACOUSTIC WAVE PROPAGATION IN ONE-DIMENSIONAL SYSTEMS

Brian V. Chapnik and I.G. Currie
University of Toronto
Department of Mechanical and Industrial Engineering
5 King's College Road
Toronto, Ontario M5S 3G8
CANADA

ABSTRACT

An investigation into the effect of finite length flexible segments on propagating acoustic waves in one-dimensional systems is presented. Flexible segments are commonly used in piping systems to reduce structure borne noise transmitted along the piping. They also have some effect on the fluid borne noise.

Computational algorithms have been developed to predict the effect of the flexible segment on transmitted fluid borne noise, with an arbitrary termination impedance and arbitrary source impedance and velocity. The fluid borne acoustic power generated by a line force applied to the flexible segment is also predicted. The model is based on a fully coupled structural-acoustic interaction over the segment, as described earlier by Chapnik and Currie (1995), and further refinements have since been introduced.

Experiments have been performed to verify the predictive algorithms, utilizing segments of hose and tubing of various geometric and material properties, with air as the contained fluid. Computational acoustic algorithms are applied to reduce the experimental data to meaningful estimates which can be used in conjunction with the predictive algorithms, both to provide realistic input parameters and to compare with the predicted results.

The experimental focus has been to use relatively simple and inexpensive engineering techniques to obtain reasonable approximations of measured parameters, as opposed to precision laboratory measurements, since the former can be more easily applied to solve problems in the field. Paired structural piezofilm sensors are used on the rigid piping upstream and downstream of the flexible segment to estimate the propagating acoustic wave, and a piezofilm actuator is applied to the flexible segment to generate the required line force.

The results of the investigation illustrate the dependence of the acoustic attenuation of the flexible segment on its geometric and material properties, and on the characteristics of the one-dimensional system in which it is placed. Some of the limitations and inaccuracies inherent in the use of approximate measurement techniques are described, and potential improvements discussed.

NOMENCLATURE

E, E_s	Young's modulus of flexible section and sensor material
F_0	applied ring force
J_0	first order bessel function
K, K_s	membrane stiffness of flexible section and ring sensor
L	length of flexible section
M_{rn}^A, M_m	acoustical and structural modal masses
R	complex pressure reflection coefficient
S	nominal cross sectional area of pipes
V_0	applied voltage to ring actuator
V_s	source particle velocity
W^+, W_0^+	transmitted fluid power with and without flexible section
Z_s, Z_t	source and termination impedance
a	nominal radius of flexible section
a_{rn}	modal coordinates of velocity potential
b_m	modal coordinates of axial displacement
c	speed of sound in fluid
d_{31}, g_{31}	piezoelectric strain and stress constants
h	thickness of tube
k, k_r	axial and radial wavenumbers
m, n, r	modal indices
m_s	surface density of tube
p^t	pressure at termination of flexible section
q_m	modal coordinates of radial displacement
t	thickness of sensor or actuator strip
x_0	location of applied ring force
ϵ_n	1 for $n=0$, 1/2 otherwise
v	Poisson's ratio
ξ_m	structural damping coefficient
ρ, ρ_s	fluid density, tube material density
ω_{rn}^A	cavity natural frequencies
ω_m^F, ω_m^L	shell flexural and longitudinal natural frequencies

REVIEW OF MODEL

A conceptual representation of the system under study is illustrated in Figure 1.

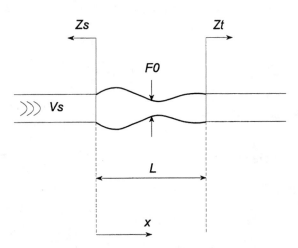

FIGURE 1: SYSTEM UNDER STUDY

A model of the coupled structural-acoustic system over the flexible segment has been presented previously (Chapnik and Currie, 1995), and can be summarized by the following three coupled differential equations governing the modal influence coefficients for the fluid velocity potential and the radial and axial displacements of the flexible section:

$$\ddot{a}_{rn} + \frac{\rho c^2}{M_{rn}^A L} \sum_k \frac{\dot{a}_{rk} M_{rk}^A}{\epsilon_k} \left(\frac{1}{Z_s} + \frac{(-1)^{n+k}}{Z_t} \right) + (\omega_{rn}^A)^2 a_{rn}$$
$$- \frac{2J_0(k_r a)c^2}{M_{rn}^A a L} \sum_m A_{mn} \dot{q}_m = \frac{V_s c^2}{M_{rn}^A L} \delta_r \qquad (1)$$

$$\ddot{q}_m + 2\xi_m \omega_m^F \dot{q}_m + (\omega_m^F)^2 q_m - \frac{v}{a} \frac{(\omega_m^L)^2}{(m\pi/L)} b_m$$
$$+ \frac{\rho}{M_m} \sum_m \dot{a}_{rn} A_{mn} J_0(k_r a) = -\frac{F_0}{M_m} \sin(m\pi x_0/L) \qquad (2)$$

$$\ddot{b}_m + 2\xi_m \omega_m^L \dot{b}_m + (\omega_m^L)^2 b_m - \frac{v}{a} \frac{m\pi}{L} \frac{K}{m_s} q_m = 0 \qquad (3)$$

The excitation to this system of equations is provided either through an assumed constant particle velocity (V_s) at the inlet plane of the flexible section, utilizing equation (1), or through an assumed constant line force input (F_0) at an arbitrary location (x_0) on the flexible section, utilizing equation (2). Note that this formulation assumes shear diaphragm boundary conditions at either end of the flexible section, and that the inlet and outlet impedances Z_s and Z_t are locally reacting and constant across the plane, although they may vary with frequency.

Once the system of equations has been solved, the acoustic power transmitted downstream of the section may be calculated using:

$$W^+ = \frac{S}{\rho c} \frac{S_{LL}}{|1+R|^2} \qquad (4)$$

where S_{LL}, the autospectrum of pressure at the end of the flexible section, includes only those modes which are not evanescent, and R, the complex pressure reflection coefficient at the outlet plane, is related to the termination impedance via:

$$R = \frac{Z_t - \rho c}{Z_t + \rho c} \qquad (5)$$

EXPERIMENTAL APPARATUS

An experiment was devised to verify the model, using readily available materials and equipment. Figure 2 illustrates the experimental apparatus.

The apparatus included a loudspeaker with good low-frequency response attached to a long conical reducer, to make the source relatively insensitive to load variations. Following this were attached a straight rigid inlet pipe, the flexible section under study, a straight rigid outlet pipe, and a variable load. The hose and piping sections were chosen to be nominally 3.8 cm in diameter, primarily for convenience. The straight inlet and outlet pipes were pieces of ABS piping, to which strips of piezoelectric film were bonded, two on each pipe, spaced approximately 10 cm apart and at a distance of approximately 10 cm from the coupling to the flexible section. The strips were long enough to completely circumscribe the pipe, and were bonded to themselves to enhance the hoop stiffness of these "ring sensors". In a similar manner, a "ring actuator" was bonded to the flexible section, at approximately its centre.

A microphone probe was inserted in the outlet pipe downstream of the ring sensors, primarily for the purpose of verifying the magnitude of the acoustic pressures estimated by the latter.

The flexible section was supported on a fibreglass bed, to avoid the effects associated with a rigid support condition and to minimize longitudinal distortions associated with the effects of gravity on the very flexible materials tested. The elastic modulus of the fibreglass is considered low enough so as to be considered negligible in the context of the small acoustic disturbances studied. The ends of the flexible section were connected to the inlet and outlet pipes using standard pipe fittings, in such a manner so as to approximate the assumed shear diaphragm end conditions. Duct tape was used to ensure no leaks at the ends of the section.

Appropriate conditioning was applied to all input and output signals. Inputs from the ring sensors were buffered with a high input impedance, as these sensors have a high related capacitance which will tend to roll off lower frequencies, especially for low input impedances. An audio transformer was used to step up voltages applied to the actuator to higher levels than can be output from standard excitation devices. It was found that, although fairly high voltages can be accommodated by the capacitive piezofilm strips, brief spikes may cause the voltage to exceed the dielectric potential across the thin band, and arcing may result in damage to the device. Smoothing of the output signal was therefore incorporated to eliminate output spikes.

EXPERIMENTAL PROCEDURE

To test various aspects of the theory, five different flexible sections were tested, each with three different loads. The flexible sections included 3 different lengths (short, medium, long) of one type of water discharge hose comprised of SBR with an embedded nylon web reinforcement, a medium length of another type of water discharge hose comprised of similar materials, and a medium length of clear PVC tubing. The loads chosen were a simple open end (i.e. the outlet pipe left unconnected at its downstream end, unflanged), a longer pipe with an open end (i.e. a second piece of pipe connected to the downstream end of the outlet pipe), and an "anechoic" end (i.e. a very long rubber hose attached to the downstream end of the outlet pipe).

For each combination of flexible section and load, a number of tests were performed. Firstly, a broadband noise input was applied to the loudspeaker, and the sensor responses recorded, to obtain a good statistical estimate of the upstream and downstream propagating power with frequency. Secondly, a stepped sine input was applied to the loudspeaker, and the sensor responses recorded, including the response of the "actuator" (which was for this test wired up as a sensor) in order to obtain a rough estimate of Young's Modulus and the structural damping factor of the flexible section. Thirdly, a stepped sine input was applied to the actuator at close to its maximum voltage capacity, to investigate the potential sound generating capability of the actuator.

The broadband noise tests were also performed on the system without any flexible section in place, to get a baseline estimate of the impedance presented by each load, and to estimate the impedance and velocity of the loudspeaker source.

All excitations were limited to a frequency range below approximately half of the frequency of the first cut-on mode in the inlet and outlet pipes, and thus plane wave theory is applicable at the sensor locations. In the flexible section, higher order radial modes could exist and were included in the model.

CALCULATED QUANTITIES

Using the measurement data, various quantities were calculated for input to and comparison with the model.

Load Characterization

Firstly, the termination impedance of each load was estimated from the data obtained without any flexible section installed, using the two-point transfer-function technique described by Chung and Blaser (1980), applied to both the upstream and downstream sensor pairs. In this method, the complex transfer function between the two sensors associated with each pair is calculated using:

$$H_{12} = S_{12} / S_{11} \tag{6}$$

where S_{11} is the autospectrum of the pressure at 1, S_{12} is the cross spectrum of the pressure between 1 and 2, and the subscripts 1 and 2 refer to the upstream and downstream sensor locations, respectively, within a given pair. The complex impedance Z_2 at the downstream sensor location is then given by:

$$Z_2 = \frac{i\rho c H_{12}\sin(kL_s)}{1 - H_{12}\cos(kL_s)} \tag{7}$$

where L_s is the distance between the two sensors of the pair. This impedance as calculated by either the upstream or downstream sensor

pairs can then be translated to the coupling location by assuming a straight pipe section in between and neglecting losses over such a small length. For the case of the downstream pair, this can be achieved using:

$$Z_t = \frac{Z_2 \cos(kL_d) + i\rho c \sin(kL_d)}{iZ_2\sin(kL_d)/(\rho c) + \cos(kL_d)} \tag{8}$$

where L_d is the distance between the coupling and the downstream sensor of the pair. Similarly, the pressure at any sensor location can be translated to the coupling location by making the same assumptions. For the pressure p_2 at the downstream sensor of the downstream pair:

$$p_t = p_2 * (\cos(kL_d) + i\rho c \sin(kL_d)/Z_2) \tag{9}$$

Loudspeaker Source Characterization

Using the estimates of p_t and Z_t thus derived for at least two different loads, the loudspeaker source characteristics can then be inferred. For any two loads, we can write:

$$Z_s = \frac{Z_t^1 Z_t^2 (p_t^1 - p_t^2)}{Z_t^1 p_t^2 - Z_t^2 p_t^1}$$

$$V_s = p_t^1 \left(\frac{1}{Z_t^1} + \frac{1}{Z_s} \right) = p_t^2 \left(\frac{1}{Z_t^2} + \frac{1}{Z_s} \right) \tag{10}$$

where the subscripts 1 and 2 refer to the two loads. For multiple loads, typically used to improve the accuracy of the prediction, a least squares solution as presented by Lavrentjev et al. (1992) can be used.

Sensor Sensitivity Characterization

Calculation of any of the above quantities requires knowledge of the acoustic pressure at the sensor locations. At low frequencies, the piezofilm sensors produce a voltage which is directly proportional to the stress applied to them, in any direction (Pinnington and Briscoe, 1994). If a perfect transfer of strain from the ABS piping to the sensor is assumed, and the frequency is well below the ring frequency of the pipe, then the induced voltage can be shown to be directly proportional to the contained acoustic pressure:

$$p = \frac{E}{E_s} \frac{h}{a} \frac{1}{g_{31}t} * V_0 \tag{11}$$

where E and h refer here to the ABS piping, not the flexible section.

Estimation of Material Properties

The method used to estimate Young's Modulus for the flexible sections can now be explained. At frequencies for which the calculated termination impedance is nearly anechoic (which in practice is observed only using the third load and over a narrow range of frequencies), the pressures observed by the sensors nearest the flexible section will be roughly the same as those inside the section. Under this assumption, equation (11) can be inverted to yield an estimate of Young's Modulus for the flexible section, as all other parameters are known.

An estimate of the damping factor associated with each flexible section was made by exciting the flexible section using the loudspeaker for long enough to reach a steady state response, and then measuring the decay of the response when the excitation was abruptly removed.

Actuator Sensitivity Characterization

The amount of force applied by the ring actuator to the flexible section depends not only on the voltage applied to it, but also on the input impedance of the section at the location of the actuator. This input impedance can readily be estimated by the model through the frequency response function, i.e. the response to a unity force input. It can be shown that the applied force F_0 for a given applied voltage V_0 can then be estimated by:

$$F_0 = \frac{K_s}{K + K_s} \frac{d_{31}a}{w_0 t} * V_0 \qquad (12)$$

where w_0 represents the radial displacement of the flexible section at x_0 when a force of unity magnitude is applied.

Use of Calculated Quantities

The calculated quantities Z_t, Z_s and V_s may be used in equation (1) to generate the predicted results of the model. Of course, equations (4) and (5) can be used for the measured data as well as for the predicted quantities, and the transmitted powers so obtained can be expressed in the form of an insertion loss, or ratio of transmitted powers with and without a flexible section installed:

$$IL = 10 \log \left(\frac{W_0^+}{W^+} \right) \qquad (13)$$

In the context of the model, this ratio compares the transmitted fluid power with no flexible section installed, as estimated from the measurements, to the predicted transmitted fluid power with a flexible section installed, the prediction utilizing quantities also estimated through measurement. This comparison is valid only for the loudspeaker source, and for each load separately. The insertion loss descriptor has no meaning in the context of the ring actuator, as there can be no transmitted power without the flexible section installed.

RESULTS

Figures 3 and 4 illustrate the measured acoustic impedance of the termination for two of the loads, the short open end and the nearly anechoic end. The third load (long open end) is omitted for brevity. The solid and dashed lines indicate the estimates for the upstream and downstream sensor pairs, respectively, while the dotted line indicates the theoretical value. As indicated by the figures, the ring sensors provide an excellent estimate of the termination impedance over the frequency range of interest. Discrepancies near 600 Hz are attributable to background noise, and the "anechoic" termination is found to be somewhat reflective at frequencies below 250 Hz.

Figures 5 and 6 illustrate the estimated source impedance and particle velocity, using all three loads to perform the estimate. Again the solid and dashed lines represent the estimates from the upstream and downstream pairs, while the dotted line represents a logarithmic mean value of these estimates, which has been used in the model to represent the source. It is interesting to note that the upstream and downstream sensor pairs produced significantly different estimates at some frequencies, particularly higher frequencies which seem to lose energy across the coupling between inlet and outlet pipes. The output from the model was fairly sensitive to the source characteristics input, and it was found that the overall mean value produced the most consistent results.

Others (Prasad and Crocker, 1983; Boden, 1988) have also found predictions to be sensitive to the source characteristics, and recommend averaging over a larger number of loads to obtain good results.

Figures 7 through 12 illustrate the performance of the model, in comparison with measured data, in terms of its prediction of the acoustical insertion loss of the flexible section and the transmitted sound power generated by the ring actuator. Solid lines indicate predicted values, while dotted lines are measured estimates. Hose #1 is a medium length of one type of water discharge hose, Hose #4 is a shorter length of the same hose, and Hose #2 is a medium length of clear PVC tubing. Two radial modes and six axial modes (both cavity and structural) were considered in the predictions.

As these results indicate, the model predicts the insertion loss of the flexible section fairly well over most of the frequency range. Discrepancies appear to be partially due to inaccuracies in the estimation of source characteristics, partially due to other measurement errors, and partially due to simplifications inherent in the model, which does not consider out-of-plane modes, energy transmitted to the supports, or other more complex effects.

The calculated sound power produced by the actuator is also in reasonable agreement with measurement, considering imperfect bonding of the actuator to the flexible section. Moreover, it was found that excitement of the actuator produced high levels of structure-borne energy on the inlet and outlet pipes, which interfered with the ability of the ring sensors to detect fluid-borne energy; the measured estimates shown in the figures use the pressure measured at the microphone probe in conjunction with the reflection coefficient previously determined through broadband testing with the loudspeaker. Discrepancies at lower frequencies are believed to be attributable to uncertainty in the source characteristics, while high frequency discrepancies are attributed to imperfect bonding, which would significantly reduce the power input for small deformations. In addition, the model neglects complex effects such as non-linear strain transfer through the shell thickness, which may be important at higher frequencies.

Finally, it is noted that the results were quite similar for all flexible sections tested, as the material properties were similar for small deformations, and the frequency range was low enough so as not to magnify differences in length. Future testing at higher frequencies will be performed to better illustrate the finite length effects.

REFERENCES

Boden, H., 1988, "Error Analysis for the Two-Load Method Used to Measure the Source Characteristics of Fluid Machines", *Journal of Sound and Vibration*, Vol.126, No.1, pp.173-177.

Chapnik, B.V., Currie, I.G., 1995, "The Effect of Finite Length Flexible Segments on Low Frequency Acoustic Wave Propagation in Piping", *Computational Aeroacoustics*, FED-Vol.219, pp.101-106.

Chung, J.Y., Blaser, D.A., 1980, "Transfer function method of measuring in-duct acoustic properties. I. Theory", *Journal of the Acoustical Society of America*, Vol.68, No.3, pp.907-913.

Lavrentjev, J., Boden, H., Abom, M., 1992, "A Linearity Test for Acoustic One-Port Sources", *Journal of Sound and Vibration*, Vol.155, No.3, pp.534-539.

Pinnington, R.J., Briscoe, A.R., 1994, "Externally Applied Sensor for Axisymmetric Waves in a Fluid Filled Pipe", *Journal of Sound and Vibration*, Vol.173, No.4, pp.503-516.

Prasad, M.G., Crocker, M.J., 1983, "Studies of Acoustical Performance of a Multi-Cylinder Engine Exhaust Muffler System", *Journal of Sound and Vibration*, Vol.90, No.4, pp.491-508.

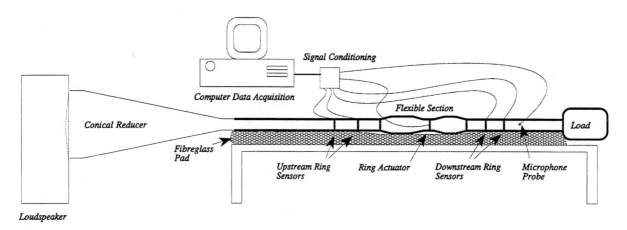

FIGURE 2: EXPERIMENTAL APPARATUS

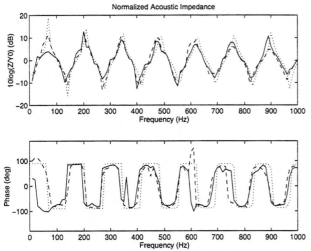

FIGURE 3: TERMINATION IMPEDANCE, OPEN END

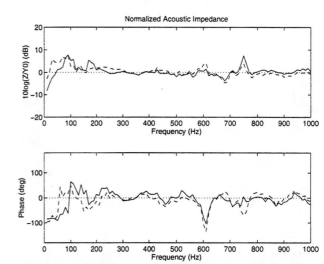

FIGURE 4: TERMINATION IMPEDANCE, ANECH. END

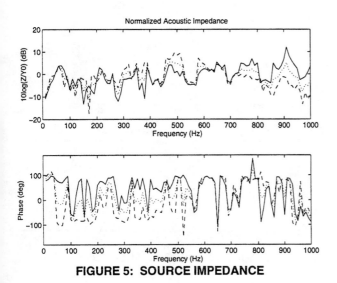

FIGURE 5: SOURCE IMPEDANCE

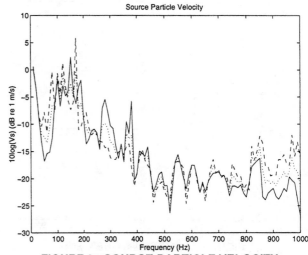

FIGURE 6: SOURCE PARTICLE VELOCITY

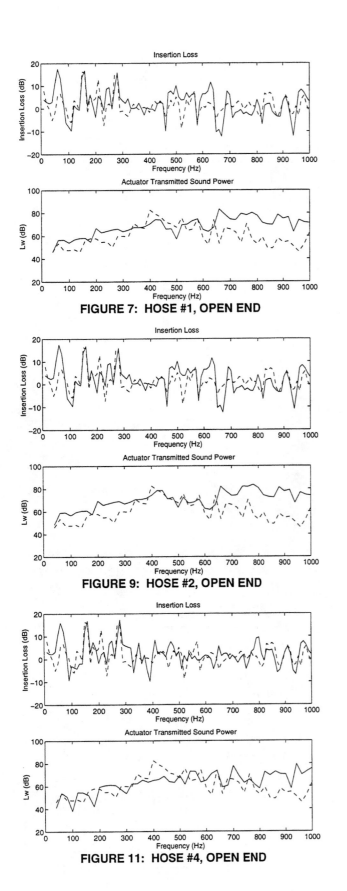

FIGURE 7: HOSE #1, OPEN END

FIGURE 9: HOSE #2, OPEN END

FIGURE 11: HOSE #4, OPEN END

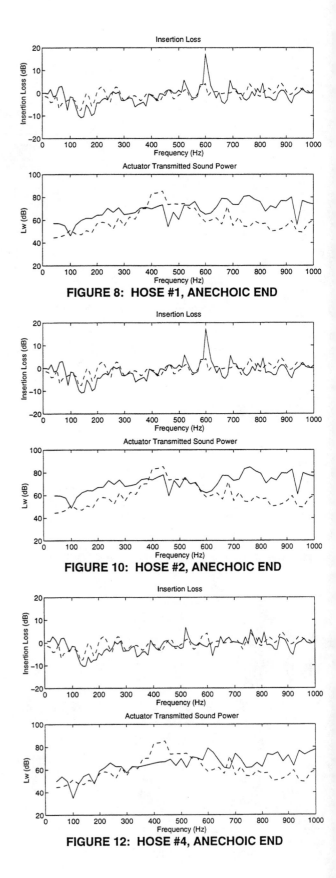

FIGURE 8: HOSE #1, ANECHOIC END

FIGURE 10: HOSE #2, ANECHOIC END

FIGURE 12: HOSE #4, ANECHOIC END

FED-Vol. 238, 1996 Fluids Engineering Division Conference
Volume 3
ASME 1996

ALGORITHMIC EXTENSIONS OF LOW-DISPERSION SCHEME AND MODELING EFFECTS FOR ACOUSTIC WAVE SIMULATION

Dinesh K. Kaushik and Oktay Baysal

Aerospace Engineering Department
Old Dominion University
Norfolk, Virginia 23529

Abstract

Accurate computation of acoustic wave propagation may be more efficiently performed when their dispersion relations are considered. Consequently, computational algorithms which attempt to preserve these relations have been gaining popularity in recent years. In the present paper, the extensions to one such scheme are discussed. By solving the linearized, 2-D Euler and Navier-Stokes equations with such a method for the acoustic wave propagation, several issues were investigated. Among them were higher-order accuracy, choice of boundary conditions and differencing stencils, effects of viscosity, low-storage time integration, generalized curvilinear coordinates, periodic sources, their reflections and interference patterns from a flat wall and scattering from a circular cylinder. The results were found to be promising en route to the aeroacoustic simulations of realistic engineering problems..

Introduction

Computational aeroacoustics (CAA) may be defined as the application of numerical techniques for the direct calculation of aerodynamic sound generation and propagation starting from the first principles. Most computational fluid dynamics (CFD) schemes, however, are not adequately accurate for solving the aeroacoustics problems (Lighthill, 1992). Their amplitudes are often orders of magnitude smaller, and yet the frequencies are orders of magnitude larger than the flow field variations generating the sound. Further, high-fidelity is paramount for the resolution of acoustic problems; but a consistent, stable, and convergent, high-order scheme is not necessarily dispersion-relation preserving and thus does not necessarily guarantee a good quality numerical wave solution for an acoustic problem. Hence, among the requirements that should be placed on a CAA algorithm are the minimal dispersion and dissipation features (Tam and Webb, 1993).

The direct simulations of acoustic wave propagation have been tried by solving the full Navier-Stokes equations. For example, Baysal et al. (1994) investigated two devices to suppress the high tones generated by a high-speed cavity flow,

using an unsteady computational fluid dynamics (CFD) method. The comparisons with experimental data were acceptable for engineering purposes. However, it was realized that the dissipative and dispersive characteristics of a typical second-order CFD method would preclude a long-term wave propagation simulation. Also, various studies (e.g. Mankbadi et al., 1993, Lyrintzis et al., 1995, and Hardin et al., 1995) have suggested that the direct simulations of the flow equations for the acoustic wave propagation using the higher-order CFD schemes could become prohibitively expensive, since the number of grid points per wavelength would be excessively high (ideally should not exceed ten).

Therefore, a fourth-order accurate dispersion-relation-preserving (DRP) method was previously investigated for a variety of wave propagation problems (Vanel and Baysal, 1995). A number of observations and recommendations were made for future investigations to extend the scheme to solve some application problems. The present investigation started precisely with this impetus. A selection of the issues explored, all for linear cases, are reported herein. These include higher-order accuracy (up to sixth-order), choice of boundary conditions and differencing stencils, effects of viscosity, low-storage time integration, generalized curvilinear coordinates, periodic sources, their reflections and interference patterns from a flat wall and scattering from a circular cylinder. The extensions for the nonlinear acoustics are deferred to another paper for brevity.

Governing Equations

The two-dimensional, compressible Navier-Stokes and Euler equations were considered in generalized curvilinear coordinates. In the absence of curved or irregularly shaped boundaries, their Cartesian expressions were preferred. By superimposing small perturbations on a mean flow field, then by neglecting the higher order terms in perturbed quantities, these equations were *linearized* to simulate the propagation of waves in a uniform mean flow.

$$\frac{\partial \hat{U}}{\partial t} = -R(\hat{U}) + S \text{ , where } R(\hat{U}) = \frac{\partial \hat{E}}{\partial \xi} + \frac{\partial \hat{F}}{\partial \eta} \qquad (1.a)$$

The flux vectors ($\hat{E}, \hat{F}$) were obtained through transformations,

$$\hat{E} = [\xi_x(E - E_v) + \xi_y(F - F_v)] / J,$$
$$\hat{F} = [\eta_x(E - E_v) + \eta_y(F - F_v)] / J \qquad (1.b)$$

where the vector of unknowns ($\hat{U}$) and the physical fluxes were

$$\hat{U} = \frac{1}{J} \begin{bmatrix} \rho \\ u \\ v \\ p \end{bmatrix}, \quad E = \begin{bmatrix} \rho_0 u + \rho u_0 \\ u_0 u + p/\rho_0 \\ u_0 v \\ u_0 p + \gamma p_0 u \end{bmatrix}, \quad F = \begin{bmatrix} \rho_0 v \\ 0 \\ p/\rho_0 \\ \gamma p_0 v \end{bmatrix} \qquad (1.c)$$

$$E_v = \frac{1}{\rho_0} \begin{bmatrix} 0 \\ \tau_{xx} \\ \tau_{yx} \\ 0 \end{bmatrix}, \quad F_v = \frac{1}{\rho_0} \begin{bmatrix} 0 \\ \tau_{xy} \\ \tau_{yy} \\ 0 \end{bmatrix} \qquad (1.d)$$

The diffusion terms in the energy equation were omitted due to their perceived secondary influence on most of the acoustic wave propagation phenomena. Also, the second coefficient of viscosity was neglected, effectively negating the rotational effect of a fluid element but leaving its deformation-rate in the shear stresses.

$$\tau_{x_i x_j} = \mu \left(\frac{\partial u_i}{\partial x_j} + \frac{\partial u_j}{\partial x_i} \right) \qquad (1.e)$$

The density (ρ), pressure (p), and velocity (u,v) of the perturbed quantities are denoted without a subscript, but those of the mean flow are demarcated using the subscript 0. These variables were normalized using the following scales for length, velocity, time, density, and pressure, respectively: Δx (mesh step size), a_0 (speed of sound), $\Delta x / a_0$ ρ_0, and $\rho_0 a_0^2$. Finally, S in eq. (1) denotes a possible acoustic source.

Computational Method

Equation (1) supports the acoustic, the entropy as well as the vorticity waves. The propagation characteristics of these waves (dispersion, dissipation, group and phase velocities, and isotropy or anisotropy) are formulated in their dispersion relations, which relate the angular frequency of the waves (ω) to the wave numbers of the space variables (α). Therefore, in order to capture the correct wave propagation characteristics, the dispersion relation of the finite-difference scheme should match as closely as possible the dispersion relation of the partial differential equations (PDE). This is equivalent to requiring that the effective wave number ($\overline{\alpha}$) and effective angular frequency ($\overline{\omega}$) of the numerical scheme must be close approximations to those of the PDE system for a large range of resolution. Such a scheme, therefore, is called a *dispersion-relation preserving* (DRP) scheme. The way in which the *baseline* DRP scheme of Tam and Webb (1993) and Tam and Shen (1993) was accomplished for the present development is given by Vanel and Baysal (1995).

In discretizing the spatial derivatives, the DRP was achieved by determining the coefficients (a_j) from the Taylor series expansion as a one-parameter family; then the remaining coefficient was determined from the minimization of the discrepancy between the numerical (effective) wave number $\overline{\alpha}$ and the exact wave number α, by integrating the square of their difference for a desired range $(-\varepsilon, \varepsilon)$, where $|\alpha \Delta x| \prec \varepsilon$. Note that, $\overline{\alpha} \Delta x$ is a periodic function of $\alpha \Delta x$ with a 2π period, and if $Real(\overline{\alpha} \Delta x) = (\alpha \Delta x)$, the scheme is nondispersive, and if $Imaginary(\overline{\alpha} \Delta x) = 0$, the scheme is nondissipative. The integration limit ε is determined depending on the shortest wavelength desired to be simulated. For example, in the 4-th order version of the present schemes, two choices of ε were tried: $\pi/2$ and 1.1, which corresponded to the minimum wavelengths of 4.5 Δx and 7 Δx, respectively. This is a remarkable improvement over a standard sixth-order scheme which can only resolve wave lengths longer than 10 Δx.

The time integration of eq. (1) was performed in two different ways. In the first approach, a four-point finite difference, which in a standard sense could be up to third-order accurate, was derived from the Taylor series as a one-parameter family. The remaining coefficient (b_j) was determined, as in the spatial coefficients, by minimizing the discrepancy between the effective and the exact dispersion relations. After discretizing all the terms in eq. (1), the resulting $\vartheta(\Delta t^2, \Delta x^{N+M-2})$-accurate DRP scheme was as follows:

$$\hat{U}_{\ell,m}^{n+1} = \hat{U}_{\ell,m}^n + \Delta t \sum_{j=0}^{3} b_j R_{\ell,m}^{n-j} \qquad (2.a)$$

where $R_{\ell,m}^n = -\frac{1}{\Delta \xi} \sum_{j=-N}^{M} a_j \hat{E}_{\ell+j,m}^n - \frac{1}{\Delta \eta} \sum_{j=-N}^{M} a_j \hat{F}_{\ell,m+j}^n \qquad (2.b)$

ℓ and m are the spatial indices and n indicates the time level. For N=M, difference eq. (2.) is central, for N=0, it is fully forward, and for M=0, it is fully backward. All the interior cells were computed using central differences. However, since these high-order stencils require multiple layers of boundary cells, all combinations between a central and a fully-one-sided difference need also be derived. Only then, it would be possible to always utilize the information from the nearest possible points for better accuracy. In the present computations a fourth-order scheme and a sixth-order scheme were derived, requiring 7-point stencil (*N takes values from 6 to 0, M takes values from 0 to 6, and N+M=6*) and 9-point stencil (*N takes values from 8 to 0, M takes values from 0 to 8, and N+M=8*), respectively.

The numerically stable maximum time step Δt was calculated from the Courant-Friedrichs-Lewy relation. For example, for the fourth-order scheme in Cartesian coordinates, the stable CFL number was found to be 0.4. However, after analyzing the numerical damping of the time integration scheme, the CFL value was set to the more stringent value of 0.19.

Since the above time integration scheme required the storage of four time levels, a relatively lower storage alternative, such as the Runge-Kutta scheme, was considered. The classical Runge-Kutta schemes, however, are intrinsically dissipative and dispersive. Recently, a class of low-dissipation and low-dispersion Runge-Kutta schemes have been developed by Hu et al. (1994). Its development was similar to that of eq. (2), such that the dissipation and dispersion errors were minimized for all the frequencies resolvable by the numerical discretization. Most importantly, these schemes can be implemented with low-storage requirements. The resulting scheme had the spatial integration identical to eq. (2b), but the time integration was replaced by the following:

$$\hat{U}^{(0)} = \hat{U}^n \qquad (3a)$$

$$\hat{U}^{(i)} = \hat{U}^{(0)} - \beta_i \Delta t R^{(i-1)}, \quad i = 1, 2, .., p \qquad (3b)$$

$$\hat{U}^{n+1} = \hat{U}^{(p)} \qquad (3c)$$

The indices n, p and i indicate the time level, and the order and the stage of the Runge-Kutta method, respectively. As for the coefficients, $\beta_1 = 0$ and the other coefficients β_i were determined from

$$c_i = \prod_{k=2}^{i} \beta_{p-k+2}, \quad i = 2, ..., p \qquad (4)$$

The coefficients c_i were computed by considering the amplification factor of the Runge-Kutta scheme, then minimizing the dispersion-relation error. The time steps to be used were determined from the stability as well as the accuracy limits. In the present study, a five-stage Runge-Kutta (p=5) was used, which required two levels of storage and it was at least second-order accurate. When it was used with 7-point spatial stencil, the CFL limit from the stability was found to be 3.05, but it was only 1.16 from the accuracy limit. Since, however, this still was larger than the CFL limit of the DRP time integration (0.19), this method was also more efficient in processing time.

Boundary Conditions

The boundaries should be transparent to the acoustic disturbances reaching them to avoid any degradation of the numerical solution. For a right-moving uniform mean flow as represented by the linearized equations, and when all the disturbances (acoustic, entropy and vorticity) are generated in the interior of the domain, only acoustic waves reach the upper, lower and upstream boundaries; but, in addition to the acoustic waves, entropy and vorticity waves can reach the downstream boundary. Therefore, following Tam and Webb (1993) and from the asymptotic solutions of the finite difference form of eq. (1), a set of *radiation* boundary conditions,

$$\frac{\partial \hat{U}}{\partial t} + A \frac{\partial \hat{U}}{\partial \xi} + B \frac{\partial \hat{U}}{\partial \eta} + C \hat{U} = 0 \qquad (5a)$$

where

$$A \equiv V \frac{x\xi_x + y\xi_y}{r}, \quad B \equiv V \frac{x\eta_x + y\eta_y}{r}, \quad C \equiv \frac{V}{2r}, \qquad (5b)$$

$$r = \frac{1}{\Delta x} \sqrt{x^2 + y^2}, \quad V = \frac{x}{r} M \sqrt{1 - (M \frac{y}{r})^2}, \qquad (5c)$$

and *outflow* boundary conditions for the downstream boundary,

$$\frac{\partial U'}{\partial t} + \hat{M}(U') = Q, \qquad (6a)$$

where the Mach-number-related operator and the source term were,

$$\hat{M} = (u_0 \xi_x + v_0 \xi_y) \frac{\partial}{\partial \xi} + (u_0 \eta_x + v_0 \eta_y) \frac{\partial}{\partial \eta} \qquad (6b)$$

$$Q = \left[\frac{\partial p}{\partial t} + \hat{M}(p), \quad -(\xi_x \frac{\partial p}{\partial \xi} + \eta_x \frac{\partial p}{\partial \eta}), \quad -(\xi_y \frac{\partial p}{\partial \xi} + \eta_y \frac{\partial p}{\partial \eta}) \right]^T \qquad (6c)$$

were obtained. In eq. (6), U' contains only the first three components of $\hat{U}$ in Eq. (1c). The pressure was obtained as in eq. (5).

For the inviscid calculations on a *solid wall*, the impermeability condition requires that the normal contravariant velocity be zero; and for the viscous computations, the no-slip condition requires that the tangential contravariant velocity also be set to zero.

$$\hat{v} = \eta_x u + \eta_y v = 0., \quad \hat{u} = \xi_x u + \xi_y v = 0 \qquad (7)$$

When above equations were used in the η-momentum and ξ-momentum equations, the wall values of pressure and shear stress were obtained, respectively. The DRP scheme coefficients for all the boundary conditions (Tam and Dong, 1994) were derived by an analogous method to that of the boundary region cells.

Results

The present schemes and their boundary conditions were evaluated by considering five wave propagation cases: (i) Single acoustic pulse; (ii) Two simultaneous acoustic pulses; (iii) Acoustic pulse near a flat wall; (iv) Periodic source near a flat wall; (v) Periodic source near a circular cylinder.

Each of the acoustic pulses, introduced into a uniform mean flow (left to right) with a Mach number of 0.5, was generated by setting u=v=0, and imposing an initial Gaussian distribution for the pressure and density:

$$p = \rho = 0.01 \exp[\frac{-\ln 2}{(3\Delta x)^2}(x^2 + y^2)] \qquad (8)$$

The pressure contours at 1500 Δt for the *single acoustic pulse* case, computed by the fourth order inviscid DRP scheme (eq. 2), are shown in Fig. 1a. The results verified the expected propagation pattern and matched the exact solution (Vanel and Baysal, 1995): the radius of the acoustic wave expanded in time while its center was being entrained downstream with the mean flow. The waves exited from boundaries without any numerical reflections. Presented in Fig. 1b is the same case computed using the optimized Runge-Kutta time integration (eq. 3) after only 150 time steps. The numerical waves matched in both the amplitude and the propagation speed. However, the latter required about *one-half* the storage memory and *one-sixth* the processing time of the former.

In the second case, *two acoustic pulses* were generated *simultaneously:* one at half-span and the other at three-quarter span of the computational domain. Presented in Fig. 2a are the pressure contours computed by the fourth-order DRP scheme with $\varepsilon = \pi/2$ and without a mean flow (M=0). It was observed that the two pulses intersected as they propagated radially. The interaction of the waves was crisply simulated. Then, the case was repeated with a mean flow of M=0.5 and $\varepsilon = 1.1$ (Fig. 2b). With the mean flow, the waves started to drift downstream. Then, the case was repeated using the sixth-order scheme (Figs. 2c, 2d). In all of the above cases minor reflections from the corners were observed. This was cured when the simulation was repeated on a four times larger domain (Figs. 2e, 2f).

In the final case with the acoustic pulse, the lower boundary was replaced by a solid flat wall. The reflection of the pulse off the wall and its interference with the incident pulse were computed once by solving the Euler equations (Fig. 3), then by solving the Navier-Stokes equations (Fig. 4). As expected, the wave strength was attenuated faster in the latter due to the physical diffusion process.

In the first *periodic acoustic source* case, the source was generated with the fourth term in the source vector of eq. (1),

$$S_4 = 0.01 \exp\left\{-\ln 2\left[\frac{x(\xi,\eta)^2 + (y(\xi,\eta) - 20)^2}{9}\right]\right\} \cdot \cos(\omega t) \qquad (9)$$

The medium was inviscid air at M=0. The interference pattern, shown in Fig. 5, reached to a steady-state pattern after some transient time.

Finally, another acoustic scattering problem (Tam and Sankar, 1996) was considered. The motivation was the physical problem of the sound field generated by a propeller scattered off by the fuselage of an aircraft. The pressure loading on the fuselage was an input to the interior noise problem. Here, the fuselage was idealized as a circular cylinder and the noise source as a line source, hence a 2-D problem. For a periodic source with $\omega=8\pi$, the fourth term in the source vector of eq. (1) was assigned the following,

$$S_4 = \exp\left\{-\ln 2\left[\frac{(x(\xi,\eta) - x_s)^2 + (y(\xi,\eta) - y_s)^2}{0.2^2}\right]\right\} \cdot \sin(\omega t) \qquad (10)$$

Due to the curved boundary, the inviscid equations were solved in their generalized curvilinear form on a conforming 251x101 grid. First, the periodic source was placed above a circular bump on a flat plate at (0, 20). The interference pattern is presented in Fig. 6. Then, the case of circular cylinder scattering, with the source at (4, 0), was simulated. Four instants from the animation are presented in Fig. 7.

By and large, the reflections and scattering computations were successful. By employing the body-fitted coordinates, solid wall boundary conditions were imposed properly, hence the wall region was properly computed. On the other hand, grid cells not being perfectly orthogonal, and the existence of the transformation metrics in the equations, caused minor degradation, as compared to the Cartesian cases.

Conclusions

Computational schemes which preserve the dispersion relation of the fundamental equations were investigated. In developing such schemes, ultimately for realistic and complex aeroacoustics problems, several necessary steps have been taken. The linearized Euler and Navier-Stokes equations were solved. Solid wall boundary conditions and differences utilizing the nearest-point information in the boundary regions were demonstrated. The spatial scheme was extended to the sixtth order accuracy, and with the optimized Runge-Kutta time-integration, the efficiency of the method was improved. For the curved wall boundary conditions, the scheme was extended for the generalized curvilinear coordinates. The schemes were successfully demonstrated for several acoustic pulse cases and several acoustic scattering cases.

In order for the scheme to be of more practical interest, it was deemed necessary to investigate its further extensions for the nonlinear equations, with a controllable amount of numerical dissipation, and multiblock nonuniform grids. Also, both from the efficiency and the accuracy points of view, replacing the present finite-difference (local) boundary conditions with integral (global) boundary conditions should prove to be profitable.

References

Baysal, O., Yen, G.W., and Fouladi, K., 1992, "Navier-Stokes Computations of Cavity Aeroacoustics With Suppression Devices," *Proceedings of DGLR/AIAA 14th Aeroacoustics Conference,* Vol. 2, pp. 940-948, Aachen, Germany. Also, *Journal of Vibration and Acoustics,* Vol. 116, No. 1, pp. 105-112.

Hardin, J.C., Ristorcelli, J.R., Tam, C.K.W., (Editors), 1995, ICASE/LaRC Workshop on Benchmark Problems in Computational Aeroacoustics, NASA Conference Publication 3300.

Hu, F.Q., Hussaini, M.Y., and Manthey, J., 1994, "Low-dissipation and Low-dispersion Runge-Kutta Schemes for Computational Acoustics," ICASE Report 94-102, Hampton, VA. Also to appear in *Journal of Computational Physics,* March 1996.

Lighthill, J., (1992), "Report on the Final Panel Discussion on Computational Aeroacoustics," ICASE Report No. 92-53, NASA Langley Research Center, Hampton, VA.

Lyrintzis, A. S., Mankbadi, R.R., Baysal, O., Ikegawa, M., (Editors), 1995, Computational Aeroacoustics, FED-Vol. 219, ASME, New-York, NY.

Mankbadi, R.R., Lyrintzis, A. S., Baysal, O., Povinelli, L. A., Hussaini, M. Y., (Editors), 1993, Computational Aero- and Hydro-acoustics, FED-Vol. 147, ASME, New-York, NY.

Tam, K. W., and Webb, J. C., 1993, "Dispersion-Relation-Preserving Finite Difference Schemes for Computational Acoustics," *Journal of Computational Physics,* Vol. 107, pp. 262-283.

Tam, C.K.W., and Shen, H., 1993, "Direct Computation of Nonlinear Acoustic Pulses using Higher-Order Finite Difference Schemes," AIAA Paper 93-4325, 15th Aeroacoustics Conference, Long Beach, CA.

Tam, C.K.W., and Dong, Z., 1994 "Wall Boundary Conditions for High-Order Finite Difference Schemes in Computational Aeroacoustics," AIAA Paper 94-0457, 32nd Aerospace Sciences Meeting, Reno, NV.

Tam, C.K.W., and Sankar, L.N., (Editors), 1996, Second Computational Aeroacoustics Workshop on Benchmark Problems, to appear as a NASA Conference Publication.

Vanel, F. O., and Baysal, O., 1995, "Investigation of Dispersion-Relation-Preserving Scheme and Spectral Analysis Methods for Acoustic Waves," Paper no. 95-093, Proceedings of First CEAS/AIAA Aeroacoustics Conference, Munich, Germany, pp. 675-682. Also, to appear in [ASME] *Journal of Vibration and Acoustics,*

Acknowledgment

This work was supported by NASA Langley Research Center Grant NAG-1-1653. The technical monitor was Dr. J.L. Thomas.

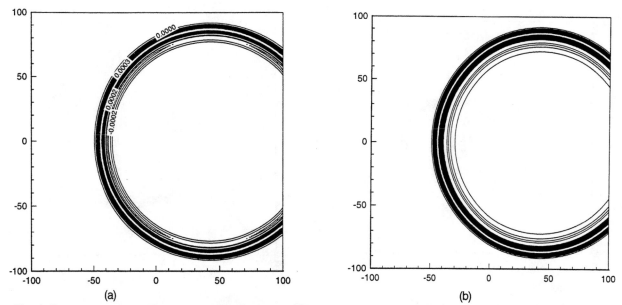

(a)

(b)

Fig. 1 Pressure contours of an acoustic pulse (eq. 8) after 1500 Δt computed with: (a) four-level DRP time integration, (b) optimized five-stage Runge-Kutta.

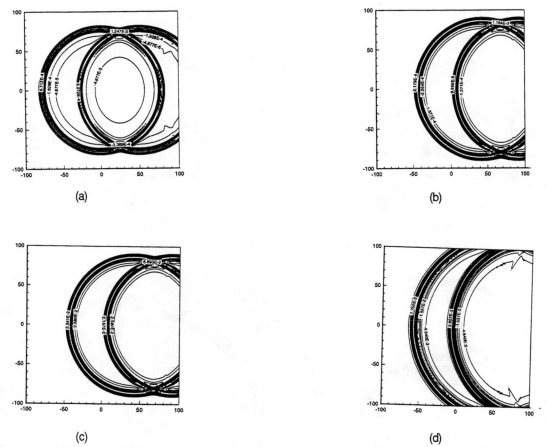

(a)

(b)

(c)

(d)

Fig. 2 Pressure contours of multiple acoustic pulses (eq. 8 at two locations). (a) M=0 case at 1000 Δt;(b) ε=1.1 case at 1500 Δt; Sixth-order scheme at (c) 1500 Δt and (d) 2000 Δt; On 400x400 domain at (e) 1000 Δt and (f) 2000 Δt.

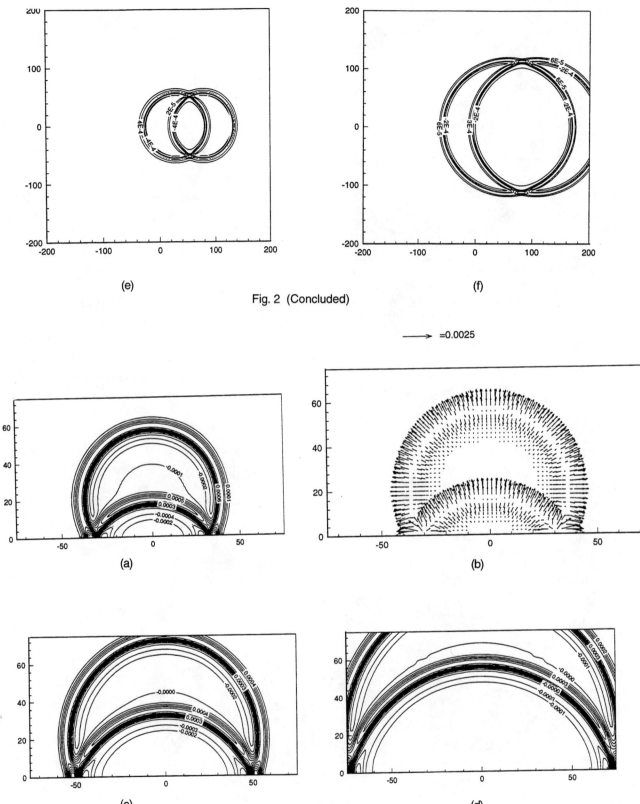

(e)

(f)

Fig. 2 (Concluded)

⟶ =0.0025

(a)

(b)

(c)

(d)

Fig. 3 Reflection of an acoustic pulse (eq. 8) from a flat wall by solving Euler equations. Pressure contours at:
(a) 500 Δt, (c) 700 Δt, (d) 1000 Δt. (b) Velocity vectors at 500 Δt.

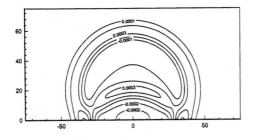 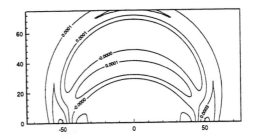

(a)   (b)

Fig. 4 Reflection of an acoustic pulse (eq. 8) from a flat wall by solving Navier-Stokes equations.
Pressure contours at: (a) 500 Δt, (b) 700 Δt.

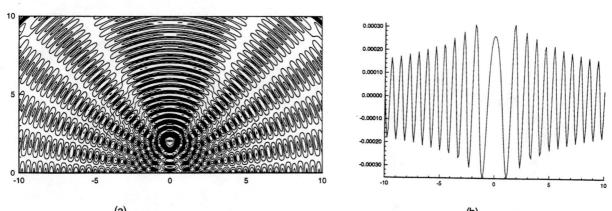

(a)   (b)

Fig. 5 Interference pattern of a periodic acoustic source (eq. 9) reflected from a flat wall:
(a) pressure contours, (b) wall pressure values.

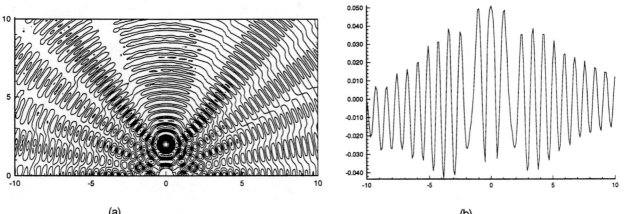

(a)   (b)

Fig. 6 Interference pattern of a periodic acoustic source (eq. 10 with source at (0,20)) from a bump on a flat wall:
(a) pressure contours, (b) wall pressure values.

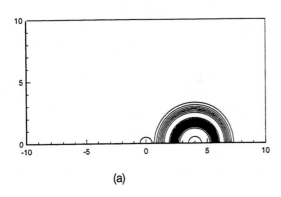

(a)

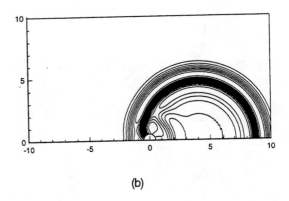

(b)

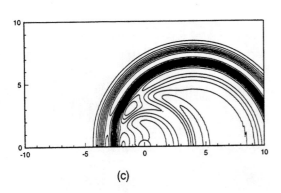

(c)

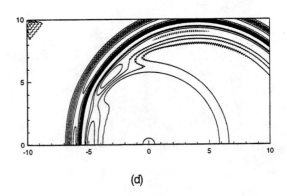

(d)

Fig. 7 Scattering of a periodic acoustic source (eq. 10 with source at (4,0)) from a circular cylinder.
Pressure contours at: (a) 200 Δt, (b) 500 Δt, (c)700 Δt, (d) 1000 Δt.

FED-Vol. 238, 1996 Fluids Engineering Division Conference
Volume 3
ASME 1996

APPROXIMATE NONREFLECTING BOUNDARY CONDITIONS
FOR CYLINDRICAL ACOUSTIC WAVES

Karl D von Ellenrieder   **Brian J Cantwell**
Stanford University, Aeronautics and Astronautics
MC 4035 Stanford, California 94305 USA
Tel. (415) 725-3290, Fax. (415) 725-3377
karl@alicec.stanford.edu, cantwell@leland.stanford.edu

ABSTRACT

The numerical treatment of boundary conditions for cylindrical acoustic waves is difficult because the parameters at a boundary depend on the state of the flow at points outside of the computational domain. Since knowledge of these external flow conditions is necessary but inaccessible for calculation, the information must be estimated. In this paper, the acoustic equations are used to derive approximate boundary conditions for axisymmetric cylindrical waves. Comparisons between analytical and numerical solutions of acoustic pulse propagation are used to test the accuracy of the method developed.

1. INTRODUCTION

While investigating two-dimensional axisymmetric compressible vortices, viscous decay and external compression and expansion of the vortex were found to give rise to radial velocities which convect mass and angular momentum into or out of the vortex. The radial mass convection can be viewed as the propagation of axisymmetric density waves. It is the accurate time-dependent representation of such waves which motivates the current numerical investigation. To simplify the analysis, acoustic wave propagation in a non-rotating fluid is considered here; the results will be extended to compressible vortex flow in future work. In this study two dimensional acoustic pulses centered at the origin of a cylindrical coordinate system are tracked as they travel out of the computational domain across a nonreflecting boundary. Computational and analytical solutions of the flow created by the travelling waves are compared to measure the performance of the boundary conditions.

Note that the propagation of axisymmetric cylindrical acoustic waves is significantly different from that of planar acoustic waves (Landau and Lifshitz 1987 and Hagstrom and Hariharan 1988): 1) A cylindrical wave must cause both compression and expansion of the medium through which it travels. At any point in the fluid, the integral over all time of the density and pressure perturbations caused by the wave will be zero. 2) Cylindrical waves possess a "tail" which decays inversely with time after the passage of the wave. 3) The outgoing and incoming characteristics of cylindrical waves are coupled. Even though a cylindrical acoustic wave may be purely outgoing, it will generate inward travelling characteristics. 4) The amplitude of a cylindrical wave scales inversely with the square root of the radius (except in the immediate vicinity of the origin).

Both the presence of incoming characteristics and the radial dependence of the wave's amplitude become especially important when nonreflecting boundary conditions are used to model wave propagation in an infinite medium. If the incoming characteristics are not accurately predicted at the boundary, significant errors in the time dependent amplitude of the wave can occur. In addition, the amplitude of waves reflected by the outer boundary will increase as the waves propagate towards the center of the domain; a constant amount of energy is being confined to a continually decreasing volume. Since the boundary should be transparent to outgoing waves, the reflected waves are essentially computational errors which grow as they travel from the boundary into the domain.

In section 2 the approximate boundary conditions are

derived and discussed. The analytical model for outgoing cylindrical waves, as well as the computational method used are presented in section 3. A comparison between the analytical and computational solutions is given in section 4. Finally, section 5 contains the conclusions reached in this study.

2. DERIVATION

Approximate boundary conditions for cylindrical acoustic waves can be found by examining the characteristic relations. Following Thompson (1987) the characteristic equations (in cylindrical coordinates) for an ideal gas under homentropic conditions are:

$$\left(\frac{\partial p}{\partial t} - \rho c \frac{\partial u_r}{\partial t}\right) + (u_r - c)\left(\frac{\partial p}{\partial r} - \rho c \frac{\partial u_r}{\partial r}\right) = -\frac{\gamma p u_r}{r} \quad (1)$$

$$\left(\frac{\partial p}{\partial t} + \rho c \frac{\partial u_r}{\partial t}\right) + (u_r + c)\left(\frac{\partial p}{\partial r} + \rho c \frac{\partial u_r}{\partial r}\right) = -\frac{\gamma p u_r}{r} \quad (2)$$

p, ρ, u_r, c, and γ, are the fluid pressure, density, radial velocity, sound speed, and ratio of specific heats respectively. Time is represented by t, and r is the radial coordinate. $(u_r - c)$ and $(u_r + c)$ represent the speed of the characteristics governed by equations (1) and (2), respectively. For acoustic wave propagation $u_r \ll c$, so that the characteristics in equation (1) are incoming, and those governed by equation (2) are outgoing. At the boundary the value of the incoming characteristics is determined by flow conditions existing outside of the computational domain. This information is unavailable for the calculation and will be approximated as shown below. Also note that the common term, $-\gamma p u_r / r$ in equations (1) and (2), is responsible for coupling the outgoing and incoming characteristics.

The expressions (1) and (2) may be rewritten in the following form:

$$\left(\frac{\partial p}{\partial t} - \rho c \frac{\partial u_r}{\partial t}\right) + \mathcal{L}_1 = 0 \quad (3)$$

$$\left(\frac{\partial p}{\partial t} + \rho c \frac{\partial u_r}{\partial t}\right) + \mathcal{L}_2 = 0 \quad (4)$$

Table 1. The acoustic approximation.

Relation	Description
ϕ	Velocity potential
$p' = -\rho_o \frac{\partial \phi}{\partial t}$	Pressure perturbation
$u_r = \frac{\partial \phi}{\partial r}, \ u_r \ll c$	Radial velocity
p_o, ρ_o	Quiescent pressure and density
$p' \ll p_o, \rho' \ll \rho_o$	Pressure and density perturbations
$-\rho_o \frac{\partial u_r}{\partial t} = \frac{\partial p}{\partial r}$	Radial momentum equation
$-\frac{1}{c^2}\frac{\partial^2 \phi}{\partial t^2} + \left(\frac{\partial^2 \phi}{\partial r^2} + \frac{1}{r}\frac{\partial \phi}{\partial r}\right) = 0$	Cylindrical wave equation

Using the relation $\gamma p = \rho c^2$, $\mathcal{L}_1$ becomes:

$$\mathcal{L}_1 = (u_r - c)\left[\frac{\partial p}{\partial r} - \rho c\left(\frac{\partial u_r}{\partial r} + \frac{u_r}{r}\right)\right] + \frac{\rho c u_r{}^2}{r} \quad (5)$$

Employing the first order acoustic approximations for outgoing cylindrical waves (Table 1), the term in square brackets on the right hand side of equation (5) is:

$$\left[\frac{\partial p}{\partial r} - \rho c\underbrace{\left(-\frac{1}{c^2}\frac{\partial^2 \phi}{\partial t^2} + \frac{\partial^2 \phi}{\partial r^2} + \frac{1}{r}\frac{\partial \phi}{\partial r} + \frac{1}{c^2}\frac{\partial^2 \phi}{\partial t^2}\right)}_{=0}\right]$$

$$= \left(\frac{\partial p}{\partial r} - \frac{\rho}{c}\frac{\partial^2 \phi}{\partial t^2}\right)$$

$$= -\left(\rho_o \frac{\partial u_r}{\partial t} - \frac{1}{c}\frac{\partial p}{\partial t}\right) \quad (6)$$

Since time derivatives at the boundary are expected to change on an acoustic time scale, the terms on the right hand side of equation (6) are approximated in the following way:

$$\left(\rho_o \frac{\partial u_r}{\partial t} - \frac{1}{c}\frac{\partial p}{\partial t}\right) \to \beta\left[\frac{\rho c u_r}{r_d} - \frac{(p - p_o)}{r_d}\right] \quad (7)$$

r_d is the radius of the computational domain, $\partial/\partial t \to \beta c/r_d$, and β is an empirically determined constant of order unity. With this approximation, the value of $\mathcal{L}_1$ is given to first order by:

$$\mathcal{L}_1 = \frac{\beta \gamma p_o u_r}{r_d} - \frac{\beta c(p - p_o)}{r_d} \quad (8)$$

As will be shown below, use of this expression for $\mathcal{L}_1$ produces boundary conditions which work fairly well for the test case studied. The boundary conditions are based on the assumption that the flow quantities at the boundary change over a time scale governed by the size of the computational domain. It is curious that a different length scale, such as the width of an acoustic pulse at half its height, does not produce boundary conditions which give similarly good results. Perhaps an explanation for this finding is that the acoustic equations do not permit cylindrical waves and pulses to have a finite length (Landau and Lifshitz 1987).

Thompson (1987) specifies the incoming characteristics with $\mathcal{L}_1 = \gamma p_o u_r / r_d$. Note that this term contributes only to the time derivative of the pressure as can be seen by adding and subtracting equations (1) and (2). Thompson remarks that his boundary conditions are not perfectly non-reflecting and that they may not work well in some circumstances. For cylindrical acoustic waves, the inward travelling characteristics are not accurately approximated with this method, and errors propagate into the domain from the outer boundary at the speed of the characteristics (Fig.

3a). The first term in Eqn. (8) is like Thompson's expression for $\mathcal{L}_1$; however, the effect of the inhomogeneous term, $\gamma p_o u_r / r_d$, is modified. For $\beta \neq 1$ this term contributes to both the time derivatives of pressure and radial velocity.

The term, $-\beta c(p - p_o)/r_d$, in $\mathcal{L}_1$ is similar to the well-posedness condition used by Poinsot and Lele (1992) and Rudy and Strikwerda (1980). This expression also resembles the form of the boundary conditions derived by Hagstrom and Hariharan (1988) using asymptotic expansions for spherical wave propagation. For the computation to be stable $\beta < 0$ is required, and this term acts to restore the flow conditions at the boundary to the quiescent state which would exist in the absence of any acoustic waves.

Algebraic manipulation of equations (3) and (4) allows the time derivatives of pressure and radial velocity at the computational boundary to be determined. The homentropic flow conditions permit the time derivative of the density to be easily related to that of the pressure, $\partial p/\partial t = c^2 \partial \rho/\partial t$. A time stepping scheme may then be used to calculate all of the flow quantities at the outer boundary of the numerical domain.

3. NUMERICAL IMPLEMENTATION

To test the performance of the approximate boundary conditions, computational solutions of outward propagating axisymmetric cylindrical pulses were compared with analytical solutions. The computations were implemented on a 1000 point, equally-spaced, one-dimensional grid using the Mac-Cormack 2-step predictor-corrector algorithm for the Euler equations. The origin of the coordinate system was located at the first grid point, while the last grid point represented the location of the nonreflecting boundary. Singularities in the inhomogeneous terms of the Euler equations in cylindrical coordinates were removed using L'Hopital's Rule. The numerical method is second order accurate in space and time, and the computations alternated between the forward-backward and backward-forward schemes to prevent the accumulation of numerical errors. Anderson, Tannehill, and Pletcher (1984) report that the MacCormack method exhibits phase errors for CFL numbers outside the range $\sqrt{0.5} < CFL < 1.0$, where $CFL \equiv c\Delta t/\Delta r$. A comparison of numerical and analytical solutions for propagating cylindrical waves suggested that a $CFL \approx 0.75$ would minimize the computational error due to dispersion for the numerical configuration used. The flow conditions given by the analytical solution when $t = 0.0$ were used to initialize the computation.

The analytical model employed for comparison with computational solutions is given by Zauderer (1989). The velocity and density perturbations,

$$u_r = Real\left\{ \frac{-\frac{Ar}{r_c^2}}{\left[(1+\frac{ict}{r_c})^2 + (\frac{r}{r_c})^2\right]^{\frac{3}{2}}} \right\} \quad (9)$$

$$\rho' = Real\left\{ \frac{\frac{Ai\rho_o}{cr_c}(1+\frac{ict}{r_c})}{\left[(1+\frac{ict}{r_c})^2 + (\frac{r}{r_c})^2\right]^{\frac{3}{2}}} \right\}, \quad (10)$$

are shown in Fig. 1 for three different times. Here $i = \sqrt{-1}$, A fixes the amplitude of the pulse, and r_c determines the initial position of the velocity perturbation's peak amplitude. The maximum velocity u_{max} occurs when $t = 0.0$ at the position $r_p = r_c/\sqrt{2.0}$. The scaling r_p/r_d, where r_d is the location of the nonreflecting boundary, provides a measure of the pulse's width, and the pulse's strength is gauged by the ratio u_{max}/c. The initial density perturbation is zero for all r locations.

4. RESULTS

The most effective value of β may be problem dependent, and is possibly a function of the pulse strength, the shape of the wave, and ratio of pulse width to domain size. The errors in velocity and density at the boundary (when the reflected wave generated by the outgoing pulse is centered at $r/r_d = 0.85$ and with $r_p/r_d = 3.0 \times 10^{-2}$) were used to determine β. Unfortunately, the velocity error increases when β is varied to make the density error smaller (Table 2). Notice that, over the range of β values studied, the density error varies more rapidly with β than the velocity error. $\beta = -0.3$ was chosen because this quantity produces the density error of smallest magnitude. As can be seen in Figs. 3 & 4, the error associated with the incoming characteristics is small when the boundary condition method derived in this paper is used; also note the comparison with computational solutions found using Thompson's (1987) method. By minimizing the error due to the inward travelling characteristics a more accurate time-dependent representation of wave propagation is possible.

Table 2. Density and pressure error vs. β

β	$\frac{(\rho_{comp} - \rho_{exact})}{\rho_o} \times 10^7$	$\frac{(u_{r\_comp} - u_{r\_exact})}{c} \times 10^6$
-0.2	-1.8	1.8
-0.3	-1.1	1.7
-0.4	3.5	1.5
-0.5	5.8	1.4
-0.6	7.7	1.2

The amount of reflection produced at a boundary depends on both the numerical method and the boundary conditions employed. When the 2-step MacCormack method is used with the approximate boundary conditions developed in this paper, it is possible to limit the amplitude of reflections produced by the computational boundary to less than one percent of the amplitude of the outward travelling pulse. To determine the percentage of reflection, the peak to peak error in density due to the reflected pulse was divided by the peak to peak value of the outgoing pulse's amplitude. Each of these quantities was measured when the respective pulse is centered at $r_p/r_d = 0.85$. In initial tests with $r_p/r_d = 3.0 \times 10^{-2}$, pulses of strength $u_{max}/c = 1.0 \times 10^{-2}$, $u_{max}/c = 1.0 \times 10^{-3}$, and $u_{max}/c = 1.0 \times 10^{-4}$ were used. The outcome of these trials suggested that the amount of reflection at the boundary is more dependent on domain size than on pulse strength. Additionally, for the same ratio of r_p/r_d and $u_{max}/c = 1.0 \times 10^{-3}$, the peak to peak amplitude of the reflected pulse remained constant $[(\rho_{comp} - \rho_{exact})/\rho_o = 2.2 \times 10^{-6}]$ when β was varied from $\beta = -0.2$ to $\beta = -0.6$. This finding suggests that the magnitude of reflections is not strongly affected by the value of β. Results for a pulse strength of $u_{max}/c = 1.0 \times 10^{-3}$, $\beta = -0.3$, and different r_p/r_d are shown in Fig. 2. The size of reflections caused by the wave at the boundary decreases as the pulse width to domain size ratio is reduced.

The majority of the initial pulse leaves the domain by $\hat{t} = 1.2$, where $\hat{t} = ct/r_d = 1$ is the acoustic time scale for the computational domain. Reflected waves created at the boundary travel back into the computational domain but remain less than one percent of the original pulse's amplitude. By $\hat{t} = 5.3$, the reflections are gone and the computational solution has converged to the steady state quiescent flow. At this time the magnitude of both the density and velocity perturbations is within the order of the truncation error, based on grid point spacing, for the numerical method used $[(\Delta r/r_d)^2 = 1.0 \times 10^{-6}]$. The magnitude of the maximum error in density and velocity at $\hat{t} = 5.3$ is $(\rho_{comp} - \rho_{exact})/\rho_o = 5.9 \times 10^{-7}$, and $u_r/c = 1.6 \times 10^{-7}$, respectively. In summary, the method developed in this paper works well for the test case under study when $\beta = -0.3$ and $r_p/r_d \approx 3.0 \times 10^{-2}$.

5. CONCLUSIONS

Good boundary conditions for acoustic waves should: 1) accurately model the propagation of waves within the computational domain, 2) produce small reflections as waves pass through the computational boundary, and 3) converge to the correct steady-state solution for the flow which is modeled. As demonstrated above, the boundary conditions derived in this paper satisfy all of these criteria for the test case under study. This method is promising because it is an easy way to implement non-reflecting boundary conditions for cylindrical waves computed in a cylindrical geom-

etry. However, further work is required to determine the usefulness of this method for other problems, to test these boundary conditions on a two-dimensional computational grid, and to characterize the behavior of the empirical parameter β.

ACKNOWLEDGEMENT

The first author is grateful for support of this work by the NASA Graduate Student Researchers Program, the NASA Ames-Stanford Joint Institute for Aeronautics and Acoustics NCC 2-55, and for the many helpful suggestions made by Prof. S. Lele.

REFERENCES

Anderson, D, Tannehill, J and Pletcher, R (1984) *Computational Fluid Mechanics and Heat Transfer* Hemisphere Publishing Corporation, Washington DC, pp 101-103

Hagstrom, T and Hariharan, S (1988) Accurate boundary conditions for exterior problems in gas dynamics. Mathematics of Computation 51 n 184 pp 581-597

Landau, L and Lifshitz, E (1987) *Fluid Mechanics, 2nd Ed.* Pergamon Press, New York, NY, pp 251-273

Poinsot, T and Lele, S (1992) Boundary conditions for direct simulations of compressible viscous flows. J Computational Physics 101 pp 104-129

Rudy, D and Strikwerda, J (1980) A nonreflecting outflow boundary condition for subsonic Navier-Stokes calculations. J Computational Physics 36 pp 55-70

Thompson, K (1987) Time dependent boundary conditions for hyperbolic systems. J Computational Physics 68 pp 1-24

Zauderer, E (1989) *Partial Differential Equations of Applied Mathematics, 2nd Ed.* John Wiley & Sons, New York, NY, pp 280-285

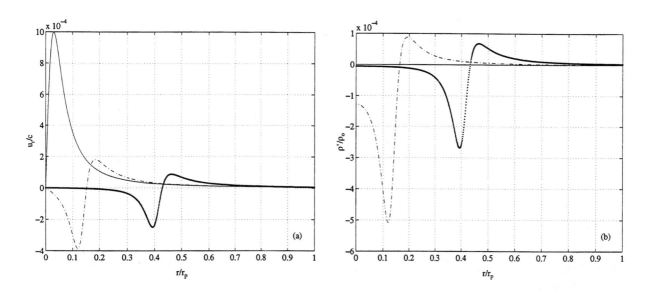

Figure 1. (a) velocity and (b) density perturbations for Zauderer's cylindrical acoustic pulse at three different times ($\hat{t} = ct/r_d$): $\hat{t} = 0.0$ (—), $\hat{t} = 0.136$ (−·), and $\hat{t} = 0.408$ (· · ·).

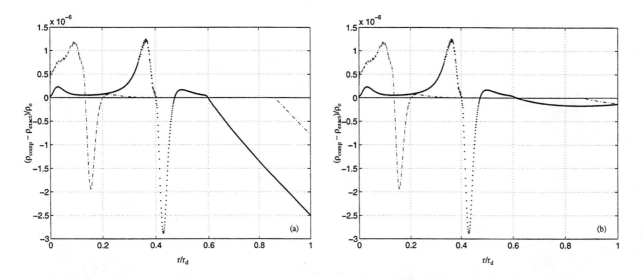

Figure 2. Density perturbation error for Zauderer's cylindrical acoustic pulse at two early times ($\hat{t} = ct/r_d$) using (a) Thompson's boundary conditions and (b) the boundary conditions developed above ($\beta = -0.3$); $\hat{t} = 0.136$ (−·), and $\hat{t} = 0.408$ (· · ·). Errors associated with incoming characteristics can be seen on the right hand side of these plots, while the error associated with numerical discretization first appears on the left and travels with the acoustic pulse. ($r_p/r_d = 3.0 \times 10^{-2}$ and $u_{mac}/c = 1.0 \times 10^{-3}$)

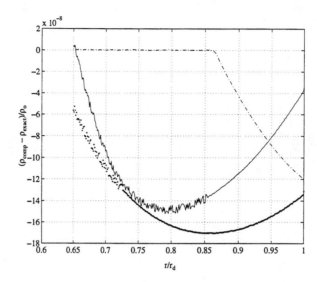

Figure 3: Closeup of density perturbation error near the nonreflecting boundary $r = r_d$ in Fig. 2(b) for $\hat{t} = 0.136$ ($-\cdot$), $\hat{t} = 0.408$ ($\cdots$), and also a later time $\hat{t} = 0.544$ (—). As can be seen by the curves shown, the error at the boundary remains small and is driven towards zero.

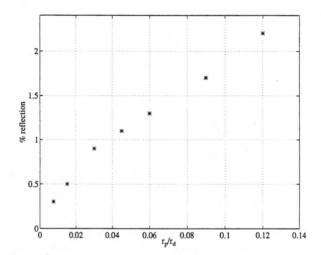

Figure 4: Reflection errors at boundary for different pulse width to domain size ratios. $\beta = -0.3$, $u_{mac}/c = 1.0 \times 10^{-3}$

CFD MODELING TECHNIQUES FOR
LARGE STRUCTURES AND FACILITIES

Introduction

Greg Sanchez
Parsons Brinckerhoff
One Penn Plaza
New York, New York 10119
Ph: 212-465-5548 — Fax: 212-465-5583
E-mail: gs@pipeline.com

Ramesh Agarwal
Department of Aerospace Engineering
Wichita State University
Wichita, Kansas 67260
Ph: 316-689-3410 — Fax: 316-689-3307
E-mail: agarwal@wsuhub.uc.twsu.edu

The ASME Fluids Engineering Division, through the Coordinating Group for CFD, has organized the Forum on CFD Modeling Techniques for Large Structures and Facilities with the intention of providing information on the applications of CFD to the mechanical, civil, architectural, and environmental engineering industries. The papers enclosed in this volume were presented at the 1996 ASME Fluids Engineering Division Summer Meeting held in San Diego, California, July 7–11, 1996.

As CFD is becoming the preferred analytical tool in the industry to study, design and build modern facilities, more and more demands are put forth to model, in full size, large facilities such as tunnel ventilation buildings, shopping malls, flow around buildings, etc. The design of such facilities often requires substantial computational resources both in memory and CPU. The facilities are in general very large and may involve turbulence, high heat release rates, chemical reactions and chemical species formation. Given the currently available computing power, even on state of the art parallel machines, it is not feasible to obtain a grid-independent solution in a cost-effective manner. However, because the design of these faciliteis has a probability factor added to some of the design constraints, customers require a trend rather than an exact solution. Most of the current CFD applications are for smaller domains, such as heat exchangers, cooling electronic boards, etc.

We express our appreciation to the authors who, with their contributions, made this forum a success. We hope that the forum and this volume will be seen as a valuable source of information to the industry which deals with the design of large structures and facilities and perhaps understand the power of CFD and its limitations. At the same time, we hope it will also be helpfull to academia and software developers who may identify areas in need of research to allow CFD to be more effectively applied to a wider range of industrial applications.

FED-Vol. 238, 1996 Fluids Engineering Division Conference
Volume 3
ASME 1996

VENTILATION REQUIREMENTS FOR NEW PHOENIX BALLPARK

S. L. Gamble, P.Eng.
Associate
Rowan Williams Davies & Irwin Inc.
Guelph, Ont. Canada

R. J. Sinclair, Ph.D.
Principal
Rowan Williams Davies & Irwin Inc.
Guelph, Ont. Canada

K. M. Matsui, P.Eng.
Project Engineer
Rowan Williams Davies & Irwin Inc.
Guelph, Ont. Canada

M. R. D. Barrett, P.E.
Principal
M E Engineers, Inc.
Denver, Co., U.S.A.

ABSTRACT

Key technical challenges have been overcome in the design of the mechanical system for the new retractable roof baseball park in Phoenix, Arizona. Wind tunnel tests and CFD model predictions aided a decision to close openings initially planned in two end walls of the stadium. To evaluate solar heat gain, a 1-D transient thermal model predicted concrete and mixed-air temperatures at various points in the seating areas. A CFD model then tested the air distribution system and helped fine tune its effectiveness in cooling the facility after the closing the roof.

Numerical airflow and temperature predictions were useful for decision making in this project because of timely feedback and easily understood results. Timely feedback was achieved by focussing the purpose of each CFD model and incorporating reasonable simplifications. Confidence in the results was achieved by establishing good estimates of the boundary conditions from local site information, wind tunnel tests and the 1-D thermal model.

1. INTRODUCTION

In buildings with large open spaces, like sports facilities, auditoria, atria, and industrial facilities, the movement of air can be a major influence on comfort, health and safety of the occupants. Designers strive to meet these objectives drawing on past experience to outline concepts and then estimate the sizes of the equipment with standard engineering calculations. Unfortunately, because little is known about the spatial distribution of the air flow, designers often use highly conservative assumptions which carry capital and operating cost penalties. Even with ample capacity in the design there is little feedback to tell the designers that the system will satisfy the needs of the occupants, or perhaps, lead to drafty and dead-flow zones.

In recent years, CFD is being used more and more to give designers and owners of large facilities feedback that improves their level of confidence in proposed designs early enough in the design process that decisions can be made to avoid potential problems and save money.

In previous work, Jones & Whittle (1992), Jones & Waters (1993), Post (1994), and Sullivan (1996) highlight a wide range of projects where CFD has been useful in designing ventilation systems. CFD is also credited as being the key tool used in the design of a novel ventilation system for the new Sydney International Aquatic Centre (HPA, 1995). In addition, CFD also played a role in assessing spectator comfort during the design of the new multi-purpose Rose Garden Arena in Portland, Oregon (Monteyne, 1995).

Bank One Ballpark, being designed for Phoenix as the home of the Arizona Diamondbacks, will be a state-of-the-art facility incorporating a number of recent technological developments in professional sports facilities. Most notable will be the use of a retractable roof system to provide shelter from sun and rain during events. It will also incorporate a natural grass playing surface.

A major technical hurdle that had to be overcome when designing mechanical ventilation for this facility was providing the grass with sufficient sunlight for proper growth and turf damage repair between ball games while ensuring that patrons will enjoy comfortable environmental conditions during the events. Sufficient grass growth rates required that the roof be open during the day in a city where summer ambient temperatures often reach 110°F (43.3°C) and can exceed 120°F (48.9°C). During the event, it is essential for the mechanical cooling system to have a closed roof for proper climate control. The design values for ambient conditions were the ASHRAE 99% design day with maximum temperature reaching 109 °F (42.8 °C) dry bulb and 71 °F (21.7 °C) wet bulb.

Several issues were of concern to the mechanical system designer in the operation of the ventilating and air conditioning (VAC) system. The non "steady state" nature of the operation of the system was an issue in that the requirement for the VAC system was to make the seating bowl comfortable within four hours after roof closure. Since most games start at 7:00pm (1900h), roof closure would occur during the heat of the day when the total quantity of heat absorbed into the concrete is at its maximum. Due to economic constraints, a single air-handler provides air to three seating levels to produce a uniform temperature distribution from the field level seats to the top of the upper deck and provides both cooling down period and game time operating functions. Buoyancy effects and differential loading of spectators were of concern to the delivery of the cool air. The system was to be similar in design to other systems that the mechanical engineers had successfully used in other large enclosed spaces. These other applications, however, were in continuously cooled spaces.

At the outset, the use of the physical, numerical and CFD models described in this paper were expected to remove as many of the unknowns from the system design as possible. For example:

• How much heat would be absorbed into the concrete and then released into the seating bowl and at what rate of release?

• What kind of temperature distribution could be expected across the seating areas from field level to upper deck seating ?

• What kind of air velocity distribution could be expected across these same areas ?

The stated goal of the VAC system in the seating bowl was to cool down the air within the stadium and then to maintain a spatial air temperature distribution of 78 °F ±5 °F (25.6 °C ± 2.8 °C) and 50% RH +10% / -20% at game time. It was expected at the outset that the temperature would vary outside this 10 °F (5.6 °C) temperature range spatially but that a stable temperature at any given seat could be maintained within ±2 °F (1.1 °C).

Chapter 2 describes the tools used in this project. Chapter 3 describes the analysis of the wind infiltration issues and Chapter 4 presents the analysis for the VAC operation issues. Chapter 5 summarizes the uses of the results achieved in this project from the perspective of the VAC system designer. Chapter 6 summarizes the general conclusions of the project.

2. METHODOLOGY

2.1 Wind Tunnel Testing

The wind tunnel is capable of providing direct simulation and measurement of surface pressures, wind speeds, wind directions and pollutant dispersion and complements CFD models. Figure 1 shows a 1:400 scale model of the Phoenix stadium in the working section of the wind tunnel and upwind fetch used in the present work.

Figure 1 - 1:400 Scale Model in Boundary Layer Wind Tunnel

The model was mounted on a turntable in the test section of the wind tunnel allowing it to be rotated to any azimuthal orientation thereby simulating wind approaching the building from any direction. Significant surrounding structures nearby the study building are also included on the turntable. Hot wire velocity measurement equipment was used to quantify the amount of outside air entering and leaving the various openings in the building's exterior envelope.

2.2 Transient Thermal Modelling

2.2.1 Model Basics. The transient effects of heating and cooling the air and concrete was predicted with an eight-layer, one-dimensional transient thermal numerical model (TTM). Figure 2 illustrates the basic physical concept of the model, which was developed with methods similar to that described by Krieth (1973).

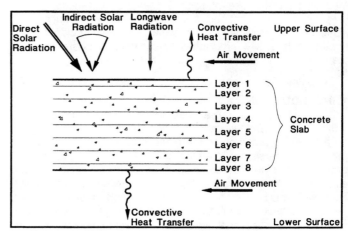

Figure 2 - Eight-Layer 1-D Transient Thermal Model of Heat Exchange in Concrete Slab

The physics which were incorporated into the model were:

- the convection heat transfer from upper and lower surfaces;

- the ambient air temperature as a function of time of day;

- the direct and diffuse solar radiation on upper surface as a function of time of day;

- the azimuthal orientation and tilt angle of surface;

- the long-wave radiation heat transfer between sky and surface; and

- the conduction and heat storage within the model layers which represent the concrete slab.

The TTM uses in a finite time step procedure to calculate the transient temperature patterns for a predefined duration. The time step used depends on the thickness and material properties of the layers and the convection heat transfer coefficients at the surfaces but typical values used in the present studies ranged between 60 and 120 seconds.

. **2.2.2 Calibration.** While thermal and radiation properties of concrete are available from handbooks, a review of these data showed a range of possible values. Early parametric runs using the TTM indicated a sensitivity to some of these properties which would be significant to the design and specification of a mechanical cooling system which has the task of removing heat stored in the concrete slab. Therefore a calibration of the model was undertaken.

To provide a measure of confidence in the selection of appropriate heat transfer properties for the concrete in the TTM, field measurements were undertaken for two days in the seating section of the Sun Devil Stadium at the Arizona State University (ASU). These recorded data measured concrete surface temperature, air temperature and solar radiation for June 14 and 15, 1995. June 14 provided conditions very similar to the design conditions assumed for the Bank One Ballpark. A peak air temperature of 108.8 °F (42.7 °C) was reached under clear sky conditions.

The measured solar radiation and temperature variations throughout June 14 were used as input for the TTM which incorporated appropriate concrete thickness and surface orientation to model the conditions at the measurement location in Sun Devil Stadium. The concrete heat conduction and storage properties, the solar absorptivity, emissivity and surface convection coefficient were fine tuned in order to reproduce a good match with the surface temperature variation in the field data. The predictions provided by the TTM are compared with the field temperature measurements in Figure 3.

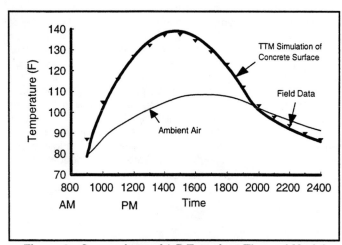

Figure 3 - Comparison of 1-D Transient Thermal Model Results with Field Measurements Taken June 14, 1995 at Sun Devil Stadium

Having determined a representative set of physical properties for the concrete slab in the stadium (Table 1) and verified that the TTM was correctly modelling the physics associated with the gain, storage and loss of heat, the TTM could then be counted upon to provide reliable estimates of heat release rates, volume average conditions within the seating bowl for use in the CFD modelling of the spatial temperature and airflow patterns.

Table 1 - Concrete Properties Obtained from Calibration

Property	Value
Thermal Conductivity	0.537 BTU/(hr ft °F) (0.93 W/(m °C))
Specific Heat	0.156 BTU/(lb °F) (653 J/(kg °C))
Mass Density	144 lb/ft^3 (2300 kg/m^3)
Solar Absorptivity	0.6
Emissivity	0.95

2.2.3 Shading. The calibration of the TTM was carried out based on field measurements of temperatures for typical seating bowl concrete in a location exposed to sunlight for the entire day. The situation in the Bank One Ballpark will be somewhat different in that several components will cause shading of the concrete. The most obvious is that the roof will be closed from approximately 3:00pm (1500h) through to midnight. This eliminates the direct and indirect solar heat gain during this period and eliminates the cold sky for long-wave energy exchange. These considerations were handled in the TTM by time-of-day dependent models for these energy exchanges.

When the roof is open from midnight through to 3:00 pm (1500h), various locations within the seating bowl will experience time periods when the building walls and retracted roof provide a shadow, eliminating the direct solar radiation. Scenarios of sun and shade for several locations within the seating bowl were formulated for daylight hours using a 3-D CAD model of the stadium with the roof open which was provided by the architects. The technique used was to position the point-of-view to that of the sun itself for a particular date and time of day and to look down upon the seating areas (Figure 4). In this way the portions of the stadium that are visible can be considered to be in sunlight and those obscured by building roof and walls are in shadow.

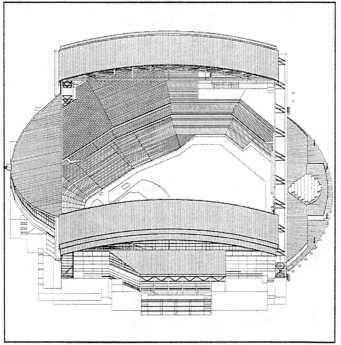

Figure 4 - Sun / Shade View - 9:00 am (0900h) Solar Time

This analysis also illustrated that continuous control over the position and width of the roof "aperture" could provide a maximization of the sunlight on the grass of the playing surface while significantly reducing the area of the seating bowl exposed to direct sunlight.

One last significant shading effect that was considered in the TTM was that of the seats which provide localized shading for concrete immediately under the seats. It was estimated that approximately 45% of the concrete surface would be shaded by seats. A long-wave radiation transfer with the backs and undersides of the lightweight, hollow seats was incorporated into the model for these areas.

2.3 CFD

Two CFD models were developed in this project. One is called the Sectional Bowl Model (SBM) and the other is called the Sectional Seating Model (SSM). The basis for this work was the commercial software package called TASCflow[1]. This software solves the three-dimensional time-averaged Navier-Stokes equations and the enthalpy equation. Turbulence effects are modelled using the standard k-ε turbulence model and natural convection effects are modelled using the Boussinesq approximations.

The transport equations are discretized using a conservative, finite-element based finite-volume method, with variables co-located on multi-block, structured, boundary-fitted grids with local grid refinement. A second-order accurate Skew Upwind Differencing Scheme with Physical Advection Correction is employed.

The solution procedure is iterative employing an algebraic multigrid solver for the coupled system of mass and momentum equations. The solution is advanced from one iteration to the next using a simple time-step marching process. RMS and MAX norms of the normalized residual fields of each transport equation are used as a measure of the degree of convergence of the equations. In this project, steady-state solutions were converged to a tolerance of less than 2.2×10^{-5} and 1.4×10^{-3} for the RMS and MAX norms, respectively.

. **2.3.1 Sectional Bowl Model.** To assess the impact of the wind driven air flow through large openings at the ends of the stadium on the performance of the chilled air supplied from the proposed VAC system, a CFD model called SBM was developed. The model represented a typical 17 ft (5.2 m) wide transverse section of the entire stadium bowl extending across the playing field.

The decision to only model a representative section of the stadium rather than the entire stadium was based on two principal factors. The first factor was that the primary objective of this analysis was to evaluate the effects of the wind infiltration resulting from the orientation of the openings under the eaves for the prevailing wind directions, which would produce essentially a two-dimensional flow through the stadium. The second factor was that it was felt that a complete stadium model would have yielded limited additional information and would have been excessively costly to set up and run within the time available.

The SBM consisted of a three-dimensional computational grid composed of 22 sub-grids. Six grids fit the CAD geometry and the remainder were used to locally refine the grid to help resolve flow details in the vicinity of the seating areas and VAC cool-air supply flows. The total number of active nodes was approximately 50,000. Schedule constraints limited grid independence tests. Previous project experience in modelling similar flow situations was used to guide the grid design decisions.

Boundary conditions for this simulation included mass-flow specified wind infiltration rates, calculated from wind tunnel measurements (Section 2.1), ambient dry-bulb temperature for a

---

[1] TM of ASC Ltd., Waterloo, Ontario.

mid-afternoon summer day, mass-flow specified supply and return flows for the proposed VAC system and estimated heat fluxes from all surfaces (i.e. concrete in the seating areas, grass on the playing field, and the closed roof).

Starting from a uniform initial guess, a total of 750 iterations were required to converge the flow to steady-state. Total CPU time was approximately 45 hours on an IBM RS/6000 Model 550 (SPECfp92 83.3). Memory requirements were of the order of 60 MB.

. **2.3.2 Sectional Seating Model.** The sectional seating model (SSM) was used to predict air speed and temperature distributions in the seating zones at two points in time which were selected as design conditions to test the performance of the initial design of the proposed VAC system, and also to optimize it. The first selected design time was 30 minutes after the beginning of operation of the VAC system after roof closure, 3:30pm (1530h). The second selected design time was at the beginning of a baseball game, approximately 4 hours after roof closure, 7:00pm (1900h).

In developing the SSM limitations were similar to that of the SBM development, with respect to the grid size and the modelling objectives. Figure 5 shows the computational grid which provided a detailed representation of half of a vertical section of a complete seating bay (width 17 ft), and extended longitudinally out to centre field. The grid topology included 25 sub-grids, for a total number of 60,000 active nodes. This total includes local refinement to better resolve the jetting flows from the drum louvre VAC supplies and the detailed flows in the seating areas. Even the backs of the seats were represented explicitly in the model to adequately account for the roughness effects of the seats on the mean airflow over them and also to better predict the convective heat transfer rates from the concrete.

Boundary conditions for this simulation included mass-flow specified supply and return flows for the proposed VAC system, estimated heat fluxes through the roof and calculated dry-bulb temperatures at the surface of the concrete in the seating areas and grass on the playing field (Figure 6). Concrete and average mixed air temperatures in the bowl were calculated for the two design times, 3:30pm (1530h) and 7:00pm (1900h), by the TTM described in Section 2.2. A volumetric heat source was applied in the region from the playing field up to the roof. The level of this heat source was determined in an iterative fashion by the modeler, as that which would maintain the known mixed air temperature in the bowl at the particular design time. With this procedure (quasi) steady-state solutions were achieved at each design time and avoided complex and lengthy true-transient simulations.

As with the SBM simulation, a broad range of time scales existed in the flow predicted in the two simulations performed with the SSM. This resulted from the broad range of length scales and air speeds for the flow in the stadium bowl, some of which were mechanically induced and others which resulted from natural convection effects. Length scales range from gap distance between seat backs (2½ ft, 750 mm) and height from the playing field to the roof (245 ft, 75 m). Air speeds ranged from the supply diffuser jets which typically discharged at speeds of in excess of

800 fpm (4 m/s), and the large scale recirculation cells above the field which turn over at speeds between 20 and 40 fpm (0.1 and 0.2 m/s).

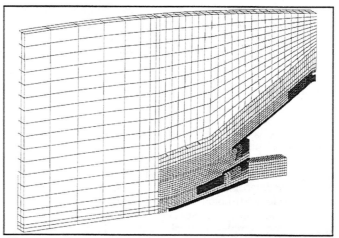

Figure 5 - Computational Grid for Sectional Seating Model

In running the simulations, achieving converged solutions required careful monitoring. Care had to be taken to select time-steps that adequately worked on the broad bandwidth of length and time scales of this flow problem.

Total CPU times for the two simulations were approximately 40 hours on a Silicon Graphics Indigo[2] 200 MHZ R4400 (SPECfp92 131) to achieve satisfactory computational effort.

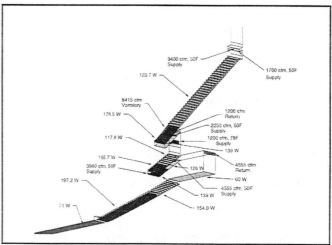

Figure 6 - Seating and Ventilation Flow Boundary Conditions for One of the Sectional Seating Model Simulations

3. INFILTRATION ISSUES

The approach to evaluating the infiltration issues was a two-step procedure. The first was to establish boundary conditions for the rate of infiltration and the second was CFD modelling of the resulting internal flows.

3.1 Wind Tunnel Testing

The initial design at the outset of the study, called for a large opening under the eaves on both the east and west ends of the stadium as mentioned earlier. These openings would align with the predominant wind directions in Phoenix and would therefore allow wind driven air flow through the stadium even when the roof is closed and the VAC system is attempting to cool the seating areas. Since these flows would be driven by the external wind pressure patterns on the stadium, appropriate boundary conditions for a CFD model of the internal flow interactions were obtained using a 1:400 model of the ball park in the boundary layer wind tunnel (Figure 1).

The open eaves were incorporated on the model and hot wire anemometry techniques were used to measure the air flow rates through the openings. Review of the meteorological data for an appropriate design value for the wind speed approaching the stadium indicated that 18.5 mph (8.2 m/s) represented a 99% design value for Phoenix. The wind tunnel measurements indicated that average air speeds in the openings at the eaves would be approximately 25% of the approaching wind speed or 400 ft/min (2 m/s). Smoke flow visualization was also used to aid in understanding the wind-induced flow patterns inside and outside the stadium.

3.2 CFD

Using the wind tunnel information as boundary conditions for the CFD model, coupled with early design values and geometry for VAC system airflows and approximate heat loads from people and lighting, the flow patterns for this case were calculated using the CFD model (Section 2.3.1). Figure 8 illustrates that the internal circulation of air caused by the wind through the openings produces strong upward motion of air at the seating levels which carries the cooling away from its intended target.

Provided with this information, the architect decided to close all major openings in the building envelope which would allow wind infiltration.

4. VAC OPERATION ISSUES

Evaluating the performance of the VAC system was carried out in three parts. The first was to use the 1-D transient numerical model to establish target volume-averaged temperatures and concrete surface heat release rates and the last two parts were quasi-steady state CFD analyses of spatial variations of temperature and air speed for cool-down and game periods.

4.1 Transient Thermal Modelling

The major unknown in the mechanical design of the stadium was the amount of heat absorbed by the concrete during roof-open periods and re-released after the roof has been closed. The TTM was formulated to help answer this question.

During cooling system operation, several changes to the physics of the TTM as calibrated to the ASU field data were necessary in order to accurately predict heat flux into the air from the surfaces for CFD boundary conditions. During the cool-down period, the occupancy gradually increases until around game time when it is at its maximum. The physical presence of the people would provide a restriction to air movement near the surface of the

concrete. For this reason the upper concrete surface convection coefficient was gradually reduced by a factor of 4 between 3:00 pm (1500h) and 7:00 pm (1900h). Also during this period, the lighting levels were gradually increased which provided a significant heat input to the surface. After the roof closes, the ambient air temperature no longer follows the outside air temperature since the VAC system is working to cool the air inside the building. For the purposes of estimating boundary conditions for a CFD model, a simplified model of this process was incorporated into the TTM. This simplification was to assume a perfect mixing calculation of internal air temperature including the internal volume of the seating bowl, VAC supply flow rates and temperatures and the heat release rates from the surfaces. This is referred to as a mixed-air temperature.

Figure 7 provides a plot of four predicted temperatures for a typical location in the lower deck of the stadium versus time of day. It can be seen that the ambient air temperature follows a typical diurnal variation up until roof closure, peaking out at 109 °F (42.8 °C) which is the design value. At roof closure, the VAC

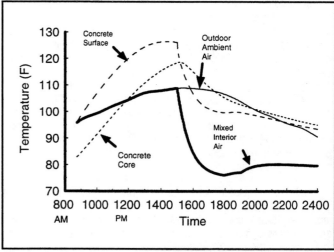

Figure 7 - Temperature Variation in Concrete and Mixed-Air Based on 1-D Transient Thermal Model

system begins to cool the internal air at a rate which decreases as the difference between the internal air and supply air temperatures reduces. Also during this period, progressively more lighting load and people occupying the stadium causes the mixed-air temperature to reach a minimum value of 77 °F (25 °C) and to increase to a steady state value during the game of 80 °F (26.7 °C). In response to the air temperature and solar radiation the concrete surface temperature rises throughout the morning and early afternoon to reach a peak of 128 °F (53.3 °C) in the hour just prior to the closing of the roof. The core temperature rise lags behind that of the surface and reaches its peak of 119 °F (48.3 °C) about 35 minutes after roof closure. These predicted concrete temperatures include the effect of an area-weighted average of seat-shaded and fully-exposed concrete.

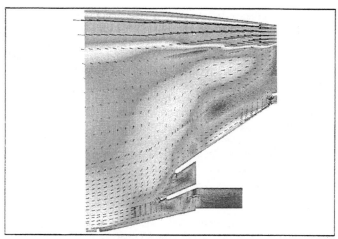

Figure 8: Impact of Wind Infiltration through Openings in East and West Walls - Vertical Plane Cutting through Seating Areas (10 fpm [0.05 m/s] blue to 400 fpm [2.0 m/s] magenta)

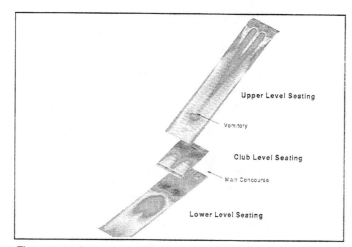

Figure 9: Air Speed Plot for Early Cool-Down (1530h) Speeds Measured 2.5 ft. (0.76 m) above Seat Backs (10 fpm [0.05 m/s] blue to 300 fpm [1.5 m/s] magenta)

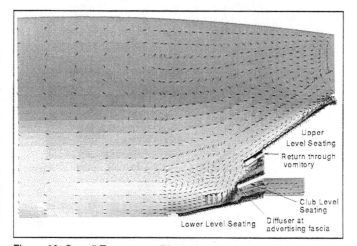

Figure 10: Overall Temperature Distribution Plot for Early Cool-Down (1530h) - Vertical Plane Cutting through Supplies at Club Level (80°F [26.7°C] blue to 100°F [37.8°C] magenta)

Figure 11: Upper Deck Close-Up Air Speed Plot for Early Cool-Down (1530h) - Vertical Plane Cutting through Supplies at Upper Ring Duct (10 fpm [0.05 m/s] blue to 300 fpm [1.5 m/s] magenta)

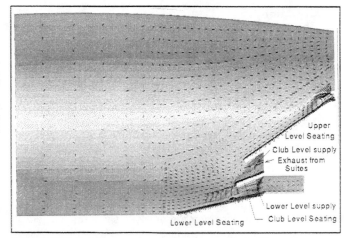

Figure 12: Overall Temperature Distribution for Start of Game Time (1900h) - Vertical Plane Cutting through Supplies at Suites and Main Concourse 70°F [21.1°C] blue to 95°F [35°C] magenta)

Figure 13: Upper Deck Close-Up Air Speed Plot for Start of Game Time (1900h) - Vertical Plane Cutting through Supplies at Upper Ring Duct (10 fpm [0.05 m/s] blue to 300 fpm [1.5 m/s] magenta)

From these TTM simulations, appropriate heat flux values from the concrete were produced. At 3:30 pm (1530h), thirty minutes after roof closure the predicted heat flux from the upper surface of the concrete into the air ranged between 18 and 40 BTUH/ft^2 (57 and 126 W/m^2) depending on location in the stadium. At the start of game time it ranged between 5 and 11 BTUH/ft^2 (16 and 35 W/m^2) with the stadium at game occupancy.

The TTM was also used to explore the effectiveness of some alternatives which would reduce the heat stored in the concrete and carried over into the interior space after the roof was closed. These alternatives were: 1) water spraying in the early afternoon while the roof was still open; and 2) temporary tarpaulins over critical seating areas to shade the concrete. Both of these options showed reductions in the stored heat but are less desirable in terms of operational considerations.

4.2 CFD

While the TTM did a good job of providing average conditions at any point in time throughout the typical day, it did not provide information on the capability of the VAC system to deliver cool air to the seating areas during the cool-down and game periods. For this, CFD was used to provide "snapshots" of the cooling performance at two important points in time.

4.2.1 Simulation of 3:30pm (1530h) Conditions.
Sample results from CFD simulation of this early cool-down period case are presented in Figures 9 to 11. Initially, the aiming of the cool air supplies was set so that the jet would exit the diffuser parallel to the plane of the seating deck. This can be seen in the close-up view of air speeds for a vertical cut through the upper deck region shown in Figure 11. The jet of cool air can be seen to quickly fall down to the seats and to continue under momentum and buoyancy forces to the field edge of the seating deck. The modelled seat backs can be seen in this figure. It was felt that while the VAC system delivers its cooling directly to the area of interest, the air speeds at seats directly in the impingement zone would be too high for the comfort of the occupants.

Lateral distribution of air speeds just above the seats is illustrated in Figure 9. The strong patterns caused by jet impingement are very evident for all three of the seating levels shown in this plot. Local speed increases near the vomitory on the upper level are evident since for this case it was used as a return air location.

Figure 10 presents the temperature profile on a vertical slice through the seating bowl from the centre of the stadium to the outside wall and from field level to ceiling. As would be expected only 30 minutes after starting the VAC system for cool-down, thermal stratification is evident. Seating area temperatures outside direct impingement regions are of the order of 90 °F (32 °C) and ceiling level temperatures exceed 100° F (38 C).

These results pointed out that while providing reasonable distributions for the cool-down function, improvements in jet aiming would be necessary for comfort during the game.

4.2.2 Simulation of 7:00pm (1900h) Conditions.
Initial jet trajectories were altered to be more horizontal, based on findings of the cool-down conditions. Figure 13 illustrates the effect on air

speeds in the upper deck region. It is seen that initial momentum carries the cool air out further from the source but buoyancy soon causes it to fall to the seats. This provides a more uniform distribution of air flow to the seating level and reduces high speed impingement zones.

The temperature distribution illustrated in Figure 12 for the start of game time indicates that thermal stratification is still present within the bowl but that temperatures within seating areas are within an acceptable range. The higher-priced field-level seating will be coolest with temperatures of approximately 72 °F (22 °C) and the upper deck will be warmest at approximately 82 °F (28 °C).

5. USE OF RESULTS

From the point of view of the VAC system designers, the most useful results of the study were as follows.

- Early wind tunnel tests and CFD simulations using initial boundary condition estimates provided timely feedback on wind induced flows through building openings and assisted in the refinement of the air distribution design.

- Once correlated with empirical data, the 1-D TTM studies provided reliable estimates of concrete heat capacity and release rates which were helpful in determining the maximum likely load the VAC system would see. This helped to size the central plant.

- The process of carrying out the detailed studies provided a helpful peer review in the design.

- The CFD results for the temperature distribution were viewed as confirmation of the VAC system designer's preconceptions of how the system would work.

- The colour graphics illustrating the flows and temperatures produced by CFD analysis were exceptional presentation tools and were very helpful in conveying the ventilation concepts to the building's owner.

6. CONCLUSIONS

The following are the general conclusions from this study which affected the design of the ventilation system.

- The original mechanical concept proved to be capable of performing both cool-down and game time operating functions.

- Wind-driven air currents in the stadium could adversely effect the distribution of chilled air. Therefore, to improve cooling performance and to reduce the cost of the air cooling systems, the design team decided to remove the under-roof openings.

- Time lags in the 4" to 5" thick concrete were such that only the thermal history over the previous six hours was significant. Additionally, hollow, lightweight seats provided significant shading for the concrete, which reduced the temperatures and improved comfort.

- Negative buoyancy of the chilled air required re-aiming the supply air jets upward from their original direction. To provide the best balance between delivery of cool air out to the extremes of the seating decks and to avoid cold drafts near the jets, they were aimed horizontally instead of parallel to the seating deck.

- Under certain conditions, return air through concourses provides sufficient cooling to eliminate the requirement for some of the supply locations.

- Photosynthesis and concrete heat gain could be optimised using continuous control of roof aperture size and positioning.

- For the low-humidity conditions in Phoenix, 100% fresh air intake capability on the VAC system is beneficial at certain times.

- Wash-down of the seating areas prior to roof closure and local shading devices are beneficial and can be used as a remedial measure for smaller areas of the stadium.

The use of CFD techniques in this project provided the design team with confidence that the stated design goals will be achieved.

7. ACKNOWLEDGEMENTS

The authors gratefully acknowledge the efforts of Glenn Schuyler, Stephen Dajka and Michael Soligo for their contributions to the successful completion of this complex project.

8. REFERENCES

HPA, 1995, "HVAC system cools indoor swimming pool Down Under", Heating/Piping/Air Conditioning, May, p. 25.

Jones, P. and Whittle, G., 1992, "Computational Fluid Dynamics for Building Air Flow Prediction - Current Status and Capabilities", Building and Environment, Vol. 27, No. 3, pp. 321-338.

Jones, P. and Waters, R., 1993, "The Practical Application of Indoor Airflow Modeling", Modeling of Indoor Air Quality and Exposure, ASTM STP 1205, Niren L. Nagda, Ed., American Society for Testing and Materials, Philadelphia, pp. 173-181.

Krieth, Frank, 1973, "Principles of Heat Transfer", 3rd Edition.

Monteyne, R., 1995, "HVAC Design Solutions for Multi-Purpose Arenas", ASHRAE Journal, Nov., pp. 22-32.

Post, N., 1994, "Airflow Models Gaining Clout", Engineering News Record, Oct., pp. 22-25.

Sullivan, A., 1996, "Modeling the Elements", Architecture, Feb., pp. 163-169.

FED-Vol. 238, 1996 Fluids Engineering Division Conference
Volume 3
ASME 1996

COMPUTATIONAL FLUID DYNAMICS TRACKING OF UF$_6$ REACTION PRODUCTS RELEASE INTO A GASEOUS DIFFUSION PLANT CELL HOUSING

Mark W. Wendel
Computational Physics and
Engineering Division
Oak Ridge National Laboratory[1]
P.O. Box 2008,
Oak Ridge, Tennessee
37831-6415
423-574-2825, Fax 423-576-0003,
e-mail mwq@ornl.gov

Norbert C. J. Chen
Seok-Ho H. Kim
Rusi P. Taleyarkhan
Engineering Technology Division
Oak Ridge National Laboratory[1]
P.O. Box 2009,
Oak Ridge, Tennessee
37831-8045
423-574-0753, Fax 423-574-2032,
e-mail ncj@ornl.gov

Kenneth D. Keith
Russell W. Schmidt
Engineering Division
Oak Ridge K-25 Site[2]
P.O. Box 2003
Oak Ridge, Tennessee
37831-7355
423-576-9687, Fax 423-576-6542
e-mail k7k@ornl.gov

ABSTRACT

A three-dimensional (3-D) computational fluid dynamics (CFD) model has been developed using CFDS-FLOW3D[3] Version 3.3 to model the transport of aerosol products formed during a release of uranium hexafluoride (UF$_6$) into a gaseous diffusion plant (GDP) process building. As part of a facility-wide safety evaluation, a one-dimensional (1-D) analysis of aerosol/vapor transport following such an hypothesized accident is being performed. The objective of this study is to supplement the 1-D analysis with more detailed 3-D results. Specifically, the goal is to quantify the distribution of aerosol passing out of the process building during the hypothetical accident. This work demonstrates a useful role for CFD in large 3-D problems, where some experimental data are available for calibrating key parameters and the desired results are global (total time-integrated aerosol flow rates across a few boundary surfaces) as opposed to local velocities, temperatures, or heat transfer coefficients.

NOMENCLATURE

Symbol	Description	Units
A	Cell-wall leakage area	m^2
K	Form loss coefficient	–
$\dot{m}$	Mass flow	kg/s
P_I	Pressure internal to cell wall	Pa
P_E	Pressure external to cell wall	Pa
ρ	Density	kg/m^3

κ	Turbulent kinetic energy	m^2/s^2
ϵ	Eddy dissipation	m^2/s^3

INTRODUCTION

In the United States, the gaseous diffusion process is used to produce enriched uranium for power generation and defense purposes. The process uses large quantities of the hazardous material uranium hexafluoride (UF$_6$) that is piped throughout the plant through large process lines. In the event of a break in a UF$_6$ line, the UF$_6$ will immediately undergo an exothermic chemical reaction (producing very high temperatures) with the moisture (H$_2$O) in the air to form hydrogen fluoride (HF) and aerosolized uranyl fluoride (UO$_2$F$_2$) that could then be spread inside and outside of the process building. As part of the facility-wide safety evaluation, a one-dimensional (1-D) analysis of aerosol/vapor transport following such an hypothesized severe accident is being performed (Kim et al., 1996). The objective of this study is to supplement the 1-D analysis with more detailed three-dimensional (3-D) results. Specifically, the goal is to quantify the distribution of aerosol passing out of the process building during the hypothetical accident.

A U.S. gaseous diffusion plant (GDP) contains multiple process buildings. The process building currently under consideration contains six "units." A unit is a group of ten "cells." A single cell contains eight axial-flow compressors that pump gaseous UF$_6$ through large cylindrical steel vessels called "converters." Each cell is contained within a sheet-metal enclosure called a cell housing. These enclosures are not air tight, but allow substantial leakage through openings and panel seams. Figure 1 shows the geometry of the cell with the eight trapezoidal protrusions to accommodate the eight compressors, each attached by a shaft passing through the cell wall to one of eight compressor motors located outside of the enclosure. The upper portion within the sheet-metal enclosure (on the level above the trapezoidal protrusions) is referred to as the penthouse. Within each unit, air is circulated outside the cell housing by the combined action of (1) the air supply blowers (three per cell) that pump air into the building, (2) the compressor motor suctions (eight per cell) that pull air out of the building, and (3) the roof vent exhaust that

---

[1]Managed by Lockheed Martin Energy Research Corp. for the U.S. Department of Energy under contract DE-AC05-96OR22464.

[2]Managed by Lockheed Energy Systems, Inc., for the U.S. Department of Energy under contract DE-AC04-84OR21400.

[3]CFDS-FLOW3D is a commercially available computational fluid dynamics program developed by AEA Technology Engineering Software, Inc.

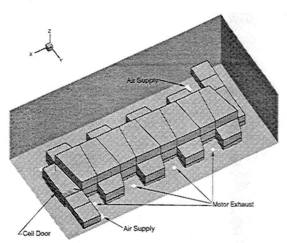

Fig. 1. Geometry of the gaseous diffusion cell with computational domain including the surrounding process building air.

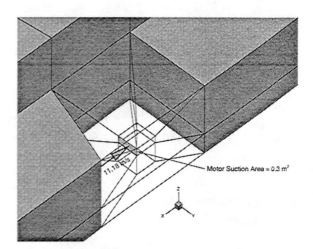

Fig. 2. Typical motor air suction boundary condition (one of eight).

allows air flow in either direction, but will typically vent the remainder of air out of the building.

A computational 3-D fluid dynamics (CFD) model has been developed using CFDS-FLOW3D[2] Version 3.3 to model the transport of aerosol products formed during a release of UF_6 into the cell housing. Because the flow domain is large (dimensions of 53 m long × 26 m wide × 16 m high), it was recognized from the beginning that a very coarse discretization was required to obtain a solution with existing computational resources (IBM RISC 6000 Model 580 with 128 Mbytes of RAM). Using such a coarse discretization would necessarily compromise the physical accuracy of the simulations. However, it is the relative distribution of aerosol flow at the boundaries of the problem that was desired, not specific local velocities and temperatures within the unit. Existing temperature and flow distribution data were also used to calibrate the steady-state solution, thus improving the accuracy of the predictions.

MODEL DESCRIPTION

An input model was developed for the CFDS-FLOW3D solver by defining the computational domain and discretization, boundary conditions, fluid properties, and solution strategy. The geometry of the problem was defined using the CFDS-FLOW3D mesh generator SOPHIA that allows the user to define 1-D edges, extrude these into two-dimensional (2-D) faces, and subsequently extrude the faces into 3-D blocks that are then discretized. The computational flow domain is shown in Fig. 1, with the rectangular holes in the floor corresponding to the locations of the two air-supply blowers that are interior to the computational domain and the eight compressor motor exhaust ducts (only five of which are visible in the figure). The blowers and motors are represented by rectangular hexahedra located as shown in Figs. 2 and 3. Approximately 50,000 control volumes were used in the discretization.

Although not shown in Fig. 1, the cell housing internals were also discretized for the flow solution. The equipment contained within the cell housing was estimated to fill between 50 and 60% of the cell volume. Refining the details of the air flow in and around this equipment is intractable, due to the large number of computational cells required, and unnecessary, since the details of the flow inside the cell housing are unimportant. However, it was still desired that the model contain the

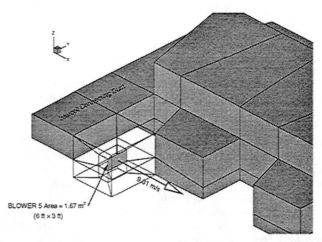

Fig. 3. Air supply blower as modeled in CFDS-FLOW3D simulations.

correct total mass of air inside the cell and maintain fairly well-mixed conditions, since the equipment is actually distributed throughout the cell. A simple solution to this dilemma is to represent the cell internals as a porous media. By using the CFDS-FLOW3D porous media model, the cell volume was defined to contain 56% solid equipment and 44% air. The porous media model allows the user to provide additional flow resistance to account for small-scale momentum losses; however, no additional flow resistance was added since it was anticipated that these momentum losses would be very small.

The air was treated as incompressible, with a buoyancy force added through the linearized Boussinesq approximation, because compressibility effects are small. Six solid hexahedra were defined to represent the heated surface of the eight converters inside the cell housing. A fixed boundary temperature was assigned to the surfaces of the hexahedra. This surface temperature was then adjusted during the steady-state solution process until the measured penthouse air temperature was matched by the computed flow solution. To match the measured penthouse air temperature, the total amount of heat transfer from the equipment to the air must be accurate. To transfer the correct amount of heat, the equipment temperature must be increased above the measured average equipment temperature. This increase is necessary because the heat transfer area of the six solid hexahedra is significantly less than the true equipment surface area.

The temperature of the air exiting the roof vent was also known from measurements taken during plant operation. This measurement was matched by specifying a heat flux on the exterior of the cell wall passing into the exterior air. This heat flux represents heat that is transmitted by conduction through the thin sheet metal wall.

To accommodate leakage of mass, enthalpy, and aerosol through openings (seams) in the sheet metal walls, 129 pairs of sources and sinks on either side of the cell wall were specified. Two "patches" are defined on each of the 129 quadrilateral surfaces comprising the discretized sheet metal cell wall that separates the heated air inside the cell housing from the forced-convected air outside. A patch is merely a CFDS-FLOW3D label for a 2-D segment attached to the computational domain which can be used in the user FORTRAN to identify certain computational cells. One patch was specified for the inside wall of each segment, and one for the outside.

A substantial amount of FORTRAN coding was supplied to the CFDS-FLOW3D steady-state simulation to simulate the leakage through the cell wall of mass and energy. Specifically, the user FORTRAN was written to accomplish the following purposes:

• Determine the magnitude of leakage mass flow through the cell wall based on the local pressure difference.
• Generate source/sink terms for the pressure (mass continuity), enthalpy and user scalar (aerosol) equations consistent with the calculated leakage through the cell wall.
• Monitor the mass flow and aerosol flow at the wall, cell door, blower exits, and motor suction locations.

At each of the 129 wall segments, an average internal pressure, P_I, and average external pressure, P_E, are calculated by considering the pressures in each of the computational cells bordering the wall segment. The leakage mass flow rate for one segment, $\dot{m}$, is then calculated using the simple form-loss relationship

$$\dot{m} = \sqrt{\frac{2\rho A^2(P_I - P_E)}{K}} \,, \qquad (1)$$

where ρ is the density, A is the leakage area, and K is the form-loss coefficient. The total leakage mass flow rate through the cell wall has been measured, and this information was used to calibrate the loss coefficient K.

The available plant data that were used in developing the computational model are given in Table 1. Some of these values could have been computed directly by the CFD model. Instead of doing so, however, the measured values are used as calibration points to minimize the inaccuracy that accompanies the use of such a coarse discretization.

STEADY-STATE SOLUTION

The flow field within the cell, through the cell wall (via various leakage pathways, including an open door and gaps between sheet metal pieces comprising the wall), and outside the cell (but within the unit) was calculated. The usual equations for transport of mass, momentum (three directions), enthalpy, and aerosol mass, as well as two additional

equations used for κ-ϵ turbulence closure, were then solved. The particle transport model in CFDS-FLOW3D does not allow transient computations, hence the aerosol mass was represented as a user scalar variable, and deposition of aerosol by settling was neglected.

The turbulent Schmidt number is assumed to be 0.9 (default value in CFDS-FLOW3D), and a very low laminar diffusivity is used (i.e., diffusion of the aerosol occurs via turbulent transport only).

The first solution obtained with the model assumed a steady-state at typical operating temperatures and flow rates. During the typical steady state, air is drawn into the cell housing near the base of the housing wall and through the door, then heated and pushed out through the seams in the top of the cell housing. Hence, a steady circulation through the cell housing occurs. The objective of this initial steady-state simulation was to determine the typical flow pattern (to be used as an initial condition for a transient simulation), and to determine the fate of the air that is passed through the cell housing.

Table 1. Assumed data used in calibrating the steady state and defining geometry and boundary conditions.

Parameter	Value
Motor suction area	0.3 m²
Motor suction velocity	11.18 m/s
Air supply blower area	1.672 m² (3 ft × 6 ft)
Air supply temperature	310 K
Air supply blower flow rate	15.57 m³/s (33,000 cfm)
Air temperature near top of cell housing (penthouse)	360 K
Total leakage flow through cell wall	9.0 m³/s (19,000 cfm)
Roof vent exit air temperature	330 K

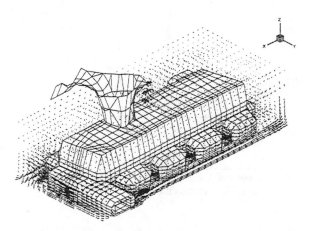

Fig. 4. Isothermal surface showing developed thermal plume during typical steady-state.

A unit source of 1 kg/s of aerosol (defined by a user scalar variable) was released inside the cell housing, distributed uniformly, and the steady-state solution was obtained. For the steady-state solution, no heat source is included to represent the reaction following the release of UF_6. This solution was calibrated to the measured through-cell circulation air flow rate (19,000 cfm), cell housing internal air temperature (360 K), and roof exhaust temperature (330 K) by adjusting leakage area, equipment temperature, and cell wall exterior convected heat flow.

The steady-state velocity vectors and one isothermal surface are shown in Fig. 4. The surface, at 330 K, shows the plume of hot air leaving the cell housing and rising to the process building ceiling. The surface also corresponds closely to a constant-user-scalar (aerosol concentration) surface since the aerosol rides along with the hot air that has left the cell housing. Results showed that 50% of the aerosol released is exhausted out the roof vent. The remaining 50% of the aerosol exits the unit building through the motor exhaust, or is passed out of the computational domain to an adjacent cell. A very small amount (less than 1%) of the circulated air is re-entrained into the cell housing.

After calibration, the calculated steady-state volumetric flow rate through the cell wall is 8.94 m³/s, the steady-state penthouse temperature is 360.7 K, and the average temperature of air passing through the roof vent is 329.0 K. These quantities were calibrated to the measurements in Table 1 by adjusting the equipment surface temperature and the available cell-wall leakage area. The resulting mass flow and user-scalar transport balance is shown in Table 2.

Table 2. Results of steady-state calculation, mass and aerosol inventory, negative value indicates loss from computational domain.

Location	Mass Flow (kg/s)	Aerosol Flow (kg/s)
Motor Suction	-30.64	-0.3617
Roof Vent	-22.71	-0.4992
Blower 1	17.81	0.00
Blower 2	-8.88	-0.069
Blower 3	17.76	0.00
Blower 4	-8.91	-0.072
Blower 5	17.78	0.00
Blower 6	17.78	0.00
TOTAL	0.00	-1.00
Cell Wall	10.21	1.007
Cell Door	1.98	0.013*

* This number is not exact due to the method of calculation for flow through an interior surface such as the cell door.

TRANSIENT SOLUTION

A transient solution was obtained by starting from the steady-state flow field and a zero initial condition assumed for the aerosol concentration. The hypothetical accident was defined by a release of 26.458 kg/s of aerosol into the cell housing, accompanied by a heat-of-reaction source of 9.635×10^6 W, lasting 5 min (300 s). The transient simulation assumed the actual heat source, and a net amount of 300 kg of user scalar (representing the aerosol) was released into the cell housing over the 300-s period. The aerosol and heat sources were again uniformly distributed through the cell internals.

The time step was fixed to 0.5 s for a requested 1500-s transient, the first 300 s of which would represent the release of aerosol into the cell environment. The simulation was terminated after only 521 s of problem time, due to a pressing deadline. These 521 s of problem time required 10 d of IBM RISC6000 Model 580 processing time. At this time, only about half of the 300 kg of user scalar (aerosol) released during the first 300 s had passed out of the computational domain. Of that aerosol that had passed out of the domain, 69% was exhausted through the roof vent boundary.

The resulting aerosol mass flow through the cell housing wall and out each of the boundaries during the transient is shown in Fig. 5. At about 330 s large oscillations in the mass flow in and out of the cell housing are observed. This is caused by poor convergence at the requested 0.5-s time step. However, the oscillations appear in the mass flow through the cell wall and not in the boundary mass flows. Also, the trend in the aerosol flow rate at the boundaries appears to be a reasonable continuation of the results before the oscillations began. Table 3 shows the fate of the 300 kg of user scalar as of 521.5 s of simulation time. Figure 6 shows the ratio between aerosol mass passing through the motor exhaust and total aerosol mass passing out of the computational domain as a function of time.

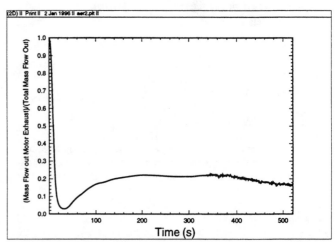

Fig. 5. Fraction of aerosol lost from the computational domain that passes through the motor exhaust as a function of time.

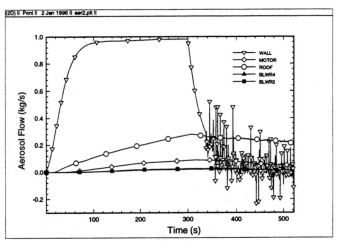

(2D) || Print || 2 Jan 1996 || aer2.plt ||

Fig. 6. Aerosol mass flow (total generated is 1 kg/s) through cell wall and mass flow boundaries during the transient simulation.

CONCLUSIONS

The results indicated that in the event of a break of a UF_6 line in the gaseous diffusion cell, at least 69% of the aerosol produced from the UF_6/H_2O reaction that passes out of the building would wind up being exhausted out of the roof vent in the process building.

This work demonstrates a useful role for CFD in large 3-D problems, where some experimental data are available for calibrating key parameters and the desired results are global (total time-integrated aerosol flow rates across a few boundary surfaces) as opposed to local velocities, temperatures, or heat transfer coefficients. A coarse discretization and large time step were required to meet the work schedule demands. All of the essential physics were included in the simulation except particle settling. This aspect was neglected due to the limitation of the CFDS-FLOW3D particle dynamics model. Some difficulties were encountered with convergence at the 0.5-s time step; however, the simulation was judged to be adequate for its purpose in providing the supplemental results to the 1-D accident simulations.

Table 3. Fate of aerosol contaminants up until 521.5 s of transient simulation.

Location	Total Mass (kg)	Percent of Release	Percent of Flow out of Domain
Out through Motor Exhaust	28.5	9.5	20.1
Out through Roof Vent	98.1	32.7	69.3
Out through Blower Boundaries	14.9	5.0	10.6
Remaining in Cell	9.4	3.1	
Remaining in Unit	149.1	49.7	
Total	300.0	100.0	100.0

REFERENCES

Kim, S. H., Taleyarkhan, R. P., Carter, J. C., Keith, K. D., Schmidt, R. W., and Dyer, R. H., March 1996, "Modeling and Analysis of Postulated UF_6 Release Accidents in Gaseous Diffusion Plant," *Proceedings, 4th International Conference on Nuclear Engineering,* published by the American Society of Mechanical Engineers, New Orleans, Lousiana.

FED-Vol. 238, 1996 Fluids Engineering Division Conference
Volume 3
ASME 1996

PROGRESS IN MODELLING EXTERNAL ATMOSPHERIC FLOWS AROUND BUILDINGS

Jon A. Peterka and Leighton S. Cochran
Cermak Peterka Petersen, Inc.
Wind Engineering Consultants
1415 Blue Spruce Drive
Fort Collins, Colorado 80524

Roger A. Pielke and Melville E. Nicholls
Colorado State University
Department of Atmospheric Sciences
Fort Collins, Colorado 80523

ABSTRACT

While Computational Fluid Dynamics (CFD) has been shown to be an effective aid in the design of airflow inside major architectural spaces (Kent, 1994), the user of CFD should be very cautious in applying the same routines to external, atmospheric flows. The constrained, often temperature differentially driven internal flows may lend themselves better to current CFD capabilities for estimating flow rates, mean pressures and ambient mean temperatures than physical experimental techniques. However, the highly turbulent flows produced by a strong wind outside a building are frequently not well represented by CFD using popular grid spacings, turbulence models and domain extents. The sharp edges of a bluff building, for example, create high Reynolds number, spatially local flow features such as separation and strong vortices that produce extremely high mean and peak pressures. Flow phenomena such as these are sensitive to the approaching and mechanically induced fine-scale turbulence.

INTRODUCTION

Wind flow about buildings includes many flow situations which cause difficulty in numerical simulations. The approach turbulent flow has an eddy structure with a spectral band ranging from scales one to two orders of magnitude larger than the building size to many orders of magnitude smaller, and can be complicated by flow in the wake of upwind structures. The distance upwind required to develop this turbulent flow can be many orders of magnitude larger than the building dimension. Flow immediately about the building involves separated, reattaching and vortex flows, all significantly influenced by the approaching turbulent structure. Pressure feedback from separated flow regions can influence flow in upwind, non-separated regions. Separated shear layers have large velocity gradients confined to thin regions which move in space and time in response to approach turbulence and to turbulence generated within the separated region. The fluctuation in separated shear layer position has a first order influence on both mean and turbulent pressures on the building surface. Given these complications, it is not surprising that numerical solutions have had difficulty matching experimental measurements; particularly for peak cladding loads.

With the First International Symposium on Computational Wind Engineering being held in Tokyo during August 1992 the progress and limitations of CFD applied to strong-wind, external building flows is starting to be seriously discussed. This is very timely since many engineering practitioners are now looking at CFD as a viable source of design wind loading data. Tuchman (1993) quotes one facade designer believing that "mathematical algorithms involving computational fluid mechanics can allow designers to quantify the loads they are dealing with

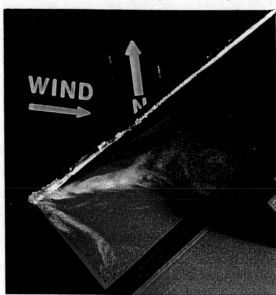

Figure 1: A typical pair of roof corner vortices. These generally cause the highest cladding loads.

on the outside of a building." This notion is of serious concern for both the computational and physical modelling sectors of the wind engineering community (Leschziner, 1992). The difficulties in mathematically modelling the turbulence, its closure, and the consequent fine-scale grid schemes required means that the use of Reynolds averaging schemes such as the K-ϵ approach can seriously under-estimate the mean and peak loads to be resisted by the building envelope in some critical edge and corner regions.

Since cladding loads on roofs and curtainwalls are caused in part by the local turbulent flow near the structure's envelope, an adequate understanding and representation of the physics contained in the turbulent make-up of the flow is required in the computer code. Investigations have shown that improper turbulence characteristics are produced by the use of K-ϵ turbulence models due to streamline curvature in the wind flow about the building (Murakami, 1993). However, recent studies with more sophisticated turbulence models, particularly in combination with an appropriate grid spacing near the building (Zhou, 1995), have been shown to produce mean surface pressures in roof vortex regions of small isolated buildings which are in better agreement with wind-tunnel or full-scale data than can be obtained with simpler approaches.

The presence of large-energy turbulence at scale sizes similar to those of the building, caused by disturbances to the flow by upwind buildings, by the building itself or the ambient atmospheric turbulence, may require a large eddy simulation model to adequately resolve turbulent structure and its impact on the building surface pressures. This approach to modelling the turbulence structure in the flow shows promise, but is computationally intensive (Murakami, 1993; Nicholls, Pielke and Meroney, 1993).

FULL-SCALE, MODEL-SCALE AND CFD PRESSURE DATA

The full-scale pressure measurements from the Texas Tech University Test Building (TTUTB) have been used to compare the physical modelling process and the CFD approach with data on a prototype building. This constitutes a most elementary first step in the development of CFD codes suitable for architectural aerodynamics since the building is a simple, rectangular, low-rise structure in an open flow environment with no neighbours to complicate the flow (Cochran, 1992a and b).

There have been several computational modeling studies of the flow around buildings using the large eddy simulation technique (Murakami, Mochida and Hibi, 1987; Murakami, Mochida and Hayashi, 1990; Tamura and Kuwahara, 1990: Nicholls et al., 1995; Frank, 1995). In a comparison of computational techniques Murakami (1993) found that the LES method produced greater accuracy than the statistical turbulence models that were tested. These comparisons with observations were made for incident flow perpendicular to a face of the building. However, wind-tunnel and field experiments have shown that the maximum wind loads on a roof occur for an oblique incident flow and are associated with the formation of corner conical vortices (Peterka and Cermak, 1976; Cochran and Cermak, 1992: Kramer and Gerhardt, 1989; Mehta, Levitan, Iverson and McDonald, 1992; Tieleman , Surry and Lin, 1994; Lin, Surry, and Tieleman, 1995). It might be expected that for oblique wind directions, the statistical turbulence models would have particular difficulty in modeling the effects of corner conical vortices, although some success has recently been reported in a study by Zhou (1995). It has yet to be established whether the LES technique can fully simulate these features.

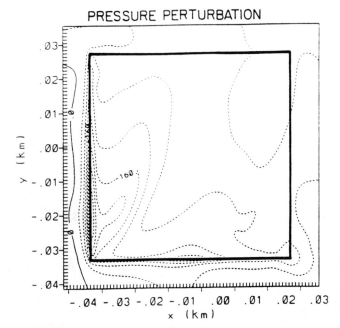

Figure 2: **Pressure perturbations at roof level on a cubic building defined by the thick solid line. The contour interval is 40 Pa.**

Corner conical vortices are small in scale relative to the height of the building and therefore, require a large number of grid points in order to be resolved. Nicholls, et. al. (1995) had some limited success simulating corner conical vortices using LES, but computational limitations precluded the simulation being run long enough to obtain results which could be statistically analyzed and compared with wind-tunnel and field data. Nevertheless, several corner conical vortices formed during the simulation which appear to have some realistic features. The simulation was performed using the Colorado State University Regional Atmospheric Modeling System (RAMS) which has been modified for LES of flow around buildings. The simulation made use of nested grids (Clark and Farley, 1984), enabling high resolution of small scale structures close to the building. The fine grid had 80 x 80 x 72 grid points and was embedded in the center of a coarse grid with a similar number of grid points. The grid increment was 1 m for the fine grid and 3 m for the coarse grid. The building was centered within the fine grid and was a cube with 60 x 60 x 60 grid points. Cyclic boundary conditions were prescribed on the coarse grid. As body induced eddies shed from the building advected through the downstream boundary, they re-emerge at the upstream boundary, eventually producing a turbulent flow field. Fig. 3 shows streamlines for a vertical cross-section (xz-plane) through the center of the building, which slices through the corner conical vortex. Although, the results of this simulation are promising, far more detailed studies are required which statistically compare the simulated wind loads with data from field experiments and wind tunnels. Since large computational resources are required for LES, particularly for oblique wind directions, its application is limited, at present. The use of nested grids is a promising procedure in LES, enabling the simultaneous representation of building scales and the larger scale atmospheric turbulent flow, such as generated by thunderstorms and hurricanes.

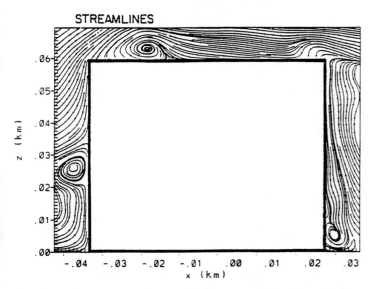

STREAMLINES

Figure 3: Streamlines for a vertical cross section through the center of the building showing the development of a roof corner vortex in Figure 2.

In order to improve the prediction of mean pressure distributions on block buildings, Zhou (1995) used the familiar K-ε turbulence closure in Reynolds averaged equations. He compared pressures predicted numerically with data at selected pressure tap locations acquired in a wind-tunnel test in a modeled atmospheric boundary layer. His predictions included wind direction cases where rooftop vortices are a prominent feature of the roof pressure distribution. In his numerical simulation, he modified the turbulence model in a thin region near the building surface using a variety of closure models suggested in the literature. A turbulence model by Norris and Reynolds (1975), in combination with a carefully selected variable grid spacing, showed better comparison to a physical model than many other simulations, particularly in the critical rooftop vortex region. Figure 4 shows that the position and magnitude of the mean pressure maxima using the Norris-Reynolds two-layer approach is in fair agreement with the wind-tunnel data. Obviously future work will need to define the extent and shape of the vortex better. This analysis shows that for applications where relatively simple building shapes occur in isolated surroundings, the computational skill level may be sufficient for limited design applications for building frames, but not the local peak cladding loads. No comparison of numerical to physical test cost was attempted, since these costs are highly dependent on other tests which might be involved, such as cladding pressures and on the experience of the test groups. In addition, no attempt was made to extend the analysis procedure to local **peak** fluctuating pressures which controls the cladding design.

CONCLUSIONS

The evidence provided by numerical simulations at this time shows an increasing level of skill in applications such as mean pressure distributions on simple block shapes in isolated environments using tailored turbulent closures in Reynolds averaged equations. There seems little likelihood that Reynolds averaged equations will be able to predict the peaks in fluctuating pressures with empirical models currently used for this purpose. Recent work shows a potential to model fluctuating pressures with Large Eddy Simulation models. The challenge in LES

simulations will be the large number of grid points and small time steps needed to resolve the highly complicated separated flow phenomena which routinely occur about buildings. The rapid advance in computing power may help to resolve this difficulty; advances in algorithms may also be necessary.

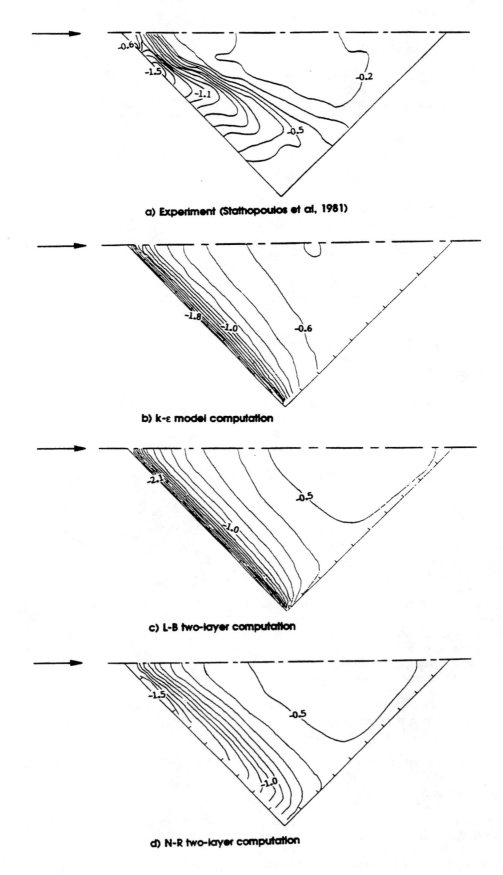

Figure 4: Mean roof pressure coefficient contours for a 45° approach flow. Note that (d) is showing some important aspects of the vortex flow given by the wind tunnel data (a). After Zhou, 1995.

REFERENCES

Clark, T.L. and Farley, R.D., "Severe Downslope Windstorm Calculations in Two and Three Spatial Dimensions Using Anelastic Interactive Grid Nesting: A Possible Mechanism for Gustiness." Journal of Atmospheric Science, Volume 4, pages 329-350, 1984.

Cochran, L.S., "Wind-Tunnel Modelling of Low-Rise Structures, Ph.D. Dissertation at Colorado State University, 509 pages, Fall 1992(a).

Cochran, L.S., "Low-Rise Architectural Aerodynamics," Architectural Science Review, Volume 35, Number 4, pages 131-136, 1992(b).

Cochran, L.S. and Cermak, J.E., "Full and Model Scale Cladding Pressures on the Texas Tech Experimental Building," Journal of Wind Engineering and Industrial Aerodynamics, Volume 41-44, pages 1589-1600, December 1992.

Frank, W., "Large-Eddy Simulation of the Three-Dimensional Flow Around Buildings," Wind Climate in Cities, NATO ASI series, Kluwer Academic Publishers, pages 669-679, 1995.

Kent, J.H., "Air Conditioning Modelling by Computational Fluid Dynamics," Architectural Science Review, Volume 37, Number 3, pages 103-113, 1994.

Kramer, C. and Gerhardt, H.J., "Wind Pressures on Roofs of Very Low and Very Large Industrial Buildings," Journal of Wind Engineering and Industrial Aerodynamics, Volume 38, pages 285-295, 1991.

Leschziner, M.A., "Computational Modelling of Complex Turbulent Flow - Expectations, Reality and Prospects," The First International Symposium on Computational Wind Engineering, pages 180-194, Tokyo, Japan, 1992.

Lin, J.X., Surry, D. and Tieleman, H., "Wind Tunnel Experiments of Pressures at Roof Corners of Flat Roof Low Buildings," Journal of Wind Engineering and Industrial Aerodynamics, Volume 56, pages 235-265, 1995.

Mehta, K.C., Levitan, M.L., Iverson, R.E. and McDonald, J.R., "Roof Corner Pressures Measured in the Field on a Low Building," Journal of Wind Engineering and Industrial Aerodynamics, Volume 41, pages 181-192, 1992.

Murakami, S., "Comparisons of Various Turbulence Models Applied to a Bluff Body," Journal of Wind Engineering and Industrial Aerodynamics, Volume 46-47, pages 21-36, 1993.

Murakami, S., Mochida, A. and Hayashi, Y., "Examining the K-ϵ Model by Means of a Wind Tunnel Test and Large Eddy Simulation of the Turbulence Structure Around a Cube," Journal of Wind Engineering and Industrial Aerodynamics, Volume 35, pages 87-100, 1990.

Murakami, S., Mochida, A, and Hibi, K., "Three-Dimensional Numerical Simulation of Airflow Around a Cubic Model by Means of Large Eddy Simulation," Journal of Wind Engineering and Industrial Aerodynamics, Volume 25, pages 291-305, 1987.

Nicholls, M.E., Pielke, R.A., Eastman, J.L, Finley, C.A., Lyons, W.A., Tremback, C.J., Walko, R.L and Cotton, W.R., "Applications of the RAMS Numerical Model to Dispersion Over Urban Areas," Wind Climate in Cities, NATO ASI series, Kluwer Academic Publishers, pages 703-732, 1995.

Nicholls, M.E., Pielke, R.A. and Meroney, R.N., "Large Eddy Simulation of Microburst Winds Flowing Around a Building," Journal of Wind Engineering and Industrial Aerodynamics, Volume 46-47, pages 229-237, 1993.

Norris, L.H. and Reynolds, W.C., "Turbulent Channel Flow with a Moving Wavy Boundary," Report Number FM-10, Stanford University, Department of Mechanical Engineering, 1975.

Peterka, J.A., and Cermak, J.E., "Adverse Wind Loading Induced by Adjacent Buildings," Journal of the Structural Division, American Society of Civil Engineers, Volume 102, No ST3, pages 533-548, 1976.

Stathopoulos, T., Surry, D. and Davenport, A.G., "Effective Wind Loads on Flat Roofs," Journal of the Structural Division, American Society of Civil Engineers, Volume 107, No ST2, pages 281-300, 1981.

Tamura, T., and Kuwahara, K., "Numerical Study of Aerodynamic Behavior of a Square Cylinder," Journal of Wind Engineering and Industrial Aerodynamics, Volume 33, pages 161-170, 1990.

Tieleman, H.W., Surry, D., and Lin, J.X. "Characteristics of Mean and Fluctuating Pressure Coefficients Under Corner (Delta-Wing) Vortices," Journal of Wind Engineering and Industrial Aerodynamics, Volume 52, pages 263-275, 1994.

Tuchman, J.L., "Curtain Walls in the Spotlight," Engineering News Record, page 7, December 13, 1993.

Zhou, Y. and Stathopoulos, T., "Application of Two-Layer Methods for the Evaluation of Wind Effects on a Cubic Building," ASHRAE Transactions, Volume 102, under review, 1996.

Zhou, Y., "Numerical Evaluation of Wind Effects on Buildings," Ph.D. Dissertation, Concordia University, Montreal, 1995.

FED-Vol. 238, 1996 Fluids Engineering Division Conference
Volume 3
ASME 1996

DESIGNING A MICRO-CLIMATE FOR A NEW INTERNATIONAL AIRPORT USING CFD TECHNIQUES TO DEVELOP PARAMETERS AND ANALYZE THE EFFECTIVENESS OF THE DESIGN

Peter Simmonds
Principal
Flak & Kurtz Consulting Engineers
343 Sansond St, Suite 450
San Francisco, CA 94104-1309

ABSTRACT

In order to consrve energy and create a comfortable climate for both passengers and workers at a new international airport in Thailand, a design concept was created where only the first 2 meters above the occupied zone is conditioned. The temperature of the air outside this area is allowed to rise above normal conditions. The idea was to let this temperature rise so that it was either equal to ot higher than the outdoor temperature thus reducing heat gains. Computer simulation programs were used to define parameters for the CFD program. Once the boundary conditions were defined, the process of design analysis began. This paper will outline steps taken to set up the CFD program. Secondly, the exploration taken to obtain an optimal climate, and thirdly, how the many results were used to explain to both fellow engineers and the architects what had been acheived. The conclusion of this analysis was the design of special supply air grilles to meet the design criteria.

FED-Vol. 238, 1996 Fluids Engineering Division Conference
Volume 3
ASME 1996

CFD Validation of Natural Smoke Movement in a Model Tunnel

M. Tabarra, B. Kenrick & R.D. Matthews

Centre for Tunnel Ventilation Research & Development
School of Engineering Systems & Design,
South Bank University,
London SE1 0AA,
UK

ABSTRACT

Preliminary results are presented of a program of research in the UK. funded by the EPSRC to study the characteristics of a hot stratified smoke layer in a 1/15 scale model tunnel under conditions of natural convection. The project uses experimental data to bench mark computational fluid dynamic output. Once the validity of the CFD model has been established, attention can be turned to modelling the movement of fire smoke in full-size tunnels, which is understood to need about five times the grid elements for a comparable level of resolution. This coupled with an investigation of aerodynamic interactions between ventilation flows and a hot stratified smoke layer will lead to the correct management of smoke from fires in vehicle tunnels and other underground spaces. The current state of CFD modelling, the memory and CPU time requirements as well as the limitations are also discussed in context of a scale model and a full-size simulation.

INTRODUCTION

This project arose from the widespread knowledge that the most immediate threat to life in tunnel fires comes not from a direct exposure to fire heat but from the effects of smoke inhalation. More recently. it has come to light that a strong ventilation system may not be the best answer to passenger safety. as this tends to mix the hot smoke layers with the cool fresh air drawn in by the fire. While city centres throughout the world are looking to Metro systems for mass transit. the horrors of King's Cross London in 1987 and Baku in 1995 make optimum ventilation and smoke movement systems mandatory.

The work done over the last four years on the longitudinal ventilation of tunnels by jet fans [1] funded by the EPSRC/DTI and industry. have

stimulated the authors' interest in the critical interaction between the smoke from a fire in a tunnel and any ventilation flows or obstructions present in the tunnel. The current phase of the project is aimed at establishing an experimental model of stratified smoke behaviour and using this to bench mark a computational fluid dynamic (CFD) model. The project has so far been a blend of experimental and theoretical study in which the steady state temperature and velocity profiles in the hot tunnel model tunnel have been compared with the CFD data. Two modes of destratification have been identified - *primary* destratification occuring near obstructions in which strong transverse or streamwise vortices bring smoke down into the cool clean air, where it cools and mixes and *secondary* destratification which occurs gradually and continuously along the tunnel as a cooling smoke boundary layer creeps down the tunnel walls and into the air below the stratified layer. It seems that the point at which primary destratification can be triggered depends mainly on the ratio of buoyancy forces to inertia forces or the Richardson number Ri.

While recent research has concentrated on accurate modelling of combustion and the realistic prediction of turbulent flames. this project will focus on far-field modelling of smoke layers and their stability under real tunnel conditions. An early paper by Heselden [2] provided the impetus for smoke movement studies and has influenced the succeeding studies. Based on full-scale fire tests, Heselden raised many illuminating questions and proposed future research fronts, many of which can only now be attempted with the advancement in CFD capabilities. The crucial role of turbulence modelling and the effect of stratification on turbulence damping was recognised early on [3], and CFD field modelling of fire smoke was underway by the mid 1980's. These studies were limited by the then current computer power and memory and were often conducted on coarse grids without radiation modelling leading to large errors. The absence of a detailed experimental data base to bench mark CFD results also added to the uncertainty of computational results. In the last three years, many researchers are using the increasing computational capacity to good effect and modelling fires in complex structures, accounting for combustion chemistry and radiation in 3D geometry [4,5]. The interest is world-wide and will be complemented by a set of comprehensive data from full-scale fire tests in the Memorial Tunnel in the U.S.A. which will be an invaluable reference for bench marking CFD results for years to come.

The ultimate beneficiaries of this work will be the travelling public, who in the event of a fire in a tunnel will receive rapid and unambiguous instructions to make good their escape. This will be due to an integrated telematic communication and ventilation control system aware of the position and power of the fire and the stability of the stratified smoke along any escape route. The commercial beneficiary of the research will be the consulting engineer, fan and ventilation system provider who will have a deeper understanding of smoke behaviour and hence a competitive edge when bidding world-wide for tunnel ventilation schemes.

EXPERIMENTAL RIG

The experimental scale model tunnel consisted of a rectangular section 300 mm wide and 500 mm high containing a variable, controlled gas fire source. The tunnel length is variable up to a maximum of 14 m, thus representing a full-scale single-lane tunnel 4.5 m wide, 7.5 m high and up to 210 m long, as shown in Figure 1. In order to avoid the undesirable effects of slight portal pressure fluctuations which could cause uncontrollable time-variant natural draughts along the tunnel, it was decided to close one end. The end wall can be effectively viewed as a plane of symmetry for an induced natural ventilation flow in a horizontal tunnel, simulating a fire in the middle of a tunnel twice the length, offering significant savings in computational time and memory space as well as experimental time. The roof was insulated with rock wool, and the side walls were made of glass to allow the laser Doppler anemometer (LDA) beams through for velocity measurements anywhere in the tunnel. The LDA system used was a Dantec two component type based on a 300 mW Argon laser

capable of giving both mean and turbulence velocity data in the axial and vertical directions. The temperatures were measured by a K-type thermocouple tree, which could be erected at predetermined (1 m interval) locations along the tunnel at mid-plane and at 20 mm off one of the glass walls. Preliminary temperature measurements verified the temperature field to be effectively two-dimensional, hence no provisions were made for further measurements across the tunnel width. A maximum fire power of 4.9 kW (representing a full-scale equivalent of ~ 4 MW) could be established which would take about an hour for the tunnel temperatures and the cold feed and hot return flow to reach steady state.

A full-scale velocity and temperature measurement rig is also under development, which will be able to supply much-needed reliable data for real size tunnel fires and other ventilation studies. This facility should be operational by the end of 1996.

CFD STUDIES

The computational fluid dynamic facilities consisted of a DEC Alpha 3000/400 computer with a processor speed of 133 MHz and 112 Mb RAM, running the CFDS-FLOW3D software package developed by AEA Technology, which is a finite-volume general purpose code with a range of features for the study of heat transfer, radiation, two-phase flow, combustion etc.

The tunnel was modelled using the SIMPLEC algorithm, a hybrid differencing scheme. The modelling initially started with the simplest approach employing a 2D adiabatic field with the fire modelled as a heat source, a standard k-ε model and no radiation effects, pertaining to stage 1 in Table 1 which shows the various modelling stages in the order of increasing complexity.

For a stage 3 approach, using a 50,000 node grid, 48 Mb of RAM space and about 6000 iterations taking 2E+05 seconds of processor time were needed. The results of a stage 3 simulation are compared with experiment in Figure 2. As expected, the CFD results follow the general trend well, but overshoot significantly in velocity and temperature in the hot stratified smoke layer. This is because the heat losses through radiation have not been modelled, giving excessive energy to the smoke layer in the CFD model. Also the sharper temperature and velocity gradients observed in the experiments have not been properly captured in the CFD, because the k-ε model used was not corrected for turbulence suppression due to density gradients.

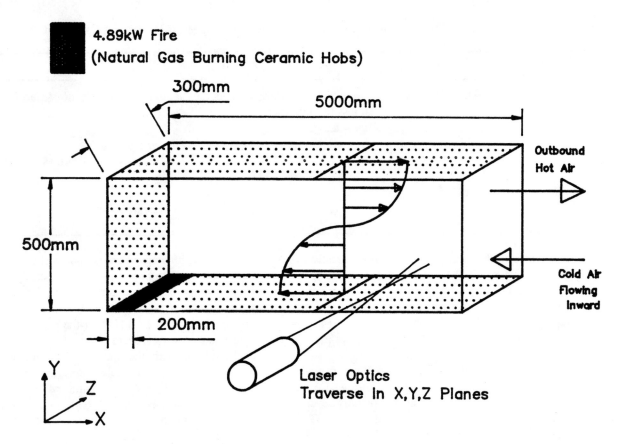

Figure 1. Experimental Test Rig

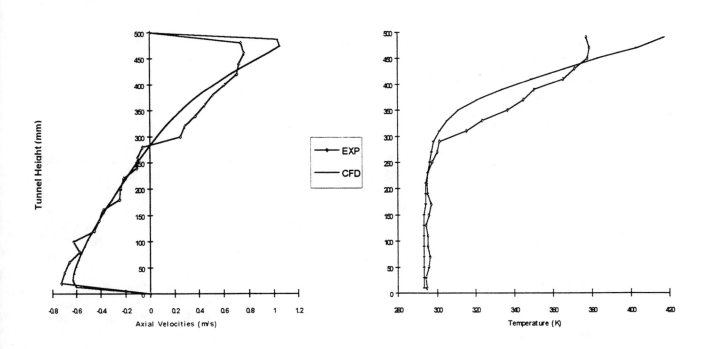

Figure 2. Comparison of CFD results with experiment
Velocity and temperature profiles for a 4.9 kW fire

Table 1. CFD modelling of Fire Smoke in Tunnels - Stages of Increasing Complexity

Stage	Modelling Approach					
1	Steady 2D,	buoyancy driven,	adiabatic,	fire as heat source,	standard k-ε model,	no radiation
2	,,	,,	heat loss through roof,	,,	,,	,,
3	Steady 3D,	,,	all heat losses,	,,	,,	,,
4	,,	,,	,,	,,	corrected k-ε model,	,,
5	,,	,,	,,	,,	,,	with radiation
6	,,	,,	,,	fire combustion model,	,,	,,
7	Transient 3D,	,,	,,	,,	,,	,,
8	,,	,,	,,	,,	Reynolds Stress model,	,,

It is expected that accuracy will improve greatly by stage 6, where all the physical complexities have been modelled in one way or another. In order to appreciate the complexities involved, Bettis recently reported a stage 7 simulation, which took 60 hours of CPU time on a Cray XMP super-computer [6].

It is realised that full-scale CFD modelling of smoke in large structures and facilities will need grid elements and hence CPU time and memory several times larger than those mentioned above. The reason for this is when scaling up from the model size to prototype, one cannot conserve all of the non-dimensional numbers (Reynolds, Froude, etc.), and has to choose the most physically significant number for the problem in hand. In the case of fire smoke, Richardson (also known as the internal Froude number) is the important dimensionless group to preserve. This means that the velocities will scale as $L^{0.5}$, flow rates and fire power as $L^{2.5}$ where L is a characteristic length of the model, resulting in a Reynolds number scaling up as $L^{1.5}$. Thus when transferring from the model to full scale, the boundary layers become relatively thinner in line with $\delta/L = Re^{-0.2}$. In order to correctly capture the boundary layers in the full-size CFD model, more grid points are needed for the same level of spatial resolution. For our 1/15 scale model, this means that the Re in full scale would be about 60 times larger, requiring 2.25 times more grid elements in each direction or about 5 times for the full cross section of the tunnel.

FUTURE WORK

Laser sheet illumination of the streamlines in the vertical mid-plane along the tunnel axis has demonstrated the existence of a sharp stable interface between the cold clear air and hot smoke layers inhibiting turbulence and smoke diffusion. Low-frequency small-amplitude gravity waves have also been observed moving along this hot/cold interface, oscillating at Brunt-Väisälä frequencies.

These oscillations are of course not observable in a steady-state CFD simulation; an unsteady time-dependent approach is required, where the memory and computation times are many times larger. It has long been suspected [2] that the point at which these internal waves become unstable and lead to smoke mixing with the clear air flow underneath depends primarily on Richardson number. The existence of such a critical value of Richardson number will be investigated both experimentally and computationally, by a parametric study varying the tunnel length, height, gradient, heat loss rate and fire orientation and power.

The project further aims to carefully examine the conditions at which external disturbances (e.g. tunnel road signs, traffic lights, etc.) may lead to breakdown of the stratified interface, leading to premature smoke mixing.

REFERENCES
1) Tabarra M., Bennett E.C. & Matthews R.D. (1995), "Optimizing Jet Fan Performance in Longitudinally Ventilated Rectangular Tunnels", ASME Conference, FED-Vol. 217, pp. 35-42
2) Heselden A.J.M. (1976), "Studies of Fire and Smoke Relevant to Tunnels", 2nd International Symposium on the Aerodynamics and Ventilation of Vehicle Tunnels, Cambridge, BHRA Fluid Engg.
3) Markatos N.C., Malin M.R. & Cox G. (1982), "Mathematical Modelling of Bouyancy-Induced Smoke Flow in Enclosures", Int. J. Heat & Mass Transfer, Vol 25, No. 1, pp. 63-75
4) Xue H., Hihara E. Saito T. (1994), "Temperature Stratification of Heated Air Flow in a Fire Tunnel", JSME Int. J., Series B, Vol. 37, No. 1, pp. 187-194
5) Fletcher D.F., Kent J.H., Apte V.B. & Green A.R. (1994), "Numerical Simulation of Smoke Movement from a Pool Fire in a Ventilated Tunnel", Fire Safety J., Vol. 23, pp. 305-325
6) Bettis R. (1995), "Controlling Smoke in Tunnel Fires", Fire Prevention, Vol. 280, pp. 19-22

FED-Vol. 238, 1996 Fluids Engineering Division Conference
Volume 3
ASME 1996

CFD MODELING CONSIDERATIONS FOR TRAIN FIRES
IN UNDERGROUND SUBWAY STATIONS

Mark P. Deng, P.E., Paul C. Miclea, P.E.
Dan McKinney

ICF Kaiser Engineers, Inc.
Oakland, California

ABSTRACT

Using Computational Fluid Dynamics (CFD) to simulate fires in subway stations and tunnels is a relatively new approach that has recently been accepted by many transit authorities, especially in the aftermath of the infamous King's Cross Station fire of November 1987 in London.

By using CFD techniques, the movement, temperature, and composition of fluid (air and smoke) can be predicted. The effects of the fire and mechanical ventilation on the evacuating patrons and on the fire fighting personnel can be predicted and visualized. Thus, the evacuation procedures and the integrity of the egress way can be better evaluated.

There are some impediments and difficulties to be overcome for this technique to be more willingly and widely accepted by the transit industry around the world. CFD analyses are expensive because of the cost of the software and hardware, intensive labor for setting up the models, and long simulation time. There are also some ambiguous areas in using the technique for this type of application, such as: how to set up boundary conditions that best represent the real situation, how to set up more realistic fire models, the accuracy of the simplified models, and the validation of CFD codes.

This paper discusses the technical issues related to grid generation, grid quality, multi-block modeling vs. single-block modeling, boundary condition setup, physical model selections, transient vs. steady-state models and how these factors affect the solution.

INTRODUCTION

The risk of fires in tunnels and subway stations requires special consideration from designers. The aim is to provide effective ventilation to remove heat and fire by-products to ensure a clear route for evacuating patrons from the fire proximity and allow access for fire-fighting crews and equipment. The *Subway Environment Simulation (SES)* computer program has been used for almost two decades to simulate tunnel fires and predict the airflow to the incident train using one-dimensional flow simulation techniques. A simple comparison between the SES predicted airflow and the required critical velocity at the fire location (based on the fire size, tunnel geometry and grade) allows a quick conclusion regarding the ventilation adequacy. This method is inappropriate, however, when the incident train is stopped at a station platform, or across secondary airways like cross-passages, vents or fan shaft connections. For fires at these locations a multi-dimensional prediction of the spread of smoke is required to determine the adequacy of the ventilation system. Since the SES program cannot predict the airflow distribution in more than one dimension, the CFD analysis is preferred.

Mathematical models of large structures such as tunnels and underground stations can be developed to analyze the spread of fire products (heat, smoke, etc.) using CFD technique. The CFD three-dimensional model divides the region of interest into small control volumes and uses the finite volume method to integrate the equations for the conservation of mass, momentum, energy and species over each control volume. This allows for a detailed analysis of the movement of air and the distribution of heat, smoke and other by-products of combustion.

ICF Kaiser Engineers Inc. has been using the CFD technique since 1992 in modeling station and tunnel fires. FLUENT, CFDS-

FLOW3D, and TASCFLOW codes have been used on a DEC ALPHA workstation. Although use of CFD technique for subway fires is relatively new, some lessons have been learned and will be discussed below.

MODEL SETUP AND GRID GENERATION

To conduct a CFD analysis, a grid of contiguous control volumes (cells) needs to be established such that the area of interest and that necessary to accommodate the established boundary conditions are represented. The value of each variable such as velocity components, pressure and temperature are calculated at the center of each of these grid cells. The mapping of meshes onto the geometry is referred to as grid generation.

The grid should be generated such that areas where substantial gradients in physical properties are likely to occur (i.e. in the vicinity of the fire) are represented by smaller cells (a finer mesh), while a coarser grid can be used in areas of fully developed flow where gradients are less severe. This is important particularly for underground stations, where relatively large volumes need to be incorporated into the model. Rail or vehicular tunnels in most cases contain double, or even multiple tracks or lanes, and tunnel widths of up to 20 m (66 ft) may be encountered. If the model is to extend to the surface, depths in the range of 10 to 30 m (30-100 ft) can be anticipated. When addressing train fires, whether in stations or in tunnels, the full extent of the train or station may need to be incorporated into the model. Additionally, there may be other features of interest to be incorporated such as escape routes, mezzanines, escalators or passage ways, that often are situated outside the station's perimeter. Of particular concern are subway stations that serve more than one line, and consequently extend to more levels. There are always connections between the mezzanine and platform areas and, in some cases, between running tunnels as well.

In general, the CFD models developed (particularly for stations) are large and tend to range from tens of thousands to hundreds of thousands of cells and nodes. Figure 1 shows the outline of a model developed for a relatively simple station, representing the platform level, the train, and stairs to the mezzanine level located above and to one side of the platform, with a fire zone shown at one end of the incident train. If super-computers could be used and the simulation time was not an issue, simulation of an entire station, including fans would be feasible and a finer mesh could be used to produce more precise results. Unfortunately, the cost of using super-computers is usually prohibitive for this kind of application. For workstations and personal computers, the model size must be limited. If the meshes are too coarse, the accuracy of the result will be compromised, so other means of reducing the model must be applied. Fortunately, the CFD engineer can take advantage of several techniques to simplify the model without substantially compromising the solution.

If the area being modeled is bilaterally symmetrical with the fire in the middle and if the airflow does not cross the line of symmetry, a symmetry boundary can be used and only one-half of the model needs to be defined and assessed. Unfortunately this option seldom

applies to tunnel or station fires as the fire location is typically on one side of the tunnel or the station. For large, multi-level stations, models can be developed for individual components and each component can be analyzed separately by maintaining continuity between components through boundary conditions. For example, results at unconstrained boundaries from an evaluation of a lower-level platform can be used to define the matching fixed boundaries for the upper-level platform. Another method of simplification, often used for stations, is to incorporate the results of a one-dimensional program such as the SES to provide boundary conditions. These boundary conditions should be setup at where the airflow is mechanically induced and fully developed (homogeneous). The three-dimensional model then would incorporate the areas of interest and extend to a location where boundary conditions can readily be defined.

MORE ON GRID GENERATION

Based on our experience, the most practical grid for this type of application is a "body-fitted, multi-block", structured grid. "Body-fitted" means that the grid boundaries fit (map to) the geometry. "Multi-block" means that the grid can be imagined as being composed of separate parts, called blocks, joined together to form the geometry. Each block is subdivided into grid cells in a regular (structured way), while the blocks join in an unstructured way. Compared to "single-block" modeling, "multi-block" modeling has the following advantages:

- It requires fewer cells, saves memory and reduces CPU usage (Figures 2, 3).

- It reduces cell distortion, which helps the calculation to converge and makes the flow solution more accurate (Figures 4, 5).

- It makes local mesh refinement possible (Figures 6, 7).

- It makes modeling complex geometry much easier.

Previously we stated that finer grids should be generated in the vicinity of the fire and coarser grids can be used in areas where the flows are fully developed and away from the fire. For some CFD codes, this may cause layers of thin and long rectangular grids extending though the whole model. The aspect ratios for some of these grids may be too high and the size difference of these grids compared to adjacent coarse grids may be significant. Some CFD codes are sensitive to these problems. However, other CFD codes provide a better solution. Fine grids can be embedded into a limited region of a general coarse mesh and make the model easier to define and solve.

Generally, CFD models are setup using the package build-in grid generator. But we found that in some situations third-party grid generators can be a better alternative. When looking for a proper third-party grid generator for specific application, a powerful, easy-to-use, interactive and user-friendly one should be the choice. These grid generators should create meshes of very high quality, more quickly and more easily than the tools that come with the CFD codes. They should generate meshes for finite difference and finite element simulation codes that model the behavior of fluids and structures. Some of them are more than mesh generators - they can generate complete input files for many simulation codes. Besides defining the mesh, physical properties can be specified on the mesh (temperatures, for example). Once the model is setup, the input file for the user's simulation code can be automatically generated.

Some of these grid generators may provide the users with many tools for generating high quality meshes including multi-linear interpolation, transfinite interpolation, and elliptic solvers and use a special projection method for mapping a block structured mesh onto one or more surfaces. This projection method removes much of the manual drudgery associated with mesh generation. Their diagnostic tools should make it easy to measure the quality of the mesh. Their graphical user interface should let the user generate mesh by "pointing and clicking". Prompts, dialogue boxes, and on-line help package should help the user create mesh easily. These grid generators should use sophisticated graphic techniques to let the user view the mesh as it is being built. These interactive features should be designed to give the user fast feedback to speed up the mesh generation process.

We have been using a third-party grid generator for awhile. With this grid generator, an object is meshed in the way an artist molds a block of clay. The raw material in this grid generator is a multiple block structured mesh. Some blocks can be removed to place holes in the mesh. Faces of the mesh are given shapes. Many functions are available to control the distribution of the mesh along the required shapes. By default, regions of the mesh are automatically interpolated. This method gives the user the control needed while minimizing the complexity of the problem. Since the shape of the mesh in the form of points, curves, and surfaces is specified independently of the mesh, it is easy to change only the geometry. For the same reason, it is easy to change only the density and nodal distribution of the mesh. By decoupling the geometry and topology of the mesh, this grid generator greatly reduces the complexity of mesh generation. Thus one can build more complex models in a shorter time. This design also makes it easier to modify an existing mesh or to build template meshes for similar models.

Usually the model of a station is complicated enough so that it is easier to make a number of separate "parts" and then put them together. Each "part" begins as a rectangular set of nodes (called a "region") in computational space, and a corresponding, similarly shaped set of nodes in physical space. We then transform and deform the simple shape into a complex shape for the part of interest. We can change a part and specify things about it in other ways too; some affect the mesh in both physical and computational space, e.g., deleting nodes or making copies. Once we have modeled all the parts, we can join them in various ways to obtain the full model (Figures 8, 9).

In addition to reducing the time of setting up a model by half or more, another benefit we get from using a third-party grid generator

is that we can use PCs to generate grids and set up models, saving the workstation for number crunching. This proved to be a great advantage when we had several stations to be modeled at the same time.

BOUNDARY CONDITIONS

Boundary conditions such as wall temperatures, flow boundaries (pressure, velocity, mass flow rate), symmetry planes, periodic planes, internal baffles (thin surfaces), and internal solids must be specified.

Boundary conditions are assigned to those cells which represent ambient boundaries and where flows enter or exit the model. As discussed in the previous section, the results of the SES program can be used extensively to limit the size of the physical model and to define the physical phenomena at the model boundaries. The average air velocity, air temperature, air density, static pressure, and wall temperature from the SES simulation can be used to define boundary conditions.

In CFD analyses, boundaries which terminate at the area of interest are defined as "inlet" or "outlet" with respect to the model (system) or as openings though which flow may pass in either direction. Either the airflow or pressure may be specified. Boundary conditions can be either time-dependent for transient analysis, or constant for steady-state analysis.

Although the SES results can be used to develop a velocity profile at a flow boundary (taking into account the tunnel roughness and air density), a uniformly distributed airflow, based on the average air velocity, is usually specified. Pressure boundaries, which can also be determined from SES simulations, are primarily selected for boundaries to ambient condition. These boundaries permit the program to determine the flow flux through the system and maintain a mass balance.

Cells representing a solid surface, such as a tunnel or station wall, may be assigned thermal properties such as heat transfer coefficient, or thermal diffusivity and conductivity. Heat flux, or constant temperature can also be assigned to these cells. For simplicity and for reduced computation time, the user may specify a "zero net heat flux" condition along the cells representing the walls, which eliminates any temperature gradient near the surfaces. If simulations are conducted to consider viscous shear along surfaces, roughness properties may also be attributed.

Depending on the specific CFD code being used, some boundary options may or may not be available. For example, the mass flow rate boundary is not available for some CFD codes, but is for others. Mass flow rate boundaries are used to model inflow or outflow where the total mass flow rate into or out of the domain is known, but the detailed temperature and velocity profile are not. This boundary type has been found helpful and more realistic for some boundaries in our applications.

549

FIRE SIMULATION

Transient CFD analyses can be conducted by simulating the progressive growth of the fire and spread of its by-products. This requires developing a time-dependent algorithm (user subroutine) which relates the release of heat, smoke, by-products of combustion, and combustion propagation with time. For transit vehicles, knowledge of the composition of the combustibles is required, as is the likely progression of combustion. A thorough transient CFD simulation of a fire in a transit tunnel or station requires extensive modeling and computation time. In addition to establishing a representative grid of control volumes, model development requires establishing time-dependent boundary conditions and fire effects. Significant time and cost savings can be realized by simulating steady-state conditions using "worst-case" heat and smoke release rates. These results are sufficient to evaluate the overall effectiveness of the ventilation system. This does not mean that the transit CFD simulations should be ruled out completely. In some cases, they can provide useful information in developing evacuation plans.

If simulation of the time-dependent propagation of the fire can be compromised, transient simulation can be conducted without a combustion model by essentially simulating the time-dependent release of hot smoke into the system. This can be accomplished by (1) developing user subroutines which convert a defined percentage of oxygen into combustion by-products (smoke) and add enthalpy at a designated rate to the selected fire cells, or (2) releasing smoke and heat into the system through a specified inlet at rates related to the simulation time. The first of these two techniques is preferred as it is more representative of the combustion process and does not contribute mass to the system as does the second approach. It also draws in fresh air to replace that removed from the fire zone by convection. This obviously does not happen if smoke is added through an inlet. Either of these two techniques may also be used for steady-state simulations when only the effectiveness of the ventilation system during the maximum heat release rate is of interest. Steady-state simulations considerably reduce run time, and are ideally suited for use with the inlet boundary conditions determined by SES simulation.

Some CFD users model the fire as a constant heat source, a source of combustion products (smoke) and a sink of air. The combustion products are assumed to be those obtained from burning a hydrocarbon which has a certain heating value. However, since no comparison study has been done for different fire models, it is difficult to quantify the effect on the results.

PHYSICAL MODELS

To represent the physical phenomena resulting from a fire in a subway station, the buoyancy effects, turbulence, and heat transfer due to convection, conduction and radiation need to be considered in the simulation. If all these factors are incorporated into the simulation, it will take forever for the simulation to converge, if it ever does. For this reason, some simplifications are necessary.

Heat transfer by radiation is time consuming to compute and has little impact on smoke distribution, although it does affect wall surface temperatures. The amount of energy released through radiation should be deducted from the fire size, if radiation is not simulated.

Turbulent flows are modeled by selecting either standard k-ε or RNG k-ε turbulence model depending on the code capability. Opinions are divided as to the merits of the RNG k-ε turbulence model for different applications. For some CFD codes, the standard k-ε is the user's only choice.

Some CFD codes have the choice of specifying the fluid as incompressible, weakly compressible for temperature variations or compressible. The ideal choice for our application is weakly compressible to save computation time. When this is not available for the code used, one should chose compressible, fully buoyant for this type of application.

COMPUTATIONAL PROCESS

Most commercial workstation and PC-based CFD codes provide the user with the ability to make adjustments during the computational process to accelerate convergence, thereby reducing the time required to reach convergence. However, some vendors claim that their codes do not need adjustments by the user during the simulation to get or accelerate convergence.

Values defining the thermodynamic and aerodynamic state computed for each cell during a computation cycle, or iteration, may be held constant for part of the computation to accelerate convergence of other parameters. Some programs have the capability of regenerating the mesh during the computation to optimize computational process and improve the resolution of the solution. Most CFD programs will allow the user to temporarily terminate the computational process and adjust solution parameters or retrieve interim results for visualization.

A number of methods may be used to determine whether or not the solution is converged. For some CFD codes, convergence is generally achieved when the total of the normalized residuals of all variables which define the aerodynamic and thermodynamic state of the system are less than 10^{-3} and the enthalpy normalized residual is less than 10^{-6}. The normalized residual is computed as a function of the residuals from the first iteration.

ANALYSIS AND PRESENTATION OF RESULTS

CFD simulations can be effectively used to determine the requirements of the mechanical ventilation system. For a tunnel fire the backlayering phenomena and the dispersion of smoke can be clearly predicted and visualized. For a station fire, the complex airflow patterns and the resulting contamination or clearing of preferred evacuation routes can readily be demonstrated.

The results of a CFD analysis are quite extensive. For each cell or volume of air, there are data available on all variables being considered: pressure, air velocity (by component direction), air temperature, species concentration, etc. For transit system fire simulations, air temperature, air velocity, and smoke concentration are the main parameters to be examined.

For a model comprised of thousands of cells, the tabular presentation of results can be overwhelming and difficult to comprehend. Since exact temperature and smoke concentration at a particular point is less of a concern than the overall distribution and flow patterns, graphical presentations are usually the best means of displaying the results of the analyses (Figures 10, 11).

The presentation can be as colored contours, velocity vectors of representative magnitude (color coded if desired), or streamlines (can also be color coded) indicating flow paths. Although velocity vectors represent airflow direction and magnitude, color coding can be used to indicate the temperature instead of the velocity magnitude, thereby providing a visual display of the buoyant effects of temperature on airflow.

Judiciously selected lateral, longitudinal, and horizontal cross-sections provide an easily comprehensible picture of the interaction of fire and ventilation and the availability of a clear evacuation route.

For transient simulations, results obtained at frequent time steps during the propagation of a fire can be combined for computer animation and displayed on the workstation or copied to video tapes for presentations.

CONCLUSIONS

CFD analyses are expensive because of the cost of the software and hardware, intensive labor for setting up the models, and long simulation time.

For most CFD analyses, setting up the models and generating grids will take about three fourth or more of the total time. It is possible to significantly shorten the grid generation time by becoming proficient with the grid generator provided by the CFD vendor or a third-party grid generator. Good grid generating skills do not only result in efficiency, but also contribute to higher grid quality, which will impact on the convergence and accuracy of the calculation and results. Besides its speed and quality of grids generated, we prefer to use third-party grid generator because:

- It is easier to use than the ones included in many CFD packages

- It works on PCs

- Essentially the same model could be used for multiple codes

- A different grid generator need not to be learned for each code.

CFD analysis can also be made more cost-effective and accurate by:

- Choosing the CFD code that best serves the purpose and gives the speed and the result expected

- Using fine local grid and coarse far field grid, symmetry, etc. to limit the size of the large models. For multi-level stations and larger areas of interest, models can be developed separately, and continuity can be maintained through boundary conditions

- Extending the CFD modeling area to just where the airflow is fully developed and using the SES program to set up boundary conditions

- Using steady-state conditions to simulate the ultimate smoke distribution from a fire in a station and tunnel, whenever only the effectiveness of the ventilation system during the maximum heat release rate is of interest

- Ignoring shear effects along surfaces for station fire analyses. For strictly smoke simulations, zero net heat flux conditions may be specified across walls.

REFERENCES

1. Miclea, P., McKinney, D., Brunner, D.: " Lessons Learned in Using the Computational Fluid Dynamic Technique in Tunnel Fire Simulation". Safety in Road and Rail Tunnels, 2nd Internal Conference, Granada, Spain, 1995.

2. Abu-Zaid, S., Bendelius, A., Santoianni D., McCleery, J.: "Using Computational Fluid Dynamics to Design an Emergency Ventilation System for a Transit Subway Station", ASME International Congress and Exposition, 1995.

3. McKinney, D., Miclea, P., Brunner, D.: "Critical Velocity of Air versus Computational Fluid Dynamics Modeling". APTA Rapid Transit Conference, Sacramento, 1994.

4. Murphy, B., Miclea P., McKinney, D.: "Station Fire Analysis Using Computational Fluid Dynamics". APTA Rapid Transit Conference, Miami, 1993.

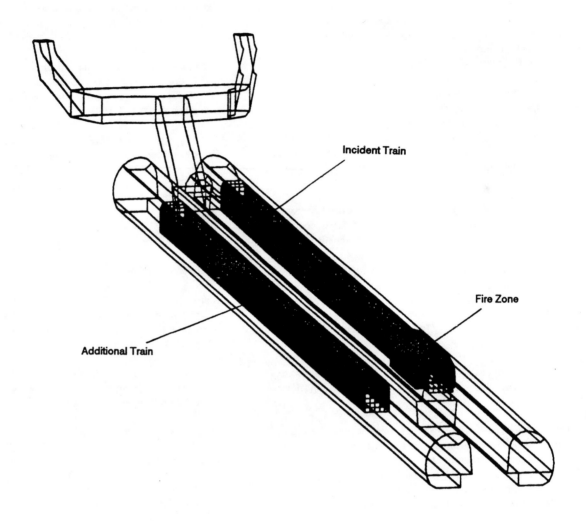

Figure 1 Sample CFD model of a subway station

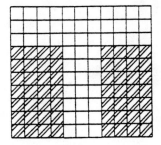

Figure 2 Single - block grid for a T- junction

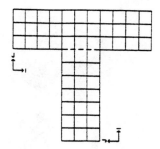

Figure 3 Two - block grid for a T- junction

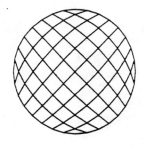

Figure 4 Single - block grid for a pipe

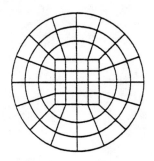

Figure 5 Multi - block grid for a pipe

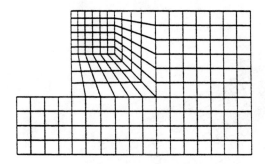

Figure 6 Local mesh refinement

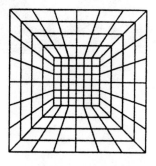

Figure 7 Local mesh refinement

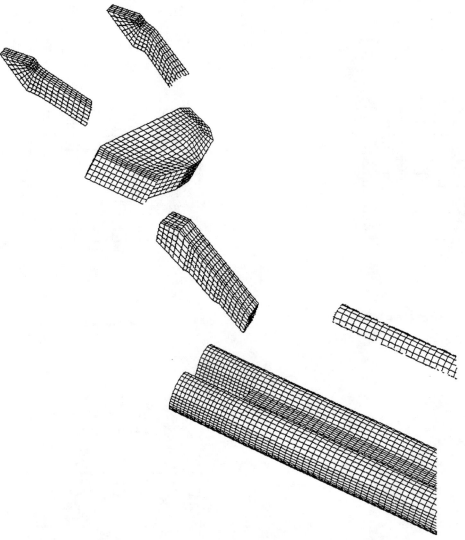

Figure 8 Sample CFD model before joining the parts

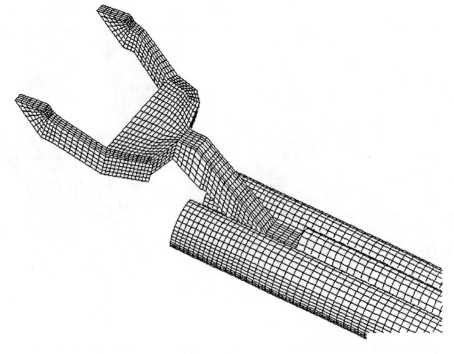

Figure 9 Sample CFD model after joining the parts

554

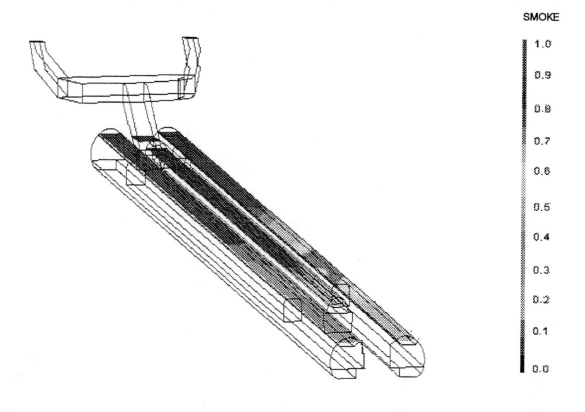

Figure 10 Smoke distribution of the sample model

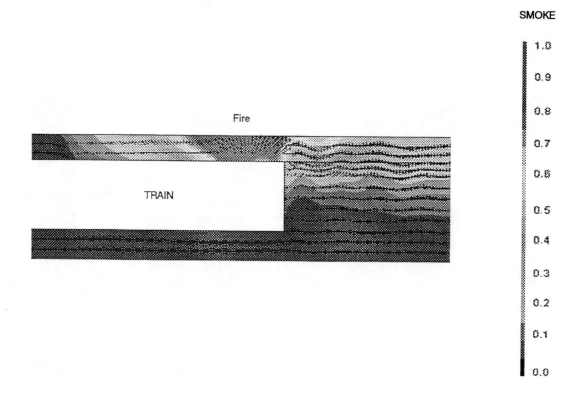

Figure 11 Smoke distribution and velocity vectors of the sample model

FED-Vol. 238, 1996 Fluids Engineering Division Conference
Volume 3
ASME 1996

NUMERICAL SIMULATION OF SUBWAY STATION FIRES AND VENTILATION

Steven R. Elias and Michael J. Raw
Advanced Scientific Computing
Waterloo, Ontario
Canada

Peter Bostwick
Toronto Transit Commission
Toronto, Ontario
Canada

ABSTRACT

Numerical methods and results are presented for the CFD simulation of subway station ventilation during a subway car fire. The fire is modeled as a volumetric source of heat, smoke and gas within the affected cars. The numerical issues related to the solution in this large structure are discussed. These topics include: multi-block hexahedral meshing, local embedded mesh refinement, and the use of a coupled Algebraic Multigrid equation solver. Computations and flow field results for three mesh densities are presented and discussed. This study shows that although the simulations can be complex and difficult to solve, the resulting information can provide valuable engineering insight into the behaviour of these flows.

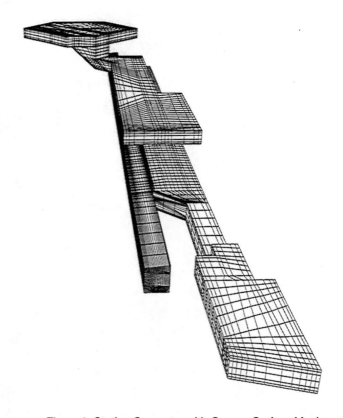

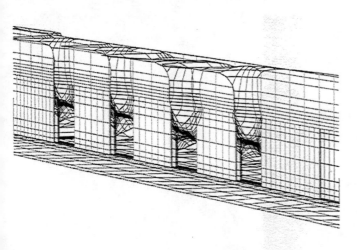

Figure 1: Smoke Plume Through Platform Edge Doors

Figure 2: Station Geometry with Coarse Surface Mesh

FED-Vol. 238, 1996 Fluids Engineering Division Conference
Volume 3
ASME 1996

CFD-BASED DESIGN OF THE VENTILATION SYSTEM
IN THE MAJOR FACILITY HALL FOR THE PHENIX DETECTOR

An Abstract

by

L. Parietti
W.S. Gregory
R. A. Martin

Los Alamos National Laboratory
Los Alamos, New Mexico 87545

The national Relativistic Heavy Ion Collider (RHIC) is a nuclear physics accelerator currently under construction by the Department of Energy at Brookhaven National Laboratory, Upton, NY. The RHIC is intended to accelerate material as heavy as gold ions to 100 GeV per nucleon in two intersecting beams, and to produce ion collisions at the locations of two sub-atomic particle detectors. These particle collisions may reveal a new phase of matter, the quark-gluon plasma, and allow investigation of plasma properties. PHENIX is one of the two complex RHIC particle detectors being designed by an international collaboration of physicists and engineers in government institutions, academia, and private industry. PHENIX will be located, operated, and maintained in a very large, existing structure called the Major Facility Hall (MFH). The dimensions of the MFH chamber occupied by PHENIX are approximately 50 ft x 60 ft x 50 ft high.

The Los Alamos National Laboratory is a collaborator on several PHENIX subsystems including the overall thermal management system for the PHENIX MFH. Because of high levels of power consumption by magnets and electronics internal to PHENIX, residual waste heat (as high as several hundred kW) is released into the MFH and must be removed to prevent overheating, hot spots, or excessive thermal gradients in the detector or its subsystems. While some of the PHENIX subsystems are internally cooled, overall thermal control to prevent thermal expansion is important because of dimensional tolerances as tight as 25 microns for some subsystems. Los Alamos engineers are responsible for conceptual design of a heating, ventilating, and air conditioning (HVAC) system for cooling and maintaining controlled humidity in the MFH. This paper summarizes progress to date in modeling the ventilation airflow and heat transfer within the MFH and around the heat-producing PHENIX for the purpose of evaluating and guiding ventilation system design.

This paper contains a brief description of the finite element CFD solver, CFX, which is being used to calculate PHENIX fluid flow and heat transfer. Computer hardware, memory requirements, CPU time, discretization (meshing), convergence studies and mesh independence studies are discussed in the paper. Regarding the flow model, descriptions are provided of the MFH geometry, boundary conditions, and heat load specifications, as well as, modeling approximations. Results include velocity field solutions and both free, and combined free and forced convection thermal solutions. The impact of computational results on the MFH ventilation system design is discussed.

Four sample figures are attached to this abstract. Figure 1 is a schematic drawing of the PHENIX detector, which shows the geometric configuration as a central octagonal cylinder (central magnet and detectors) connecting two truncated octagonal cones (muon trackers) on the north and south ends, respectively. The detector can be modeled as a flow obstacle and heat source in the MFH, which is shown schematically in Figure 2. Here, for simplicity, the PHENIX detector is represented inside the MFH as a box, bounded on the north and south ends by muon identifier plates. This figure also depicts the location of four ventilation duct openings, all of which penetrate the west wall of the MFH. An example finite element mesh used to obtain numerical solutions is presented in Figure 3. The mesh has been refined in the vicinity of the two smaller vents on the left-front face with the right vent providing inlet airflow and the left vent (with an exhaust duct extension) providing exhaust airflow. Preliminary steady-state, MFH velocity field results for the mesh of Figure 3 are shown in Figure 4 for a representative inlet flow boundary condition. A matrix of numerical experiments to determine the preferred ventilation configuration, with flow distribution and control for adequate PHENIX cooling using the existing four apertures, is presented and discussed in the full paper.

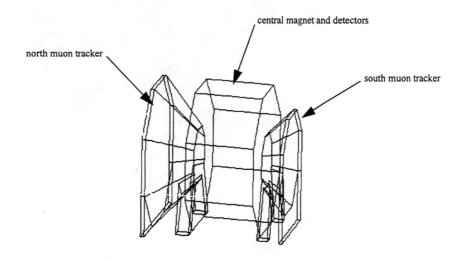

Figure 1: PHENIX detector.

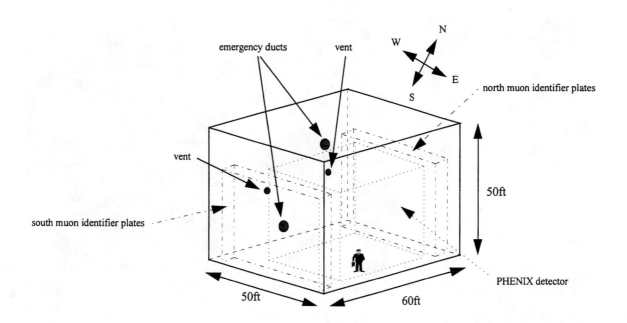

Figure 2: MFH layout.

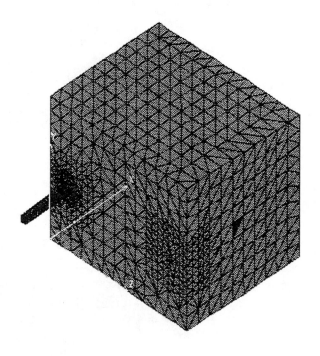

Figure 3: MFH finite element mesh.

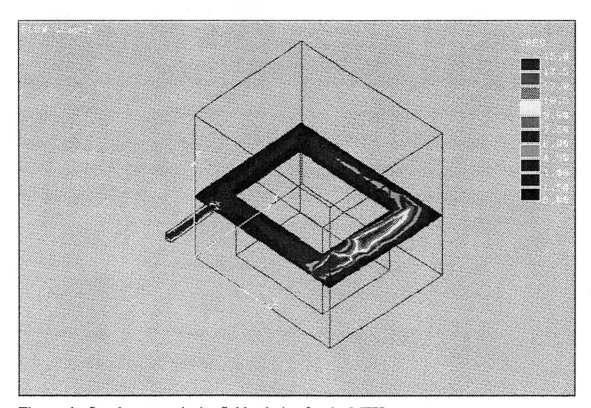

Figure 4: Steady-state velocity field solution for the MFH.

FED-Vol. 238, 1996 Fluids Engineering Division Conference
Volume 3
ASME 1996

ANALYSIS OF AIRFLOW AROUND AN OIL PRODUCTION PLATFORM

Mark Seymour, Paul Rose, and Farzad Baban
Flomerics Inc.
2 Mount Royal Ave.
Marlborough, MA 01752
Voice: (508) 485-0445
Fax: (508) 624-0559
Email: flovent@flomerics.com

ABSTRACT

The ventilation performance of an open-sided oil production platform, the Hamilton Oil Douglas Complex at Liverpool Bay, is presented. A thorough computational investigation was undertaken to evaluate the effectiveness of the air flow through these decks in removing contamination caused by gas leaks. The primary goal was to assess whether the gas leaks were sufficiently dispersed by the on-coming wind so as to prevent the occurrence of a potentially life-threatening explosion by the mixture of gases. It was also critical to identify suitable locations throughout the structure for proper placement of leak detectors.

Traditionally, in applications similar to this, a number of wind-tunnel studies used to be performed to predict the wind pressures resulting from the interaction of flows off various structures within the Complex. Pressure fields then used to be mapped for a number of approaching wind directions. However, these experimental investigations would not be able to provide detailed information regarding the ventilation rates. That is why empirical models had to be used to predict gross air change rates. By using a CFD model, we provided the capability for addressing air change rate and mapping the detailed flow field. The possibility for a potential explosion was then conveniently assessed by mapping the concentration of different gases throughout the domain.

In order to predict the detailed flow field, a knowledge of the wind distribution around the production platform was required. Thus, the modeling was carried out in two phases. The first phase was a simplified model of the Douglas Complex equivalent to a wind tunnel model, but without the approximation resulting from scaling. The results of this phase were used to provide the wind distribution data around the Complex for the detailed modeling of the two decks undertaken in the second phase. In the second phase, a detailed study of the ventilation performance within the production platform was carried out.

During the normal operation, there were three platforms in a line: production, accommodation, and wellhead platforms. These platforms covered a distance of 250 m. Of primary interest was the ventilation performance in the cellar deck and the mezzanine deck of the production platform. The production platform was situated in between the other two platforms. Hence, a global model was built to correctly assess the interaction of the flow with all three platforms. For a number of months following installation, a drilling platform was present close to the wellhead platform. Hence, one more platform had to be considered and included in the modeling.

The information obtained from the global model was used as boundary conditions for a more detailed study of local airflow within the cellar and the mezzanine decks of the production platforms. Further investigations were carried out to study the effectiveness of the airflow through these decks in removing contamination caused by gas leaks. This paper summarizes these results and provides the ventilation performance in and around the complex for a number of different wind directions and speeds.

INTRODUCTION

This paper describes a study undertaken to investigate the ventilation effectiveness of open sided decks of an oil production platform operated by Hamilton Oil Company. The analysis was carried out using the Computational Fluid Dynamics (CFD) software FLO*VENT* under contract with Brown and Root Vickers Limited, the company responsible for the design.

The project was nominally divided into two sections. Firstly an analysis of the wind flow patterns around the complex and secondly a detailed study of the ventilation performance within the production platform. The two parts have to be undertaken separately simply to make the calculation tractable from a numerical point of view.

The production platform formed one part of the Douglas complex in Liverpool Bay. During normal operation there would be three platforms (accommodation platform, production platform and wellhead platform) in a line running west to east. These covered a distance of some 250 m. Of primary interest was the ventilation performance in the cellar deck and mezzanine deck of the production platform. Since this was sandwiched between the other two platforms the effect of these platforms had to be considered. Hence a global model was built to correctly assess the wind shadow these may cast onto the production platform. In addition one further platform was to be considered. For a number of months following installation a drilling platform would be present, either to the north or south of the wellhead platform. For the purposes of this modelling exercise the drilling

platform was assumed to be to the north of the complex.

To obtain a better understanding of the ventilation performance in and around the complex a number of different wind directions and speeds were analysed. The information obtained from the global model was to be used as boundary conditions for a more detailed study of local airflows within the cellar and mezzanine decks of the production platform. Further an investigation was to be carried out to study the effectiveness of the airflow through these decks in removing contamination caused by gas leaks. It is critical that alarms are correctly placed to detect leaks, or, the gas is dispersed such that potentially explosive mixtures are not present.

OBJECTIVES

This study was commissioned to study the airflow in and around platforms of the Douglas complex in Liverpool Bay. The objectives were:

• To study the effect of the complex on the airflow around the production platform, providing boundary conditions for detailed analysis.

• To study in more detail the effectiveness of the natural ventilation scheme on the cellar and mezzanine decks of the production platform.

MODEL DESCRIPTION

The primary concern of this project was to establish the ventilation performance of the cellar and mezzanine decks on the production platform.

Traditionally wind tunnel models would have been used to predict the wind pressures which result from the interaction of the entire Douglas complex in conjunction with a number of wind directions. Such models are unable to give detailed information regarding the ventilation rates and so empirically based models could be used to predict gross air change rates. FLO*VENT* provides the capability to address not only the air change rate, but also the detailed flow and thus the question of the potential for explosive concentrations of gases leaking from equipment.

For the overall wind patterns studied in phase 1 each of the four platforms were constructed separately then combined to produce the model for the overall flow analysis. Separate, detailed, models were made of the cellar and mezzanine decks of the production platform. This section describes the models and highlights assumptions and simplifications made. Elevations were measured from a datum set as the water level of the lowest astronomical tide for the location.

The accommodation platform was a jack up platform with the legs penetrating the hull to support it on the seabed. With platforms of this type the whole structure is floated to its position and the legs lowered to the seabed to raise the hull clear of the water. The hull was essentially a triangular wedge some 75 m in length and 64 m wide

The accommodation platform had its own HVAC system. There were two intake plenums on the forward side of the accommodation block, and four exhaust vents on the stern deck. A total airflow of 78 m^3/s (92.82 kg/s) passed equally through these vents.

The drilling vessel was almost identical to the accommodation platform. The difference was that the switchroom and equipment mounted on the stern was replaced by a drilling derrick.

The smallest platform in the complex was the wellhead platform, covering an area of some 30 m by 30 m.

Of primary interest for the flow analysis was the flow within the production platform. This was the largest and probably most intricate of the platforms in the Douglas complex. In total there were four decks. The cellar and mezzanine decks were modelled in greater detail for the internal flow analysis. The overall schematic of all the platforms is shown in figure 1.

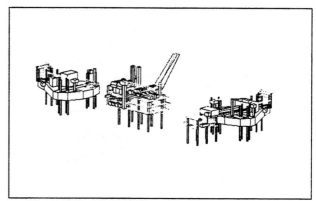

Figure 1. The FLOVENT model of the entire complex.

LOCAL DECK MODELS

Within the production platform, two decks were studied in detail: the cellar deck and mezzanine deck. An overall picture of the cellar deck viewed from the South-West is shown in Figure 2. Top deck is removed for clarity.

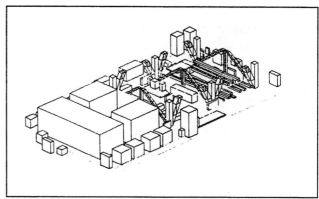

Figure 2. View of cellar deck.

Heat output from pump motors was prescribed by the client. These figures were calculated with the assumption that heat emissions from pump shaft bearings/couplings and fluid inefficiencies were negligible. Within the detail of the model it was not possible to model the individual motors, therefore the heat output was considered to be emitted from the whole of the pump.

An overall picture of the mezzanine deck viewed from the South West is shown in Figure 3.

565

The top deck is removed for clarity. A number of the vessels on the deck were identified as being possible sources of heat transfer to the air. The heat transfer was of two types. Either a surface temperature was identified or an actual heat output.

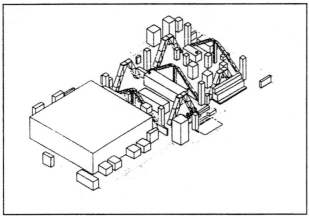

Figure 3. View of mezzanine deck

To investigate the effectiveness of dealing with gas leaks simulations were to be carried out to analyse the dispersion of concentration from a number of specified leaks. It was assumed that the gas was of the same density as the surrounding air. It was reasoned that this was applicable since it would probably be made from a number of different substances which would mix out rapidly. The location and direction of the gas leaks were specified during discussions with the client who also supplied details of the flow rate and temperature of the escaping gas

The gas release positions were placed on equipment items which were thought, by the client, to be most prone to the possibility of a leak. It was felt that a leak was most likely to occur at a flange so the position of such a leak reflected this concept. The direction of the release was based upon examination of the flow patterns predicted during Phase 1, as well as the geometry of the case.

SIMULATIONS PERFORMED

The individual platforms were arranged in an L shape the longer side running east - west

(Figure 1). Phase 1 on the project considered the effect of the complex as a whole and the wind shadows which may be cast onto the two decks of primary interest. Phase 2 investigated the detail of the flow within the cellar and mezzanine decks of the production platform. A total of six wind directions were considered (wind blowing from 45, 90, 180, 225, 270 and 315 degrees from north) with primarily two wind speeds (1.2 m/s and 5.5 m/s). A third wind speed (3.6 m/s) analysed from the same directions with the exception of 180 degree. Finally the worst case direction (270 degree) was also analysed for 0.6 m/s. The wind direction and velocity information was selected by the client based upon prevailing weather data for the region in which the complex was located.

RESULTS AND DISCUSSION

The results of the FLO*VENT* analysis have been displayed in diagrammatic form showing air speed (m/s) as either solid fills or as velocity vectors. The latter show the direction as well as the magnitude of air flow. The vectors are plotted so that the tail of the arrow is at the point where the value was calculated and show the direction of air movement. In 2-D views (plan or elevation), the length of the arrow indicates the 2-D velocity magnitude (i.e. the velocity projected onto the plane of viewing) when compared to the reference vector, while the color indicates the overall magnitude of air speed at the tail. All diagrams have been drawn such that north is at the top.

To aid analysis the colour scales were set the same on different diagrams. The velocity range was set from 0.0 m/s to 1.4 m/s. Values outside this range appears as blank areas (either in the solid fill or a region with no vectors). If lower than the scale, this area would be surrounded by colours at the bottom of the scale and above by colours at the top of the scale. Concentrations of gases are calculated and displayed as fractional values (kg gas per kg air). In the text percentages are used.

The external flow analysis was carried out to gain knowledge of the effect of the entire

Douglas complex on the flow around the open cellar and mezzanine decks of the production platform. Of particular importance were the wind shadows cast by individual platforms in the complex. This was found to be significant. Figure 4 shows a diagram of air speed around the complex due to a wind of 1.2 m/s blowing from the North East at the level of the cellar deck.

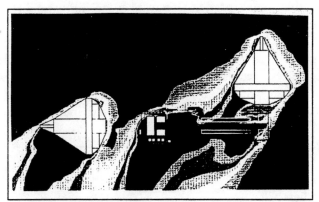

Figure 4. Wind speed around Douglas platforms --- wind direction 45 degrees.

The velocity vector field is shown in Figure 5. In this view, the shadow cast by the drilling support vessel can be seen to have some effect on the ventilation of the cellar deck of the production platform.

Figure 5. Velocity vectors around the platforms --- wind direction 45 degrees.

The effect of the accommodation platform when the wind was blowing from a westerly direction was found to be much more critical. In this instance, the production platform decks were almost completely in a wind shadow and the ventilation was significantly reduced (Figure 6).

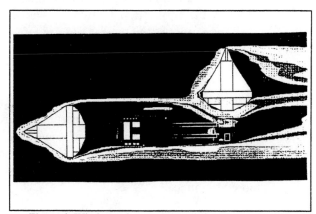

Figure 6. Wind speed around the platforms --- wind direction 270 degrees.

It was found that the lowest air change rates occurred when the wind blew from the east or the west. On the mezzanine deck with the wind blowing over the accommodation module, the air change rate was calculated to be between 8 and 11 air changes per hour. It should be noted however that this was the only case when the air change rate was in this range. The next lowest (cellar deck same wind) the ventilation rate was up to 20 air changes per hour. This direction was shown by a wind rose for the location[5] to occur approximately 20% of the time for all wind speeds. This is significant as the air change rate for the wind from the west appeared independent of wind speed, however the flow patterns can be seen to be quite different. For example at low wind speeds on the cellar deck the flow appears to be pulled in due to thermal loads. Indeed it was felt that the cellar deck had greater air change rates due to the higher thermal loads having greater influence when compared to the mezzanine deck. With higher wind speeds the air tended to flow straight past the module. In some areas it was pushed into the module.

In general the air change rate was the same on the cellar and mezzanine decks. The exceptions to this were the case with wind blowing from 270 degree (as described in previous paragraph) and wind from a easterly direction. In this case the lower air change rate occurred on the cellar deck. The reason was felt to be a blastwall across the wellhead platform at the same elevation as the cellar deck on the production platform. The mezzanine deck was above this and so received relatively unhindered air flow.

The average air change rate was calculated such that it was weighted depending upon the frequency of the wind from a particular direction. As expected, the average air change rate did not vary linearly with wind speed. As the wind speed dropped, the decrease in air change rate became more pronounced.

In addition to analysing the global air change rate through each module, the air change rate in individual computational cells was calculated. A Volume of the inner zone with an air change rate between particular values was then predicted. This information was then used to identify the amount of the module which was not well ventilated. As expected, the 270 degree wind direction produced the worst air changes.

However, it should be stressed that less than 1 m^3 had ventilation rates less than 12 air changes. Even when the global air change rate was close to the value of 12 it was found that very little of the decks were stagnant. This was possibly due to the area reduction due to equipment blocking the path of air movement and hence increasing the local velocities.

In each of the decks, three leaks were specified and simultaneously simulated. For the mixture of gases specified, there would be the danger of explosion between the limits of 2.2% gas in air (lower explosion level - LEL) and 9.5% (upper explosion level - UEL). The percentage of the inner zone of the module which was occupied by a potentially explosive mixture was calculated. It was found that the amount of gas residual in the module was proportional to the amount of gas released. Consequently the greatest volume of explosive gas (and the greatest potential risk of explosion) was found with leak 1 on the cellar deck. when more than one eighth (12.5%) of the module

was occupied by an explosive mixture, the damage was considered to be severe in the case of an explosion.

In the case of the cellar leak 1 (Figure 7), it was discovered that this criteria was exceeded even at what would be considered good ventilation rates with a wind speed of 1.2 m/s. This value was also exceeded at high wind speeds for wind directions 90 and 270 degrees. In general it was found that the volume of explosive mixture decreased as wind speed increased; the latter causing increased ventilation rates. The exception was the westerly wind. As previously discussed the ventilation rate in this case seemed to be independent of speed.

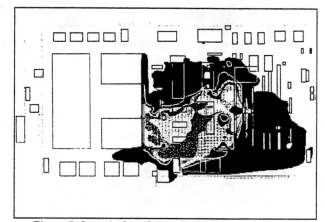

Figure 7. Spread of gas from cellar leak 1 --- 1.35 m above deck, wind direction 45 degrees.

CONCLUDING REMARKS

This report describes the work initiated to provide an analysis of the ventilation performance of two naturally ventilated decks of a production platform. This formed a part of the Douglas Complex to be run by Hamilton Oil Company in Liverpool Bay.

It was found that the surrounding platforms had a significant influence upon the ventilation performance of the production platform. In particular the wind shadows cast when the wind blew from either the east or west.

In general it was found that the ventilation rate was dependent on the wind speed. This was not a linear relationship. The air change rate dropped more sharply at the lower wind speeds. However in the worst case (wind from West) the ventilation rate remained constant no matter what the wind speed. This was not only due to the large accommodation module, but also the large rooms at the westerly end of the production platform, preventing wind from entering the module. This may be a critical finding since the wind blows from this direction some 20% of the year and on the mezzanine deck the ventilation rate was between 8 and 11 air changes per hour.

Taking into account the other wind directions, a weighted average air change rate was calculated. This took into account the time that wind of a particular velocity blew from each direction. In this case the minimum air change rate was a little under 30 air changes per hour (1.2 m/s - wind speed is equal to or exceeds this value 95% of the year).

The amount of gas which remains in the module was found to be dependent on the size of the leak. For a large leak (e.g. cellar deck leak 1) the module filled with an explosive concentration to quite an extent at low wind speeds. Higher wind speeds were more effective at clearing the gas since the ventilation rate was greater.

REFERENCES

1. Flomerics, "How to Use FLOVENT - Lecture Course", Document no. FLOVENT / LC / 0594/ 1/1, 1994.

2. Patankar, S V, "Numerical Heat Transfer and Fluid Flow", Hemisphere Publishing Corporation.

3. Perry and Chilton, "Chemical Engineers Handbook", McGraw Hill, 1973.

4. I E Idelchik, "Handbook of Hydraulic Resistance", Hemisphere Publishing Corp. 1986.

5. Hamilton Oil Company, "Scope of Work for a Natural Ventilation Study by 3D Computational Fluids Dynamics Analysis", Document no. D-500-HR-003, 1994.

FLUID MACHINERY

Introduction

Ali Ogut
Rochester Institute of Technology
Rochester, New York

Upendra Singh Rohatgi
Brookhaven National Laboratory

The Fluid Machinery Forum of the 1996 ASME Fluids Engineering Division Summer Meeting (FED) is sponsored by the FED Fluid Applications and Systems Technical Committee. It provides an opportunity for presentation of current work in the area of fluid machinery. The informal nature of the forum allows the presentation of the results of ongoing work which are not yet complete for ASME formal presentation. The forum also provides an avenue of discussion and an exchange of information.

The Fluid Machinery Forum is scheduled to take place at every FED Summer Meeting. It is the seventh in the series of forums and reflects the current interest of the Fluid Applications and Systems Technical Committee.

The forum will include short papers dealing with different areas of fluid-handling machinery such as, but not limited to, design methods, theoretical analysis, experiments, performance characteristics, off-design performance, scaling, NPSH, etc. The types of machinery which could be included are various types of compressors, pumps, turbines, transmissions, etc., and also specific sections such as inlets, guide vanes, scrolls, gates, diffusers, nozzles, valves, seals, etc.

The current forum has 16 papers, including a keynote paper. The papers have been contributed from industry, academia, and govenment, and reflect some of the ongoing research in the fluid machinery area in many countries, including Egypt, France, Japan, Korea, Malaysia, Norway, Portugal, South Africa, United Kingdom, and U.S.A.

Thanks are extended to all authors for their contribution; the ASME publications and technical staff, Dr. Edwin Rood, chair of the Fluids Engineering Division; Dr. Hugh Coleman, the Program Chair of the 1996 Fluids Engineering Division Conference; and the Fluid Applications and Systems Technical Committee.

FED-Vol. 238, 1996 Fluids Engineering Division Conference
Volume 3
ASME 1996

FLUID DYNAMICS AND PERFORMANCE
OF AUTOMOTIVE TORQUE CONVERTERS: AN ASSESSMENT

T. W. von Backström[1] and B. Lakshminarayana[2]
Center for Gas Turbine and Power
Pennsylvania State University
University Park, PA 16802

ABSTRACT

Experimental investigations by various groups over the past decade have uncovered the main features of the flow in hydraulic torque converters. Measurement techniques include laser velocimetry, hot wires, fast response and conventional five hole probes and wall static pressure measurement. In both the pump and turbine most of the flow is concentrated in the pressure surface shell corner while the flow in the suction surface core corner is highly turbulent and may be separated and reversed. The position of the stator in a passage curved in the meridional plane leads to secondary flow and low velocities at the core near the pump inlet. Velocity gradients coupled with flow turning and rotor rotation lead to strong secondary flows. By using data from a combination of measurement techniques torque converter torque, power and efficiency could be calculated, and the effect of element efficiency on overall efficiency could be demonstrated.

NOTATION

$(C_{p_o})_{Abs}$ $2((P_o)_{Abs} - p_{hub}) / \rho V_{ref}^2$

C_{pb} blade static pressure coefficient $2(p - p_{ref}) / \rho U_{tip}^2$

C chord length

C_{P_s} $= 2(p_s - p_{hub}) / \rho V_{ref}^2$

FHP five hole probe

L length

LV laser velocimetry

PSU The Pennsylvania State University

P power

P_o stagnation pressure normalized by $\rho V_{ref}^2 / 2$

P_f^* non-dimensional fluid power $= P_f / [(0.5\rho\, V_{ref}^2)(V_{ref} R_P^2)]$

P_s^* non-dimensional shaft power $= P_s / [(0.5\rho\, V_{ref}^2)(V_{ref} R_P^2)]$

PS, SS pressure and suction surface

p, p_s static pressure normalized by $0.5\rho\, V_{ref}^2$

p_{hub} reference pressure on hub

Q volume flow normalized by $V_{ref} R_P^2$

R radius

r radial coordinate

SR speed ratio (turbine/pump)

T torque

TR torque ratio (T_T/T_p)

U_{pt} pump tip blade speed

UV University of Virginia

V absolute velocity normalized by V_{ref}

V_r, V_θ, V_x absolute radial, tangential and axial velocity

V_{ref} $U_{pt}(1-SR)^{0.5}$

$\underline{V}_{sec}$ secondary velocity

W, W_θ relative total and tangential velocity

x coordinate normal to chosen radial line and to axis

y coordinate parallel to chosen radial line

z axial coordinate

Δ difference operator

η efficiency

θ tangential coordinate

ρ fluid density

Ω angular velocity normalized by $(0.5 V_{ref}/R_P)$

ν Kinematic viscosity

---

[1]Adjunct Senior Scientist, Aerospace Engineering, presently Head of the Department of Mechanical Engineering, University of Stellenbosch, South Africa.

[2]Evan Pugh Professor of Aerospace Engineering and Director, Center for Gas Turbine and Power.

Superscripts

‾	passaged averaged
=	Area averaged

Subscripts

Abs	absolute
f	fluid
h	hydraulic
P	pump,
Pt	pump tip radius
ref	reference
s	stator
T	turbine
r,θ,z	components in r,θ,z directions
TC	torque converter
0	stagnation
x,y,z	components in x, y, z, directions

INTRODUCTION

Recent interest in reducing automobile fuel consumption and air pollution has stimulated continued research into the fluid dynamics of hydraulic torque converters (Fig. 1). Its elements are a pump driven by an input shaft, a turbine driving an output shaft and a stator blade disc that may freewheel forward, but is prevented from rotating backwards by a one way clutch. An automotive type torque converter typically produces an output torque that changes smoothly from to two to three times the input torque at stall (zero turbine speed), to a torque equal to the input torque at the coupling point. The coupling point is reached when the turbine torque equals the pump torque and the stator starts to freewheel. Industrial type torque converters may have maximum torque ratios of up to ten.

Torque converter flow fields are very complex. They are three-dimensional, viscous and unsteady due to the close coupling between rotor and stator elements. Additional complexities arise due to the differential in rotor speed between the pump and the turbine. The turbine and the pump passages are narrow, long and dominated by viscous, curvature and rotation effects, separation and secondary flow. Potential and viscous interactions at the rotor-rotor and rotor-stator interfaces generate unsteadiness. The nature and magnitude of the unsteadiness vary with the spacing between two blade rows, the number of blades in both the rotors and the stator, the thickness of blade trailing edges, location of areas of flow separation, blade wake profiles, secondary flows and other geometrical and operating parameters.

The main objective of this paper is to examine the flow in automotive type torque converters, to try to recognize and describe the main characteristics of the flow field. While this paper is a review in the sense of integrating information and insights from various sources, the emphasis is on assembling a clear picture of the typical flow fields in hydrodynamic torque converters and its impact on performance and design. Much of the discussion will focus on the mean flow field, as its control will probably remain the main objective of the design and improvement process.

BACKGROUND

Most if the insights in the present paper were based on the experimental investigations of groups at the Ruhr-Universitat in Bochum, Germany, and at two universities in the USA: The Pennsylvania State University (PSU) and the University of Virginia (UV). The group at the Ruhr-Universitat investigated the flow and performance of an industrial type torque converter (Adrian, 1985 and Browarzik, 1994). It consisted of an unshrouded radial outflow (centrifugal) pump of conventional design. The torque converter had a stall torque ratio of 5.7 and a peak efficiency of 87 % at a speed ratio SR = 0.55.

The discussion of the flow in automotive torque converters is primarily based on pump and turbine measurements at the UV by Brun et al. (1994a,b), Brun and Flack (1994, 1995a,b), Gruver, et al., (1994); blade static measurements at General Motors by By and Lakshminarayana (1991, 1995a,b,c); stator, pump, and turbine exit measurements at PSU by Marathe and Lakshminarayana (1995), and Marathe et al. (1994, 1995a, b). In many instances these data are reprocessed to examine critical flow features. Unpublished data from these groups are also reviewed. Furthermore, the flow field only at the peak efficiency conditions (SR = 0.8) is examined in detail to assess the nature of flow field, even though a brief assessment at stall conditions is also included for completeness.

These groups carried out their research on models of the same automotive type torque converter with 230 mm outer diameter as shown in Fig. 1. The blade numbers were typically 27, 29, and 19 in the pump, the turbine, and the stator respectively. The gaps between the elements were small and there was meridional flow curvature in all the elements including the nominally axial flow stators, due to the torus curvature. The stall torque ratio was 2.1. The facilities were operated typically at 1100 rpm. PSU used Shell Diala oil with $v = 5 \times 10^{-6}$ at 60°C and UV used Shell Flex 212 oil with $v = 2.2 \times 10^{-6}$ m²/s. The main flow measurement techniques employed were laser two spot anemometry (UV), hot film anemometry (RU) and fast response five hole probe (PSU) and wall static pressure measurements (PSU). The FHP measurements were acquired at station 1 (stator exit), station 4 (pump exit), station 8 (turbine exit or stator inlet) shown in Fig. 1. The LV data was acquired at station 2 (pump inlet), station 3 (pump mid-chord), station 4 (pump exit), station 5 (turbine 1/4 chord), station 6 (turbine mid-chord), and station 7 (turbine exit). These data are interpreted together to provide an integrated assessment of the flow field. The main flow visualization methods were the spark tracer method and the wall tracer method (Numazawa, 1983; Lee et al., 1994). A fundamental difference between the flow in torque converters and all other types of turbomachinery, except multi-spool gas turbines, is the presence of at least two rotors affecting the time-dependent flow. Further complications are the proximity of the elements to each other and the recirculating nature of the flow. Added to this is the random flow fluctuations due to flow separation and turbulence. Browarzik (1994), Brun and Flack (1994, 1995a, b) and Marathe et al. (1995a,b) have explained in detail how to acquire and analyze time dependent data in torque converters. The conclusion is that the non-random flow at a particular point in a particular element of a torque converter depends on the instantaneous relative positions of all the other elements.

The computational effort is vigorously pursued by several groups (e.g., By et al. 1995c, Schulz et al., 1994, Kost et al., 1994, Marathe et al., 1994, and Tsujita et al., 1996). The computational effort is not reviewed in this paper due to limitations on the length of the paper and due to the fact that the torque converter flow field has not yet been computed satisfactorily. In addition to reviewing the experimental efforts at RU, PSU, and UV, an attempt is made to list additional useful references (not quoted in the text) at the end of the paper.

PUMP FLOW FIELD

Flow at the stator exit and at the pump inlet

The assessment of the pump inlet field is based on the UV data (station 2, Fig. 1) presented by Gruver et al. (1994) and the stator exit flow field (station 1, Fig.1) is based on PSU data (Marathe et al., 1994). There are some very interesting and undesirable flow features as the flow progresses from the stator exit (data taken at 0.36 axial chord downstream of the stator) and the pump inlet (very near the leading edge). The convex curvature of the core tends to decelerate the flow. The absolute stagnation pressure contours at the exit of the stator acquired with a five-hole probe, shown in Fig. 2, reveal the presence of a low pressure region near the shell, high pressure region near the core, and a distinct wake. But the passage averaged (mass) values of $(C_p)_{Abs}$ shows nearly uniform distribution from the core to the shell (Fig. 3). The axial velocity contours show lower axial velocities near the core region (Fig. 4). The passage averaged axial velocities shown in Fig. 5 indicate that the axial velocity near the core region is about 70% of that near the shell.

The axial velocity at the pump inlet (Fig. 6) shows some dramatic change occurring between the stator trailing edge and the pump inlet. The schematic shown in Fig. 1 is not the actual flow path. The flow path changes from axial to radial, with considerable torus curvature effects as the flow progresses from station 1 to 2. The velocity in the core region has decreased drastically (from a value of 0.335 to -0.013), resulting in reversed flow across the entire pitch within 20% of the spanwise distance from the core. This is caused by convex curvature of the flow path near the core. The flow deceleration occurs due to the convex curvature near the core (opposite effect on the concave side, where there is flow acceleration), combined with the adverse pressure gradient, resulting in flow separation. It is clear from comparing the passage-averaged distribution of axial velocity (Figs. 5 & 7) that the axial velocity in the mid-span region has accelerated, while those near the core have decelerated substantially, resulting in back flow. The relative tangential and relative total velocity is nearly zero; and the absolute tangential and total velocity is highest in the core region at the pump inlet. This effect is caused by the fact that the pump "drags" the separated or back flow along and behaves like a "drag pump" near the core region. The incidence to pump blade row in the

20% span from the core is very high. This should result in flow separation near the leading edge of the pump. This is evident from the plot of secondary velocity vectors (not shown), where region of flow separation at the suction surface near the inlet is visible as a disturbed flow region.

At the pump inlet (SR=0.800), a strong tangential velocity component is directed at the pressure surface of the pump, with low energy flow along the suction surface. The incipient right-handed circulation pattern shows near all surfaces, especially near the pressure surface where the flow with the increased angular momentum is flung outwards towards the core. The backflow at the pump inlet near the core is also evident in the pitch-averaged axial velocity profile (Fig. 7). It is caused by a combination of the effects of the sudden increase in flow area where the stator core shroud ends, and the relatively large mean inlet incidence angle of 15.3°. Having had angular momentum added to it in the rotor, the back flowing fluid has a zero relative and a high absolute tangential velocity. The back flowing fluid has been accelerated to a tangential velocity equal to that of the pump rotor at that radius.

At SR=0.065 the contour plot of the axial velocity (not shown) indicates only small local regions of backflow concentrated in the suction and pressure corners in the spanwise range of about 10 % from the core. The flow is more disturbed near the pressure surface at SR=0.065 and less disturbed near the suction surface than at SR=0.800. No backflow was evident in the pitch-averaged flow near the core, but the through flow velocity decreases continuously from mid section to core. The average relative flow angle is -3.1°. Since it implies that the flow enters the pump with virtually no relative whirl velocity, the backflow inducing diffusing action in the pump inducer is absent. As the angular momentum of this flow is reduced by impingement on the blade suction side, the radial pressure gradient forces it inwards. This mechanism contributes to setting up the circulatory secondary flow pattern.

Flow at the mid-chord plane of pump

The pump mid-chord plane is a plane perpendicular to the radial direction at a radial position between the centers of curvature of the core and the shell where the radius is 86.04 mm (station 3, Fig.1). This plane would correspond approximately with the outlet plane of the pumps in the torque converters of Adrian (1985) and Browarzik. (1994). At a speed ratio of 0.065, the through flow velocity is fairly uniform, but at 0.800 there is a velocity gradient from the suction to the pressure surface, with a strong jet on the shell and pressure side occupying nearly half the flow passage (Fig. 8).

At both SR=0.80 and at SR=0.065 there is a clockwise circulation centered near the suction surface core corner, as shown in Fig. 9. The secondary flow components are as large as the through-flow components. At a speed ratio of 0.8, the average through-flow secondary flow velocities and vorticity decreases with decreasing pump speed, but at a slower rate than the pump speed.

The axial velocity contours, show in Fig. 8, when compared with axial velocities at inlet (Fig. 6), clearly reveals major changes between these two stations. The strong secondary flow that exists in this region (Fig. 9) has transported the core region (Shell to 80% of span) towards the pressure surface and the separation zone (up to 20% of span near the core, Fig. 6) has been transported toward the suction side spread across the entire core to shell region. This is not caused by adverse pressure gradient on the suction surface as evidenced by the blade pressure data presented by By & Lakshminarayana (1995a), but by the secondary flow induced due to shear layers, rotation and curvature effects (Lakshminarayana, 1996, p. 321-330). The secondary flow pattern shown in Fig. 8 has been captured reasonably well by a Navier-Stokes solver (By et al., 1995c).

Numazawa et al (1983) found that the streamlines generally show a shell-to-core flow on the pump pressure surface at mid-chord, especially for SR = 0.8, indicating a circulation with the pump rotation, while at the exit there is a core-to-shell flow at a speed ratio of 0.8 and a converged flow towards the center of the surface at SR = 0.0. Lee et al. (1994) found that just before the mid-chord position the shell flow starts flowing up the pressure surface wall, more or less aligning itself with the exit meridional direction. This flow then migrates crosswise and downstream along the core surface towards the suction surface, but does not attach to it. The effect is the by now familiar clockwise circulation at mid-chord shown in Fig. 9. In general the data of Lee et al. (1994) tend to confirm those of Numazawa et al (1983), Gruver et al. (1994).

Flow at the exit of pump

The axial velocity and the secondary flow pattern at the exit of the pump (Station 4) are shown in Figs. 10, and 11 respectively. The secondary flow is now counter clockwise, with dominant "jet" flow pattern near the suction surface, moving from shell to core. It should by remarked that the magnitude and the direction of the Coriolis force ($2\Omega \times \underline{W}$) changes as the flow progresses, acting nearly in the blade-to-blade direction near the leading edge and core-to-shell at the pump exit. This indicates that the rotation induced secondary flow dominates the flow field in the torque converters. The counter-clockwise movement transports high energy mean flow from the pressure surface near the mid-chord location to the shell suction surface (Fig. 8). This is evident by comparing Figs. 8 & 10, and the corresponding secondary velocity vector in Figs. 9 & 11. The separated region now has moved to the corner formed by the core and suction surface. The flow at the exit of the pump resembles the "jet-wake" pattern observed in centrifugal compressors (Eckardt, 1980). It is interesting to note that the pitchwise center of the back flow (Fig. 10) is also the center of the vortex.

The passage-averaged mean stagnation pressure (Fig. 3) and the axial velocity (Fig. 5)clearly shows the effect of secondary flow on the spanwise mixing of the flow. The stagnation pressure and the axial velocity are both lower near the core region at the pump exit. In ordinary industrial pumps non-uniform exit profiles and flow separation are to be avoided because these two phenomena generally inhibit pressure recovery in the diffuser or volute of the pump. These effects do not seem to be as serious in torque converters that are primarily momentum transfer devices and have no diffusers.

The pitch averaged velocity profiles for SR=0.065 (not shown) are very similar to those at SR=0.800. The axial velocity at SR=0.065 varies more with pitch than with the span except near the core. No backflow region is evident at the core, but the axial velocity is low near the core. The secondary flow pattern (not shown) looks similar to that at SR=0.800. The core-to-shell velocity gradient is smaller than at the mid-chord plane.

The relative exit flow angle and the slip factor at SR=0.065 are found to be -7.0 ° and 0.897, for the LV data. Wiesner (1967) gave the following equation for the slip factor of centrifugal impellers:

$$\sigma = 1 - (\cos \beta_{out})^{0..5} / Z_n^{0.7}$$

where β_{out} is the blade outlet angle and Z_n the number of blades. With $\beta_{out} = 0.0$ ° and $Z_n = 27$ the calculated slip factor is 0.900 which agrees well with the data. The Wiesner slip factor relationship was empirically derived for radial turbomachines but Strachan et al (1992) have found that it predicted the pump torque and the overall performance of Jandasek's (1963) torque converter well for various pump exit blade angles.

Blade static pressure distributions for the pump

By et al. (1995a) measured the blade static pressures near the mid-span, core and shell regions at speed ratios of 0.0, 0.6, 0.8. The data at SR=0.8 is shown in Fig. 12. His general observations are as follows. For the 0.0 speed ratio condition the static pressure distribution near the leading edge at the shell and mid-span is reversed, indicating negative incidence. The pump static pressure field changes drastically from shell to core and the centrifugal and Coriolis force have dominant effect as analyzed in Lakshminarayana (1996, p 277). A reversal of pressure distributions at the core over the last 25% indicates poor flow conditions at the suction surface core corner near the exit. The pressure distributions are better (presumably this means that the pressure surface pressures are everywhere higher than the suction pressure and both vary fairly smoothly) for a speed ratio of 0.6, and slightly worse at 0.8 than at 0.6. At mid section a three-dimensional potential code can reasonably predict the static pressure distribution. A Navier Stokes code can be used to effectively predict the pump flow field (By et al. 1995c).

Discussion of flow fields in pumps

As discussed before, the main features of the flow are the concentration of the flow near the pressure surface-shell corner and the secondary velocity. Since the main flow in automotive type mixed-flow pumps has a velocity gradient with the higher velocity near the shell, the blade curvature turns the near-core flow more than the near-shell flow thereby contributing to the secondary flow circulation in the same direction as the pump rotation looking downstream. And since in the automotive type mixed flow pump, at a speed ratio of 0.800, the main flow has a gradient with a slightly higher velocity near the suction than near the pressure side, the curvature in the meridional plane deflects the flow on the pressure surface towards the core more than the flow near the suction side, also contributing to a secondary flow circulation in the same direction as the pump rotation, looking downstream.

The effects mentioned so far act whether the pump rotates or not, but only when there is a velocity gradient at the inlet. This is one of the reasons why By (1993) found such large differences between the computed flow fields with uniform and non-uniform inlet velocity profiles. As the pump inlet flow has a profile with a higher velocity near the shell than near the core, the passage curvature in the meridional plane will keep the high momentum flow near the shell. As this flow moves outward beyond the quarter chord point it is forced in the direction of the pressure surface by the Coriolis force, while the low momentum fluid is turned more in the direction of rotation. Once the main flow has accumulated near the pressure surface, it will be kept there by the Coriolis force. These effects explain why the high velocity flow accumulates near the pressure surface-shell corner, and why there is typically a secondary flow circulation at the mid-chord plane in the same direction as the pump rotation. The accumulation of boundary layer flow near the insides of the flow passage also explains the existence of the wake region near the core and why the flow there is highly turbulent.

A schematic of the flow features, based on the present knowledge of the torque converter flow field is shown in Fig. 13. The assessment of the data in an automotive mixed flow pump reveals the following:

1.   The inlet velocity profile typically shows a small region of low velocity at the casing and separated flow at the core, depending on how much the pump shell to core span is larger than that of the stator. Strong secondary flows move this separation region to suction surface (shell-to-core) near mid-chord region and back to core region at the exit. A wake region exits near the core and the suction surface at the exit of pump. This indicates considerable spanwise and blade-to-blade mixing as the flow proceeds from the inlet to the exit.

2.   The flow is smooth along the initial part of the pressure surface. At the mid-chord section, most of the flow is already concentrated near the pressure surface shell corner, with evidence of a wake in the suction surface core corner.

3.   In a pump that rotates clockwise when looking downstream at the pump inlet, there is a strong right handed flow circulation at mid-chord, and in the opposite direction at the exit.

4.   The inlet axial velocity profile is affected by whether the stator is positioned where there is curvature in the meridional plane or not.

5.   At the pump exit, most of the flow is concentrated near the shell and pressure surface with little flow near the core, in both the radial and the mixed flow type of pump.

6.   The agreement between the CFD predictions and measurements were good, even with the present k-ε turbulence models.

TURBINE FLOW FIELD

The LV measurement at inlet (station 4, Fig. 1), quarter chord (station 5), mid-chord location (station 6), (Brun & Flack, 1995a) and the five-hole probe measurements at the exit (station 8) of the turbine (Marathe & Lakshminarayana, 1995) are interpreted in this section to assess the flow features in the turbine.

Flow at the inlet of an automotive torque converter turbine

The axial velocity profile shown at pump exit, (Fig. 10) at SR=0.8 (Brun et al., 1994a), undergoes substantial changes as it approaches the turbine inlet. The flow becomes more uniform in the blade-to-blade direction, with highest axial velocity occurring near the shell, and flow separation in the core region (about 10% of blade height) measured across the entire passage. The pump blade wake can be clearly seen at this location. It is the secondary velocities that undergo major change. The magnitudes of secondary velocities are substantially reduced at this location.

The main difference between the pump exit and the turbine inlet axial velocity profiles at SR=0.800 is that at the turbine inlet, the velocities decrease more sharply near the core and shell compared to that at the pump exit. At SR=0.800 the through flow component is only about a quarter of the absolute tangential component. A fractional adjustment in tangential velocity profile will then result in a noticeable adjustment in through flow profile. The turbine inlet blade angle changes from 55 ° at the core through 52 ° at mid span to 49° at the shell, but the flow inlet relative angle plot has a more negative slope, such that closer to the shell the flow impinges with increasing angle on what is normally the suction side of the turbine blades. In these regions the turbine blades do work on the fluid, thereby increasing its energy. But the geometry of the flow and the blade passage is such that the flow relative to the turbine is turned farther away from the axial direction, and the relative total velocity increases. The through flow leaving the pump and entering the turbine near the shell is then accelerated and the flow is retarded near the core. This results in the flow lifting off the core, causing a velocity deficit at the core at the quarter and mid-chord sections.

At SR = 0.065, the outer half of the velocity profiles is almost uniform, but the inner half decreases towards the core. Relative flow angles are almost uniform, but the decrease in the pump exit through flow velocity results in an increased relative yaw angle into the turbine near the core. Consequently the fluid does relatively more work near the core. The fluid energy is then reduced more near the core than elsewhere in the vicinity of the turbine inlet. Near the core, the turbine blades have to turn the flow through a greater angle towards the axial direction. Since this is a diffusing action, the already relatively energy deficient total relative flow near the core experiences a further reduction in velocity. The inlet pitch angle shows that the flow does not lift off the core at the inlet. However, since the inlet incidence angle is large (27°) and the turbine blades are thin plates (about 1 mm), the flow separates at the leading edge of the suction surface. Both the centrifugal and the meridional pressure gradient force the low momentum flow inwards towards the axis, causing separation at the core and preventing flow re-attachment to the core before mid-chord.

Flow at the quarter- and mid- chord planes of a turbine

At SR=0.800 no flow separation is evident at the quarter chord plane, but there is a low velocity region at the suction surface-core corner. Minimum and maximum non-dimensional through flow velocities here are 0.08 and 0.59, and the circumferential component is 0.34. At mid-chord (Fig.14), the velocity field is relatively uniform with no separation or significant deficit in the through flow velocity. Maximum velocity is 0.56 near the core and 0.12 near the pressure surface. Complex secondary flow pattern, which undergoes dramatic changes is observed as the flow progresses from turbine inlet to mid-chord (Fig 15). The secondary flow pattern is from shell to core near suction surface quarter-chord as the flow approaches mid-chord. But, no vortex pattern is observed at these locations.

At the quarter-chord plane the flow is separated for SR = 0.065 over about 30 % of the area. At the mid-chord plane the picture is similar except that the reversed flow now covers only about 15 % of the flow area. A complex secondary flow pattern exists, consisting of two triangular flow regions. In the one, bounded by the core and suction surfaces, the secondary flow is directed to the suction surface-core corner feeding the reversed flow.

Lee et al. (1994) did flow visualization in automotive type torque converter turbines by means of a wall tracer method as a described earlier. At a speed ratio of 0.8 in the circular section torus torque converter, there is flow separation on the suction surface near the turbine inlet. Where the flow reattaches, it more or less follows the blade passage in the meridional plane up to the quarter chord plane where it starts to deviate towards the core, eventually resulting in lift-off from the suction side and reversed flow at the three quarter point. On the pressure surface, there is an immediate flow deviation towards the core, which is strongest at about the quarter chord plane and then decreases again towards the exit.

Flow at the exit of a turbine

The stagnation pressure coefficient at the exit, plotted in Fig. 16, shows largest stagnation pressure drop (work done) near the shell and mid-span regions, and lowest work extracted and losses near the core region. The wake decays rapidly due to larger flow path as well as downstream potential effect due to stator blades. The flowfield is uniform for about 80% of span from the shell. The high absolute stagnation pressures and low relative stagnation pressures observed near the core is attributed to possible flow separation near the core inside the turbine passage caused by convex curvature of the torus. This is confirmed by the axial velocity distribution shown in Fig. 17, derived from a high response five-hole probe. The low velocity region near the core region observed from quarter-chord to trailing edge region can be attributed to the curvature effects on the convex side. The flow decelerates (even in the absence of flow turning by the blades) in this region and accelerates near the shell region. Hence, the observed velocity profile increasing from the core to the shell is a attributed to curvature effects. The blade pressure distribution due to By & Lakshminarayana (1995b), shown in Fig. 12, does not indicate presence of adverse pressure gradient in this region.

The low velocity regions observed near the core at quarter chord can be attributed to both adverse pressure gradient (Fig. 12) and curvature effect, while similar features near mid-chord and exit are attributed mainly to the curvature effect.

The passage and mass averaged distribution of absolute stagnation pressure coefficient, shown in Fig 3, indicate that the stagnation pressure drop is highest near the shell and lowest near the core. This is consistent with axial velocity distribution. The radial distribution of the passage averaged axial velocity distribution (Fig.5) shows a substantial reduction in axial velocity from shell to core, except at the last measuring point near the core.

The secondary flow pattern, derived from high frequency response five-hole probe, plotted in Fig. 18, shows that substantial secondary flow occurs near the core region. A vortex pattern, with counter-clockwise circulation, exists in the core region. The outward (towards the shell) secondary flow in the core region near the suction surface tends to move the low velocity and low pressure regions slightly outward as shown in Figs. 16 and 17.

General Discussion of Turbine Flow Field

By & Lakshminarayana (1995b) measured the wall static pressure distributions on the turbine blade along the mid-span and on the shell and core surfaces near the passage corners. They came to the following conclusions: Simple assumptions like one-dimensional flow and simple radial equilibrium were not valid in the turbine. The pressure distribution was better at SR =0.600 than at 0.800. A three-dimensional potential code could not accurately predict the static pressure distribution even at mid span under all speed ratio conditions, since the flow was not irrotational.

The blade pressure distribution at the mid-span, core, and shell regions, shown in Fig. 12, indicates that the flow in the initial part of the turbine (leading edge to about 10-15 percent chord) develops under adverse pressure gradient. The blade static pressure actually increases, thus behaving like a pump. The pressure drop is continuous and well behaved beyond this location. Thus, it is clear that there is a mismatch between the pump exit flow and the turbine inlet flow. This is perhaps an area for improvement.

In an automotive type torque converter with a mixed flow pump and turbine, the turbine operates under a much larger range of conditions than the pump, because under normal working conditions its speed changes much more than that of the pump. At low turbine speeds, the pressure gradient due to flow curvature in the meridional plane obviously has a much larger effect than that due to flow turning, while in the pump, as at high speed ratios in the turbine, both effects play their parts.

At low speed ratios the mismatch between the direction of the flow in the turbine relative frame and the turbine inlet blade angle causes separation at the suction surface as reported by Brun and Flack (1995a), Lee et al. (1994) and By & Lakshminarayana (1995b). Because of its momentum the main flow tends to accumulate in the pressure surface-shell corner, but the blade leaning angle is such that it tends to force the flow inwards, towards the torque converter axis, resulting in some shift in the main flow from the shell to the core, near the pressure surface. Because, at mid-chord the flow passage is turning in two planes, with roughly the same radius of curvature, both curvatures affect the flow distribution. The turning in the meridional plane forces the main flow towards the shell, and the blade boundary layers towards the core, while the turning perpendicular to the meridional plane forces the main flow towards the pressure surface, and the core and shell boundary layers towards the suction surface. These two effects result in the main flow migrating towards the pressure surface-shell corner, a process that is assisted by the forward lean of the blades at the mid-chord plane. The low momentum boundary layers are forced to the suction surface-core corner by the pressure gradients as reported by Brun and Flack (1995a). In the design of the torque converter under discussion there is little curvature in the turbine blades beyond mid-chord. Consequently only the meridional curvature influences the flow beyond mid-chord at low speed ratios. The main flow is then found near the shell at the turbine exit, with the low momentum boundary layer fluid near the core. The disappearance of the blade-to-blade pressure gradient beyond turbine exit causes a flow adjustment, resulting in a flow from pressure to suction surface at the exit.

Brun and Flack (1995a) found that the flow in the turbine at SR = 0.800 was not fundamentally different from that at SR = 0.065. Flow conditions at SR = 0.8 are generally better, however, because firstly the flow does not separate from the suction surface at the inlet, and secondly, there is a centrifugal pressure gradient component acting in the opposite direction to the meridional gradient near the exit, thereby reducing the non-uniformity of the exit profile and the concentration of low momentum fluid near the core.

A schematic of all the flow features in a turbine discussed in this section is shown in Fig. 19.

STATOR FLOW FIELD

The only function of a stator in a torque converter is to impart additional angular momentum to the flow, beyond that imparted by the pump. The high torque ratio at the stall condition, when the turbine is stationary, requires a large flow deflection of about 120°, while the unity torque ratio requirement at a high speed ratio demands zero flow deflection. In the torque converter under consideration the stator blade inlet design angle is 7°, the outlet angle is 63° and the incidence angle varies between about plus and minus 50°. The dilemma of the designer is to design a blade row capable of a very high flow deflection, but with a low loss coefficient at a high negative incidence angle (Marathe et al., 1994).

To further complicate matters, it has been found that at off design conditions the stator flow field is highly three-dimensional (Bahr et al. 1990, By and Lakshminarayana, 1991, and Marathe et al. 1994, 1995a). The main flow approaching the stator from the turbine has a higher through flow velocity near the shell than that near the casing, and the circumferential component near the core increases faster with speed ratio than that near the shell.

Consequently Bahr et al. (1990) found that the effect of the varying incidence angle with operating point was severe and that the one-dimensional theory was inaccurate: velocity profiles and torque distribution over the blade length were not uniform. The flow averaged turbulence intensity was high near the walls (approximately 20 % compared to 10 % near the mid-span).

Marathe et al. (1994) measured the stator inlet flow field (turbine exit flow) with a five-hole probe coupled to five fast response transducers in an automotive type torque converter using oil as working fluid. The pressure signals were divided into five parts: the temporal average, the rotor-rotor interaction aperiodic component, the blade periodic component, the blade aperiodic component and the unresolved component. They found that pressure and velocity fluctuations were moderate but flow angle fluctuations were high. The turbine blade wakes were thin, and near the shell the wake decay was rapid. The secondary flow pattern in the turbine frame of reference showed overturning in the separation region near the core, underturning in the rest of the passage and a radial inflow in the entire passage (Fig. 18).

By & Lakshminarayana (1991) investigated the static pressure distribution over the axial flow stator blades of an automotive torque converter, measuring at the midspan and on the shell and core surfaces near the passage corners. They found that a panel method could predict the pressure distributions well only at mid-span. The blade pressure distribution (Fig.12) indicates very large positive incidence (+57°) at SR=0 and large negative incidence (-47°) at SR=0.8. Most of the static pressure drop at SR=0.8 occurs from the leading edge to 50% chord, while the static pressure drop at SR=0 occurs aft of the mid-chord.

Marathe et al. (1995b) also measured the time dependent stator blade surface pressures at five points in the stator mid-chord plane. The location of transducers were at the leading edge and near the leading and trailing edges on the suction and pressure surfaces. The unsteady blade static pressures were found to be high near the leading edge and insignificant near the trailing edge. Unlike conventional turbomachinery, the source of unsteadiness is found to be upstream wake as well as the upstream static pressure variation (potential effect).

The stator exit flow is presented in an earlier section (Figs. 2 - 5). At SR=0.800 the pitch-averaged axial velocity profile at stator exit indicates large gradients from core-to-shell. The axial velocity is lower near the core. The deviation angle of 1.2 ° derived from FHP measurements at SR=0.800 indicates that there is almost no flow deflection in the stator: the stator inflow angle is 54.6 ° and the outflow angle is 61.8 °. The flow deflection at SR=0.065 is found to be large. A deviation angle of 5.8° and turning angle of 95° is reported.

Discussion of stator flow fields

One of the major features of the flow in the stator under consideration is large areas of separation found at SR=0.800 when the flow deflection is small, and the absence of separation at SR=0.065 when the flow deflection is large. A schematic of the flow field in the stator is shown in Fig. 20.

At SR=0.800 there is separation on the pressure surface extending over the full span at mid-chord. It is caused by the combination of a large negative incidence angle and the concave shape of the stator blade profile. The separation over the full chord near the core is caused by the high incidence angle due to turbine rotation and flow overturning at the turbine exit near the core. The secondary flow at the exit consists of two weak circulation cells near the two blade walls. They induce core-to-shell flow near the walls, indicating a core pressure higher than the shell pressure, which is borne out by the static pressure distribution, although the gradient is very small. The low momentum boundary layer flow transported from core to shell along the suction surface eventually causes flow separation in the suction-shell corner near the exit.

At SR=0.065 the high velocity exit flow is near the pressure shell corner, with a low velocity core near the suction shell corner, more or less coincident with a left handed vortex. The static pressure decreases from shell to core with a gradient that can be explained by a simple streamline curvature model that takes into consideration both the effect of the circumferential and the meridional velocity.

One of the major differences between the industrial and automotive types of torque converter lies in the stator exit meridional through flow velocity profile. In the industrial type the higher velocity is near the core (Adrian, 1985), while in the automotive type it is near the shell as shown in Fig. 2 (Bahr et al. 1990, Marathe et al. 1994). This trend must be due to the presence of the stator blades near the torque converter axis of the automotive type. It is caused by the passage vortices associated with the curvature of the flow in the meridional plane between the turbine exit and the pump inlet. Consequently the pumps in the automobile type torque converters are exposed to less favorable meridional inlet velocity profiles than ordinary pumps and certain industrial torque converter pumps; the critical part of the flow passage, the core region where boundary layer flow accumulates, now starts with a low through flow velocity at inlet.

A schematic showing of all features discussed in this and earlier sections is shown in Fig. 20. This is based on an assessment of LV data (UV) and the five-hole probe data (PSU).

TORQUE CONVERTER FLOW FIELD AND PERFORMANCE -- AN INTEGRATED ASSESSMENT

The global features of the torque converter flow can be ascertained by examining Fig. 3, 5, 12, 13, 19 and 20. The stator inlet and exit stagnation pressure distribution is uniform from core to shell, with maximum losses occurring in the outer and inner third of the blade height. The stagnation pressure distribution at the exit of both turbine and pump is non-uniform, with lower values near the core. Low axial velocity near the core, and in some instances separated flow, in both of these components contribute to low pressure rise in the pump and low pressure drop in the turbine. This is also confirmed by passage average axial velocity distribution shown in Fig. 5.

The blade static pressure distribution (Fig.12) shows that the stator provides a smooth entry to the pump (except in the core region as indicated earlier) at both SR=0.8 and 0.065. The pump exit and the turbine inlet have not been matched well, with the initial part of turbine behaving like a pump at SR=0.8. The stator inlet and turbine exit matches well only at SR=0.6, with large positive and negative angles at SR=0.8 and 0.

The area-mass averaged stagnation and static pressure distribution derived from five-hole probe data (Marathe, 1996) is given in Table 1. The stagnation pressure loss between the turbine exit and stator exit is lowest at SR=0.6, and very high at both SR=0.8 and 0.065.

Angular Momentum and Torque Converter Efficiency

Definition of the various efficiency used in this paper is given in Appendix A.

The torque converter efficiency is the turbine power divided by the pump power. The efficiency is then essentially equal to the speed ratio multiplied by the torque ratio, placing an upper limit on efficiency at any particular speed ratio. The "lost" energy is dissipated in the working fluid, increasing its temperature. Zero efficiency at zero speed ratio in torque converters is unavoidable, as the output power is proportional to the turbine speed. At this condition, when there is no conversion of fluid energy into shaft energy, they become essentially mechanical heaters of the paddle wheel type.

Using area-mass averaged values of angular momentum at the inlet and exit of each of the components, a torque ratio (T_T / T_P) of 1.079 at SR=0.8 was calculated yielding the torque converter efficiency of $\eta_{TC} = 0.863$. This is a fairly realistic internal efficiency for this torque converter, since from Bahr et al. 1990, η_{TC}=0.820 at SR=0.800 measured directly by a torque meter. The data (Fig. 12) based on blade static pressure (By, 1993) yields η_{TC}=0.828 and TR=1.034.

If at SR=0.065 the LV pump exit and turbine inlet data are used in conjunction with the FHP stator exit and turbine exit data results in TR=2.52, with η_{TC}=0.163. The corresponding data from blade static measurements are TR=2.09 and η_{TC}=0.136 which includes drag torque on the pump. The direct measurement yields η_{TC}=0.13, and TR=2.0. Thus, it is clear that the flow measurements should provide detailed information on flow field as well as losses in each component.

Stagnation Pressure, Energy Balance And Efficiency

The non-dimensional flow (area and mass) averaged stagnation pressures are given in Table 1. Stagnation pressures are required to calculate the hydraulic efficiencies of the rotating elements and the stator efficiency as defined in Appendix A. The efficiencies calculated are shown in Table 1.

Table 1: Element power and efficiency and overall efficiency (based on inlet & exit stagnation pressure of each component).

SPEED RATIO	Component	Exit Average Stagnation Pressure $\overline{(Po)}_{Abs}$	Rotor Power	Fluid Power	Element efficiency	Overall efficiency
0.8	Pump Turbine Stator	7.562 0.995 0.8036	1.579 1.362	1.430 1.362	η_{hP} = 0.906 η_{hT} = 1.000 η_{S} = 0.953	η_{TC}=0.863
0.065	Pump Turbine Stator	1.3522 0.8345 0.5929	0.2081 0.0332	0.1627 0.0848	η_{hP} = 0.782 η_{hT} = 0.398 η_{S} = 0.522	η_{TC}= 0.163

At SR=0.800 all the element efficiencies are high, as they must be to give a torque converter efficiency of 86.3 %. The rotor power input is 1.579 of which 1.430 (90.6 %) is converted into useful fluid energy and the rest dissipated. Of the 1.430 added to the fluid, the turbine extracts 1.362 at an efficiency of 100 %, resulting in 1.362 transferred to the rotor. The value of 100 % for efficiency is obviously optimistic, but it does indicate a very high turbine rotor efficiency at this condition. The percentage of the fluid power dissipated in the stator (and elsewhere, but not in the pump or turbine) is 100-95.3=4.7%.. Clearly, if a high peak efficiency is desired, every element should be very efficient, and extreme care should be taken to eliminate every possible loss source in the flow path.

At SR=0.065 the turbine and stator efficiencies are much lower, because they operate under adverse incidence angles. The pump efficiency is still reasonably high in spite of negative incidence angles. One way to minimize these losses is to design components with wider operating ranges.

By combining LV and FHP data fairly realistic values for element and torque converter efficiency were calculated. As more data at different speed ratios become available, the trends of component efficiencies with speed ratio could be determined. This information should be useful in deciding where to concentrate the effort when working to improve torque converters.

ACKNOWLEDGMENTS

This work was sponsored by the power train division of General Motors Corporation. The authors wish to express their appreciation to D. Maddock & R. By for technical discussions, R. Flack and K. Brun of the University of Virginia for making their data available, and B. Marathe and Y. Dong (PSU) for their assistance in the preparation of the paper. The first author's stay at PSU was funded by the University of Stellenbosch, the Foundation for Research Development and the Howden Group of South Africa.

REFERENCES (QUOTED)

Adrian, F. W., 1985, "Experimental and Analytical investigation of Flows in Hydrodynamic Torque Converters," Ph.D. thesis (in German), The Ruhr University, Bochum, Germany.

Bahr, H. M. et al., 1990, " Laser Velocimeter Measurements in the Stator of a Torque Converter," SAE paper 901769

Browarzik, V., 1994, "Experimental Investigation of Rotor/Rotor Interaction in a Hydrodynamic Torque Converter Using Hot-Film Anemometry," ASME paper 94-GT-246.

Brun, K., R. D. Flack, and J. K. Gruver, 1994a, "Laser Velocimetry Measurements in the Pump of an Automotive Torque Converter," Part II Unsteady Measurement. ASME paper 94-GT-48.

Brun, K., R. D. Flack, and S. B. Ainley, 1994b, "Secondary Flow Measurement in a Mixed Flow Pump Using Laser Velocimetry," Seventh international symposium on applications of laser techniques to fluid mechanics, Lisbon, Portugal.

Brun, K. and R.D. Flack, 1995a, "Laser Velocimeter Measurements in the Turbine of an Automotive Torque Converter," Part I - Average Measurements, ASME paper 95-GT-292.

Brun, K. and R.D. Flack, 1995b, "Laser Velocimeter Measurements in the Turbine of an Automotive Torque Converter," Part II - Unsteady Measurements, ASME paper 95-GT-293.

By, R., 1993, "An Investigation of Three-Dimensional Flow Fields in the Automobile Torque Converter," Ph.D. thesis, Dept. of Aerospace Engineering, Pennsylvania State University.

By, R. and B. Lakshminarayana, 1991"Static Pressure Measurement in a Torque Converter Stator," Journal of Passenger Cars, Vol. 100, p 1756-1764.

By, R. and B. Lakshminarayana, 1995a, "Measurement and Analysis of Static Pressure Field in a Torque Converter Pump," ASME J. of Fluids Engineering, Vol. 117, p 109-115

By, R. and B. Lakshminarayana, 1995b, "Measurement and Analysis of Static Pressure Field in a Torque Converter Turbine," ASME J. of Fluids Engineering, Vol. 117, No. 2, p 473-478.

By, R., R. Kunz, and B. Lakshminarayana, 1995c, "Navier-Stokes Analysis of the Pump Flow Field of an Automotive Torque Converter," ASME J. of Fluids Engineering, Vol 117, p 11.

Eckardt, D., 1980, "Flow Field Analysis of Radial and Back Swept Centrifugal Impellers," in Performance Prediction of Compressors & Pumps, ASME

Fister, W., and F.-W. Adrian, 1983, "Experimental Researches of Flow in Hydrodynamic Torque Converters," presented at the 7th Conference on Fluid Machinery, Hungary, Vol. 1.

Gruver, J. K., R. D. Flack, and K. Brun, 1994, "Laser Velocimeter Measurements in the Pump of a Torque Converter," ASME paper 94-GT-47.

Jandasek, V. J., "The Design of a Single Stage Three-element Torque Converter. Passenger Car Automatic Transmissions," SAE Transmission workshop meeting, Second edition, Advanced Engineering, Vol 5, p 201.

Kost, A., N. K. Mitra, and M. Fiebig, 1994, "Computation of Unsteady 3D Flow and Torque Transmission in Hydrodynamic Couplings," ASME paper 94-GT-70.

Lakshminarayana, B., 1996, Fluid Dynamics & Heat Transfer of Turbomachinery, John Wiley & Sons, Inc., New York, NY.

Lee, J. -S. et al., 1994, "Surface Flows Inside Automotive Torque Converters," Proc. 5th Int. Symposium on Transport Phenomena and Dynamics of Rotating Machinery, Vol. B., p 887 (ISRO MAC), Maui, Hawaii.

Marathe B. V., 1996, "Experimental Investigation of Steady and Unsteady Flow Field in Automotive Torque Converters," Ph.D. Thesis, Dept. of Aerospace Engineering, PSU, (in preparation).

Marathe, B.V. and B. Lakshminarayana, 1995, "Experimental Investigation of Steady and Unsteady Flow Field Downstream of an Automotive Torque Converter Turbine and Stator," International J. of Rotating Machinery, Vol. 2, p 67-84.

Marathe, B.V., B. Lakshminarayana, and Y. Dong, 1994, "Experimental and Numerical Investigation of Stator Exit Flow Field of an Automotive Torque Converter," ASME paper 94-GT-32.

Marathe, B. V., B. Lakshminarayana, and D. G. Maddock, 1995a, Investigation of Steady and Unsteady Flow Field Downstream of an Automotive Torque Converter Turbine and Inside the Stator," Part I - Flow at the exit of the turbine, ASME paper 95-GT-231.

Marathe, B.V., B. Lakshminarayana, and D. G. Maddock, 1995b, "Investigation of Steady and Unsteady Flow Field Downstream of an Automotive Torque Converter Turbine and Inside the Stator," Part II- Unsteady pressure on the stator blade surface, ASME paper 95-GT-232.

Numazawa, A. et al., 1983, "An Experimental Analysis of Fluid Flow in a Torque Converter," SAE paper, 830571.

Schulz, H., R. Greim, and W. Volgmann, 1994, "Calculation of Three-dimensional Viscous Flow in Hydrodynamic Torque Converters," ASME paper 94-GT-208.

Strachan, P.J., F. P. Reynaud, and T. W. von Backstrom, 1992, "The Hydrodynamic Modeling of Torque Converters," South African Inst. Mech.. E R&D Journal, Vol 8, No. 1.

Tsujita, H., S. Mizuki, and E. Ejiri, 1996, "Analysis of Flow Within Pump Impeller of Torque Converter," ASME paper 96-GT-XXX, to be presented at ASME IGTI meeting in Birmingham, England, June 1996.

Wiesner, F.J., 1967, "A Review of Slip Factors for Centrifugal Impellers," ASME J. of Engineering for Power.

Additional References (Not Quoted)

Abe, K. and T. Kondoh, 1991, "Three-Dimensional Simulation of the Flow in a Torque Converter," SAE paper 910800.

Bai, L., A. Kost , M. Fiebig, and N. K. Mitra, 1994, "Numerical Investigation of Unsteady Incompressible 3D Turbulent Flow and Torque Transmission in Fluid Couplings, ASME paper 94-GT-69.

By, R. R., J. E. Mahoney, 1988, "Technology Needs for the Automotive Torque Converter,"Part I: Internal Flow, Blade Design and Performance, SAE paper 880482.

Ejiri, E. 1990, "A New Approach to Developing a More Efficient Torque Converter Stator," SAE paper 901765.

Folchert U., A. Menne, and H. Waller, 1994, "Experimental Identification of the Dynamic Characteristic of Hydrodynamic Torque Converters and Couplings," ASME paper 94-GT-360.

Fujitani, K. R. R. Himeno, and M. Takagi, 1988, "Computational Study on Flow Through a Torque Converter," SAE paper 881746.

Hoshino, A. et al. 1990, "A Consideration on Performance improvement of Hydraulic Torque Converters," Industrial Applications of Fluid Mechanics, ASME FED Vol. 100, p 65-70

Ishihara, T., 1955, "A Study of Hydraulic Torque Converters," 1995, Ph. D. Thesis, University of Tokyo, AHO Report of the Institute of Industrial Science, Vol. 5, No. 7.

Jandasek, V. J., 1962, "The Design of a Single-Stage Three-Element Torque Converter," SAE Design Practices, AE-5.

Ma, W., B. J. Luo, and S. Wu, 1991, "The Research on Quasi-Three-Dimensional Flow Design of Hydrodynamic Torque Converter Blades," SAE paper 912701.

Maddock, D. G., 1991, "Application and Design of Automotive Torque Converters," GM Powertrain Division, Class notes for an Automatic Transmission Course.

Mercure, R. A., 1979, "Review of the Automotive torque Converter," SAE paper 790046.

Minato, K. et al., 1989, "A Performance Prediction of Hydrohynamic Torque Converter," SAE paper 900555.

Nagornaya, N. K., 1961, "Impact Losses and Coefficients in Hydraulic Torque Converter Blade Systems," Russian Engineering Journal, Vol. 6, pp 21-24.

Sakamoto, H., K. Suyama, and T. Saka, 1992, "Study on Torque Converter Circuit Profile," SAE paper, 920765.

Wada, A. et al., 1995, "A PTV Analysis of Torque Converter Internal Flow," ASME paper, ASME FED Vol. 218.

Ziebart, E., 1953, "Investigations on a Foettinger Hydraulic Torque Converter, "Z-VDI, Vol. 95, No, 30, pp. 1027-1036.

APPENDIX A: EFFICIENCY RELATIONSHIPS

For the sake of simplicity we assume here that the volume flow, Q is constant in the torus. We also disregard mechanical losses and drag torques. To eliminate the need to keep track of algebraic signs, the symbol Δ always denotes a positive change, for example $Q\Delta p_{0T}$ is the fluid energy decrease (not increase, which would be negative)in the turbine.

The hydraulic efficiencies of the pump and turbine are:
$\eta_{hP} = (Q \, \Delta p_{0P}) / (T_P \Omega_P)$, $\eta_{hT} = (T_T \Omega_T) / (Q \, \Delta p_{0T})$

The efficiency of the torque converter is:
$\eta_{TC} = P_{T\,shaft} / P_{P\,shaft}$, $= [\eta_{hT} \, Q \Delta p_{0T}] / [(Q \Delta p_{0P}) / \eta_{hP}] = \eta_{hP} \, \eta_{hT}$
$(\Delta p_{0T} / \Delta p_{0P})$

From the equation above it is clear that to define a stator efficiency such that:
$\eta_{TC} = \eta_{hP} \, \eta_{hT} \, \eta_{S}$
the definition of the stator efficiency must be:
$\eta_{S} = \Delta p_{0T} / \Delta p_{0P} = 1 - (\Delta p_S / \Delta p_{0P})$

Where $\Delta p_S / \Delta p_{0P}$ represents the fraction of the pump input energy dissipated in the stator, and η_S is a measure of how well the stator minimizes dissipation of pump input energy. In the simple model it was assumed that any additional losses to those occurring in the pump and turbine occur in the stator, because of the close proximity of the pump exit and turbine inlet. In a real torque converter η_S really accounts for all internal losses except those in the pump and turbine. The stator can be expected, however to be the major contributor to the additional losses.

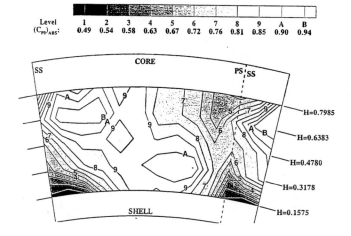

Fig 2. Contours of absolute stagnation pressure coefficient $(C_{p_0})_{Abs}$ at stator exit at SR=0.8 (PSU data from Marathe et al., 1994)

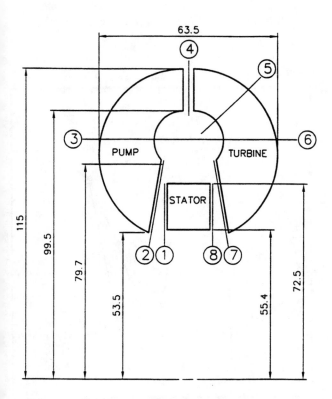

Fig 1. Schematic of automotive torque converter showing measurement stations (dimensions are in mm)

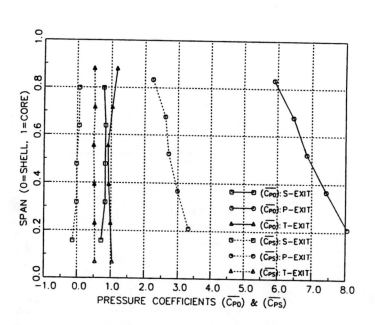

Fig 3. Spanwise distribution of passage-mass averaged pressure coefficients $(\bar{C}_{p_0})_{Abs}$ and $(\bar{C}_{P_S})$ (PSU data from Marathe, 1996)

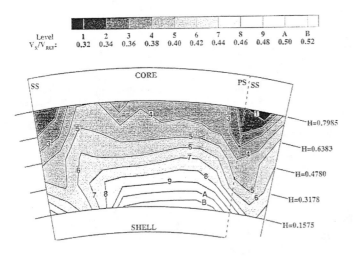

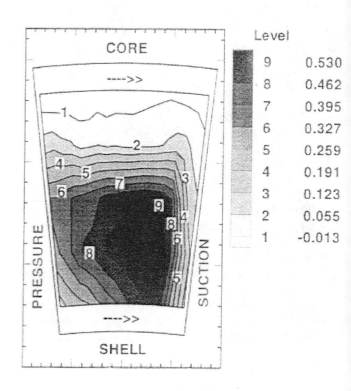

Fig 4. Normalized axial velocity (V_x/V_{ref}) contours at stator exit at SR=0.8 (PSU data from Marathe, et al., 1994)

Fig 6. Pump inlet axial velocity (V_x / V_{ref}) contours from LV at SR=0.800 (UV Data from Gruver et al., 1994)

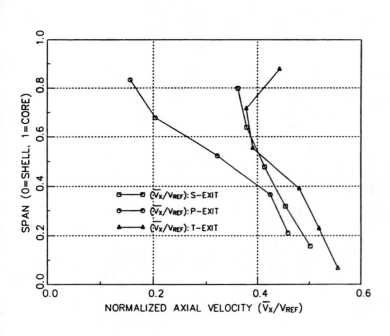

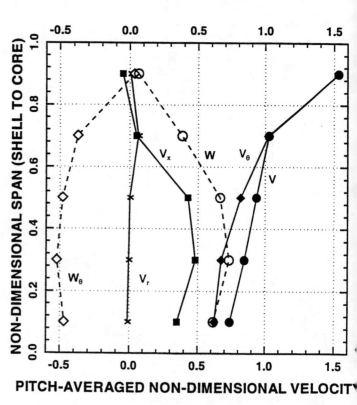

Fig 5. Spanwise distribution of passage-mass averaged normalized axial velocity (V_x/V_{ref}) (PSU data from Marathe, 1996)

Fig 7. Pump inlet velocity components from LV at SR=0.800 (UV Data from Gruver et al., 1994)

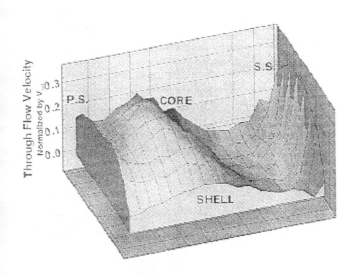

Fig 8.   Axial velocity at pump mid-chord from LV at SR=0.800
         (UV Data from Gruver et al., 1994)

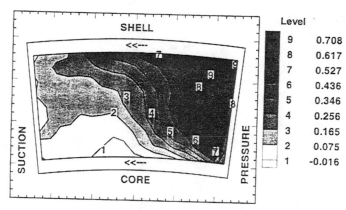

Fig 10.   Pump exit axial velocity contours from LV at SR=0.800
          (UV Data from Gruver et al., 1994)

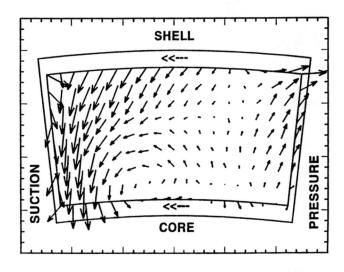

Fig 11.   Pump exit secondary velocity (V_{sec}) vector plot from LV
          at SR=0.800 (UV Data from Gruver et al., 1994)

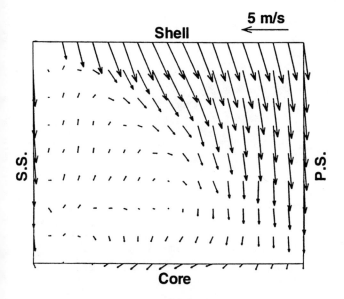

Fig 9.   Secondary velocity vector ($\underline{V}_{sec}$) at pump mid-chord
          from LV data at SR=0.800 (UV Data from Gruver
          et al., 1994)

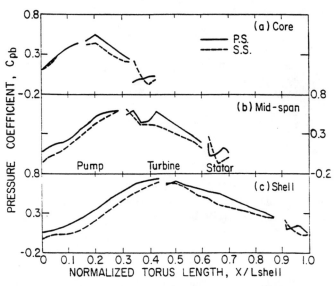

Fig 12.   Blade static pressure distribution at SR=0.800 (adapted
          from By, 1993)

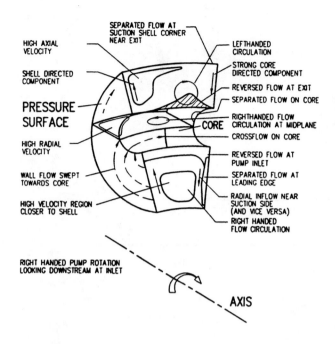

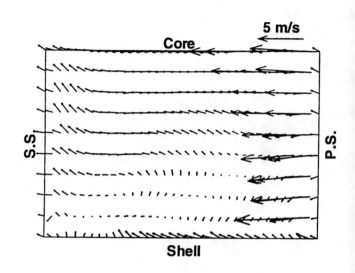

Fig 15. Secondary velocity vectors (V_{sec}) at SR=0.800 at turbine mid-chord from LV data (UV data from Brun & Flack, 1995a)

Fig 13. Main flow features in a torque converter pump at SR=0.800

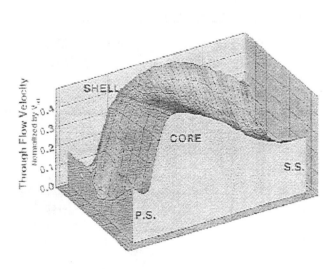

Fig 14. Axial velocity contours at turbine mid-chord from LV at SR=0.800 (UV data from Brun & Flack, 1995a)

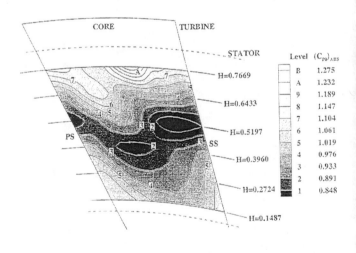

Fig 16. Coefficient of absolute stagnation pressure $(C_{p_o})_{Abs}$ at turbine exit at SR=0.800 (PSU data from Marathe et al., 1995a)

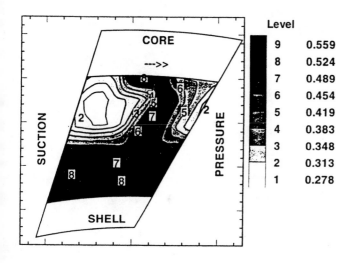

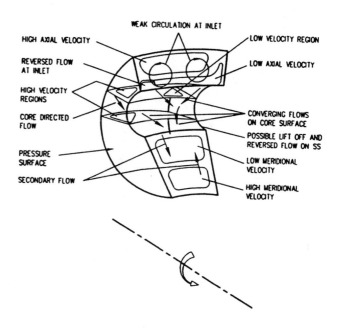

Fig 17. Turbine exit axial velocity contours at SR = 0.800
(PSU data from Marathe & Lakshminarayana, 1995a)

Fig 19. Main flow features in a torque converter turbine at
SR=0.800

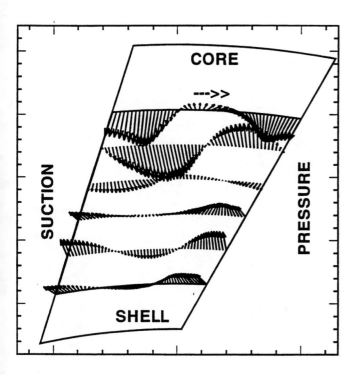

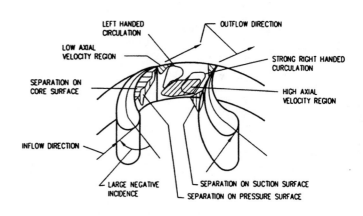

Fig 18. Turbine exit secondary velocity ($\underline{V}_{sec}$) vector plot at
SR=0.800 (PSU data from Marathe &
Lakshminarayana, 1995a)

Fig 20. Main flow features in a torque converter stator at
SR=0.800

FED-Vol. 238, 1996 Fluids Engineering Division Conference
Volume 3
ASME 1996

PERFORMANCE OF DIFFERENT DIFFUSERS FOR CENTRIFUGAL COMPRESSORS

Abraham Engeda
Turbomachinery Lab, Mechanical Engineering Dept.,
Michigan State University, E. Lansing, MI

ABSTRACT

Centrifugal compressors have the widest compressor application area, covering aircraft engines, small stationary gas turbines, process and refinery industries, the refrigeration industry, and turbochargers. The objective of this paper is to improve the understanding of the performance of diffuser systems of centrifugal compressors. The centrifugal compressor user is often interested in a class of diffusers that:

• require less radius ratio than current diffusers, primarily to minimize casing size,
• are readily adaptable to different flow capacities by means of simple reprofiling, and
• capable of offering as much pressure recovery potential as any other style.

On the basis of experimental results the performance of vaneless, conventional vaned and low solidity vaned diffuser systems are assessed and compared.

NOMENCLATURE

a	m/s	sonic velocity
b	-	diffuser height
C	m/s	velocity
CVD		conventional vaned diffuser
C_p		press. recovery coefficient
d	m	diameter
h	KJ	enthalpy
L	m	length
LSVD		Low Solidity Vaned Diffuser
LWR	-	length-to-width-ratio
ṁ	kg/s	mass flow
M	-	Mach number
p	N/m^2	pressure
r	m	radius
R		gas constant
T	k	temperature
t	m	blade thickness
W	-	width
z	-	blade or vane number
α		flow angle in the cyl. coord.
β		blade angle
φ		angle
γ		ratio of specific heats
η		efficiency
θ		divergence angle
σ		solidity
ρ	kg/m^3	density
ψ	radians	blade pitch

Subscripts

2	impeller outlet
3	vaned diffuser inlet
4	vaned diffuser outlet
h	at hub
r	radial direction
s	at shroud
u	tangential direction

INTRODUCTION

The diffuser system of a centrifugal compressor comes basically in two general categories either as a vaneless or vaned diffuser, each followed by a collector, a volute or the next stage. Vaned diffusers can further be subdivided into two categories depending on channel geometry as straight or curved channel or depending on solidity, as conventional or low solidity. Figure 1 schematically shows two types of conventional vaned diffusers (cambered and vane island) and a low solidity vaned diffuser.

Generally vaneless diffusers are known to possess wide operating range with relatively low efficiency while current conventional vaned diffusers have narrow range and high efficiency. Cambered and vane island diffusers, hereafter called Conventional Vaned Diffusers (CVD) represent generally the current conventional vaned diffuser family.

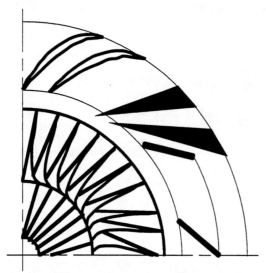

Figure 1. Schematic view of various diffusers

The Low Solidity Vaned Diffuser, hereafter called LSVD, is showing good performance both in range and efficiency level. It seems to combine and posses the good qualities of both vaneless and conventional vaned diffusers.

Through the years many different designs of centrifugal compressor diffusers have been presented, no one of them appears to be distinctly superior to the others. Diffusers for centrifugal compressors, especially the vaned type, are still designed mostly by art.

The vaneless diffuser has probably the simplest geometrical turbomachinery flow passage that can be described by three parameters. However, the flow through it is as complex as in any complex geometrical passage. The vaneless diffuser is characterized by simple and inexpensive construction, wide operating range, and the ability to reduce sonic absolute velocity to a subsonic one without the formation of shock waves.

As already stated current conventional vaned diffusers are designed empirically,

industrial design practice consists of initially determining the:

• Blade number,
• Blade profile,
• Maximum blade thickness,
• Total diffusion,
• Mean blade loading, and
• Vaneless diffuser width distribution.

The choice of these parameters results from qualitative study of losses, channel blockage, and sensitivity at off design, based on experimental results. The vaned diffuser inlet diameter d_3 is also determined based on a qualitative study of Mach number influence on the attainable efficiency, off design sensitivity, and noise level.

LSVD - THE LOW SOLIDITY VANED DIFFUSER

Recent works /1, 2, 3, 4, 5, and 6/ have confirmed the good potential of a LSVD. Basically a LSVD geometry consists of blunt leading edge, short length, and small number of vanes, as shown in figure 1. Its distinctive feature being the absence of a throat.

Based on figure 2, a basic geometrical relationship for the LSVD can be developed relating, the vane angles, vane numbers, solidity, and radius ratio as:

$$[\sigma]^2 = \frac{\left(\dfrac{r_4}{r_3}\right)^2 + 1 - 2\left(\dfrac{r_4}{r_3}\right)\cos(\beta_4 - \beta_3)}{2 - 2\cos\left(\dfrac{360}{Z}\right)} \qquad [1]$$

This geometrical relationship can be summarized graphically as in figure 3, where flow turning $(\beta_4 - \beta_3)$ is expressed as a function of blade number, solidity, and radius ratio.

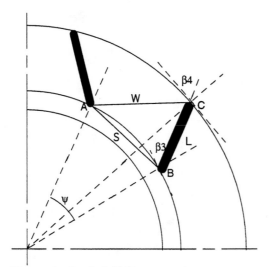

Figure 2.: Basic LSVD geometry

MSU TEST FACILITY

The comparative performance tests of the vaneless, camber vaned and a LSVD were performed at the Michigan State University Turbomachinery Lab. The tests were performed on Test Rig I of the lab's two major centrifugal compressor rigs, each of which has a 225 KW drive with variable speed and fully automated data acquisition and monitoring system. Both test rigs have been designed to accommodate a wide configuration of impellers and diffuser systems. Figure 4 shows a top view of both Test Rig I and II, and Figure 5 shows a side view of Test Rig I.

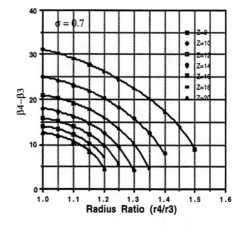

Figure 3.: LSVD geometrical relationship

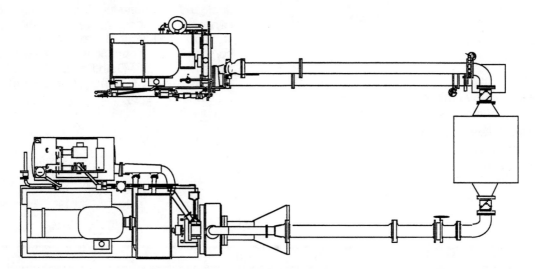

Figure 4:. Top view of Test Rig I and II

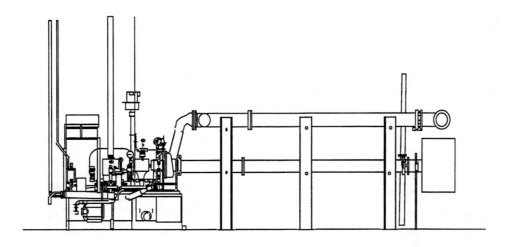

Figure 5:. Side view of Test Rig I

TEST RESULTS

As representatives of vaneless and CVD, typical good performing designs of a vaneless and cambered vaned were selected to be compared with two new LSVD designs.

The two LSVD were designed and matched to the same impeller at 28,000 RPM. The impeller had the following configuration:

- tip diameter, d_2 = 244 mm
- exit blade width, b_2 = 12.85 mm
- inlet shroud diam., d_{s1} =147 mm
- inlet hub diameter, d_{h1} = 47.09 mm
- exit blade angle, β_2 =70.70°
- inlet blade angle, β_{s1} =28.60°
- blade number, Z   = 19

The two tested LSVD, hereafter referred as LSVD#1 and LSVD#2 had the following configuration shown in Table I.

Both LSVD#1 and LSVD#2 have been designed after careful study of past LSVD performances documented in the open literature. Figure 6 to 9 show the comparative performances of the two LSVD systems with a CVD and a vaneless diffuser for two speeds in terms of stage pressure ratio and efficiency.

Table I

DIFFUSER	Z	β_3 (deg)	β_4 (deg)	σ
LSVD#1	14	17	31.6	0.7
LSVD#2	16	17	29.6	0.7

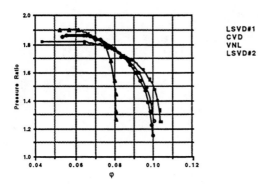

Figure 6.: Stage [tot/tot] pressure ratio comparison for a vaneless, CVD and LSVD at 24,000rpm

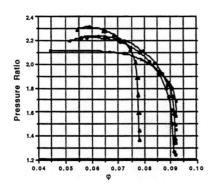

Figure 7.: Stage [tot/tot] pressure ratio comparison for a vaneless, CVD and LSVD at 28,000rpm

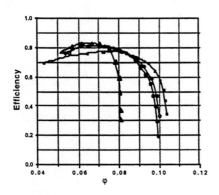

Figure 8.: Stage [tot/tot] efficiency comparison for a vaneless, CVD and LSVD at 24,000rpm

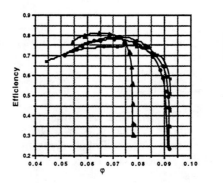

Figure 9.: Stage [tot/tot] efficiency comparison for a vaneless, CVD and LSVD at 28,000rpm

All figures show that both LSVD designs posses typical good performance of a centrifugal compressor stage run over a flow range, i.e. relative high efficiency over a wide stable operation range. Especially at the higher speed figures 7 and 9 shows a typical unchoked diffuser system possessing a wide operation range at high efficiency.

CONCLUSION

The performance of a vaneless, a CVD and two new designs of LSVD has been compared. Results show that Low Solidity Vaned Diffusers, LSVD, for centrifugal compressors may be the compromise solution between:

- vaneless diffuser system which possess low efficiency and wide range, and
- conventional vaned systems which possess high efficiency and narrow range.

Even though LSVD systems are showing promising signs of a good diffuser, the exact mechanism by which the pressure recovery occurs in LSVD systems is unknown and there is no clear procedure for LSVD design.

This paper has once again confirmed through test results and performance comparison that more future work on LSVD systems may be beneficial.

ACKNOWLEDGMENT

The author wishes to acknowledge the support of the Elliott Turbomachinery Company.

REFERENCES

1) E. Sutton: The performance and Flow Conditions Within a Radial Diffuser Fitted with Short Vanes, British Hydromech. Res. Assn., Report 946, 1968

2) Y. Senoo : Low Solidity Circular Cascade for wide Flow Range Blower, Proceddings of Advanced Concepts in Turbomachinery, Fluid Dynamics Institute, Hanover-NH, 1981

3) Y. Senoo and. H. Hayama: "Low Solidity Tandem Cascade Diffusers For Wide Flow Range Centrifugal Blowers, ASME-Paper 83-GT-3, 1983.

4) C. Osborne and J. Sorokes: The Application of Low Solidity Diffusers in Centrifugal Compressors , ASME Winter Annual Meeting 1988, FED Symposium, Chicago

5) J.M. Sorekes and J.P. Welch: Experimental Results on a Rotatable Low Solidity Vaned Diffuser, ASME Paper, 92-GT-19, 1992

6) W.C. Hohlweg, G.L. Direnzi, and R.H. Aungier: Comparison of Conventional and Low Solidity Vaned Diffusers, ASME Paper, 93-GT- , 1993

FED-Vol. 238, 1996 Fluids Engineering Division Conference
Volume 3
ASME 1996

A STUDY OF FUNDAMENTAL INTERRELATION BETWEEN THE MAGNITUDE OF CENTRIFUGAL FORCES AND THE HYDRAULIC ENERGY LOSSES, CAUSED IN AN AXIAL FLOW PUMP

Takaharu Tanaka
Department of Mechanical Engineering
Kobe University
Nada, Kobe
Japan

ABSTRACT

In the practical operation of axial flow pump, it seems that the magnitude of centrifugal forces and the hydraulic energy losses are regularly interrelated with respect to flow rate. However, they are not regularly interrelated with respect to flow rate in an axial flow pump. If the axial flow pump is practically operated in the region between the flow rate at maximum efficiency point and zero flow rate, centrifugal forces may increase their magnitude regularly in the flow passage with the increase of hydraulic energy losses for the decrease in flow rate. However, between the largest flow rate and the flow rate at maximum efficiency point, centrifugal forces may not decrease their magnitude, but increase, while the hydraulic energy losses decrease for the decrease in flow rate.

NOMENCLATURE

A = cross area of flow passage
H = head
n = rotational speed
Q = flow rate
η = efficiency

Subscripts
1,2,··· = arbitrary condition
d = impeller outlet
design = design condition
s = impeller inlet
η max = maximum efficiency condition
th = theoretical condition

∗ = practical value for favorable efficiency pump at design condition
+ = practical value for less favorable efficiency pump at design condition
※ = practical value for favorable efficiency pump at off design condition
= practical value for less favorable efficiency pump at off design condition

1. INTRODUCTION

In practical operation, the initial flow rates at which upstream and/or downstream backflow starts and their characteristics at lower region of off design flow rates may differ one another among axial flow pumps. Their experimental characteristics and relative interrelations have been reported so far by many investigators, such as those by Lakshminarayana (1973), Fraser (1981), Tanaka (1982), Engeda (1988), and so on.

The grade (quality) of internal flow condition at an equivalent flow rate, that is the grade of efficiency characteristics may differ one another among axial flow pumps. Usually, it is believed that the grade of internal flow conditions and the grade of efficiency characteristics are regularly interrelated each other, as shown by Tanaka (1987). However, their physical interrelations among axial flow pumps have not been clear from previous investigations.

From these view points, in the present paper, fundamental interrelation between the magnitude of centrifugal forces and the hydraulic energy losses, caused in an axial flow pump is discussed universally at design and off design conditions.

2. ESTABLISHMENT OF OPERATING CONDITIONS

To develop the discussion in general, it would be reasonable to assume that most of the concrete design factors: such as heads, flow rates, and geometrical sizes (blade angles, lengths, diameters, etc.) are not given concretely. Then, it would be reasonable to pay our attention to practical facts obtained through experimental data.

In practical operation of an axial flow pump, there is an optimum operating condition at where operating condition becomes most convenient. This optimum operating condition may differ one another by axial flow pumps. Therefore, the characteristics of all the practical axial flow pumps under consideration may be classified based upon the optimum operating condition.

Fig. 1 shows a practical example on the performance characteristics of an axial flow pump, operated at constant rotational speeds. We can see that there exists an optimum operating condition.

3. HYDRAULIC ENERGY OUTPUT AT DESIGN CONDITION

The hydraulic energy outputs at maximum efficiency point could be recognized as the energy outputs, practically produced at its most efficient flow condition in an axial flow pump. It may be explained simply as a function only of head $H_{\eta max}$ and flow rate $Q_{\eta max}$. However, their values, practically produced at each of maximum efficiency points, may differ one another by the grade (quality) of optimum internal flow conditions among axial flow pumps.

In general, on an axial flow pump A, if theoretical rotational speed $(n_A)_{th}$ and practical rotational speed at optimum operating condition $(n_A)_{\eta max}$ are identical, then their hydraulic energy outputs are comparable. Generally, they have the relation:

$$f(\gamma \mathbf{Q}_{th} \mathbf{H}_{th}) > f(\gamma \mathbf{Q}^*_{\eta max} \mathbf{H}^*_{\eta max}), \qquad (1)$$

On the axial flow pump B, if its practical rotational speed $(n_B)_{\eta max}$ at optimum operating condition is identical to that of axial flow pump A, then their hydraulic energy outputs are comparable. If its practical maximum efficiency is lower than that of axial flow pump A, then they have the relation

$$f(\gamma \mathbf{Q}^*_{\eta max} \mathbf{H}^*_{\eta max}) > f(\gamma \mathbf{Q}^+_{\eta max} \mathbf{H}^+_{\eta max}). \qquad (2)$$

4. DISCHARGE HEAD AT MAXIMUM EFFICIENCY CONDITION

In practical operation of an axial flow pump, practical internal flow condition is most significant and representative at maximum efficiency point. Therefore, it seems reasonable to compare their internal flow conditions at each of maximum efficiency points at an equivalent flow rate among axial flow pumps. For this purpose, as a matter of convenience, it would be possible to pick out arbitrarily two different kinds of axial flow pumps in relative grade of efficiencies; one is high and the other is not high at each of maximum efficiency points. Then, to compare these two internal flow conditions, following operating condition may be requested between them [See Fig. 2]

$$\mathbf{Q}^*_{\eta max} = \mathbf{Q}^+_{\eta max} \equiv \mathbf{Q}_{\eta max}. \qquad (3)$$

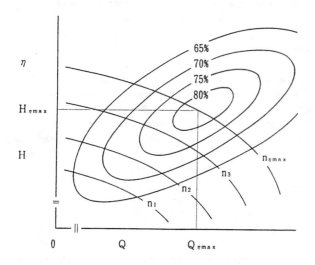

Fig. 1 Performance characteristics of an axial flow pump operated at constant rotational speeds.

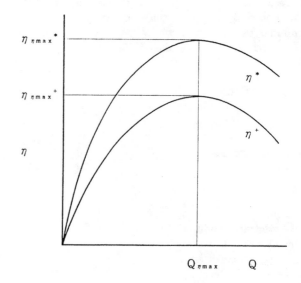

Fig. 2 Efficiency characteristics of two axial flow pumps with an equivalent flow rate $Q_{\eta max}$ at maximum efficiency point.

Then, following relation may be obtained at maximum efficiency point ;

$$H^*_{\eta max} > H^+_{\eta max}. \qquad (4)$$

In other words,

$$(H_d{}^* - H_s{}^*)_{\eta max} > (H_d{}^+ - H_s{}^+)_{\eta max}. \qquad (5)$$

This indicates that the discharge head $H_d{}^*{}_{\eta max}$, which is practically produced by axial flow pump whose maximum efficiency is high, may always become larger than that $H_d{}^+{}_{\eta max}$ of other axial flow pump whose maximum efficiency is not high.

From above discussion, it could be said that although the hydraulic energy outputs are identical, the internal flow condition at impeller discharge may differ one another among axial flow pumps by the relative grade of maximum efficiencies whether it is high or not high at optimum operating condition, and that on the axial flow pump whose maximum efficiency is high, its discharge head $H_d{}^*{}_{\eta max}$ may always become larger than that $H_d{}^+{}_{\eta max}$ of other axial flow pump, whose maximum efficiency is not high. This result at maximum efficiency point may be applicable in common to all and among the axial flow pumps, regardless to relative grade of efficiency characteristics whether they are favorable or less favorable at off design condition.

5. HYDRAULIC ENERGY OUTPUT AT OFF DESIGN CONDITION

To simplify the discussion and to consider the off design condition, it would be reasonable to assume that all the hydraulic energy outputs at each of maximum efficiency points are same (identical) for all the tested practical axial flow pumps, regardless to relative grade of efficiency characteristics whether they are favorable or less favorable at off design condition. In addition to this, it would be reasonable to pick out again, for convenience, arbitrarily two different kinds of axial flow pumps in relative grade of efficiency characteristics, one is a favorable and the other is a less favorable at off design condition.

Then, following relations could be considered between them at maximum efficiency point

$$f(\gamma Q^*_{\eta max} H^*_{\eta max}) = f(\gamma Q^\#_{\eta max} H^\#_{\eta max}), \qquad (6)$$

The physical quantities nominated by symbol ✻ in equation (6) may indicate, for example, the hydraulic energy outputs at maximum efficiency point for favorable pump in efficiency characteristics at off design condition, and those physical quantities nominated by symbol # may indicate the energy outputs at maximum

efficiency point for less favorable pump at off design condition.

To simplify the discussion, it could be assumed that the fundamental flow rates at maximum efficiency point, $Q^*_{\eta max}$ and $Q^\#_{\eta max}$, are identical between them as hydraulic energy outputs are. Therefore, the same could be assumed about the heads, $H^*_{\eta max}$ and $H^\#_{\eta max}$ [See Fig. 3] .

Then, relative comparison of two hydraulic energy outputs in two different grades: favorable and less favorable at off design condition, at an equivalent flow rate Q_A, may indicate the comparison of two internal flow conditions between two different axial flow pumps in efficiency characteristics at off design condition, such as those of pump Ⅰ (solid line) and pump Ⅱ (dotted line) in Fig. 3. That is, the former symbol ✻ may be applicable, for example, to those of favorable axial flow pump in efficiency characteristics and the latter symbol # to those of less favorable pump.

6. DISCHARGE HEAD AT OFF DESIGN CONDITION

It is obvious that in the practical axial flow pump, whose efficiency characteristic is favorable at off design condition, its hydraulic energy output, at an equivalent flow rate Q_1, is larger than that of less favorable axial flow pump. That is,

$$f(\gamma Q_1 H_1{}^*) > f(\gamma Q_1 H_1{}^\#). \qquad (7)$$

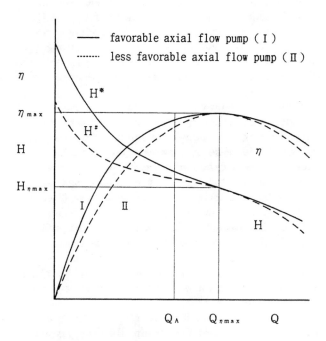

Fig. 3 Efficiency characteristics of two axial flow pumps. Each of efficiencies, flow rates, and heads at maximum efficiency point are identical.

Therefore, they have the following relation at off design condition,

$$H^* > H^\#. \qquad (8)$$

In other words,

$$H_d{}^* > H_d{}^\#, \qquad (9)$$

Therefore, it could be concluded at off design condition that internal flow condition may differ one another among axial flow pumps by the relative grade of efficiency characteristics. On the axial flow pump whose efficiency characteristics is favorable at off design condition, the head at impeller discharge may always become larger than that produced by less favorable axial flow pump.

7. EFFICIENCY CHARACTERISTICS AND CENTRIFUGAL FORCES

From above discussion it became clear that on the axial flow pump whose relative grade of efficiency is favorable at an equivalent flow rate, the discharge head becomes larger than that for the less favorable axial flow pump. Fundamentally, these relative interrelationships may be held among axial flow pumps, regardless to flow rate whichever they are operated at design or off design flow rate.

Therefore, if all the practical geometrical flow passages, except those at impelling blade section, are made identical, then to accomplish the flow rate Q_1 in equivalent, as a matter of course, the hydraulic resistance against the fluid flow has to be made stronger for the favorable axial flow pump than that for the less favorable axial flow pump, as much the efficiency is much favorable.

In practical operation of an axial flow pump, each of the flow rates $Q_1, Q_2, Q_3, ...$ is used to be performed in artificial way, for example, by operating the discharge valve. To decrease the flow rate, cross area has to be closed at the location of discharge valve in the pipe line. That is, the hydraulic resistance against the flowing fluids is increased at the location of discharge valve. And the flow rate is decreased. This indicates that for the favorable axial flow pump, as the produced head is larger, the cross area has to be closed much tight at the location of discharge valve than that for less favorable axial flow pump. It may be closed narrower as much the efficiency characteristic is much favorable [see Fig. 4].

On the other hand, it is clear that in the practical operation of an axial flow pump, the flow passage is closed with the decrease in flow rate, and the geometrical shape of flow passage in the region between the impelling blade and the discharge valve section is changed forcibly by the discharge valve with the decrease in flow rate so that it constructs (forms) a kind of semi closed vessel with a rotating impeller in it. It may form a flow passage similar to a kind of closed vessel as much the efficiency characteristic is much favorable. At zero flow rate, a closed vessel may be performed perfectly in the flow passage with a rotating impeller in it.

This indicates that in an axial flow pump, the flow passage is formed continuously as a closed vessel by the discharge valve with the decrease in flow rate. Then, as a rotating impeller is installed in it, as a matter of course, centrifugal force may increase continuously in the flow passage with the decrease in flow rate. That is, the centrifugal forces may act to fluid particles ordinarily in the flow passage at whole range of flow rates from largest flow rate to zero flow rate, that is, regardless to flow rate at design and off design flow rate.

From these results it could be said that the centrifugal forces, caused throughout the impelling action are strongly interrelated with efficiency characteristics at design and off design flow rates among axial flow pumps. The centrifugal forces may act to fluid particles stronger for the favorable axial flow pump than that for the less favorable axial flow pump. It may act stronger as much the efficiency characteristic is much favorable, both at design and off design flow rate.

8. DESIGN FLOW RATE AND CENTRIFUGAL FORCES

It is needless to say that when the axial flow pump is operated at largest flow rate, the discharge valve is fully opened in the flow passage. However, even at the largest flow rate, as a rotating impeller is set in it, it could be said that in the flow passage some centrifugal forces may affect to fluid particles, and their magnitudes may differ by the grade of efficiency characteristics among axial flow pumps.

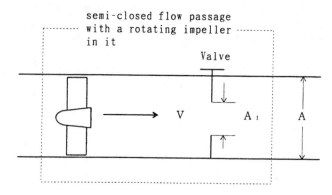

Fig. 4 Semi−closed flow passage of an axial flow pump in a conduit pipeline.

Generally speaking, the cross area is closed by the discharge valve with the decrease in flow rate. This indicates that with the start to decrease its largest flow rate, the flow passage starts to form a geometrical shape similar to closed vessel. That is, the centrifugal forces starts to increase its magnitude in the flow passage with the start to decrease its largest flow rate. And at zero flow rate, the cross area is fully closed, and a fully closed vessel is performed. Therefore, it could be said that the effect of centrifugal forces may be the smallest at the largest flow rate, and the strongest at the zero flow rate. This changing process of geometrical shape by the discharge valve may indicate that centrifugal forces may increase in the flow passage continuously with the decrease in flow rate from the largest flow rate to zero flow rate.

As described above, in an axial flow pump, the cross area for the fluid flow becomes narrower with the decrease in flow rate, and the effect of centrifugal forces increases in the flow passage. However, it is well known that at some operating condition between the fully opened and the fully closed of discharge valve, its fluid flow condition becomes most convenient. In other words, the geometrical shape of flow passage, which locates between the impelling section and the discharge valve section, may start to form a flow passage similar to a closed vessel with the start to decrease its largest flow rate. And on the way to perform a closed vessel, its operating condition becomes most convenient at a certain shape of flow passage similar to semi closed vessel.

That is, on the way to increase centrifugal forces, its internal flow condition becomes optimum at a certain magnitude of centrifugal forces. It would be obvious that this optimum flow condition corresponds to maximum efficiency point in the practical operation of an axial flow pump. Therefore, it could be concluded that some magnitude of centrifugal forces affects to fluid particles at maximum efficiency point in the flow passage of an axial flow pump.

☆ NOTE

In general, in the practical operation of an axial flow pump, to obtain a certain flow rate or to control the operating flow condition, the hydraulic resistance has to be loaded more or less to the fluid flow in the conduit pipeline. To add the hydraulic resistance to the fluid flow, or to subtract the hydraulic resistance from the fluid flow, there are two practical methods in substance: one is the artifical method and the other is in a sense the natural method.

The former method may indicate the artifical accomplishment. For example, the operation by a discharge valve is one of them. The cross area is controlled artifically by the discharge valve, and its operating condition (flow rate) is changed, as mentioned above.

And the latter method may indicate the natural accomplishment. For example, the operation by changing the friction losses is one of them. That is, if the length of conduit pipeline is adjusted naturally at impeller discharge, then the operating condition (flow rate) may be changed. The hydraulic resistance becomes larger as the length of conduit pipeline becomes longer. This method is theoretically available, but its practical operation is very difficult. In the practical operation of an axial flow pump, the length zero of the conduit pipeline may correspond to the largest flow rate and the infinite length may correspond to zero flow rate.

Again, from the latter point of view, it would be possible to say that in an axial flow pump, the centrifugal forces may start to increase its magnitude in the flow passage with the start to decrease its largest flow rate, and increases its magnitude continuously with the decrese in flow rate. And, at the flow condition with a certain magnitude of centrifugal forces, that is, at a certain flow rate between the largest and the zero flow rates, its operating condition becomes most convenient (optimum). That is, at the design condition, its internal flow condition is already set under the condition effected by centrifugal forces.

9. HYDRAULIC LOSSES AND CENTRIFUGAL FORCES

Generally speaking, all kinds of axial flow pumps are designed so that all the impelling blades may direct fluids forcibly to flow toward axial direction. Therefore, it could be considered that all the fluids may flow toward axial direction in the flow passage as they may flow most closely by following the shape of impelling blades at the maximum efficiency point. This may induce the idea that there is no radial flow at design condition and that there is no effect of centrifugal forces in the axial flow pumps.

If the operating condition is different from optimum flow rate, and if the flow rate is larger or smaller than that, it could be said that the hydraulic energy losses may become larger, because the rate of hydraulic energy outputs becomes smaller at those flow rates. This energy losses may be caused because of the fluid particles which do not flow along the flow passage in the impelling blades.

This idea may induce the assumption that if fluid particles flow different way from their theoretical flow passage, then hydraulic energy losses may increase in the flow passage. And the centrifugal forces may affect to fluid particles different way from that of expected direction. That is, the axial flow becomes smaller and the radial flow becomes larger. This may indicate the idea that the efficiency characteristics become better, the hydraulic energy losses become smaller and the effect of centrifugal forces becomes smaller. Conversely speaking, these idea may indicate the reason why the centrifugal forces which effect to fluid particles may take its smallest (minimum) value at maximum efficiency point.

Finally, this consideration may lead to the conclusion that the fluid flow condition caused by centrifugal forces may not need to be considered at design flow rate because it is natural to assume that fluid particles may flow in the axial direction along the flow passage in an axial flow pump.

However, the results obtained here in this investigation indicate that centrifugal forces may increase their magnitude certainly and continuously in the flow passage with the decrease in flow rate from the largest flow rate to zero flow rate in the pumping system.

It is obvious that the flow rate at maximum efficiency point situates quite downstream from the flow rate at the largest flow rate in the practical operation. Then, it would be reasonable to consider that the magnitude of centrifugal forces at maximum efficiency point is quite larger than that of largest flow rate. This indicates that centrifugal forces may not become a minimum at the maximum efficiency point. It may become a certain magnitude which is larger than that at the largest flow rate. Over against this, the hydraulic energy losses may take the smallest value at the maximum efficiency point.

It is believed that centrifugal forces may increase their magnitude regularly in the flow passage with the increase of hydraulic energy losses, as descrived above. If we look at the operating condition between the flow rate at maximum efficiency point and zero flow rate, then centrifugal forces may increase regularly in the flow passage with the increase of hydraulic energy losses. This result may consist with those of general concepts.

However, if we look at the operating condition between the largest flow rate and the flow rate at maximum efficiency point, then it is obvious that centrifugal forces become larger certainly and continuously with the decrease in flow rate. Their magnitude may not become a minimum at maximum efficiency point, but it may become a larger value than that at the largest flow rate. Whilst, the hydraulic energy losses may take its smallest (minimum) value at the maximum efficiency point. That is, for the decrease in flow rate, although the hydraulic energy losses at maximum efficiency point become smaller than that at largest flow rate, the effect of centrifugal forces at the maximum efficiency point becomes larger than that of largest flow rate. This result may be opposed to those general consepts.

These opposed two results may indicate that the magnitude of centrifugal forces and the energy losses are not regularly interrelated for different flow rates in the practical operation of axial flow pumps. At least, in the operating condition between the largest flow

rate and the flow rate at maximum efficiency point, it could be said that the increasing of hydraulic energy losses may not indicate the increasing of the effect of centrifugal forces in the flow passage of conduit pipeline.

These indicate that for the success in improvement of efficiency characteristics in axial flow pumps, the fluid flow condition at maximum efficiency point which is effected by centrifugal forces may need to be considered in the theoretical analysis.

10. CONCLUSIONS

It is believed that centrifugal forces may increase their magnitude regularly in the flow passage with the increase of hydraulic energy losses in the axial flow pumps. However, the magnitude of centrifugal forces and the hydraulic energy losses may not regularly interrelated in the fluid flow of axial flow pump. Their interrelations are bounded by the flow rate at the maximum efficiency point in the practical operation of axial flow pump.

In the operating condition between the flow rate at maximum efficiency point and zero flow rate in performance characteristic curve, the centrifugal forces may increase their magnitude regularly in the flow passage with the increase of hydraulic energy losses for the decrease in flow rate. However, the centrifugal forces may increase their magnitude in the operating condition between the largest flow rate and the flow rate at maximum efficiency point as the hydraulic energy losses decrease with the decrease in flow rate.

REFERENCES

Engeda, A. and Rautenberg, M., 1988, "Pump Instabilities at Partial Flow," Part−Load Pumping Operation, Control, and Behaviour, Proceedings of the Institution of Mechanical Engineers, C330/88, pp. 1−6.

Fraser, W. H., 1981, "Recirculation in Centrifugal Pumps", ASME Winter Annual Meeting, Washington.

Lakshminarayana, B., 1973, "Three−Dimensional Flow Field in Rocket Pump Induceds, Part 1: Measured Flow Field Inside the Rotating Blade Passage and at the Exit," Journal of Fluids Engineering, Trans. ASME, pp.567−578.

Tanaka, T., 1982, "An Evaluation of Efficiency Characteristics based on Internal Flow Condition of Pumps", Proceedings "Small Hydro Power Fluid Machinery−1982", ASME, pp.67−71.

Tanaka, T., 1987, "An Experimental Study of Backflow Phenomena in a High Specific Speed Turbomachinery", Proceedings of the 10th International Conference of the British Pump Manufacturers' Association, BHRA Fluids Engineering, pp. 41−60.

FED-Vol. 238, 1996 Fluids Engineering Division Conference
Volume 3
ASME 1996

AEROTHERMODYNAMIC PARAMETERS INFLUENCE ON THE

NOISE AND VIBRATION OF A RECIPROCATING COMPRESSOR

by

N. H. Mostafa[*]   and   **Larry D. Mitchell**
Visiting Professor   **Randolph Professor**
Mechanical Engineering Department
VIRGINIA POLYTECHNIC INSTITUTE
AND STATE UNIVERSITY
Blacksburg, VA 24061-0238

ABSTRACT:

An important task in the design and operation of reciprocating compressor units is the understanding and control of noise and vibration levels . Vibrations from single elements such as valves, crankshaft, etc., from collection of elements, or from fluid flow in reciprocating compressor may be the sources of noise.

One of the causes of excitation of the housing of the hermetic compressors in commercial refrigeration is the periodic gas pressure variations which interact with many compressor elements. These variations are mainly due to the opening and closing movement of the suction and exhaust valves. Unbalanced pressure effects cause shaking of the compressor which in turn, cause compressor suspension forces to excite the compressor shell. The compressor shell then radiates acoustic noise.

The excitation frequencies seam in sound pressure response that are most influenced by the fluid dynamics of the are found as follows 700 Hz, 912.5 Hz, 1162.5 Hz, 1737.5 Hz, 1862.5 Hz, 2387.5 Hz and 4337.5 Hz. These frequencies will be used to plot the sound pressure levels as a function of aerodynamic variables.

Also, the frequencies dominate the vibration acceleration level that affected by the aerothermodynamic parameters on the compressor levels are 700 Hz, 1275 Hz, 1512.5 Hz, 1962.5 Hz, and 4750 Hz. Also, optimize the acoustic and vibration performance with the operating characteristics are demonstrated at various operating parameters.

NOMENCLATURE:

a : Vibration acceleration level on casing (m/s^2).
I_s : Near field sound intensity (dB).
N : Rotor seed (rpm).
P_1: pressure of fluid at compressor inlet (Pa).
P_2 :Pressure of fluid at compressor outlet (Pa).

---

*Associate Prof. Mechanical Depart., Zagazig university, Egypt.

P_{DB}: Dynamic pressure at bottom of cylinder (Pa).
P_{Dh} :Dynamic pressure at housing cavity (Pa).
P_{DT} :Dynamic pressure at top of cylinder (Pa).
T : Temperature. (C$^\circ$)
Subscript:
1 : Compressor inlet.
2 : Compressor outlet.
S : Static.
D : Dynamic.

INTRODUCTION:

The following research is part of a series of studies to more fully understand the phenomenon of sound propagation from a hermetic reciprocating compressors.

The sound levels emitted from the operation of the reciprocating compressor were studied by Craun (1994). Compressor assembly modeling by Ramani et al. (1994) involves detailed solid modeling of internal component for inertia properties, developing reduced-degrees-of-freedom by finite element models of the mounting springs, modeling of shockloop and modeling of the sealed external shell. Eighty seven natural frequencies below 2000 Hz (excluding the rigid-body modes) were found using the finite-element-based compressor assembly model. This model can be used to predict velocity responses on the surface of the sealed shell. These velocities are used in sound emission predictions. A finite element analysis model attempted to predicts the same dynamic characteristics that were discovered in the actual compressor through the experimental modal analysis.

Experimental modal testing was performed by Rose (1994) using impact testing to determine the compressor frequencies response function. Twenty three natural frequencies were identified for the compressor housing in the frequency range below 2000 Hz. These were correlated and the Finite Element Model updated by Ramani et al.(1994).

Through the use of multiple-input /single-output (MISO) modeling, the propagation paths of sound within a reciprocating hermetic compressor have been investigated and ranked by Craun (1994). From experimental data of compressor far-field sound output, from suspension spring forces, and from internal suction, exhaust, and general housing pressure fluctuations, a MISO model has been developed. From this model, the importance of the suspension system forces in generating the compressor far-field sound spectrum has been identified. In the frequency range above 800 Hz, forces passing through the suspension system appear to be the dominant contribution to shell excitation and sound radiation as opposed to the influence of internal acoustic pressure fluctuations on the generation of external far-field sound.

Furthermore, the compressor's vibrations change with different operation conditions as discussed by Mostafa (1994) in other industrial centrifugal compressor. The aerothermodynamic parameters such as output-to-input pressure ratio and rotor speed have an influence upon vibration level. This relation can be described in a second-degree polynomial form. Aerothermodynamic vibrations is synchronized with the fluid blade interaction frequencies in centrifugal compressor. The non-uniform distribution of pressures, velocity and temperature along the various section of the turbines cause a series of excitation on the rotor. These pressure fluctuation generate dynamic forces which cause vibration (Mostafa 1994,2).

The aim of the current work is to determine the vibration and acoustic signature for a range of compressor performances. This performance is concerned with the influence of the thermodynamic parameters such as pressure, pressure ratio and (suction, discharge, evaporator inlet and condenser outlet) temperatures on the noise and vibration levels. These thermodynamic parameters are thought to influence the structureborne vibrations that have been shown to directly and dominantly control the noise emission. This means that the determination of vibration and noise level at various thermal loads will be helpful to the designer and to maintenance persons in their quest for a quite machine.

COMPRESSOR TEST SETUP:

The test loop was built and installed at the Virginia Polytechnic Institute and State University, Mechanical Engineering Department, with the help of Bristol Compressor Company. The compressor (model H25A) is a two-cylinder, reciprocating, hermetically sealed refrigeration compressor used in commercial settings.

The volumetric efficiency of the H25A62QDBL compressor is 79.8%. This efficiency was calculated by the manufacturer using the ARI (American Refrigeration Institute) rating condition (45°F evaporator, 20°F superheat, 130°F condenser, 15°F subcooling, 95°F ambient) and assumes a running speed of 3500 rpm. The version studied here is driven by a 4.92 hp(3730w), squirrel-cage, three-phase, AC electric motor. The compressor was set on its standard rubber mounting grommets and placed on hard concrete floor. The compressor / test bench system was charged with R-22 refrigerant .

EXPERIMENTAL INSTRUMENTATION:

In order to discuss the aerothermodynamic parameters that affect vibration and noise, it was necessary to collect spectral data from a compressor operating under different conditions. Thus,

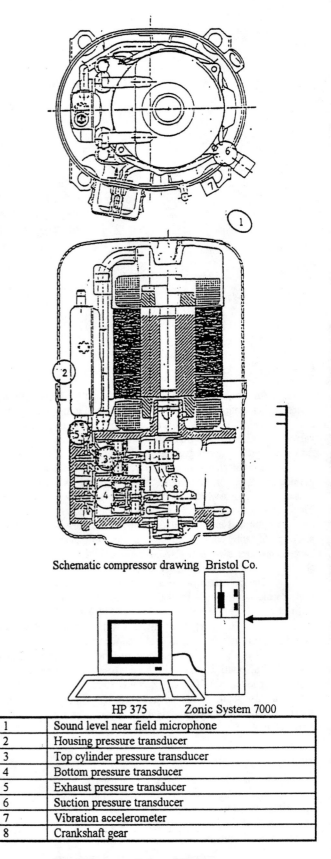

Schematic compressor drawing Bristol Co.

HP 375   Zonic System 7000

1	Sound level near field microphone
2	Housing pressure transducer
3	Top cylinder pressure transducer
4	Bottom pressure transducer
5	Exhaust pressure transducer
6	Suction pressure transducer
7	Vibration accelerometer
8	Crankshaft gear

Fig. (1) Instrumentation of H25A compressor

it is necessary to install instrumentation inside the compressor housing as shown in Fig. (1).

To measure the pressure fluctuation which might drive the shell vibration, five piezoelectric pressure transducers were placed inside the compressor. One within the compressor shell cavity, one near the compressor suction line and one within the compressor exhaust line. The other two pressure transducers were placed in the compressor cylinder top and bottom. Shell vibration and near-field sound were also measure with piezoelectric sensor and microphone, respectively.

As can be seen in Fig.(1),the instrumentation were routed to their appropriate signal conditioning amplifiers and then into a Zonic System 7000 data acquisition unit. This unit was then connected via Ethernet cable to a Hewlett-Packard HP375 workstation running Zonic Zeta (Ver. 4.22) software to control the System 7000.

To begin simultaneous data collection and to reference the signals to the compression process, a gear was installed on the compressor crankshaft near a stationary magnetic pickup. This gear (72 tooth) had one tooth removed to indicate the top dead center of the piston motion. A circuit was built to convert this missing pulse in the square pulse train to act as a trigger signal. For each test, 5 consecutive data blocks were acquired simultaneously from the microphone, pressure transducer, and other instrumentation. Data blocks were 1024 data points long, with sampling rate of 0.0781 ms/sample. This resulted in a spectral resolution 12.5 Hz and baseband analysis frequencies up to 5000 Hz. Fast response thermocouples type (T) were installed at compressor inlet and outlet, and at the expansion valve inlet and outlet. The static pressure at compressor inlet and outlet was measured.

RESULTS:

The acoustic and vibration response of the compressor are caused by the periodic variation of the gas pressures in the compressor system. These are mainly due to the opening and closing movement of the suction and exhaust valves which generate a pressure field on the internal surfaces of the valves themselves. For this reason figure (2) shows the spectrum of the internal pressure in the top and bottom cylinders, the exhaust pressure, and the suction pressure, respectively. The pressure spectrum for top and bottom of cylinder are similar. The main peaks appears at the running speed and its harmonics, especially, the second and the third. But, in the exhaust pressure and suction pressure the first and the third harmonic of running speed disappear completely. This is caused by the two pistons being exactly 180 degrees out of phase. The base frequency in the suction and exhaust is twice running speed. The peak of the second harmonic of running speed in the exhaust and suction is reduced to 1/10 and 1/27 of the cylinder pressures, respectively.

Figure (3) shows the dynamic pressure of bottom cylinder (P_{DB}) function of the dynamic pressure of top cylinder (P_{DT}) at 112.5 Hz. This is a linear relation which means P_{DB} increases linearly with increasing P_{DT}. Also, dynamic suction and exhaust pressures of the compressor ($P_{D1}P_{D2}$) at 112.5 Hz increase with polynomial form with increasing P_{DT}. Thus, it is clear also the sound pressure level inside the housing cavity is also increasing with increasing P_{DT} with much lower magnitude.

Figures (4) & (5) represent the sound pressure spectrum inside and outside the compressor housing respectively. The peaks

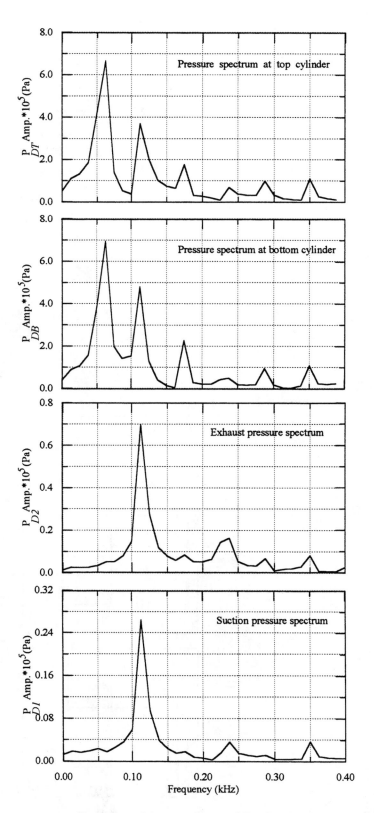

Fig. (2) Dynamic pressure spectrum of P_{Dt}, P_{DB}, P_{D2} , and P_{D1} at (P_{1S}=4.86x10^{5}Pa & P_{2S}=19.44x10^5 Pa)

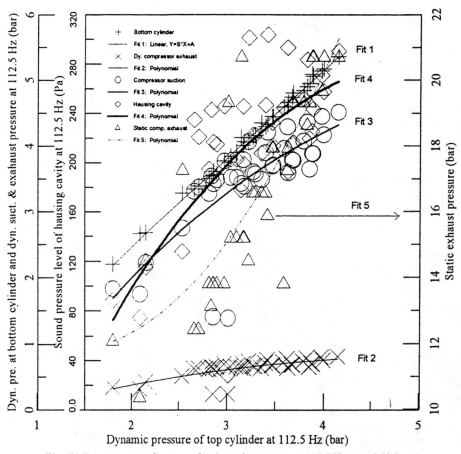

Fig. (3) Compressor performance for dynamic pressure at 112.5 Hz (speed 58.3 rps)

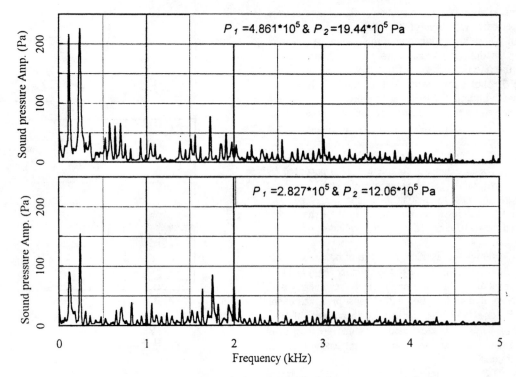

Fig. (4) Sound pressure spectrum inside housing cavity at different operating condition.

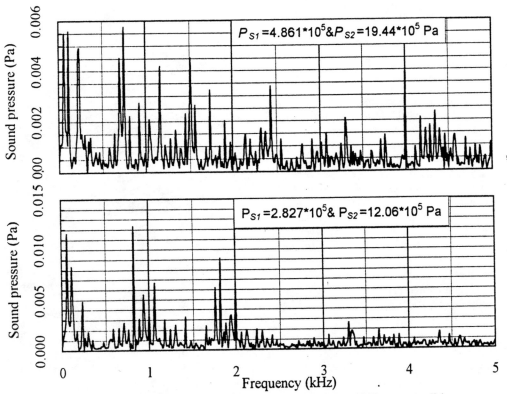

Fig. (5) Sound spectrum outside the compresor at different conditions.

shown in figures (4) and (5) are the harmonics of the running speed of 57.774 Hz. The excitation of the compressor systems is caused by the periodic action of the pistons and valves system. These actions cause a rich harmonic complement of forces exciting the compressor system. When a particular harmonic component approaches a system resonance frequency one might expect an increase in compressor vibration and/or sound. From these figures and other operating conditions the following peaks appears to be a function of the operating condition; 700, 912.5, 1162.5, 1737.5, 1862.5, 2387.5, and 4337.5 Hz. Ofcourse other peaks appear in these figures. They, however, remain substantially steady with load variation. The first three of the listed peaks are nearly matched with resonance frequencies for the assembled compressor as demonstrated by Rose (1994). The fourth peak is between all known system resonance. Thus, the variation sound pressure with load can be attributed solely to the forcing function variations themselves. The fifth peak is also near an assembly resonance. By following the amplitudes at these frequencies for various operating conditions, one will develop different response surfaces shown in fig.(6). These figures show the sound pressure level as a function of the static suction and exhaust pressures. Note that the overall sound pressure level has a relation increasing along the diagonal from minimum to maximum suction and exhaust pressures. This relation is highly significant with that second degree form (where P value <0.00001):-

$$I_s(Overall\ sound)= 96.86 -3.732\ (Ps_1 x 10^{-5})+1.698(Ps_2 x 10^{-5})$$
$$+0.2094(Ps_1 x 10^{-5})^2+ 0.1184(Ps_1 Ps_2 x 10^{-25}) \qquad (1)$$

Figure (6) shows also that the first three frequencies (700, 912.5 and 1162.5 Hz) have the maximum peaks at maximum exhaust pressure with suction pressure around 4.2 bar. These relations are highly significant with the following three equations:-

$$I_{s(at\ 700\ Hz)} = 22.195 +12.58\ (Ps_1 x 10^{-5}) -1.29(Ps_1 x 10^{-5})^2$$
$$-0.0177(Ps_2 x 10^{-5})^2 \qquad (2)$$

$$I_{s(at\ 912.5\ Hz)} = 6.5+15.09\ (Ps_1 x 10^{-5})-1.996(Ps_1 x 10^{-5})^2$$
$$+0.144(Ps_1 Ps_2 x 10^{-25}) \qquad (3)$$

$$I_{s(at\ 1162.5\ Hz)} = 16.31-15.5\ (Ps_1 x 10^{-5}) -1.63(Ps_1 x 10^{-5})^2$$
$$- 0.0144(Ps_2 x 10^{-5})^2 \qquad (4)$$

At 1737.5 and 1862.5 Hz other important peaks appears at lower exhaust pressure around (13.5 bar) with suction pressure equal 4 bar . Otherwise, the higher exhaust and suction pressure result in lower noise level. These relation is highly significant with these equations:-

$$I_{s(at\ 1737.5\ Hz)} = 24.514+0.185(Ps_1 Ps_2 x 10^{-25}) \qquad (5)$$

$$I_{s(at\ 1862.5\ Hz)} = 8.811+16.639(Ps_1 x 10^{-5})-1.969(Ps_1 x 10^{-5})^2 \qquad (6)$$

At 2387.5 and 4337.5 Hz the peaks increase at higher suction and exhaust pressure with the following significant equations:-

$$I_{s(at\ 2387.5\ Hz)} = 2.877+17.351(Ps_1 \times 10^{-5})-2.072(Ps_1 \times 10^{-5})^2 \qquad (7)$$

$$I_{s(at\ 4337.5\ Hz)} = 50.44-2.68(Ps_2 \times 10^{-5})-1.26(Ps_1 \times 10^{-5})^2$$
$$+0.1184(Ps_1Ps_2 \times 10^{-25}) \qquad (8)$$

Figure (7) represents the vibration spectrum at the long face of the compressor, fig.(1), which is recommended to pickup most of the radiated frequencies by Craun (1994). From this figure and other operating conditions with respect to the peaks that change significantly with load, the following amplitude of these frequencies were found, 700, 1275, 1512.5, 1962.5 and 4750 Hz. The first and the fourth one are matched with resonances of the compressor system. By following the amplitudes at these frequencies for various operating conditions, one will develop different response surfaces shown in fig.(8). These figures show the acceleration level as a function of the static suction and exhaust pressures. The response surface at 700 and 1275 Hz have the same trend with different amplitude. In both cases the acceleration peaks are at an exhaust pressure of 14.5 and maximum suction pressure (6.25 bar). These relations are highly significant with that second degree form (where P value <0.00001):-

$$a_{(at\ 700\ Hz)} = -12+1.698(Ps_2 \times 10^{-5})+ 0.33(Ps_1 \times 10^{-5})^2$$
$$-0.0463(Ps_2 \times 10^{-5})^2 -0.0897(Ps_1 Ps_2 \times 10^{-25}) \qquad (9)$$

$$a_{(at\ 1275\ Hz)} = -2.58+1.658(Ps_1 \times 10^{-5})-0.032(Ps_1 Ps_2 \times 10^{-25}) \qquad (10)$$

Also, the response surface of 1512.5 Hz, 1962.5 Hz, and the overall acceleration appear to be have the same trend, but with different amplitudes. These frequencies have the maximum values at maximum exhaust and near maximum suction pressure with the following significant equations:-

$$a_{(at\ 1512.5\ Hz)} = -1.071-0.0069(Ps_2 \times 10^{-5})^2 +0.09(Ps_1 Ps_2 \times 10^{-25}) \qquad (11)$$

$$a_{(at\ 1962.5\ Hz)} = 5.385-2.658(Ps_1 \times 10^{-5})+ 0.208(Ps_1 \times 10^{-5})^2-$$
$$-0.00697(Ps_2 \times 10^{-5})^2+ 0.0656(Ps_1 Ps_2 \times 10^{-25}) \qquad (12)$$

The response surface of 4750 Hz have the same trend with maximum peaks occur along a line of suction pressure equal about 4.4 bar and starting at exhaust pressures of 12 bar with the following significant equations:-

$$a_{(at\ 4750\ Hz)} = 0.07179 +0.008461(Ps_1 Ps_2 \times 10^{-25}) \qquad (13)$$

All the above relation are significant within the tested operating range ($Ps_1 = (1.6\ TO\ 5.9) \times 10^5$ Pa & $Ps_2 = (10.4\ to\ 20.83) \times 10^5$ Pa).

Figure (9) represent the sound pressure level function of suction and exhaust compressor temperature. This figure shows that maximum sound pressure level appears around (105-120 C°) with higher temperature suction.

Figure (10) represent the sound pressure level function of compression ratio and acceleration of vibration level. This figure

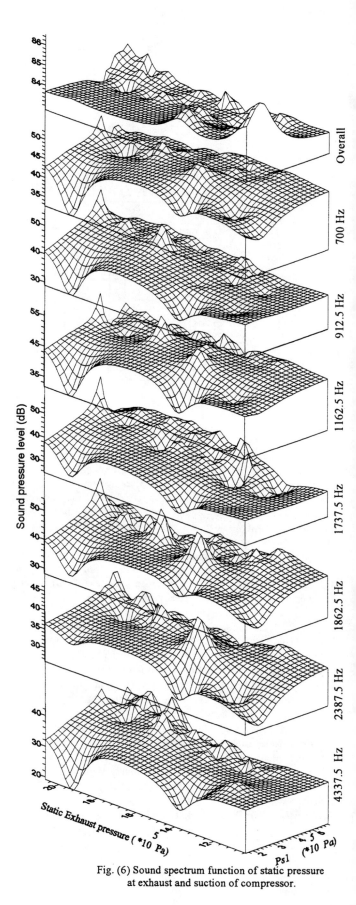

Fig. (6) Sound spectrum function of static pressure at exhaust and suction of compressor.

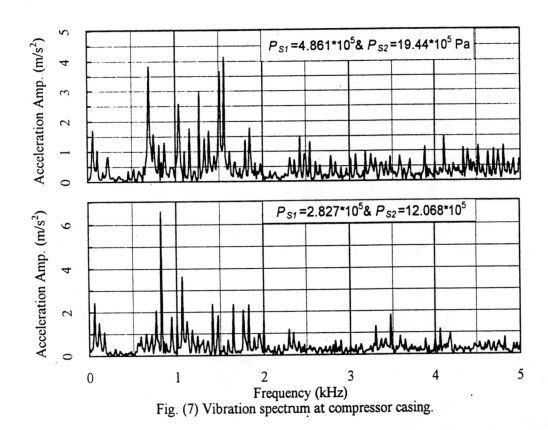

P_{S1} =4.861*10⁵& P_{S2} =19.44*10⁵ Pa

P_{S1} =2.827*10⁵& P_{S2} =12.068*10⁵

Fig. (7) Vibration spectrum at compressor casing.

shows that maximum sound pressure level appears from 4.7 to 5 compression ratio.

CONCLUSION:

One of the causes of excitation of the housing of the hermetic refrigeration compressors is the periodic gas pressure variations which interact with many compressor elements

* The sound pressure level inside the housing cavity have higher values at the highest dynamic pressure of bottom and top of cylinder with (frequency equal to running speed multiply by numbers of cylinders 180 degrees out of phase). The same trend is also gained with dynamic suction and exhaust pressure.

* The main frequencies of sound pressure level that affected by the aerothermodynamic parameters is 712.5 Hz, 912.5 Hz, 1162.5 Hz, 1737.5 Hz, 1862.5 Hz, 2387.5 Hz and 4337.5 Hz which is corresponding to 12, 16, 20, 30, 32, 41, 75 of the running speed. The first three and the fifth are matched with the compressor resonances.

* The main frequencies of vibration acceleration level that affected by the aerothermodynamic parameters are 700 Hz, 1275 Hz, 1512.5 Hz, 1962.5 Hz and 4750 Hz. which is corresponding to 12, 22, 26, 34, , 82, of the running speed. the first three is matched with the compressor response.

* The sound pressure level and vibration at these corresponding frequencies have significant second degree relations function of pressure suction and exhaust of the compressor.

* The maximum sound pressure level appears around (105-120 C°) with higher temperature suction of the compressor and from 4.7 to 5 compression ratio.

In the future this data could provided a knowledge base for an expert system which would enable to spot instantaneously the parameters which are affecting the compressor performance.

ACKNOWLEDGMENTS

The authors wish to acknowledge Bristol compressor company for its support and cooperation.

REFERENCES:

Rose, J. A., April, 1994, "*The Experimental Characterization of the Dynamics of a Reciprocating Freon Compressor System*" M. Sc. Thesis, Virginia Polytechnic Institute and State University, Mechanical Eng. Department, Blacksburg, VA, U.S.A.

Craun, M. A., May, 1994, "*Identification of Sound Transmission Paths within a Hermetic Reciprocating Refrigeration Compressor Via Multiple-Input/ Single-Output Modeling*" M. Sc. Thesis, Virginia Polytechnic Institute and State University, Mechanical Eng. Department, Blacksburg, VA, U.S.A.

Ramani, A., Rose, J., Knight, C. E. and Mitchell, L. D., July 19-22, 1994. "Finite Element Modeling of a Compressor For Sound Prediction Purpose" *Proceeding of The International Compressor Engineering Conference at Purdue*, West Lafayette, Indiana, U.S.A., Vol. I, pp. 7-11.

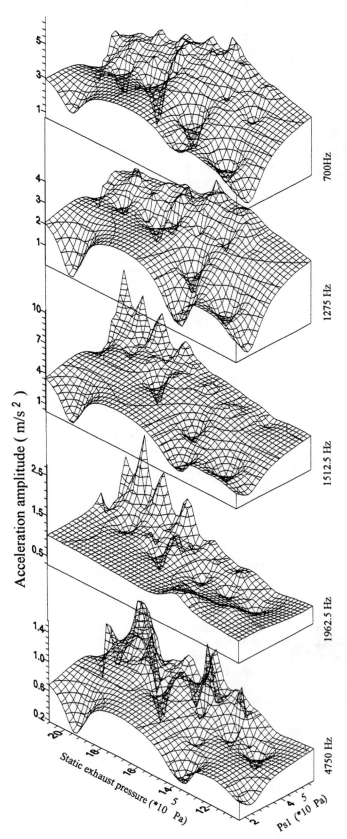

Fig. (8) Vibration spectrum function of exhaust and suction pressure.

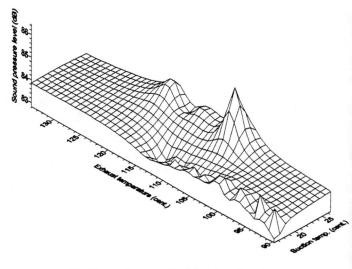

Fig. (9) sound pressure level function of suction and exhaust temperatures.

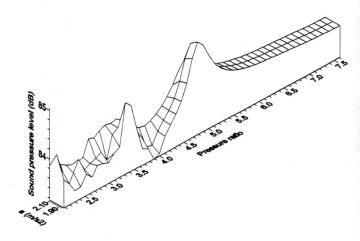

Fig. (10) Sound pressure level function of pressure ratio and acceleration of vibration.

Mostafa, N. H., June 19-23, 1994, "Aerothermodynamic Vibration Correlation in an Industrial Compressor Turbine Unit", *Proceeding of ASME The Fluids Engineering Division Summer Meeting*, Fluid Machinery Forum, Nevada, U.S.A., FED Vol. 195. PP. 35-41.

* Mostafa, N. H., June 19-23, 1994, "Steam Distribution Excitation Between High & Medium Pressure Turbines" *Proceeding of ASME The Fluids Engineering Division Summer Meeting*, FED, Fluid Machinery Forum, Nevada, U.S.A., Vol. 195. PP. 19-23.

FED-Vol. 238, 1996 Fluids Engineering Division Conference
Volume 3
ASME 1996

THEORY, DESIGN, AND TEST OF AN EFFICIENT SUBSONIC DIFFUSER

G. Fonda-Bonardi

Meruit, Inc.

ABSTRACT

One of the classical results of velocity potential theory is the solution of the problem of an axially symmetrical, inviscid jet impinging on a flat plate. The pressure and velocity distribution pertaining to this geometry lends itself to the design of an extremely efficient diffuser in which the side wall of the duct is shaped to conform with one streamsurface of the theoretical flow. The resulting adverse pressure gradient along the diffuser wall would cause detachment of the flow and consequent obliteration of the prescribed flow geometry. Detachment is prevented by the injection of high-speed gas along the wall through a series of slots, each injecting a thin layer of gas just before the previous one becomes detached. The injected air is collected from the core flow by means of a scoop located in a region of the diffuser where the undisturbed potential flow generates a static pressure higher than the pressure at the injection point(s). Hence the recirculation loop requires no external power input and contains only static structures. The practical design of such a diffuser requires the use of CFD programs for the detailed computation of the merging of the flow from the slots with the core flow and with each other such that the local stagnation pressure of each wake is always higher that the static pressure at each point, thus preventing reversed internal flow and destruction of the flow geometry. Extensive testing of an experimental diffuser proved pressure recovery efficiencies in excess of 90% for an inlet Mach number of 0.95. We call this design the Radial Recirculating Diffuser (RRDf).

1. INTRODUCTION

The RRDf is an extremely efficient diffuser capable of compressing a gas stream to a final pressure very close to its stagnation pressure.

Conventional subsonic diffusers achieve recompression by slowing the gas down in a long conical duct with a small divergence angle, which is chosen as a compromise between the need to avoid boundary layer separation and the desire to limit the length of the diffuser. However, when the pressure ratio (and therefore the area ratio) exceeds a certain limit, boundary layer separation is very difficult to prevent, unless the diffuser is so long that frictional losses consume more kinetic energy than is converted in pressure recovery. A good engineering compromise yields divergence angles between 3 and 7 degrees, with a pressure recovery up to perhaps 80% of stagnation.

2. BASIC GEOMETRY

One of the classical results of velocity potential theory is the solution of the problem of an axially symmetrical, inviscid jet impinging on a flat plate. Since the solution is easily obtained in closed form, it is often presented as an example in textbooks (e.g. Prandtl and Tietjens, 1957), which usually deal with the incompressible case. Since the corresponding flow for a compressible fluid can be found later by a transformation of coordinates (Shapiro, 1953), this is a convenient way to proceed. Briefly it is found that the streamlines are cubic hyperbolas of the form

$$zr^2 = C \tag{1}$$

in each meridian plane, and that the lines of equal pressure (isobaric lines) are ellipses of the form

$$4z^2 + r^2 = R^2 \tag{2}$$

in the same plane (see Fig. 1). Other properties of this type of flow may be derived as follows:

As a fluid element moves along a streamline in this geometry, the pressure at first increases, and then decreases, while the velocity of course first decreases, and then increases. For each streamline the point of maximum pressure occurs where the streamline is tangent to an isobaric line, such as point T in Fig. 1. This point is found by differentiating equations (1) and (2) and equating the two derivatives:

$$\frac{-\sqrt{C}}{2z^{3/2}} = \frac{-4z}{r} \qquad \text{and therefore}$$

$$C = \frac{64z^5}{r^2} \tag{3}$$

which, substituted in (1), gives

$$zt = r/\sqrt{8} = (c/8)^{1/3} \tag{4}$$

where zt and rt are the coordinates of the point T of maximum pressure on the streamline. All such points lie on straight line passing through the origin and forming an angle $arctan\sqrt{8}$ with the axis, as shown by the dashed line of Fig. 1. The major semiaxis of the isobaric ellipse passing through T is found by substituting zt and rt in (2)

$$R_t = r_t \sqrt{3/2} \qquad (5)$$

A diffuser can be built by placing hard walls along any suitable streamline and extending them to the point of maximum pressure given by (4), and then extending the end plate to the radius given by (5) as shown in Fig. 1. All diffusers designed by this method are geometrically similar, and only one parameter (the constant c) determines the scale factor: the mass flow m (kg/sec) is proportional to c.

Whereas conical diffusers decelerate the gas by trying to pull the streamlines apart (as long as they stick to the walls), the principle of operation of the subject diffuser is basically different. The fluid is slowed down by letting it impinge on the end plate, where the axial streamline actually stops, thereby achieving the full stagnation pressure $p0$ at the center of the plate. The fluid then accelerates radially away from this point towards the edge of the plate, and the pressure correspondingly drops; the plate is extended to the point where the pressure is equal to the desired terminal pressure $pt < p0$; a hard wall is placed along the streamline tangent to the isobaric ellipse passing through this point; the coordinates of this point determine the value of the constant c pertaining to the streamline coincident with the wall, which in turn determines the scale factor of the diffuser.

It is therefore desirable at this point to compute the effective area available to the flow in the diffuser, so as to relate the dimensions of the diffuser to the desired area ratio and pressure ratio. The effective area A is most easily found by integrating the flow through a surface of constant velocity, which coincides with an isobaric surface (2). The element dA is accordingly:

$$dA = 2\pi r \, ds \cos g \qquad (6)$$

where ds is the element of length along the ellipse (2), and g is the angle between the normal to the streamline and the tangent to the ellipse (see Fig. 2):

$$ds = dr / \cos g, \text{ and } \qquad g = a - b. \qquad (7)$$

We also have

$$\tan a = dr/dz \bigg|_{ellipse} = -4z/r \qquad (8)$$

$$\tan b = -dz/dr \bigg|_{streamline} = 2z/r \qquad (9)$$

By writing $\cos a$ and $\cos(a-b)$ in terms of $\tan a$ and $\tan b$ one obtains a rather cumbersome expression which, surprisingly, can be simplified to the following:

$$dA = \pi \frac{2R^2 - 3r^2}{R\sqrt{R^2 - r^2}} \qquad \text{and}$$

$$R = 4z^2 + r^2 = 4z^2 + c/z \qquad (10)$$

This can be integrated in closed form between two points of ordinate $z1$ and $z2$:

$$A = \pi[2zr - 8^3]_{z1}^{z2} \qquad (11)$$

If we extend the integration between the outside wall (described by equation $r^2 z = c$) and the axis $(z = z1)$ we have on the axis

$$z1 = R/2, \qquad \text{and}$$
$$2z1R - 8z1^3 / R \equiv 0 \qquad (12)$$

which substituted into (5) gives simply

$$A = \pi(2zR - 8z^3 / R) \qquad (13)$$

This is the effective area of the diffuser corresponding to a point (r,z) on the wall, so that (6) can be used to compute the pressure that will be measured at that point in the wall. The effective terminal area of the diffuser is found by substituting the values (4) and (5) in (13) for the point of maximum pressure:

$$A = \pi r^2 / \sqrt{3} = 2\Pi c^{2/3} / \sqrt{3} \qquad (14)$$

This is the effective area corresponding to the polar cap of the isobaric ellipsoid between the rim (rt, zt) and the axis; it is also the effective area of the equatorial zone between the rim (rt, zt) and the edge of the plate $(r0, Rt)$. This is also the maximum area anywhere in the diffuser: if the walls are extended beyond point (rt, zt) and the plate the radius Rt, then (13) shows that the effective area decreases again, as it must because the pressure decreases and the fluid velocity increases.

It is convenient to define a length y equal to the radius of a circle having an area equal to the effective area A at a point of the duct:

$$y^2 = A / \pi \qquad \text{and}$$

$$Y_t = r_t / 3^{1/4} \qquad (15)$$

Fig. 3 shows the variation of y along a diffuser of this type; also shown for comparison is a conventional conical diffuser with a divergence angle of 4 degrees for the same area ratio. Certain other geometrical properties of the flow are of interest and have some influence on the performance

610

of the diffuser. The family of the orthogonal trajectories of the streamlines is easily found to be

$$r^2 - 2z^2 = C \qquad (16)$$

which is seen to be a family of hyperbolas in the meridian plane.

The curves intersect the axis for $C < 0$ and intersect the line $z = 0$ for $C > 0$; the corresponding three-dimensional surfaces are accordingly polar caps of two-sheeted hyperboloids in the neck of the diffuser and equatorial zones of one-sheeted hyperboloids in the bell. The case $C = 0$ corresponds to a cone (the common asymptote to all hyperboloids with the vertex at the origin and an apical half-angle equal to $arctan\sqrt{2}$ (see Fig. 4).

This geometry points up a basic difference with conical diffusers. In the case of conical flow the streamlines are straight lines and the isobaric surfaces are concentric spheres which coincide everywhere with the orthogonal surfaces. In the case of the impact diffuser the isobaric surfaces do **not** coincide with the orthogonal surfaces and strong pressure gradients exist across the streamlines (this of course accounts for the curvature of the streamlines).

Considering a streamsurface as a flexible, frictionless, massless wall separating two fluid streams, it is easy to see that when the isobaric surfaces are everywhere orthogonal to the streamsurfaces, these are in an indifferent equilibrium: in other words, a virtual displacement of a streamsurface generates no restoring nor upsetting forces. As a consequence when the boundary layer becomes separated in a conical diffuser, the flow is easily transformed in a constant-area, constant-velocity, isobaric free jet which is in complete equilibrium with its environment and which may randomly stick to one or the other side of the diffuser.

In the case of an impact diffuser, the streamlines are in a stable equilibrium. A virtual displacement generates strong restoring forces which are the difference between the inertial forces due to the path curvature and the acting pressure gradient. If the boundary layer becomes separated, the flow tends to resist deformation and remains quite close to the wall; this proximity helps reattach the flow.

3. BOUNDARY LAYER SEPARATION

There is a vast body of literature on the subject of boundary layers, but not much specific information is available on the details of turbulent boundary layer separation in an adverse pressure gradient.

There are three well known ways of dealing with a separating boundary layer, each with advantages and disadvantages such as make each more or less suitable for a given situation. The first employs suction through holes and slits; the second involves the use of vortex generators; both were examined theoretically and experimentally and were discarded as solutions to the problems at hand.

The third method consists of blowing a thin sheet of high velocity fluid into the boundary layer through a slot tangential to the wall (North, 1975). Since the static pressure p in the diffuser under consideration is everywhere lower than the external atmospheric pressure pt, the slot(s) can be fed, at least in principle, from the atmosphere without any auxiliary pump, simply utilizing the pressure drop $pt-p$ across the diffuser wall to accelerate the injected air. In this case the stagnation pressure of the injected air ps is equal to the external air pressure pt, except for such small losses as may occur by friction in the slot itself; and the Mach number of the injected air is that which pertains to the pressure p/pt.

Under the assumptions prevalent in all analytical efforts (Schlichting, 1960) it is possible to compute in closed form the detachment point as a function of the free stream velocity decrement, and one finds that detachment occurs when the free stream velocity is smaller by the ratio $\eta = 0.842$ of the velocity at the onset of the adverse pressure gradient, i.e. the point of the injection of a new slot flow.

In this case (as illustrated in Fig. 5) the n slots would be located where the free stream velocities are in a geometric series:

$$u0 : u1 : u2 : .... : un = 1 : \ \eta^1 : \eta^2 : ... \eta^n$$

with $\qquad \eta = 0.842 \qquad (17)$

The width of each slot is chosen to provide a mass flow adequate to the task of accelerating by turbulent mixing the slow fluid contained in the boundary layer at that point; a new, thin, boundary layer appears at the outer wall of the slot. Another slot is placed before this new boundary layer becomes separated. The profile of the wall between slots is computed by assigning appropriate values $c1, c2, c3, c4, ... cn$ to the constant C in (1). The bell and end plate are extended to the appropriate radii rtn and Rtn in accordance with (4) and (5). The total number n of slots required depends of course on the velocity ratio $u0/ut$ between the velocity $u0$ at the entrance of the diffuser and the required terminal velocity at the exhaust, with $ut/un >= 1$.

This simple design procedure was used to design the experimental diffuser, but it soon became apparent that it could be considered only a starting point for the design of the slot cascade; in practice it is necessary to take into account the interaction of all preceding wakes and jets with the developing boundary layer of each new slot, and purely analytical procedures are inadequate to describe these interactions. A detailed numerical solution of the problem was developed with a FORTRAN subroutine ("BLAYER") that computes the developing velocity profiles across the boundary layer along a wall with arbitrary pressure gradients for compressible flows with Mach numbers between 0 and 1. This subroutine also merges the developed boundary layer with the injected flow from the slots, and tracks the wakes of the slot walls.

From the velocity profile BLAYER calculates the displacement thickness and the momentum thickness, which are used by the calling program to calculate the correction to the position of the wall, so as to maintain the correct duct area for the core flow, and the width of each subsequent slot so as to inject the correct momentum at each stage. In addition the subroutine returns a warning of impending separation so that the slots may be located where needed, not necessarily at points of constant velocity ratio η.

The calling program can perform one of two functions:

a. Given a desired pressure gradient profile, generate the wall profile that will result in that pressure profile without detachment, returning the number, position, and width of the needed slots, and the mass flow m through the slots (program DIFDES).

b. Given a fixed duct diffuser with a fixed set of slots, compute the resulting pressure profile for each set of inlet pressure, inlet stagnation pressure (in the core flow), slot supply pressure, and inlet boundary layer profile (i.e. the off-design operation of a given RRDf), (program DIFRUN).

This procedure solves the problem of the two refinements to the theoretical diffuser profile mentioned above.

The third refinement is of a more fundamental nature. If the core flow has a stagnation pressure $p0 > pt$, (the external atmospheric pressure) and if the diffuser is required to recompress the flow to a final terminal pressure pt, and if the slots are fed from a source pressure $ps = pt$, then an infinite number of slots would be required, because in no case the flow from the last slot could be recompressed to a final pressure pt without boundary layer separation. It becomes necessary therefore to feed at least some of the slots from a reservoir held at some pressure $ps > pt$, such that the last slot operates at a Mach number (pertaining to the pressure ratio pn/ps) sufficient to give $ut/un >= \eta n$.

The inconvenience of a blower to feed the slots at a pressure $ps>pt$ can be avoided by noting that the stagnation pressure $p0$ of the core flow is (as it must be) higher than the terminal pressure, and that the fluid everywhere in the bell of the diffuser in front of the end plate is at a static pressure higher than pt. The streamlines and the isobaric lines form a curvilinear coordinate system where a point is identified by two independent parameters. Once the total mass flow through the slots ms and the supply pressure are identified, it is possible to find a point

$Q = (rq,zq)$ such that the mass flow through the circle (concentric with, and perpendicular to the axis) passing through Q is equal to ms, and such that the pressure at this point is equal to ps.

The entire mass flow ms than passes through the flowtube of equation $r^2z = c_q$, where $c_q = r_q^2 z_q$; and a hard wall can be placed in coincidence with this surface without otherwise changing the flow between it and the diffuser wall. The inner flow can then be collected and fed to the slots as shown in Fig. 6. Boundary layer separation does not occur along the new wall, which replaces the end plate, because the pressure gradient is favorable over all of its surface. The cross-sectional area of the tube connecting the scoop at Q with the plenum chamber feeding the slots must be, of course, large enough to keep the frictional pressure losses to an acceptable level.

4. PRACTICAL DESIGN PROCEDURE

The design procedure is simple in principle, since it consists in choosing the appropriate overall area ratio for the desired outlet Mach number and pressure ratio, determining the corresponding value of $y/y*$ ($y*$ being the value of y at the inlet), and subdividing this in a sequence of steps so as to generate a geometric series of velocity ratios. Then slots are located at the corresponding values of y.

In practice the process is complicated since the pressure ps in the plenum feeding the slots is lower than the stagnation pressure of the core flow (due to frictional losses in the recirculating ducting), and additional losses occur in the developing boundary layer from one slot to the next. Therefore the measured stagnation pressure profiles show two distinct regions, the core flow having a stagnation pressure equal to $p0$, and the region next to the slotted wall having a stagnation pressure appreciably lower. The ripples introduced by the successive alternations of injected slot air and residual wakes of boundary layers decay rapidly, being obliterated by mixing in about three slot distances downstream of each slot in turn.

Whereas the distance between successive slots is related to the duct area increase required to yield the desired velocity decrement without detachment, the width of each slot (and therefore the mass of air injected at that point) is related to the thickness of the arriving boundary layer so as to produce a mixed layer with an appropriate stagnation pressure. It is important that the stagnation pressure of the mixed streamtube associated with each slot be as close as possible to that of all the others, so that the stagnation pressure in the terminal plane be essentially constant across the entire mixed layer; if the stagnation pressure varies appreciably across the mixing region, the lowest stagnation pressure acts as a ceiling for the terminal pressure of the entire diffuser, since that streamtube expands to fill the available area as the static pressure approaches the (lowest) stagnation pressure.

This complete design procedure, including the numerical computation of slot parameters, was experimentally verified. It was also found that the simple scoop profile used for illustration in Fig. 6 caused serious instabilities to develop, and it had to be modified near point Q to insure stable flow conditions; but a discussion of the stability of the flow in the recirculation system is beyond the scope of this paper.

[The geometry of the RRDf lends itself to a simple adaptation to the exhaust of a gas turbine, where the flow is confined to an annular area between the outer shroud and the hub of the last turbine stage. In this case the diffuser comprises an outer wall and an inner wall placed in coincidence with two suitable streamlines chosen to include the appropriate flow, as shown in Fig. 7. Both inner and outer walls would be equipped with slots for boundary layer control as described, and would be fed by gas suitably scooped from the core flow.]

5. EXPERIMENTAL RESULTS

A heavily instrumented test bed, originally built with a long conical diffuser, was modified to test an experimental diffuser designed to accept the flow from a circular duct of 280 mm (11-inch) diameter at a Mach number near 1, with an initial boundary layer approximately 10 mm thick. Since this duct was fed from the atmosphere by means of an inlet bell, the stagnation pressure of the core flow was between 750 and 760 Torr absolute, and the static pressure at the inlet of the diffuser could be as low as 400 Torr absolute.

The original configuration of the test installation is shown in Fig. 7, comprising a 200 Hp. blower with adjustable inlet vanes, pulling the air from a plenum chamber and discharging it through a stack through the roof of the building. The test diffuser was located between the inlet bell, designed to provide uniform velocity across the duct except for the developing boundary layer, and the plenum chamber evacuated by the blower. All elements of the duct and the diffuser were suspended from an overhead rail for easy access to any segment of the apparatus, which could be altered by removing and substituting parts as needed. The static pressure in the plenum as controlled by the adjustable vanes in the blower, was the actual discharge pressure of the diffuser, and the actual value of this, compared with the static pressure at the inlet, was the measure of the performance of the diffuser.

The original long conical diffuser was built from cylindrical aluminum castings, each 160 mm. long, each carrying four static pressure taps (cf. Fig. 9) with the inner surface carefully machined to match the desired profile,

including the displacement thickness of the developing boundary layer. This form of construction proved very convenient when it was decided to shorten the diffuser and add slots implementing the new design, as shown in Fig. 8, which shows it as it was first conceived; later it underwent substantial modification (see Fig. 11).

The instrumentation consisted of a bank of 46 mercury manometers plus two mercury U-tubes mounted in front of a ruled, graduated board that could be moved so as to set the zero of the graduation to the level of a barometer tube, thus providing absolute pressure readings for local atmospheric pressure as well as for each of the manometer tubes. A schematic side view of the arrangement is shown in Fig. 10. The manometers were connected to the static pressure taps along the duct (Fig. 9), along the slotted diffuser, at several points along the collecting scoop, and/or to a special Pitot tube (Fig. 11). This last had a micrometer drive for precise measurements across the boundary layer and across the wakes of the slots, and could be placed in correspondence with any of the static pressure taps. The bank of manometers was photographed by a permanently mounted Polaroid camera for documentation of the instantaneous pressure profile together with readings of thermometers, barometers, and other associated instruments (Fig. 13).

Fig. 13 is one such Polaroid photograph recording the performance of run #1027. Tubes 1 through 5 indicate the pressure in the inlet; tubes 6 through 15, the pressure in the test section, showing a minimum pressure of 431 Torr in Tube 9. Tubes 16 through 21 show the static pressure at the first slots, and the remaining tubes show the static pressure at various points in the system. Tubes 27, 28, and 46 are not connected, and measure the atmospheric pressure at 750 Torr. Tube 37 shows the blower suction in the plenum at 705 Torr.

A common measure of diffuser performance is the pressure recovery coefficient Cp defined as

$$Cp = (pt-p) / (p0-p) \qquad (19)$$

which, for a given diffuser geometry, is a function of the inlet Mach number and the inlet blockage factor (North, 1975). Careful measurements of the boundary layer profiles at the inlet of the diffuser yielded a value for the blockage factor of 0.09, almost independent of Mach number. The measurement illustrated in Fig. 13 is near the low end of the measured performance range, reading only

$$Cp = (705 - 431) / (750-431) = 0.86 \qquad (20)$$

$p/p0 = 431/750 = 0.575$, which corresponds to a Mach number of 0.92.

Fig. 11 shows the micrometer-driven Pitot tube mounted to measure the details of the flow from the first slot as it mixed with the boundary layer from the test section (the static pressure is provided by the static pressure taps, which are omitted for clarity in Fig. 11. Note the difference of the slot configuration from Fig. 8, the result of several resesigns)..

Fig. 12 shows the measured results; it is interesting to note that the minimum pressure in the wake of the wall appears to be displaced from the point corresponding to the slot width (19 mm), This displacement is due to the fact the filling of the pressure valley occurs mostly with air from the slot, since the velocity gradient is initially steeper on that side; in addition there is the displacement thickness of the new boundary layer developing on the new wall.

The measured values of Cp as a function of inlet Mach number are shown in Fig. 14. The shaded band shows the range obtained by changing slot plenum pressure and/or scoop geometry. Also shown for comparison are data from Figure 22 of North (1975), representing typical performance of state-of-the-art conical diffusers for the same blockage factor (0.09). The Cp of this experimental radial recirculating diffuser ranges from 0.84 to 0.92 over the range of Mach 0.2 to 0.95, while the conical diffusers sampled by Rundstadler et al. (1975) ranged from 0.75 to 0.67 over the same Mach number range. It should be noted that Cp is here computed using the value of $p0$ at the center of the core flow. This is a very conservative choice; still better performance could be presented if, more realistically, the mass weighted average of each streamtube $pavg$ were to be used instead of $p0$ for computing Cp .

6. SUMMARY AND CONCLUSIONS

An effective and economical method has been demonstrated for preventing the detachment of the boundary layer in a short diffuser. The fact that no detachment occurs in the presence of very strong adverse pressure gradients permits the design and construction of diffusers with arbitrary and very high area ratio. The very high pressure recovery ratio and total pressure ratio obtainable with this Radial Recirculating Diffuser makes it useful in all those applications where the energy efficiency of a fluidynamic device is strongly dependent on the transformation of the kinetic energy of a fluid into pressure.

BIBLIOGRAPHY

[1]   L. Prandtl, and O. G. Tietjens, *"Fundamentals of Hydro- and Aeromechanics"*, Dover New York, 1957, pg.. 143-144.

[2]   A. H. Shapiro, *"The Dynamics and Thermodynamics of Compressible Fluid Flow"*, The Ronald Press Co, New York, 1953, Vol. 1, pg. 291-297.

[3]   H. Schlichting, *"Boundary Layer Theory"*, McGraw-Hill Co., New York, 1960, pg. 578.

[4]   North, Paul, *"The Suppression of Flow Separation by Sequential Wall Jets"*, ASME publication 75-WA-FE-9, 1975.

[5]   P. W. Rundstadler, F. X. Dlan, and R.C. Dean, *"Diffuser Data Book"*, TN-186, Creare Inc., Hanover, New Hampshire 1975.

ASMERRDf4Tech95

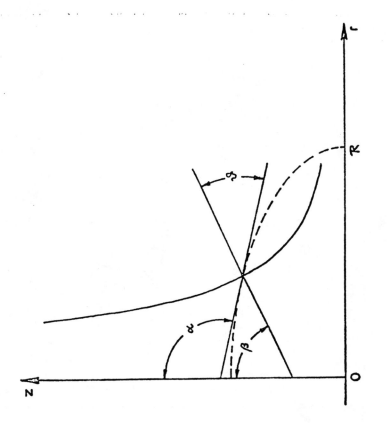

Fig. 2: Angles Between Streamlines and Isobaric Lines

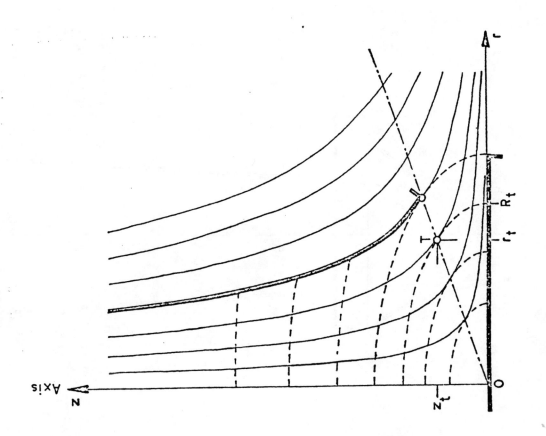

Fig. 1: Flow Geometry

615

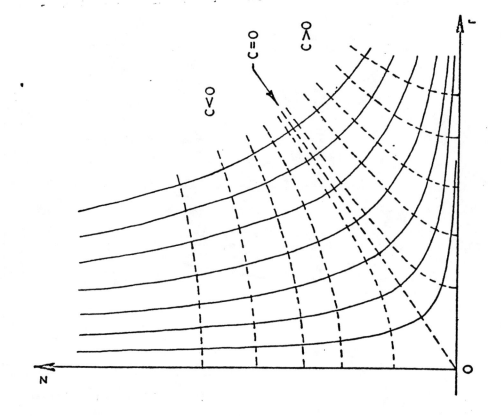

Fig. 4: Orthogonal Trajectories of
Streamlines

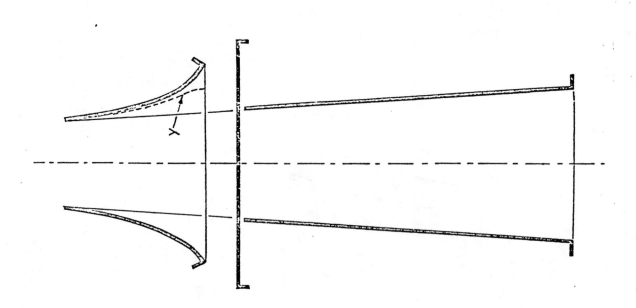

Fig. 3: Comparison of Impact Diffuser
and Conical Diffuser

616

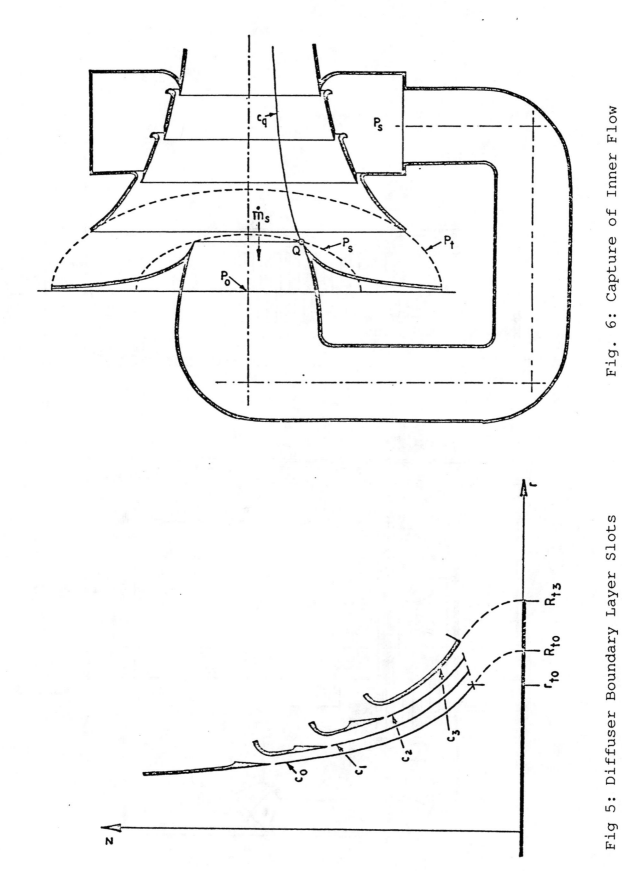

Fig. 6: Capture of Inner Flow

Fig 5: Diffuser Boundary Layer Slots

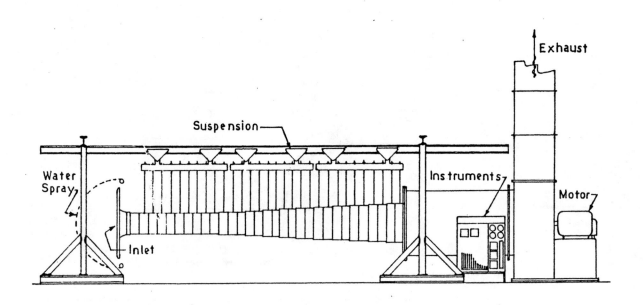

Fig. 7: Original Conical Diffuser

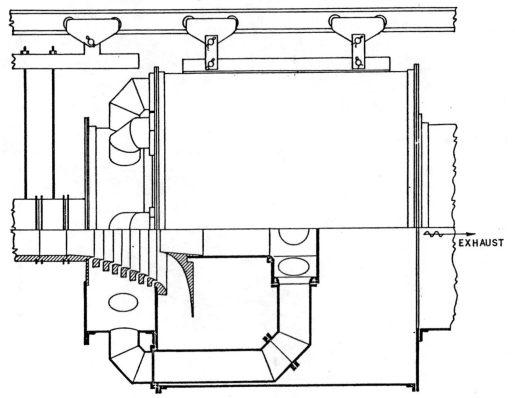

Fig. 8: Diffuser Scoop Geometry

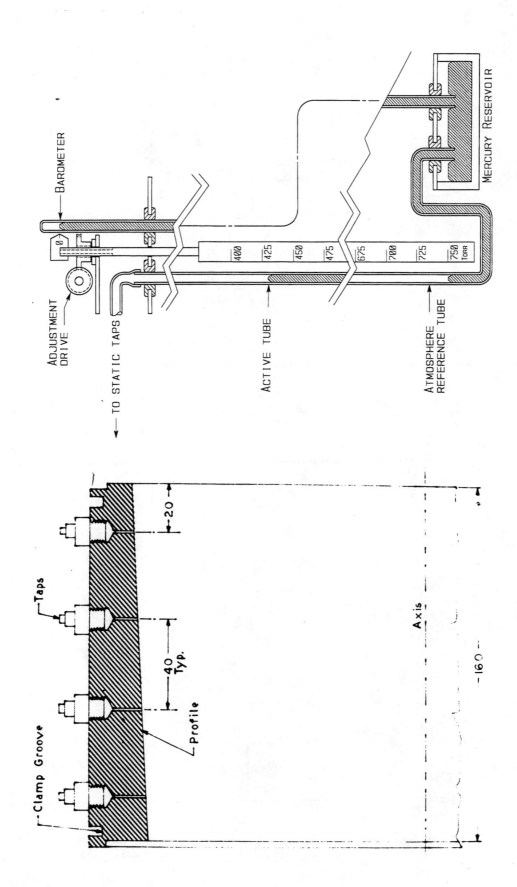

BAROMETER

ADJUSTMENT
DRIVE

TO STATIC TAPS

ACTIVE TUBE

ATMOSPHERE
REFERENCE TUBE

MERCURY RESERVOIR

400
425
450
475
675
700
725
750 TORR

Fig.10: Edge View of Manometer Board

Clamp Groove

Taps

20

40
Typ.

Profile

Axis

160

Fig. 9: Typical Wall Segment with
Static Pressure Taps

619

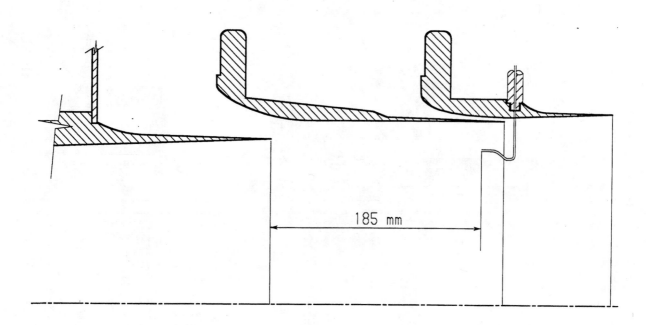

Fig.11: Micrometer-Driven Pitot Tube Downstream of First Slot

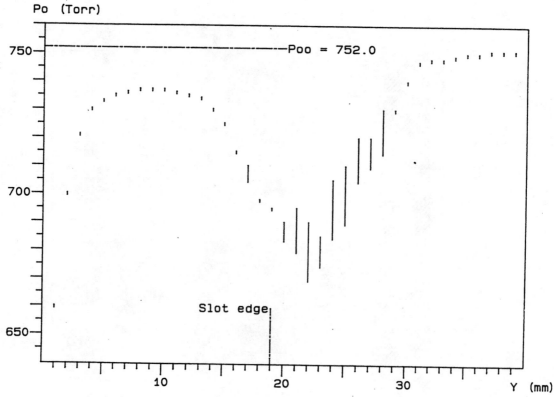

Fig.12: Survey of Stagnation Pressures in Wake
of First Slot Gas Injection

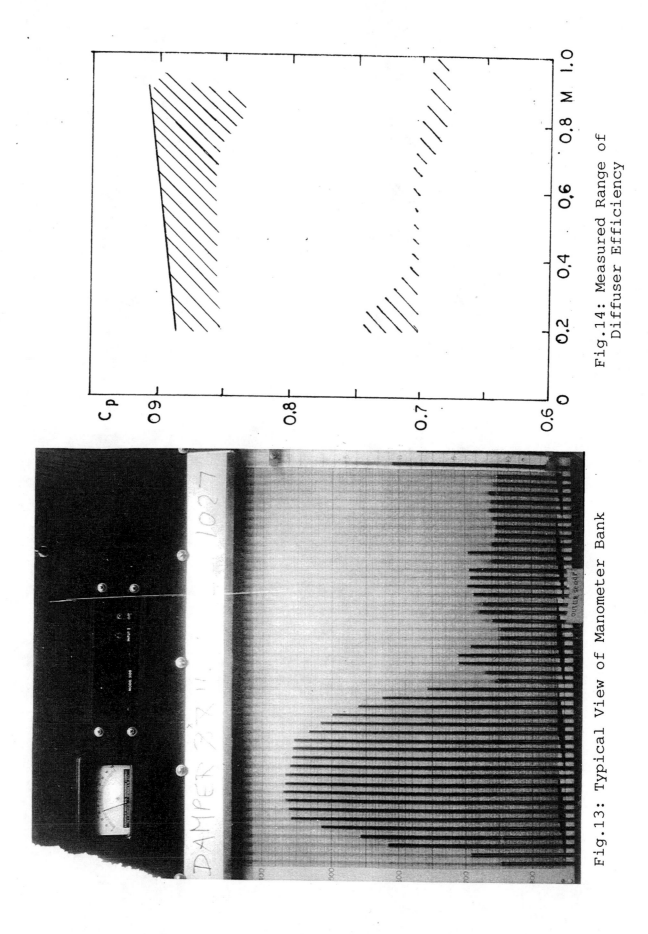

Fig.14: Measured Range of
Diffuser Efficiency

Fig.13: Typical View of Manometer Bank

FED-Vol. 238, 1996 Fluids Engineering Division Conference
Volume 3
ASME 1996

OPTIMIZATION OF SYMMETRICAL PROFILES FOR THE WELLS TURBINE ROTOR BLADES

L.M.C. Gato and J.C.C. Henriques
Department of Mechanical Engineering, Instituto Superior Técnico
Universidade Técnica de Lisboa
Lisbon
Portugal

ABSTRACT

The paper describes a numerical optimization study of symmetrical blades for the Wells turbine, which is a self-rectifying axial-flow turbine suitable for wave power plants. The optimization method is based on a two-dimensional potential flow calculation, and on Polak-Ribière's conjugate gradient algorithm. The aim is to control the shape of the pressure distribution around the profiles and postpone separation and stall, so as to extend the turbine's operating range. Results of the inviscid flow design method are presented for a Wells turbine rotor cascade and validated in the case of isolated aerofoils, against XFOIL viscous flow calculations.

NOMENCLATURE

c = chord

C_D = $2D/(\rho V_\infty^2 c)$, drag coefficient

C_L = $2L/(\rho V_\infty^2 c)$, lift coefficient

C_p = $2(p_s - p_\infty)/(\rho V_\infty^2)$, pressure coefficient

D = drag force per unit of span

L = lift force per unit of span

m = position of maximum thickness

p = static pressure

r, θ, x = cylindrical co-ordinate system

r_t = leading edge radius

Re = $(\rho V_\infty c)/\mu$, Reynolds number

S = cascade pitch

t = aerofoil maximum thickness

$\mathbf{U}_\infty$ = far field velocity, Fig. 2

$\mathbf{V}, \mathbf{W}$ = absolute, relative velocity

V_∞ = U_∞ (isolated airfoil), W_m (cascade)

$\mathbf{W}_m$ = $(\mathbf{W}_1 + \mathbf{W}_2)/2$, Fig. 3

w = complex velocity

x = distance along chord from leading edge

y = aerofoil ordinate perpendicular to chord

(x, y) = cartesian co-ordinate system

α = angle of attack

α_d = design angle of attack

β = angle of relative velocity

Γ = total circulation

λ = cascade stagger angle

μ = viscosity

ρ = density

ω = rotor angular speed

Subscripts

opt = optimum value

p = pressure surface

s = at the profile surface, suction surface

sep = separation point

x, θ = axial, tangential velocity component

$1, 2$ = far upstream, downstream

∞ = far field

1. INTRODUCTION

The motion of ocean waves has been recognized as a potential source of renewable energy. Several different principles for wave power extraction have been developed, such as the oscillating water column (OWC). This device converts the water wave motion into a reciprocating air flow, which can in turn be directed through an air turbine to drive an electrical generator.

The Wells turbine is an axial flow turbine consisting essentially of a rotor with untwisted aerofoil blades of symmetrical cross section set radially at a stagger angle $\lambda = 90°$ (Raghunathan and Tan, 1983a; Raghunathan, 1995; Gato and Falcão, 1984; 1988), as shown in Fig. 1. Being symmetrical about a plane normal to the turbine axis, these

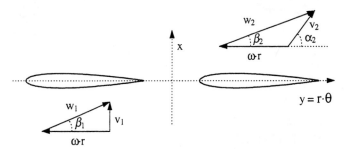

Fig. 1 Blade geometry and velocity diagram.

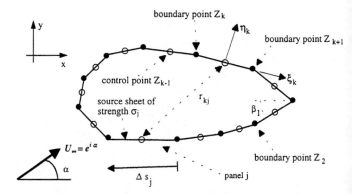

Fig. 2 Surface panel distribution.

blades are not sensitive to the direction of the approaching axial air flow and therefore provide an unidirectional torque from an oscillating airflow. Different versions of the turbine have been considered and studied with and without guide vanes, e.g. the biplane (Raghunathan and Tan, 1983b; Inoue et al., 1986; Gato and Curran, 1996a), the contra-rotating (Beattie and Ragunathan, 1993; Gato and Curran, 1996b) and the variable-pitch Wells turbines (Gato and Falcão, 1989; Sarmento et al., 1990; Salter, 1993).

One of the main points to consider in the design of a Wells turbine rotor for wave energy applications is the maximization of the range of sea conditions during which the turbine can operate efficiently. For high flow rates, the operational range of all fixed-pitch configurations is limited by the flow stalling around the rotor blades. This is due to the turbine's sensitivity to the angle of the relative airflow approaching the blades, Fig. 1. At high flow rates the incident flow angle to the blade increases. If this angle becomes too large, the flow over the blade separates and stalls resulting in a loss of lift from the blade and a marked increase in drag, culminating in a loss of torque in the turbine rotor.

The paper describes an inviscid flow methodology for the numerical optimization of symmetrical blade profiles aiming at the extension of the Wells turbine operating range for large flow rates. The basic idea behind the method is to control the shape of the pressure distribution around the turbine rotor blade sections, so as to postpone separation and stall. Results of the inviscid optimization method were obtained and are presented, both for isolated aerofoils and for a cascade of blades. The method is validated by comparing the results of the inviscid optimization method for single aerofoils with results from corresponding viscous analysis using the XFOIL code (Drela, 1989).

2. PANEL METHOD FOR INVISCID INCOMPRESSIBLE FLOW

In many engineering applications the fluid flow around an aerofoil can be closely approximated as two-dimensional and incompressible. Making further assumptions and considering an inviscid and irrotational flow, it can be shown that the equations of motion are reduced to the simple Laplace equation (see, e.g. Katz and Plotkin (1991)). The linearity of Laplace equation is used in the theory of the panel method to decompose the flow around an aerofoil in two basic flows: the first is a non-lifting flow resulting from an uniform stream; the other is a pure circulatory flow that is superposed to the non-lifting flow, to satisfy the Kutta condition. The panel method has become a standard aerodynamic tool for the numerical solution of low-speed flows, since the late 1960s. However, various formulations of the

panel method have been proposed, differing essentially in the way they implement these basic flows.

2.1 Isolated Aerofoil

In the present approach, we follow the methodology described by Eça (1987), which allows the calculation of cusped trailing edges. The aerofoil contour and its mean line are divided, respectively, in small flat N and M segments (panels) and then sources or vortexes are distributed in each panel to obtain the combined lifting flow.

The non-lifting flow is simulated as a combination of a source sheet distribution of constant strength σ_j at each surface panel j, and an uniform stream at an incidence angle α, Fig. 2. The complex velocity at a control point k is obtained adding the complex velocities evaluated, respectively, for the source sheets (Gato and Henriques, 1994),

$$w_k = -\frac{i}{2}\sigma_k + \sum_{j=1,N}^{j \neq k} Q_{kj}\sigma_j , \qquad (1)$$

and the onset uniform stream of unitary velocity,

$$w_k^\infty = e^{(-\alpha+\beta_k)i} . \qquad (2)$$

Here β_k is the angle of the panel k with respect to the real axis x, Fig. 2. For a single aerofoil, the induction coefficient Q_{kj} is given by (Gato and Henriques, 1994)

$$Q_{kj} = \frac{e^{i(\beta_k-\beta_j)}}{2\pi}\ln\left(\frac{z_k - c_{j_1}}{z_k - c_{j_2}}\right). \qquad (3)$$

In Eq. (3) z_k is a complex variable representing the coordinates of the control point k and c_{1_j}, c_{2_j}, are the values of the end points of panel j, in the local coordinate system $(\xi, i\eta)$ shown in Fig. 2.

The imposition of the boundary condition of zero normal velocity at the body surface for the non-lifting flow, at $k = 1,...,N$ control points, results in a simple linear system of N equations,

$$\text{im}(w_k) + \text{im}(w_k^\infty) = 0 , \qquad (4)$$

which can be solved for σ_j.

The circulatory flow is obtained combining vortex sheets of constant strength at the mean line and source sheets in the surface panels, as for the non-lifting flow. Knowing that the overall circulation distribution in the aerofoil is arbitrary, as shown in (Hess,

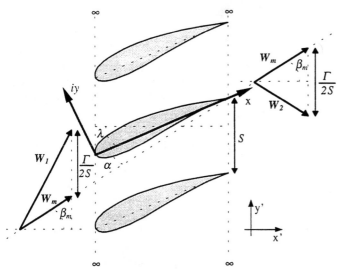

Fig. 3 Vector diagram showing inlet and outlet velocities and angles.

1974), we will follow Eça's (1987) recommendation and use an overall hyperbolic variation that reaches zero at the trailing edge, as physically required,

$$\gamma_l = \gamma^0 s_l^{0.4}, \qquad (5)$$

where γ_l is the strength of the vortex sheet in panel l of the mean line, s_l is the mean line length measured from the trailing edge to control point l, and γ^0 is such that the Kutta condition is satisfied. The total circulation around the aerofoil Γ is then obtained integrating Eq. (5) along the aerofoil mean line, from the leading edge to the trailing edge.

Taking into account the simple relationship between the complex velocity induced by a vortex sheet (w_v) and a source sheet (w_s) of equal geometry and unitary strength, $w_v(z) = i\,w_s(z)$, the velocity induced by the M vortex sheets in the k panel, per unit of γ^0, can then be written as

$$w_k^* = \sum_{l=1}^{M} i Q_{kl} s_l^{0.4}, \qquad (6)$$

where Q_{kl} is given by Eq. (3). The source strength σ_j^c required to satisfy the boundary condition of zero normal velocity at the body surface can be calculated from

$$\text{im}(w_k^c) + \text{im}(w_k^*) = 0, \qquad (7)$$

where w_k^c is obtained introducing σ^c in Eq. (1). To impose the Kutta condition, we specify equal velocity (pressure) at the two control points adjacent to the trailing edge (Hess, 1974), from which we finally obtain the required constant value

$$\gamma^0 = -\frac{\text{re}(w_1^\infty + w_N^\infty + w_1 + w_N)}{\text{re}(w_1^* + w_N^* + w_1^c + w_N^c)}. \qquad (8)$$

2.2 Cascade

For a cascade of blades, we adopt the global coordinate system (x, iy) shown in Fig. 3. Using the same panel discretization in all the blades, we find $N+M$ rows of an infinite number of similar panels set with a pitch S along straight lines normal to the cascade axis. Instead of Eq. (3), derived for a single aerofoil, the induction coefficient Q_{kj} for a cascade of blades, Fig. 3, is (Gato and Henriques, 1994)

$$Q_{kj} = \frac{e^{i(\beta_k - \beta_j)}}{2\pi} \ln\left\{ \frac{\sinh\left[\pi\left(z_k - c_{1j}\right)\big/Se^{\lambda i}\right]}{\sinh\left[\pi\left(z_k - c_{2j}\right)\big/Se^{\lambda i}\right]} \right\}. \qquad (9)$$

It can be shown that the coefficient of self induction given by Eq. (9) at $(\xi, i\eta) = (0, +0i)$ is the same as that obtained for the isolated aerofoil (Eq. (3)), i.e. $Q_{kk} = -1/2i$. Therefore, cascade calculations can be performed along the same lines as described in Section 2.1 for the isolated aerofoil, simply replacing Eq. (3) by Eq. (9). This is the main advantage of using complex variables in the calculations.

Having determined the blade circulation, the inlet and the outlet velocities (Fig. 3) are easily computed from

$$w_1 = e^{i\beta_m} + \frac{i\Gamma}{2S} \quad \text{and} \quad w_2 = e^{i\beta_m} - \frac{i\Gamma}{2S}. \qquad (10)$$

In addition, the inlet and outlet flow angles are given by

$$\beta_1 = \arg(w_2) \quad \text{and} \quad \beta_2 = \arg(w_2). \qquad (11)$$

3. OPTIMIZATION METHOD FOR SYMMETRICAL BLADES

3.1 Optimization Technique

Starting with a design space D defined by a set of geometric parameters $\mathbf{x}$ describing the blade geometry,

$$D = \left\{ \mathbf{x} = \{x_i\} : x_{i_{\min}} \le x_i \le x_{i_{\max}}, \ x_i \in \Re^1, i = 1, \ldots, n \right\} \quad (12)$$

the problem consists in minimizing an objective function

$$f(\mathbf{x}) : D(\mathbf{x}) \subset \Re^n \to \Re^1, \qquad (13)$$

subject to side constraints,

$$\min\{f(\mathbf{x}) : \mathbf{x} \in D\}. \qquad (14)$$

Almost all the optimization algorithms use the following procedure: given a certain starting point, $\mathbf{x}^0$, and a search direction unit vector, $\mathbf{s}^0$, compute a travel distance, α^q, such as

$$f^{q+1} = \min\{f(\mathbf{x}^q + \alpha^q \mathbf{s}^q) : \alpha^q \ge 0\}, \text{ and} \qquad (15)$$

$$\nabla f(\mathbf{x}^q) \cdot \mathbf{s}^q < 0, \qquad (16)$$

where q is the iteration number. Then, calculate a new direction, $\mathbf{s}^q$, and repeat the procedure starting with the new point, $\mathbf{x}^q$, until $|\alpha^q| < \varepsilon$, where ε is the desired tolerance. In the present work, the algorithm chosen to determine the search direction is based on the well known Polak-Ribière's conjugate gradient method (for theoretical considerations see (Polak, 1971); for an engineering approach see (Vanderplaats, 1984)). Furthermore, this method uses a directional gradient, which in the present implementation is obtained by the following finite difference scheme:

$$\nabla f \cdot \mathbf{s} \cong \frac{f(\mathbf{x}^q + \delta \cdot \mathbf{s}) - f(\mathbf{x}^q)}{\delta} \quad . \qquad (17)$$

In order to have a similar round-off error in all variables of the previous finite difference, we apply the following parametric variable transformation

$$x_i = \left(x_{i_{max}} - x_{i_{min}}\right) \cdot t_i + x_{i_{min}} \quad , \qquad (18)$$

where t_i stands for the new design variables, which have a constraint $t_i \in [0,1]$.

In the present blade design we are restricted to the constraints defined by Eq. (12). Geometrically, this means that our space of feasible designs is an hipercube.

3.2 Blade Shape

The blade shape was described using the NACA Four and Five digit thickness distribution series, which are defined by the following two equations (Abbott and Doenhoff, 1959):

$$\pm y_t(x) = \begin{cases} a_0 \sqrt{x} + a_1 x + a_2 x^2 + a_3 x^3 & ,x < m \\ d_0 + d_1(1-x) + d_2(1-x)^2 + d_3(1-x)^3 & ,x \geq m \end{cases} \qquad (20)$$

where y_t, x and m are, respectively, the dimensionless ordinate and abscissa of a point on the surface, and the position of maximum thickness divided by the blade chord c.

The four coefficients d_0, d_1, d_2, d_3 are determined from the following conditions:

• Maximum thickness: $y_t(m^+) = \pm 0.5\,t$; $y_t'(m^+) = 0$. (21)

• Trailing edge angle: $y_t'(1) = -f(m,t)$, where $f(m,t)$ is a polynomial interpolation of NACA's recommended table of values

$$f(m,t) = t \cdot \left(-12.5m^4 + 35.833m^3 - 13.625m^2 + 2.517m + 0.775\right). \quad (22)$$

• Trailing edge thickness: $y_t(1) = 0.01t$. (23)

The other four coefficients a_0, a_1, a_2, a_3 are determined from the following conditions:

• Maximum thickness: $y_t(m^-) = \pm 0.5t$, $y_t'(m^-) = 0$. (24)

• Leading edge radius: $r_t = 0.5\,a_0^2$. (25)

• Radius of curvature R at the point of maximum thickness:

$$R = \left(2d_2 + 6d_3(1-m)\right)^{-1}. \qquad (26)$$

Finally, we supply the maximum thickness t, the leading edge radius r_t and the position of maximum thickness m. Based on geometrical considerations we impose the following constraints to the main variables:

$$0.01 \leq r_t \leq 0.06 \quad , \qquad 0.06 \leq m \leq 0.6 \,. \qquad (27)$$

3.3 Objective Function

The optimization aims at controlling the shape of the pressure distribution around the profile in order to postpone separation and stall using inviscid flow methods. Separation is known to be strongly dependent on the adverse pressure gradient and, therefore, it is expected that a smoother adverse pressure gradient results in postponing stall. For this reason we considered the minimization of the adverse pressure gradient of the inviscid flow as the objective function,

$$Obj = \min\left[\oint H(\vartheta)\,\vartheta^2 \mathrm{d}s\right] \quad , \qquad (28)$$

where $H(\vartheta)$ is the Heaviside function, $\vartheta = -\partial c_p / \partial s$, c_p the surface pressure coefficient, and $\mathrm{d}s$ is a line element on the blade contour.

The use of other design criteria normally suited for conventional turbine cascades, e.g. the minimization of the normalized load,

$$Obj = \min\left[\int_0^c \left(c_{p_s} - c_{p_p}\right)^2 \mathrm{d}x\right], \qquad (29)$$

where dx is a line element on the blade mean-line, was seen to produce unrealistic designs due to the adopted thickness distribution (Section 3.2).

When we apply the Kutta condition to a cusped blade, the resulting trailing edge velocity is not necessarily zero, as is the case when we consider it to have a finite angle. Therefore, in inviscid flow, the trailing edge pressure gradient found is usually smoother for a cusped section than for an aerofoil ending with a finite angle. In early calculations the trailing edge angle was considered as a design variable, and the design method always generated cusped blades. Due to manufacturing restrictions, it is necessary to impose the slope of the profile at the trailing edge, for which we decided to use the NACA recommendation that determines the slope as a function of the leading edge radius and the position of maximum thickness (Eqs. (22) and (23)). Furthermore, the objective function is subject to the side constraints given by the inequalities (27).

4. VISCOUS FLOW STUDY

Although adverse pressure gradient and separation are related, it was intended to validate the inviscid flow optimization criteria against a viscous calculation. It is well known that these effects are of primary importance in the characterisation of the performance of an aerofoil especially at high angles of attack, as is required for the operation of the Wells turbine. For such incidence angles, separation is expected to occur in a large area of the turbine blades surface. Under these flow conditions only a Navier-Stokes code seems accurate enough to predict the pressure distribution. The major problem of such implementation is the computation time required. In the latest workstations, several hours are necessary to achieve convergence of a two-dimensional Navier-Stokes code. If the optimization method requires, say a hundred objective function evaluations, the overall execution time will amount to several days. A design method based on an optimization technique definitely requires a faster analysis method.

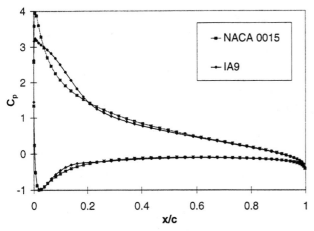

Fig. 4 Surface pressure distribution of NACA 0015 and IA9 aerofoils at $\alpha = 9°$, in potential flow.

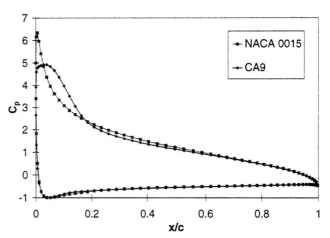

Fig. 6 Cascade blade surface pressure distribution: NACA 0015 and CA9 aerofoils at $\alpha = 9°$, for $\lambda = 90°$ and S/c=1.5, in potential flow.

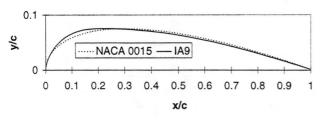

Fig. 5 NACA 0015 and IA9 aerofoils.

4.1 The XFOIL Code

Viscous flow calculations were performed using the XFOIL code (Drela, 1989), which is based upon a two-equation lagged dissipation integral method. The transition between laminar and turbulent flow is determined by an e^9-type amplification formulation. The boundary layer and transition equations are solved simultaneously with the inviscid flow field by a global Newton method. The viscous-inviscid coupling is modelled by a wall transpiration concept where the local source strength is equal to the local gradient of mass defect. Drela's method is considered reliable in the prediction of transition separation bubbles in single aerofoils, even at low Reynolds number flows. However, XFOIL does not take into account the cascade interference among blades which would eventually discourage its use in the design of Wells turbine blades. In fact, cascade interference is seen to have a strong influence on the aerofoil pressure distribution when performing inviscid flow analysis based on the panel method. Knowing that inviscid effects generally control the modification of the aerofoil surface pressure distribution due to cascade interference, it was thought that if the inviscid optimization method proved to be effective in the design of isolated profiles it would also be adequate for the design of profiles in cascade. For this reason, it was decided to use XFOIL as a means of assessing and validating the inviscid optimization method considering only isolated aerofoils.

4.2 Optimization Method Using XFOIL

The methodology used before in inviscid flow for the design of symmetrical aerofoils with high stalling angles was initially adopted to be used together with the XFOIL code. If Eq. (29) were adopted as the objective function for the viscous flow calculations, we would obtain aerofoils subject to large separated flow regions, which is exactly the opposite of what is intended. The obvious reason is that in the separated flow regions the pressure gradient is almost null.

The objective function was then chosen to be the minimization of the ratio between the drag and lift forces at a given design angle of attack, α_d. The optimization procedure was found not to work properly due to numerical inaccuracies inherent to the boundary layer integral method. (The drag evaluation using XFOIL is only three significant digits accurate). In fact, from different starting conditions the solution usually converged to a local minimum point rather than to the true optimum. Since the method was seen to rely on only two design variables (leading edge radius and position of maximum thickness), it was decided to replace the exact approach used in the inviscid flow optimization method by a graphic analysis of the objective function, based upon an XFOIL calculation of the flow within a broad window of the design space, centred in optimum values given by the inviscid flow design method, at given incidence angles and Reynolds number.

5. RESULTS

The numerical optimization techniques discussed above have been used to design several aerofoils. A thickness ratio $t/c = 0.15$ was selected for the aerofoil design in order to compare the aerodynamic characteristics of the new sections with those of the standard NACA 0015.

Results of the optimization are a function of the design angle of attack, α_d, and calculations were performed for different types of flow situations. The values used were:

- $\alpha_d = 9°$, attached flow or incipient trailing edge separation;

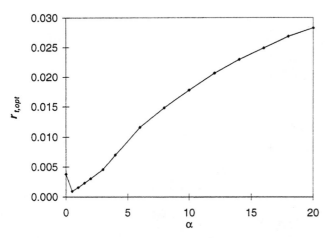

Fig. 7 Variation of the optimum leading edge radius with
the design angle of attack.

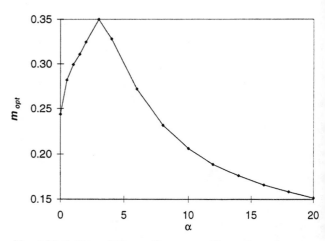

Fig. 8 Variation of the optimum position of maximum
thickness with the design angle of attack.

	Design Type	Name	m	r_t	c_L at $\alpha=9°$	Min. c_p at $\alpha=9°$	c_L at $\alpha=18°$	Min. c_p at $\alpha=18°$
Isolated	NACA	0015	0.300	0.0159	1.11	-4.0	2.20	-12.7
	Eq. (29), $\alpha_d = 9°$	IL9	0.516	0.0018	1.10	-17.4	2.18	-65.1
	Eq. (28), $\alpha_d = 9°$	IA9	0.218	0.0165	1.11	-3.2	2.20	-11.9
	Eq. (28), $\alpha_d = 14°$	IA14	0.176	0.0230	1.12	-3.4	2.20	-9.9
	Eq. (28), $\alpha_d = 18°$	IA18	0.158	0.0264	1.12	-3.6	2.21	-8.9
Cascade[(*)]	NACA	0015	0.300	0.0159	2.06	-6.4	4.07	-22.0
	Eq. (28), $\alpha_d = 9°$	CA9	0.198	0.0214	2.08	-5.1	4.11	-18.5

[(*)] $\lambda=90°$; $S/c=1.5$

Table 1 Design variables and some aerodynamic characteristics of
the optimized profiles in comparison with the NACA 0015.

- $\alpha_d = 14°$, flow with moderate trailing edge separation;
- $\alpha_d = 18°$, flow with massive trailing edge separation.

In all the calculations the aerofoil shape was represented by 100 panels. The integrals that appear in the objective functions of Section 3.3 were evaluated using the trapezoidal rule. The surface velocity derivative was calculated using a cubic spline interpolation.

5.1 Inviscid Flow Optimization

Calculations were performed both for the case of an isolated aerofoil and for a Wells turbine cascade. The results of the inviscid optimization method are summarized in Table 1.

It can be seen from Table 1 that the load minimization method (Eq. (29)) generates an aerofoil without practical interest, due to the huge pressure peak found in its leading edge. This proves the inability of the present method to design uncambered aerofoils subject to an approximately uniform pressure load through its chord, taking into account the thickness distribution restrictions of Section 3.2.

Figure 4 compares the chordwise pressure distribution of two isolated aerofoils at an incidence angle $\alpha = 9°$: the NACA 0015 section and the IA9 profile, designed with the objective function given by Eq. (28) for a design incidence angle $\alpha_d = 9°$. While for constant flow incidence the lift coefficient is almost the same for both profiles,

the new design provides a lower pressure peak and a smoother pressure recovery. Furthermore, the results show that the design method moves the maximum thickness position of the modified profiles towards the leading edge, and a leading edge radius increase when compared with the NACA 0015 aerofoil, Fig. 5.

The results presented in Table 1 and Fig. 6 for a cascade of blades, with stagger angle $\lambda = 90°$ and pitch-to-chord ratio $S/c = 1.5$, also show, as for the isolated aerofoils, that the method based on Eq. (28) has produced a profile with a lower pressure peak and smoother pressure recovery in comparison with the standard NACA 0015 section. Although the geometric differences of the isolated aerofoil, in comparison with the cascade sections, are not too pronounced for the same design incidence angle, α_d, (the point of maximum thickness is moved only 2% towards the leading edge, and the leading edge radius slightly increased, see Table 1), larger differences are found when the sections are compared for approximately the same design lift coefficient (e.g. comparing the IA18 with the CA9). This means cascade effects are to be taken into account in the optimization process of Wells turbine rotor blade sections.

Figures 7 and 8 show the optimum leading edge radius, $r_{t_{opt}}$, and the position of maximum thickness, m_{opt}, of the optimized isolated aerofoils (adverse pressure gradient method, Eq. (28)), as a function of

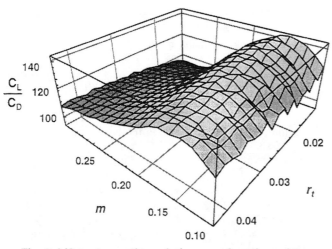

Fig. 9 Lift to drag ratio variation as a function of the leading edge radius and position of maximum thickness, at $\alpha_d = 14°$ and Re = 5×10⁶.

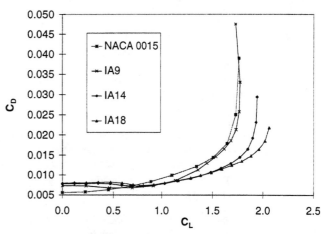

Fig. 10 Lift and drag characteristics of the NACA 0015, IA9, IA14 and IA18 aerofoils.

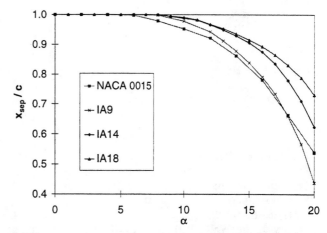

Fig. 11 Position of the separation point at the suction surface of NACA 0015, IA9, IA14 and IA18 aerofoils, as a function of the incidence angle.

the design incidence angle α_d. The figures show a monotonic variation of the leading edge radius with the increase in α_d, whereas the position of maximum thickness presents a maximum for $\alpha_d \approx 3°$. This is a consequence of the geometrical restrictions imposed upon the function that generates the thickness distribution (see Section 3.2).

5.2 Viscous Flow Optimization

Viscous flow calculations were performed only for the case of isolated aerofoils, since XFOIL does not allow the calculation of cascade flows. Figure 9 presents the lift-to-drag ratio for 15% relative thickness aerofoils (thickness distribution as defined in Section 3.2), for a wide range of design variables, centred in the optimum values given by the inviscid flow design method, i.e. $0.014 \leq r_t \leq 0.044$ and $0.1 \leq m \leq 0.3$, at $\alpha_d = 14°$ and a Re = 5×10⁶. The figure shows that maximum lift-to-drag ratio is almost insensitive to a change in the leading edge radius. Furthermore, the maximum lift-to-drag ratio is obtained for a value m near the one achieved with the inviscid optimization (see Table 1), but with the position of the maximum thickness moved further towards the leading edge. This behaviour was also seen to occur for $\alpha_d = 9°$ and 18°.

Figures 10 and 11 compare the aerodynamic characteristics of four optimized profiles, as given by both the inviscid and the viscous flow optimization methods at $\alpha_d = 9°$, 14° and 18°, with respect to the standard NACA 0015 section in terms of lift, drag, and separation point at the suction surface. Figure 10 clearly shows that the optimization methods were successful in producing blades which significantly delay the onset of separation. In fact, the optimized sections are seen to achieve substantially higher maximum lift coefficients than the NACA 0015, more prone to stall as indicated by the sharp increase in drag. The postponement of stall can also be seen in Fig. 11, which represents the non-dimensional co-ordinate x_{sep} where the onset of separation occurs for each section as a function of the angle of attack.

The optimized sections have higher drag at low incidence angles (below 8°) when compared to the NACA 0015 section (Fig. 10). This constitutes a disadvantage for the optimized sections, since low aerofoil drag at small incidence angles is known to be a very important characteristic to bear in mind in the design of Wells turbine rotor blades. However, the NACA 0015 presents higher drag for high incidence angles, up to $\alpha = 19°$. This fact is in close relationship with the extent of the boundary layer separation, as can be seen from Figs. 10 and 11.

Finally, it should be noted that the XFOIL results presented for high incidence angles have a large degree of uncertainty due to the turbulence modelling. The effects of compressibility in the aerodynamic characteristics of the optimized sections should also be studied in the future.

6. CONCLUSION

This paper presents a methodology for the numerical optimization of Wells turbine symmetrical blades using a generic panel method for the calculation of two-dimensional potential flow around aerofoils, as well as an optimization algorithm based on the Polak-Ribière's conjugate gradient method. The objective function aims at controlling the shape of the pressure distribution around the profiles, in order to postpone separation and stall.

The inviscid flow optimization criteria were validated against XFOIL viscous flow calculations, in the case of isolated aerofoils. It is concluded that the inviscid flow optimization is far more robust and its results are in good qualitative agreement with the ones obtained for viscous flow. In comparison with a standard NACA 0015 section, the results clearly show that the proposed optimization methods were successful in designing derivatives of the NACA 0015 section which significantly delay the onset of separation. However, the optimized sections are seen to have higher drag at low incidence angles, which is undesirable for the Wells turbine applications.

ACKNOWLEDGEMENTS

The work was partially financially supported by IDMEC and contract JOU2-CT93-0333 (DG 12 WSME) from the EU.

REFERENCES

Abbott, I., and von Doenhoff, A., 1959, "Theory of Wing Sections," Dover Publications Inc., New York.

Drela, M., 1989, "XFOIL: An Analysis and Design System for Low Reynolds Number Airfoils," in "Low Reynolds Number Aerodynamics", Springer-Verlag Lecture Notes in Engineering, Vol. 54.

Eça, L. C. R., 1987, "Calculation of the Aerodynamic Characteristics of Aerofoils," (in Portuguese) MSc. Thesis, Instituto Superior Técnico, Lisbon.

Gato, L. M. C., and Falcão, A. F. de O., 1984, "On the Theory of the Wells Turbine," ASME Journal of Engineering for Gas Turbines and Power, Vol. 106, No. 3, pp. 628-633.

Gato, L. M. C., and Falcão, A. F. de O., 1988, "Aerodynamics of the Wells Turbine," International Journal of Mechanical Sciences, Vol. 30, No. 6, pp. 383-395.

Gato, L. M. C., and Henriques, J. C. C., 1994, "Optimization of Symmetrical Blades for Wells Turbine", Air Turbine Development and Assessment for Wave Power Plants, contract JOU2-CT93-0333, Progress Report, Instituto Superior Técnico, Lisbon.

Gato, L. M. C., and Curran, R., 1996a, "Performance of the Biplane Wells Turbine," accepted for publication in ASME International Journal of Offshore Mechanics and Arctic Engineering.

Gato, L. M. C., and Curran, R., 1996b, "Performance of the Contrarotating Wells Turbine," ISOPE International Journal of Offshore and Polar Engineering, Vol. 6, No. 1.

Hess, J. L., 1974, "Review of Integral-Equation Techniques for Solving Potential Flow Problems with Emphasis on the Surface-Source Method", Computational Methods in Applied Mechanics Engineering, Vol. 5, pp. 145-196.

Inoue, M., Kaneko, K., Setoghuchi, T., and Raghunathan, S., 1986, "Starting and Running Characteristics of Biplane Wells Turbine," Proceedings, 5th International Offshore Mechanics and Arctic Engineering Symposium, ASME Tokyo, Vol. 2.

Katz, J, and Plotkin, A, 1991, "Low Speed Aerodynamics," McGraw-Hill Publications, New York.

Polak, E., 1971, "Computational Methods in Optimization", Academic Press, New York.

Raghunathan, S., 1995, "The Wells Air Turbine for Wave Energy Conversion," Progress Aerospace Sciences, Vol. 31 pp. 335-386.

Raghunathan, S., and Tan, C. P., 1983a, "Aerodynamic Performance of a Wells Air Turbine," Journal of Energy, Vol 7, No. 3, pp. 226-230.

Raghunathan S., and Tan, C. P., 1983b, "The Performance of Biplane Wells Turbine," Journal of Energy, Vol. 7, No. 6 pp. 741-742.

Vanderplaats, G., 1984, "Numerical Optimization Techniques for Engineering Design", McGraw-Hill Publications, New York.

Salter, S. H., 1993, "Variable Pitch Air Turbines," Proceedings, European Wave Energy Symposium, eds. G Elliot and G Carati, NEL, East Kilbride, Scotland, pp 435-442.

Sarmento, A. J. N. A, Gato, L. M. C., and Falcão, A. F. de O., 1990, "Turbine-controlled Wave Energy Absorption by Oscillating-water-column Devices," Ocean Engineering, Vol. 17, No. 5, pp. 481-497.

APPENDIX

Table 2 presents the coefficients of Eq. (20) describing the thickness for each optimized section.

Name	a_0	a_1	a_2	a_3	d_0	d_1	d_2	d_3
IL9	0.060000	0.190774	-0.29907	0.09527	0.0015	0.372417	-0.597637	0.293262
IA9	0.181659	0.266613	-2.17336	3.41187	0.0015	0.152869	-0.030396	-0.057414
IA14	0.214476	0.294056	-3.33976	6.73552	0.0015	0.146887	-0.031768	-0.046410
IA18	0.229783	0.318200	-4.16172	9.45178	0.0015	0.144907	-0.033180	-0.041860
CA9	0.206882	0.233701	-2.49175	4.42615	0.0015	0.149713	-0.030534	-0.052206

Table 2 Coefficients of eq. (20) for the optimized aerofoils.

FED-Vol. 238, 1996 Fluids Engineering Division Conference
Volume 3
ASME 1996

SIMULATION OF THE THREE-DIMENSIONAL TURBULENT FLOW INSIDE A CENTRIFUGAL FAN IMPELLER

R. I. Issa and G. Xi*
Imperial College of Science, Technology and Medicine
Dept of Mechanical Engineering, London, SW7 2BX
United Kingdom

ABSTRACT

Calculations of the three dimensional turbulent flow in a low pressure centrifugal fan impeller have been made using the multi-purpose,commercial CFD code: STAR-CD. Three different turbulence models were utilised: the standard $k - \varepsilon$ model, its RNG variant and one with Coriolis force modifications(or so called $k - \varepsilon - cm$ model). A systematic comparison between the calculated results and experimental data has been conducted and the results indicate that the general flow characteristics such as the formation of jet-wakes and secondary vortical flow can be well predicted qualitatively. The calculated mean velocities as well as the turbulence kinetic energy are also in good quantitative agreement with the experimental data in most parts of the passage. The comparisons between the three different turbulence models show that, the $k - \varepsilon - cm$ turbulence model presents a substantial improvement on the prediction of turbulence kinetic energy. However, the RNG-based $k - \varepsilon$ model does not show any improvement over the standard model for this case.

INTRODUCTION

The flow in centrifugal impellers is one of the most complex phenomena exhibiting a strong interaction of curvature, rotation and frictional effects. Although existing invisid mean stream surface analysis techniques have achieved much success in improving the aerodynamic performance of centrifugal compressors, fans and pumps, they still have some essential limitations. For example, they cannot provide accurate performance data from surge to choke; they also need a lot of empirical data in the design process. Recently, therefore a number of investigations(for example,Moore,1985;Han and Krain,1990;Dawes,1987;Xi et al.,1991) have resorted to the solution of the full time-averaged N-S equations (including turbulence models) to study flows in centrifugal impellers.From such calculations, important features of the flow such as the development of jet-wakes and secondary vortical flow can be studied and these studies will be of great utility in the endeavour to improve centrifugal turbomachinery design. However, so far, very little work has been done to study the effects of turbulence models on the computed fields; and there has not been a systematic and thorough comparison with experimental data. Thus, it is difficult for engineers to judge to what extent the viscous analysis results can be relied upon in the design of centrifugal turbomachinery.

In this paper , a low pressure centrifugal shrouded fan impeller, in which both the mean and turbulent flow fields were measured(Kjork and Lofdahl,1989) is chosen to validate the numerical method used to compute the flow which was taken to be incompressible and steady in a frame of reference rotating at the impeller speed. The method solves the time-averaged Navier-Stokes equations in conjunction with three alternative turbulence models, the standard $k - \varepsilon$ model(Launder and Splading,1974), the RNG-based $k - \varepsilon$ model(Yakhot et al.,1992) and the $k - \varepsilon$ model with Coriolis force modifications(Howard et al., 1980) or so called the $k - \varepsilon - cm$ model.

This paper presents a qualitative analysis of the flow characteristics in the low speed centrifugal impeller studied, and gives a quantitative comparison between the

---

*Permanent address: Xi'an Jiaotong University,China

calculated and measured mean velocities and turbulence kinetic energy. The performance of the above mentioned turbulence models is also assessed in relation to the measurements.

GOVERNING EQUATIONS

The flow in the centrifugal impeller is considered as three-dimensional, steady, incompressible, turbulent in a relative frame fixed to the impeller. The continuity, momentum and turbulence model equations solved are stated in Cartesian tensor notation as follows:

Continuity

$$\frac{\partial}{\partial x_j}(\rho \tilde{u}_j) = 0 \qquad (1)$$

Momentum

$$\frac{\partial}{\partial x_j}(\rho \tilde{u}_j u_j - \tau_{ij}) = -\frac{\partial p}{\partial x_i} + S_i \qquad (2)$$

Turbulence kinetic energy

$$\frac{\partial}{\partial x_j}\left(\rho \tilde{u}_j k - \frac{\mu_{eff}}{\sigma_k}\frac{\partial k}{\partial x_j}\right) = \mu_t P - \rho\varepsilon + G_c \qquad (3)$$

Dissipation rate

$$\frac{\partial}{\partial x_j}\left(\rho \tilde{u}_j \varepsilon - \frac{\mu_{eff}}{\sigma_\varepsilon}\frac{\partial \varepsilon}{\partial x_j}\right) = C_{\varepsilon 1}\frac{\varepsilon}{k}\mu_t P$$

$$-(C_{\varepsilon 2} + C_c)\rho\frac{\varepsilon^2}{k} + G_c\frac{\varepsilon}{k} \qquad (4)$$

where

$x_i \equiv$ cartesian coordinate(i=1,2,3)

$u_i \equiv$ absolute fluid velocity component in direction x_i

$\tilde{u}_j \equiv u_j - u_{cj}$, relative velocity between fluid and moving coordinate frame which moves with velocity u_{cj}

$p \equiv$ static pressure

$\rho \equiv$ density

$S_{ij} \equiv$ strain tensor rate($=0.5\left(\frac{\partial u_i}{\partial x_j} + \frac{\partial u_j}{\partial x_i}\right)$)

$\tau_{ij} \equiv$ stress tensor components($=2\mu S_{ij} - \frac{2}{3}\mu\frac{\partial u_k}{\partial x_k}\delta_{ij} - \overline{\rho u'_i u'_j}$)

$S_i \equiv$ momentum source components from rotational forces

$P \equiv 2S_{ij}\frac{\partial u_i}{\partial x_j}$, $\mu_{eff} \equiv \mu + \mu_t$, $\mu_t \equiv \rho C_\mu \frac{k^2}{\varepsilon}$

$-\overline{\rho u'_i u'_j} \equiv 2\mu_t S_{ij} - \frac{2}{3}\rho k \delta_{ij}$

For the standard $k - \varepsilon$ model:

$G_c = 0, C_c = 0, C_\mu = 0.09, \sigma_k = 1.0, \sigma_\varepsilon = 1.3$

$C_{\varepsilon 1} = 1.44, C_{\varepsilon 2} = 1.92$

For the $k - \varepsilon - cm$ model:

$G_c \equiv 9\omega\mu_t\frac{\partial \tilde{u}_r}{r\partial\theta}, C_c = 0$, other constants are kept the same

as that of standard $k - \varepsilon$ model

$r, \theta \equiv$ radial and tangential coordinates in relative cylindrical coordinate frame

$\omega \equiv$ impeller rotation speed

For RNG-based $k - \varepsilon$ model:

$G_c \equiv 0, C_c \equiv C_\mu\eta^3(1.0 - \eta/\eta_0)/(1 + \beta\eta^3)$

$\eta \equiv Sk/\varepsilon, S \equiv (2S_{ij}S_{ij})^{0.5}$

$C_\mu = 0.085, \sigma_k = 0.719, \sigma_\varepsilon = 0.719, C_{\varepsilon 1} = 1.42$

$C_{\varepsilon 2} = 1.68, \eta_0 = 4.38, \beta = 0.012$

NUMERICAL PROCEDURE

The governing equations are solved numerically using a method, which is embodied in the multi-purpose CFD code STAR-CD(1994). The method is of the finite-volume type utilising non-structured, non-orthogonal mesh discretisation, with a non-staggered variable arrangement. The discretisation scheme selected is the second-order central difference scheme to which some numerical dissipation is added in the form of blending with the upwind scheme. The results presented here were obtained using 100% central differencing for momentum equations, and 70% for the $k - \varepsilon$ equations.

Since neither the inlet flow conditions nor the precise geometry of the suction pipe of the impeller was given by Kjork and Lofdahl(1989), the computational domain had to be limited in extent so as to locate the inlet boundary of the domain at the same position of the first measuring station in the experimental set-up, where data are available ; those were then used as inlet conditions for the calculations. Because the turbulence energy dissipation rate is not directly measured, it was estimated using the empirical formula : $\varepsilon_{in} \equiv C_\mu^{0.75}k^{1.5}/l$, where l is an appropriate length scale taken to be 0.02b2 (b2 is the exit width of the impeller). On the solid walls of hub, shroud and blade surfaces, no-slip condition together with the wall-fuction(Launder and Splading,1974) are used. On the outlet boundary, the gradients of all dependent variables were set to zero. Several different computational meshes have been used in order to test the influence of mesh density and configuration, and a solution with a mesh of 48 × 32 × 60 (Fig.1), was finally accepted as mesh-independent.

RESULTS AND DISCUSSION

The case studied is a low pressure centrifugal shrouded fan impeller, in which the flow field was measured by Kjork and Lofdah(1989). The impeller has nine backward blades with inlet angle of 23 degrees and outlet angle of 25 degrees relative to the tangential direction. The inner and outer diameters are respectively 0.45 m and 0.8 m, and the inlet width b1 and outlet width b2 are same with a value of 0.125 m. The measurements and calculations were carried out at design point of the fan, which corresponds to an impeller speed of 890 rpm , and flow rate of $1.9 m^3/s$.

Quantitative Comparison

Mean Velocities. Figures 2 to 4 give the comparison between the measured and calculated values of the mean velocities with different turbulence models(where, Up is blade tip velocity , z/b2=0.0 at the hub and z/b2=1.0 at the shroud). From Fig.2, it can be seen that the calculated z direction velocity is very close to the experimental data in the region around z/b2=0.5, and the deviation is only about 1.5 percent of the impeller tip speed Up. Near the wall region of the hub and shroud , the maximum deviation increases to about 2.5 percent of Up; the distribution is still in good agreement with the experimental data. In Fig.3, it can be seen that the calculated radial velocity is in very good agreement with the experimental data in the whole domain. The largest absolute deviation is only about 4 percent of blade tip speed Up, which occurs near the blade suction surface. Figure 4 gives the comparison of tangential mean velocity. The calculated values is found to be quite close to the experimental data over about 70 percent of the passage, but considerable deviations of 4 to 12 percent of the impeller tip speed Up appear near the blade suction region. It can also be noticed that the prediction of mean velocities is improved to some extent by the $k - \varepsilon - cm$ model, especially in the corner region between the hub and blade suction surface. However,quantitatively, the influence of the three different turbulence models is quite small on the prediction of the mean velocities.

The above comparisons suggest that the turbulence structure near the blade suction surface could be more anisotropic than that of other regions due to the effect of Coriolis forces, and the eddy viscosity model used here may bring large errors when applied to this region. The wall-fuction used in the calculations is another possible factor which might be responsible for the above discrepancy.

Turbulence Kinetic Energy. Figure 5 presents the comparison of the turbulence kinetic energy. It can be seen that, unlike the prediction of mean velocities, different turbulence models have a large influence on the prediction of turbulence kinetic energy. The maximum relative deviation between calculated and measured values, which occurs near the blade suction surface region, is under 30 percent. In general, the $k - \varepsilon - cm$ model gives the best prediction against the experimental data , and this implies that the modification due to Coriolis forces on the

standard $k - \varepsilon$ model is appropriate. However, the RNG-based $k - \varepsilon$ model does not demonstrate better prediction than the standard model in this case.

Turbulence Viscosity. Figure 6 (a) and (b) show that the predicted turbulence viscosity distributions with different models(where,vist/visl is the ratio of turbulence viscosity to laminar viscosity). In Fig.9 (a),it is seen that near the inlet the different turbulence models yield similar answers. However, with the flow development downstream, for example, on the r=350 mm surface(Fig.9 (b)) , the difference becomes large. The peak of the viscosity field predicted by the standard $k - \varepsilon$ and RNG $k - \varepsilon$ models is located near the blade suction surface region, and the maximum value is about 400 times of the laminar viscosity. The $k - \varepsilon - cm$ model gives quite uniform distribution across the suction and pressure surfaces,and the predicted maximum values is only 200 times that of the laminar viscosity.

The Jet-wake and Secondary Flow

The jet-wake structure of the throughflow velocity has been traditionally considered as the basic flow model in centrifugal impellers, especially, after the measurement of Eckardt(1976) on an impeller of a high-speed compressor, which indicated that the wake(the low streamwise momentum region) indeed appears in the corner between the shroud and the blade suction surface near the exit of impeller. However , some recent research shows quite different results. For example, the measurement of a modern impeller of a centrifugal compressor by Krain(1988) indicates that the wake is maximum inside the impeller rather than at the exit , and also it occurs near the shroud and pressure surface,rather than near the suction surface. Therefore, it is interesting to study whether the jet-wake structure exists and where it occurs in the present configuration.

Figure 7 (a), (b) and (c) present the predicted relative velocity magnitude isoline pattern at three different positions from the middle to the exit of the impeller(here,only the results of the standard $k - \varepsilon$ model are presented because the RNG $k - \varepsilon$ model and $k - \varepsilon - cm$ model give very similar results). It can be clearly seen that a high momentum region which shifts from the suction to the pressure surface along the flow, and a low momentum region (so called wake) appears at the corner of the shroud and suction surfaces near the exit of the impeller.This predicted pattern is verified by the measurements of Kjork and Lofdahl(1989).

Figure 8 (a),(b) and (c) show the secondary flow velocity vector plots at different radial positions (again only the standard $k - \varepsilon$ model's results are presented). Here, the 'secondary flow' is defined as the projection of the total relative velocity vector on the surfaces normal to the local streamwise CFD grid lines. From Fig.8, it can be seen that, on the r=310 mm surface, only one large secondary vortex appears near the shroud side. Towards the exit of the impeller two new secondary vortices appear near the blade suction on the r=350 mm surface. On the r=398 mm surface(almost the exit of the impeller), the above two vortices become very large and strong. These secondary flow vortices move low momentum fluid to the suction surface, and force the high momentum fluid to shift to the pressure surface. This is the main reason why the wake usually appears near the suction surface at the exit of impellers. These Coriolis force-dominated secondary flow patterns may however be singnificantly changed by centrifugal forces arising from different blade curvature, contour of shroud and hub as well as tip leakage flow (for unshrouded impellers), especially in modern three-dimensional impellers with twisted blades.

SUMMARY AND CONCLUSIONS

This paper presents an extensive CFD study of the flow field in a low-pressure centrifugal fan shrouded impeller with different turbulence models. The study indicates that the streamwise throughflow development and the secondary flow vortex structure in the impeller can be qualitatively well predicted by the CFD method used. Quantitatively,the calculated mean velocities are in good agreement with the experimental data in most parts of the passage, but deviate near the blade suction surface, especially for the relative tangential velocity. This discrepancy is most probably due to the turbulence anisotropy which cannot be accounted for by the eddy viscosity turbulence models used.

Compared with the standard $k - \varepsilon$ model, the Coriolis force modified turbulence model ($k - \varepsilon - cm$ model) can improve the prediction of turbulence kinetic energy; the RNG-based $k - \varepsilon$ model does not provide better prediction than the standard $k - \varepsilon$ model in this case. As for the mean velocity prediction, the influence of different turbulence models is relatively small.

ACKNOWLEDGEMENT

The anthors wish to thank Computational Dynamics Ltd for making available their STAR-CD code to perform the computations.

REFERENCES

Dawes, W. N.,1987, "Application of a three-dimensional viscous compressible flow solver to a high-speed centrifugal compressor rotor-secondary flow and loss generation," Proceedings of IMechE, C261/87

Eckardt, D., 1976, "Detailed Flow Investigations Within a High-Speed Centrifugal Compressor Impeller," ASME , J. of Fluids Engineering , vol.98 ,pp-402

Howard, J. H. G.,Patankar, S. V. and Bordynuik, R. M.,1980,"Flow Prediction in Rotating Ducts Using Coriolis-Modified Turbulence Models," ASME, J. of Fluids Engineering, vol.102, pp. 456-461

Hah,C. and Krain H. ,1990,"Secondary Flow and Vortex Motion in a High-Efficiency Backswept Impeller at Design and Off-Design Conditions," ASME, J., of Turbomachinery,vol.112, pp. 7-13

Krain, H.,1988,"Swirling Impeller Flow," ASME , J. of Turbomachinery ,vol.110, pp. 122-128

Kjork, A. and Lofdahl, L. ,1989,"Hot-Wire Measurements Inside a Centrifugal Fan Impeller ," ASME , J. of Fluids Engineering , vol.111, pp.365-368

Launder, B. E. and Spalding, D. B. ,1974,"The Numerical Computation of Turbulent Flow," Comp. Meth. in Appl. Mech. and Engr., vol.3, pp.269

Moore, J. , Moore, J. G. and Timmis, P. H.,1985, "Performance Evaluation of Centrifugal Compressor Impellers Using Three-Dimensional Viscous Flow Calculations," ASME J. of Engineering for Gas Turbine and Power,vol.106 , pp. 475-481

STAR-CD manual, 1994, Computational Dynamics Ltd

Xi, G., Wang, S. J. and Miao, Y. M.,1991,"A calculation procedure for three-dimensional turbulent flow in a centrifugal impeller with any blade geometry," ASME paper, 91-GT-171

Yakhot, V. and et al,1992,"Development of Turbulence Models for Shear Flows by a Double Expansion Technique," Physics of Fluids A, vol.4 no.7,pp. 1510-1520.

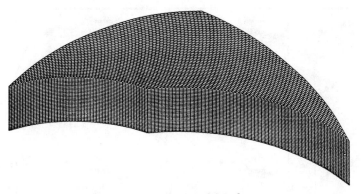

Fig.1 Computational Mesh

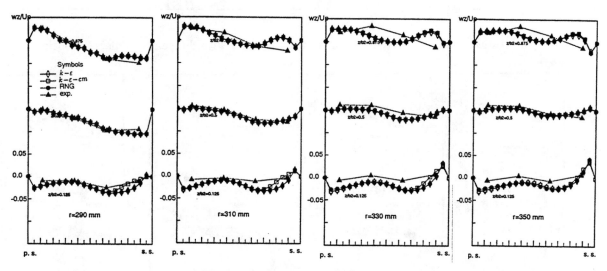

Fig.2 Measured and Calculated z direction mean velocity with different turbulence models

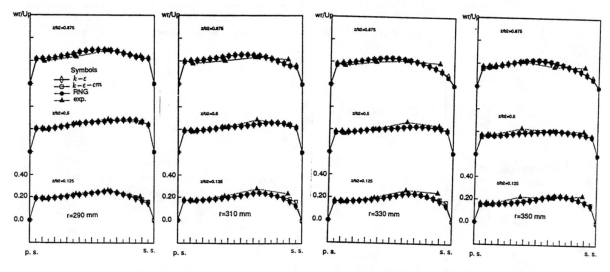

Fig.3 Measured and Calculated radial mean velocity with different turbulence models

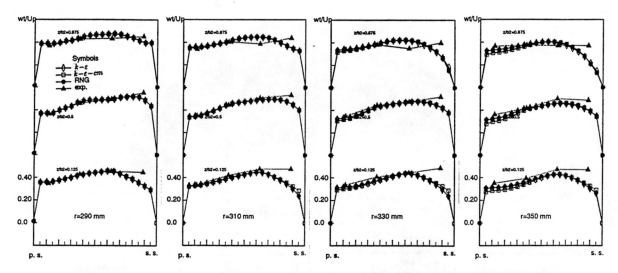

Fig.4 Measured and Calculated tangential mean velocity with different turbulence models

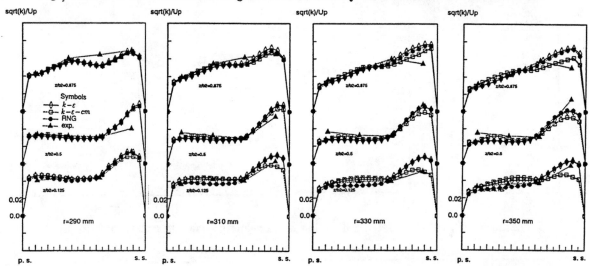

Fig.5 Measured and Calculated turbulence kinetic energy with different turbulence models

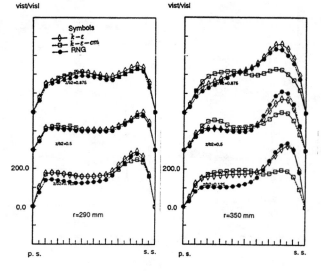

Fig.6 Calculated turbulence viscosity
with different turbulence models

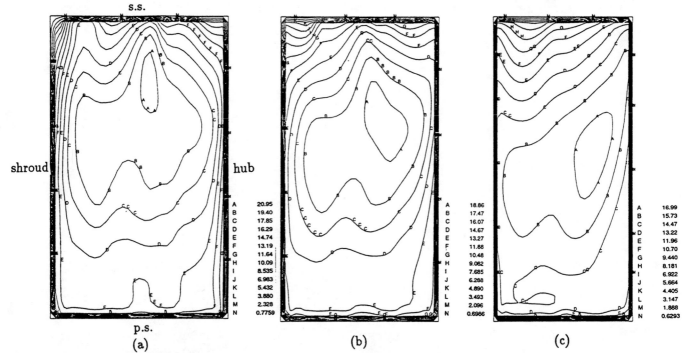

Fig.7 Calculated relative Velocity Magnitude Isoline Pattern at three different
Positions($k - \varepsilon$ model) (a) r=310 mm (b) r=350 mm (c) r=398 mm

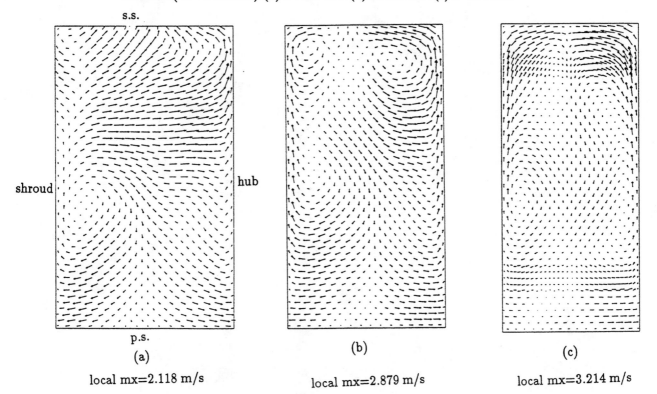

local mx=2.118 m/s   local mx=2.879 m/s   local mx=3.214 m/s

Fig.8 Calculated secodary flow velocity vector plots at
(a) r=310 mm (b) r=350mm (c) r=398 mm

FED-Vol. 238, 1996 Fluids Engineering Division Conference
Volume 3
ASME 1996

DEVELOPMENT OF A RAPID METHOD OF ANALYSING THE FLOW THROUGH

TURBOMACHINERIES

Thabet Belamri   Robert Rey   Farid Bakir

Smaîne Kouidri   Riccardo Noguera

LEMFI-URA CNRS 1504

ENSAM-151, Bd de l'Hôpital

75013 PARIS, FRANCE

Phone : (33)-1 44-24-64-12

e-mail : belamri@cumana.paris.ensam.fr

ABSTRACT

The singularities method is used to analyze the blade-to-blade flow through a plane cascade. Computed values of the flow turning angle and the pressure distribution are compared with experimental ones. The agreement between theory and experiment is very interesting. From the plane cascade, the use of the conformal mapping has allowed us to visualize the recirculation and cavitation zone through a centrifugal pump impeller.

INTRODUCTION

In recent years, the development of the numerical calculation means, the calculation time and their price reduction have allowed us to know more about the flow structure through turbomachineries, to detail the physical process which governs their function and to analyze accurately the internal phenomena.

The singularities method is used to analyze the flow through the turbomachineries. This method permits us to find a particular solution of the Laplace equation which satisfies the boundary conditions imposed. The method is very useful because it permits us, when the calculation programs are ready, to study the flows assimilating them to an elimentaries flows superposition (Belamri, et al 1996) corresponding to :

- A base uniform flow
- Springs, snikes or vortices located at well chosen points of flow field.

Martensen (1959) was one of the original investigators of this method by using a discrete distribution of vortices on the blade.

surfaces. Douglas and Neumann (1965) have used the continuous distribution of source. Bahately (1968), Stevens et al (1971) and Marvrilis (1971) used Douglas and Neumann's work and developed similar results by using a continuous distribution of vortices. Corniglion and Luu (1976) applied the method to analyze the flow through a stage of turbine and took into account the vorticity emission. Concerning the circular cascades, the flow study was facilitated by the transition to the plane cascade using a conformal mapping. In this way, a number of authors, notably Acosta (1954), Ayyubi and Rao (1971) used this conformal mapping for analysis of flow through a centrifugal pump impeller in which the blades, without thickness, had a logarithmic spiral shape. This restriction is the major defect of this approach. Recently, Visser and Brouwers (1993) resolved analytically the problem of the flow through the pump impeller fitted with straight radial blades by using a Fourier series, with the Fourier coefficients given by the hypergeometric function.

The principle of the method is being exposed and applied to determine the flow through a plane cascade of airfoils and through a circular one using a conformal tranformation which takes into account the thickness of the blades.

BASIC EQUATIONS

The method was developed with the following assumptions :
- The fluid is inviscid and incompressible
- The absolute flow is irrotational and bidimensionnal
- The singularities chosen are vortices

Expression of the velocity induced by a sucession of vortices

The flow is periodic and all the singularities are reputed parallel to the Oy axis with the space t corresponding to the step of the profiles (all the profiles are the same) "Fig. 1.".
The integral equation giving the velocity field has the following expression (Fagard, 1991) :

$$C' = u - i.v = \frac{i}{2.t} \int_{(c)} \coth\left(\frac{\pi}{t}\left[(x-x_0)+(y-h(x_0))\right]\right) . \gamma(s) . ds \qquad (1)$$

Where (c) is the blade contour.
the flow through the cascade is modeled by the superposition of all the singularities and a uniform flow of α_m direction and C_m modulus.

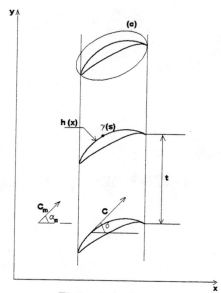

Fig 1 : plane cascade

The velocity $\vec{C}$ in the plane is given by the following system :

$$\vec{C} \begin{cases} u = C_m \cos \alpha_m + \text{Re}(C') \\ \\ v = C_m \sin \alpha_m - \text{Im}(C') \end{cases} \qquad (2)$$

_____Nomenclature _____

A : matrix of influence, m^{-1}
B : second member of the linear system, m/s
$Cz\infty$o : camber of the profiles
C : absolute velocity of a point of the plane (x, y), m/s
C' : conjugate velocity, m/s
Im : imaginary part
K : the scale of the conformal mapping, m
Na : number of blades
N : rotational speed, tr/mn
P : static pressure distribution on the blade surface, bars
Qn: nominal flow, m^3/s
Re : real part
S : pressure coefficient
U : training velocity, m/s
l : cord of the profiles, m
s : curviline coordinate, m
t : step of the profiles, m
u, v : the axial and tengential component of the absolute flow velocity, m/s
z = x + iy : complex coordinate of a general point

Γ : vortex intensity, m^2/s
$\Delta\alpha$: flow turning angle, degrees ($\alpha_1 - \alpha_2$)
Δs : length of a segment, m
α : direction of the uniform flow, degrees
γ : stager angle, degrees
$\gamma(s)$: vortex strength per unit length of airfoil contour, m/s
δ : angle between the segment carrying a vortex and the Ox axis, degrees
λ : parameter ($\lambda = 0$ for a fixed cascade; $\lambda = 1$ for a rotating cascade)
ρ : fluid density, kg/m^3
σ : solidity of the profiles (l/t)
μ : parameter ($\mu = 1$ for the influence of the vortex on the blade surface, $\mu = 0$ for all the other cases)
ω : angular speed of the impeller, rd/s
Subscripts
ex: upper side
in : lower side
m : average flow
1 : inlet of the impeller
2 : outlet of the impeller

We set :

$$X = \frac{\pi}{t}(x - x_0)$$

$$Y = \frac{\pi}{t}(y - h(x_0))$$

$$Z = X + i.Y$$

Then we find the following identity :

$$i.\coth(Z) = \frac{\sin 2Y + i.sh2X}{ch2X - \cos 2Y}$$

The velocity expression becomes :

$$\vec{C} \quad \begin{vmatrix} u = C_m \cos \alpha_m + \frac{1}{2.t} \int_{(c)} \frac{\sin 2Y}{ch2X - \cos 2Y} . \gamma(s)ds \\[4mm] v = C_m \sin \alpha_m - \frac{1}{2.t} \int_{(c)} \frac{sh2X}{ch2X - \cos 2Y} . \gamma(s)ds \end{vmatrix} \qquad (3)$$

These expressions permit us to introduce the function of influence :

$$fx = \frac{\sin 2Y}{ch2X - \cos 2Y}$$

$$fy = \frac{sh2X}{ch2X - \cos 2Y}$$

The zero tengential velocity condition

The vortex distribution checks the zero tengential velocity on the profile surface of equation $y = h(x)$.

$$\frac{dh}{dx} = tg\delta(x,y) = \frac{v(x,h(x)) + \lambda.U}{u(x,h(x))} \qquad (4)$$

The Kutta-Joukowski condition

It is checked by equaling the velocity modulus on the upper and lower side at the trailing edge.

Determination of the linear system

In practice the profile is divided in k (k = 400) segments carrying vortices. The integral equations yielding the velocity field are replaced by a discrete sum, the velocity expression becomes :

$$\vec{C} \quad \begin{vmatrix} u = Ca + \frac{1}{2.t} . \sum_{j=1}^{k} fx.\Gamma_j \pm \mu \left(\frac{\Gamma_i + \Gamma_{i+1}}{2.\Delta s} \right).\cos\delta \\[5mm] v = \lambda.U + Ca.tg\,\alpha_m - \frac{1}{2.t} . \sum_{j=1}^{k} fy.\Gamma_j \pm \mu \left(\frac{\Gamma_i + \Gamma_{i+1}}{2.\Delta s} \right).\sin\delta \end{vmatrix} \qquad (5)$$

with $Ca = C_m.\cos \alpha_m$, axial velocity

The term $\left(\dfrac{\Gamma_i + \Gamma_{i+1}}{2.\Delta s} \right)$ represents the influence of the vortex on itself (limit when z tends to z_o in "Eq. 1.")
(+) corresponds to the upper side and (-) to the lower side

Taking into account the equations (5) into (4), then we obtain :

$$tg\delta(x,y) = \frac{\lambda.U + Ca.tg\alpha_m - \frac{1}{2t}\sum\limits_{j=1}^{k} fy\Gamma_j \pm \mu \left(\frac{\Gamma_i + \Gamma_{i+1}}{2.\Delta s} \right).\sin\delta}{Ca + \frac{1}{2t}\sum\limits_{j=1}^{k} fx\Gamma_j \pm \mu \left(\frac{\Gamma_i + \Gamma_{i+1}}{2.\Delta s} \right).\cos\delta} \qquad (6)$$

let after developement :

$$tg\delta(x,y). \sum_{j=1}^{k} fx\Gamma_j + \sum_{j=1}^{k} fy\Gamma_j = 2.t.\lambda.U + 2.t.Ca.[\,tg\,\alpha_m - tg\,\delta(x,y)\,]$$

for one triplet (x_i, y_i, δ_i) on the surface blade, we developed this last equation :

$$tg\delta_i. \left[fx_{i,1}.\Gamma_1 + fx_{i,2}.\Gamma_2 + ... + fx_{i,k}.\Gamma_k \right] +$$

$$\left[fy_{i,1}.\Gamma_1 + fy_{i,2}.\Gamma_2 + ... + fy_{i,k}.\Gamma_k \right]$$

$$= 2.t.\lambda.U + 2.t.Ca.[\,tg\,\alpha_m - tg\,\delta_i\,]$$

let :

$$tg\delta_i. \left[fx_{i,1}.\Gamma_1 + fx_{i,2}.\Gamma_2 + ... + fx_{i,k}.\Gamma_k \right] +$$

$$\left[fy_{i,1}.\Gamma_1 + fy_{i,2}.\Gamma_2 + ... + fy_{i,k}.\Gamma_k \right] = 2.t.\lambda.U + 2.t.Ca.[\,tg\,\alpha_m - tg\,\delta_i\,]$$

Given also :

$$[tg\delta_i.fx_{i,j} + fy_{i,j}].\Gamma_j = 2.t.\lambda.U + 2.t.Ca.[\,tg\,\alpha_m - tg\,\delta_i\,]$$

then we obtain the linear system :

$$A_{ij}.\Gamma_j = B_i \qquad (7)$$

with

$$A_{ij} = tg\,\delta_i.fx_{i,j} + fy_{i,j} \qquad 1 \leq i \leq k\,, 1 \leq j \leq k$$

$$B_i = 2.t.\lambda.U + 2.t.Ca.[\,tg\,\alpha_m - tg\,\delta_i\,]$$

Note :
The isolate profile is a particular case of the cascade where the solidity tends to zero. The function of influence expression becomes :

$$fx = \frac{(y - h(x_0))}{(x - x_0)^2 + (y - h(x_0))^2}$$

$$fy = \frac{(x - x_0)}{(x - x_0)^2 + (y - h(x_0))^2}$$

APPLICATIONS

Plane cascade fixed or rotating

In order to compare the results with those of experiment (NACA -TN 3916), (Herrig, et al, 1958), the flow turning angle calculation is done at a constante inlet angle for a given cascade (cambrer Cz∞o, solidity σ).

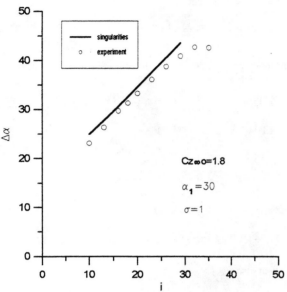

For every angle of attack (i), we determine the pressure coefficient (calculated by " Eq. 8.") and the flow turning angle. The difference between the two results stems from the fact that we are working with a perfect fluid and we did not take into account the effect of the boundaries layers in our calculation " Fig. 2.".

$$S = 1 - \frac{P - P_1}{\frac{1}{2}\rho.C^2_1} \qquad (8)$$

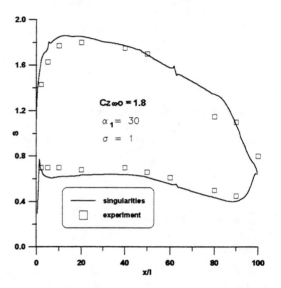

Fig 2 : Turning angle and pressure coefficient evolution

Circular cascades

Conformal transformation

The calculation of the blade-to-blade flow is facilitated by the transition to the plane cascade where the profile step is the same at the inlet and the outlet of the cascade. This transition uses a conformal transformation. The flow in the real plane (m, θ), corresponds to the flow in the mapping plane (x, y) "Fig. 3.".
The relations between the points of the two planes is given by (Rey, 1995) :

$$\begin{vmatrix} x = K. \int_{m_o}^{m_L} \dfrac{dm}{r} \\[4mm] y = K. \int_{\theta_o}^{\theta_L} d\theta \end{vmatrix} \qquad (9)$$

where
- (m_o, θ_o) et (m_L, θ_L) are respectively the loading and the trailing edge of the real profile
- K is the scale of the transformation given by :

$$K = \frac{t.Na}{2.\pi}$$

Velocity field

The velocity field in the real plane is deduced from that which we obtain in the mapping plane by the inverse transformation. This result, which is calculated by the singularities method applied to the plane cascade, takes into account the impeller width variation by the intermidiate of Ca in a quasi-tridimensional calculation. The following expressions give the relative components of the velocity in the real plane :

$$\begin{vmatrix} W_m = u.\dfrac{K}{r} \\[4mm] W_\theta = v.\dfrac{K}{r} \end{vmatrix} \qquad (10)$$

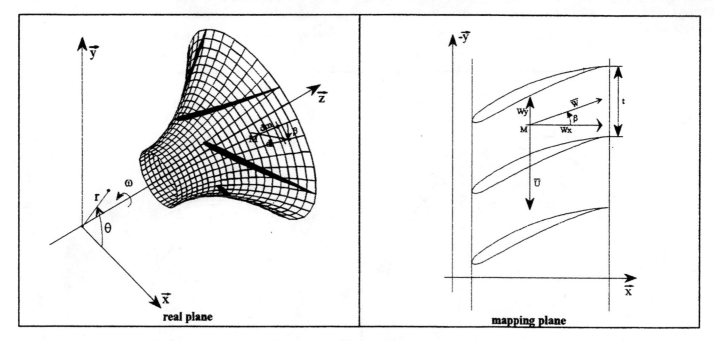

Fig 3 : Conformal transformation

The method was applied to a centrifugal impeller in which the 5 blades are obtained by the inverse transformation from the NACA 65 profiles. The inlet and outlet radius impeller have the value of R_1 = 0.115 m and R_2 = 0.2042 m respectively. The flow rate value is 0.1575 m³/s when the impeller rotates at N = 1500 tr/mn "Fig. 4" and "Fig. 5". The first results obtained permit us to make evident two phenomena the recirculation zone for the reduced flow rate and also the cavitaion zone.

Illustration, Fig. 6. shows the evolution of the two phenomena for a reduced and nominal flow rate.

The discontinuous curvature, seen on the blade surface, is caused by the blade-to-blade grid. This grid requires a better definition.

We note finally that the calculation time of the field, executed on PC DX2 - 66 Mhz, is by the minute.

Fig 4 : Centrifugal impeller in the mapping plane

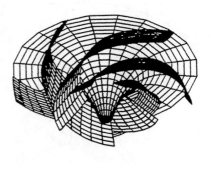

Fig 5 : Centrifugal impeller in the real plane

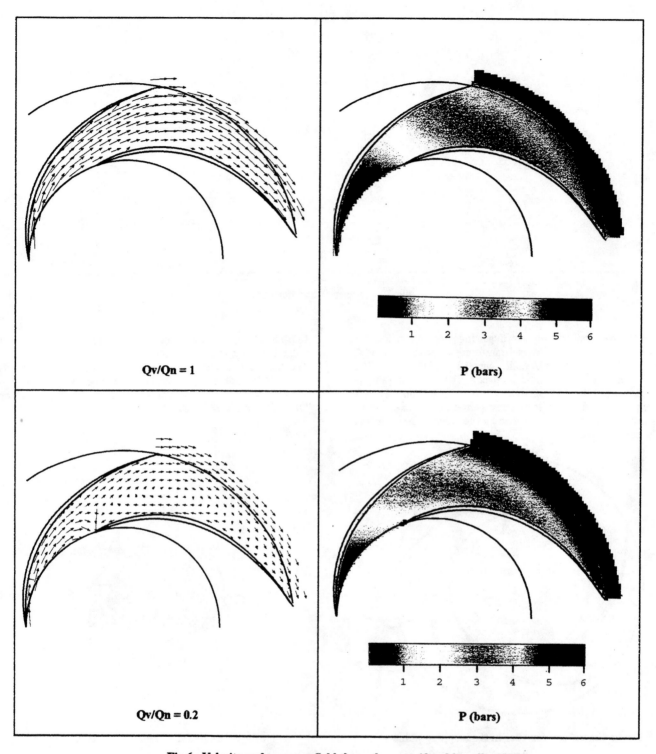

Fig 6 : Velocity and pressure field through a centrifugal impeller NS 32
(N = 1500 tr/mn, Qn = 0.1575 m³/s)

CONCLUSION

The present study has permitted us to further master the singularities method not only for the theoretical part but also for the numerical aspect and programming: precision, stability, number of points, the matrix condition number[1] .The program was done on a PC and the calculation time is measured in minutes. Its structure offers the user a choice between many profiles for analysing. The transition from the cascade to an isolated profile is facilitated by using the functions of influence. The internal flow through the turbomachineries will be further analyzed by introducing the following aspects :
- Boundaries layers model
- Unsteady flow
- Cavitation study

BIBLIOGRAPHY

Acosta, A. J., 1954, " An Experimental and Theoretical Investigation of a two-Dimensional Centrifugal Pump Impeller," Trans. ASME, Vol. 76, 1954, pp.749.

Ayyubi, S. K., Rao, Y. V. N., 1971, " Theoretical Analysis of Flow Through Two-Dimensional Centrifugal Pump Impeller by Method of Singularities ," ASME Journal of Basic Engineering ,pp. 35-41.

Belamri, T., Rey, R., Noguera, R., Bakir, F.,Kouidri, S., 1996, " Flow Analysis Around An Isolated Porfile By The Singularities Method," IV CEM-NNE/96, IV Congresso De Engenharia Mecânica Norte-Nordeste, Recife, Bresil.

Bhatelay, I. C., 1968, "Investigation of Invicid Incompressible Flow, Part IV : Potential Flow Analysis About Arbitrary Multiple Two-Dimensional Bodies by the Method of Distributed Singularities," Genral Dynamics, Fort Worth Division, Rep. No. ERR-FW-669, Mar. 1968.

Corniglion, J., Luu, T. S., 1976, " Etude théorique et expérimentale des interactions instationnaires dans un étage de turbomachine, " Technical Report, CETIM, France.

Herrig, L., Emery, C., Erwin, R., 1957, " Systematic Two-Dimensionnal Cascade Tests of NACA 65-Series Compressor Blades At Low Speeds, " Langley Aeronautical Laboratory, Washington.

Fagard., M., 1991, " Etude des écoulements décollés en grille d'aubes en régime sous-sonique compressible, " Ph.D. thesis, LEMFI, FRANCE.

Hess, J. L., Smith, A. M. D., " Calculation of potential flow about arbitrary bodies, " Progress in aeronautical sciences, Vol 8., Pergamon press.

Mavrilis, F., " Aerodynamic Research on High Lift System, " Canadian Aeronautics and Space journal, May 1971, pp. 175-184.

Minassian, L. M., 1976, " A study On Multielement Cascades and Airfoils, ", ASME Journal of Fluids Engineering, Jun 1976, pp. 208-215.

Stevens, W. A., Goradia, S. H., et Braden, J. A., " Mathematical Model for Two-Dimensional Multi-Component Airfoils in Viscous Flow, " NASA CR-1843, July 1971.

Rey, R., 1995, " Dimensionnement des turbomachines, " Technical Report, ENSAM, Paris, France.

Visser, F. C., Brouwers, J. J., 1993, " Review Of Status Of Potential Flow Calculations In Radially Bladed Pump Impellers, " ASME Pumping Machinery, Vol. 154,pp. 219-226.

---

(1) This aspect will be published later

FED-Vol. 238, 1996 Fluids Engineering Division Conference
Volume 3
ASME 1996

NUMERICAL SIMULATION OF THREE-DIMENSIONAL VISCOUS FLOW
IN A MULTIBLADE CENTRIFUGAL FAN

Xi Chen, Kwang-Yong Kim, Se-Yun Kim

Dept. of Mechanical Engineering, Inha University,
Incheon, 402-751, KOREA

ABSTRACT

Numerical study is presented for the analysis of three-dimensional incompressible turbulent flows in a multiblade centrifugal fan, which is used in household air-conditioning system. Reynolds averaged Navier-Stokes equations with k-ε turbulence model are transformed to a non-orthogonal curvilinear coordinates, and are discretized with finite volume approximations. The computational area is divided into three blocks. The flow inside of the fan is regarded as steady flow, and empirical formulas are employed to simulate the flow through the impeller.

NOMENCLATURE

d_1 : Inner diameter of impeller

d_2 : Outer diameter of impeller

k : Turbulent kinetic energy

ε : Dissipation rate of k

b : Width of blade

z : Number of blades

c_{1r} : Radial velocity at inlet of blade

c_{2u} : Tangential velocity at outlet of blade

β_{2A}: Blade angle at outlet of blade

f_c : Circumferential force of blade

ε : Velocity coefficient or slip factor

$\bar{r}$: Average radius

$\dot{m}$: Flow rate

INTRODUCTION

Multiblade fans have been widely used in automobiles and household air-conditioning systems due to relatively high flow rates and high pressures. In order to design multiblade fans with high efficiency and low noise, it is worth to analyze the flowfield inside of the fan by numerical method. Since the flows inside of multiblade fans are, however, unsteady and three-dimensional viscous flows, it is very difficult to simulate the flowfield by conventional computational fluid dynamics.

The flowfield inside of centrifugal fan can be divided into three parts; core, impeller and scroll. In case of general centrifugal fan, the flows in core and impeller are usually assumed to be axisymmetric and periodic, respectively, and then can be calculated in a computational domain bounded by blades, hub and shroud[Zhang and Lakshiminarayana, 1990, Zhang et al., 1994, Casey et al., 1992, Moore and Moore, 1981]. Consequently, the inlet flows in the scroll are assumed to be uniform for numerical simulation in this block. However, in the case of multiblade fans, the flows are more complex. The main features of the fan are large diameter ratio, large relative width and large number of blades which are of the forward-curved design. Thus, the flowfield inside of impeller has following characteristics.

Because of the large diameter ratio($d_1/d_2 > 0.8$), the path length from inlet to outlet of impeller is relatively short, and the flowfield in scroll affects the flows in impeller and core significantly. Therefore, the distributions of velocity and pressure in the inlet and outlet of impeller change in circumferential direction, significantly. By that reason, the inlet flows of the impeller and scroll can not be regarded as uniform anymore. And the large relative width of blade(b/d_2 >0.4) make the distributions of velocity and pressure in impeller change in axial direction, significantly. According to the visualization of the flowfied in impeller of multiblade fan[Kadota et al., 1994], there are dead zones and backward-flow zones in the impeller, which take about 30% of the flowfield in impeller. Therefore, the simulation of flow in multiblade fan must be fully three-dimensional and carried out in all of three blocks from inlet of core to exit of scroll.

Special method such as with moving boundaries can be used to simulate this kind of unsteady flow in principle. However, a large number of computational grids will be needed if we want calculate all of the flows which go through every blades of the impeller. Thus, it will take too long computing time and need too many memories to engineering applications. Due to the large number of blades(z>50), the aerodynamic load on each blade is relatively low, and the variations of velocity and pressure between blades are relatively small, comparing with those of the time-average flow along the scroll. Therefore, in this study, the flow inside of the fan is regarded as steady flow by modeling the impeller force for economic calculations.

NUMERICAL METHODS

The governing equations, i. e., continuity, momentum, turbulent kinetic energy and its dissipation rate equations for steady, incompressible flow can be written as

$$E_x + F_y + G_z = S \tag{1}$$

where x, y, z represent the Cartesian coordinates, and

$$E = \begin{bmatrix} \rho u \\ \rho u^2 - \mu_t u_x \\ \rho uv - \mu_t v_x \\ \rho uw - \mu_t w_x \\ \rho uk - \mu_t k_x/\sigma_k \\ \rho u\varepsilon - \mu_t \varepsilon_x/\sigma_\varepsilon \end{bmatrix} \qquad F = \begin{bmatrix} \rho v \\ \rho uv - \mu_t u_y \\ \rho v^2 - \mu_t v_y \\ \rho vw - \mu_t w_y \\ \rho vk - \mu_t k_y/\sigma_k \\ \rho v\varepsilon - \mu_t \varepsilon_y/\sigma_\varepsilon \end{bmatrix}$$

$$G = \begin{bmatrix} \rho w \\ \rho uw - \mu_t u_z \\ \rho vw - \mu_t v_z \\ \rho w^2 - \mu_t w_z \\ \rho wk - \mu_t k_z/\sigma_k \\ \rho w\varepsilon - \mu_t \varepsilon_z/\sigma_\varepsilon \end{bmatrix}$$

$$S = \begin{bmatrix} 0 \\ (\mu_t u_x)_x + (\mu_t v_x)_y + (\mu_t w_x)_z - p_x \\ (\mu_t u_y)_x + (\mu_t v_y)_y + (\mu_t w_y)_z - p_y \\ (\mu_t u_z)_x + (\mu_t v_z)_y + (\mu_t w_z)_z - p_z \\ \rho P - \rho\varepsilon \\ \rho\frac{\varepsilon}{k}(c_{\varepsilon 1}P - c_{\varepsilon 2}\varepsilon) \end{bmatrix} \tag{2}$$

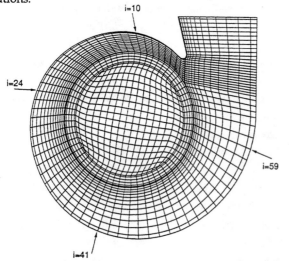
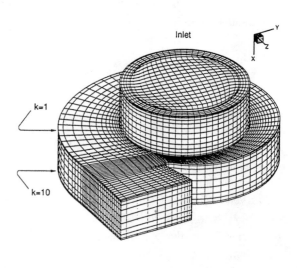

Fig. 1 Grid system and index for multiblade centrifugal fan

The production rate of turbulent kinetic energy, P is defined as follows,

$$P = c_\mu \frac{k^2}{\varepsilon} [(u_y + v_x)^2 + (v_z + w_y)^2 +$$
$$(w_x + u_z)^2 + 2(u_x^2 + v_y^2 + w_z^2)] \qquad (3)$$

For the computations of turbulent flow, the present work employs k–ε turbulence model. The standard k–ε model solves the equations for turbulent kinetic energy, k and its dissipation rate, ε, and obtains the eddy viscosity, μ_t by following relation.

$$\mu_t = \rho c_\mu \frac{k^2}{\varepsilon} \qquad (4)$$

The model constants used are c_μ =0.09, σ_k =1.0, σ_ε =1.3, $c_{\varepsilon 1}$ =1.44, and $c_{\varepsilon 2}$ =1.92.

The equations for k and ε involved in Eq. (1) are only valid in the region far from the wall where the turbulent Reynolds number is sufficiently high. Thus, the widely used empirical wall function is employed to provide the near wall boundary conditions for momentum equations and the k–ε model.

The governing equations in Cartesian coordinates are transformed to a non-orthogonal curvilinear coordinate system as described by Demirzic[1982]. The governing transport equations are integrated over a finite number of control volumes in physical space as in the work of Peric[1985]. As a numerical scheme for the convection terms, linear upwind differencing scheme is used. SIMPLEC algorithm is employed to calculate the pressures. The SIP(strongly implicit procedure)[Fletcher, 1991] was used to solve linear algebraic equations.

Because of the complexity of the flow, it is very important to generate suitable grids. In this study, the computational domain is divided into three blocks ; core, impeller and scroll. Therefore, the technique for the multi-block calculation is used to match the flows between different blocks.

MODELING OF IMPELLER FORCE

The flow through the impeller is pushed by moving blades, and then changes its direction. The moving blades in the flowfield receive the reaction load from the flow.

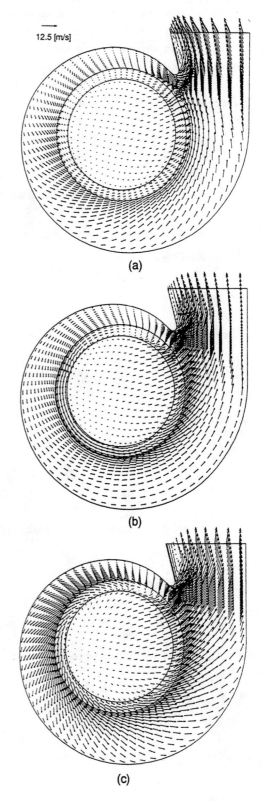

12.5 [m/s]

(a)

(b)

(c)

Fig. 2 Velocity vectors on ξ-η planes
(a) k=2   (b) k=5   (c) k=9

Therefore, the rotation of blades can be considered as a force, so called "blade force". Usually, the "blade force" can be divided into lift and drag as in the case of airfoil, and also can be divided into radial and circumferential forces. The circumferential force is most important because only this force changes the momentum and the total energy of the flow.

The circumferential force can be obtained from the difference between the outgoing and incoming momentums, and from the difference between the velocities at outlet and inlet of the impeller. The incoming and outgoing angular momentums are $r_1 c_{1u}$ and $r_2 c_{2u}$ per unit mass about impeller axis, respectively. And, the torque for a flow rate $\dot{m}$ is obtained as follows,

$$T = \dot{m}(r_2 c_{2u} - r_1 c_{1u}) \tag{5}$$

Thus, the circumferential force, f_c can be written as

$$f_c = T / \bar{r} = \dot{m}(r_2 c_{2u} - r_1 c_{1u}) / \bar{r} \tag{6}$$

where $\dot{m}$ can be obtained by c_{1r}, and c_{2u} can be calculated by c_{1r}, β_{2A} and velocity coefficient, ε.

$$\varepsilon = c_{2u} / c_{2uth} \tag{7}$$

In this study, velocity coefficient, ε is calculated by the empirical formula given by Eck[1975].

$$\varepsilon = \cfrac{1.0}{1.0 + \cfrac{1.5 + 1.1\,\beta_{2A}/90°}{z[1.0 - (r_1/r_2)^2]}} \tag{8}$$

Finally, we obtain the following circumferential force.

$$f_c = \dot{m}(r_2(r_2\omega - c_{2r}ctg\beta_{2A})\varepsilon - r_1 c_{1u}) / \bar{r} \tag{9}$$

The force, f_c is employed in the impeller block as body force to simulate the rotation of the blades.

RESULTS AND DISCUSSIONS

Numerical calculation was carried out in a multiblade fan

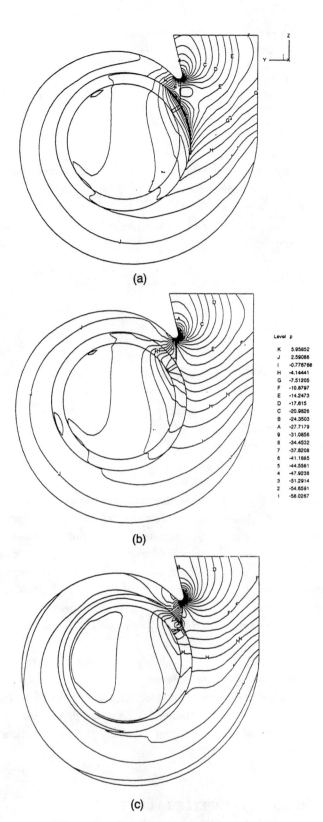

(a)

Level p

K	5.95852
J	2.59088
I	-0.776766
H	-4.14441
G	-7.51205
F	-10.8797
E	-14.2473
D	-17.615
C	-20.9826
B	-24.3503
A	-27.7179
9	-31.0856
8	-34.4532
7	-37.8208
6	-41.1885
5	-44.5561
4	-47.9238
3	-51.2914
2	-54.6591
1	-58.0267

(b)

(c)

Fig. 3 Pressure contours on ξ - η planes
(a) k=2   (b) k=5   (c) k=9

with d_1/d_2=0..835, b/d_2=0.41, z=50, and β_{2A}=139.6° where d_2 is 190 mm. The operating fluid is 20° C air with 1.25 kg/m³ density and 1.8×10^{-5} N·s/m² viscosity. The rotational speed of the impeller is 770 rpm. And, the velocity of uniform inlet flow is 1.5 m/s.

Grid system is shown in Fig. 1. As shown in this Figure, each of the three blocks has a independent grid system, which matches with the other blocks at block surfaces.

Figs. 2 to 4 show velocity vectors and pressure contours. In Fig. 2, velocity vectors are displayed on three sections; near inlet of fan(k=2), at the middle(k=5) and near endwall(k=9) of the fan, respectively. The augmentation of rotational velocity due to circumferential force. in impeller block are noted because of the circumferential force. The magnitudes of velocities at 0.96b height from inlet section of scroll(k=9) are relatively larger than those on the other sections, and the radial velocities on that section are also larger than the others. In this aspect, it can be thought that considerable mass flow goes through between middle and endwall sections. The distribution of radial velocity along the circumferential direction is not uniform, obviously. The radial velocities near the outlet of scroll are larger than the others. The flow directions near inlet section(k=2) and endwall section (k=9) in scroll are much different. It means that the flow in scroll has swirling structure as shown in Fig. 5. Fig. 6 shows the distributions of pressure on outer wall of scroll, the highest pressure locates on inner face of the tongue near endwall. On the middle section of scroll(k=5), very large gradients of pressure are found around the tongue in Fig. 3(b). The increase in pressure along the outlet duct is not shown due to the insufficient exit length. The sections in Fig. 4 are perpendicular to the direction of main flow. Secondary flows of relatively large magnitude are found in three sections. In Fig. 4(b), most of inflow turns to the scroll of exit part(i=59) as it reach endwall, because the maximum pressure occurs near i=24 section, as shown in Fig. 3(b)

A comparisons is made between the numerical simulation and experiment in Fig. 7. Fig. 7(a) shows the velocity vectors calculated on the middle section of the fan. And, Fig. 7(b) shows the velocity vectors measured by LDV[Kim et al., 1995].

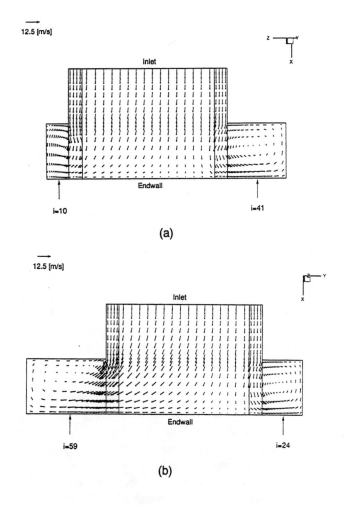

Fig. 4 Velocity vectors on η-ζ planes
(a) i=10,41 (b) i=24,59

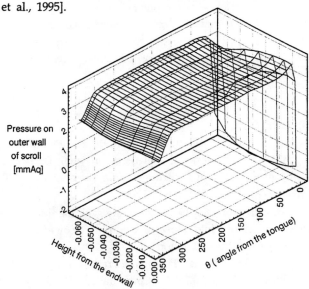

Fig. 5 Pressures on the outer wall of scroll

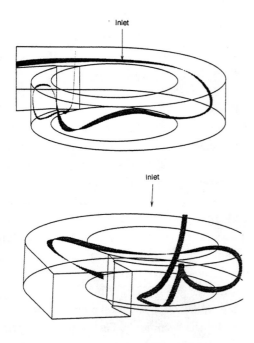

Fig. 6 Three-dimensional stream ribbon from
inlet to outlet of the fan

CONCLUSION

A numerical simulation of the flow in a multiblade centrifugal fan was carried out by the use of "blade force", which replaces the role of the rotating impeller, and results in the changes of velocity and pressure through the impeller. The computational results show that this kind of simplification leads to economic calculation but, gives detailed characteristics of three-dimensional flow in multiblade fan. Further measurements are needed to modify the "blade force" in both of circumferential and radial directions.

REFERENCES

Casey, M. V., Dalbert, P., and Roth, P., 1992, "The Use of 3D Viscous Flow Calculations in the Design and Analysis of Industrial Centrifugal Compressors," ASME J. of Turbomachinery. vol. 114, pp. 27-37.

Demirdizic, I. A., 1982, "A Finite Volume Method For Computation of Fluid Flow in Complex Geometries," Ph.D Thesis, University of London.

Eck, B., 1975, "Fans," Pergamon Press.

Fletcher, C. A. J., 1991, "Computational Techniques for Fluid Dynamics 1," Springer-Verlag.

Kadota, S., Kawaguchi, K., Suzuki, M., Matsui, K., and Kikuyama, K., 1994, "Experimental Study on Low-Noise Multiblade Fan," JSME Paper, vol 60, no. 570, pp. 102-113.

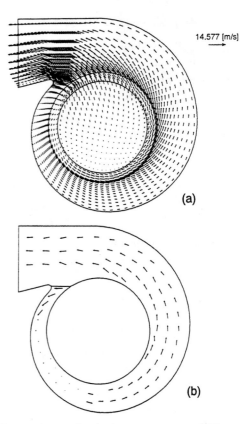

14.577 [m/s]

(a)

(b)

Fig. 7 Comparison of velocity vectors on middle section
(a) calculation   (b) measurement

Kim, T. J., Lee, D. J., Liu, H. S., Son, Y. H., and Jung, C. M., 1995, "Developments of Sirocco Fan and Crossflow Fan: 1st Report," LG Electronics. Co.

Launder, B. E., and Spalding, D. B., 1974, "The Numerical Computational of Turbulent Flows", Computer Methods in Applied Mechanics and Engineering, vol. 3, pp. 269-289.

Moore, J., and Moore J. G., 1981, "Calculations of Three-Dimensional Viscous Flow and Wake Development in a Centrifugal Impeller," ASME J. of Engineering for Power, vol. 103, pp. 367-372.

Pantankar, S. V., 1980, "Numerical Heat Transfer and Fluid Flow," McGraw-Hill Book Co.

Peric, M., August 1985, "A Finite Volume Method for the Prediction of Three-Dimensional Fluid Flow in Complex Ducts," Ph.D Thesis, Imperial College, London.

Zhang, L., and Lakshminarayana B., 1990, "Computational and Turbulence Modeling for Three-Dimensional Boundary Layers Including Turbomachinery Rotor Flows," J. of AIAA, vol. 28, pp. 1861-1869.

Zhang, M. J., Gu, C. G., and Miao, Y. M., 1994, "Numerical Study of the Internal Flow Field of a Centrifugal Impeller," ASME Paper, 94-GT-357.

FED-Vol. 238, 1996 Fluids Engineering Division Conference
Volume 3
ASME 1996

AN ANALYTICAL DESIGN METHOD FOR LINEARIZED

FREE-VORTEX TYPE FLOW IN TURBOMACHINES

Nhan T. Nguyen

Aeronautical Test and Simulation Division

NASA Ames Research Center

Moffett Field, CA

ABSTRACT

An analytical solution based on the velocity perturbation method and radial equilibrium theory is derived for a 3-D axisymmetric flow through constant-diameter turbomachines with a free-vortex type tangential velocity distribution. The linearized equation of motion for inviscid flow is solved by approximation using an asymptotic expansion method. The derived solution sufficiently describes the behavior of the axial and radial velocities upstream and downstream near a blade row as well as the far field velocities. A new design method based on this analysis is presented to enable the designer to compute the velocity field near a blade row without directly solving the 3-D Euler equations for axisymmetric flow. The results of this analytical method demonstrate a very good agreement with the well-established streamline curvature method which is frequently used in turbomachinery design and analysis.

NOMENCLATURE

Symbols

A	Velocity Perturbation Amplitude
c	Blade Chord
c_p	Constant-Pressure Specific Heat
K	Product of Tangential Velocity and Radius
k	Eigenvalue of the Boundary Value Problem
M	Mach Number
$\dot{m}$	Mass Flow Rate
P	Pressure
R	Gas Constant
r	Radial Coordinate, Radius
s	Entropy
T	Temperature
V	Velocity
x	Axial Coordinate

Greeks

γ	Specific Heat Ratio
ω	Rotational Speed
ρ	Density

Subscripts

h	Blade Hub
m	Mid-Radius Streamline
o	Stagnation Condition
r	Radial Coordinate
s	Streamline
t	Blade Tip
x	Axial Coordinate
θ	Tangential Coordinate
∞	Far Field Condition
1	Upstream
2	Downstream

INTRODUCTION

In the design of axial-flow turbomachines, the designer frequently faces the task of selecting a suitable radial distribution of the tangential velocity in order to design the blade airfoil to provide the proper flow turning requirement. Clearly, the choice of the tangential velocity distribution has a profound impact on the performance of the turbomachine, as some distributions may provide certain advantages over others in meeting the design requirements and/or off-design performance. There are many such distributions that the designer can select, one of which is the free-vortex type. This distribution is a textbook classic due to its simplicity when used in the context of radial equilibrium, which dictates that the axial velocity must be radially uniform in the absence of the radial velocity and radial gradient of the entropy. With the proliferation of computational fluid dynamic methods accompanied by a rapid growth in computing power, the radial equilibrium is no longer an important consideration in designing turbomachines. Its chief limitation is the lack of treatment of the radial flow near a blade row, leading to incorrect blade angles and overestimation of the design efficiency [1], particularly in turbines and high pressure ratio compressors. In these instances, the assumption of no radial flow is no longer valid because of the significant shift in the streamlines through a blade row. In the current turbomachinery design, an inviscid 3-D axisymmetric method, based on the streamline curvature formulation, is frequently used to account for such radial flow. This paper presents an alternate method for turbomachinery design based on an approximate analysis of the 3-D axisymmetric flow in constant-diameter turbomachines with a free-vortex type tangential velocity distribution. In this method, the velocity field is postulated as the superposition of the far field velocity components and small local perturbations near a blade row. The radial equilibrium theory can be readily applied to solve for the far field axial velocities; whereas the perturbations are to be obtained from the equation of motion, which has been linearized and solved by an asymptotic expansion method. The design based on this analytical method can be implemented most efficiently by a numerical scheme. The advantage of the present analytical method lies in its simple, yet intuitive formulation, which enables the designer to compute the velocities without solving directly the 3-D Euler equations for axisymmetric flow. The method demonstrates a very good agreement with the traditional streamline curvature method; therefore it can be readily implemented in the design of a special class of turbomachines with constant-diameter or slightly varying area ducts.

3-D AXISYMMETRIC FLOW ANALYSIS

The flow through a turbomachine is approximately axisymmetric if the inlet condition does not vary circumferentially and the blade rows possess large number of blades. This axisymmetry in the flow field effectively eliminates any variation of the flow property and velocity in the tangential direction. Thus, only the axial and radial coordinates are of interest to the designer. In addition, a uniform inlet condition, particularly the enthalpy, is usually required at the inlet of the turbomachine. This is important since the present analysis is based on the assumption of no radial gradient of the enthalpy at the inlet. For a free-vortex type tangential distribution, this assumption further leads to the condition of constant radial distribution of the enthalpy throughout the flow field, thereby greatly simplifying the design method.

In the design of turbomachines, the thermodynamic properties of the flow ahead and behind a blade row must be determined. The principal parameters for determining the blade shapes are the velocities at the leading edge and trailing edge of the blade row, which can be obtained from the equations of motion. The flow in a turbomachine can be regarded as consisting of two regions: the inviscid core where the flow is not affected by the viscous effect of the fluid and the viscous layer near the end walls. It is customary in the turbomachinery design to treat these two flow regions separately. The viscous effect in a turbomachine, usually dominating the flow near the end walls, is a highly complex phenomenon which can be best accounted for by empirical correlation of the boundary layer displacement thickness established from a priori experimental knowledge and/or correlations. So long as the boundary layer growth is small compared to the overall area of the inviscid core, the flow in this region can be essentially decoupled from the viscous boundary layer. This condition is approximately met in turbines where the

pressure gradient is favorable or in compressors with a few number of stages, e.g. 3 or 4. As the number of stages increases in a compressor, the viscous effect will become more dominant and increasingly interact with the inviscid core. Hence, the viscous effect must then be fully accounted for and the flow equations can no longer be decoupled. In the present analysis and a typical design of turbomachines, the axial velocity in the inviscid core is usually modified in the continuity equation for the boundary layer displacement thickness by the use of blockage factors [2]. The flow in this inviscid region is thus governed by the Euler equations. In order to simplify the Euler equations, the flow inside the blade row is not considered, thereby enabling the blade force terms to be eliminated. This in no way reduces the validity of the solution since the flow outside of the blade row where the blade forces do not exist is computed to provide the necessary information for the flow within the blade row to be subsequently analyzed. This approach is often referred to as the hub-to-tip and blade-to-blade solution [3]. In the design of turbomachines, the hub-to-tip flow or flow in the meridional plane is always carried out; but the blade-to-blade flow or flow within the blade passage can be estimated either by cascade correlations or CFD methods. Frequently, the cascade correlation method is the preferred choice such as the use of NACA-65 series blades in compressor design. In the present analysis, the Euler equations of motion are:

$$-\frac{1}{\rho}\frac{\partial P}{\partial x} = V_x \frac{\partial V_x}{\partial x} + V_r \frac{\partial V_x}{\partial r}$$

$$-\frac{1}{\rho}\frac{\partial P}{\partial r} = V_x \frac{\partial V_r}{\partial x} + V_r \frac{\partial V_r}{\partial r} - \frac{V_\theta^2}{r} \tag{1}$$

For an adiabatic flow, the energy equation is:

$$c_p (T_o - T) = \frac{1}{2}\left(V_x{}^2 + V_r{}^2 + V_\theta{}^2\right) \tag{2}$$

The free-vortex type tangential velocity distribution is:

$$r\, V_\theta = K = constant \tag{3}$$

It can be shown that for isentropic flow with uniform axial velocity, this distribution guarantees that the flow is irrotational everywhere as all the vorticity components completely vanish in the flow field. That is:

$$\frac{\partial V_r}{\partial x} = \frac{\partial V_x}{\partial r} \tag{4}$$

The condition of irrotationality can greatly simplify the method of analysis. However, in general, the flow in a turbomachine is only irrotational in the region between the inlet and the first blade row because the inlet condition is required to be uniform, according to the problem statement. Following the first blade row, the total pressure is no longer uniform because the total pressure loss across the blade row varies radially. This total pressure loss is due to blade profile loss, viscous loss, secondary flow loss, and all other losses occurring within a turbomachinery blade row. Since the entropy production is proportional to the total pressure loss, it follows that the radial gradient of the entropy is also non-zero according to:

$$\frac{ds}{dr} = \frac{d}{dr}\left(R\ln\left[\left(\frac{T_{o,2}}{T_{o,1}}\right)^{\frac{\gamma}{\gamma-1}}\left(\frac{P_{o,2}}{P_{o,1}}\right)^{-1}\right]\right) \tag{5}$$

Applying the Gibb's relation to Eq.'s (1) and (2), the general radial equilibrium equation without consideration for the radial flow is given as [4]:

$$c_p \frac{dT_o}{dr} - T_\infty \frac{ds}{dr} = \frac{V_\theta}{r} \frac{d}{dr}(r V_\theta) + V_{x,\infty} \frac{\partial V_{x,\infty}}{\partial dr} \qquad (6)$$

For free-vortex flow, the momentum equation in the tangential direction results in:

$$c_p (T_{o,2} - T_{o,1}) = \omega (K_2 - K_1) \qquad (7)$$

Substituting Eq.'s (5) and (7) into Eq. (6), the radial equilibrium equation for free-vortex flow is obtained:

$$V_{x,\infty} \frac{dV_{x,\infty}}{dr} = -T_\infty \frac{ds}{dr} = R\left(T_o - \frac{V_{x,\infty}^2 + V_\theta^2}{2 c_p}\right) \frac{d}{dr}\left[\ln\left(\frac{P_{o,2}}{P_{o,1}}\right)\right] \qquad (8)$$

Equation (8) applies to the flow in the far field where the radial velocity is zero. Thus, it can be seen that the radial gradient of the far field axial velocity is non-zero for a non-uniform radial profile of the total pressure. Therefore, in the absence of the radial velocity in the far field, the condition of irrotationality according to Eq. (4) is not satisfied if the total pressure profile is not uniform. Hence, the flow is generally rotational downstream of the first blade row.

Although the flow is rotational as a result of a non-zero radial gradient of the entropy, the flow along a streamline remains isentropic upstream and downstream of a blade row, since there is no source of dissipation in the inviscid flow field [4]. Therefore, the isentropic relation still holds along a streamline in a rotational flow field. The isentropic relation for the density is then given as:

$$\frac{\rho}{\rho_o} = \left(\frac{T}{T_o}\right)^{\frac{1}{\gamma-1}} = \left[1 - \frac{V_x^2 + V_r^2 + V_\theta^2}{2 c_p T_o}\right]^{\frac{1}{\gamma-1}} \qquad (9)$$

where all the state properties are determined at each streamline.

In a constant-diameter turbomachine, the velocity field is axial far upstream and downstream of a blade row. Equation (8) can be applied to solve for the far field axial velocity using a convenient numerical method such as finite-difference:

$$V_{x,\infty,i+1} = V_{x,\infty,i} + f_i \frac{\Delta r}{V_{x,\infty,i}} \qquad (10)$$

where f is the expression on the right hand side of Eq. (8), which can be evaluated readily from the knowledge of the upstream and downstream total pressures. The starting velocity value is selected such that the continuity equation is satisfied:

$$\dot{m} = \int_{r_h}^{r_t} \rho_\infty V_{x,\infty} 2 \pi r \, dr \qquad (11)$$

If the flow is irrotational downstream of the blade row, then the far field axial velocity is constant and thus can be solved analytically from Eq.'s (3), (9), and (11) for a specific heat ratio of 1.4 as follows:

$$V_{x,\infty} = \frac{\dot{m}}{2 \pi \rho_o [m(r_t) - m(r_h)]} \qquad (12)$$

where m(r) is equal to:

$$m(r) = \left(A^2 - \frac{B^2}{r^2}\right)\left(\frac{A^4 r^2}{2} + \frac{7 A^2 B^2}{3} - \frac{B^4}{3 r^2}\right) - \frac{5 A^3 B^2}{2} \ln\left[\frac{r}{B}\left(A + \sqrt{A^2 - \frac{B^2}{r^2}}\right)\right]$$

and

$$A^2 = 1 - \frac{V_{x,\infty}^2}{2 c_p T_o}$$

$$B^2 = \frac{K^2}{2 c_p T_o}$$

Near the blade row, the streamlines shift due to the existence of the radial gradient of the density across the blade row (Fig. 1). The radial velocity no longer remains zero. The axial velocity is also redistributed radially in the presence of the radial velocity. In order to accurately determine the blade shape, this radial flow must be accounted for. It is postulated that the velocity field is composed of two components: the far field velocity and the local perturbation. Horlock [5] used this approach in his "actuator disk" analysis for an irrotational flow with a uniform axial velocity. In his analysis, he showed that the perturbation component of the axial velocity contains an exponential decay expression, which would make the velocity perturbation vanish far upstream and downstream of the blade row. The present analysis makes use of the exponential expression and further enhances the generality of the solution by not restricting the flow to just being irrotational. Restating another way, the far field axial velocity is permitted to vary along the radial direction. The present analysis further improves the perturbation approach by imposing the condition of irrotationality to the local velocity perturbation. This supposition is justifiable since any rotational effect in the flow is derived primarily from the far field velocity as discussed earlier. This new approach will greatly simplify the subsequent analysis. Thus, it is postulated that the velocities upstream and downstream of a blade row are described by:

$$V_x(x,r) = V_{x,\infty}(r) - \text{sgn}(x) e^{-k\left(|x| - \frac{c}{2}\right)} g(r) \quad , \quad |x| \geq \frac{c}{2} \qquad (13)$$

$$V_r(x,r) = \frac{1}{k} e^{-k\left(|x| - \frac{c}{2}\right)} g(r) \qquad (14)$$

where c is the blade chord and sgn(x) is the sign function:

$$\text{sgn}(x) = \begin{cases} 1 & , \quad x > 0 \\ -1 & , \quad x < 0 \end{cases}$$

The significance of the sgn(x) function in Eq. (13) is that while the radial velocities must maintain the same direction through a blade row in order to satisfy the conservation of the radial momentum, the local velocity perturbation has an additive effect on the far field upstream axial velocity and a reverse effect for the downstream velocity, or vice versa. This means that if both the upstream and downstream far field axial velocities are uniform then the local perturbation will make the velocities switch slope across the blade row. The implication of this is that the local perturbation will result in a difference in the turning angle and thus the blade camber, while the stagger angle of the blade section remains relatively unaffected by the local radial flow. The deviation in the camber will result in the incidence angle not being at the minimum loss or intended design condition, which can lead to a reduced design efficiency of the turbomachine.

From Eq.'s (13) and (14), it follows that:

$$\frac{\partial V_x}{\partial r} = \frac{dV_{x,\infty}}{dr} + \frac{\partial V_r}{\partial x} \tag{15}$$

Equation (15) reduces identically to Eq. (4) if the far field axial velocity is radially uniform. This is a reassertion that the free-vortex flow field is irrotational if the axial velocity is uniform.

Applying Eq.'s (2) and (15) together with the ideal gas law to Eq. (1), the density relation becomes:

$$\frac{\partial}{\partial x}(\ln \rho) = \frac{1}{\gamma - 1}\frac{\partial}{\partial x}(\ln T) - \frac{V_r}{RT}\frac{dV_{x,\infty}}{dr}$$

$$\frac{\partial}{\partial r}(\ln \rho) = \frac{1}{\gamma - 1}\frac{\partial}{\partial r}(\ln T) + \frac{V_x}{RT}\frac{dV_{x,\infty}}{dr} \tag{16}$$

The expressions containing the radial gradient of the far field axial velocity in Eq. (16) represent the gradient of the entropy in the axial and radial directions, which are non-zero for a rotational flow. It is noted that the radial component of Eq. (16) reduces identically to Eq. (8) for a zero radial velocity.

To complete the description of the free-vortex flow field, the axial and radial velocities are now determined from the continuity equation:

$$\frac{\partial}{\partial x}(\rho V_x r) + \frac{\partial}{\partial r}(\rho V_r r) = 0 \tag{17}$$

Substituting Eq.'s (2) and (16) into Eq. (17), the equation of motion in terms of the velocity components is obtained:

$$\left(1 - \frac{V_x^2}{\gamma RT}\right)\frac{\partial V_x}{\partial x} + \left(1 - \frac{V_r^2}{\gamma RT}\right)\frac{\partial V_r}{\partial r} - \frac{V_x V_r}{\gamma RT}\left(\frac{\partial V_x}{\partial r} + \frac{\partial V_r}{\partial x}\right) + \frac{V_r}{r}\left(1 + \frac{V_\theta^2}{\gamma RT}\right) = 0 \tag{18}$$

It should be noted that the irrotational condition imposed on the perturbation components enables the radial gradient of the far field axial velocity to be mathematically eliminated from the equation of motion, thereby simplifying the analysis. Equation (18) is highly nonlinear, but can be linearized by substituting Eq.'s (13) and (14) into Eq. (18) and eliminating small terms. Therefore, the equation of motion in terms of the velocity perturbation becomes:

$$g'' + \frac{1}{r}\left[1 + \frac{M_{\theta,h}^2}{\left(\frac{r}{r_h}\right)^2 - \frac{\gamma - 1}{2}M_{\theta,h}^2} + \frac{r}{\gamma R}\frac{ds}{dr}\right]g' + \left[1 - \frac{M_{x,\infty}^2}{1 - \frac{\gamma - 1}{2}M_{\theta,h}^2\left(\frac{r_h}{r}\right)^2}\right]k^2 g = 0 \tag{19}$$

where:

$$M_{x,\infty}^2 = \frac{V_{x,\infty}^2}{\gamma R T_o - \frac{\gamma - 1}{2}V_{x,\infty}^2}$$

$$M_{\theta,h}^2 = \frac{V_{\theta,h}^2}{\gamma R T_o - \frac{\gamma - 1}{2}V_{x,\infty}^2}$$

The far field axial velocity term in Eq. (19) in general is a function of the radial coordinate. However, it might be replaced by the average value without any loss of generality. The entropy term represents the irreversibility of the flow across the blade row. Equation (19) resembles the Bessel's differential equation, but because of the additional non-constant terms in the coefficients, the solution becomes mathematically intractable. In fact, it can be shown that the solution will converge asymptotically to the Bessel functions. Hawthorne [6] suggested an asymptotic expansion method for large values of k, which can be shown that this is tantamount to the geometric condition of high hub-to-tip ratio in the turbomachines. Since the asymptotic expansion of the Bessel functions contains a sinusoidal term, the solution is then also assumed to be sinusoidal in the form of:

$$g_n = c_n e^{i\left[k_n r + \frac{f(r)}{k_n}\right]} \tag{20}$$

Substituting Eq. (20) into Eq. (19) and eliminating terms containing k in the denominator since they are considered to be small if k is large, an approximate solution for f(r) is obtained:

$$\frac{f(r)}{k} \approx -\frac{M_{x,\infty}^2}{2}k_n r + i\ln\left(\sqrt{\frac{r}{r_h}}\left[1 - \frac{\gamma - 1}{2}M_{\theta,h}^2\left(\frac{r_h}{r}\right)^2\right]^{\frac{1}{2(\gamma - 1)}}\right) + i\frac{s - s_h}{2\gamma} \tag{21}$$

Using the expression for the entropy in Eq. (5), upon simplification, the solution for g_n becomes:

$$g_n \approx c_n\left(\frac{P_o}{P_{o,h}}\right)^{\frac{1}{2\gamma}}\sqrt{\frac{r_h}{r}}\left[1 - \frac{\gamma - 1}{2}M_{\theta,h}^2\left(\frac{r_h}{r}\right)^2\right]^{-\frac{1}{2(\gamma - 1)}} e^{i\left[\left(1 - \frac{M_{x,\infty}^2}{2}\right)k_n r\right]} \tag{22}$$

Substituting Eq. (22) into Eq.'s (13) and (14) and imposing the boundary condition of zero radial velocity at the hub and tip radii, the axial and radial velocities then become:

$$V_x \simeq V_{x,\infty} + \text{sgn}(x)\, h(r)\sum_{n=1}^{\infty} c_n e^{-k_n\left(|x| - \frac{c}{2}\right)}\cos\left[n\pi\left(\frac{r - r_h}{r_t - r_h}\right)\right] \tag{23}$$

$$V_r \simeq \left(1 - \frac{M_{x,\infty}^2}{2}\right)h(r)\sum_{n=1}^{\infty} c_n e^{-k_n\left(|x| - \frac{c}{2}\right)}\sin\left[n\pi\left(\frac{r - r_h}{r_t - r_h}\right)\right] \tag{24}$$

where:

$$h(r) = \left(\frac{P_o}{P_{o,h}}\right)^{\frac{1}{2\gamma}}\sqrt{\frac{r_h}{r}}\left[1 - \frac{\gamma - 1}{2}M_{\theta,h}^2\left(\frac{r_h}{r}\right)^2\right]^{-\frac{1}{2(\gamma - 1)}}$$

$$k_n \simeq \frac{n\pi}{\left(1 - \frac{M_{x,\infty}^2}{2}\right)(r_t - r_h)}$$

Since the validity of the solution is predicated on the assumption that the eigenvalue k is large, by examining the above expression, this would imply that for this condition to be satisfied, the hub-to-tip ratio should be large, e.g. 0.6 and above. In such cases, the solutions can be approximated by the first few terms since the series converges rapidly; whereas for smaller hub-to-tip ratios, more terms will be needed to improve the accuracy of the calculated velocity profiles. In most cases, however, reasonable accuracy can be obtained by using just the first term because of the exponential decay in the solution. Hence, the radial distributions of the velocities at the leading edge and trailing edge of the blade row are now approximately equal to:

$$V_x \simeq V_{x,\infty} + A \, sgn(x) \, h(r) \cos\left[\pi\left(\frac{r - r_h}{r_t - r_h}\right)\right] \tag{25}$$

$$V_r \simeq \left(1 - \frac{M_{x,\infty}^2}{2}\right) A \, h(r) \sin\left[\pi\left(\frac{r - r_h}{r_t - r_h}\right)\right] \tag{26}$$

It remains then to determine the velocity perturbation amplitude A to complete the description of the velocity field. Since the radial velocity exists as a result of the streamline shift through a blade row, its value can be deduced from the slope of the streamline, which can be expressed as:

$$\frac{\partial r_s}{\partial x} = \frac{V_r}{V_x} = \frac{\left(1 - \frac{M_{x,\infty}^2}{2}\right) A \, h(r) \sin\left[\pi\left(\frac{r - r_h}{r_t - r_h}\right)\right] e^{-k\left(|x| - \frac{c}{2}\right)}}{V_{x,\infty} + sgn(x) \, A \, h(r) \cos\left[\pi\left(\frac{r - r_h}{r_t - r_h}\right)\right] e^{-k\left(|x| - \frac{c}{2}\right)}} \tag{27}$$

It follows from Eq. (27) that the mid-radius streamline slopes at the leading edge and trailing edge are related to that at the mid-chord as follows:

$$\left.\frac{\partial r_s}{\partial x}\right|_{|x|=0} = e^{k\frac{c}{2}} \left.\frac{\partial r_s}{\partial x}\right|_{|x|=\frac{c}{2}} \tag{28}$$

Since the streamline across the blade row is smoothly varying with a gradual change in the slope as described by Eq. (27), the streamline slope at the mid-chord can be approximated by the ratio of the change in the radial location of the mid-radius streamline between the leading edge and trailing edge to the blade chord. This enables the streamline slopes at the leading edge and trailing edge to be estimated as,

$$\left.\frac{\partial r_s}{\partial x}\right|_{|x|=\frac{c}{2}} \simeq \frac{r_{m,2} - r_{m,1}}{c} \, e^{-k\frac{c}{2}} \tag{29}$$

and the radial locations of the streamline can be determined from the continuity equation such that the mass flow within the volume bounded by the stream surfaces is conserved:

$$\int_{r_h}^{r_m} \rho \, V_x \, 2\pi r \, dr = \rho_{\infty,1} V_{x,\infty,1} \pi \left[\left(\frac{r_t + r_h}{2}\right)^2 - r_h^2\right] \tag{30}$$

Finally, the perturbation amplitude A can be evaluated using Eq. (27) applied at the mid-radius streamline location. This method is well-suited for an iterative solution, whereby the streamline locations are initially determined from the far field axial velocities upstream and downstream of the blade row, and successively refined as the new axial and radial velocities at the leading edge and trailing edge become known.

It should be noted that the streamline slope is conveniently evaluated at the mid-radius location in the above formulation. Other locations could as well be used instead of the mid-radius to evaluate the streamline slope. In fact, the accuracy may be improved if the perturbation amplitude is to be computed at a number of radial locations and an average is then obtained.

An interesting observation can be made from Eq. (29). For the same shift in the streamline radii, as the aspect ratio of the blades (blade span over blade chord) reduces, the streamline slope also reduces. Thus for a given pressure rise, the radial flow could be reduced by the use of low aspect ratio blading [7]. However, as pointed out in the literature [8], this reduction in the radial flow may come at the expense of the secondary flow, which may increase the losses for the low aspect ratio blades.

Thus far, the analysis has been performed for a single blade row with undisturbed flow far upstream and downstream. In reality, the adjacent blade rows within the turbomachine interact with each other to produce a perturbation which is the combination of all the perturbations caused by the individual blade rows since the perturbed flow is linear [5]. If the blade rows are sufficiently far apart, the perturbation between two adjacent blade rows can be assumed to be only affected by the blade rows themselves. Thus, the perturbation amplitude at the trailing edge of the upstream blade row and at the leading edge of the downstream blade row is the sum of the contributions from the two blade rows. Therefore, the amplitude in Eq.'s (25) and (26) may be modified as follows:

$$\left(1 - \frac{M_{x,\infty}^2}{2}\right) A \, e^{-k\left(|x| - \frac{c}{2}\right)} = \sum_{i=1}^{2} \left(1 - \frac{M_{x,\infty i}^2}{2}\right) A_i \, e^{-k_i\left(|x_i| - \frac{c_i}{2}\right)} \tag{31}$$

where i = 1,2 denotes the upstream and downstream blade rows, respectively. The amplitude A_i can be solved from a system of linear equations by evaluating Eq. (27) at the mid-radius location:

$$A_1 + \left(\frac{2 - M_{x,\infty,2}^2}{2 - M_{x,\infty,1}^2}\right) e^{-k_2 \Delta} A_2 \simeq \frac{V_{x,\infty,1} \left.\frac{\partial r_s}{\partial x}\right|_{x_1 = \frac{c_1}{2}}}{\left(1 - \frac{M_{x,\infty 1}^2}{2}\right) h_1\left(\frac{r_t + r_h}{2}\right)}$$

$$\left(\frac{2 - M_{x,\infty,1}^2}{2 - M_{x,\infty,2}^2}\right) e^{-k_1 \Delta} A_1 + A_2 \simeq \frac{V_{x,\infty,2} \left.\frac{\partial r_s}{\partial x}\right|_{x_2 = -\frac{c_2}{2}}}{\left(1 - \frac{M_2^2}{2}\right) h_2\left(\frac{r_t + r_h}{2}\right)}$$

In general, however, the contributions of all blade rows must be considered. Hence, the resulting matrix of the perturbation amplitudes can be solved from the streamline slopes at all blade row stations.

DESIGN METHOD

The design of a turbomachine usually is specified by the pressure ratio and mass flow rate. A design RPM is then selected to match the operating characteristics of the motor or generator. In addition, a uniform inlet condition is also specified from which the inlet axial velocity and density can be determined. A typical design procedure using the analytical method developed above may be as follows:

(1) Determine the stage pressure ratio and enthalpy rise.

(2) Select an appropriate pre-swirl tangential velocity distribution of free-vortex type upstream of the rotor, if necessary. This can be accomplished by the use of inlet guide vanes. The downstream tangential velocity can then be computed from the enthalpy change using Eq. (7). Thus, K_1 and K_2 are determined. For subsonic compressors, the selected tangential velocities should be checked along with the axial velocities at all radial stations for critical Mach number limitation at the inlet of the blade row. There are numerous methods available to enable the critical Mach numbers in a subsonic compressor to be estimated [9].

(3) Compute the far field axial velocity upstream of the blade row using Eq.'s (10) or (12).

(4) Compute cascade correlation parameters for compressors or turbines, such as diffusion factors, Reynolds numbers, and/or momentum thickness to estimate the total pressure loss across the blade row, which may include profile, skin friction, secondary, and tip clearance losses.

(5) Compute the total pressure downstream of the blade row from the cascade loss correlation. In general, the profile of the total pressure will not be uniform because of varying losses along the blade span.

(6) Compute the far field axial velocity downstream of the blade row from Eq.'s (10) or (12).

(7) Compute the initial streamline radii at the leading edge and trailing edge along the mid-radius using Eq. (30) with the perturbation amplitude A set to zero.

(8) Compute the streamline slopes at the leading edge and trailing edge from Eq. (29).

(9) Compute the perturbation amplitude A from Eq. (27). If A differs from the previous value, then set A equal to the average of the new value and the previous value and go back to step (7). For multiple blade rows, the matrix of the perturbation amplitudes must be set up and solved for in similar fashion as Eq. (31).

(10) Compute the flow angles at the leading edge and trailing edge of the blade row from the axial and tangential velocities.

(11) Determine the camber and stagger angles from the flow angles using cascade correlations or other appropriate methods [2].

In general, in the design of compressors, particularly subsonic compressors, there is a practical limit as to how much pressure rise can be achieved by a blade row before flow separation on the airfoil will be encountered. As such, the stage pressure rise is usually limited to a low or moderate value, typically less than 1.15. This means that the radial flow effect will tend to be less important. Furthermore, this effect can be lessened by the use of low aspect ratio blading, e.g. 2 or less, as discussed previously. In these cases, one can design a compressor based on the simple radial equilibrium theory, and therefore steps (7) to (9) in the above design procedure can usually be neglected. The situation of radial flow becomes significant in turbines or modern high pressure ratio compressors since the enthalpy change across a blade row is very high. In these cases, the designer must fully account for the radial shift in the streamlines.

SAMPLE CALCULATION

A sample calculation for a large-scale single stage compressor rotor is performed using the present method and then validated by the streamline curvature method. The following is the pertinent design information:

$$\dot{m} = 16,000 \text{ lb/sec} \, (7,257.6 \text{ kg/sec})$$

$$P_{o,1} = 4,268 \, \frac{\text{lb}}{\text{ft}^2} \, (204.4 \text{ kPa})$$

$$\frac{P_{o,2}}{P_{o,1}} = 1.2225$$

$$T_{o,1} = 580 \, ^\circ\text{R} \, (577.6 \, ^\circ\text{K})$$

$$\text{RPM} = 700$$

$$r_h = 8.5 \text{ ft} \, (2.59 \text{ m})$$

$$r_t = 12.0 \text{ ft} \, (3.66 \text{ m})$$

A streamline curvature code [10] is used to obtain the required pressure ratio. The code uses NACA 65-series cascade correlation to predict the performance of compressor blades. After a number of iterations, a tangential velocity downstream of the rotor is arrived at and equal to:

$$r \, V_{\theta,2} = 4521.56 \, \frac{\text{ft}^2}{\text{sec}} \, \left(420.07 \, \frac{\text{m}^2}{\text{sec}}\right)$$

Using this information and the total pressure profile downstream of the rotor, a calculation is then performed using the analytical method to derive the axial and radial velocities upstream and downstream of the rotor. The results of the calculation are plotted in Fig.'s (2) to (6).

Figure 2 shows the computed far field and local axial velocities upstream and downstream of the rotor. As can be seen, the velocity field is uniform far upstream since this is a specified condition. At the leading edge of the rotor, because of the presence of the radial flow, the axial velocity profile becomes distorted. The hub velocity is reduced by the amount of the velocity perturbation amplitude, while the tip velocity increases roughly by the same amount. The perturbation is opposite at the trailing edge where the hub velocity is greater than the far field velocity. This condition is necessary because the radial flow near the blade row has to satisfy the conservation of the radial momentum, which dictates that the radial velocities cannot alter the direction through the blade row. It should be noted that the skew in the far field axial velocity downstream of the rotor is entirely arbitrary due to the radial gradient of the entropy increase across the rotor, which in this case is higher at the tip than it is at the hub. The amplitude of the velocity perturbation is about 2% of the far field velocity, which is not unreasonable for this high pressure ratio compressor. In general, as the enthalpy change across a blade row increases, so does the velocity perturbation. In turbines or modern high pressure ratio compressors, these values can become quite significant. Figure 3 demonstrates the validity of the method by showing a very good agreement between the axial velocities computed by the present method as compared to the streamline curvature code, particularly at the upstream location. Figure 4 is the plot of the radial velocities at the leading edge and trailing edge of the rotor for the two methods. In general, they seem to match reasonably well. The maximum amplitude of the radial velocity is approximately the perturbation amplitude which modifies the axial velocity. The negative values of the radial velocities indicate that the streamlines shift inward toward the hub due to the increase in the axial velocity inboard of the blade at the trailing edge. The agreement in the radial velocity at the leading edge is excellent, while the radial velocity at the trailing edge is off somewhat. However, the conservation of the radial momentum dictates that the radial velocities at the leading edge and trailing edge must be approximately the same in magnitude. This implies that the results from the analytical method satisfy the radial momentum condition better than the streamline curvature method. Therefore, this may suggest that the difference could be due to some artifacts in the numerical methods of both approaches as opposed to a deviation in the present analysis. In any case, the difference in the radial velocity at the trailing edge is less than 15%, which is still acceptable for design purposes. Further improvement in the accuracy of the radial velocity was made by computing the perturbation amplitude at three different radii: 25%, 50%, and 75% of blade span. The results from this calculation did reduce the error to about 10%. Figures 5 and 6 illustrate the effect of the radial flow on the blade camber. The turning angles computed with and without radial flow consideration are plotted in Fig. 5. The difference is not marked, since there is only about a 1° difference at the tip and the hub and no difference at the mid span of the blade. However, when translated into the blade camber using NACA 65-series cascade correlation, a 1° difference in the turning angle at the tip becomes a 3° difference in the blade camber, which results in a noticeable difference in the blade shape as shown in Fig. 6. This deviation in the blade camber is one of the primary causes for the loss in the design efficiency. For a compressor, this effect is usually more pronounced at the hub than anywhere else along the blade span because the blade sections in this region tend to be most highly loaded, and any small underturning or overturning of the flow can cause the blade section to operate at a non minimum loss or intended design incidence angle.

DISCUSSION

In the design of axial flow turbomachines, a knowledge of the radial flow in the vicinity of a blade row is of paramount importance for the designer because this enables the designer to accurately determine the flow angles, from which a particular blade profile can be determined. The current design method of turbomachines usually employs the streamline curvature method, which directly solves the 3-D axisymmetric flow, in conjunction with either an empirical cascade correlation or a 2-D numerical method in the circumferential plane to predict the flow through the blade passage. The viscous effect in the through-flow region is usually accounted for by correlation and is reflected in the inviscid calculation by the use of blockage factors in the continuity equation. The compressor designer faces a difficult challenge in how to accurately estimate the boundary layer growth in the end walls because of the highly complex flow in these regions involving viscous dissipation and secondary cross flow. For multistage machines, it has been shown in the literature that the viscous effect in the boundary layers gradually degrades the axial velocity profile and reduces the inviscid core of the flow [9]. The design in this region thus can no longer be done purely with an inviscid code such as the streamline curvature or the present method as the interaction of the viscous effect begins to dominate the flow field. The typical degradation of the performance in the latter stages of a turbomachine can be attributed to the increasing viscous effect.

In the present analytical method, the 3-D axisymmetric flow is postulated as the superposition of the far field velocity and

perturbation of a linearized flow field. The far field problem is governed by the radial equilibrium condition where the radial velocity is simply neglected. The velocity perturbation is then obtained from the linearized equation of motion by an asymptotic expansion, which yields simple expressions for the perturbation. The superposition of these two flow problems complete the description of the velocity field in the blade region. It should be mentioned that Hawthorne [6] and Horlock [5] had studied this problem extensively using analytical methods, which led to mathematically unwieldy solutions that did not quite blend themselves to simple design. Horlock's formulation of the problem did not account for the radial distribution of the tangential velocity and neither formulations considered the radial gradient of the entropy. More importantly, both formulations relied on velocity matching conditions at the discontinuity to derive the perturbation amplitude via Bessel series expansion, which is adequate for uniform far field velocities but renders itself impractical for non-uniform axial velocity profiles. The present method is much less restrictive of the radial gradient of the entropy or the far field axial velocity and has been shown to provide a good agreement with the traditional streamline curvature method (Fig. 3), therefore it can be used as an alternate method for turbomachinery design. The advantage of the present method lies in its simple, yet intuitive formulation of a 3-D axisymmetric flow. Since the method is intrinsically 2-D as compared to the 3-D streamline curvature method, it is speculated that numerical implementation will probably be more efficient than the streamline curvature method. The limitation of the present analytical method lies in its applicability to only turbomachines with constant diameter or slightly varying area ducts. Flow in the entrance nacelle or aft nacelle of turbomachines with significant changes in the slopes at the physical boundaries still requires the streamline curvature or other true 3-D method to better handle the presence of a large radial velocity. Future development work based on the approach presented herein might provide a new method of analyzing these types of flow in turbomachines.

CONCLUSION

A new analytical design method for free-vortex type flow in axial-flow turbomachines has been presented. The method takes into account the radial flow near a blade row, which otherwise causes the turning angle across the blade row to be either under or overestimated, thereby leading to incorrect blade camber while not significantly affecting the stagger angles. This is one of the major contributions to the loss in the design efficiency of turbomachines, particularly gas turbines and high pressure ratio compressors. The free-vortex type tangential velocity distribution simplifies the problem, since the radial gradient of the enthalpy is zero everywhere for a uniform inlet flow condition. In the problem formulation of the 3-D axisymmetric flow in the vicinity of the blade row, the velocity perturbation method was used. The velocities are then considered to have two contributions: a far field velocity and a velocity perturbation near the blade row. The radial equilibrium equation can be applied to derive the far field axial velocity, whereas the perturbation component has to be solved from the linearized equation of motion. Using an asymptotic expansion procedure, a simple expression for the velocity perturbation was derived with an undetermined perturbation amplitude. By considering the streamline slope, which can be computed from the change in the streamline radius across the blade row, this amplitude can be evaluated. For multiple blade rows, superposition of the perturbations due to the individual blade rows can be used to estimate the local velocities near each blade row. A design method based on this analytical method has been presented as an alternate design procedure to the traditional streamline curvature method. A good agreement with the streamline curvature code has been obtained using the present method. Thus, the validity of the method has been demonstrated.

The advantage of the method is the reduction of the 3-D flow problem into a 2-D problem superposed by a predetermined perturbation component. Thus, the numerical implementation of the method might be more efficient than the streamline curvature method, which is a direct 3-D axisymmetric flow solver. The limitation of the present method is that it can be applied to turbomachines of constant diameter or slightly varying area ducts. However, these types of machines constitute an important class of turbomachines, for which the present method can be readily used with confidence. While the method has been formulated for a free-vortex distribution of the tangential velocity, its general approach can still be used to derive the far field velocity and perturbation for other types of distribution. With a non free-vortex distribution, the complexity of the radial equilibrium equation will increase, but is still manageable by numerical methods such as finite-difference, while the linearized equations of motion for the velocity perturbation can probably still be solved approximately by the asymptotic expansion method.

REFERENCES

1. Cumpsty, N.A., 1989, "Compressor Aerodynamics", Longman Scientific & Technical, Essex, England.

2. Lieblein, S., 1965, "The Aerodynamic Design of Axial Flow Compressor", NASA SP-36.

3. Wu, C.H., 1951, "A General Through Flow Theory of Fluid Flow with Subsonic or Supersonic Velocity in Turbomachines of Arbitrary Hub and Casing Shapes", NACA Tech. Note 2302.

4. Shapiro, A.R., 1953, "The Dynamics and Thermodynamics of Compressible Fluid Flow", John Wiley & Sons, New York.

5. Horlock, J.H., 1982, "Axial Flow Turbines", Robert E. Krieger Publishing Company, Malabar, Florida.

6. Hawthorne, W.R., 1964, "Aerodynamics of Turbines and Compressors", Princeton, New Jersey.

7. Hetherington, R., 1967, "Computer Calculations of the Flow in Axial Compressors", published in "Internal Aerodynamics", Institution of Mechanical Engineers, Westminter, London.

8. Wennerstrom, A.J., October 1986, "Low Aspect Ratio Axial Flow Compressors: Why and What It Means", Third Cliff Garrett Turbomachinery Award Lecture, SAE SP-683.

9. Dixon, S.L., 1989, "Thermodynamics of Turbomachinery", Pergamon Press, Oxford, England.

10. Hearsey, R. M., 1995, "Program HTO-300 NASA ARC 1994 Version", The Boeing Company.

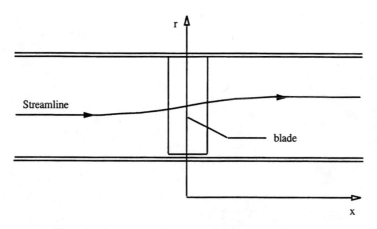

Figure 1 - Illustration of Streamline Shift through a Blade Row

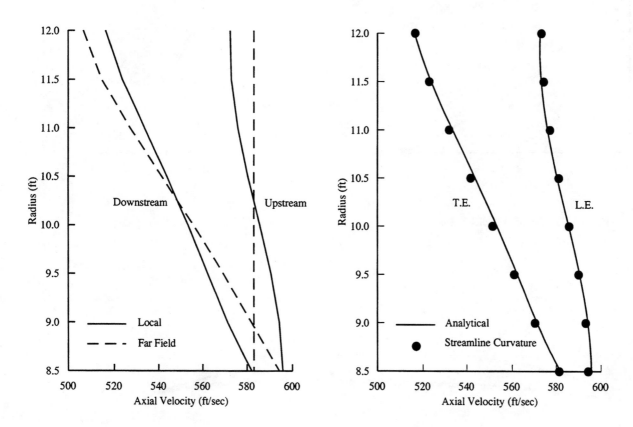

Figure 2 - Far Field and Local Axial Velocities

Figure 3 - Comparison of Axial Velocities

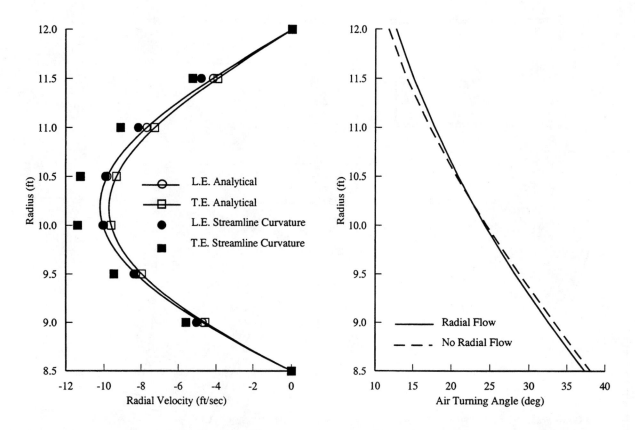

Figure 4 - Comparison of Radial Velocities

Figure 5 - Comparison of Air Turning Angle

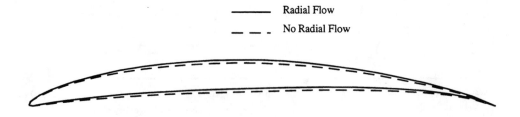

Figure 6 - Comparison of NACA 65-Series Blade Sections at Tip

FED-Vol. 238, 1996 Fluids Engineering Division Conference
Volume 3
ASME 1996

A DESIGN PROCEDURE FOR TURBOCHARGING COMPRESSORS

Sarim N. AL-Zubaidy
Faculty of Engineering - Mechanical Program
University Malaysia Sarawak (UNIMAS)
Kota Samarahan, Sarawak
Malaysia

ABSTRACT

The highly competitive nature of the turbocharger industry demands that the performance of compressors and turbines of small turbochargers be continuously improved. This should come through improving aerodynamic performance without compromising reliability. This paper proposes an inverse procedure for the design of impellers for centrifugal compressors. The design sequence is based on using a simplified fluid dynamic model which sufficiently incorporates the important physical phenomena, which is then coupled with a numerical algorithm to optimize the design within the imposed constraints.

INTRODUCTION

A turbocharger is essentially a small gas turbine which comprises a compressor, a turbine and a bearing housing. It is used for raising the fresh charge density in internal combustion engines by recovering some of the thermal energy of the exhaust gas which would otherwise be wasted. The effectiveness of turbocharging depends on:

firstly, the efficiencies of the turbocharging processes; and *secondly,* the matching of the compressor and the turbine with each other and with the breathing characteristics of the engine.

This paper addressees the first issue of the turbocharging process by proposing a rapid design procedure to allow the designer to produce impellers with acceptable performance and acceptable levels of accuracy.

For automotive applications, the desirable characteristics of turbocharging compressors are:

 a) high isentropic efficiency, i.e. ($\eta \geq 78\%$);
 b) broad flow characteristics;
 c) surge line as far to the left on the mass flow
   vs. pressure ratio map as achievable;
 d) minimum weight for a given duty.

There are a large number of design variables which influence the performance of centrifugal compressors. A computer model is proposed which would serve as a valuable design tool to aid the study of the influence of the various design parameters on the performance of the impellers.

THEORETICAL ASPECTS

For given performance requirements (i.e. mass flow rate, total to total pressure ratio and in some cases rotational speed), the equations of continuity, momentum and energy could be solved at the rotor inlet and exit. The assumption is made that the flow is steady and one dimensional. The dimensionless mass flow parameter based on the impeller inlet conditions could be written as:

$$\frac{m\sqrt{C_p T_{01}}}{d_2^2 P_{01}} = \frac{\left(\frac{\pi}{4}\frac{\gamma}{\sqrt{\gamma-1}}\right)e^2\left[1-\left(\frac{h}{e}\right)^2\right]\sqrt{\left[M_e^2-(e-k)^2\left(\frac{U_2}{a_0}\right)^2\right]}}{\left[1+\frac{\gamma-1}{2}\left\{M_e^2-\left(e^2-2ek\right)\left(\frac{U_2}{a_0}\right)^2\right\}\right]^{\frac{\gamma+1}{2(\gamma-1)}}}$$

$$\dots\dots\dots\dots\dots\dots\dots(1)$$

The equation for the dimensionless speed parameter could be written as:

$$\frac{d_2 N}{\sqrt{C_p T_{01}}} = \frac{1}{\pi} \sqrt{\frac{\left(\frac{P_{02}}{P_{01}}\right)^{\frac{\gamma-1}{\gamma}} - 1}{\eta_c \left[\phi_s - k\left(\frac{d_1}{d_2}\right)\right]}} \qquad \ldots\ldots\ldots\ldots (2)$$

The mass flow parameter based on the impeller exit conditions could be written as follows:

$$\frac{m\sqrt{C_p T_{01}}}{d_2^2 P_{01}} = \left(\pi\frac{\gamma}{\gamma-1}\right)\left(B_2 \frac{b_2}{d_2}\sin\alpha_2\right)\left(\frac{P_{02}}{P_{01}}\right)\left(\frac{T_{01}}{T_{02}}\right) *$$

$$\left(\frac{C_2}{\sqrt{C_p T_{02}}}\right)\left\{1 - \frac{1}{2}\left(\frac{C_2}{\sqrt{C_p T_{02}}}\right)^2\right\}^{\frac{1}{\gamma-1}} \qquad \ldots\ldots\ldots\ldots(3)$$

The detailed derivation of the above relations can be found in AL-Zubaidy (1995) and Gulati (1979).

Figure 1 shows the effect of improving the impeller efficiency on the overall stage efficiency. It can be seen that as the diffuser efficiency increases (at a constant degree of reaction), improving the impeller efficiency will have a great effect on stage efficiency. This improvement in impeller efficiency can be brought about by improving the aero thermodynamic design and through controlling the secondary flow effects.

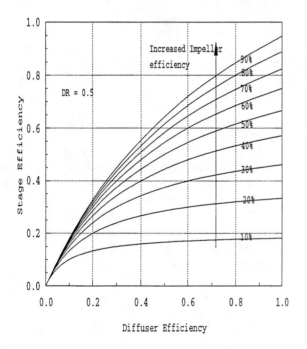

FIGURE 1: EFFECT OF IMPELLER EFFICIENCY ON STAGE EFFICIENCY

The systematic solution of equations 1-3 for a given total to total pressure ratio (given here to be 2.5:1) will result in a design chart that will enable designers to select the overall principal dimensions of the impeller. Figure 2 shows the effect of inducer tip relative Mach number on the dimensionless mass flow parameter for values of U_2/a_0 ranging from 0.5 to 1.7. The inducer to tip diameter ratio and the hub to tip diameter ratio were held constant being 0.6 and 0.2 respectively. It can be seen that for every value of speed ratio, there is a unique optimum value for the mass flow parameter. The position of optimum however shifts from the left to the right as the value of the relative Mach number increases.

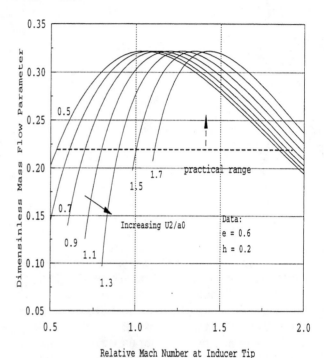

FIGURE 2: RELATION BETWEEN MACH NUMBER AND MASS PARAMETER

Figure 3 shows the effect of the velocity parameter on the dimensionless mass flow parameter for varying values of tip width to dip diameter ratio (ranging from 0.04 - 0.06) and a total to total pressure ratio of 2.5:1, outlet blade blockage of 0.94 and an axial flow angle of 30 degrees. As can be seen from the figure, the maximum value of the mass flow parameter is located at the same value of the velocity parameter no matter what impeller tip width to impeller tip diameter ratio is selected.

From the information available so far, the designer can select the best combination to suit the particular design requirements. Based on the above, it is considered that for a pressure ratio of 2.5:1, the following parameters to be selected are:

$\dfrac{m\sqrt{C_p T_{01}}}{d_2^2 P_{01}} = 0.23$	
e	= 0.6
β_e	= 40°
h	= 0.2

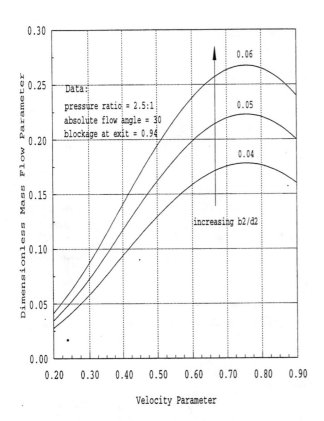

FIGURE 3: EFFECT OF SPEED ON MASS PARAMETER

Figure 4 shows the radial-axial profile of three impellers (A, B and C). They have the same dimensionless parameters as above and also the same projected inlet areas, but the areas normal to the relative flow are different because of the different values of inducer tip angle. It can be appreciated, that even at this stage further design optimization is needed to narrow the choice of candidate impellers.

PRELIMINARY OPTIMIZATION

The one dimensional optimization program is based on the assumption that the flow inside the rotor is controlled by the maximum achievable diffusion which for a given geometry approximates to the location of flow separation.
Downstream of this point the flow splits into a jet and wake. It is further assumed that the jet flow has a constant Mach number in the flow direction and the only losses are due to friction along the walls.
The wake static pressure is fixed by a tangential equilibrium between jet and wake taking into account centrifugal and coriolis forces Frigne (1978). This non-uniformity of the relative velocity at the impeller exit gives rise to mixing losses at the inlet to the diffuser section. Loss in impeller efficiency due to clearance losses is assumed to vary in accordance with the following relation Takashi (1989):

$$\Delta \eta_{impeller} = K \left\{ \frac{\Delta b_2}{b_2} \right\} \qquad \dots\dots\dots\dots\dots\dots\dots\dots(4)$$

The above relation illustrates the importance of reducing the clearance to the limiting capabilities of the machining process.
During the calculation procedure, the impeller efficiency was closely related to the impeller geometry, this provided a very valuable tool for mapping the complete range of variation of the impeller possible geometrical dimensions.
The results indicated that very low values of tip width to tip diameter ratio (its relation to mass flow parameter is given in Figure 3) will result in lower separation and mixing losses but higher friction and clearance losses.

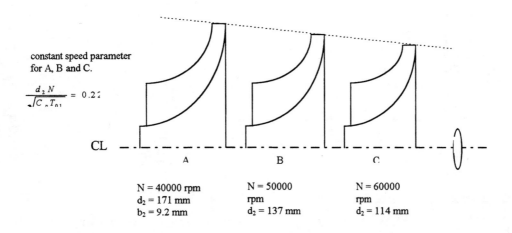

FIGURE 4: POSSIBLE IMPELLER CONFIGURATIONS

Extremely high values result in less friction losses in the impeller but early flow separation might result and hence higher mixing losses.

The designer at this stage could predict the flow at the diffuser entrance by starting with the jet-wake mixing calculation extended to compressible flow Hendriks (1981) and continue downstream with a non-isentropic compressible flow calculation using a friction coefficient Stanitz (1952).

THE DETAILED DESIGN PROCEDURE

The equations of equilibrium for an element of compressible fluid in a cylindrical coordinate system (these are simply expressions of Newton's second law) could be written as follows:

$$\rho\left(r\frac{d^2}{dt^2}\theta + Z\frac{dr}{dt}\frac{d\theta}{dt}\right) = -\frac{\partial P}{r\partial\theta} \quad \ldots\ldots\ldots(5)$$

$$\rho(\frac{d^2}{dt^2}r - r\left(\frac{d\theta}{dt}\right)^2) = -\frac{\partial P}{\partial r} \quad \ldots\ldots\ldots(6)$$

$$\rho\frac{d^2}{dt^2} = -\partial\frac{\partial P}{\partial Z} \quad \ldots\ldots\ldots(7)$$

The above equations are assumed to hold along the three main streamlines within the fluid (i.e. hub, mean and shroud). A further assumption is the existence of an infinite number of blades. This enables the equation of tangential equilibrium (6) to be reduced to an ordinary differential equation that can be solved in a step by step manner along the flow path.

Since the design procedure described in this paper is based on an inverse approach, it therefore requires knowledge of the distribution and overall characteristics of the relative through flow velocity. Figure 5 shows the prescribed relative velocity schedule which has the following desirable characteristics:

    a- gradual deceleration throughout
    b- little diffusion at the point of flow
        turning from the axial to the radial direction
    c- the achievement of the overall diffusion
        requirements (from the previous stage).

The differential pressure along the flow path could be written as:

$$dP = \rho\{r\omega^2 dr - W_r dW_r - W_z dW_z\} + \frac{\partial P}{\partial\theta}d\theta$$

$$\ldots\ldots\ldots(8)$$

The summation of the elemental pressure rise from inlet to outlet will allow the calculation of the theoretical pressure along the impeller to be established.

OPTIMIZATION ALGORITHM

In order to optimize the overall shape of the impeller (within a given set of constraints), an optimization algorithm has been employed. Only a brief description of the algorithm is given here but detailed information can be found in the User's Manual (1992).

The algorithm used is called OPTDES and it is an interactive program for computer aided optimization and design. OPTDES is executed in three steps. The first step is to interface the user's analysis software (the computer model of the user's design problem) to OPTDES. The second step is to define the optimization problem (i.e. objective function and constraints). The third step is to optimize and explore design space. Each of these steps is accomplished in the package by executing independent programs which communicate with each other through data files.

The optimization problem could be stated mathematically as follows:

    Find
    $X = X^*$ such that
    $F(X)$ is minimum (or maximum)
subject to the constraints:
    $g_j(X) \leq 0$
    $X_l \leq X \leq X_u$
Where;
$X^* \in R^n$ = optimal values of design variables
$F(X)$ = given objective function
$g_j(X)$ j=1...m = design constraints
$X_l \in R^n, X_u \in R_n$ = lower and upper limits of variables

In the current design, the objective function was stated to be the following:

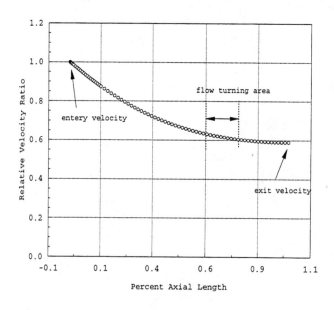

FIGURE 5: PRESCRIBED VELOCITY SCHEDULE

666

$$ds = \left\{C_d\right\}\left\{\frac{2f(W)^3}{d_h T C_m}\right\}\{dl\} \quad \dots\dots\dots\dots(9\text{-}a)$$

The density is calculated from the equation of state for a given perfect gas in the following form:

$$\rho = f(h,s) \quad \dots\dots\dots\dots\dots\dots\dots\dots(9\text{-}b)$$

The entropy change along the streamline (with reference to Figure 6) can be written as:

$$s_q = s_p + \Delta s_{pq} \quad \dots\dots\dots\dots\dots\dots(9\text{-}c)$$

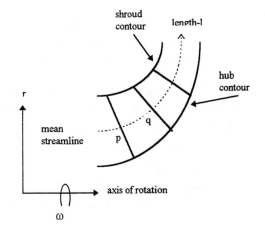

FIGURE 6: GEOMETRY OF MERIDIONAL STREAMLINE

The objective function (9) has been solved in a step by step manner along the mean streamline for an optimum passage shape (within the specified constraints). This also allowed the monitoring of the effect of changes in geometry on various dependent and independent parameters. Calculations have shown that the blade shape is rather insensitive to variations in the density distributions, but on the other hand, the distribution of relative velocity components (particularly the radial component) is important. This has allowed the use of the axial radial profile as a controlling instrument on the blade shape.

Figure 7 shows the distribution of the radial, axial and tangential relative velocity along the dimensionless axial length (Z/Z_{total}). It can be seen that in each case the variation is smooth and continuous from the impeller inlet station to outlet.

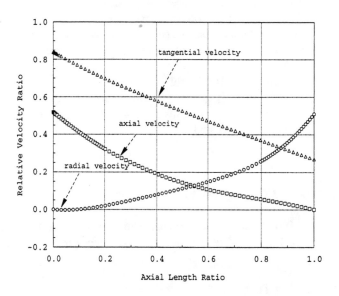

FIGURE 7: DISTRIBUTION OF RELATIVE COMPONENTS

Figure 8 shows the distribution of the pressure ratio (i.e. P_x/P_{outlet}) against the meridional length ratio. It can be seen that the characteristics of the pressure rise (both along the pressure and suction side) are in line with the general behavior of existing successful designs.

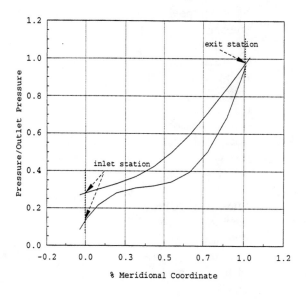

FIGURE 8: PRESSURE VS MERIDIONAL COORDINATE

CONCLUSIONS

The paper proposes a computer based design procedure that enables the designer to work right through from a basic performance specification to the working manufacturing drawing of a turbocharger compressor impeller. The design sequence is based on an inverse approach. This provides a rapid, rational and systematic procedure which allow the monitoring of effects of various geometrical parameters on performance.

The approach used enables the language of research to be moved closer to design and thus narrows the gap which might exist between highly meritorious findings reported by research workers and very simple aged rules of thumb used by designers.

ACKNOWLEDGMENTS

The author wishes to thank Universiti Malaysia Sarawak (UNIMAS) for their support and kind permission for using computational facilities.

NOTATION

a	speed of sound
C	absolute velocity
C_d	dissipation coefficient
C_p	specific heat at constant pressure
d	diameter
DR	degree of reaction (figure 1)
e	inducer to tip diameter ratio
h	hub to tip diameter ratio
k,K	numerical constant
m	mass flow rate
M	Mach number
N	rotational speed
P	pressure
p	calculation station
q	calculation station
r	radius, radial coordinate
s	entropy
T	temperature
U	peripheral velocity
Z	axial coordinate

Greek Symbols

γ	ratio of specific heats
ϕ_s	slip factor
η	efficiency
α	absolute flow angle
β	relative flow angle
ρ	density
θ	tangential coordinate

Subscripts

0	stagnation condition
1	impeller inlet condition
2	impeller exit condition
c	compressor
e	inducer tip condition
h	hydraulic
m	meridional
r	radial
z	axial

REFERENCES

AL-Zubaidy, S. N. and Bhinder, F.S., 199 "Preliminary Inverse Design Procedure for Centrifug Impellers", I.Mech.E. AEROTECH conference Birmingham, UK.

Gulati, P. S., Rebling, P. and Bhinder, F. S., 197 "Some Design Considerations in High Flow Rat Centrifugal Compressors for Turbochargers". CINAC paper Number D30, Vienna.

Frigne, P., and Ven den Braembussche, R.,1978, "On Dimensional Design of Centrifugal Compressors Takin Into Account Flow-Separation in the Impeller". VK TN 129.

Takashi Mikogrami et al., 1989, "Recent Aerodynami Advancements in Turbocharger Compressor an Turbine Wheel Design". SAE paper Number 890643.

Hendriks, R. and Farrell, W. M., 1981, "Performanc andConstruction of a High Efficiency Gas Turbine wit an Output of 7.5 MW". CIMAC paper Number GT9.

Stanitz, J., 1952, "One Dimensional Compressible Flo in Vaneless Diffusers of Radial and Mixed Flo Compressor; Including Effects of Friction, Hea Transfer and Area Change". NACA TN 2610.

User's Manual,1992, "OPTDES.BYU - A Softwar System for Optimal Engineering Deign", Release 4.0 Design Synthesis Inc.

FED-Vol. 238, 1996 Fluids Engineering Division Conference
Volume 3
ASME 1996

Transient Response of Multiphase Pumps in Petroleum Applications

Rune Mode Ramberg

Dr.ing cand., Norwegian University of Technology and Science

Lars E. Bakken

Principal Research Advisor, Statoil, Norway

ABSTRACT

There exist several concepts for multiphase boosting. Depending on application, positive displacement or rotodynamic pumps may be selected. Focus is placed on the Poseidon multiphase concept, the development work, testing and first operational experience.

Operational experience from the Gullfaks A platform demonstrates the booster's capability and its ability to handle different operating conditions, including transient operations. The shift in performance is far beyond the experience from traditional turbomachinery.

As with centrifugal compressors, the pump flow is restricted by unstable flow condition (surge). Both the shape and location of the surge line are influenced by the actual operation condition. Unlike compressors, the performance characteristics change towards a "negative slope" as the discharge pressure drops continuously in the surge approach area.

To ensure stable operation on Gullfaks A, a transient multiphase model has been developed. Understanding the booster system constraints and responses are essential to verify start-up, shut-down and adaptability to operating conditions. The proposed transient model is tuned against field test data. A good agreement between model predictions and test data has been obtained.

In future applications, manifoil operation and subsea boosting of unprocessed wellstream, and transient system analysis are essential for successful integration of the booster system. Understanding the booster adaptability to changes in operating conditions and fluid properties is a major challenge to ensure stable and effective operation.

1. INTRODUCTION

Since 1984 Statoil has been working with the development of the Poseidon concept for multiphase boosting. The work covers different phases, including development of theory and design tools, model development and laboratory scale testing, and design and testing of a full scale prototype pump in real well fluid application. This work forms the fundamentals of successful topside operation offshore.

Operational experience from the Gullfaks A platform (PFD given in figure 1), and test experience from ELSMUBS (Electrical Subsea Multiphase Booster Station) demonstrates the rotodynamic boosters ability to handle different operating conditions, including transient operations.

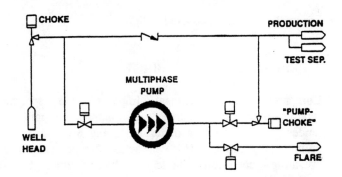

Figure 1. PFD Gullfaks A pump.

The rotodynamic pump principle used in a multiphase flow usually would create phase separation between the boosted gas and liquid, which degradate the performance and may cause the pump head to collapse. The specific shape of impellers and vanes, prevent phase separation of the fluid inside the operating range. In general the hydraulic design of rotodynamic multiphase pumps may be related to inducers for single phase pumps.

An important criteria when handling multiphase fluid is to achieve low net positive suction head (NPSH). To obtain this, multistage co-axial design is used (figure 2.), which include an impeller design with very low inlet and exit angles (β_1: 3 - 10^0, β_2: 13 - 19 °). The diffuser area ratio of 2, resulting in a low specific nominal head of 40 m at reference speed and flow. Free vortex design improve the hydraulic design and prevent phase separation in the impeller. In addition rotodynamic pumps may be equipped with a mixer at the pump inlet to provide a suitable blend of liquid and smoothen variations in flow regimes (slugging). Fluid velocities are designed conservatively in consideration to the multiphase sound velocity. Typical the ciricumferenisial impeller u, is below 70 m/s, and the relative fluid velocity v, below 60 m/s.

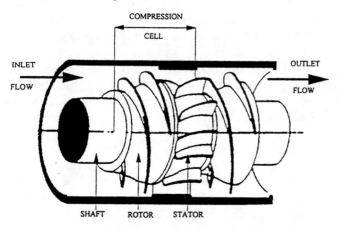

Figure 2. Multistage co-axial design.

2. PERFORMANCE AND SURGE

Compared with centrifugal impellers, the specific rotodynamic design counteracts the fluid phase separation tendency which reduces performance and may cause the pump head to collapse. However, actual fluid properties and operating conditions largely influence the pump performance and head degradation. Factory tests at low suction pressure (5 - 10 bar) and site tests at 40 to 60 bar clearly demonstrates the impact of changed fluid density ratios, and the significant impact both on the characteristic curves and stability limits.

Multiphase performance degradation

On site the unprocessed wellstream contains sand as well as emulsions. Experience with characterising "North Sea crude" shows a clear need for adapting thermodynamic

analysis to the specific area of application. Actual fluid properties are established using PVT analysis and computer predictions based on STEP (Statoil Thermodynamic Estimation Package). However, the impact of changed thermodynamic and fluid properties on the booster performance are not fully established. One major challenge is the Mach-number impact on performance. Even though the design normally restricts the fluid velocities, gas volume fraction and pressure have great impact on sonic velocity in multiphase fluid. The algorithm given in [1], results in a sonic velocity at 145 m/s or Mach-number at approximately 0.5 for the pump used at Gullfaks. Two-phase sonic velocity for air/water mixture at 25 °C are given in figure 3.

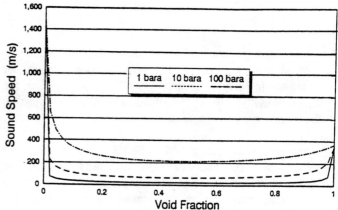

Figure 3. Two-phase sonic velocity for air/water mixture.

Fluid test analysis confirm the variations in fluid viscosity, which is strongly dependant on pressure, water content and the formation of emulsion and foam. Laboratory analysis of the recombined well fluid at Gullfaks (oil, water and natural gas) show viscosity variation between 2.2 to 19 cP. The variation is strongly dependant on share rate, pressure and water cut. Test data for the specific Gullfaks fluid is given in figure 4. The viscosity measurements reflects actual stratified emulsion flow.

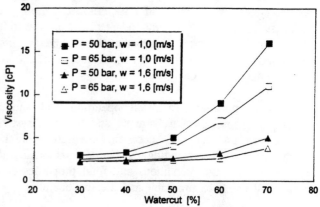

Figure 4. Viscosity data for Gullfaks fluid.

The change in viscosity is consistent to the standard deviation in viscosity of emulsion, given in figure 5. The asymptotic viscosity increase is related to the phase inversion point (water in oil inverse to oil in water). At operating conditions water and crude potentially form emulsions. This potential is raised when the liquid is boosted through a multiphase pump, because the shear stress applied by the pump. The magnitude of the shear stress induce turbulence and forces the liquids to mix. In this respect the pump might be regarded a as huge stirrer.

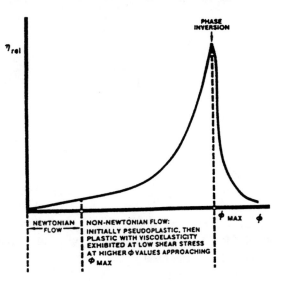

Figure 5. Standard deviation in viscosity of emulsion

Concerning the viscosity effect on performance, few data are presently available. However, at gas volume fractions below 0.75, a change in viscosity from 2 cP to 40 cP may modify the booster performance.

Site performance analysis verifies the impact increased suction pressure (changed density ratio) has on performance. With a constant gas volume fraction (GVF) of 0.34 a density ratio change from 0.01 to 0.04 (suction pressure increase from 10 to 60 bar) reduces the impact related to compression of multiphase fluid from 0.84 to 0.94. The numbers are defined as the ratio between measured multiphase head, divided by single phase head calculated from the head characteristic. The effects of changed fluid and flow regime on performance are to be taken into consideration. Performance diagram at changed suction density ratios and GVF is given in figure 6.

Several investigations have been conducted to determine the multiphase flow through pumps and its influencing parameters. Gaard [2] showed that centrifugal pumps lost

the ability to pump two-phase fluids when GVF exceeded 15% at low pressure (1 bar).

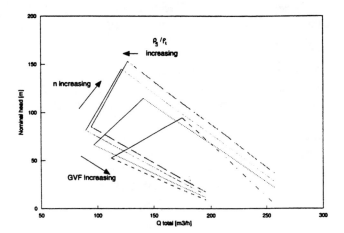

Figure 6. Performance diagram.

Murakami and Minemura [3,4] have photographically observed bubble behaviour of an air -water mixture in an impeller using a stroboscope and a high-speed camera. For input GVF less than 4%, no bubble-accummulation was observed at the impeller eye. Beyond an input void fraction of 6%, accumulation of air bubbles was observed in the impeller, as well as system vibrations with a frequency of 10 seconds.

Lea and Bearden [5] did a qualitative study on the effect of gas interference on the produced head. They concluded that decreasing the pump inlet pressure will increase the amount of degradation. Increasing the GVF at the inlet also reduces the produced head. A tendency for the pump to surge and gas-lock towards the best efficiency point was observed.

Patel and Runstadler [6] showed that impeller head degradation substantially exceeded the head degradation in the volute. Flow regimes will influence the pump performance. They postulated that two different flow regimes existed:
• Bubbly flow, where small bubbles exists and degradation is small.
• Bubble flow, with large voids and larger bubbles in the impeller causing high head degradation.

The bubble size will affect the degradation, and Patel and Runstadler [6] observed chopping of large bubbles by the impeller into smaller bubbles. Because of the drag forces and pressure gradients within the impeller, the bubbles tend to lag behind the liquid phase. Increasing the void fraction increases the lag and causes the bubbles to coalescence, leading to the formation of larger voids within the impeller. A further increase in the inlet voidfraction increases the lag even more and causes gas and liquid phases to separate in the impeller. At flow coefficients below the designpoint the fluid velocities are restricted, resulting in a gas accumulation at the impeller eye.

The velocity difference between gas and liquid leads to accumulation of gas at the inlet region, Gaard [2] The difference will increase due to the volume occupied by the gas, and the accumulation of gas will increase. This process will continue until there is a continuous gas pocket running from inlet to outlet of the impeller, resulting in loss of pressure raise. Sachdeva [10] reports the same mechanism and states that surging occurs near the best efficiency point, mainly due to the velocity difference.

As shown the different phase-velocities are important factors in determining the multiphase performance degradation. Runstadler and Doland [9] did a qualitative study of data from centrifugal pump flowing an air-water mix. They concluded that pumpsurging is eliminated when the liquid superficial velocity is more than 50 % of the velocity corresponding to the best efficiency point.

The superficial velocities of each phases determine the flow regime. Two- phase flow regimes in horizontal and vertical pipes are well investigated. Coste and Vilagines [7] states that the transverse forces (Centrifugal, curvature effects and Coriolis forces) will lead to the same kind of flow regimes in the blade channel as in horizontal pipes and especially to stratified flow regimes. Its difficult to determine the transition from stratified to non stratified flow. Bratu [8] presents a one dimensional formula based on a modified Fronde number as a function of Coriolis acceleration, centrifugal acceleration and acceleration due to the radius of curvature.

The curvature and mixing ability of rotodynamic pumps may not be sufficient to establish homogeneous flow at all conditions. Low volumetric flow, high GVF and density ratio between gas and liquid may lead to separation inside the impeller channels.

Separation of the multiphase flow causes performance degradation. Based on the literature survey and test experiences, the density ratio $\frac{\rho_g}{\rho_l}$, GVF, viscosity, bubble size and fluid velocities are the most important parameters characterising the rate of phase separation and performance degradation.

Performance calculation/ model

Several empirical performance correlation have been published. In majority these correlation's implies non slip homogenous bubble flow.

Mikielewicz et al [11] derived a method for correlating the characteristics of centrifugal pumps in two-phase flow based on Eulers equation for each of the two phases. They defined a two phase flow function:

$$f_{tp} = \frac{(1+a)(1+as^2)}{(1+as)^2}$$

where

$$a = \left(\frac{\alpha}{1-\alpha}\right)\left(\frac{\rho_g}{\rho_l}\right)$$

and

$$s = \frac{c_g}{c_l}$$

The two phase flow function was implemented in the formula for the work coefficient ψ, which implies a degradation in Euler head.

Based on the literature review and test result, its concluded that the following parameters are mainly characterising the multiphase head degradation:

- GVF
- Gas and liquid density
- Single phase liquid head
- Pump speed
- Viscosity, including emulsions
- Slip ratio between gas and liquid.

The latter two are not incorporated in the model at the present stage.

The relationship between multiphase head and pressure rise is given by [12]:

$$H_{mp} = \frac{\Delta P}{\rho_{mp} g}$$

The pump pressure rise is also affected by the tuning of impeller/diffuser design to the actual multiphase flow characteristics. At present no 3 D multiphase flow simulation is valid. The pump design is therefore, mainly based on single phase flow regime.

Test experience and literature clearly demonstrates the degradation in head when handling multiphase flow. The head degradation is illustrated in figure 7 [10], which implies multiphase head degradation.

$$H_{mp} = H_s \xi$$

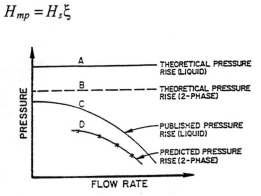

Figure 7. Multiphase head degradation.

The degradation ξ is mainly affected by the density ratio and actual GVF. The following correlation between single- and multiphase head is proposed:

$$H_{mp} = H_s \left(\frac{\rho_{mp}}{\rho_l} \right)(1 + \alpha)$$

The model is a first approach to the flange to flange calculation. The single phase head is given by the performance characteristics.

The model is verified against field test data from Gullfaks A, given in figure 8. In figure 8 (a) the model is verified at variable flow, with a constant inlet pressure at 56 bar and GVF at 0.31. The data in figure 8 (b) include variation in suction pressure (41 bar to 56 bar) and GVF (0.33 to 0.44). Further verifications have been performed with pressure variations between 10 to 60 bar, at air water and natural gas/curde fluids, and gas volume fractions up to 0.5. The nature of the model restricts the variations in GVF fraction to 0 - 0.65.

Stability limits/ surge

As with centrifugal and axial compressor, the multiphase pump volume flow will be restricted by unstable flow conditions. The form and location of the surge line are found to be a function of the actual operation condition, particularly the gas-liquid density ratio and GVF are important. Figure 6 illustrate the variation in surge line location according to variations in density ratio and GVF.

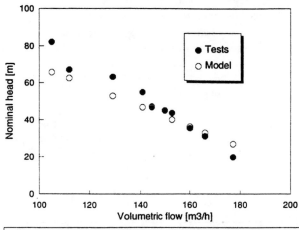

The test points are calculated as average nominal head for each stage. Pump speed is 3500 rpm. The testpoints are adjusted with the laws of affinity

Figure 8 (a). Model verification, constant P_1, and GVF.

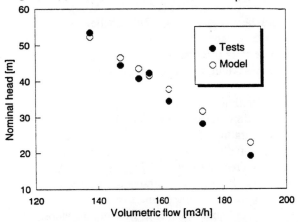

The test points are calculated as average nominal head for each stage Pump speed is 3500 rpm. The testpoints are adjusted with the laws of affinity

Figure 8 (b). Model verification, variable P_1, and GVF.

Lea and Bearden [5] indicated that the onset of surge was dependent on :
- Pump type: mixed flow pumps perform best.
- Fluid Properties: in diesel-CO_2 flow, the breakdown of pumping capacity was observed at lower GVF than for air-water flow.
- Inlet void fraction: higher GVF lead to onset of surge at a higher flow rate.

Rothe et al. [13] describes two types of unstable flow in the pump: One due to the nature of the pipeline (slug flow) that occurred at high inlet GVF. Another unstable flow occurred at low GVF (< 20%) and stable inlet flow. The latter was studied, and a surge frequency of 1 Hz was measured.

Experience from the rotodynamic pump tests indicated that the pumps enter surge at low volumetric flow. At surge $\frac{dP}{dt}$ becomes negative, and the discharge pressure drops continuous for about 10 to 15 sec. The onset of full surge causes typical heavy discharge pressure fluctuations. Typical surge is given in figure 9.

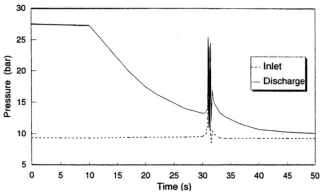

Figure 9. Typical surge.

It should be noted that a major challenge when testing multiphase pumps is to obtain accurate and updated multiphase flow measurements. Especially this is related to transient behaviour, including phase slip relations.

Pump operation at constant speed and reducing the volumetric flow, forces the pump into surge cycles. In this unstable operating condition, the pump discharge pressure decreases rapidly to a certain level. During surge the discharge increases to normal level and remain stable for about 50 sec. Figure 10 illustrates the transient behaviour. During the pressure decrease/increase process, lasting about 10-15 sec, the liquid volumetric flow almost stops, and the gas volumetric flow is reduced as well. For a short period of time the pump is only processing gas. The liquid flow is then gradually increased. The section numbers given in figure 10 correspond to the pictures in figure 11.

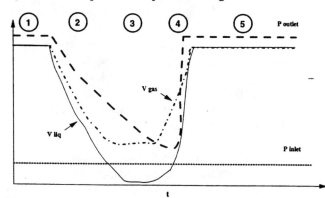

Figure 10. Surge cycle.

Observations made through the at transparent tube section at the pump inlet (figure 11) indicate that the volumetric gas flow is higher than the liquid flow at minimum pressure raise. A film was taken to detect velocity profiles, phase slip and gas accumulation. From observations its concluded that increasing gas velocity, causes formation of mist, and growing liquid waves, which finally leads to a complete mixture of gas and liquid.

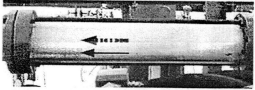

1. Normal operating point, equal gas and liquid velocity

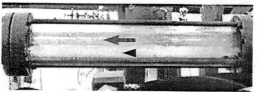

2. Separatated phases, low pressure raise. Increasing gas velocity, forming of mist, some liquid waves.

3. High gas velocity, more mist, increasing liquid velocity , bigger waves.

4. Increasing liquid level and velocity in the tube, foam forming.

5. Foam , annular flow, equal gas and liquid velocity, normal operating point.

Gas velocity
Liquid velocity

Figure 11. Transparent tube section.

Reducing the volumetric flow to the point of surge onset, causes the homogeneous flow to separate inside the channels and gas to accumulate at the inlet. The phase separation at the impeller, causes a major disturbance to the flow pattern. The gas flow will act on its one , resulting in a jet/wake flow at the surge point, while the liquid flow will have no energy recovery in the diffuser. This leads to a very low pressure rise in the diffuser, resulting in a liquid build up until the pumping action is recovered. At the pump inlet the flow level increases until a point where the pump suddenly is able to handle it. The gas flow is then accelerate faster than the liquid, causing the observed behaviour of the flow in the transparent tube section.

In the surge approach area the head degradation my be represented by the rate of change in GVF and suction volumetric flow.

$$\frac{d\alpha}{dt} = f(\frac{dQ_1}{dt}, n, P_1)$$

This function is at present not implemented.

3. ADAPTABILITY AND TRANSIENT SYSTEM BEHAVIOUR

An important aspect when utilising multiphase pumps in a production network, is to ensure the network stability, including booster surge protection and performance control. The booster adaptability to fluid and operating conditions is vital with respect to transient response. These aspects are analysed by:
- transient reference tests at site conditions
- development and tuning of a dynamic multiphase model
- experimental and theoretical verification of booster adaptability

Transient reference test

Several transient tests are conducted during the different test campaign of Poseidon pumps. These tests are related both to transient flow conditions (i. e. slugging) and production system constrains.

This work focuses on the transient reference tests performed at the Gullfaks A production facility. System configuration is given in figure 1. The booster operating pressure and flow rate may be changed largely to analyse the production

system transient response. Of specific interest is the booster self-adaptability to flow regime and operating conditions. The well fluid is characterised by PVT-analysis:
- watercut (standard conditions) : 0.65
- hydrocarbon density : 644 kg/m^3
- hydrocarbon gas mol. weight : 25.4 kg/kmol

Several tests have been conducted to investigate the transient system responses. In verifying the booster flexibility and stability, the pump choke valve was closed from 90° to 35° in one step. The step-change causes a dramatic discharge pressure increase, until the pump was tripped due to high discharge pressure. The suction and discharge pressure response are given in figure 12.

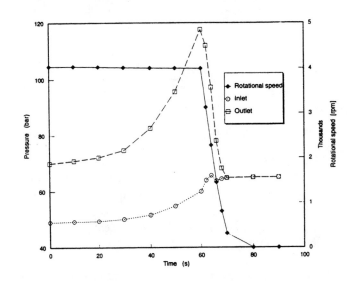

Figure 12. Shutdown of pump chocke valve.

Similar test has been performed by giving the pump control system a step-change in speed, from 3525 to 4017 rpm. The pressure responses are given in figure 13.

Experience from single phase pumping and natural gas compression underlines the multiphase pump damped transient response to sudden changes in operating conditions. The response is related to the shift in actual pump performance at different operating conditions. These effects are further analysed in the following sections.

Dynamic model

The shift in performance, related to thermodynamic and fluid properties is a major contributor to stable and effective operation. A better understanding of these effects is vital in analysing performance at different operating conditions.

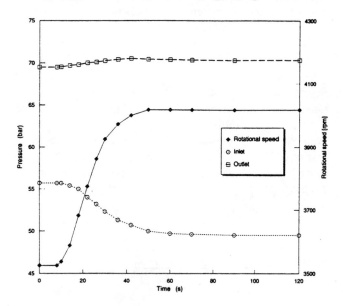

Figure 13. Step-change in speed.

The multiphase pump behaviour at transient operating conditions is a complex relationship between the rate of change in flow regime, and the pump performance shift at different operating conditions. It is not surprising that there is not a single dynamic model for transient pump behaviour in the literature.

An important constraint for a transient model accuracy is the head degradation in multiphase flow. The proposed dynamic model is based on a quasi steady state model approach. The model include the following basic equations :

$$
\begin{bmatrix}
\Delta P \\
H_{mp} \\
H_s \\
Q_{tot} \\
c \\
P_1 \\
P_2
\end{bmatrix}
=
\begin{bmatrix}
P_2 - P_1 \\
\dfrac{\Delta p}{\rho_{mp} g} \\
\dfrac{H_{mp} \rho_l}{(1+\alpha)\rho_{mp}} \\
\dfrac{H_s - b}{a} \\
\dfrac{4 Q_{tot}}{\pi d^2} \\
p_0 - \lambda c^2 \rho_{mp} \dfrac{\Sigma l + \Sigma le}{2d} \\
p_3 + \lambda c^2 \rho_{mp} \dfrac{\Sigma l + \Sigma le}{2d}
\end{bmatrix}
$$

Which leads to:

$$
\frac{dP_2}{dt} = g \frac{d}{dt}\left(H_s \left(\frac{\rho_{mp}^2}{\rho_l} \right)(1+\alpha) \right) + \frac{dP_1}{dt}
$$

The single phase characteristic curves are represented by a polynomial function, wich are corrected with the laws of affinity within the operating range:

$$
H_s = a + b * Q
$$

The dynamic multiphase pump model is incorporated in a total process model, including well performance, production choke, flowlines, valves and inlet separator. Model input- and output variables are set by the overall process model. System configuration and model flow sheet are given in figure 14.

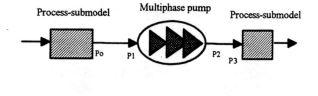

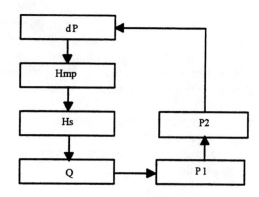

Figure 14. System configuration and model flow sheet.

The proposed prototype model is verified against field performance data at Gullfaks A. The pump and system response to step-change in choke position is given in figure 15. At present its concluded that the model represents the actual pump transient behaviour to a acceptable degree of accuracy.

To ensure stable operation at the Gullfaks installation all major components such as pump unit, driver, control system

676

and piping were modelled in a dynamic system model. Understanding the total system's constraints and responses were essential to verify start-up procedures, ensure stable operation at different operating conditions and prevent pressure transients during shut down. During certain process shut-downs, the pump unit will be exposed to full dynamic shut-in pressure of the actual well, which may cause the suction pressure to increase from 55 bar to 170 bar during a short period of time. Tuning of stroke times for the suction and discharge isolation valves effectively dampened the associated pressure transients.

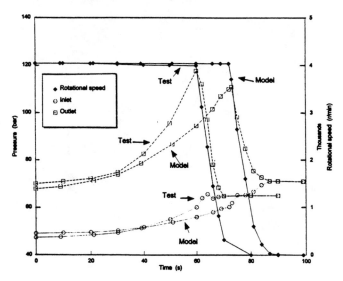

Figure 15. Transient model verification.

Adaptability

In petroleum applications, handling medium to high gas volume fractions, the production system flexibility and stability have a direct impact on the income. The multiphase pump is a key element, which has a great impact on both production flexibility and system stability. In this respect the pump adaptability to process set-ups is vital. Reference tests and infield experience have demonstrated the rotodynamic pump capability of handling variations in operating conditions. The pump adaptability is mainly dictated by the performance variation at different operating conditions.

However, process equipment response to variation in flow regimes must be taken into consideration. A fixed trottle valve position at pump discharge may cause a large variation in discharge pressure according to variation in GVF. The effects, related to the variation in GVF have to be analysed separately, and not included in the multiphase pump response.

Transient tests have been conducted at the Gullfaks installation to verify the multiphase pump response and adaptability to variation in operating conditions. The reference tests underlines the pump damped response to operating conditions.

The adaptability to variation in operating conditions may be visualised as follows. A sudden reduction in suction pressure increases the amount of flash gas from the crude oil. The flashing is strongly dependant on the crude hydrocarbon composition, and is found much more dominant in specific condensate crudes. In addition the gas fraction of the total flowrate is expanded according to the pressure variation. The suction GVF is changed according to the gas flashed off, and the expansion of the "free gas".

A step change in production choke position, or shut in of one well during manifold operation causes a sudden reduction in the pump suction volumetric flowrate and pressure, at constant pump speed. The multiphase pump response is affected by the rate of change in GVF and the shift in the multiphase fluid density ratio. The pump performance is shifted towards lower head, resulting in a damped response to the variation in operating conditions.

A similar perturbation of a single phase system, utilising a single phase pump would have caused far greater transients with respect to variation in suction pressure and suction volumetric flowrate.

The single- and multiphase pump response is illustrated in figure 16.

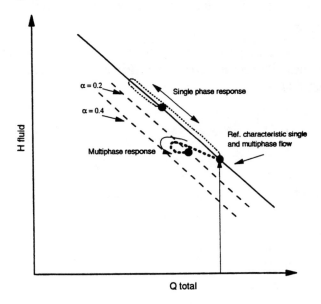

Figure 16. Single- and multiphase pump response

The verification of adaptability to variations in flow regimes and operating conditions is important related to future development of multiphase boosters. Particularly in subsea applications the adaptability is vital in the production system design. The damped response to variation in operating conditions limit the need for a sophisticated, fast acting control system.

SUMMARY AND CONCLUSIONS

Operational experience from the Gullfaks A platform demonstrates the rotodynamic booster's capability and its ability to handle different operating conditions, including transient operations. The shift in performance is far beyond the experience from traditional turbomachinery.

Separation of the multiphase flow causes performance degradation. Based on the literature survey and test experiences, the density ratio, GVF, viscosity, bubble size and fluid velocities are the most important parameters characterising the rate of phase separation and performance degradation.

The model is verified against field test data from Gullfaks A. Verifications have been performed with pressure variations between 10 to 60 bar, at air water and natural gas/curde, and gas volume fractions up to 0.5. The nature of the model restricts the variations in GVF fraction to 0 - 0.65.

At present its concluded that the model represents the actual pump transient behaviour to a acceptable degree of accuracy.

The transient reference tests underlines the pump damped response, and adaptability to variation in operating conditions.

NOMENCLATURE

Latin symbols

a	constant
b	constant
c	absolute velocity
d	pipe diameter
g	gravitational acceleration
H	pump head
l	pipe length
n	pump speed
P	pressure
Q	volumetric flow
t	time
u	ciricumferenisial velocity
v	relative velocity
w	shear rate

Greek symbols

α	gas volume fraction
β	angel of flow
φ	work coeffisient
λ	frictional coefficient
ρ	fluid density
π	3.14159
τ	shear stress
ξ	degradation

Indices

0	outlet preceding process-sub model
1	inlet multiphase pump
2	outlet multiphase pump
3	inlet succeeding process-sub model

Abbreviations

GVF	gas volume fraction
PFD	process flow diagram
dP	differential pressure

Subscript

1	inlet
2	outlet
e	equivalent
g	gas
l	liquid
mp	multiphase
s	single phase

References

[1] Gudmundsson, J. S., Dong, L., Rødøy, F:"Two-Phase Flow Metering by Pressure Pulse Propagation". SPE, 67. Annual Technical Conference and Exibition. Oct. 4-7, 1992. SPE 24778.

[2] Gaard S. :"Modelling of Two-Phase Bubble Flow in Centrifugal Pumps. Dr.ing dissertation, Norwegian Institute of Technology, 1992.

[3] Murakami, M., Minemura, K. :"Effects of Entrained Air on the Performance of a Centrifugal Pump, First Report - Performance and Flow Conditions," Bulletin of JSME, Vol 17. No.110, 1047-1055, Aug. 1974.

[4] Murakami, M., Minemura, K. :"Effects of Entrained Air on the Performance of a Centrifugal Pump, Second Report - Effects of number of blades," Bulletin of JSME, Vol 17. No.112, 1286-1295, Oct. 1974.

[5] Lea.J. F., Bearden, J. L. : " Effect of Gaseous Fluids on Subersible Pump Performance, " JPT, (Dec.1982), SPE 9218.

[6] Patel, B.R., Runstadler, P-W.:"Investigations Into the Two-Phase Behavior of Centrifugal Pumps" ASME Symposium on Polyphase Flow in Turbomachinery, Dec. 1978, San Francisco.

[7] Coste, P., Vilangines, R.: "Use of the Cathare 1D Pump Model to Predict the Two-Phase Characteristic of a Pump for Petroleum Fluids", European Two-Phase Flow Group Meeting, Hannover, Jun. 1993.

[8] Bratu, C.: "Rotodynamic Two-Phase Pump Performances", SPE 28516, 1994.

[9] Runstadler, P. W., Doland, F. X.: "Two-Phase Flow Pump Data for a Scale Model NSSS Pump", ASME Symposium on Polyphase Flow in Turbomachinery, Dec. 1978, San Francisco.

[10] Sachdeva, R.: "Two-Phase Flow Through Electric Submersible Pumps", PhD dissertation, Uni. of Tulsa, 1988.

[11] Mikielewicz, J. , Wilson, D. G., Chan, T-C., Goldfinch A. L.:"A Method for Correlating the Characteristics of Centrifugal Pumps in Two-Phase Flow", Journal of Fluids Engineering, Vol. 100, 395-409, Dec.1978.

[12] Lea, J. F., Turpin, J. L., Bearden, J.L.:"Correlation of Performance Data for Electric Subersible Pumps With Gas-Liquid Flow", SouthWestern Petroleum Short Course-86, p.267-281.

[13] Rothe, P.H. et al.:"Pump Surge Due to Two Phase Flow", ASME Syposeum on Polyphase Flow in Turbomachinery, Des. 1978, San Francisco.

FED-Vol. 238, 1996 Fluids Engineering Division Conference
Volume 3
ASME 1996

MODELING TECHNIQUES FOR PREDICTING COMPRESSOR PERFORMANCE DURING SURGE & ROTATING STALL

By

E. S. El-Mitwally
Professor

M. Abo-Rayan*
Professor

N.H. Mostafa
Assoc. Prof.

A.H. Hassanien
Ph. D. Candidate

Mechanical Power Dept., Faculty of Engineering
Zagazig University, Zagazig, Egypt

ABSTRACT

The tendency for compressors to exhibit flow instabilities and surge at low flow rates limit their operating range. Narrow operating ranges result in poor acceleration characteristics for a gas turbine engine. It Also result in uneconomical operation for industrial compressors because of preventing the operation at maximum efficiency. In this paper, different techniques to simulate surge and rotating stall are compared with each other. Both of the thermodynamic effect of the real process and the development of the rotating stall cell are taken into consideration during the solution. The validity of the new model is tested by comparing the results with published experimental data. This model has a higher coefficient of correlation which has been increased by 30% and 6% over Hansen's model for flow and pressure performance respectively.

INTRODUCTION

Using on-line expert systems to control centrifugal compressors requires solid knowledge of the behavior of the whole system. This expert system not only requires an accurate method to simulate the actual process but also requires a fast algorithm to determine the status of the process as quickly as possible.

NOMENCLATURE

A	Flow area	m^2
a_0	Sonic velocity	m/s
B	Dimensionless parameter	-
C	$p_2 - p_{o1}$	
C'	$d(p_2 - p_{o1})/dm$	--
c_p	Specific heat at constant pressure	J/(kg.K)
D	Impeller diameter	m
e	Internal energy	
F	Distributed body force	N/m^2
F'	$d(p_3 - p_{o3})/dm$	
FX	Force of compressor blading & casing acting on fluid including wall pressure area force	
H	Head	J/kg
h	Enthalpy	
IMP	Impulse function	
KE	Kinetic Energy	
k	Polytropic exponent	--
L	Effective length of equivalent ducting	m
m	Mass flow parameter	kg/s
m_b	Leakage mass flow per unit length	(kg/s)/m
N	Rotational speed	rpm
p	Pressure	N/m^2
$\tilde{p}$	$\Delta p/(1/2\rho u^2)$	
Q	Rate of heat addition to control volume	
$\mathcal{R}$	Gas constant	J/(kg.K)
S	Valve parameter = $(A_C/A_T)^2$	--
SW	Rate of shaft work	
T	Temperature	K
u	Blade peripheral speed	m/s
V	Volume	m^3
X	Compressibility function	m/s
x	Axial coordinate	
Z	Compressibility	--
Δt	Integration time step	s
Δx	Grid point spacing	
γ	Ratio of specific heats	c_p/c_v
η	Efficiency	--
ρ	Density	kg/m^3
τ	compressor flow relaxation time	
ω	Helmholtz frequency	

*Mech. Dept., Mansoura University., Mansoura, Egypt

stresses while the second (surge) may also have a disastrous effect on the whole system of which the compressor is a component. Surge and Rotating stall typically occur in a frequency range of 3 to 15 and 50-100 Hz sequentially. When rotating stall occurs, one or more "stall cells" travel around the compressor annulus in the direction of rotation of the compressor, with a rotational speed closely to one-half of the compressor rotational speed [Stenning, 1980]. On the other hand, surge is a large oscillations of the total mass flow rate through the compressor as shown in Fig. (1). Both of surge and rotating stall can occur in both axial and centrifugal compressors. Within each stall cell, the blades are so severely stalled that there is virtually no flow through the blade row. Once rotating stall is encountered, it may not be possible to return to an unstalled condition merely by opening the throttle because of system hysteresis effects. In this situation the only way to come out of stall may be to change the rotational speed; resulting in a sizable loss in pressure ratio.

Compressor performance during surge and rotating stall can be predicted using three different methodologies. A brief comparison between these methodologies is shown in Table (1). **Davis [1986]** proposed a new model to simulate the compression system of a multi-stage axial compressor. Figure (2) shows the physical compression system and control volume concept of MacCormake technique. This model is based on one dimensional flow and is used to solve the basic equations (continuity, momentum and energy) using MacCormake numerical technique. The governing equations for this model are as follows :

Predictor equation

$$\overline{U}_{[i]}^{[P]} = \overline{U}_{[i]} - \frac{\Delta t}{\Delta x_{[i-1]}}\left(\overline{f}_{[i]}^{[n]} - \overline{f}_{[i-1]}^{[n]}\right) + \Delta t\,\overline{Q}_{[i]}^{[n]} \tag{1}$$

Corrector equation:

$$\overline{U}_{[i]}^{[C]} = \overline{U}_{[i]} - \frac{\Delta t}{\Delta x_{[i]}}\left(\overline{f}_{[i+1]}^{[P]} - \overline{f}_{[i]}^{[P]}\right) + \Delta t\,\overline{Q}_{[i]}^{[P]} \tag{2}$$

New time step

$$\overline{U}_{[i]}^{[n+1]} = \frac{1}{2}\left(\overline{U}_{[i]}^{[C]} + \overline{U}_{[i]}^{[P]}\right) \tag{3}$$

Where the three vectors (U, Q and f) represent the continuity, momentum and energy equation.

$$\overline{U} = \begin{bmatrix} \rho A \\ \rho A u \\ \rho A(e + u^2/2) \end{bmatrix}, \overline{Q} = \begin{bmatrix} -m_b \\ FX \\ -h_{ob} + SW + Q \end{bmatrix}$$

$$\overline{f} = \begin{bmatrix} \rho A u \\ \rho A u^2 + pA \\ \rho A u[e + (p/\rho) + (u^2/2)] \end{bmatrix}$$

Rotating stall time lag equation

$$FX_{SS} = \tau \frac{dFX}{dt} + FX \tag{4}$$

where $FX = p_S \dfrac{\partial A}{\partial x} + F_b$

Davis' model is a slow algorithm since it consumes a lot of time. (1:100 real processing time to simulation time on 486, 25 MHz based system **[Harvell, 1992]**). This disadvantage makes this model not suitable for on-line expert system. This model needs a complete details about the compressor geometry and the steady state performance during normal operation and reverse flow.

Greitzer [1976] developed a one-dimensional time-dependent, nonlinear mathematical model of an axial compression system to predict the transient response of that system while undergoing a perturbation from steady operating conditions. Figure (3) shows Greitzer's equivalent compression system. The equations governing the model are transformed into non-dimensional form by dividing the pressure, mass flow and time by the quantities $(\rho u^2/2)$, $(\rho u A_C)$ and $(1/\omega)$ respectively.

The rate of mass flow within the compressor duct and throttle as :

$$\frac{d\tilde{\dot{m}}_C}{d\tilde{t}} = (\tilde{C} - \Delta\tilde{p})B \tag{5}$$

$$\frac{d\tilde{\dot{m}}_T}{d\tilde{t}} = (\Delta\tilde{p} - \tilde{F})B/G \tag{6}$$

The mass equation for the plenum can be written as :

$$\frac{d\Delta\tilde{p}}{d\tilde{t}} = (\tilde{\dot{m}}_C - \tilde{\dot{m}}_T)/B \tag{7}$$

where $B = \dfrac{u}{2a_0}\sqrt{\dfrac{V_P}{A_C L_C}}$ and $G = \dfrac{L_T A_C}{L_C A_T}$

SUBSCRIPTS

b	Blade
C	Compressor
D	Delay (lag in revolution)
[i]	Control volume station number
[i+1],[i-1]	Previous and next control volume station numbers
m	Mean
o1	Total condition at inlet
o2	Total condition at exit
P	Plenum
p	Polytropic
S	Static
SS	Steady state
T	Throttle valve ducting

SUPERSCRIPTS

●	First derivative with respect to time
′	First derivative with respect to mass
~	Dimensionless parameter
[P]	Predictor
[C]	Corrector
[n]	Present value
[n+1]	Future value

Table (1) Comparison Between Modeling Techniques for Predicting Compressor Performance During Surge & Rotating Stall

Method / Parameter	Distributed Parameters	Non-Linear Lumped Parameters			Linear Lumped Parameters
Equations	Continuity, energy, and momentum	Analytical Lumped Equations			Analytical Lumped Equations
Time needed	Very High	Small			Very Small
Surge prediction	Yes	Yes			Yes
Accuracy	Very Accurate	Accurate			Not Acceptable
Model by	Davis	Greitzer	Hansen	Elder	Stenning
Compressor type	Axial	Axial	Centrifugal	Centrifugal	Axial
No. of stages	three	three	one	one	one
Treatment	Multi-stage	Single	Single	Single	Single
Rotating stall	Yes	Yes	Yes	No	Yes
Non-linear Eqs.	Yes	Yes	Yes	Yes	No

A first order time lag was imposed on the compressor pressure rise by the following equation :

$$\frac{d\tilde{C}}{d\tilde{t}} = (\tilde{C}_{SS} - \tilde{C}) / \tilde{\tau} \qquad (8)$$

where $\tilde{\tau} = \dfrac{\pi D N_D}{2 L_C B}$

The pressure drop is written in terms of the velocity at the throttle discharge plane or in terms of throttle mass flow as

$$F = \frac{\dot{m}_T^2}{2\rho A_T^2} \qquad (9)$$

Greitzer did not take the thermodynamic effect of the real process into consideration. The steady state performance during normal operation and reverse flow are required to complete the solution of the model.

Hansen [1981] applied Greitzer's model to a small single-stage centrifugal compressor. He suggested a new value for the delay period N_D (0.5 instead of 2.0).

Elder et al., [1983] introduced a new model to simulate a large single stage centrifugal compressor. Figure (4) shows the components of the compressor. The model was based on one dimensional flow but, they inserted a new equation to the system. The new equation is the steady state energy equation. also, they neglected the equation which represents the time lag to complete the rotating stall. This is because they applied their model between two stable points. The following equations represent this model.

Momentum equation:

$$\frac{dm_1}{dt} = \frac{A_m}{\Delta x} (p_{o1} - p_{o1} + F_{NET}) \qquad (10)$$

where $k = \dfrac{ZR}{c_p}\left(\dfrac{1}{\eta_p} + X\right)$

and $F_{NET} = p_{o1}\left[\left(\dfrac{H_p}{c_p T_1}\left(\dfrac{1}{\eta_p} + X\right) + 1\right)^{1/k} - 1\right]$

Element continuity equation :

$$\frac{dp_2}{dt} = \frac{ZRT_1}{(1-k)V}(m_1 - m_2) \qquad (11)$$

Energy equation in steady state form :

$$h_2 = h_1 + SW \qquad (12)$$

and polytropic head equation :

$$H_p = \frac{c_p T_1}{\left(\dfrac{1}{\eta_p} + X\right)}\left(\left(\dfrac{p_{o2}}{p_{o1}}\right)^k - 1\right) \qquad (13)$$

Elder's model has not the capability to simulate either the deep surge cycles or rotating stall. The model becomes more complex when inserting more elements into the model (in case of simulating multi-stage compressors) consequently, consuming more time.

Stenning [1980] introduced a new model based on Greitzer's one. The non linearity of the Greitzer's model is removed from the model. Figure (5) shows a schematic diagram of the lumped model. The final equation is a second order differential equation in one variable Z only.

$$\left(\frac{LF'V}{AkART_3}\right)\ddot{Z} + \left(\frac{L}{A} - \frac{C'F'V}{kRT_3}\right)\dot{Z} + (F' - C')Z = 0 \qquad (14)$$

where Z may be any variable (p_2, p_3, m_3, m_2). Stenning's model was based on the following equations :

$$p_2 - p_3 = \frac{L}{A} \dot{m}_2 \qquad (15)$$

$$m_2 - m_3 = \frac{V_P}{kRT_3} \dot{p}_3 \qquad (16)$$

$$p_3 = F' m_3 \qquad (17)$$

$$p_2 = C' m_2 \qquad (18)$$

Since Stenning's model is based on a second order differential equation so, he introduced a criterion for starting surge oscillations. The system will start oscillating if

$$\left(\frac{L}{A} - \frac{C'F'V}{kRT_3} \right) = 0 \quad \text{or} \quad C' = \frac{LkRT_3}{F'VA}$$

The steady state performance during normal operation and reverse flow and the throttle characteristics is required to complete the solution of Stenning's model. The model is not validated by comparing its results with experimental data. Although the experimental data presented by **Hansen [1981]** shows that the characteristics of the non-dimensional pressure or non-dimensional flow are different, this model assumes that they will have the same characteristics.

In this paper, a new model is aimed to simulate process plant compressor transients. The model should have a fast algorithm in order to incorporate it in on-line expert system. The model should be able to represent the thermodynamic effects of the real process with accepted accuracy. More over, the model should be simple (i.e. it does not need a complicated data).

THEORETICAL MODEL

In this model the principles of mass, energy, and linear momentum are applied to the flow as shown in Fig. (6). To simplify the model, It's assumed that the flow is one dimensional flow. The dynamics of the energy equation is neglected because its minor effect on the solution. The process in the plenum is polytropic

The rate of change of mass flow at the compressor exit can be related to pressure difference across the compressor ($\Delta p = p_2 - p_1$) and the pressure rise across the compressor. C,

$$p_1 - p_2 + C = \rho L_C \frac{dc_x}{dt} \qquad (19.a)$$

in terms of the compressor mass flow and inserting the plenum pressure this equation becomes:

$$(p_1 - p_p) + (p_p - p_2) + C = \frac{L_C}{A_C} \frac{d\dot{m}_C}{dt}$$

or in other form

$$C - \Delta p + \Delta p_p = \frac{L_C}{A_C} \frac{d\dot{m}_C}{dt} \qquad (19.c)$$

in non-dimensional form equation (19.c) will be

$$\frac{d\tilde{\dot{m}}_C}{d\tilde{t}} = (\tilde{C} - \Delta\tilde{p} + \Delta\tilde{p}_p)B \qquad (19.d)$$

An analogous equation can be written to describe the flow in the throttle duct:

$$\Delta p - F = \frac{L_T}{A_T} \frac{d\dot{m}_T}{dt} \qquad (20)$$

The pressure drop across the throttle can be described by the following relation

$$F = \frac{1}{2} \rho c_{xT}^2 \qquad (21.a)$$

in terms of the mass flow

$$F = \frac{\dot{m}_T^2}{2\rho A_T^2} \qquad (21.b)$$

The momentum equation through the plenum

$$\frac{d\tilde{\dot{m}}_T}{d\tilde{t}} = (\Delta\tilde{p} - \tilde{F})B / G \qquad (22)$$

The continuity equation across the plenum is

$$\dot{m}_C - \dot{m}_T = V_p \frac{d\rho_p}{dt} \qquad (23.a)$$

After some manipulation this equation becomes

$$\dot{m}_C - \dot{m}_T = \frac{\rho V_p}{\gamma p} \frac{dp_p}{dt} \qquad (23.b)$$

in a non-dimensional form the equation becomes

$$\frac{d\Delta\tilde{p}}{d\tilde{t}} = (\tilde{\dot{m}}_C - \tilde{\dot{m}}_T) / B \qquad (23.c)$$

The time needed for development of the stall cell can therefore be long enough so that the compressor mass flow undergoes a significant change during this process. Under these conditions, a first order transient response model to simulate this lag is adopted. Explicitly, the approximation for the transient compressor response can be written as

$$\tau \frac{dC}{dt} = (C_{SS} - C) \qquad (24.a)$$

where $\tau = \dfrac{\pi D N_D}{u}$ and $u = \dfrac{\pi D N}{60}$

in a non-dimensional form this equation will be

$$\frac{d\tilde{C}}{d\tilde{t}} = (\tilde{C}_{SS} - \tilde{C}) / \tilde{\tau} \qquad (24.b)$$

The energy equation (in its steady state form) is represented by the following relation [Elder, 1983] where the dynamic part of the equation is neglected:

$$h_2 = h_1 + \frac{E_{NET}}{\dot{m}_C} \qquad (25)$$

where $E_{NET} = SW * \dot{m}_C$

consequently

$$T_2 = T_1 + \frac{SW}{c_p} \qquad (26)$$

$$n = \frac{k\,\eta_p}{1 - k(1 - \eta_p)} \qquad (27)$$

$$\eta_p = \frac{(k-1)\,\ln\left(\frac{p_2}{p_1}\right)}{k\,\ln\left(\frac{T_2}{T_1}\right)} \qquad (28)$$

The previous set of equations (19-28) are solved simultaneously to get the variations of the non-dimensional flow and pressure as a function of time. Both of the thermodynamic effect of the real process and the development of the rotating stall cell are taken into consideration during the solution.

The steady state performance and reverse flow are required to complete the solution of the model. These data are given to the program as equation representing the curve fitting of the experimental data. Usually, the experimental data representing the performance during reverse flow are difficult to be obtained. Consequently, another model is developed to predict the performance of the centrifugal compressors during the reverse flow. This model is based on the model proposed by Galvas [1973]. This modified model can predict the performance of the multi-stage centrifugal compressors with variable stage dimensions and multi-compressors arranged in series. Figure (7) shows the results of this model.

RESULTS AND DISCUSSION

The validity of the new model is tested by comparing the results with published experimental data and three models proposed by other authors. The model needs the performance during steady state and reverse flow. Actually, the reverse flow performance is difficult to be obtained specially in industrial compressors.

The model is configured with initial parameters such that it can be compared with **Hansen's model [1981]** at 54000 rpm. **Hansen [1981]** used a centrifugal compressor with a single stage. The results of this comparison will be demonstrated on figures (8,9, and 10). The non-dimensional mass flow is plotted on Fig. (8) where the abscissa represents the time in seconds. The model shows a higher coefficient of correlation **(Cr)** with the experimental data than Hansen's model (developed model Cr= 0.97, Hansen's model Cr=0.76).On the contrary of Hansen's model, the new model introduces an oscillating frequency equals the experimental one. While Hansen's model produces a shift in predicting the negative flow peaks (e.g. at time $\cong 0.157$ seconds), the existing model predicts these peaks more accurately. Figure (9) shows the non-dimensional pressure drop against the time. The model succeeded in predicting

the maximum of the upper and lower peaks of the oscillations. Moreover, the model predicts the oscillating frequency. The model coefficient of correlation is higher than Hansen's model (developed model Cr= 0.96, Hansen's model Cr=0.90) Figure (10) shows the non-dimensional pressure drop when plotted against the non-dimensional mass flow.

The model is configured with the initial parameters such that it can be compared with **Greitzer [1976]**. **Greitzer [1976]** used a three stage axial compressor. The results are shown on figure (11). The non-dimensional pressure drop is plotted against the non-dimensional mass flow. The results are more fitted with the experimental data than Greitzer's model specially near the negative flow regime. It should be noted that, Greitzer did not plot the variations of both non-dimensional pressure and mass flow against time.

The model is configured with the initial parameters such that it can be compared with **Davis [1986]**. **Davis [1986]** used a three stage axial compressor. The figures presented by Davis are simulation results and not compared with experimental data. Consequently, the data shown on figures (12,13, and 14) represents a comparison between the new model and Davis' model only. It should also be noted that the initial values have a great influence on the output results (e.g. the critical value of the "S" parameter). The non-dimensional pressure drop is plotted on Fig. (12) where the abscissa represents the time. On Fig. (13) the non-dimensional mass flow is plotted against the time. The difference in predicting the peaks of the oscillations on Figs (12&13) may be due to the difference in the "S" parameter between the two models. The non-dimensional pressure drop is plotted on Fig. (14) against the non-dimensional mass flow. The model shows the same trend as Davis' model for the three figures (12, 13 and 14). The present model has a faster algorithm than Davis' model. Davis' model uses 1:100 real processing time to simulation time based on 486, 25 MHz system **[Harvell, 1992]** but, the new model, has a ratio 1: 0.5 per stage.

CONCLUSIONS

A new model is developed for predicting the compressor performance during surge and rotating stall.

- The new model takes into account the thermodynamic effects of the real process by inserting the energy equation into the model.

- The representation of the time lag equation in the model simulates the real development of the stall cell by increasing its initial value during steps of integration to the maximum value.

- The model have the capability to predict both of axial and centrifugal compressors by changing the maximum limit of the delay period. (in axial compressors $N_D = 2$ while in centrifugal ones N_D is taken equal to 0.5).

- The model is not only simple but also more accurate than other models which treat the same phenomenon.

- The model has a faster algorithm than the distributed model. Thus, this model is more suitable for on-line expert systems specially, for large compressors in petrochemical plants.

REFERENCES

Davis, M.W., 1981 *"Stage-by-Stage Post-Stall Compression System Modeling Technique: Methodology, Validation, and Application,"* Ph.D. Thesis, Blacksburg, Verginia, USA.

Davis, M.W., and O'Brien, W.F., 1991 "Stage-by-Stage Poststall Compression System Modeling Technique," *AIAA J. of Propulsion & power Vol. 7, pp. 997-1005.*

Elder, R.L., and Macdougal I., 1983 "Simulation of Centrifugal Compressor Transient Performance for Process Plant Applications, " *ASME Journal of Engineering for Power, July, 83-GT-25, pp. 1-5.*

Elder, R.L. and Gill, M.E., 1984 "A Discussion of the Factors Affecting Surge in Centrifugal Compressors, " *ASME Journal of Engineering for Power, 84-GT-194, pp. 1-8.*

Galvas, M.R., Nov., 1973 "FORTRAN program for predicting off-Design Performance of Centrifugal Compressors," *NASA Technical note.*

Greitzer, E.M., 1976a "Surge and Rotating Stall in Axial Flow Compressors. Part I: Theoretical Compression System Model," *ASME Power, April, pp.190-198.*

Greitzer, E.M., 1976b "Surge and Rotating Stall in Axial Flow Compressors. Part II: Experimental Results and Comparison with Theory," *ASME Power, April, pp. 199-211.*

Hansen, K.E., and Jorgensen, P., 1981 "Experimental and Theoretical Study of Surge in a Small Centrifugal Compressor," *ASME Fluid, Sep., Vol. 103, pp. 391-395.*

Harvell, J. K. and O'Brien, W.F., 1992 "Computational Considerations Associated with the Development of Near-Real-Time Dynamic Simulation for Propulsion Applications," *AIAA 28th joint propulsion Conference Monterey CA., July, AIAA 92-0560.*

O'Brien, W.F., 1992 "Dynamic Simulation of Compressor and Gas Turbine Performance," *AGARD Lecture Series 183, May, pp. 5.1-5.28.*

Stenning, A.H. 1980 "Rotating Stall and Surge," *ASME Trans. Journal of Fluids Engineering, March, Vol. 102, pp. 14-20.*

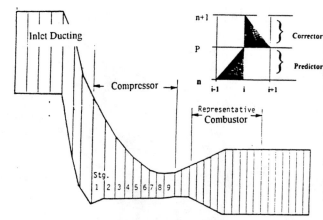

Fig. (2) Physical Compression System and Control Volume of MacCormake Numerical Technique [Davis, 1986]

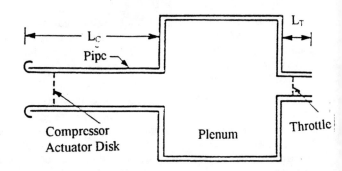

Fig. (3) Eqivalent Compression System [Greitzer, 1976]

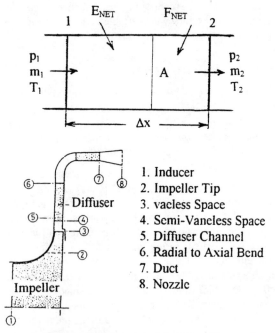

1. Inducer
2. Impeller Tip
3. vaeless Space
4. Semi-Vaneless Space
5. Diffuser Channel
6. Radial to Axial Bend
7. Duct
8. Nozzle

Fig. (4) Elements Considered in Modeling Compressors with Vaned Diffusers [Elder, 1983].

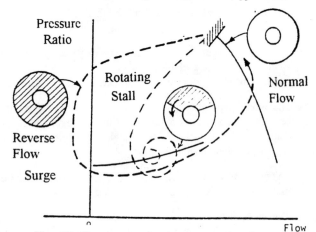

Fig. (1) Compressor Surge and Rotating Stall

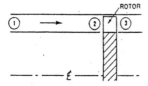

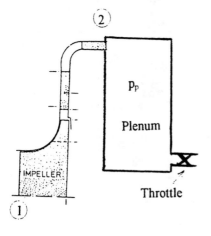

Fig. (5) Equivalent Compression System [Stenning, 1980]

Fig. (6) Schematic Diagram of the Compression System

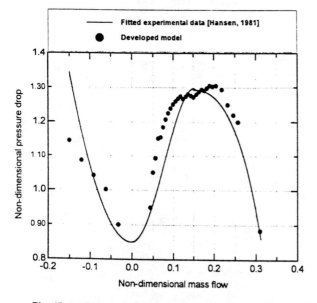

Fig. (5. 7.) Comparison of the reverse flow performance of the developed model and fitted experimental data [Hansen, 1981] assuming steady state perforrmance

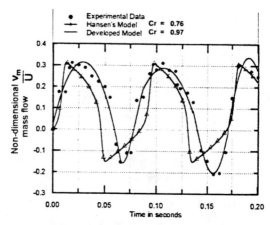

Fig.(8) Comparison of the non-dimensional mass flow fluctuation (at 54000 rpm) of the developed model, experimental data and Hansen's model [Hansen, 1981]

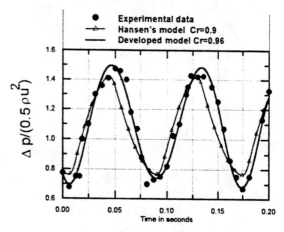

Fig.(9) Comparison of the non-dimensional pressure drop fluctuation (at 54000 rpm) of the developed model, experimental data and Hansen's model [Hansen, 1981]

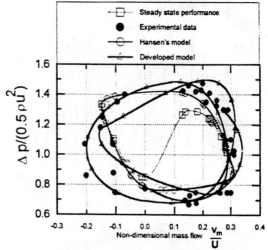

Fig. (10) Comparison of the fluctuation of the non-dimensional mass flow and pressure drop (at 54000 rpm) of the developed model, experimental data and Hansen's model [Hansen, 1981]

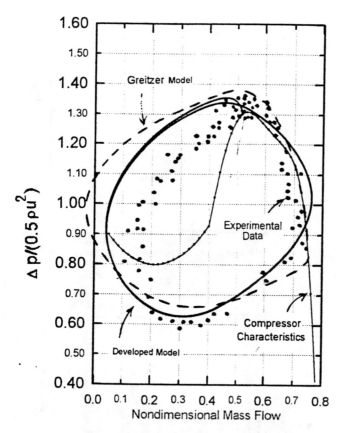

Fig.(11) Comparison Between Greitzer's
Model [1976] and the Developed
Model at B=1.29

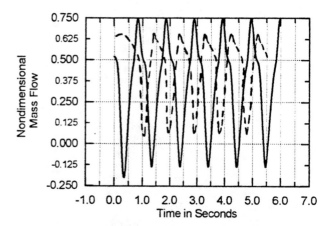

Fig.(13) Comparison Between Davis'
Model [1986] and the Developed
Model When B=1.00

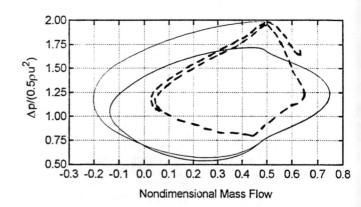

Fig.(14) Comparison Between Davis'
Model [1986] and the Developed
Model When B=1.00

┌───┐
│ - - Davis' Model   ── Developed Model   │
└───┘

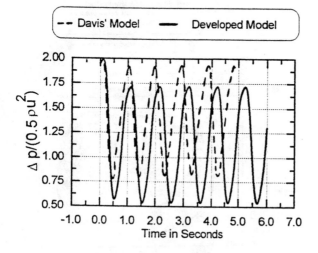

Fig.(12) Comparison Between Davis'
Model [1986] and the Developed
Model When B=1.00

FED-Vol. 238, 1996 Fluids Engineering Division Conference
Volume 3
ASME 1996

Commentary ASME Code Section III Pumps

by

Douglas B. Nickerson[1], Consultant
Chairman, ASME Boiler Code, Section III
Working Group on the Design of Pumps

Paul Burchett, Ontario Hydro
Working Group on the Design of Pumps

Robert E. Cornman, Ingersoll Dresser Pumps
Working Group on the Design of Pumps

Alex Fraser, Weir Pumps
Working Group on the Design of Pumps

Hassan Tafarrodi, GE Nuclear
Working Group on the Design of Pumps

ABSTRACT

This Commentary will explain how the ASME Code requirements are implemented for a nuclear pump. One of the most critical elements in a nuclear power plant are the pumps. These pumps provide the driving force for the movement of liquids in the various systems. The Code is limited to pressure boundary requirements. Many of the things necessary to the satisfactory design of a nuclear pump are not subjected to Code rules. This paper will outline the responsibilities and duties of the various agencies involved in the construction of a nuclear power plant, as applied to the pumps. The authors have outlined what is necessary for a satisfactory, safety related, nuclear pump. Some of the requirements are found in the Boiler Code, others are found in the QME document but most must depend on the engineers who write the design specification and the pump designers who design and produce the

product. A satisfactory pump depends, in the last analysis, on the skill of the pump designer and the integrity of the manufacturer.

INTRODUCTION

One of the most critical elements in a nuclear power plant are the pumps. These pumps provide the driving force for the movement of liquids in the various systems. A pump is used in the main reactor circulating system to create the fluid flow that transfers the nuclear energy to the steam generator. A pump provides the coolant flow that serves the steam condenser. There are pumps in all the fluid systems that make up a nuclear power plant. The provision of pumps best able to perform their function is a team effort. The system designer must outline the requirements for each of the required pumps. The Architect and Engineer, A&E, must prepare a clear, unambiguous design specification. The pump manufacturer must design and build a pump that fully meets the system needs.

This paper will discus how ASME Code requirements, are implemented for a nuclear pump. The paper will be based on the

---

[1] Address correspondence to:
Douglas B, Nickerson
Consultant Mechanical Engineer
1115 Gateway Tower
3452 E. Foothill Blvd.
Pasadena, CA. 91107
dnickers@interserv.com

Revised 03/05/96

current issue of Section III of the Boiler Code, 1995 edition and QME-1-1994 which lists the qualification requirements for pumps.

REQUIREMENTS

General Section III Requirements

Historically, the Code was written to cover pressure boundary items. This derives from the fact that the Code, which was originally issued in 1914, was a set of rules to protect the public from boiler explosions. In 1958 a committee was formed to develop rules for pressure vessels "of superior quality". This effort is the foundation of Section III of the Boiler Code. This section was first published in 1963. In 1971 Section III was renamed "Nuclear Power Plant Components". Pumps and valves were included in this edition for the first time. Because the Code had been written to define the requirements for pressure vessels, the rules for pumps and valves were limited to pressure retaining parts. For pumps and valves, where operational considerations are equally as important as the pressure boundary, the implementation of the ASME Code has caused some confusion.

Article NCA-3000 outlines the responsibilities and duties of the various agencies involved in the construction of a Nuclear power plant. NCA-3200 "Owner's Responsibilities" provides the rules applicable to the Owner of the power plant. Among the owners responsibilities are the designation of the appropriate Edition of the Code. An important requirement of the Code is the provision of a Design Specification for each safety related pump. This appears in Article NCA-3250 "Design Specifications". This Article includes an outline of the required contents of a design specification. This information is supplemented by a pump specification check list which appears in Appendix QP-A to QME-1-1994, "Qualification of Active Mechanical Equipment Used in Nuclear Power Plants. It cannot be overemphasized that this design specification must contain all the operational requirements the pump must meet."

NCA-3255 and NCA-3260 cover the preparation and review of the design report which becomes the permanent record of the pump design. This requirement is only for the pressure boundary part of the pump. The Code specifies pressure boundary and baseplate mounting structure stress levels. This document must be updated if design changes are made to the pump. NB, NC and ND-4000 cover fabrication and installation. of the pump.

NB, NC, and ND-5000 cover examination and NB, NC and ND-6000 cover testing. All these items are usually more completely specified in the design specification.

NCA-3500 Responsibilities of an "N" Certificate Holder. The pump manufacturer must have an "N" stamp. This signifies he has been evaluated by an ASME survey team and his quality control manual has been approved. He is responsible for supplying design documents and material certification. These items must be in accordance with his approved Quality Assurance program which permits him to stamp the final item with his "N" stamp. Code articles relevant to these responsibilities are NCA-3552 "Design Documents", NCA-3560 "Quality Assurance", NCA-3800 "Material Requirements" and NCA-8000 "Stamping".

These documents only cover the requirements to be included in a design specification they do not suggest specific values, nor do they impose operational limitations. The Code does not cover much of the information necessary to define a satisfactorily pump. Operational items are excluded by the Code. The Design Specification is the definitive document for a safety related nuclear pump. It should include all the operational requirements so that the pump will perform its intended service as an active component of a nuclear power plant.

Specific Pump Requirements

NB, NC, ND-3400 Pump Design

NB-3400 contains information specific to Class 1 pumps. Subarticle NB-3411.1 lists the specific items the Code covers. They are:, (a) "pump casings", (b) "pump inlets and outlets", (c) "pump covers", (d) "clamping rings", (e) "seal housing and seal glands", (f) "related bolting", (g) "pump internal heat exchanger piping", (h) pump auxiliary nozzles, (i) "piping identified with the pump and external to and forming part of the pressure retaining boundary and supplied with the pump" and (j) "mounting feet or pedestal supports when integrally attached to the pump pressure retaining boundary and supplied with the pump".

Subarticle NB-3411.2 specifies the exemptions. They are (a) "pump shafts and impellers", (b) "nonstructural internals", (c) "seal packages". The jurisdictional boundary between pressure retaining parts and pump internals is further defined in subarticle NB-1132.2. Section NC and ND present similar requirements for Class 2 and 3 pumps. Non-mandatory Appendix U further lists pump and valve internal parts and sets up requirements for their quality level.

Pumps are classified as Class 1, 2 or 3. Class 1 pumps are defined as pumps included in the fluid containing pressure boundary of the reactor. Failure of the pump pressure boundary would violate the integrity of the reactor pressure boundary. Class 2 pumps are defined as pumps which are not part of the pressure boundary of the reactor but are important for reactor shutdown, emergency core cooling, post accident containment heat removal or post accident fission product removal. This class also includes pumps in the secondary system of the steam generator. Class 3 pumps are those pumps not included in Classes 1 and 2 but are required for cooling water, auxiliary feedwater, post accident atmospheric cleanup and seal water systems important to safety. The design service loadings must be specified. The remaining pumps used in a nuclear power plant can be classified as not safety related and commercial grade components may be used.

Only a small fraction of the pumps in a nuclear power plant are active and safety related. A nuclear pump costs from 5 to 15 times as much as the same pump classified as not safety related. This is a real cost borne by the manufacturer because of the quality control system and complex paper trail that must be maintained for classified components. Pumps, not truly safety related, should not be so classified.

NCA-2142 defines the various levels of service loadings. NB-3112 sets forth the pressure, temperature and mechanical loads that must be sustained. Service condition A, is defined in NCA-2142.4 as design operation. Level B service limits are those design conditions the pump must be able to sustain without needing repair. Level C service limits are loadings which may require that the pump be removed from service for repair but the pressure boundary may not be compromised. Level D service limits are for one time load applications which may cause gross distortions which may affect the functioning of the pump but may not compromise the pressure boundary.

NB-3200 requires that the design of the pressure boundary for Class 1 pumps be designed by analysis. This involves computing stress intensity levels and comparing them with values in the allowable stress table in Section II. Stress intensity is defined as the algebraic difference between the maximum and minimum stress at any specific point.

Section III NC-3100 contains nearly the same requirements for Class 2 pumps. The essential difference between NB and NC/ND is that under article NC/ND-3100 design by analysis is not required and therefore the stress limits are not "stress intensity" values but are the more usual stress values quoted in the literature. Whereas Article NB-3400 contains types A through F and type J pumps, Article NC-3400 includes types G, H and K in addition. These types are added because they can be expected to meet less stringent x-ray quality requirements. Article ND-3400 follows the requirements of NC-3400 but includes type L pumps as well. This type is included because Class 3 pumps do not require x-ray inspection of the pump bowl castings.

SubSection NF contains the requirements for the pump supports. It specifies baseplate mounting structure stress levels. This section contains much less stringent material and inspection requirements than NB, NC and ND.. This relaxation is not too important because the foundation stiffness requirements are overriding for the satisfactory operation of a pump. The Code does not address mounting stiffness required to produce equipment that operates at acceptable vibration levels.

It is important that the A&E and systems engineer consider the effect of pipe

Revised 03/05/96

loads on the pump. Pump costs can escalate significantly when high pipe loads are imposed as the design must be more robust to resist displacement effects on the pump rotor, seal and coupling. The pump should not be used as an anchor point. Therefore system piping layout and pipe support positioning are crucial in minimizing the effect on the pump.

QME-1 REQUIREMENTS

QME-1-1994 "Qualification of Active Mechanical Equipment Used in Nuclear Power Plants", was written to set forth the requirements for the qualification of mechanical equipment used in nuclear power plants *ie,* pumps and valves. It is divided into three sections. The QR portion establishes general principles, philosophy and items that are generally applicable. The QV section is appropriate for valves. The QP section defines the methods for qualifying pumps for use in nuclear power plants. QP-4000 includes definitions of some of the terms used in the definition of pump components and appurtenances. Section QP-5000 specifies qualification principles and philosophy. QP-6000 Qualification Specification itemizes the information that should be in a pump qualification specification. Appendices QP-A and B provide check lists to suggest items that should be included in the pump design specification. Appendix QP-B is applicable to the seal system. In case the pump is powered by a turbine, QP-C provides a check list for this equipment. This document does not contain any values specific to pump performance.

Design Specification

The Design Specification is an important document, it establishes the basis on which the pump is designed, manufactured and tested as well as all operational requirements. QP-A & B of QME-1 provide a check list of what should be included in the specification but do not offer any advice on acceptable values or problem areas to be avoided.

The Code does not impose design and construction rules for assuring operability of components. However, NCA-3252(a)(6) states that "where operability of a component is a requirement, the Design Specification shall make reference to the appropriate documents which specify the operating requirements".

The Design Specification is part of the contract between the owner and the pump manufacturer. It incorporates the design requirements as well as many detail requirements such as accessories and appurtenances, inspection, testing and preparation for shipment and storage. Operational requirements included are; discharge head, pressure, suction pressure and temperature together with mechanical loads and test conditions. It is important that the design specification define the minimum service temperature. This will determine the need for material with low temperature properties and impact test requirements.

Safety related pumps and their drivers fall under the "active equipment" category and as such, must be designed with the clear objective of being capable of satisfying the dynamic and environmental qualification rules which exist in national standards and regulations. These standards and regulations are normally referenced in the Design Specification. The design specification must include drawing and data requirements to conform to the Code requirements. The preparation of this document is normally assumed by the A&E who is responsible for the design and construction of the plant. In the last analysis, however it is the Owner's responsibility.

Current examples of national standards are:

(1) ASME QME-1: 1994 "Qualification of Active Mechanical Equipment used in Nuclear Power Plants"

(2) IEEE 344:1987 "Recommended Practice for Seismic Qualification of Class 1E Equipment for Nuclear Power Generating Stations".

(3) IEEE 323: 1983 "Standard for Qualifying Class 1E Equipment for Nuclear Power Generating Stations"

For non-pressure boundary components Appendix U recommends component quality requirements. This Appendix also provides some additional materials, available for pump internal parts.

Operability over the complete operating range can be proven either by test or (more usually) by analysis. Testing is employed where the equipment and environmental effect is too complex to satisfy by analytical techniques on a valid mathematical model. For example, shaker table testing may be required for engines or turbine drivers with complex control gear. Thermal shock or debris testing of critical Class 2 pumping equipment may be required when the pump has to operate under adverse suction conditions following a major LOCA (Loss of Coolant Accident).

Analytical techniques can be employed where structures, capable of analysis, exist and classical methods can be used to validate the model. For example, a simple static analysis can be used when the equipment can be shown to be rigid, (*ie* where the fundamental structural frequency is greater than 33 Hertz).

When harsh conditions exist, environmental qualification of non-metallic components such as seals, bearings, lubricants, thermal and electrical insulation, may be required to be proven by simulated testing to justify the aging effects of operational and system conditions on equipment. The types of aging include thermal, radiation, wear and vibration effects.

The Design Specification usually does not specify the pump type. The NPSH usually determines the pump speed. The head and flow then determine the specific speed. This parameter suggests a pump type. As an example, low total head coupled with high flow suggest a type B or D pump. These are pumps having a horizontally split case with double suction. For high heads one of the multistage pumps will be required. A type K vertical pump is used when the pump suction must be lowered to obtain static head for a reasonable NPSH.

High energy pumps (more than 500 HP) require special consideration. They cannot be operated for long periods over a wide range of flows. Operation at off peak flows will usually result in high bearing loads. These high bearing loads can lead to reduced life expectancy. Operation at or near shut off will cause extreme temperature rises since the energy input to the pump is not dissipated with the through flow. Operation in this regime must be avoided. The specification should clearly state the conditions under which the pump will be operated.

Appendix S, "Pump Shaft Design Methods" is a non-mandatory appendix. The methodology is very good but the loads can only be approximated. Such things as torsional load reversal and bending loads cannot be determined by the designer with any degree of accuracy. This is particularly true at off design conditions. Experience on the part of the pump designer is much more important than any particular design method.

The specification should establish what vibration tests or analysis is to be carried out. For pumps an acceptable vibration level can be set and confirmed by test. Typical acceptance values can be found in the Hydraulic Institute Standard (HIS) for pumps.

For custom built pumps the dynamic requirements that must be met are an essential part of the design. These may be included by requiring the manufacturer to test or include in his design analysis the following items:

1.   Shaft lateral vibrational frequency analysis and critical speed, wet and dry. In order to be sure there are no resonances, the analysis should include at least three vibration modes above the fundamental.

2.   A shaft torsional analysis should be prepared if the pump is engine driven. A comparison of the calculated frequencies with the blade passing frequencies and engine torsional frequencies should be made.

3.   In order to assure satisfactory operation when the pump is mounted in the power plant allowable vibration levels of the installed pump should be called out. It may be appropriate to specify allowable unbalance values for the rotating element.

Vibration problems with the pump may occur due to the natural frequency of the system being coincident with the rotational speed. This can occur because of the mounting being less rigid than assumed or due to unanticipated piping loads. These problems arise in spite of careful design and installation. The structural natural frequencies of custom built pump assemblies and the shaft vibrations should be measured as part of the suppliers performance tests. This vibration data can be very valuable in overcoming on site vibration problems later.

This often is controversial between the owner and the pump manufacturer. It is not easy to assign responsibility for problems only discovered when the pump is installed. If the pump has vibration problems when it is installed they must be resolved by cooperation between the owner and the manufacturer.

One of the important elements in determining the cost of the pump is the complexity of the sealing configuration. The pump shaft seal requirements should be defined in the specification but the final selection of seal type and cooling system should be negotiated between the owner and supplier. Typical arrangements for seal cooling can be found in the API 610 pump specification.

Most design specifications itemize the materials to be used in the pump's construction. This will be based upon the owners experience in operation. If the pump is a new application negotiations between the owner and supplier are recommended before the specification is finalized. The materials are selected based on experience with corrosion and erosion problems. The system designer is often more knowledgeable in this field. The material of the case is an essential item included in this list of pump materials. The pump designer is usually not as familiar with the effects of the pumped fluid upon his pump material as the system designer. Since the case forms the pressure boundary the specified material must be in the Code. Often this requirement may not permit the owner to specify the best material for the service. Ultimately, (if the pump casing material is not specified) the pump supplier must be responsible for material selection and should consider effects such as corrosion/erosion to determine the optimum selection. If Code materials are unsuitable, then a Code Case must be submitted and approved by the ASME Code Committee. The Code Case must then be approved for use by the owner. As part of the material specifications welding requirements should be included if applicable.

The type of driver must be selected. If the drive is a steam turbine or a gear drive the speed should be defined.

The instrumentation required by the power plant to monitor the pump operation should be included so that either it is provided with the pump or provisions for connections are available.

If auxiliary fluid piping is required it must be defined in the design specification.

The test requirements for acceptance of pumps should be provided by the Owner. These tests will include a proof pressure test of the assembly, as specified in the Code. Most pumps are designed to withstand full discharge design pressure. However, the mechanical seals may not be satisfactory for this condition. If this is the case special arrangements must be made for proof pressure testing. Hydraulic and mechanical performance tests will provide data so that the efficiency and head-capacity of the pump may be determined. If seal leakage is critical, special tests of this component may be required.

The Design Specification should provide for finish requirements, shipping and storage provisions. It should include drawing and data requirements to conform to the Code.

The installation drawing is the document which defines the installation of the pump. This document includes location and configuration of all external connections. It includes mounting points and weight of the pump and its driver. The design report will include the stress levels for the various loading conditions.

CONCLUSION

The authors have tried to outline what is necessary for a satisfactory pump to be used in a Nuclear power plant. Some of the requirements are found in the Boiler Code, others are found in the QME document but most depend on the engineers who write the design specification and the engineers who design and produce the product. A satisfactory pump depends on the skill of the pump designer and the integrity of the manufacturer. Even though the Code has rules for quality control and guidance for the design of the pump pressure boundary this is only a small fraction of what is necessary. The operational suitability depends on the input from the design specification as agreed to between the owner and the pump manufacturer. This document depends on the experience of the system designer and the free interchange of information between all parties involved.

Safety related pumping equipment must be designed, constructed and rigorously analysed and/or tested for reliable and safe operation to ensure a high standard of structural and operational integrity.

No specification can be substituted for the skill and experience of a good pump engineer and no quality control system can ensure a quality product from an unscrupulous vendor. The ultimate utility of the pump system requires experience, skill and communication between both the pump designer and system owner at an engineering level. Having all the above factors right, there will be unanticipated hydrodynamic interactions between the pump and the system. The pump, being the driving force in system flow, will be influenced by everything else in the system. These factors can only be anticipated by an experienced A&E who is skilled in system design. In a word, a satisfactory pump will only result from the cooperation between the Owner, A&E and the pump designer. With each organization working as a member of the team the results will be a well designed system with the pumps contributing to its smooth, efficient operation.

REFERENCES

ASME CODE, SECTION III, 1995 edition, "ASME Boiler & Pressure Vessel Code"

QME-1-1994, "Qualification of Active Mechanical Equipment Used in Nuclear Power Plants"

IEEE 344: 1987, "Recommended Practice for Seismic Qualification of Class 1E Equipment for Nuclear Power Generating Stations"

IEEE 323: 1983, "Standard of Qualifying Class 1E Equipment for Nuclear Power Generating Stations"

API-610, Seventh Edition, Feb. 1989, "Centrifugal Pumps for General Refinery Service"

HIS "Standards of the Hydraulic Institute, Centrifugal Pump Section", 14th Edition, 1983, Figure 77 "Acceptable Field Vibration Limits for Vertical Pumps & Horizontal Pumps With Piggyback Mounted Motors (Non-rigid Structures).

API 610, Seventh Edition, Feb. 1989, "Centrifugal Pumps for General Refinery Service".

Revised 03/05/96

FED-Vol. 238, 1996 Fluids Engineering Division Conference
Volume 3
ASME 1996

SURGE PREDICTION MODELING FOR
LOW PRESSURE COMPRESSION PROCESS

M. A. Rayan[1]
Mechanical Power Department,
Mansoura University,
Mansoura, EGYPT.

R. N. Azoole[2]
Mechanical Power Department,
Mansoura University,
Mansoura, EGYPT.

ABSTRACT:

This paper presents theoretical and experimental investigation on *surge* prediction of low pressure compression process. The main research effort focused on operation stability and transient operation came across particularly in centrifugal compressor operation known as *surge* phenomenon. Theoretical and experimental analysis have been done to predict *surge* based on transient response analysis. The purpose of this analysis is to protect these centrifugal compressors from *surge* onset and to increase it's efficiency by minimizing energy power waste. This is done by stating a closer anticipated new set point of minimum flow rate in order to minimize gas recirculation. Since it is difficult to apply this study on a real and large centrifugal compressor process, a simulator (PMC) as a hydraulic circuit uses low pressure compression process is used. Data acquisition system (DAS) and PC computer with relevant software packages designed for this research and similar applications are used. Operation monitoring and logging of the compressed air system flowing to the hydraulic circuit are exhibited. The model used for theoretical modeling is non linear lumped parameter model monitoring of the unsteady operation of the compressed air through the Test Rig and logging of *surge* onset during both start up and throttling procedures. Then plotting the experimental data on charts to compare this experimental data with theoretical data for the same process. The benefits of this research actually is the employment of the obtained results to construct a process control system to overcome *surge* onset. The obtained results shows a reasonable agreement between the theoretical model based on Greitzer's and Hansen's models and the simulator experimental results, for prediction and onset of *surge*. The model will presents an efficient and economical mean of process monitor for conditions similar to the real industrial plants.

KEY WORDS:

Centrifugal compressors, Surge and Instability Operation, Process Monitoring and Control (expert systems), Numerical Analysis and Simulation.

NOMENCLATURE:

a	=	speed of sound	(mps)
A	=	Flow through area	(m^2)
B	=	Greitzer's compressor stability	$(\sim)$
$(P_r)_c$	=	Compressor pressure rise	$(\sim)$
F	=	Throttle pressure drop.	$(\sim)$
m	=	Mass flow parameter	$(\sim)$
G	=	Geometric parameter	$(\sim)$
L	=	Duct length	(m)
N	=	Compressor Speed	(r. p. m.)
R	=	compressor rotor mean radius	(m)
ΔP	=	Plenum pressure rise	$(\sim)$
V_P	=	Exit plenum Volume.	(m^3)
τ	=	Compressor flow time constant	$(\sim)$
ω	=	Helmholtz resonator frequency	$(\sim)$

Subscripts :
P = Plenum   C = Compressor
T = Throttle   ss = Steady state condition
Superscript: $(\sim)$ = (non-dimensional)

1. INTRODUCTION:

Centrifugal compressors operations are limited by a *surge* region where unstable operation encountered at low flow rates, so flow levels must be maintained at levels high enough to keep the compressor out of *surge* region. S*urge* phenomenon will be analyzed, discussed for centrifugal compressor used to compress air, the mass flow rate required to achieve a safe operation away of *surge* and away of stone wall on the performance curve of compressor will be determined. The analysis of *surge and rotating stall* (which occur directly before *surge*) was first observed by the group developing centrifugal compressor for whittle turbojet in 1938 [Chesir, 1945]*.

A comprehensive list of publications on *Rotating stall* up to 1967 has been assembled by [Fabri, 1967]*. All of these analysis is to describe the theory of the onset of *rotating stall and surge* but does not yield the criterion for the onset of *Rotating stall* or *surge* which could be applicable to single stage compressors and multistage compressors. [Metcalf, 1972] represent how to calculate and eliminate *surge* using Daniel flow computation techniques and using relays control scheme. [Dunham, 1962]** found that *rotating stall* followed by *surge* occurs at the peak of the performance curve of centrifugal compressors at this point, which separates stable operating area than unstable operating area. [Whitfield, 1977] agrees with the authors in the difficulties of predicting the flow through centrifugal compressor which is often highly separated and fully three dimensional, he also states that up to this time, the computing technique have not provided the ability to predict this three - dimensional separated flow.

The first Modeling technique is done by [Stening, 1980] using linear differential equations, linearizing the compressor characteristic in the vicinity of the steady state operating point, using simple lumped parameter mode. [Stening, 1980], assumes a pressure drop from the plenum to the atmosphere as a function of the mass flow through value, which represents small disturbances away from the steady state, then he linearized these equations leading to his characteristic equation. This technique of Stening is a good approach to model the *surge* but is *not accurate* enough for simulation using *expert system* for predicting *surge* and allowing anti surge control to over come surge.

The second Modeling technique is done by [O'Brine, 1991] using partial differential equations which is far accurate but at the same time far long and slow to be implemented in industry by means of expert system. O'Brien used distributed parameters which needs parallel computers to simulate the unsteady condition, this technique formulates a stage - by stage dynamic system model which included details of internal features of a compression system such as effects of off - design stage mismatching, interstage bleeds, and variable geometry could be studied. There are several the difficulties for implementing this technique in *expert system* applications for similar cases.

The third Modeling technique is done by [Grietzer, 1975] allowing to use Non - linear lumped parameter he developed a non - linear model to predict the transient response of a compression system subsequent to a perturbation from steady operating conditions he developed a non dimensional parameters on which this response depends, for value above the critical, the system will exhibit the large amplitude oscillatory behavior characteristic of *surge*, while for values below the critical, it will moves toward operation in *rotating stall*, at a substantially reduced flow rate and pressure ratio. The overall dynamics of *surge* and *rotating stall* in axial flow compression systems has been studied theoretically and experimentally by [Grietzer, 1975]. Flow instabilities can be of two types :*Rotating stall* and *surge*, the first describes bladding oscillating stresses while the second may have a disastrous effect on the whole system of which the compressor is a component, but *surge*

consists of large amplitude oscillations of the flow through the entire compressor while also produces large oscillations in compressor delivery pressure [Hansen, 1981]. Throttling the flow through an *turbo* compressor from design point to the *stall* limit, the steady flow pattern that exists becomes unstable. [Hansen, 1981] presents study depending on Greitzer's study to further explore the Greitzer model and test its applicability to describe *surge* in a small single-stage centrifugal compressor system, to test the dynamic behavior prediction based on measured steady- state branches of centrifugal compressor characteristics. So modeling is enough accurate and the solution offered of solving the four non - linear differential equations will be done using fifth - order Rung - Kutta integration. This computer program could be easily implemented in Expert system used for process monitoring and control systems. Transient response of a certain compressor depends on non-dimensional parameters, system modeling during unsteady operation is done by means of numerical simulation using non-linear lumped parameters for on line prediction of surge and *rotating stall* utilizing expert system.

2. MODELING TECHNIQUE:

The present analysis is based on a modified Greitzer and Hansen analysis. The analysis is done using the non linear system behavior, using Helmholtz resonator type of compression system model introduced by [Stening, 1980]. The analysis shows that for a given compression system i-e specified compressor characteristics, there are an important non-dimensional parameters on which the system response depends. A modified Greitzer and Hansen model was used, the modification is based mainly to expand the modeling in order to handle different geometric conditions and characteristics and different system performance. Using numerical analysis: non- linear deferential equations (fifth order Rung Kutta integration) to solve the four Greitzer's equations, as a *Fortran* executable file driven by an expert system simulation package then the modeling program produces a data file including all initial parameters essential for modeling. Plotting these parameters against each other to get the required charts in unsteady operation analysis (transient compression system).

2.1. *Rota* Case Modeling:

Greitzer model was applied to axial compressor, and Hansen model (modified Greitzer model) was applied to single stage centrifugal compressor. Using Hansen modified model to be applied here on *low compression system* Fig (1) as a study case. The objective of this experimental work is to have a hydraulic process system with an obstruction elements are installed in series, in a 2.54 cm diameter pipe, mounted on a portable panel (Fig. 1). Hansen modified model is applied in this study, The available compressed air is used instead of centrifugal compressor, taking in consideration the following:

1. Using calculated C_r from measured flow rate is:

$[Q = (\pi Db) \varepsilon C_r]$ instead of C_x of the flow at inlet as Hansen did. The term (πDb) represents the compressor flow area (A_c).

2. The equivalent calculated axial velocity is:

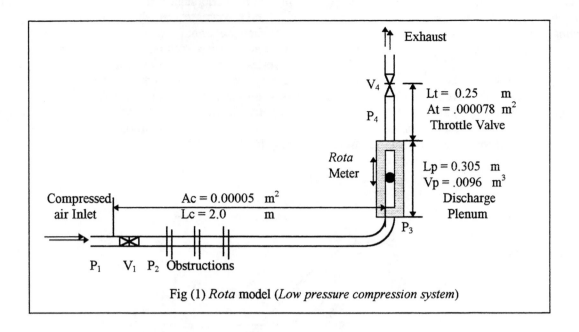

Fig (1) *Rota* model (*Low pressure compression system*)

$[C_r = Q / A \, \epsilon \ (\text{mps})]$.

3. The resultant head of compression system is a function of pressure coefficient (ϕ).

4. The pressure coefficient for turbomachines is:
$\phi = 2g H / U^2$.

5. The equivalent calculated impeller tip velocity
is $U = (\sqrt{2g H}) / \phi$ (mps)

6. The equivalent calculated velocity is
$U = \pi D N / 60$ (mps)

7. The equivalent calculated speed is:
$N = 60 * U / \pi D$ (rpm)

8. The characteristic real case performance curve data (P_r - Q%) is used instead of (C_{ss} - m) of the system under study for simplicity of modeling.

9. The characteristic curve fitting equation is mapped according to curve fitting with polynomial coefficients of fourth order.

Where:

    D = impeller tip diameter

    ϵ = contraction ratio of compressor blades

    $= [(\pi * D) - (t * z)] / \pi D$

    t = Blade thickness.

    z = Number of blades.

The proposed modified model equations will be as follow:

Momentum balance for the compressor duct represented by equation:
$$dQ_c / dt = B[(P_r)_c - (P_r)_P] \tag{1}$$
Momentum balance for the throttle duct represented by equation:
$$dQ_t / dt = B/G(\Delta P - F) \tag{2}$$

Mass balance for the plenum represented by equation:
$$d\Delta P / dt = (Q_c - Q_t) / B \tag{3}$$

Relaxation response to departure from steady represented by equation:

$$dP_r / dt = (1/\tau) [(P_r)_c - (P_r)_P] \tag{4}$$

Throttle characteristics represented by equation:
$$F = S Q_t^2 \tag{5}$$

where:
$$B = U / 2\omega L_c \underline{\hspace{2cm}} \tag{6}$$
$$\text{or} \ \ B = U / \ 2a \sqrt{V_p / A_c * L_c} \tag{7}$$

G = Geometric Parameter = $(L_t / A_t) / (L_c / A_c)$ (8)

Q_c = Flow rate through compressor

Q_t = Flow rate through throttling valve

$(P_r)_P$ = Plenum Pressure ratio (P_3 / P_4)

$(P_r)_c$ = Compressor Pressure ratio (P_1 / P_2)

ΔP = Pressure difference ($P_1 - P_2$)

Equation (1) - (4) were solved numerically for different compression and throttle characteristic curves, and for a range of values of the parameter B, using fourth order predictor corrector in order to determine the dynamic behavior of the compressor system. Although the forgoing arguments have been focused on the behavior of the simplified compression system. The basic qualitative conclusions can be extended to the more general case described by equation (1) - (4). Modified Hansen modeling is enough accurate and the solution offered of solving the four non - linear differential equations will be done using fifth - order Rung - Kutta integration. This solution is fast enough, computer program can be easily implemented through expert system used for process monitoring and control tasks. The previous studies indicate that neither a complete picture of mechanisms, nor an application quantitative flow model describing the *Rota* of flow breakdown appears to be available at this time to assist in the prediction of overall *surge* behavior. Never the less, for an engineering application in the system dynamics analysis a lumped parameter model, such as that of

699

Greitzer is used by [Hansen, 1981].A modified model was used, the modification is based mainly to expand the modeling in order to handle different geometric conditions and characteristics. Using numerical analysis {Non-linear deferential equations (fifth order Rung Kutta integration)}to solve the four Greitzer's equations, as a *Fortran* executable file driven by an expert system simulation package to simulate both Hansen's cases and test rig *Rota* cases enabling to change initial geometric data entry and the polynomial coefficients of the fitting curve of the performance curve (Pr- Q%). The modeling program produces a result file including all initial parameters essential for modeling, plotting these parameters against each other to get the required charts in unsteady operation (transient compression system). Test rig *Rota* system was simulated and modeled at three cases (three different S-values) enabling to change initial geometric data entry and the polynomial coefficients of the fitting curve of the performance curve [(Pr) $_c$ - Q $_c$ %].

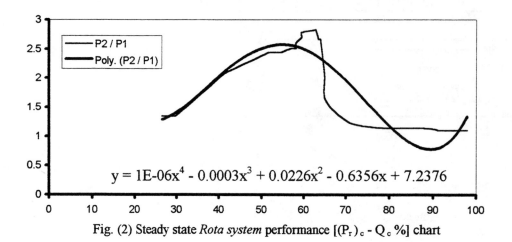

$$y = 1E\text{-}06x^4 - 0.0003x^3 + 0.0226x^2 - 0.6356x + 7.2376$$

Fig. (2) Steady state *Rota system* performance [(P$_r$)$_c$ - Q$_c$ %] chart

Fig (2) shows the *Rota* system performance curve so the steady state pressure rise **P$_r$** was mapped as:

$$\mathbf{P_r = 7.162 - 0.62*Q_c + 0.022*Q_c^2 - 0.0003* Q_c^3} \qquad (9)$$

3. THEORETICAL MODELING RESULTS:

Using numerical analysis {non-linear deferential equations (fourth order Rung Kutta integration)}to solve the four proposed modified Greitzer's equations, as a *Fortran* executable file driven by an expert system simulation package then the modeling program produces a results file including all initial parameters essential for modeling, plotting these parameters against each other to get the required charts in unsteady operation analysis (transient compression system*), Rota* surge analyses is shown in Fig (3,4,5). Here are the modeling charts that explains the unsteady operation condition utilizing the Rung-Kutta fourth order *Fortran* program, plotted from results file by excel software package. Fig. (3) showing the Qc- Time chart where the mass flow rate is surging with time and the *surge* dissipate gradually according to the initial compression system performance curve Fig (2). The three curves for different (S) values are identical. Fig (4) Shows the Pr- Time chart, that easily exhibits the fluctuation of the pressure ratio against the time indicating the *surge* onset at this transient operation. Also the three curves for different (S) values are identical. Here in Fig (5) is the Pr- Qc chart for the same case, this chart reflects the unsteady behavior of the system, the flow starts at the center of the whirl surging hardly and then begin to relax at the end of the whirl lump as the steady state performance curve show before at Fig (2), note the departure of the curve in the negative region of Qc indicating the occurrence of the reverse flow during *surge* onset which is the main evidence of *surge* onset in this case. Also the three curves for different (S) values are identical.

4. EXPERIMENTAL RESULTS: (*Rota* system monitoring and logging at transient condition):

During start- up at low flow rate and High pressure ratios it is noticed that due to the large losses resulted from obstruction devices on the discharge line as in fig (1) , a clear visual & audible evidence are easily observed. This means that the *float (pop)* of the *Rota* Meter as a flow measuring device was surging hardly until the flow rate increased and excess the critical value. The *surging* of the float of the *Rota* Meter was so interested for monitoring & logging to analyze this phenomenon and correlate it against Hansen's & Greitzer's analysis in the next section. The monitoring of the Compression system at unsteady condition which occur at partially opening of exhaust valve (V$_4$) had been done at several cases as follow: **Fig (6);** this curve is plotted while an audible and visual *surge* onset on *Rota* bob causing the curve of Flow (Q) against time to be as a sin curve at two fixed valve (V$_4$) opening setting: (S=125, S=250) (Flow uncertainty is _+2%). **Fig (7);** Shows the operating the system over a range of regulating valve (V$_1$) setting while keeping the exhaust valve (V$_4$) partially opened so performance curves fig (5) exhibit the system performance of pressure ratio

(Pr) against flow rate (Q%), the flow was surging hardly while start up until the flow across the value of 63 % of STD flow rate. (Flow uncertainty is _+2%). **Fig (8)**; Here it is interested to plot pressure ratio (Pr) against the (S) Valve parameter $\{S = (A_c/A_t)^2\}$ to note that the system behavior here is similar to the last curve, this means that the (S) parameter is a quantitative parameter to represent the flow through the compression system. ("S" uncertainty is _+5%). **Fig (9)**; In this chart the plotting of the unstable flow which starts to *surge* at low flow rates and surging becomes strong and hard until the flow passed the flow percentage of 63 %, then the flow becomes steady at the rest of the range, the flow represented here against time (Sec.) (Flow uncertainty is _+2%). **Fig (10)**; shows the plotting of the Valve parameter (S) against the flow(Q%) , it is found that the surging progress while (S) value is high starting with max. (S) value at valve (V_1) closing sate, until the (S) value decreases to equal value of 105, which is associated with value of 63 % of flow rate and pressure ratio (Pr) at value of 2.8.

5. DISCUSSION:

The analysis of theoretical modeling techniques based on the non linear lumped parameter [Greitzer, 1975], were very useful and powerful especially for axial compressors, during *transient* operation. It is not easy to predict *surge* onset without taking Hansen's valve parameter (S) in considerations. It is considered as the main quantitative parameter related to the flow rate through the compression system especially for centrifugal compressors. This analysis answers clearly definite questions; such as for *surge* prediction, when *surge* occurs? Which quantitative parameters are concerning *surge* onset? Which parameter (S) are suitable for Anti - s*urge* control system? The theoretical modeling done for both Hansen's cases shows typical identical similarity for his experimental modeling charts published on his paper. That similarity proved the validity of the modeling technique's program to simulate and solve any other similar conditions. This modeling program was applied for *Rota* compression system case to study the response of the system at three (S) values that been identical in there response behavior. After analyzing the *unsteady operation analysis of experimental data logging of Rota compression system* it was found that; *Rota float* surging occurs at flow rates below critical value of 63 % of STD reference flow rate and high pressure ratio of Pr = 2.8 at valve parameter S > 105 at max. Pressure drop in discharge line downstream the discharge control valve. Damping occurs after increasing the flow rate above 63 % and S < 105. The same behavior occurs during throttling the system. Comparing the theoretical modeling of *Rota* system results with Hansen's results similarity found except the decay of the *Rota* theoretical modeling oscillations, but in experimental the oscillation continues at the same *Rota* until the valve (V_4) setting changed to the safe limit. The *Rota surge* occurs at the Greitzer's parameter B = 0.256 (at theoretical modeling) that is less than the critical "B" value of 0.6, but Hansen mentioned

that the min. value of parameter (B) = 0.105 at low speeds of (7000-9000 rpm), this satisfies this condition under study. There is another reason may cause this compression system to *surge* at value of (B) of less than the critical (B = 0.6), due to the obstruction devices on the discharge side (up stream of plenum). That makes the **(S)** parameter is the great concern of *surge* onset, in this case in conjunction of parameter (B). Discharge flow (Q) and valve parameter **(S),** are good quantitative parameters for Anti- surge control scheme. [Patlovany, 1986] Analyzed a large air compressor for the purpose of minimizing energy costs and protecting the compressor from *surge*, his analysis shows that *surge* occurs for two different multi stage compressors (low pressure and high pressure), at the *Rota* of 66 % and 69.5 % of discharge flow at different *rotating* speeds (from 4280 rpm to 5110 rpm), this agrees with the results obtained from experimental that indicates the safe flow rate is more than 63 % for this case. The visual and audible surging of the *Rota* pop was an enough evidence of *surge* onset instead of using vibration detectors in this case. The experimental results from this case regarding the safe operating limit of the flow rate (Q = 63%) should be incremented with at least more 5% as a safe margin for steady operation. During experimental monitoring analysis another important parameter appears that the energy losses were max. at *surge* onset.

6. CONCLUSION & RECOMMENDATIONS:

The analytical study of both theoretical and experimental studies of the simulated compression system during transient operation was very useful and powerful. This analysis answers clearly definite questions; such as for *surge* prediction, when *surge* occurs? Which quantitative parameters related with *surge* onset? And which parameters are more suitable for Anti *surge* control scheme. Considering the present investigation, the following conclusions and recommendations are concluded: The theoretical modeling done for *Rota* cases using the modified model, shows a reasonable agreement with the experimental results using hydraulic simulator. Greitzer compressor characteristic's parameter **(B)** has a clear effect on *surge* onset for value of (B = 0.256) that agrees with Hansen's min. Value of (B= 0.105 for low rpm of about 7000 rpm) that is less than Greitzer's value of **B< 0.6** (Critical value).The valve parameter "S" has an effect on *surge* onset for values of **S > 105** (Experimental logging) his agrees with Hansen's min. value of **S= 47** (critical value is S = 125).*Rota* float surging occurs at flow rates below critical value of 63 % of STD reference flow rate and high pressure ratio of Pr = 2.8 at valve parameter S > 105 at max. pressure drop in discharge line downstream the discharge control valve. The same oscillations occurs during throttling the system at normal operation, or (experimental data). The *Rota surge* occurs even the Greitzer's parameter B = 0.256 that is much lower than critical B value of 0.6, this is may be due to obstruction devices installed on the discharge line (up stream of plenum). Damping occurs after increasing the flow rate (experimentally) above 63 % and

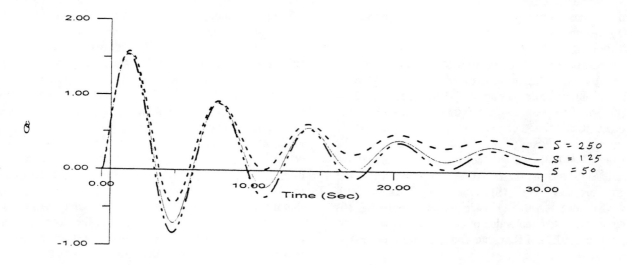

Fig (3) ROTA modeling (Qc-Time) chart at B = 0.256

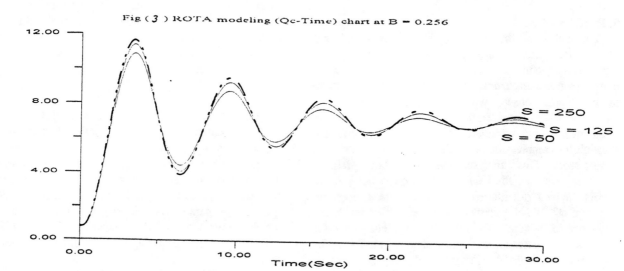

Fig (4) ROTA modeling (Pr - Qc%) chart at B = 0.256

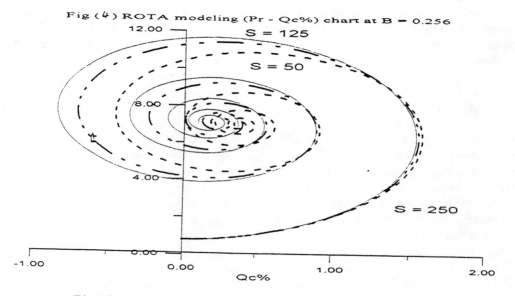

Fig (5)   ROTA modeling (Pr-Qc%) chart at B=0.256

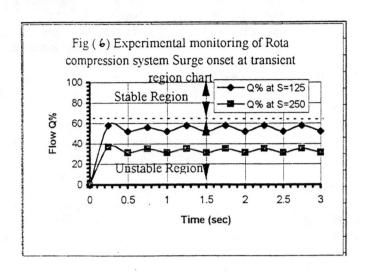

Fig (6) Experimental monitoring of Rota compression system Surge onset at transient region chart

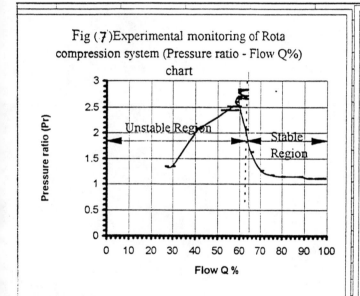

Fig (7)Experimental monitoring of Rota compression system (Pressure ratio - Flow Q%) chart

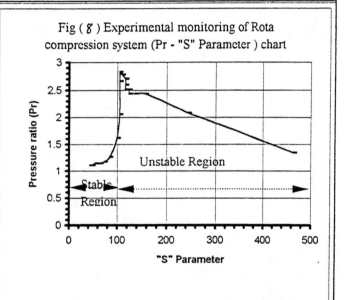

Fig (8) Experimental monitoring of Rota compression system (Pr - "S" Parameter) chart

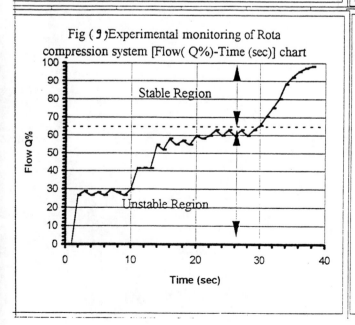

Fig (9)Experimental monitoring of Rota compression system [Flow(Q%)-Time (sec)] chart

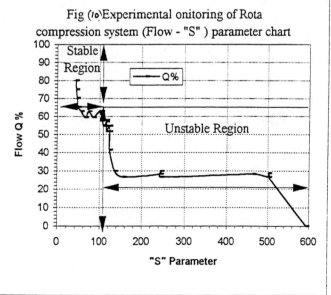

Fig (10)Experimental onitoring of Rota compression system (Flow - "S") parameter chart

S <105 (_+5%).Comparing the theoretical *Rota* modeling results with Hansen's results, similarity found except the decay of *Rota* theoretical modeling charts. Discharge flow as a percentage of STD flow and throttling (S) is a good quantitative parameter for anti-surge control scheme. The presented model in this form is adequate for use in computer based expert system, for its quick response. The use of such model will be of a great help for *surge* prediction and building up the reasonable Anti-*surge* control system.

REFERENCES:
1. Stenning, A. H. "Rotating Stall and Surge", *Trans ASME,* March 1980.
2. Whitfield A. "Rationalization of Empirical Loss Coeff. And Their Application In One Dimensional Performance Prediction Procedure For Centrifugal Compressors", *ASME*, Dec. 28 1977.
3. Patlovany, D. and A. B. Focke "Predictive *Surge* Control and Optimization For A Centrifugal Compressor", *Mech. Eng. ASME, 1986.*
4. Greitzer, E. M. *"Surge and Rotating Stall In Axial Flow Compressors, ASME,* April 1975.
5. Metcalf, J. "How To Calculate and Eliminate Compressor Surge", *Daniel Ind. LTD*, UK, 1972.
6. Hansen, K. H "Experimental and Theoretical Study of Surge In A Small Centrifugal Compressor ", *Journal of Fluid Mechanics*, Vol. 103/391, Sept. 1981.
7. O'Brien W. F. and Davis M. W "Stage - By - Stage Post Stall Compression System Model Technique" *AIAA, ASME, CA, Joint propulsion conference, San-Diego* June-29- July-2 1987, published on Nov. 20. 1990.

AUTHOR INDEX

FED-Vol. 238
1996 Fluids Engineering Division Conference
Volume 3

Abo-Rayan, M. 681
Agarwal, Ramesh K. 233, 485, 517
Al-Zubaidy, Sarim N................................. 663
Almgren, Ann S...355
Assanis, Dennis N.................................... 165
Azoole, R. N..697
Baban, Farzad..563
Bakir, Farid 639
Bakken, Lars E. 669
Bangalore, Ashok....................................... 465
Bar-Yoseph, Pinhas Z...............................105
Barrett, M. R. D. 519
Baysal, Oktay 463, 503
Belamri, Thabet 639
Bell, John B. 355
Bernard, Peter S....................................1, 33
Bernstein, Edward L. 323
Bin, Fu 75
Bostwick, Peter... 557
Bourgault, Yves 209
Buffard,Thierry 189
Burchett, Paul 689
Burt, David J. 439
Cantwell, Brian J....................................... 511
Chapnik, Brian V. 497
Chen, Norbert C. J.....................................529
Chen, Xi 647
Chen, Zuxing 57
Chippada, S. 409
Chorin, Alexandre J................................... 129
Christon, Mark A.......................................277
Chyczewski, Thomas.................................. 465
Cochran, Leighton S...................................535
Colella, Phillip... 355
Constantinescu, George.............................. 173
Cornman, Robert E....................................689
Cottet, Georges-Henri 135
Currie, I. G. 497
Dawson, C. N.. 409
de Melo, José Ronaldo C. 385
Debelak, Kenneth A....................................271
Demuren, Ayodeji O..............................1, 121
Deng, Mark P..547
Dhaubhadel, M. N................. 149, 239, 249
Dompierre, Julien 209
Donescu, Pompiliu 421
Eghbali, Davoud A.....................................309
El-Mitwally, E. S..681
Elias, Steven R..557
Engeda, Abraham......................................589
Engelman, Michael S. 205, 317, 427
Esmaeeli, Asghar 375
Estivalezes, J. L. 473
Fabris, Drazen.. 49

Fadda, Dani.. 335
Ferguson, John W......................................439
Fiorentino, Luigi 241
Fonda-Bonardi, G. 609
Fortin, Michel 209
Foss, John F.. 83
Fraser, Alex...689
Gamble, S. L...519
Gamet, L. 473
Ganjoo, Deepak 331
Gato, L. M. C. 623
Gelfgat, Alexander Y.................................. 105
Gharakhani, Adrin 13
Ghoniem, Ahmed F....................................13
Gregory, W. S. 559
Habashi, Wagdi G........................209, 299
Handler, Robert A...................................... 57
Haroutunian, Vahé 205
Hassanien, A. H.. 681
Hayder, M. E. 479
Henriques, J. C. C. 623
Hérard, Jean-Marc 189
Hirano, Hirokazu 445
Hodges, Ben R..361
Hou, T. Y..403
Howell, Louis H...355
Hsiao, Chao-Tsung.....................................65
Huang, Tom T. 331
Huh, Kevin S. 485
Hussein, Hussein J. 271
Issa, R. I. 159, 631
Jameson, Antony....................................... 349
Javareshkian, M. H.....................................159
Jiang, Bo-nan 433
Jianzhong, Lin 75
Joo, S. W..415
Jordan, Stephen A..................................... 141
Juric, Damir.. 341
Kaushik, Dinesh K.....................................503
Kawahara, Mutsuto 331, 445, 451, 457
Keith, Kenneth D..529
Kenrick, B. 543
Kim, Kwang-Yong 647
Kim, Se-Yun 647
Kim, Seok-Ho H...529
Kleijn, Chris R...151
Kocatulum, Bulent 255
Kollmann, Wolfgang 277
Kondo, Hirokasu 451
Kornblum, Barbara T..................................277
Kouidri, Smaine 639
Krishnamoorthy, S. 415
Laforgia, Domenico 241
Lakshminarayana, B. 573

Langerman, Michael A. 285
Lathouwers, Danny 151
Li, Hui...97
Li, Jeffrey Guoping... 197
Liepmann, Dorian.. 49
Liou, Biing-Horng... 349
Liping, Shen 75
Lockard, David P. 465
Long, Lyle N. 465
Lyrintzis, A. S. 463
Madarame, H. 113
Marcus, Daniel..49
Martin, R. A. 559
Martinelli, Luigi... 349
Martinez, M. L. 409
Maruoka, Akira...445
Matsui, K. M. 519
Matthews, R. D. 543
McCallen, Rose C. 277
McKinney, Dan... 547
Meiners, Matthew J. 285
Metzger, D. 293
Miclea, Paul C. 547
Mitchell, Larry D. 601
Miyake, Yutaka...41
Mobasher, Amir A. 323
Moen, Christopher D. 181
Morris, Philip J. 465
Mostafa, N. H. 601, 681
Najjar, Fady M. 225
Nguyen, Nhan T... 653
Nicholls, Melville E. 535
Nickerson, Douglas B. 689
Nieckele, Angela O. 385
Noguera, Riccardo 639
Nozaki, Tsutomu.. 97
Ogut, Ali 571
Ohta, Shinji.. 445
Okamoto, K. 113
Ozyoruk, Yusuf...465
Parietti, L. 559
Park, Ounyoung 323
Pauley,Laura L. 65
Peeters, M. F. 299
Peterka, Jon A. 535
Pielke, Roger A.. 535
Pordal, Harbi.. 439
Prasad,V. 403
Raad, Peter E. 217, 331, 335, 369
Ramanan, Natarajan 205, 427
Ramaswamy, B... 331, 415
Ramberg, Rune Mode... 669
Raw, Michael J. 557
Rayan, M. A. 697
Rey, Robert.. 639
Rice, Warren 285

Riziotis, Vasislis A. 25
Robichaud, M. P.. 299
Rohatgi, Upendra Singh 571
Rose, Paul 563
Rosenberg, J. 317
Rubinstein, R. 479
Sabau, Adrian S.. 217, 369
Sahoo, R. K. 263
Sakai, S. 113
Sakakiyama, Tsutomu..391
Sanchez, Greg..517
Sarkar, A. 263
Sastri, V. M. K. 263
Sauvé, R. 293
Schmidt, Russell W. 529
Seymour, Mark 563
Shariff, Maher M. 271
Shih, T. S. 249
Simmonds, Peter 541
Sinclair, R. J. 519
Solan, Alexander 105
Sotiropoulos, Fotis... 173
Strain, John A. 3
Street, Robert L. 333, 361
Sussman, Mark...355
Swearingen, Jerry D... 57
Tabarra, M. 543
Tabatabai, M. 293
Tafarrodi, Hassan 689
Tafti, Danesh K. 225
Takagi, Toshimitsu...................................... 451, 457
Taleyarkhan, Rusi P. 529
Tanaka, Takaharu 595
Tong, Albert Y. 397
Tryggvason, Grétar....................... 331, 341, 375
Tsujimoto, Koichi...41
Vallet, Marie-Gabrielle 209
Van Den Akker, Harry E. A. 151
Van Santen, Helmar... 151
Virgin, Lawrence N... 421
von Backström, T. W. 573
von Ellenrieder, Karl D. 511
Voutsinas, Spyros G. 25
Welcome, Michael 355
Wendel, Mark W. 529
Wendl, Michael C. 233
Wheeler, M. F. 409
Williamson, John W. 271
Wilson, Robert V. 121
Wu, Jie 433
Xi, G. 631
Yu, Sheng-Tao 433
Zhang, Guoqing 165
Zhang, H. 403
Zhou, J.-M. 299
Zhou, Y...479